# The UK Scanning Directory

## *7th Edition*

## Interproducts

*Publishers of Specialist Radio Books*

**Scotland**

www.interproducts.ukf.net

The UK Scanning Directory

© Copyright Interproducts 1999

7th Edition published November1999

ISBN 1 900445 09 3

Published by

**Interproducts**

**8 Abbot Street, Perth, PH2 0EB, Scotland**
**Telephone: 01738 441199**
**Fax: 01738 626953**
**email: interproducts@ukf.net**
**www.interproducts.ukf.net**

# Contents

# Contents

# *Introduction*

Welcome to the 7th edition of *The UK Scanning Directory*, the country's largest and most comprehensive guide to users of the VHF and UHF spectrum. Through our commitment to detail and with the help of PROMA, the Professional Radio Operators Monitoring Association, *The UK Scanning Directory* has again grown to include many thousands of new frequencies. In fact, *The UK Scanning Directory* is now viewed by professional bodies with such respect that it is used as a standard reference book not only by radio enthusiasts but also by numerous government agencies, police forces, military units and industrial users around the country.

Over the past year or so, we have all witnessed the rapidly changing face of radio communications. The continuing increase in user numbers has created an over subscription of available bandwidth leading to the implementation of new technologies to cope with demand. Trunking systems are one such solution, but advances in spectrum management are mirrored in listener technology allowing you to monitor these transmissions with the aid of a home computer.

In this edition, we have focused on keeping you informed of new developments in the communications industry. That's why we have included articles on civil and military airband listening, an alphabetic listing of every airport in the UK and Ireland and a beginners guide to the practical aspects of VHF/UHF radio communications.

When you start to thumb through this edition, you will very quickly see just why *The UK Scanning Directory* has become Britain's most popular radio book.

We thank all our contributors who have taken the time to send us frequencies and information. Your help and support are always welcome and appreciated.

Editor
November 1999

# Scanning - A Beginners Guide

## Scanning from the ground up!

Beginning a new hobby can often be a daunting prospect. You are filled with enthusiasm, eager to find out as much as you can and get the most out of the hobby. It is often at this point that some enthusiasts begin to have second thoughts because the information they require is just not that easily available, or they can't find anyone to answer that burning question about some form of transmission. Well, if that is the position you find yourself in, then read on because we've got the solution to all your problems - a beginner's guide to the world of VHF/UHF scanning, practical tips and advice, sources of information and most important of all, names of groups that you can contact to learn more about your hobby and have all those questions answered.

## Where can I learn more?

The first stop in your search for information on the scanning hobby should be your local newsagents, where radio related magazines are on sale. Magazines such as *Shortwave Magazine, Radio Active* and *Radio Today* are packed with the latest information and useful listening tips from the professionals. Their addresses are given on page 17.

Listeners groups are also an important source of information. PROMA (Professional Radio Operators Monitoring Association) is such a group that specialises in monitoring the VHF and UHF bands. The group produces regular frequency lists for its members. If you would like to join them, contact Paul Wey at 2 Icknield Way, Baldock, Hertfordshire, SG7 5AJ. It is worth checking out their website *www.geocities.com/SiliconValley/Station/6670*.

And while we're on the subject of the Internet, let's not forget that this too is a valuable resource of information on scanning. Many of pages focus on scanning in the US with some of the information being relevant here. For example, there was recently an article circulating the Net about a piece of software called *Trunker* that is reported to be able to follow the trunked radio transmissions of the Metropolitan Police in London. Don't forget the newsgroups. *Alt.radio.scanner* concentrates on US scanning but there are frequent questions and threads that are relevant to UK and European listeners. *Alt.radio.scanner.uk* focuses almost entirely on the UK scanning.

## How the VHF/UHF Spectrum works

Many VHF/UHF beginners have graduated from shortwave, or HF, where signals bounce of the ionosphere high above the earth's surface allowing signals to travel many thousands of miles before reaching your radio. The VHF/UHF spectrum is a little different. You may remember from your school days that energy is directly related to frequency, the higher the frequency, the more energetic the wave. This is true of all waves, including radio waves. At shortwave frequencies, below 30 MHz, wave energies are low enough to be reflected by the ionosphere. At VHF/UHF frequencies, the waves are so energetic that they pass straight through the ionosphere and out into space. It's a bit like trying to bounce a ping-pong ball and a bullet off a wall.

Since there are few things capable of reflecting VHF/UHF radio waves, they can't be heard behind hills or some buildings. In fact, VHF/UHF operate on the principle of Line of Sight, if you can see it, you can hear it!

So this explains why you cannot hear signals from towns and cities miles away from your location. On average, you should be able to receive ground signals within a radius of 25 miles, providing the terrain around you is perfectly flat. As soon as this terrain begins to change and becomes more uneven, the range of receivable signals is reduced. Aircraft are a bit different. Because they fly so high, they act like giant radio stations in the sky and it is possible to receive their signals up to 240 miles away. So don't be disappointed if you can't hear a ground signal 30 miles away, it's not your scanner that is at fault, it's just the way the VHF/UHF radio waves works.

There is one exception to all of this. On the lower VHF bands, below around 80 MHz, the lower regions of the ionosphere are capable of reflecting signals if they are suitably excited by solar activity. As we approach a more active period in the solar cycle, low band skip, as it is known, will become more common and it is not uncommon to pick up US stations on 30 or 40 MHz from here in the UK.

## Frequencies and Modes

Transmission modes have always caused confusion amongst scanner listeners. The basic transmission modes are AM, or Amplitude Modulation and FM or Frequency Modulation.

If you tune in an AM signal and it seems distorted, it is probably an FM signal, and visa versa. Most PMR transmissions are in narrow FM or NFM. Wide FM, or WFM, is only used by broadcasting stations and the audio carriers from TV stations. You just might pick up a few PMR users using AM but they are few and far between.

Another confusion is FM on the airbands. Well, simply put, it just never happens. All civil and military aeronautical voice transmissions are carried out in AM. If your scanner is receiving them better in FM, then that is a quirk of your scanner, but the original transmission is AM.

One of the biggest problems that faces a new scanner enthusiast is "How do I tune in a frequency with 5 decimal places if I only have three decimal places on my scanner?"

Let's say you're trying to hear a BBC outside broadcast in Cardiff on a frequency of 141.75625 MHz, but your scanner only displays three decimal places. How do you do it? First of all, look at the frequency steps your scanner is capable of tuning. These are usually 25, 12.5, 10, 5, 1 or 0.1 kHz for a table top scanner and 25, 12.5, 10 and 5 kHz for a handheld, although many scanners now allow you to programme which step you want, for example 250 kHz.

Once you've found the smallest tuning step, use the table below to work out which "closest" frequency you should tune. Don't worry about being off frequency. Both AM and FM transmissions are wide enough to allow a small margin of error. So, if your scanner's smallest step is 5 kHz, you should tune 141.755 MHz. You will be 1.25 kHz off frequency but that should not cause any distortion in the audio quality of the signal.

| Smallest Step | Frequency to Tune (Decimal Places) | | | |
|---|---|---|---|---|
| | 2 | 3 | 4 | 5 |
| 25 kHz | 141.75 | 141.750 | 141.7500 | 141.75000 |
| 12.5 kHz | 141.75 | 141.750 | 141.7500 | 141.75000 |
| 10 kHz | 141.75 | 141.750 | 141.7500 | 141.75000 |
| 5 kHz | | 141.755 | 141.7550 | 141.75500 |
| 1 kHz | | 141.756 | 141.7560 | 141.75600 |
| 0.1 kHz | | | 141.7562 | 141.75620 |

Now you can use this table to tune in any frequency.

## Simplex or Duplex?

What's the difference? A simplex radio channel is where both base and mobile transmit on the same frequency, say 81.9375 MHz. A duplex channel is where all users transmit on say 171.5000 MHz and receive on 166.7000 MHz. This arrangement is generally associated with repeaters, which we will look at next.

There is yet another possibility, the dual frequency simplex. In this arrangement, user A transmits on say 86.0125 MHz and receives on 72.6250 MHz while user B receives on 86.0125 MHz and transmits on 72.6250 MHz.

## Repeaters

The directionality exhibited by VHF/UHF radio waves introduces a unique problem in radio communications. If signals cannot bend around or over obstacles like mountains, large buildings or even the horizon, how can two radios communicate under these circumstances.

Here's a little thought experiment. Image you are walking down the street of a major city such as Manchester. How much of the city can you see? Well not very much because your view is obstructed by all the buildings. Now imagine that you are standing at the top of one of those buildings looking across the city. How much of the city can you see now? With height on your side, you can see lots more. If you apply that same principle to VHF/UHF radio, a receiver placed on top of a tall building is going to hear much more than one at street level, and similarly, a transmitter is going to be able to transmit further.

Repeaters work on exactly the same principle. By locating a transceiver on top of one of these obstacles and using it to relay radio signals, communications can be carried out over much further distances.

From a technical point of view, repeaters work like this.

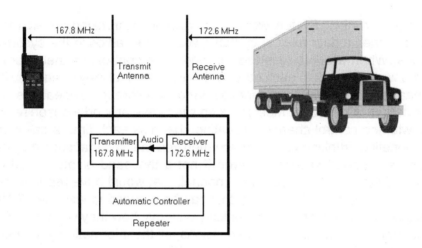

## *Trunking*

Over the past ten years or so, the demand for frequencies in the VHF/UHF radio spectrum has continued to increase as more and more users take advantage of the benefits of two-way radio communications. This demand, however, has produced an interesting problem in that the number of required frequencies now exceeds the numbers available within the restricted bandwidth of the radio spectrum. In essence, there just isn't enough space to fit in all the users.

One solution is to reduce channel spacing. For example, in a 2 MHz bandwidth, there are 80 individual channels, each spaced at 25 kHz. If this spacing is halved to 12.5 kHz, the common channel spacing used in most PMR sub-bands, a total of 160 channels can be fitted into the same bandwidth. This can and has been taken a step further on some sub-bands, particularly those used for public utilities and television outside broadcasts, where channel spacing is now only 6.25 kHz.

Of course, you might think that channel spacing can be reduced indefinitely thus always keeping the problem of spectrum overcrowding at bay. Unfortunately, that is not the case, for at some point, adjacent channels will begin to interfere with each other and all the initially perceived benefits will be lost.

Solving this problem is far more difficult that you might think. To find the solution, we must go back and look at the way frequencies are allocated. One of the major problems of allocating individual channels to each user is that although the channel might be registered for use, it need not actually be in use. So while our 2 MHz sub-band might have all 80 of its 25 kHz channels allocated to 80 different companies, only one or two frequencies might be in use at any one time. With all channels allocated, no new users can join the band even though many of the frequencies are dormant.

The ingenious solution to this seemingly impossible problem is Trunking. Trunking takes all these factors into account and provides a solution that is both user friendly and spectrum-efficient.

So how does a Trunking System work? Each radio in the trunking system monitors a control channel, a data frequency that gives all the radios in the system their instructions. When a call is received, or made, the control channel informs the radios who wish to speak to each other which free channel they need to switch to. When speaking on their voice channel a normal "talk-through" repeater is used to allow the sets to talk to each. Most trunking sites have around a dozen repeaters on them with the control channel allocating channels each time a call is made. The real benefit of trunking can be seen when you realised that such a system of repeaters can support several hundred if not a thousand or more customers. Using the old system of one user per channel, that would have required around 12 MHz of bandwidth. With trunking, that can be reduced to less than 2 MHz. If you would like to learn more about trunking systems, how they work, how to beat them and how to follow trunked transmissions, all the information you need is in *Scanner Busters 2*, by D.C. Poole (see page 596).

The new digital trunking system, TETRA, (Trans European Trunked Radio) operates in the 410-430MHz band and will become more prevalent in the coming years. Listeners is the London area may already have noticed that trunking is now being used by the Metropolitan Police in an effort to alleviate spectrum congestion.

But listener technology is hot on the heels of the radio companies. Already a trunk-decoding package is available in the US that decodes data from the control frequency and can be used to control your scanner. It is rumoured that a similar package might be able to be adapted to monitor government trunking systems. And in the UK, there is a system that can be used to monitor trunking called *FTrunk*. It consists of a decoder box which plugs into the back of a PC and a scanner is conected to the decoder. The example of the software below shows which frequency to tune into, or if you have a scond scanner it will automatically switch to the channel. It is manufactured by Talkback Systems Australia, PO Box 8054, Northland Centre, Victoria, 3072, Australia (email: mpt1327@tbsa.com.au), or you can contact Interproducts (tel. 01738 441199 fax 01738 626953) for general information.

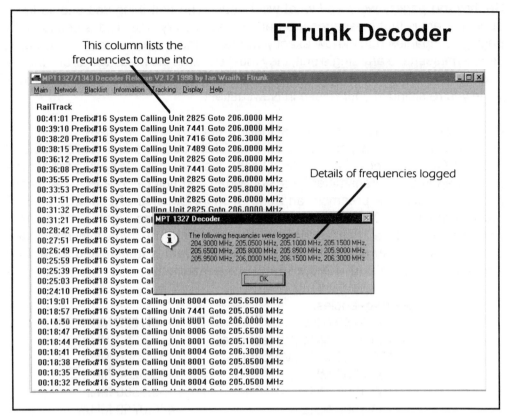

# FTrunk Decoder

This column lists the frequencies to tune into

Details of frequencies logged

## Paging

Ever wondered exactly what all those data transmissions are around 138 MHz and 153 MHz. The answer is simple: Pagers - those little gadgets that clip onto your belt and tell you all manner of information from "Happy Birthday" to "Don't go home the Police are looking for you." Like mobile telephones, they can be an asset or a hindrance, but from the listeners' point of view, they can be a real catch. When digital GSM telephones were introduced a few years ago, many in the scanning community thought that marked the end of eavesdropping on their neighbours. But the information vacuum did not last long. Enthusiasts throughout Europe and the US focused on Pagers as their next great target. Since the signals when not encryption, it was only a matter of decoding the data to read the messages.

So, can you read these messages? Well of course you can. All you need is a piece of software that decodes the transmissions and here's the good news, the software is shareware and can be downloaded from the Internet! All you need do is run an audio line from the speaker jack of your scanner to the input port of your PC's soundcard, adjust the volume to the correct level, and soon messages will start scrolling up your screen.

So, how do pagers work and what will I hear? The first thing you should know about pagers is that messages are transmitted countrywide. That's because the paging companies don't know exactly where all there pagers are so in order to send a message to any single unit, they must transmit the message all around the country. So don't be too surprised if you read a message for someone in London while you're sitting in your house in Newcastle!

Pagers work like this: The basic signalling pattern used in many pagers is a sequence of coded binary data using the Post Office Code Standardisation Advisory Group (POCSAG) code. The POCSAG code is a synchronous paging format that allows pages to be transmitted in a single-batch structure. The POCSAG code format consists of a preamble and one or more batches of codewords. Each batch comprises a 32-bit frame synchronisation code and eight 64-bit address frames of two 32-bit addresses or idle codewords each. The frame synchronisation code marks the start of the batch of codewords. Data is transmitted as an FSK signal at a bit rate of 512, 1200, or 2400 bits per second.

Pager frequencies:

| | |
|---|---|
| 137.9750 MHz | 153.1750 MHz |
| 138.0750 MHz (Vodaphone) | 153.2250 MHz |
| 138.1750 MHz (Mercury) | 153.2500 MHz |
| 153.0250 MHz | 153.3250 MHz |
| 153.1250 MHz | 153.3500 MHz |
| 153.1500 MHz | 466.0750 MHz |

If you would like a copy of the pager decoding software, it can be downloaded from *http://home.foni.net/~fliegl//*. The file to download is the self-extracting zip archive called poc32205.exe. This is the German version of poc32 (version 2.05) of the package, however, an English version of the earlier version 1.04 can be downloaded at *http://www.geocities.com/ CapeCanaveral/Hangar/4783/ poc32eng.zip.*

## Encryption

Encryption is one of those subjects that keeps on coming up and readers keep on asking if there is any way to beat the system. So, let's take a brief look at how encryption works.

As children, we all played with codes and ciphers, A = 1, B =2, etc. Using such a cipher, any message can be reduced to a series of apparently meaningless numbers. Modern encryption is surprisingly similar, but instead of letters being converted into numbers, whole messages or segments of speech are digitised. Now, prior to transmission, the encryption takes place. This is done by adding a series of pseudo-random numbers to the digitised message, which has the effect of scrambling the message.

Let's assume our original message is APPLE, or 1-16-16-12-5. By adding the series of pseudo-random numbers to our message, it is transformed into 23-13-24-1-5, or WMYAE and this is what is transmitted over the air. To get around the encryption requires that you have some knowledge of the mathematical algorithm that generates the number series. The problem is this: the number series that an encryption algorithm produces depends on the encryption key used by system and encryption keys have literally millions upon millions of possible combinations. In fact, some systems are so secure that to test every possible key at a rate of one key per second would take longer than the age of the universe! Someone once calculated than there are fewer grains of sand on earth than there are possible key combinations for some ciphers. Imagine being asked you find that single grain - truly a daunting prospect. With such a large number of combinations, these codes are said to be computationally infeasible to break. It's just not worth even trying.

So, to answer all these readers out there who would like to tap into the local Regional Crime Squad or Drugs Squad, it's just not currently possible. However, things might not be quite as black as they seem. Here are a few questions you might like to think about. Have you ever seen a Drugs Squad officer using a radio? Don't they all use mobile telephones these days? Is that because mobile 'phones are less suspicious than radios or don't the police trust their own encryption system?

## *Buying a Scanner*

Finally, let's take a look at buying a scanner. Scanners come is two forms, the base station which is a table top radio best suited for listening at home, and the handheld scanner, which can easily be slipped into the inside pocket of a jacket so that you can wonder around town listening to what is going on.

Before you commit to buying a scanner, firstly decide what you want to use it for. If you're going to be out and about with it, then you're better going for a handheld. If you plan on spending long hours tuning in from the comfort of your own home then a table top radio is for you. Once you've decided, you now have the task of choosing which is the best scanner for your needs. There are a few essentials that you should look out for: a digital readout is an absolute must, so are both FM and AM reception modes.

Frequency coverage is also very important. Many US built scanners have huge chunks of the spectrum blocked out to comply with legal constraints in that country. They might be cheap, but once you start to use them you'll discover why! The FM broadcasting band, air band, PMR bands, military bands and television bands are all blocked out. This information is often given on a label on the back. So, when you choose a scanner, go for one for that has "continuous tuning" from around 25 MHz up to at least 1 GHz. Failing that, choose a scanner that is as close to this specification as possible.

Besides frequency blocking, there is another quirk that cheaper scanners have - bad image rejection. Simply put, you'll pick up lots of signals but many will be on the wrong frequency. For example, the local skip hire company might transmit on 166.1875 MHz, but you will also hear it on 130.4125 MHz, that's right in the middle of the aviation band. If you've new to the hobby, having just bought you're very first scanner and hear Joe talking about his skip on 130.4125 MHz, you're not going to query the frequency. The real problem occurs when you look up the frequency in *The UK Scanning Directory*, Joe's Skip won't be listed on 130.4125 MHz. Not only will you be listening to the wrong frequency, you will also not be able to get the full benefit of *The UK Scanning Directory*. So don't be fooled by that "very reasonable" price tag.

Look through the radio magazines, like *Shortwave Magazine, Radio Active and Radio Today* for scanner adverts and reviews. Find a local scanner dealer who also sells amateur radio equipment and go pay them a visit. Talk to the sales people, try out the scanner and find out if it does everything you want. If it does, buy it, if not, keep looking. Of course, there is always the second hand market that is advertised in most radio magazines.

## Antennas

Now that you have your scanner, the inevitability of antenna design looms. Radio antenna design is a huge subject that could easily fill this book, so in the interests of brevity, let's just look at a few simple antennas that will allow you to hear transmissions for around you. Most handheld scanners come with a short whip antenna already fitted. These are usually fine for strong signals but are a bit lacking with weak signals. Table top radio are usually sold with a trusty telescopic antenna. This type of antenna is ideal for the novice scanning enthusiast as it has a broad enough bandwidth to capture signals all over the band. Once you start to specialise in a particular branch of scanning, such as military aviation, you might want to either built or buy an antenna cut to that frequency range. Most radio magazines publish regular articles on antenna building. Alternatively, scrap yards always seem to have a collection of VHF/UHF antennas gathered from building sites. Another source is a company undergoing a move - many companies who operate VHF/UHF radios leave their old antennas behind when they move to new premises!

---

Unfortunately we are unable to answer questions by telephone due to the sheer volume of work in maintaining *The UK Scanning Directory*. If you do have any questions, please either e-mail, fax or send them to us by letter.

---

# Using the UK Scanning Directory

Each page of *The UK Scanning Directory* is set out in five column; Base and Mobile frequencies, Mode, Location and User & Notes.

**Base Frequency:** This is the most acive frequency where most will be heard so the best one to monitor.

**Mobile Frequency:** In a Simplex arrangement, this frequency will be the same as the Base frequency. However, in a Duplex arrangement, this frequency will carry only signals from mobiles.

**Mode:** This is the mode that should be selected on your scanner for best reception.

**Location:** This is generally the area from where the signal originates. For example, if you are in Cambridge and you heard a signal on a particular frequency, then the location of the signal will be Cambridge.

**User & Notes:** This column contains details of who uses a particular frequency, their callsign, channel number and any other relevant notes.

Below is an example of a typical page.

Column 1:    Base & Repeater Transmit Frequency (Duplex)
             Base & Mobile Transmit Frequency (Simplex)

Column 2:    Mobile Transmit Frequency (Duplex)
             Mobile & Base Transmit Frequency (Simplex)

Column 3: Transmission Mode (i.e. AM, NFM, WFM, etc)

Column 4: Location (The approximate area where the signal will be heard, i.e. City, Town, District, Village, or County.

Column 5: User, Callsign & Remarks

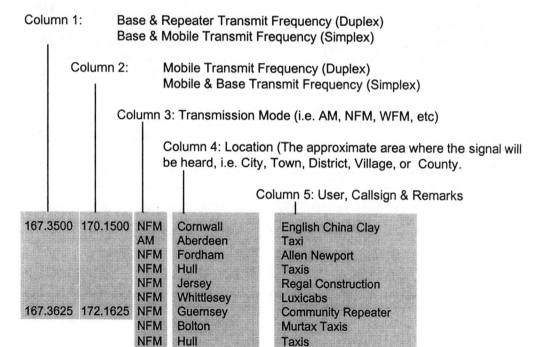

| | | | | |
|---|---|---|---|---|
| 167.3500 | 170.1500 | NFM | Cornwall | English China Clay |
| | | AM | Aberdeen | Taxi |
| | | NFM | Fordham | Allen Newport |
| | | NFM | Hull | Taxis |
| | | NFM | Jersey | Regal Construction |
| | | NFM | Whittlesey | Luxicabs |
| 167.3625 | 172.1625 | NFM | Guernsey | Community Repeater |
| | | NFM | Bolton | Murtax Taxis |
| | | NFM | Hull | Taxis |

A great deal of confusion has arisen from the gaps left after certain frequencies, for example, the gaps that follow 167.3500/170.1500 in the above extract. These gaps have been introduced to make the page less cluttered and more user friendly. Any gaps that follow a frequency indicates that the same frequency applies of all entries below the first. Therefore, the 167.3500/170.1500 group means:

| | | | | |
|---|---|---|---|---|
| 167.3500 | 170.1500 | NFM | Cornwall | English China Clay |
| 167.3500 | 170.1500 | AM | Aberdeen | Taxi |
| 167.3500 | 170.1500 | NFM | Fordham | Allen Newport |
| 167.3500 | 170.1500 | NFM | Hull | Taxis |
| 167.3500 | 170.1500 | NFM | Jersey | Regal Construction |
| 167.3500 | 170.1500 | NFM | Whittlesey | Luxicabs |

If you are new to scanning the following list of the main users of the VHF/UHF bands will help you to quickly find their frequencies.

List of Abbreviations and Terms

| | |
|---|---|
| AA | Automobile Association |
| AFIS | Aerodrome Flight Information Service |
| AFSATCOM | US Air Force Satellite Communications |
| AM | Amplitude Modulation |
| ARA | Air Refuelling Area |
| ATC | Air Traffic Control or Air Training Corps |
| ATCC | Air Traffic Control Centre |
| ATIS | Aerodrome Terminal Information Service |
| AWACS | Airborne Warning & Control System |
| BAe | British Aerospace |
| BBC | British Broadcasting Corporation |
| BGS | British Geological Survey |
| BNFL | British Nuclear Fuels Ltd |
| BR | British Rail |
| BT | British Telecom |
| BTP | British Transport Police |
| CAC | Centralised Approach Control |
| CB | Citizen Band |
| CEGB | Central Electricity Generating Board |
| CMD | Command |
| Comms | Communications |
| CW | Continuous Wave (Morse) |
| DAB | Digital Audio Broadcasting |
| DATIS | Digital Aerodrome Terminal Information Service |
| DME | Distance Measuring Equipment |
| DTI | Department of Trade and Industry |
| DSRR | Digital Short Range Radios |
| FLTSATCOM | US Navy Satellite Communications |
| FM | Frequency Modulation |
| GCHQ | Government Communications Headquarters |
| GSM | New digital mobile phones |
| IBA | Independent Broadcasting Authority |
| IFR | Instrument Flight Rules |
| ILR | Independent Local Radio |
| ILS | Instrument Landing System |
| ITN | Independent Television News |
| ITV | Independent Television |
| LBS | Low Band Skip |
| LWT | London Weekend Television |
| MoD | Ministry of Defence |
| Mould | MoD National Home Defence Repeater Network |
| MRSA | Mandatory Radar Service Area |

| | |
|---|---|
| MWL | Mid-Wales Railway Line |
| NATO | North Atlantic Treaty Organisation |
| NASA | National Aeronautics and Space Administration |
| NB | Narrow Band |
| NCB | National Coal Board |
| NFM | Narrow Band FM |
| O/B | Outside Broadcast |
| Ops | Operations |
| PAR | Precision Approach Radar |
| PFA | Popular Flying Association |
| PMR | Private Mobile Radio |
| PR | Personal Radio |
| R | Runway (Left & Right) |
| RAF | Royal Air Force |
| RCA | Radiocommunications Agency |
| RN | Royal Navy |
| RTTY | Radio Teletype |
| SAR | Search and Rescue |
| SCS | Shopping Centre Security |
| Spec. | Specification |
| SRE | Surveillance Radar Element |
| SSB | Single-Side Band |
| SSTV | Slow Scan Television |
| Std | Standard |
| Surv. | Surveillance |
| TACAN | Tactical Air Navigation |
| TMA | Terminal Manoeuvring Area |
| TX . | Transmission |
| UACC | Upper Air Control Centre |
| UHF | Ultra High Frequency (300 - 3000 MHz) |
| UKAEA | UK Atomic Energy Authority |
| USAF | US Air Force |
| USAFE | US Air Force Europe |
| USB | Upper Side Band |
| VFR | Visual Flight Rules |
| VHF | Very High Frequency (30 - 300 MHz) |
| VOLMET | Aviation Weather Broadcast |
| VOR | VHF Omni-Directional Radio Range |
| WFM | Wide Band FM |

# Longwave, Medium Wave and Shortwave Allocations

Many scanners now cover frequencies down to 100 kHz and allow access to the exciting world of Shortwave radio. Below is a list of frequency allocations, but if you want to learn more about receiving stations from around the world, turn to the back of this book for a list of publications what will introduce you fascinating subject.

| | |
|---|---|
| 148.5 - 283.5 kHz | Longwave Broadcasting AM |
| 283.5 - 320 kHz | Maritime NDB, Aeronautical Navigation |
| 320 - 405 kHz | Aeronautical Navigation NDB |
| 405 - 435 kHz | Aeronautical Navigation NDB, Maritime Mobiles |
| 435 - 495 kHz | Maritime Mobiles |
| 495 - 505 kHz | Mobile (Distress and Calling) |
| 505 - 526 kHz | Maritime Mobiles |
| 526 - 1626 kHz | Medium Wave Broadcasting |
| 1626 -2850 kHz | Maritime |
| 2850 -2000 kHz | 160 metres Amateur Radio |
| 2300 - 2495 kHz | 120 metres Tropical Braodcasting |
| 2851 - 3019 kHz | En-Route Aeronautical Mobiles |
| 3023 - 3152 kHz | Off-Route Aeronautical Mobiles |
| 3155 - 3200 kHz | Fixed and Land & Maritime Mobiles |
| 3200 - 3400 kHz | 90 metres Tropical Broadcasting and Fixed & Land Mobiles |
| 3401 - 3497 kHz | En-Route Aeronautical Mobiles |
| 3500 - 3800 kHz | 80 metres Amateur Radio |
| 3950 - 4000 kHz | 75 metres European Braodcasting |
| 4000 - 4435 kHz | Maritime Fixed & Mobiles |
| 4438 - 4650 kHz | Fixed and Land & Maritime Mobiles |
| 4651 - 4696 kHz | En-Route Aeronautical Mobiles |
| 4700 - 4995 kHz | Off-Route Aeronautical Mobiles |
| 4750 - 5060 kHz | 60 metres Tropical Broadcasting |
| 5060 - 5450 kHz | Fixed and Land & Maritime Mobiles |
| 5450 - 5477 kHz | Off-Route Aeronautical Mobiles |
| 5481 - 5676 kHz | En-Route Aeronautical Mobiles |
| 5680 - 5726 kHz | Off-Route Aeronautical Mobiles |
| 5730 - 5960 kHz | Fixed and Land & Maritime Mobiles |
| 5950 - 6200 kHz | 49 metres Broadcasting Band |
| 6200 - 6526 kHz | Maritime Mobiles |
| 6526 - 6682 kHz | En-Route Aeronautical Mobiles |
| 6685 - 6765 kHz | Off-Route Aeronautical Mobiles |
| 6765 - 7000 kHz | Fixed and Land Mobiles |
| 7000 - 7100 kHz | 40 metres Amateur Radio |
| 7100 - 7300 kHz | 41 metres Broadcasting Band |
| 7300 - 8100 kHz | Fixed and Land Mobiles |
| 8100 - 8195 kHz | Fixed and Maritime Mobiles |
| 8195 - 8812 kHz | Maritime Mobiles |
| 8816 - 8960 kHz | En-Route Aeronautical Mobiles |
| 8965 - 9037 kHz | Off-Route Aeronautical Mobiles |
| 9040 - 9500 kHz | Fixed |

| | |
|---|---|
| 9500 - 9900 kHz | 31 metres Broadcasting Band |
| 9900 - 9995 kHz | Fixed |
| 10006 - 10096 kHz | En-Route Aeronautical Mobiles |
| 10100 - 10150 kHz | 30 metres Amateur Radio |
| 10150 - 11175 kHz | Fixed and Land & Maritime Mobiles |
| 11175 - 11271 kHz | Off-Route Aeronautical Mobiles |
| 11276 - 11396 kHz | En-Route Aeronautical Mobiles |
| 11400 - 12230 kHz | Fixed |
| 11650 - 12050 kHz | 25 metres Broadcasting Band |
| 12230 - 13197 kHz | Maritime Mobiles |
| 13200 - 13257 kHz | Off-Route Aeronautical Mobiles |
| 13261 - 13357 kHz | En-Route Aeronautical Mobiles |
| 13360 - 13600 kHz | Fixed and Land & Maritime Mobiles |
| 13600 - 13800 kHz | 22 metres Broadcasting Band |
| 13800 - 14000 kHz | Fixed and Land Mobiles |
| 14000 - 14350 kHz | 20 metres Amateur Band |
| 14350 - 14990 kHz | Fixed and Land & Maritime Mobiles |
| 15010 - 15097 kHz | Off-Route Aeronautical Mobiles |
| 15100 - 15600 kHz | 19 metres Broadcasting Band |
| 15600 - 16360 kHz | Fixed |
| 16360 - 17407 kHz | Maritime Mobiles |
| 17410 - 17550 kHz | Fixed |
| 17550 - 17900 kHz | 16 metres Broadcasting Band |
| 17901 - 17967 kHz | En-Route Aeronautical Mobiles |
| 17970 - 18027 kHz | Off-Route Aeronautical Mobiles |
| 18030 - 18068 kHz | Fixed |
| 18068 - 18168 kHz | 16 metres Amateur Band |
| 18168 - 18780 kHz | Fixed |
| 18780 - 18900 kHz | Maritime Mobiles |
| 18900 - 19680 kHz | Fixed |
| 19680 - 19797 kHz | Maritime Mobiles |
| 19800 - 21000 kHz | Fixed & Land Mobiles |
| 21000 - 21450 kHz | 15 metres Amateur Band |
| 21450 - 21850 kHz | 13 metres Broadcasting Band |
| 21850 - 21870 kHz | Fixed |
| 21870 - 21924 kHz | Aeronautical Fixed |
| 21925 - 21998 kHz | En-Route Aeronautical Mobiles |
| 22000 - 22852 kHz | Maritime Mobiles |
| 22855 - 23000 kHz | Fixed |
| 23000 - 23200 kHz | Fixed and Land & Maritime Mobiles |
| 23200 - 23350 kHz | Off-Route Aeronautical Mobiles |
| 23350 - 24890 kHz | Fixed & Land Mobiles |
| 24890 - 24990 kHz | 12 metres Amateur Band |
| 24990 - 25070 kHz | Fixed & Land Mobiles |
| 25070 - 25210 kHz | Maritime Mobiles |
| 25210 - 25520 kHz | Fixed and Land & Maritime Mobiles |
| 25550 - 25600 kHz | Radio Astronomy |
| 25600 - 26100 kHz | 11 metres Broadcasting Band |
| 26100 - 26172 kHz | Maritime Mobiles |
| 26175 - 26235 kHz | Fixed and Land & Maritime Mobiles |

# *Useful Addresses*

| | |
|---|---|
| *Practical Wireless* | PW Publishing Ltd. Arrowsmith Court, Station Approach, Broadstone, Dorset, BH18 8PW. Tel: 01202 659910 Fax: 01202 659950 |
| *Radio Active* | Radio Active Publications, 189 London Road, North End, Portsmouth, Hants, PO2 9AE. Tel: 01705 6138000 Fax: 01705 690626 |
| Radio Authority | Holbrook House, 14 Great Queen Street, London, WC2B 5DG. Tel: 0171 430 2724 Fax: 0171 405 7062 www.radioauthority.org.uk |
| Radiocommuncations Agency | South Quay 3, 189 Marsh Wall, London, E14 9SX. Tel: 020 7211 0502 Fax: 020 7211 0507 www.open.gov.uk/radiocom/ |
| Radio Society of Great Britain | Lambda House, Cranborne Road, Potters Bar, Herts, EN6 3JE. Tel: 01707 659015 Fax: 01707 645105 www.rsgb.org |
| Radio Today | RSGB Sales, Lambda House, Cranborne Road, Potters Bar, Herts, EN6 3JE. Tel: 01707 659015 Fax: 01707 645105 www.rsgb.org |
| Shortwave Magazine | PW Publishing Ltd. Arrowsmith Court, Station Approach, Broadstone, Dorset, BH18 8PW. Tel: 01202 659910 Fax: 01202 659950 |

# Scanning and the Law

We are often asked about the legal position of scanning. In a nut shell 95% of what you listen to is illegal! According to the authorities all you can listen to are broadcasts and amateur radio. Tuning into the airband, ships or even the local dust cart is a no go area. If you hear a Mayday call from a fishing boat and inform the Coastguard you can be prosecuted and have your equipment confiscated.

Go to any airport or airshow and you will find many people tuned into the aircrafts and nobody minds. On the other hand during the past year we have learnt of several people who have been successfully prosecuted for listening to the police, even though they were not caught in the act. Because they had police frequencies in their scanner's memory this was enough to convict them, therefore store sensitive frequencies in your head. A helpful leaflet on this subject entitled *Receive only - Scanner etc. Information Sheet* (RA169) is obtainable free of charge from The Information and Library Service, Radiocommunications Agency, South Quay 3, 139 Marsh Wall, London, E14 9SX (telephone 020 7211 0502 or 0505: web site www.open.gov.uk/radiocom/). Therefore scanning should be done with common sense and discretion, and don't tell everybody in the pub how you hear PC Plod arrest your mother-in-law for shop lifting a bottle of gin.

A last thought. This is a hypercritical situation because the government is listening into us more and more. For example your telephone calls, faxes and e-mail are being monitored by GCHQ, Cheltenham, and the US listening post at Menwith Hill near Harrogate. Britain must be the only country in the world which allows a foreign power into its country to monitor its population!

# Part 1

# Frequencies for the UK and Republic of Ireland

## 26.1000 - 27.5000 MHz   Fixed, Land and Mobile

## Except Aeronautical Mobile

**26.1000 - 26.1750 MHz   MARITIME MARITIME MOBILE USB**

**26.100 - 27.450 MHz       ONE-WAY PAGING SYSTEMS AND ALARMS**

| Base | Mode | Location | User and Notes |
| --- | --- | --- | --- |
| 26.2500 | NFM | Nationwide | JFMG Talkback |
| 26.3500 | NFM | Nationwide | JFMG Talkback |
| 26.4500 | NFM | Nationwide | JFMG Talkback |
| 26.5880 | NFM | Nationwide | Common Paging Channel |
| 26.8350 | NFM | Nationwide | Short term hire pagers |
| 26.9200 | NFM | Nationwide | Short term hire pagers |
| 26.9950 | NFM | Nationwide | Vehicle radio keys |
| 27.0450 | NFM | Nationwide | Vehicle radio keys |
| 27.0950 | NFM | Nationwide | Vehicle radio keys |
| 27.1200 | NFM | Nationwide | Paging tests and development |
| 27.1450 | NFM | Nationwide | Vehicle radio keys |
| 27.1625 | NFM | St Helier | Jeanne Jugan Hospital Paging |
| 27.1950 | NFM | Nationwide | Vehicle radio keys |
| 27.4500 | NFM | Nationwide | Short range alarm for the elderly and infirm |

**GENERAL TELEMENTRY AND TELECOMMAND SYSTEMS FOR INDUSTIAL,**

**SCIENTIFIC AND MEDICAL APPERATUS**

| Base | Mode | Location | User and Notes |
| --- | --- | --- | --- |
| 26.995 | NFM | Nationwide | Industrial, scientific and medical apparatus |
| 27.045 | NFM | Nationwide | Industrial, scientific and medical apparatus |
| 27.095 | NFM | Nationwide | Industrial, scientific and medical apparatus |
| 27.145 | NFM | Nationwide | Industrial, scientific and medical apparatus |
| 27.195 | NFM | Nationwide | Industrial, scientific and medical apparatus |

**26.9650 - 27.4050 MHz   CEPT (UK & EUROPE) CITIZEN BAND RADIO**

| Base | Mode | Location | User and Notes |
| --- | --- | --- | --- |
| 26.965 | NFM | Nationwide | Channel 01 |
| 26.975 | NFM | Nationwide | Channel 02 |
| 26.985 | NFM | Nationwide | Channel 03 |
| 27.005 | NFM | Nationwide | Channel 04 |
| 27.015 | NFM | Nationwide | Channel 05 |
| 27.025 | NFM | Nationwide | Channel 06 |
| 27.035 | NFM | Nationwide | Channel 07 |
| 27.055 | NFM | Nationwide | Channel 08 |
| 27.065 | NFM | Nationwide | Channel 09 |
| 27.075 | NFM | Nationwide | Channel 10 |
| 27.085 | NFM | Nationwide | Channel 11 |
| 27.105 | NFM | Nationwide | Channel 12 |
| 27.115 | NFM | Nationwide | Channel 13 |
| 27.125 | NFM | Nationwide | Channel 14 |
| 27.135 | NFM | Nationwide | Channel 15 |
| 27.155 | NFM | Nationwide | Channel 16 |
| 27.165 | NFM | Nationwide | Channel 17 |
| 27.175 | NFM | Nationwide | Channel 18 |
| 27.185 | NFM | Nationwide | Channel 19 |
| 27.205 | NFM | Nationwide | Channel 20 |
| 27.215 | NFM | Nationwide | Channel 21 |
| 27.225 | NFM | Nationwide | Channel 22 |

| Base | Mobile | Mode | Location | User and Notes |
|------|--------|------|----------|----------------|
| 27.235 | | NFM | Nationwide | Channel 24 |
| 27.245 | | NFM | Nationwide | Channel 25 |
| 27.255 | | NFM | Nationwide | Channel 23 |
| 27.265 | | NFM | Nationwide | Channel 26 |
| 27.275 | | NFM | Nationwide | Channel 27 |
| 27.285 | | NFM | Nationwide | Channel 28 |
| 27.295 | | NFM | Nationwide | Channel 29 |
| 27.305 | | NFM | Nationwide | Channel 30 |
| 27.315 | | NFM | Nationwide | Channel 31 |
| 27.325 | | NFM | Nationwide | Channel 32 |
| 27.335 | | NFM | Nationwide | Channel 33 |
| 27.345 | | NFM | Nationwide | Channel 34 |
| 27.355 | | NFM | Nationwide | Channel 35 |
| 27.365 | | NFM | Nationwide | Channel 36 |
| 27.375 | | NFM | Nationwide | Channel 37 |
| 27.385 | | NFM | Nationwide | Channel 38 |
| 27.395 | | NFM | Nationwide | Channel 39 |
| 27.405 | | NFM | Nationwide | Channel 40 |

## 26.960 - 27.280 MHz　　GENERAL MODEL CONTROL

| Base | Mobile | Mode | Location | User and Notes |
|------|--------|------|----------|----------------|
| 26.995 | | NFM | Nationwide | 'Brown' Model Channel |
| 27.045 | | NFM | Nationwide | 'Red' Model Channel |
| 27.095 | | NFM | Nationwide | 'Orange' Model Channel |
| 27.145 | | NFM | Nationwide | 'Yellow' Model Channel |
| 27.195 | | NFM | Nationwide | 'Green' Model Channel |
| 27.245 | | NFM | Nationwide | 'Blue' Model Channel |

## 27.60125 - 27.99125 MHz　　UK CB

| Base | Mobile | Mode | Location | User and Notes |
|------|--------|------|----------|----------------|
| 27.60125 | 27.60125 | NFM | Nationwide | Channel 01 |
| 27.61125 | 27.61125 | NFM | Nationwide | Channel 02 |
| 27.62125 | 27.62125 | NFM | Nationwide | Channel 03 |
| 27.63125 | 27.63125 | NFM | Nationwide | Channel 04 |
| 27.64125 | 27.64125 | NFM | Nationwide | Channel 05 |
| 27.65125 | 27.65125 | NFM | Nationwide | Channel 06 |
| 27.66125 | 27.66125 | NFM | Nationwide | Channel 07 |
| 27.67125 | 27.67125 | NFM | Nationwide | Channel 08 |
| 27.68125 | 27.68125 | NFM | Nationwide | Channel 09 emergency |
| 27.69125 | 27.69125 | NFM | Nationwide | Channel 10 |
| 27.70125 | 27.70125 | NFM | Nationwide | Channel 11 |
| 27.71125 | 27.71125 | NFM | Nationwide | Channel 12 |
| 27.72125 | 27.72125 | NFM | Nationwide | Channel 13 |
| 27.73125 | 27.73125 | NFM | Nationwide | Channel 14 calling |
| 27.74125 | 27.74125 | NFM | Nationwide | Channel 15 |
| 27.75125 | 27.75125 | NFM | Nationwide | Channel 16 |
| 27.76125 | 27.76125 | NFM | Nationwide | Channel 17 |
| 27.77125 | 27.77125 | NFM | Nationwide | Channel 18 |
| 27.78125 | 27.78125 | NFM | Nationwide | Channel 19 calling |
| 27.79125 | 27.79125 | NFM | Nationwide | Channel 20 |
| 27.80125 | 27.80125 | NFM | Nationwide | Channel 21 |
| 27.81125 | 27.81125 | NFM | Nationwide | Channel 22 |
| 27.82125 | 27.82125 | NFM | Nationwide | Channel 23 |
| 27.83125 | 27.83125 | NFM | Nationwide | Channel 24 |
| 27.84125 | 27.84125 | NFM | Nationwide | Channel 25 |
| 27.85125 | 27.85125 | NFM | Nationwide | Channel 26 |
| 27.86125 | 27.86125 | NFM | Nationwide | Channel 27 |

| Base | Mobile | Mode | Location | User and Notes |
|---|---|---|---|---|
| 27.87125 | 27.87125 | NFM | Nationwide | Channel 28 |
| 27.88125 | 27.88125 | NFM | Nationwide | Channel 29 |
| 27.89125 | 27.89125 | NFM | Nationwide | Channel 30 |
| 27.90125 | 27.90125 | NFM | Nationwide | Channel 31 |
| 27.91125 | 27.91125 | NFM | Nationwide | Channel 32 |
| 27.92125 | 27.92125 | NFM | Nationwide | Channel 33 |
| 27.93125 | 27.93125 | NFM | Nationwide | Channel 34 |
| 27.94125 | 27.94125 | NFM | Nationwide | Channel 35 |
| 27.95125 | 27.95125 | NFM | Nationwide | Channel 36 |
| 27.96125 | 27.96125 | NFM | Nationwide | Channel 37 |
| 27.97125 | 27.97125 | NFM | Nationwide | Channel 38 |
| 27.98125 | 27.98125 | NFM | Nationwide | Channel 39 |
| 27.99125 | 27.99125 | NFM | Nationwide | Channel 40 |

### 28.0000 - 29.7000 MHz    10M AMATEUR BAND

| Base | Mobile | Mode | Location | User and Notes |
|---|---|---|---|---|
| 28.120 | | NFM | Nationwide | Packet Radio |
| 28.215 | | CW | Didcot | GB3RAL Beacon |
| 28.680 | | NFM | Nationwide | Slow Scan TV and Fax Calling |
| 29.200 | | NFM | Nationwide | Packet Radio (FM 2.5kHz) |
| 29.300 | | NFM | Nationwide | Satellite downlinks |
| 29.600 | | NFM | Nationwide | FM calling channel |

### 29.7000 - 29.9700 MHz    MOD TACTICAL CHANNELS 25 kHz SIMPLEX NFM

### 30.0050 - 31.0250 MHz    NASA SPACE TO EARTH NFM SIMPLEX

| Base | Mobile | Mode | Location | User and Notes |
|---|---|---|---|---|
| 30.01000 | | NFM | Space | Downlink |

### 30.0250 - 31.7000 MHz    USAFE COMMUNICATIONS 25 kHz SIMPLEX

| Base | Mobile | Mode | Location | User and Notes |
|---|---|---|---|---|
| 30.02500 | | NFM | USAF Fairford | Base Security |
| 30.12500 | | NFM | Swansea | TA HQ camp communications |
| 30.17500 | | NFM | Salisbury Plain | Army |
| 30.20000 | | NFM | Salisbury Plain | Army |
| 30.25000 | | NFM | Nationwide | Historic Flights |
| 30.32500 | | NFM | Salisbury Plain | Army |
| 30.35000 | | AM | Nationwide | U.S. 352 Sqdn. Air to Air |
| 30.35000 | | NFM | Nationwide | Army Forward Air Controllers |
| 30.45000 | | NFM | Nationwide | US Military MARS Network |
| 30.50000 | | NFM | London | US Embassy Security (Eagle) |
| 30.50000 | | NFM | USAF Fairford | Base Security |
| 30.82500 | | NFM | Nationwide | Royal Anglia Regiment, 1st Battalion |
| 30.98750 | | NFM | USAF Fairford | Base Security |
| 31.00000 | | NFM | USAF Fairford | Tanker Ground Ops |
| 31.18250 | | NFM | USAF Fairford | Fence Security |
| 31.20000 | | NFM | Salisbury Plain | Army |
| 31.20000 | | NFM | USAF Fairford | Ground Maintenance |
| 31.25000 | | NFM | USAF Fairford | Base Security |
| 31.30000 | | NFM | USAF Fairford | Base Medical Services |
| 31.40000 | | NFM | USAF Fairford | Tanker Ground Operations |
| 31.43750 | | NFM | Nationwide | Digital Signalling |
| 31.50000 | | NFM | Brighton | TA Barracks |
| 31.50000 | | NFM | Preston | TA Barracks |
| 31.57500 | | NFM | Nationwide | RAF Regiment |
| 31.67500 | | NFM | Salisbury Plain | Army |
| 31.70000 | | NFM | Salisbury Plain | Army |

## 31.0875 - 31.2125 MHz   CORDLESS TELEPHONES (1998 ALLOCATION)

| Base | Mobile | Mode | Location | User and Notes |
|------|--------|------|----------|----------------|
| 31.0375 | 39.9375 | NFM | Nationwide | Cordless Telephones |
| 31.0625 | 39.9625 | NFM | Nationwide | Cordless Telephones |
| 31.0875 | 39.9875 | NFM | Nationwide | Cordless Telephones |
| 31.1125 | 40.0125 | NFM | Nationwide | Cordless Telephones |
| 31.1375 | 40.0375 | NFM | Nationwide | Cordless Telephones |
| 31.1625 | 40.0625 | NFM | Nationwide | Cordless Telephones |
| 31.1875 | 40.0875 | NFM | Nationwide | Cordless Telephones |
| 31.2125 | 40.1125 | NFM | Nationwide | Cordless Telephones |

## 31.7125 - 31.7875 MHz   HOSPITAL PAGING OUTGOING SPEECH
### (RETURN SPEECH ONLY IN EMERGENCIES)

| Base | Mobile | Mode | Location | User and Notes |
|------|--------|------|----------|----------------|
| 31.725 | 161.000 | NFM | Nationwide | Hospital Paging |
| 31.750 | 161.025 | NFM | Worcester | Ronkwood Hospital Paging |
| 31.750 | 161.025 | NFM | Nationwide | Hospital Paging |
| 31.775 | 161.050 | NFM | Eastbourne | Hospital paging |
| 31.775 | 161.050 | NFM | London | LWTV Park Royal Ch 2 |
| 31.775 | 161.050 | NFM | Nationwide | Hospital Paging |

## 31.8000 - 34.9000 MHz   USAFE COMMUNICATIONS 25 kHz SIMPLEX

| Base | Mobile | Mode | Location | User and Notes |
|------|--------|------|----------|----------------|
| 31.80000 | | AM | Nationwide | RAF Cadets Channel V12 |
| 31.91250 | | NFM | Nationwide | Digital Signalling |
| 31.95000 | | NFM | Salisbury Plain | Army |
| 32.20000 | | NFM | Nationwide | USAF Base Security |
| 32.25000 | | NFM | Salisbury Plain | Army |
| 32.30000 | | NFM | Brighton | TA Barracks |
| 32.30000 | | NFM | Preston | TA Barracks |
| 32.30000 | | NFM | USAF Fairford | Base Security |
| 32.32500 | | NFM | Salisbury Plain | Army |
| 32.35000 | | NFM | Salisbury Plain | Army |
| 32.35000 | | NFM | USAF Mildenhall | Security |
| 32.42500 | | NFM | Salisbury Plain | Army |
| 32.52500 | | NFM | Salisbury Plain | Army |
| 32.57500 | | NFM | Salisbury Plain | Army |
| 32.70000 | | NFM | Nationwide | RAF Regiment |
| 32.90000 | | NFM | Salisbury Plain | Army |
| 33.12500 | | NFM | Nationwide | Army |
| 33.20000 | | NFM | Salisbury Plain | Army |
| 33.25000 | | NFM | USAF Lakenheath | Birdscare operations |
| 33.25000 | | NFM | USAF Mildenhall | Birdscare operations |
| 33.30000 | | NFM | Nationwide | USAF War Training |
| 33.50000 | | NFM | USAF Lakenheath | Birdscare operations |
| 33.50000 | | NFM | USAF Mildenhall | Birdscare operations |
| 33.67500 | | NFM | Brighton | TA Barracks |
| 33.67500 | | NFM | Preston | TA Barracks |
| 33.70000 | | NFM | USAF Mildenhall | Fire Control |
| 33.77500 | | NFM | Salisbury Plain | Army |
| 33.86250 | | NFM | USAF Mildenhall | Ambulance |
| 34.10000 | | NFM | Nationwide | USAF Medical |
| 34.12500 | | NFM | Salisbury Plain | Army |
| 34.15000 | | NFM | USAF Lakenheath | Crash operations |
| 34.15000 | | NFM | USAF Mildenhall | Crash operations |
| 34.30000 | | NFM | Salisbury Plain | Army |
| 34.40000 | | NFM | Nationwide | Army Forward Air Controllers |

| Base | Mobile | Mode | Location | User and Notes |
|------|--------|------|----------|----------------|
| 34.76250 | | NFM | USAF Mildenhall | Security |
| 34.90000 | | NFM | USAF Lakenheath | Base security |
| 34.90000 | | NFM | USAF Mildenhall | Security |

**34.9250 - 34.9750 MHz**    LOW POWER ALARMS FOR ELDERLY AND INFIRM

| Base | Mobile | Mode | Location | User and Notes |
|------|--------|------|----------|----------------|
| 34.925 | | NFM | Nationwide | Emergency alarms for the elderly |
| 34.950 | | NFM | Nationwide | Emergency alarms for the elderly |
| 34.950 | | NFM | West Midlands | Emergency alarms for the elderly |
| 34.975 | | NFM | Nationwide | Emergency alarms for the elderly |
| 34.975 | | NFM | West Midlands | Emergency alarms for the elderly |

**35.0000 - 35.2500 MHz**    RADIO CONTROLLED MODELS 10 kHz (100 mW MAX)

| Base | Mobile | Mode | Location | User and Notes |
|------|--------|------|----------|----------------|
| 35.000 | | NFM | Nationwide | Channel 60 |
| 35.010 | | NFM | Nationwide | Channel 61 |
| 35.020 | | NFM | Nationwide | Channel 62 |
| 35.030 | | NFM | Nationwide | Channel 63 |
| 35.040 | | NFM | Nationwide | Channel 64 |
| 35.050 | | NFM | Nationwide | Channel 65 |
| 35.060 | | NFM | Nationwide | Channel 66 |
| 35.070 | | NFM | Nationwide | Channel 67 |
| 35.080 | | NFM | Nationwide | Channel 68 |
| 35.090 | | NFM | Nationwide | Channel 69 |
| 35.100 | | NFM | Nationwide | Channel 70 |
| 35.110 | | NFM | Nationwide | Channel 71 |
| 35.120 | | NFM | Nationwide | Channel 72 |
| 35.130 | | NFM | Nationwide | Channel 73 |
| 35.140 | | NFM | Nationwide | Channel 74 |
| 35.150 | | NFM | Nationwide | Channel 75 |
| 35.160 | | NFM | Nationwide | Channel 76 |
| 35.170 | | NFM | Nationwide | Channel 77 |
| 35.180 | | NFM | Nationwide | Channel 78 |
| 35.190 | | NFM | Nationwide | Channel 79 |
| 35.200 | | NFM | Nationwide | Channel 80 |
| 35.210 | | NFM | Nationwide | Channel 81 |
| 35.220 | | NFM | Nationwide | Channel 82 |
| 35.230 | | NFM | Nationwide | Channel 83 |
| 35.240 | | NFM | Nationwide | Channel 84 |
| 35.250 | | NFM | Nationwide | Channel 85 |

**35.2500 - 37.7500 MHz**    MoD TACTICAL COMMUNICATIONS 25 kHz SIMPLEX

| Base | Mobile | Mode | Location | User and Notes |
|------|--------|------|----------|----------------|
| 35.250 | | NFM | Salisbury Plain | Army |
| 35.275 | | NFM | Salisbury Plain | Army |
| 35.350 | | NFM | Brecon Beacons | Army |
| 35.400 | | NFM | Brecon Beacons | Army |
| 35.575 | | NFM | Salisbury Plain | Army |
| 35.600 | | NFM | USAF Mildenhall | Security |
| 35.625 | | NFM | Salisbury Plain | Army |
| 35.775 | | NFM | Salisbury Plain | Army |
| 35.900 | | NFM | USAF Mildenhall | Security |
| 35.975 | | NFM | Nationwide | Royal Signals |
| 36.000 | | NFM | Brighton | TA Barracks |
| 36.000 | | NFM | Preston | TA Barracks |
| 36.200 | | AM | Nationwide | 847 Sqdn Navy Tactical |

| Base | Mobile | Mode | Location | User and Notes |
|------|--------|------|----------|----------------|
| 36.250 | | AM | Yeovilton | 847 Sqdn Navy |
| 36.350 | | NFM | Bovington | Army training camp |
| 36.350 | | AM | Nationwide | 27 Sqdn Air to Air |
| 36.450 | | NFM | Nationwide | JFMG Talkback |
| 36.610 | | NFM | Nationwide | JFMG Touring Conference Radio Mics |
| 36.750 | | NFM | Nationwide | Army Forward Air Controllers |
| 36.790 | | NFM | Nationwide | JFMG Touring Conference Radio Mics |
| 36.800 | | NFM | Nationwide | Air Training Corps V12 |
| 36.850 | | NFM | Salisbury Plain | Army |
| 37.010 | | NFM | Nationwide | JFMG Touring Conference Radio Mics |
| 37.025 | | NFM | Cinque Ports | Signal Regiment |
| 37.025 | | NFM | Nationwide | RAF Regiment |
| 37.190 | | NFM | Nationwide | JFMG Touring Conference Radio Mics |
| 37.200 | | NFM | East Anglia | Regiment |
| 37.225 | | NFM | Stanford Battle Area | Army |
| 37.300 | | AM | Nationwide | RAF Cadets Channel V11 |
| 37.325 | | NFM | Salisbury Plain | Army |

36.6100 - 36.7900 MHz　Cordless Domestic Audio Equipment

37.0100 - 37.1900 MHz　Cordless Domestic Audio Equipment

37.7500 - 38.2500 MHz　Radio Astronomy within 80 km
of Cambridge

37.9000 - 40.1000 MHz　MoD Tactical Communications
25 kHz Simplex

| Base | Mobile | Mode | Location | User and Notes |
|------|--------|------|----------|----------------|
| 38.000 | | NFM | Nationwide | Army Air Corps 653 & 663 Sqdn |
| 38.000 | | USB | Nationwide | Racal Comsec |
| 38.025 | | AM | Nationwide | 3 Cas Gazelle Close Air Support |
| 38.100 | | AM | Nationwide | 18 Sqdn Chinook Air/Air |
| 38.100 | | AM | Nationwide | RAF Cadets Channel V13 |
| 38.320 | | NFM | Nationwide | Fish Tagging (Salmon) |
| 38.325 | | NFM | Cinque Ports | 44 Signal Regiment |
| 38.425 | | NFM | Cinque Ports | 44 Signal Regiment |
| 38.575 | | NFM | Sennybridge | Army |
| 38.625 | | NFM | Okehampton | Army 657 Sqn Ops |
| 38.825 | | NFM | Carlisle | Army Ground Station |
| 39.000 | | NFM | Ludford Cove | Range Patrol Vessel |
| 39.000 | | NFM | Salisbury Plain | Army |
| 39.500 | | NFM | Nationwide | Army Tanks Channel |
| 39.600 | | NFM | Ludford Cove | Army Patrol Vessel |
| 39.650 | | NFM | Nationwide | Army Tanks Channel |
| 39.725 | | NFM | London, Westminster | Royal Yeomanry |
| 39.750 | | NFM | Nationwide | Royal Signals public display |
| 39.800 | | NFM | Nationwide | Puma Air to Air exercises |
| 39.850 | | AM | Nationwide | 3 Cas Gazelle Close Air Support |
| 39.900 | | NFM | USAF Fairford | Base Security |
| 40.000 | | NFM | Salisbury Plain | Army |
| 40.050 | | NFM | Nationwide | Army Distress Frequency |
| 40.080 | | NFM | London | Sky News Link |
| 40.200 | | AM | Nationwide | RAF Cadets Channel V14 |
| 40.275 | | NFM | London | Royal Military Police |

| Base | Mobile | Mode | Location | User and Notes |
| --- | --- | --- | --- | --- |
| 40.6650 - 41.0000 MHz | | | RADIO CONTROLLED SURFACE MODELS 10 KHZ (E.G. CARS AND BOATS) | |
| 40.665 | | NFM | Nationwide | Channel 665 |
| 40.675 | | NFM | Nationwide | Channel 675 |
| 40.685 | | NFM | Nationwide | Channel 685 |
| 40.695 | | NFM | Nationwide | Channel 695 |
| 40.700 | | NFM | Bovington | Army Training Camp |
| 40.700 | | NFM | Salisbury Plain | Army |
| 40.705 | | NFM | Nationwide | Channel 705 |
| 40.715 | | NFM | Nationwide | Channel 715 |
| 40.725 | | NFM | Nationwide | Channel 725 |
| 40.735 | | NFM | Nationwide | Channel 735 |
| 40.745 | | NFM | Nationwide | Channel 745 |
| 40.750 | | NFM | Bovington | Army Training Camp |
| 40.755 | | NFM | Nationwide | Channel 755 |
| 40.765 | | NFM | Nationwide | Channel 765 |
| 40.775 | | NFM | Nationwide | Channel 775 |
| 40.785 | | NFM | Nationwide | Channel 785 |
| 40.795 | | NFM | Nationwide | Channel 795 |
| 40.805 | | NFM | Nationwide | Channel 805 |
| 40.815 | | NFM | Nationwide | Channel 815 |
| 40.825 | | NFM | Nationwide | Channel 825 |
| 40.835 | | NFM | Nationwide | Channel 835 |
| 40.845 | | NFM | Nationwide | Channel 845 |
| 40.855 | | NFM | Nationwide | Channel 855 |
| 40.865 | | NFM | Nationwide | Channel 865 |
| 40.875 | | NFM | Nationwide | Channel 875 |
| 40.875 | | NFM | Salisbury Plain | Army |
| 40.885 | | NFM | Nationwide | Channel 885 |
| 40.895 | | NFM | Nationwide | Channel 895 |
| 40.905 | | NFM | Nationwide | Channel 905 |
| 40.915 | | NFM | Nationwide | Channel 915 |
| 40.925 | | NFM | Nationwide | Channel 925 |
| 40.935 | | NFM | Nationwide | Channel 935 |
| 40.945 | | NFM | Nationwide | Channel 945 |
| 40.955 | | NFM | Nationwide | Channel 955 |
| 41.0000 - 46.6000 MHz | | | MoD TACTICAL COMMUNICATIONS 25 KHZ SIMPLEX | |
| 41.10000 | | AM | Odiham | Chinook Wing Ops |
| 41.12500 | | NFM | Salisbury Plain | Army |
| 41.17500 | | NFM | Nationwide | Army Ground Station |
| 41.25000 | | NFM | Cinque Ports | 44 Signals Regiment |
| 42.05000 | | NFM | Jersey | Territorial Army |
| 42.05000 | | NFM | Salisbury Plain | Army |
| 42.12500 | | NFM | Nationwide | Army War Training |
| 42.15000 | | NFM | Cinque Ports | 44 Signals Regiment |
| 42.32500 | | NFM | Salisbury Plain | Army |
| 42.55000 | | NFM | Salisbury Plain | Army |
| 43.10000 | | NFM | Salisbury Plain | Army |
| 43.22500 | | NFM | Salisbury Plain | Army |
| 43.45000 | | NFM | Nationwide | 7 Sqdn Chinook Air to Air. |
| 43.55000 | | NFM | Salisbury Plain | Army |
| 43.72500 | | NFM | North West England | Army Ground Station |
| 43.77500 | | NFM | Salisbury Plain | Army |

| Base | Mobile | Mode | Location | User and Notes |
|------|--------|------|----------|----------------|
| 44.00000 | | NFM | Bovington | Army Training Camp |
| 44.00000 | | NFM | Salisbury Plain | Army |
| 44.42500 | | NFM | Salisbury Plain | Army |
| 44.45000 | | NFM | Nationwide | Army War Training |
| 45.30000 | | NFM | Salisbury Plain | Army |
| 45.30000 | | NFM | Stanford Battle Area | Army |
| 45.40000 | | NFM | Sennybridge | Army |
| 45.42500 | | NFM | Stanford Battle Area | Army |
| 45.70000 | | NFM | Wiltshire | Dunge Hill War Games |
| 45.71250 | | NFM | Nationwide | Army War Training |
| 45.75000 | | NFM | Nationwide | RAF Regiment |
| 46.00000 | | NFM | Nationwide | Royal Signals Display |
| 46.12500 | | NFM | Nationwide | Army War Training |
| 46.32500 | | NFM | Nationwide | Army War Training |

### 46.6100 - 46.9700 MHz — US SPEC. CORDLESS TELEPHONES BASE (SPLIT + 3.06 MHz)

| Base | Mobile | Mode | Location | User and Notes |
|------|--------|------|----------|----------------|
| 46.610 | 49.670 | NFM | Nationwide | US Specification Channel 1 |
| 46.630 | 49.845 | NFM | Nationwide | US Specification Channel 2 |
| 46.670 | 49.860 | NFM | Nationwide | US Specification Channel 3 |
| 46.710 | 49.770 | NFM | Nationwide | US Specification Channel 4 |
| 46.730 | 49.875 | NFM | Nationwide | US Specification Channel 5 |
| 46.770 | 49.830 | NFM | Nationwide | US Specification Channel 6 |
| 46.830 | 49.890 | NFM | Nationwide | US Specification Channel 7 |
| 46.870 | 49.930 | NFM | Nationwide | US Specification Channel 8 |
| 46.930 | 49.990 | NFM | Nationwide | US Specification Channel 9 |
| 46.970 | 49.970 | NFM | Nationwide | US Specification Channel 10 |

### 47.0000 - 47.4000 MHz — FUTURE PMR ALLOCATION, CURRENTLY MoD

### 47.309375 - 47.365625 MHz — LONG RANGE AND VEHICLE SECURITY ALARM SYSTEMS 12.5 kHz BANDWIDTH

| Base | Mobile | Mode | Location | User and Notes |
|------|--------|------|----------|----------------|
| 47.30938 | | NFM | Nationwide | Long Range Security Alarms Ch 1 (6.25 kHz bandwidth) |
| 47.31875 | | NFM | Nationwide | Long Range Security Alarms Ch 2 |
| 47.33125 | | NFM | Nationwide | Long Range Security Alarms Ch 3 |
| 47.34375 | | NFM | Nationwide | Long Range Security Alarms Ch 4 |
| 47.35625 | | NFM | Nationwide | Long Range Security Alarms Ch 5 |
| 47.36563 | | NFM | Nationwide | Long Range Security Alarms Ch 6 (6.25 kHz bandwidth) |
| 47.40000 | | NFM | Nationwide | Car Theft Paging Alarms |

### 47.41875 - 47.43125 MHz — EXTENDED RANGE CORDLESS PHONES

| Base | Mobile | Mode | Location | User and Notes |
|------|--------|------|----------|----------------|
| 47.41875 | 77.55000 | NFM | Nationwide | Extended Range Telephone |
| 47.43125 | 77.51250 | NFM | Nationwide | Extended Range Telephone |

### 47.45625 - 47.54375 MHz — CORDLESS TELEPHONES

| Base | Mobile | Mode | Location | User and Notes |
|------|--------|------|----------|----------------|
| 47.45625 | 1.64200 | NFM | Nationwide | Channel 1 |
| 47.46875 | 1.66200 | NFM | Nationwide | Channel 2 |
| 47.48125 | 1.68200 | NFM | Nationwide | Channel 3 |
| 47.49375 | 1.70200 | NFM | Nationwide | Channel 4 |
| 47.50625 | 1.72200 | NFM | Nationwide | Channel 5 |
| 47.51875 | 1.74200 | NFM | Nationwide | Channel 6 |
| 47.53125 | 1.76200 | NFM | Nationwide | Channel 7 |
| 47.54375 | 1.78200 | NFM | Nationwide | Channel 8 |

| Base | Mobile | Mode | Location | User and Notes |
|------|--------|------|----------|----------------|

**47.5500 - 48.5500 MHz**  BROADCASTING LINKS

| Base | Mobile | Mode | Location | User and Notes |
|------|--------|------|----------|----------------|
| 47.55000 | | NFM | Nationwide | JFMG Location Talkback Base |
| 47.57000 | | NFM | Cardiff | BBC Radio Wales studio sound channel |
| 47.64500 | | NFM | Nationwide | BBC O/B |
| 47.94375 | | NFM | Nationwide | ITV Engineers Channel 1 |
| 47.94375 | | NFM | Stockport | ITV Engineers |
| 47.95625 | | NFM | Nationwide | ITV Engineers Channel 2 |
| 47.96875 | | NFM | Nationwide | ITV Engineers Channel 3 |
| 48.05625 | | NFM | Isle of Wight | Isle of Wight Radio Feeder |
| 48.08125 | | NFM | London | Sky TV Talkback |

**48.4000 - 48.5000 MHz**  CORDLESS RADIO MICROPHONES 12.5 KHz

| Base | Mobile | Mode | Location | User and Notes |
|------|--------|------|----------|----------------|
| 48.30000 | 52.75000 | WFM | Nationwide | JFMG Stereo Sound Link |
| 48.40000 | | NFM | Nationwide | Channel 1 |
| 48.40625 | 52.85625 | NFM | Nationwide | ASP-Hi Talkback |
| 48.41250 | | NFM | Nationwide | Channel 2 |
| 48.41250 | 52.86875 | NFM | Nationwide | ASP-Hi Talkback |
| 48.42500 | | NFM | Nationwide | Channel 3 |
| 48.42500 | | WFM | Nationwide | JFMG Mono Sound Link |
| 48.42500 | 52.87125 | NFM | Nationwide | A3P-I li Talkback |
| 48.43750 | | NFM | Nationwide | Channel 4 |
| 48.43750 | 52.90375 | NFM | Nationwide | ASP-Hi Talkback |
| 48.45000 | | WFM | England, south | Coastway Hospital Link South Coast |
| 48.45000 | | WFM | Essex | Radio Caroline Link TX Essex |
| 48.45000 | | NFM | Nationwide | Channel 5 |
| 48.45000 | 52.90625 | NFM | Nationwide | ASP-Hi Talkback |
| 48.46250 | | NFM | Nationwide | Channel 6 |
| 48.46250 | 52.91875 | NFM | Nationwide | ASP-Hi Talkback |
| 48.47500 | | NFM | Nationwide | Channel 7 |
| 48.47500 | | WFM | Nationwide | JFMG Mono Sound Link |
| 48.47500 | 52.93125 | NFM | Nationwide | ASP-Hi Talkback |
| 48.48750 | | NFM | Nationwide | Channel 8 |
| 48.50000 | 52.94375 | NFM | Nationwide | ASP-Hi Talkback |
| 48.52500 | | WFM | Nationwide | JFMG Mono Sound Link |
| 48.80000 | | NFM | Nationwide | JFMG Location Talkback Base |

**48.97500 - 48.98750 MHz**  SHORT TERM HIRE PAGING

| Base | Mobile | Mode | Location | User and Notes |
|------|--------|------|----------|----------------|
| 48.9750 | | NFM | Nationwide | Short Term Hire Paging |
| 48.9875 | | NFM | Nationwide | Short Term Hire Paging |

**48.99375 - 49.49375 MHz**  ONE WAY NON SPEECH PAGING SYSTEMS

| Base | Mobile | Mode | Location | User and Notes |
|------|--------|------|----------|----------------|
| 49.0000 | | NFM | Nationwide | Channel 1 |
| 49.0125 | | NFM | Nationwide | Channel 2 |
| 49.0250 | | NFM | Nationwide | Channel 3 |
| 49.0375 | | NFM | Nationwide | Channel 4 |
| 49.0500 | | NFM | Nationwide | Channel 5 |
| 49.0625 | | NFM | Nationwide | Channel 6 |
| 49.0750 | | NFM | Nationwide | Channel 7 |
| 49.0875 | | NFM | Nationwide | Channel 8 |
| 49.1000 | | NFM | Nationwide | Channel 9 |
| 49.1125 | | NFM | Nationwide | Channel 10 |
| 49.1250 | | NFM | Nationwide | Channel 11 |
| 49.1375 | | NFM | Nationwide | Channel 12 |
| 49.1500 | | NFM | Nationwide | Channel 13 |

| Base | Mobile | Mode | Location | User and Notes |
|---|---|---|---|---|
| 49.1625 | | NFM | Nationwide | Channel 14 |
| 49.1750 | | NFM | Nationwide | Channel 15 |
| 49.1875 | | NFM | Nationwide | Channel 16 |
| 49.2000 | | NFM | Nationwide | Channel 17 |
| 49.2125 | | NFM | Nationwide | Channel 18 |
| 49.2250 | | NFM | Nationwide | Channel 19 |
| 49.2375 | | NFM | Nationwide | Channel 20 |
| 49.2500 | | NFM | Nationwide | Channel 21 |
| 49.2625 | | NFM | Nationwide | Channel 22 |
| 49.2750 | | NFM | Nationwide | Channel 23 |
| 49.2875 | | NFM | Nationwide | Channel 24 |
| 49.3000 | | NFM | Nationwide | Channel 25 |
| 49.3125 | | NFM | Nationwide | Channel 26 |
| 49.3250 | | NFM | Nationwide | Channel 27 |
| 49.3375 | | NFM | Nationwide | Channel 28 |
| 49.3500 | | NFM | Nationwide | Channel 29 |
| 49.3625 | | NFM | Nationwide | Channel 30 |
| 49.3750 | | NFM | Nationwide | Channel 31 |
| 49.3875 | | NFM | Nationwide | Channel 32 |
| 49.4000 | | NFM | Nationwide | Channel 33 |
| 49.4125 | | NFM | Nationwide | Channel 34 |

### 49.4250 - 49.4750 MHz    HOSPITAL PAGING

| Base | Mobile | Mode | Location | User and Notes |
|---|---|---|---|---|
| 49.4250 | | NFM | Bournemouth | Hospital Paging |
| 49.4250 | | NFM | Nationwide | Hospital Channel 35 |
| 49.4375 | | NFM | Nationwide | Hospital Channel 36 |
| 49.4500 | | NFM | Jersey | Hospital Cardiac Bleep & Voice |
| 49.4500 | | NFM | Nationwide | Hospital Channel 37 |
| 49.4500 | | NFM | Oxford | J Radcliff Hospital emergencies |
| 49.4625 | | NFM | Nationwide | Hospital Channel 38 |
| 49.4750 | | NFM | Nationwide | Hospital Channel 39 |

### 49.5000 - 49.7875 MHz    BBC CORDLESS MICROPHONES NFM

### 49.8200 - 49.9875 MHz    LOW POWER DEVICES, WALKIE TALKIES, RADIO CONTROLLED TOYS AND BABY MONITORS

| Base | Mobile | Mode | Location | User and Notes |
|---|---|---|---|---|
| 49.800 | | WFM | Nationwide | Wireless Headphones new frequency |
| 49.820 | | NFM | Nationwide | Channel 1 |
| 49.820 | | NFM | Nationwide | JFMG Touring Conference Radio Mics |
| 49.830 | | NFM | London | Maxon Ch 1 Metropolis motorcycle training |
| 49.830 | | NFM | Nationwide | Channel 2 |
| 49.830 | | NFM | Nationwide | Channel A |
| 49.830 | | NFM | Nationwide | Maxan Channel 1 |
| 49.840 | | NFM | Kingston | JJB Sports |
| 49.840 | | NFM | Milton Keynes | JJB Sports |
| 49.840 | | NFM | Nationwide | Channel 3 |
| 49.840 | | NFM | Nationwide | Channel UK1 |
| 49.845 | | NFM | Nationwide | Channel B |
| 49.845 | | NFM | Nationwide | Maxan Channel 2 |
| 49.850 | | NFM | Nationwide | Channel 4 |
| 49.860 | | NFM | Ayr | Sports Division stock control |
| 49.860 | | NFM | Nationwide | Channel 5 |
| 49.860 | | NFM | Nationwide | Channel C |
| 49.860 | | NFM | Nationwide | Maxan Channel 3 |
| 49.870 | | NFM | Nationwide | Channel 6 |

| Base | Mobile | Mode | Location | User and Notes |
|------|--------|------|----------|----------------|
| 49.875 | | NFM | Nationwide | Channel D |
| 49.875 | | NFM | Nationwide | Maxan Channel 4 |
| 49.880 | | NFM | Nationwide | Channel UK2 |
| 49.890 | | NFM | London | CSM motorcycle training |
| 49.890 | | NFM | Nationwide | Channel 7 |
| 49.890 | | NFM | Nationwide | Channel E |
| 49.890 | | NFM | Nationwide | Maxan Channel 5 |
| 49.900 | | NFM | Nationwide | Channel 8 |
| 49.910 | | NFM | Nationwide | Channel 9 |
| 49.920 | | NFM | Nationwide | Channel 10 |
| 49.930 | | NFM | Nationwide | Channel 11 |
| 49.940 | | NFM | Nationwide | Channel 12 |
| 49.950 | | NFM | Nationwide | Channel 13 |
| 49.960 | | NFM | Nationwide | Channel 14 |
| 49.960 | | NFM | Nationwide | Channel UK3 |
| 49.970 | | NFM | Nationwide | Channel 15 |
| 49.980 | | NFM | Nationwide | Channel 16 |
| 49.980 | | NFM | Nationwide | JFMG Touring Conference Radio Mics |

| 50.0000 - 52.0000 MHz | | | 6M UK AMATEUR RADIO BAND ALL MODES | |
|------|--------|------|----------|----------------|
| 50.00000 | | CW | Buxton | Beacon (GB3BUX) |
| 50.04200 | | CW | St Austell | Beacon (GB3MCB) |
| 50.05000 | | CW | Potters Bar | Beacon (GB3NHQ) |
| 50.06000 | | CW | Inverness | Beacon (GB3RMK) |
| 50.06200 | | CW | Ballymena | Beacon (GB3NGI) |
| 50.06400 | | CW | Lerwick | Beacon (GB3LER) |
| 50.06550 | | CW | St Helier | Beacon (GB3IOJ) |
| 50.09000 | | CW | Nationwide | CW calling channel |
| 50.20000 | | USB | Nationwide | SSB calling |
| 50.27500 | | CW | Darlington | Repeater (GB3IFX) |
| 50.30000 | | CW | Nationwide | CW calling |
| 50.51000 | | SSB | Nationwide | Slow scan TV |
| 50.55000 | | SSB | Nationwide | Fax |
| 50.60000 | | SSB | Nationwide | RTTY (afsk) |
| 50.63000 | | SSB | Nationwide | Packet Radio |
| 51.22000 | 50.72000 | NFM | Ipswich | Amateur Repeater GB3EF |
| 51.22000 | 50.72000 | NFM | Tenby | Amateur Repeater GB3AE |
| 51.24000 | 50.74000 | NFM | Leicester | Amateur Repeater GB3UM |
| 51.27000 | 50.77000 | NFM | Lancashire | Amateur Repeater GB3UK |
| 51.28000 | 50.78000 | NFM | Royston | Amateur Repeater GB3PX |
| 51.29000 | 50.79000 | NFM | Stoke-on-Trent | Amateur Repeater GB3SX |
| 51.30000 | 50.80000 | NFM | Huddersfield | Amateur Repeater GB3HX |
| 51.31000 | 50.81000 | NFM | Farnham | Amateur Repeater GB3FX |
| 51.32000 | 50.82000 | NFM | Nottingham | Amateur Repeater GB3RR |
| 51.32000 | 50.83000 | NFM | Shaftesbury | Amateur Repeater GB3WX |
| 51.34000 | 50.84000 | NFM | Amersham | Amateur Repeater GB3AM |
| 51.35000 | 50.85000 | NFM | Portsmouth | Amateur Repeater GB3PD |
| 51.51000 | | SSB | Nationwide | FM calling channel |
| | | | | |
| 50.50000 | | FM | Nationwide | Video transmissions for railways, track to train, using leaky feeder techniques. |

### 52.0000 - 52.3875 MHz — BROADCASTING LINKS NFM

### 52.8500 - 52.9500 MHz — CORDLESS RADIO MICROPHONES 12.5 kHz

| Base | Mode | Location | User and Notes |
|------|------|----------|----------------|
| 51.56000 | AM | Nationwide | Army Helicopters. |
| 52.00000 | NFM | Nationwide | JFMG Location Talkback Mobile |
| 52.58750 | WFM | Peterborough | E of England Show radio station link motorcycle rally |
| 52.70000 | NFM | Nationwide | RAF Regiment |
| 52.75000 | WFM | Nationwide | JFMG Stereo Sound Link |
| 52.85000 | NFM | Nationwide | Channel 1 |
| 52.85000 | WFM | Perth | Hospital Radio |
| 52.86250 | NFM | Nationwide | ASP Talkback Sound Links |
| 52.86250 | NFM | Nationwide | Channel 2 |
| 52.87500 | NFM | Nationwide | ASP Talkback Sound Links |
| 52.87500 | NFM | Nationwide | Channel 3 |
| 52.87500 | WFM | Nationwide | JFMG Mono Sound Link |
| 52.87500 | WFM | Nationwide | JFMG Mono Sound Link |
| 52.88750 | NFM | Nationwide | Channel 4 |
| 52.90000 | NFM | Nationwide | ASP Talkback Sound Links |
| 52.90000 | NFM | Nationwide | Channel 5 |
| 52.91250 | NFM | Nationwide | ASP Talkback Sound Links |
| 52.91250 | NFM | Nationwide | Channel 6 |
| 52.92500 | NFM | Nationwide | ASP Talkback Sound Links |
| 52.92500 | NFM | Nationwide | Channel 7 |
| 52.92500 | WFM | Nationwide | JFMG Mono Sound Link |
| 52.93750 | WFM | Castlepoint & Benfleet | OAP Homes Radio Net |
| 52.93750 | NFM | Nationwide | ASP Talkback Sound Links |
| 52.93750 | NFM | Nationwide | Channel 8 |
| 52.95000 | NFM | Nationwide | ASP Talkback Sound Links |
| 52.95000 | NFM | Nationwide | JFMG Location Talkback Mobile |
| 53.20000 | NFM | Swansea | BBC Wales |
| 53.52500 | NFM | Nationwide | BBC O/B Continuity |

### 53.7500 - 55.7500 MHz — BBC 5W CORDLESS MICROPHONES

| Base | Mode | Location | User and Notes |
|------|------|----------|----------------|
| 53.575 | NFM | Taunton | BBC O/B Mics (Somerset Sound) |
| 53.750 | NFM | Nationwide | BBC O/B Microphone Ch. 1 |
| 53.750 | NFM | Nationwide | JFMG Portable Audio Links |
| 53.800 | NFM | Nationwide | JFMG L/Power Fixed Site Conference |
| 53.800 | WFM | Nationwide | JFMG WFM Conference Use |
| 53.850 | NFM | Nationwide | BBC O/B Microphone Ch. 2 |
| 53.950 | NFM | Nationwide | BBC O/B Microphone Ch. 3 |
| 54.050 | NFM | Nationwide | BBC O/B Microphone Ch. 4 |
| 54.100 | NFM | Nationwide | JFMG L/Power Fixed Site Conference |
| 54.100 | WFM | Nationwide | JFMG WFM Conference Use |
| 54.150 | NFM | Nationwide | BBC O/B Microphone Ch. 5 |
| 54.250 | NFM | Nationwide | BBC O/B Microphone Ch. 6 |
| 54.300 | NFM | Nationwide | JFMG L/Power Fixed Site Conference |
| 54.300 | WFM | Nationwide | JFMG WFM Conference Use |
| 54.350 | NFM | Nationwide | BBC O/B Microphone Ch. 7 |
| 54.450 | NFM | Nationwide | BBC O/B Microphone Ch. 8 |
| 54.550 | NFM | Nationwide | BBC O/B Microphone Ch. 9 |
| 54.650 | NFM | Nationwide | BBC O/B Microphone Ch. 10 |
| 54.700 | NFM | Nationwide | JFMG Lipower Fixed Site Conference |
| 54.700 | WFM | Nationwide | JFMG WFM Conference Use |
| 54.760 | NFM | Nationwide | BBC O/B Microphone Ch. 11 |
| 54.800 | AM | Nationwide | 845 Sqdn Navy Sea King. |

| Base | Mobile | Mode | Location | User and Notes |
|------|--------|------|----------|----------------|
| 54.850 | | NFM | Nationwide | BBC O/B Microphone Ch. 12 |
| 54.950 | | NFM | Nationwide | BBC O/B Microphone Ch. 13 |
| 55.050 | | NFM | Nationwide | BBC O/B Microphone Ch. 14 |
| 55.150 | | NFM | Nationwide | BBC O/B Microphone Ch. 15 |
| 55.250 | | NFM | Nationwide | BBC O/B Microphone Ch. 16 |
| 55.350 | | NFM | Nationwide | BBC O/B Microphone Ch. 17 |
| 55.400 | | NFM | Nationwide | JFMG Lipower Fixed Site Conference |
| 55.400 | | WFM | Nationwide | JFMG WFM Conference Use |
| 55.450 | | NFM | Nationwide | BBC O/B Microphone Ch. 18 |
| 55.500 | | NFM | Nationwide | JFMG L/Power Fixed Site Conference |
| 55.500 | | WFM | Nationwide | JFMG WFM Conference Use |
| 55.550 | | NFM | Nationwide | BBC O/B Microphone Ch. 19 |
| 55.750 | | NFM | Nationwide | JFMG Portable Audio Links |

**55.7500 - 60.75000 MHz  Future PMR**

**54.000 - 60.000 MHz   MoD Tactical Communications 25 kHz Simplex**

| Base | Mobile | Mode | Location | User and Notes |
|------|--------|------|----------|----------------|
| 56.62500 | | NFM | Nationwide | Royal Signals Public Displays |

**60.7500 - 62.7500 MHz     BBC 5W Cordless and Outside Broadcast Mics**

| Base | Mobile | Mode | Location | User and Notes |
|------|--------|------|----------|----------------|
| 56.97500 | | NFM | Nationwide | BBC O/B Continuity |
| 60.29500 | | NFM | Nationwide | BBC O/B Continuity |
| 60.75000 | | NFM | Nationwide | BBC O/B Microphone Ch. 20 |
| 60.75000 | | NFM | Nationwide | JFMG Portable Audio Links |
| 60.80000 | | NFM | Nationwide | BBC O/B Microphone |
| 60.85000 | | NFM | Nationwide | BBC O/B Microphone Ch. 21 |
| 60.90000 | | NFM | Nationwide | BBC O/B Microphone |
| 60.95000 | | NFM | Nationwide | BBC O/B Microphone Ch. 22 |
| 61.00000 | | NFM | Nationwide | BBC O/B Microphone |
| 61.05000 | | NFM | Nationwide | BBC O/B Microphone Ch. 23 |
| 61.10000 | | NFM | Nationwide | BBC O/B Microphone |
| 61.15000 | | NFM | Nationwide | BBC O/B Microphone Ch. 24 |
| 61.25000 | | NFM | Nationwide | BBC O/B Microphone Ch. 25 |
| 61.30000 | | NFM | Nationwide | BBC O/B Microphone |
| 61.35000 | | NFM | Nationwide | BBC O/B Microphone Ch. 26 |
| 61.40000 | | NFM | Nationwide | BBC O/B Microphone |
| 61.45000 | | NFM | Nationwide | BBC O/B Microphone Ch. 27 |
| 61.50000 | | NFM | Nationwide | BBC O/B Microphone |
| 61.55000 | | NFM | Nationwide | BBC O/B Microphone Ch. 28 |
| 61.65000 | | NFM | Nationwide | BBC O/B Microphone Ch. 29 |
| 61.70000 | | NFM | Nationwide | BBC O/B Microphone |
| 61.75000 | | NFM | Nationwide | BBC O/B Microphone Ch. 30 |
| 61.80000 | | NFM | Nationwide | BBC O/B Microphone |
| 61.85000 | | NFM | Nationwide | BBC O/B Microphone Ch. 31 |
| 61.90000 | | NFM | Nationwide | BBC O/B Microphone |
| 61.95000 | | NFM | Nationwide | BBC O/B Microphone Ch. 32 |
| 62.05000 | | NFM | Nationwide | BBC O/B Microphone Ch. 33 |
| 62.15000 | | NFM | Nationwide | BBC O/B Microphone Ch. 34 |
| 62.20000 | | NFM | Nationwide | BBC O/B Microphone |
| 62.25000 | | NFM | Nationwide | BBC O/B Microphone Ch. 35 |
| 62.27500 | | NFM | Nationwide | Royal Signals |
| 62.35000 | | NFM | Nationwide | BBC O/B Microphone Ch. 36 |
| 62.45000 | | NFM | Nationwide | BBC O/B Microphone Ch. 37 |
| 62.55000 | | NFM | Nationwide | BBC O/B Microphone Ch. 38 |

| Base | Mobile | Mode | Location | User and Notes |
|---|---|---|---|---|
| 62.60000 | | NFM | Nationwide | BBC O/B Microphone |
| 62.75000 | | NFM | Nationwide | JFMG Portable Audio Links |
| 62.92500 | | NFM | Nationwide | BBC O/B Microphones (spare) |
| 64.03750 | | NFM | Nationwide | BBC O/B Microphones |

**62.75000 - 68.0000 MHz**     FUTURE PMR

**64.0000 - 68.0000 MHz**     MoD TACTICAL COMMUNICATIONS
25 kHz SIMPLEX

| Base | Mobile | Mode | Location | User and Notes |
|---|---|---|---|---|
| 66.77500 | | NFM | Nationwide | Royal Signals |
| 68.02500 | | AM | Cheltenham | MoD Transport |
| 68.02500 | | AM | Nationwide | UKAEA Transport Movements |
| 68.10000 | | NFM | Nationwide | MoD Engineering |
| 68.12500 | | NFM | Brecon Beacons | Army Range Ops |
| 68.15000 | | NFM | Maidenhead | Army Stores |
| 68.15000 | | NFM | Nationwide | Army Stores |
| 68.15000 | 68.15000 | NFM | Nationwide | Army Pye Channel 6 |
| 68.15000 | 79.35000 | NFM | Camberley | Army Stores |

**68.08125 - 70.00625**     PMR LOW BAND MOBILE SIMPLEX

| Base | Mobile | Mode | Location | User and Notes |
|---|---|---|---|---|
| 68.20000 | | NFM | Isle of Man | Highways & Transport |
| 68.48750 | | NFM | Doncaster | Carr Hill Parcels |
| 69.40000 | | NFM | Nationwide | RAC Network Q Rally Control |
| 69.45000 | | NFM | Nationwide | RAC Network Q Rally Control |
| 69.48750 | | NFM | Nationwide | RAC Network Q Rally Control |
| 69.98750 | | NFM | Nationwide | RAC Network Q Rally Control |

**68.0000 - 69.5000 MHz**     MoD, MOULD & TACTICAL COMMUNICATIONS
25 kHz

| Base | Mobile | Mode | Location | User and Notes |
|---|---|---|---|---|
| 68.20000 | | NFM | Nationwide | Royal Signals |
| 68.20000 | 78.40000 | NFM | Nationwide | Army Pye Channel 4 |
| 68.22500 | | NFM | Nationwide | Royal Signals |
| 68.23750 | | NFM | Kent | Customs & Excise car to car Ch.5 |
| 68.26250 | | NFM | Nationwide | Royal Signals |
| 68.27500 | | NFM | Dartmoor | Military Range |
| 68.30000 | 79.22500 | NFM | Nationwide | Army Pye Channel 1 |
| 68.32500 | | AM | Nationwide | Military Airfield Ground services |
| 68.35000 | | NFM | Dartmoor | Military Range |
| 68.35000 | 68.35000 | NFM | Nationwide | Army Pye Channel 5 |
| 68.36250 | | NFM | Nationwide | Army Cadet Force Ch 1 |
| 68.38750 | | NFM | Bristol | MoD Transport |
| 68.40000 | 79.25000 | NFM | Nationwide | Army Pye Channel 2 |
| 68.42500 | | NFM | Dartmoor | Military Range |
| 68.42500 | | NFM | Northern Ireland | British Army |
| 68.42500 | 79.27500 | NFM | Nationwide | Army Pye Channel 3 |
| 68.50000 | | NFM | RN Rosyth | Dockyard Ops |
| 68.50000 | | NFM | Rosyth | RN Dockyards Operations |
| 68.50000 | 79.80000 | NFM | Nationwide | Army Pye Channel 7 |
| 68.52500 | 79.70000 | NFM | Nationwide | Army Pye Channel 8 |
| 68.56250 | | AM | RAE Farnborough | Emergency Services |
| 68.60000 | 79.95000 | NFM | Nationwide | Army Pye Channel 9 |
| 68.61250 | | AM | RAE Farnborough | Tractor Control |
| 68.62500 | | NFM | Larkhill | Army Range |
| 68.63750 | | AM | Nationwide | Army Pye Channel 1 |
| 68.63750 | | NFM | Northern Ireland | British Army |

| Base | Mobile | Mode | Location | User and Notes |
|------|--------|------|----------|----------------|
| 68.63750 | | AM | RAE Farnborough | ATC Ch 6 |
| 68.67875 | | NFM | Nationwide | Royal Signals |
| 68.68750 | | AM | Cheltenham | MoD Transport |
| 68.68750 | | AM | Hampshire | MoD transport |
| 68.68750 | | AM | RAE Farnborough | Ground Services |
| 68.69380 | | AM | RAE Farnborough | Repair Workshop |
| 68.72000 | | NFM | Machynlleth | ManWeb |
| 68.76250 | | NFM | Salisbury Plain | Army Transport (Tenor Base) |
| 68.78750 | | AM | Cheltenham | MoD Transport |
| 68.86880 | | AM | RAE Farnborough | Fire |
| 68.90630 | | AM | RAE Farnborough | Medical |
| 68.98750 | | NFM | Brecon Beacons | Mould |
| 69.00000 | 75.00000 | NFM | Nationwide | JFMG Owned Band BBC Closing Yr 2000 |
| 69.07500 | | NFM | Okehampton | Military Range |
| 69.12125 | | NFM | Nationwide | Royal Signals |
| 69.12500 | | NFM | Isle of Man | Highways & Transport |
| 69.12500 | | NFM | Northern Ireland | British Army |
| 69.15500 | | NFM | Northern Ireland | British Army |
| 69.17500 | | NFM | Okehampton | Military Range |
| 69.20000 | | NFM | Northern Ireland | British Army |
| 69.22500 | | NFM | Berkshire | Cadet Training Net |
| 69.25000 | | NFM | Northern Ireland | British Army |
| 69.30000 | | AM | Smethwick | Sea Cadets |
| 69.32500 | | NFM | Brecon Beacons | Army |
| 69.32500 | | NFM | Northern Ireland | British Army |
| 69.35000 | | AM | Brecon Beacons | Army Cadets Hike Control |
| 69.37500 | | NFM | Northern Ireland | British Army |
| 69.40000 | | WFM | Nationwide | Eastern European Low Band Skip |
| 69.40000 | | NFM | Northern Ireland | British Army |
| 69.47500 | 84.52500 | NFM | Nationwide | 39 Inf Bgd/Sig Chan A9 |

## 69.5000 - 69.8000 MHz    MoD Tactical Communications
### 25 kHz Simplex

| Base | Mobile | Mode | Location | User and Notes |
|------|--------|------|----------|----------------|
| 69.50000 | | NFM | Okehampton | Military Range |
| 69.50000 | | NFM | RN Rosyth | Security |
| 69.55000 | | NFM | Northern Ireland | British Army |
| 69.57500 | | NFM | Northern Ireland | Army Bomb Squad |
| 69.75000 | | NFM | Northern Ireland | British Army |
| 69.80000 | | NFM | Northern Ireland | British Army |
| 69.70000 | | WFM | Nationwide | Eastern European Low Band Skip |

## 69.82225 - 69.9625 MHz    Television O/B "System One" CMCR
### Studio Manager Talkback

| Base | Mobile | Mode | Location | User and Notes |
|------|--------|------|----------|----------------|
| 69.82250 | 74.70000 | NFM | Nationwide | BBC Studio Manager Ch. 3 |
| 69.82500 | | NFM | Manchester | ITN Studio Link |
| 69.82500 | | NFM | Nationwide | BBC CMCR Channel 7 |
| 69.82500 | | NFM | Northern Ireland | British Army |
| 69.83500 | 75.26880 | NFM | Nationwide | BBC Studio Manager Ch. 4 |
| 69.83750 | | NFM | Nationwide | BBC CMCR Channel 8 |
| 69.83750 | | NFM | Scotland | BBC Scotland CMCR |
| 69.84500 | | AM | Salisbury Plain | Army |
| 69.84750 | | NFM | Nationwide | BBC Studio Manager Ch. 5 |
| 69.85000 | | NFM | Nationwide | BBC CMCR Channel 9 |
| 69.85000 | | NFM | Northern Ireland | British Army |
| 69.86000 | | NFM | Nationwide | BBC Studio Manager Ch. 6 |

| Base | Mobile | Mode | Location | User and Notes |
|---|---|---|---|---|
| 69.86250 | | NFM | Nationwide | BBC CMCR Channel 10 |
| 69.86250 | | AM | RNAS Yeovilton | Radio Somerset link at air display |
| 69.87250 | | NFM | Nationwide | BBC Studio Manager Ch. 7 |
| 69.87500 | | NFM | Nationwide | BBC CMCR Channel 11 |
| 69.88500 | | NFM | Nationwide | BBC Studio Manager Ch. 8 |
| 69.89750 | | NFM | Nationwide | BBC Studio Manager Ch. 9 |
| 69.90000 | | NFM | Birmingham | BBC Talkback |
| 69.90000 | | NFM | Goodwood | BBC Goodwood OB |
| 69.90000 | | NFM | Haydock Park | TV O/B |
| 69.90000 | | NFM | Scotland | BBC Scotland Channel 12 |
| 69.90000 | 75.29375 | NFM | Swansea | BBC Wales O/B |
| 69.90750 | 75.28750 | NFM | Nationwide | BBC Studio Manager Ch. 2 |
| 69.92500 | | NFM | Nationwide | BBC Studio Continuity |

**69.9650 - 70.0000 MHz**      MoD TACTICAL COMMUNICATIONS 25 kHz

| Base | Mobile | Mode | Location | User and Notes |
|---|---|---|---|---|
| 69.95000 | | NFM | Northern Ireland | British Army |
| 69.96250 | 75.26250 | NFM | Nationwide | BBC Studio Manager Ch. 1 |
| 69.97500 | | NFM | Berkshire | Cadet Training Net |
| 69.98000 | | FM | Northern Ireland | Ulster Defence Regiment |

**70.0000 - 70.5000 MHz**      4M AMATEUR RADIO BAND

| Base | Mobile | Mode | Location | User and Notes |
|---|---|---|---|---|
| 70.00000 | | CW | Buxton | Beacon (GB3BUX) |
| 70.01000 | | CW | Camberley | Repeater (GB3REB) |
| 70.02000 | | CW | Dundee | Beacon (GB3ANG) |
| 70.02500 | | CW | St Austell | Beacon (GB3MCB) |
| 70.20000 | | CW | Nationwide | CW calling channel |
| 70.20000 | | SSB | Nationwide | SSB calling channel |
| 70.26000 | | AM | Nationwide | AM calling channel |
| 70.30000 | | NFM | Nationwide | FAX calling channel |
| 70.30000 | | NFM | Nationwide | RTTY calling channel |
| 70.30000 | | NFM | Salisbury Plain | Army |
| 70.31250 | | NFM | Nationwide | Packet channel |
| 70.32500 | | NFM | Nationwide | Packet channel |
| 70.35000 | | NFM | Nationwide | Raynet channel |
| 70.37500 | | NFM | Nationwide | Raynet channel |
| 70.40000 | | NFM | Nationwide | Raynet channel |
| 70.45000 | | NFM | Nationwide | FM calling channel |
| 70.48750 | | NFM | Nationwide | Packet channel |

**70.5125 - 71.5000 MHz**      FIRE BRIGADES (ENGLAND & WALES) 12.5
**kHz**      [MOBILE 80.5000 - 81.5000 MHz]

| Base | Mobile | Mode | Location | User and Notes |
|---|---|---|---|---|
| 70.51250 | 80.18750 | AM | Coventry | Fire Brigade (FB) |
| 70.51250 | 80.18750 | NFM | Northumberland | Fire Brigade (M2LJ) |
| 70.51250 | 80.43750 | AM | West Midlands | Fire Brigade (FBW) |
| 70.52500 | 80.10000 | AM | Ipswich | Fire Brigade |
| 70.52500 | 80.10000 | AM | London | Fire Brigade (FH) Ch 1 |
| 70.52500 | 80.73750 | AM | Manchester | Fire Brigade (FT) Ch 2 |
| 70.53750 | 80.11250 | AM | North Yorkshire | Fire Brigade (M2LY) |
| 70.53750 | 80.18750 | AM | Nottinghamshire | Fire Brigade (M2NZ) |
| 70.55000 | 80.00000 | AM | Manchester | Fire Brigade HQ (FT) Ch 1 |
| 70.56250 | 80.60000 | AM | Mid Glamorgan | Fire Brigade (WF) |
| 70.56250 | 80.98750 | AM | Lincolnshire | Fire Brigade (NV) |
| 70.57500 | 80.46250 | AM | West Midlands | Fire Brigade (FBW) Ch 3 |
| 70.58700 | 80.76250 | AM | Manchester | Fire Brigade (FT) Ch 3 |
| 70.58750 | 80.18750 | AM | Hampshire | Fire Brigade (HX) Ch 2 |

| Base | Mobile | Mode | Location | User and Notes |
|---|---|---|---|---|
| 70.60000 | 80.00000 | AM | Derbyshire | Fire Brigade (M2ND) |
| 70.60000 | 81.26250 | NFM | Warwickshire | Fire Brigade (M2YS) |
| 70.61250 | 80.12500 | AM | Dyfed | Fire Brigade (WV) |
| 70.61250 | 80.12500 | NFM | Surrey | Fire Brigade (HF) |
| 70.61250 | 80.12500 | NFM | West Yorkshire | Fire Brigade (M2XF) |
| 70.62500 | 80.61250 | AM | Essex | Fire Brigade (VD) Ch 1 Mobilising |
| 70.62500 | 80.61250 | AM | Merseyside | Fire Brigade (M2FO) Ch 3 |
| 70.63750 | 80.00000 | AM | Doncaster | Fire Brigade (M2XV) |
| 70.63750 | 80.11250 | AM | South Yorkshire | Fire Brigade (XV) |
| 70.63750 | 80.21250 | AM | East Sussex | Fire Brigade (KD) |
| 70.65000 | 80.98750 | AM | Wiltshire | Fire Brigade (QM) |
| 70.66250 | 80.45000 | AM | Leicestershire | Fire Brigade (M2NK) |
| 70.67500 | 80.52500 | AM | South Glamorgan | Fire Brigade (WD) |
| 70.67500 | 80.55000 | NFM | Lancashire | Fire Brigade (BE) Ch 1 |
| 70.67500 | 80.55000 | AM | Liverpool | Fire Brigade |
| 70.68750 | 80.91250 | AM | Hereford & Worcester | Fire Brigade (YB) |
| 70.70000 | 80.00000 | AM | Norfolk | Fire Brigade (M2VF) |
| 70.70000 | 80.82500 | NFM | Merseyside | Fire Brigade (M2FO) Ch 4 |
| 70.70000 | 81.12500 | NFM | Gwent | Fire Brigade (WP) Ch 4 |
| 70.71250 | 80.35000 | AM | East Sussex | Fire Brigade Ch 2 |
| 70.71250 | 80.35000 | AM | Manchester | Fire Brigade |
| 70.71250 | 80.80000 | AM | Derbyshire | Fire Brigade (M2ND) |
| 70.72500 | 80.03750 | AM | Devon | Fire Brigade (M2QD) |
| 70.72500 | 80.67500 | AM | Essex | Fire Brigade (VD) Ch 2 |
| 70.74000 | 70.74000 | NFM | West Midlands | Data Link for Fire Brigade |
| 70.75000 | 80.75000 | AM | Northamptonshire | Fire Brigade (NO) |
| 70.76250 | 80.15000 | AM | East London | Fire Brigade (M2FE) Ch3 |
| 70.76250 | 80.15000 | AM | London | Fire Brigade Ch.3 (FE) |
| 70.76250 | 80.98750 | NFM | West Yorkshire | Fire Brigade (M2XF) |
| 70.77500 | 80.50000 | AM | Cheshire | Fire Brigade (M2CF) |
| 70.77500 | 80.50000 | AM | Hampshire | Fire Brigade (HX) Ch 1 |
| 70.78750 | 80.80000 | NFM | Buckinghamshire | Fire Brigade (HK) |
| 70.78750 | 80.80000 | AM | Cornwall | Fire Brigade (QA) |
| 70.80000 | 80.51250 | AM | West Sussex | Fire Brigade (KW) |
| 70.81250 | 81.21250 | AM | Gwynedd | Fire Brigade (WC) |
| 70.82500 | 80.03750 | AM | Devon | Fire Brigade (M2QD) |
| 70.82500 | 80.78750 | AM | Manchester | Fire Brigade (FT) Ch 4 |
| 70.83750 | 80.00000 | AM | Cambridgeshire | Fire Brigade |
| 70.83750 | 80.03750 | NFM | Cumbria | Fire Brigade (BC) |
| 70.83750 | 80.03750 | AM | Galashiels | Fire Brigade (ZF) |
| 70.83750 | 80.12500 | AM | Kent | Fire Brigade (KF) |
| 70.85000 | 80.96250 | AM | Powys | Fire Brigade (WB) |
| 70.86250 | 80.55000 | AM | Dorset | Fire Brigade (QK) |
| 70.87500 | 80.66250 | NFM | West Yorkshire | Fire Brigade (M2XF) Ch.2 |
| 70.88750 | 80.21250 | AM | Durham | Fire Brigade (LF) |
| 70.88750 | 80.21250 | AM | Hertfordshire | Fire Brigade (M2KP) |
| 70.90000 | 80.03750 | AM | Hertfordshire | Fire Brigade (M2VI) |
| 70.90000 | 80.40000 | NFM | Suffolk | Fire Brigade (VN) |
| 70.90000 | 80.60000 | NFM | Lancashire | Fire Brigade (BE) Ch 2 |
| 70.91250 |  | FM | London | Fire Brigade Data Channel |
| 70.91250 | 80.00000 | NFM | Essex | Fire Brigade (M2VD) Ch3 |
| 70.93750 |  | NFM | England & Wales | Fire Brigade Data Channel |
| 70.95000 | 80.00000 | FM | West Glamorgan | Fire Brigade (WZ) |
| 70.96250 | 80.11250 | AM | London | Fire Brigade (FS) Ch.2 NE and SE |
| 70.96250 | 81.08750 | AM | Merseyside | Fire Brigade (M2FO) Ch 2 |
| 70.97500 | 80.65000 | NFM | Norfolk | Fire/Rescue Service |

| Base | Mobile | Mode | Location | User and Notes |
|------|--------|------|----------|----------------|
| 70.97500 | 80.65000 | AM | Shropshire | Fire Brigade (YU) |
| 70.97500 | 80.65000 | NFM | Stockport | Fire Brigade |
| 70.98750 | 80.00000 | NFM | Gwynedd | Fire Brigade (M2WC) |
| 71.01250 | 80.17500 | AM | Avon | Fire Brigade (M2QC) |
| 71.01250 | 80.17500 | AM | Bristol | Fire Brigade |
| 71.03750 | 81.16250 | AM | Merseyside | Fire Brigade (M2FO) Ch.1 Central & South |
| 71.07500 | 80.15000 | AM | Bristol | Fire Brigade |
| 71.07500 | 80.15000 | AM | Humberside | Fire Brigade (XT) MOB Ch. |
| 71.07500 | 80.62500 | AM | Gloucester | Fire Brigade (QF) |
| 71.10000 | | NFM | Humberside | Fire Brigade data |
| 71.10000 | 80.37500 | AM | Humberside | Fire Brigade (M2XT) Ch.1 |
| 71.10000 | 80.66250 | AM | Oxfordshire | Fire Brigade (M2HI) |
| 71.11250 | 80.00000 | AM | Cleveland | Fire Brigade (M2LT) |
| 71.11250 | 80.41250 | AM | Bedfordshire | Fire Brigade (M2VM) |
| 71.12500 | 80.11250 | AM | Somerset | Fire Brigade (M2QI) |
| 71.13750 | 80.11250 | AM | Buckinghamshire | Fire Brigade (M2HK) |
| 71.13750 | 80.43750 | AM | North Yorkshire | Fire Brigade (M2LY) East Area |
| 71.15000 | 80.51250 | AM | West Midlands | Fire Brigade (FBW) Ch.2 Western D+E |
| 71.16250 | 80.87500 | AM | Clwyd | Fire Brigade (M2WK) |
| 71.17500 | 80.21250 | AM | London | Fire Brigade (M2FN) Ch 4 Central & North |
| 71.17500 | 81.11250 | AM | North Yorkshire | Fire Brigade (M2LY) West Area |
| 71.20000 | 80.00000 | NFM | Lancashire | Fire Brigade (M2BE) Ch2 |
| 71.20000 | 80.05000 | NFM | Humberside | Fire Brigade |
| 71.20000 | 80.22500 | NFM | Berkshire | Fire Brigade (M2HD) |
| 71.20000 | 80.22500 | NFM | Scunthorpe | Fire Brigade (M2HQ) |
| 71.25000 | 80.00000 | NFM | Gloucester | Fire Brigade (M2YP) |
| 71.27500 | 81.06250 | AM | Isle of Wight | Fire Brigade (M2HP) |
| 71.27500 | 81.08750 | NFM | Suffolk | Fire Brigade (M2VN) |
| 71.30000 | | AM | Tyne and Wear | Fire Brigade (M2LP) Ch 1 |
| 71.31250 | | NFM | England & Wales | Fire Brigade data channel |
| 71.33750 | | NFM | England & Wales | Fire Brigade data channel |
| 71.33750 | | AM | South Glamorgan | Fire Brigade (M2WD) |
| 71.33750 | | AM | Tyne and Wear | Fire Brigade M2(LP) Ch 2 |
| 71.33750 | 80.00000 | NFM | London | Fire Brigade (M2FHO) Ch5 1200 Baud data |
| 71.37500 | | AM | Gwent | Fire Brigade (M2SD) |
| 71.37500 | | NFM | West Glamorgan | Fire Brigade (M2WF) |
| 71.38750 | | AM | Gloucestershire | Fire Brigade M2QC) |
| 71.38750 | 80.00000 | NFM | Lancashire | Fire Brigade (M2BE) Ch 3 |
| 71.41250 | 80.76250 | AM | Moreton In The Marsh | Fire Brigade College Ch.3 |
| 71.42500 | 80.52500 | AM | Cambridgeshire | Fire Brigade (VC) |
| 71.45000 | | AM | Nottinghamshire | Fire Brigade (NZ) |
| 71.46250 | 81.38750 | AM | Moreton In The Marsh | Fire Brigade College Ch.2 |
| 71.48750 | 80.60000 | AM | Moreton In The Marsh | Fire Brigade College Ch.1 |

## 72.8000 - 73.9250 MHz    MOD TACTICAL COMMUNICATIONS
### 25 KHz DUPLEX

| Base | Mobile | Mode | Location | User and Notes |
|------|--------|------|----------|----------------|
| 72.80000 | | NFM | Brecon Beacons | Army Range Ops |
| 72.80000 | | NFM | Nationwide | Secure Government Mobiles |
| 72.81250 | | NFM | Portsmouth | Navel Base Transport & Security |
| 72.81250 | | NFM | Southampton | Royal Navy Loading |
| 72.82500 | | NFM | USAF Fairford | Base Ops |
| 72.98750 | | NFM | HMS Drake | Naval Provost |
| 73.00000 | | NFM | Brecon Beacons | Army Range Ops |
| 73.00000 | | NFM | High Wycombe | RAF Police |
| 73.00000 | 78.90000 | NFM | Nationwide | Army Pye Equipment Ch. 7 |

| Base | Mobile | Mode | Location | User and Notes |
|---|---|---|---|---|
| 73.02500 | 78.65000 | NFM | Nationwide | Army Pye Equipment Ch. 8 |
| 73.07500 | | NFM | Cinque Ports | 44 Signals Regiment |
| 73.10000 | | NFM | Aldershot | Military Police |
| 73.12500 | 78.40000 | NFM | Nationwide | Army Pye Equipment Ch. 1 |
| 73.15000 | 78.42500 | NFM | Nationwide | Army Pye Equipment Ch.2 |
| 73.20000 | | NFM | DRA Farnborough | Ground Movements |
| 73.20000 | 78.45000 | NFM | Nationwide | Army Pye Equipment Ch. 3 |
| 73.21250 | | NFM | Southampton | Royal Navy Transport |
| 73.22500 | 78.47500 | NFM | Nationwide | Army Pye Equipment Ch. 4 |
| 73.25000 | 78.50000 | NFM | Nationwide | Army Pye Equipment Ch. 5 |
| 73.25600 | | NFM | Midlands | Army Base Security |
| 73.27500 | | NFM | Kent | Tour de France French PMR |
| 73.32500 | | NFM | Plymouth | Royal Marines |
| 73.32500 | 78.80000 | NFM | Nationwide | Army Pye Equipment Ch. 6 |
| 73.33750 | | NFM | RN Portsdown | Base Ops |
| 73.35000 | | NFM | Nationwide | MoD Security Police |
| 73.35000 | | NFM | RAF High Wycombe | Security |
| 73.35000 | | NFM | West Midlands | USAF Police |
| 73.37500 | | NFM | South Staffs | Army |
| 73.38750 | | NFM | Nationwide | Sea Cadets |
| 73.40000 | | NFM | Plymouth | MoD Operations |
| 73.42500 | | NFM | RN Faslane | Transport |
| 73.43750 | | AM | RAE Farnborough | Ground Control |
| 73.45000 | | NFM | RN Portsdown | Security |
| 73.46250 | | AM | RAE Farnborough | Ground Vehicles (linked to 444.200 MHz) |
| 73.46875 | | AM | RAE Farnborough | Workshop Ch 5 |
| 73.47500 | | NFM | Blandford Forum | Royal Military Police |
| 73.47500 | | NFM | Nationwide | MoD Police |
| 73.48750 | | NFM | RAE Farnborough | Ground Service Ch 1 |
| 73.50000 | 78.65000 | NFM | Nationwide | Army Pye Equipment Ch. 1 |
| 73.51250 | | NFM | Fairford | MoD Police Special Events (Div. South & South West) |
| 73.51250 | | NFM | London | MoD Police (Sometimes input for 443.5125 & 443.575 + repeater) |
| 73.51250 | | NFM | Mildenhall | MoD Police Special Events (Div. East Anglia) |
| 73.51250 | | NFM | Nationwide | MoD Police |
| 73.52500 | 78.72500 | NFM | Nationwide | Army Pye Equipment Ch. 2 |
| 73.53750 | | NFM | Farnborough Air Show | MoD Police |
| 73.53750 | | NFM | Plymouth | MoD Operations |
| 73.55000 | | NFM | Portland | MoD Police |
| 73.55000 | 78.77500 | NFM | Nationwide | Army Pye Equipment Ch. 9 |
| 73.56250 | | NFM | RN Faslane | Security (Alpha Control) |
| 73.56750 | | NFM | RN Poole | Royal Marines |
| 73.57500 | | NFM | Plymouth | Military Police |
| 73.57500 | | NFM | RN Dartmouth | Navy Ops |
| 73.58750 | | NFM | London | Royal Military Police Ch.10 |
| 73.61250 | | NFM | Plymouth | MoD Police |
| 73.63750 | | NFM | Plymouth | MoD Police |
| 73.63750 | | NFM | RAE Farnborough | Movements Control Ch 6 |
| 73.65000 | | NFM | London | MoD Police |
| 73.66875 | | NFM | RAE Farnborough | Fire Ch 4 |
| 73.70000 | | NFM | Nationwide | Army Cadet Force |
| 73.70000 | | NFM | RN Faslane | MoD Police |
| 73.70000 | 84.12500 | NFM | Nationwide | 61 Sig Sqn Channel 1 |
| 73.70625 | | NFM | RAE Farnborough | Medical Ch 2 |
| 73.72500 | 84.15000 | NFM | Nationwide | 61 Sig Sqn Channel 2 |
| 73.73750 | | NFM | Bedfordshire | British Inteligence Centre |

| Base | Mobile | Mode | Location | User and Notes |
|------|--------|------|----------|----------------|
| 73.73750 | | NFM | London | Royal Military Police Ch.11 |
| 73.75000 | 84.17500 | NFM | Nationwide | 61 Sig Sqn Channel 3 |
| 73.77500 | 84.25000 | NFM | Nationwide | 61 Sig Sqn Channel 4 |
| 73.80000 | | NFM | Brecon Beacons | Army Range Control |
| 73.80000 | 84.27500 | NFM | Nationwide | 61 Sig Sqn Channel 5 |
| 73.82500 | 84.32500 | NFM | Nationwide | 61 Sig Sqn Channel 6 |
| 73.85000 | | NFM | Nationwide | Army Cadet Force |
| 73.85000 | | NFM | Nationwide | MoD Police Ch 5 |
| 73.85000 | 84.35000 | NFM | Nationwide | 61 Sig Sqn Channel 7 |
| 73.87500 | 84.37500 | NFM | Nationwide | 61 Sig Sqn Channel 8 |
| 73.90000 | 84.42500 | NFM | Nationwide | 61 Sig Sqn Channel 9 |
| 73.92500 | 84.47500 | NFM | Nationwide | 61 Sig Sqn Channel 10 |

### 73.9250 - 74.1000 MHz    MoD MOULD REPEATERS 12.5 kHz DUPLEX

| Base | Mobile | Mode | Location | User and Notes |
|------|--------|------|----------|----------------|
| 74.01250 | | NFM | London | Mould |
| 74.01250 | | NFM | Northamptonshire | Mould |
| 74.01250 | | NFM | Scarborough | Mould |
| 74.01250 | | NFM | Swansea | Mould |
| 74.02500 | | NFM | Baldock | Mould |
| 74.02500 | | NFM | Lincolnshire | Mould |
| 74.02500 | | NFM | Suffolk | Mould |
| 74.02500 | | NFM | West Midlands | Mould |
| 74.02500 | 79.01250 | NFM | Hampshire | Mould |
| 74.03750 | | NFM | Shropshire | Mould |
| 74.03750 | | NFM | Wiltshire | Mould |
| 74.05000 | | NFM | Brecon Beacons | Mould |
| 74.05000 | | NFM | Northamptonshire | Mould |
| 74.05000 | | NFM | Nottinghamshire | Mould |
| 74.05000 | | NFM | West Midlands | Mould |
| 74.06250 | | NFM | Manchester | Mould |
| 74.06250 | | NFM | Northamptonshire | Mould |
| 74.06250 | | NFM | Swindon | Mould |
| 74.06250 | | NFM | West Midlands | Mould |
| 74.06250 | | NFM | West Yorkshire | Mould |
| 74.07500 | | NFM | Devon | Mould |
| 74.07500 | | NFM | Gwent | Mould |
| 74.07500 | 79.03750 | NFM | Catterick | MoD Police (WATCHDOG) |
| 74.07500 | 79.03750 | NFM | Midlands (North) | Mould |
| 74.08750 | | NFM | Glasgow | Mould |
| 74.08750 | | NFM | Gwent | Mould |
| 74.08750 | | NFM | Manchester | Mould |
| 74.08750 | | NFM | Tayside | Mould |
| 74.08750 | | NFM | West Midlands | Mould |

### 74.1000 - 74.7875 MHz    MoD MOULD & TACTICAL CHANNELS 12.5 kHz

| Base | Mobile | Mode | Location | User and Notes |
|------|--------|------|----------|----------------|
| 74.10000 | | NFM | Baldock | Mould |
| 74.10000 | | NFM | RAF Honington | RAF Police Ch 3 |
| 74.11250 | | NFM | Baldock | Mould |
| 74.11250 | | NFM | Colchester | Barracks |
| 74.11250 | | NFM | Gwent | Mould Ch 1 |
| 74.11250 | | NFM | Manchester | Mould |
| 74.11250 | | NFM | West Midlands | Mould |
| 74.12500 | | NFM | Brecon Beacons | Mould |
| 74.12500 | | NFM | West Midlands | Mould |
| 74.13750 | | NFM | Brecon Beacons | Mould |

| Base | Mobile | Mode | Location | User and Notes |
|------|--------|------|----------|----------------|
| 74.15000 | | NFM | Manchester | Mould |
| 74.15000 | | NFM | Shropshire | Mould |
| 74.15000 | | NFM | West Midlands | Mould |
| 74.16250 | | NFM | Manchester | Mould |
| 74.16250 | | NFM | Strathclyde | Mould |
| 74.16250 | | NFM | Swansea | Mould |
| 74.16250 | | NFM | West Midlands | Mould |
| 74.18750 | | NFM | Baldock | Mould |
| 74.18750 | | NFM | Midlands (North) | Mould |
| 74.18750 | | NFM | West Yorkshire | Mould |
| 74.20000 | | NFM | Nationwide | Military Transport Security |
| 74.20000 | | NFM | Norfolk | Mould |
| 74.20000 | 79.30000 | NFM | Nationwide | RAF Police Transport |
| 74.21250 | | NFM | Catterick | MoD Police (WATCHDOG) |
| 74.21250 | | NFM | Manchester | Mould |
| 74.21250 | | NFM | Strathclyde | Mould |
| 74.21250 | 79.21250 | NFM | Gwent | Mould |
| 74.22500 | | NFM | Colchester | Mould |
| 74.22500 | | NFM | Lincolnshire | Mould |
| 74.22500 | | NFM | Nationwide | Royal Ordnance Corps |
| 74.22500 | | NFM | Nottinghamshire | Mould |
| 74.22500 | | NFM | Upper Heyford | Mould |
| 74.22500 | | NFM | West Midlands | Mould |
| 74.23750 | | NFM | Lincolnshire | Mould |
| 74.23750 | | NFM | Shropshire | Mould |
| 74.23750 | | NFM | Tayside | Mould |
| 74.25000 | | NFM | Suffolk | Mould |
| 74.25000 | 79.28750 | NFM | Colchester | Barracks |
| 74.25000 | 79.35000 | NFM | Norfolk | Mould |
| 74.26250 | | NFM | Gwent | Mould |
| 74.26250 | | NFM | Swindon | Mould |
| 74.27500 | | NFM | Strathclyde | Mould |
| 74.28750 | | NFM | Edinburgh | Mould |
| 74.28750 | | NFM | Suffolk | Mould |
| 74.30000 | | NFM | Stanford | Battle Ground Command Ch 0 |
| 74.31250 | | NFM | Gwent | Mould |
| 74.31250 | | NFM | Shropshire | Mould |
| 74.32500 | | NFM | Baldock | Mould |
| 74.33750 | | NFM | Baldock | Mould |
| 74.33750 | | NFM | Manchester | Mould |
| 74.35000 | | NFM | London | Mould |
| 74.35000 | 79.45000 | NFM | Brecon Beacons | Mould |
| 74.36250 | | NFM | Chester | Mould |
| 74.36250 | | NFM | Hampshire | Mould |
| 74.36250 | | NFM | Southampton | Mould |
| 74.37500 | | NFM | Brecon Beacons | Mould |
| 74.38750 | | NFM | Gwent | Mould |
| 74.38750 | | NFM | London | Mould |
| 74.38750 | | NFM | Swindon | Mould |
| 74.38750 | 79.41250 | NFM | Devon | Mould |
| 74.40000 | | NFM | Brecon Beacons | Mould |
| 74.41250 | | NFM | Brecon Beacons | Mould |
| 74.41250 | | NFM | Hertfordshire | Mould |
| 74.41250 | | NFM | Shropshire | Mould |
| 74.41250 | | NFM | West Yorkshire | Mould |
| 74.42500 | | NFM | London | Mould |

| --- | --- | --- | --- | --- |
| 74.42500 | | NFM | Soffolk | Mould |
| 74.43750 | | NFM | Midlands (North) | Mould |
| 74.43750 | | NFM | Strathclyde | Mould |
| 74.43750 | | NFM | West Midlands | Mould |
| 74.43750 | 79.66250 | NFM | Norfolk | Mould |
| 74.45000 | | NFM | Swansea | Mould |
| 74.45000 | 79.45000 | NFM | Brecon Beacons | Mould |
| 74.46250 | | NFM | Gwent | Mould |
| 74.46750 | 79.71250 | NFM | Gwent | Mould |
| 74.48750 | | NFM | Hertfordshire (North) | Mould |
| 74.48750 | | NFM | London | Mould |
| 74.48750 | | NFM | Norfolk | Mould |
| 74.48750 | | NFM | Wiltshire | Mould |
| 74.48750 | 79.92650 | NFM | Hampshire | Mould |
| 74.51250 | | NFM | Brecon Beacons | Mould |
| 74.51250 | | NFM | West Midlands | Mould |
| 74.52500 | | NFM | Brecon Beacons | Mould |
| 74.53750 | | NFM | Brecon Beacons | Mould |
| 74.53750 | | NFM | Hertfordshire (North) | Mould |
| 74.53750 | | NFM | Lincolnshire | Mould |
| 74.53750 | | NFM | West Midlands | Mould |
| 74.55000 | 79.55000 | NFM | Nationwide | RAF Police |
| 74.56250 | | NFM | Brecon Beacons | Mould |
| 74.57500 | | NFM | Brecon Beacons | Mould |
| 74.57500 | | NFM | Manchester | Mould |
| 74.57500 | | NFM | Richmond | MoD Police |
| 74.57500 | | NFM | Shropshire | Mould |
| 74.57500 | | NFM | West Yorkshire | Mould |
| 74.58750 | | NFM | Devon | Mould |
| 74.58750 | | NFM | Gwent | Mould |
| 74.58750 | | NFM | Hampshire | Mould |
| 74.58750 | | NFM | Swansea | Mould |
| 74.58750 | | NFM | Wiltshire | Mould |
| 74.60000 | | NFM | Kent | Tour de France French PMR |
| 74.60000 | | NFM | London | Mould |
| 74.60000 | | NFM | West Midlands | Mould |
| 74.61250 | | NFM | Brecon Beacons | Mould |
| 74.61250 | | NFM | West Midlands | Mould |
| 74.62500 | | NFM | Brecon Beacons | Mould |
| 74.62500 | | NFM | Devon | Mould |
| 74.62500 | | NFM | Suffolk | Mould |
| 74.65000 | | NFM | Midlands (North) | Mould |
| 74.65000 | 79.61250 | NFM | Hants (Crabwood Farm) | Mould |
| 74.66250 | | NFM | Brecon Beacons | Mould |
| 74.66250 | | NFM | Swindon | Mould |
| 74.67500 | | NFM | Strathclyde | Mould |
| 74.67500 | 79.71250 | NFM | Gwent | Mould |
| 74.68750 | | NFM | Suffolk | Mould |
| 74.68750 | 79.68750 | NFM | Cambridgeshire | Mould Ch 15 |
| 74.70000 | | NFM | Gwent | Mould |
| 74.70000 | | NFM | Hertfordshire (North) | Mould |
| 74.70000 | | NFM | Tayside | Mould |
| 74.70000 | 79.71250 | NFM | Brecon Beacons | Mould |
| 74.71250 | | NFM | Oxfordshire | Mould |
| 74.72500 | | NFM | Brecon Beacons | Mould |
| 74.72500 | | NFM | Manchester | Mould |

| Base | Mobile | Mode | Location | User and Notes |
|---|---|---|---|---|
| 74.72500 | | NFM | Shropshire | Mould |
| 74.73750 | | NFM | Hampshire | Mould |
| 74.73750 | | NFM | London | Mould |
| 74.75000 | | NFM | Devon | Mould |
| 74.75000 | | NFM | Manchester | Mould |
| 74.75000 | | NFM | Shropshire | Mould |
| 74.75000 | | NFM | Wiltshire | Mould |
| 74.76250 | | NFM | Gwent | Mould |
| 74.78750 | | NFM | Gwent | Mould |
| 75.02500 | | NFM | RAF Marham | Security |
| 75.25000 | | AM | Pendine (MoD) | Range Ops |
| 75.25000 | | AM | West Midlands | USAF Police |

**74-8000 - 75.2500 MHz**     CIVIL AVIATION OUTER, MIDDLE & INNER RUNWAY MARKERS

| Base | Mobile | Mode | Location | User and Notes |
|---|---|---|---|---|
| 75.00000 | | AM | Nationwide | Runway Marker Beacons |

**75.2500 - 75.3000 MHz**     BBC O/B TALKBACK

| Base | Mobile | Mode | Location | User and Notes |
|---|---|---|---|---|
| 75.26250 | 69.96250 | NFM | Nationwide | BBC O/B Talkback Ch 1 |
| 75.26250 | 75.30000 | NFM | Nationwide | JFMG Airborne Use |
| 75.26860 | 69.83500 | NFM | Nationwide | BBC O/B Talkback Ch 4 |
| 75.28130 | 69.87250 | NFM | Nationwide | BBC O/B Talkback Ch 7 |
| 75.28750 | 69.90750 | NFM | Nationwide | BBC O/B Talkback Ch 2 |
| 75.29380 | 69.89750 | NFM | Nationwide | BBC O/B Talkback Ch 9 |

**75.3000 - 76.7000 MHz**     MoD POLICE, MOULD & USAFE SECURITY 12.5 kHz

| Base | Mobile | Mode | Location | User and Notes |
|---|---|---|---|---|
| 75.30000 | | AM | Pendine (MoD) | Range Ops |
| 75.30000 | | AM | Porton Down | Security |
| 75.30000 | | AM | Suffolk | USAF Police |
| 75.32500 | | NFM | Nationwide | USAF Ground Common |
| 75.32500 | | NFM | USAF Lakenheath | Ground Ops |
| 75.32500 | | NFM | USAF Mildenhall | Ground Ops |
| 75.40000 | | AM | Pendine (MoD) | Range Ops |
| 75.40000 | | AM | Suffolk | USAF Police |
| 75.45000 | | NFM | Nationwide | USAF Base Security |
| 75.47500 | | NFM | Brecon Beacons | Mould |
| 75.50000 | | AM | Christchurch | Military |
| 75.50000 | | AM | Glasgow | RAF Security |
| 75.50000 | | NFM | Gwent | Royal Air Force |
| 75.50000 | | NFM | Northamptonshire | Security |
| 75.53750 | | NFM | RAE Farnborough | Medics |
| 75.57500 | | NFM | Nationwide | USAF Ground Common |
| 75.57500 | | NFM | USAF Lakenheath | Ground Ops |
| 75.57500 | | NFM | USAF Mildenhall | Ground Ops |
| 75.60000 | | NFM | Plymouth | MoD |
| 75.66250 | | NFM | Wattisham Barracks | Royal Military Police |
| 75.67500 | | NFM | Plymouth | MoD Dockyard Ops |
| 75.67500 | | NFM | USAF Lakenheath | Security |
| 75.67500 | | NFM | USAF Mildenhall | Security |
| 75.71250 | | NFM | Hampshire | Mould |
| 75.71250 | | NFM | Oxfordshire | Mould |
| 75.73750 | | NFM | London | Mould |
| 75.73750 | | NFM | Nationwide | Military Close Protection Ch 11 |

| Base | Mobile | Mode | Location | User and Notes |
|------|--------|------|----------|----------------|
| 75.75000 | | NFM | Devon | Mould |
| 75.75000 | | NFM | Gwent | Mould |
| 75.75000 | | NFM | Wiltshire | Mould |
| 75.76250 | | NFM | Salisbury Plain | Close Support Group |
| 75.78750 | | NFM | Gloucester | Mould |
| 75.78750 | | NFM | Gwent | Mould |
| 75.78750 | | NFM | Lothian and Borders | Mould |
| 75.81250 | | NFM | Brecon Beacons | Army |
| 75.82500 | | NFM | London | Barnard Link for Remembrance Sunday |
| 75.82500 | | NFM | London | Used by military for state visits |
| 75.82500 | | NFM | London | Wellington Barracks and Buckingham Palace guards |
| 75.82500 | | NFM | Nationwide | Military Close Protection Ch 12 |
| 75.82500 | | NFM | Nationwide | T19 Tactical Support Team. |
| 75.82500 | | NFM | Nationwide | USAF Special Agents |
| 75.83750 | | NFM | East Anglia | MoD Police G Division |
| 75.83750 | | NFM | RN Faslane | Security (CHARLIE CONTROL) |
| 75.83750 | | NFM | USAF Mildenhall | Security |
| 75.86250 | | NFM | Oxfordshire | Mould |
| 75.87500 | | NFM | Devon | Mould |
| 75.87500 | | NFM | Dorset | Territorial Army Mould |
| 75.87500 | | NFM | Gwent | Mould |
| 75.87500 | | NFM | London | Mould |
| 75.87500 | | NFM | Nationwide | Military Close Protection Ch 10 |
| 75.90000 | | NFM | Gwent | Mould |
| 75.91250 | | NFM | Gwent | Mould |
| 75.91250 | | NFM | Plymouth | Mould |
| 75.93750 | | NFM | Fife | Mould |
| 75.93750 | | NFM | Gwent | Mould |
| 75.93750 | | NFM | Hampshire | Mould |
| 75.93750 | | NFM | Salisbury Plain | Army cadets |
| 75.93750 | | NFM | Tayside | Mould |
| 75.93750 | | NFM | Warminster | Mould |
| 75.94000 | | NFM | Salisbury Plain | Army |
| 75.95000 | | NFM | Gwent | Mould |
| 75.96250 | | NFM | Hampshire | Mould |
| 75.97500 | | NFM | Nationwide | Royal Signals |
| 75.98750 | | NFM | Edinburgh | DVP Military |
| 76.00000 | | NFM | Nationwide | USAF Police |
| 76.00000 | | NFM | Taunton | Taunton Deane Council |
| 76.01250 | | NFM | Gwent | Mould |
| 76.01250 | | NFM | Hampshire | Mould |
| 76.01250 | | NFM | Plymouth | MoD Dockyard Ops |
| 76.01250 | | NFM | West Midlands | Mould |
| 76.05000 | | NFM | USAF Lakenheath | Security |
| 76.05000 | | NFM | West Midlands | USAF Maintenance Ch 6 |
| 76.06250 | | NFM | Devon | Mould |
| 76.06250 | | NFM | Gwent | Mould |
| 76.06250 | | NFM | Nationwide | Military Close Protection Ch 15 |
| 76.07500 | | NFM | Hampshire | USAF |
| 76.07500 | | NFM | Wiltshire | USAF |
| 76.11250 | | NFM | Gwent | Mould |
| 76.11250 | | NFM | Hampshire | Mould |
| 76.12500 | | NFM | Gwent | Mould |
| 76.12500 | | NFM | West Midlands | Mould |
| 76.16250 | | NFM | Hampshire | Mould |
| 76.22500 | | NFM | Devon | Mould |

| Base | Mobile | Mode | Location | User and Notes |
|---|---|---|---|---|
| 76.22500 | | NFM | Gwent | Mould |
| 76.22500 | | NFM | Nationwide | Military Close Protection Ch 16 |
| 76.22500 | | NFM | Nationwide | USAF Base to Mobile |
| 76.22500 | | NFM | USAF Mildenhall | Security |
| 76.25000 | | NFM | Brecon Beacons | Army |
| 76.25000 | | NFM | USAF Mildenhall | Security |
| 76.26250 | | NFM | Gwent | Army |
| 76.30000 | | NFM | RNAS Culdrose | Ground Services |
| 76.30000 | | NFM | RNAS Yeovilton | Navy Provosts |
| 76.32500 | | NFM | Devon | Mould |
| 76.32500 | | NFM | Hampshire | Mould |
| 76.32500 | | NFM | London | MoD Police Ruislip |
| 76.32500 | | NFM | Lothian and Borders | Mould |
| 76.32500 | | NFM | Nationwide | Military Close Protection Ch 14 |
| 76.32500 | | NFM | Tayside | Mould |
| 76.32500 | | NFM | USAF Lakenheath | Security |
| 76.32500 | | NFM | USAF Mildenhall | Security |
| 76.35000 | | NFM | USAF Lakenheath | Crystal Palace |
| 76.36250 | | NFM | Northamptonshire | Mould |
| 76.36250 | | NFM | Salisbury | Mould |
| 76.36250 | | NFM | West Midlands | Mould |
| 76.38750 | | NFM | Hampshire | Mould |
| 76.43750 | | NFM | Hampshire | Mould |
| 76.43750 | | NFM | London | Mould |
| 76.43750 | | NFM | Manchester | Mould |
| 76.43750 | | NFM | Nationwide | Military Close Protection Ch 09 |
| 76.43750 | | NFM | Oxfordshire | Mould |
| 76.43750 | | NFM | Salisbury Plain | Army |
| 76.43750 | | NFM | West Midlands | Mould |
| 76.44000 | | NFM | Salisbury Plain | Army |
| 76.45000 | | NFM | USAF Fairford | Security |
| 76.47500 | | NFM | Hampshire | USAF |
| 76.47500 | | NFM | London | Mould |
| 76.47500 | | NFM | South Wales | Mould |
| 76.50000 | | NFM | London | MoD Police Ruislip |
| 76.50000 | | NFM | London, North | DVP Military |
| 76.50000 | | NFM | Nationwide | Military Close Protection Ch 13 |
| 76.52500 | | NFM | Camberley | WRAC Gate Security |
| 76.52500 | | FM | Neath, Glamorgan | Knight Hawk Security |
| 76.52500 | | NFM | USAF Lakenheath | Security |
| 76.56250 | | NFM | Kent | Tour de France (French) |
| 76.57500 | | NFM | USAF Lakenheath | Security Ch 2 |
| 76.60000 | | NFM | Cumbria | Range Control |
| 76.61250 | | NFM | Hampshire | USAF |
| 76.67500 | | NFM | USAF Lakenheath | Security |
| 76.70000 | | NFM | Cumbria | Range Control |
| 76.70000 | | NFM | Nationwide | British Telecom Channel A |
| 76.70000 | | NFM | Nationwide | USAF Police |
| 76.72500 | | NFM | RAF Leeming | Ground |

### 76.70625 - 77.99375 MHz    PMR Low Band Mobiles 12.5 kHz Duplex

| Base | Mobile | Mode | Location | User and Notes |
|---|---|---|---|---|
| 76.73750 | | NFM | Nationwide | British Telecom Channel B |
| 76.75000 | | NFM | Nationwide | British Telecom Channel C |
| 76.76250 | | NFM | Nationwide | British Telecom Channel D |
| 76.82500 | | NFM | Nationwide | Thames TV Talkback |
| 77.13750 | | NFM | Hampshire | Motorway Surveyors |

| Base | Mobile | Mode | Location | User and Notes |
|------|--------|------|----------|----------------|
| 77.21250 | | NFM | Hampshire | Netley Country Park Rangers |
| 77.21250 | | NFM | Leicester | Council Ch2 |
| 77.23750 | | NFM | Hampshire | New Forest Council |
| 77.25000 | | NFM | Hampshire | Motorway Surveyors |
| 77.25000 | | NFM | RNAS Culdrose | Ground Services |
| 77.25000 | 87.25000 | NFM | Stockton | Borough Council |
| 77.26250 | 87.26250 | NFM | Stockton | Borough Council |
| 77.28750 | | NFM | Galway | Tone Repeater |
| 77.41250 | | NFM | Oxford | Terry's Taxis |
| 77.70000 | | NFM | Swansea City | Royal Mail |
| 77.87500 | 77.87500 | NFM | Nationwide | ITN O/B Film Mobiles |

## 77.8000 - 79.0000 MHz    MoD & USAFE, BBC O/B Networks 12.5 kHz

| Base | Mobile | Mode | Location | User and Notes |
|------|--------|------|----------|----------------|
| 77.98750 | | NFM | Hampshire | Marchwood Miltary Port |
| 78.00000 | | NFM | Hampshire | Army Ops |
| 78.02500 | | NFM | Pembroke | Military Range |
| 78.05000 | | NFM | London | Military |
| 78.10000 | | AM | Nationwide | ATC Channel V3 |
| 78.10000 | | AM | Nationwide | RAF Cadets Channel V1 |
| 78.10000 | | NFM | Nationwide | BBC O/B |
| 78.11250 | | NFM | RN Faslane | Security (Papa Control) |
| 78.12500 | | NFM | Guilford | Army |
| 78.13750 | | NFM | Blandford | Royal Signals Security |
| 78.15000 | | NFM | Nationwide | BBC O/B Talkback Channel 1 |
| 78.15000 | 84.50000 | NFM | Okehampton | Military Range |
| 78.16250 | | NFM | Aldermaston | Atomic Weapons Establishment |
| 78.16250 | | NFM | Burghfield, Suffolk | Atomic Weapons Establishment |
| 78.16250 | | NFM | RN Faslane | Security (Bravo Control) |
| 78.16250 | 73.61250 | NFM | Plymouth | MoD Police |
| 78.16250 | 73.61250 | NFM | Salisbury Plain | MoD Police (scrambled) |
| 78.16250 | 73.61250 | NFM | Southend | MoD Police |
| 78.16250 | 84.66250 | NFM | Okehampton | Military Range |
| 78.17500 | 84.67500 | NFM | Okehampton | Military Range |
| 78.18750 | 78.18750 | NFM | Nationwide | BBC O/B Camera Channel 1 |
| 78.20000 | 78.20000 | NFM | Nationwide | BBC O/B Camera Channel 2 |
| 78.21250 | 78.21250 | NFM | Nationwide | BBC O/B Engineering Ch. 3 |
| 78.21550 | | NFM | Nationwide | BBC O/B |
| 78.22500 | | AM | Avon | Air Training Corps |
| 78.22500 | | NFM | Birmingham | BBC Microwave set up |
| 78.22500 | | NFM | Nationwide | BBC O/B Engineering Ch. 4 |
| 78.22750 | | NFM | Nationwide | BBC O/B |
| 78.23150 | | NFM | DRA Farnborough | DRA Security |
| 78.23750 | | NFM | Aldermaston | Atomic Weapons Establishment Ch.1 (A and L) |
| 78.23750 | | NFM | Nationwide | BBC O/B Engineering Ch. 5 |
| 78.23750 | | NFM | Salisbury Plain | MoD Police (Hippy Surveillance) |
| 78.24000 | | NFM | Nationwide | BBC O/B Rigging |
| 78.25000 | | NFM | Nationwide | BBC O/B Lighting Channel 6 |
| 78.25250 | | NFM | Nationwide | BBC O/B |
| 78.27500 | | NFM | Bovington | Army Camp Ch 3 |
| 78.27500 | | NFM | Colchester | Barracks |
| 78.27500 | | NFM | Dover | Army |
| 78.27500 | | NFM | Hampshire | Army Ops |
| 78.27500 | | NFM | Waterbeach Barracks | MoD Police |
| 78.28750 | | NFM | Colchester | Barracks Ch 4 |
| 78.30000 | | NFM | Aberystwyth | Royal Welsh Fusilliers TA Centre |
| 78.30000 | | NFM | Bovington | Army Camp Ch 4 |

| Base | Mobile | Mode | Location | User and Notes |
|------|--------|------|----------|----------------|
| 78.30000 | | NFM | Colchester | Barracks Ch 2 |
| 78.30000 | | NFM | Middle Wallop | Army Air Corps |
| 78.30000 | | NFM | Nationwide | Combined Cadet Force |
| 78.30000 | | NFM | Stanford Battle Area | Stanford Ops |
| 78.30000 | | NFM | Waterbeach Barracks | Security |
| 78.31250 | | NFM | Aldershot | Military Police |
| 78.31250 | | NFM | Salisbury Garrison | Military Police |
| 78.32500 | | NFM | Colchester | Barracks Ch 3 |
| 78.32500 | | NFM | Hampshire | Military Police |
| 78.32500 | | NFM | London | Bassington Barracks Military Police |
| 78.32500 | | NFM | Stanford Battle Area | Stanford Ops |
| 78.32500 | | NFM | Waterbeach | Security |
| 78.32500 | | NFM | West Moors | Army Ch 3 |
| 78.33750 | | NFM | London | MoD Police |
| 78.35000 | | NFM | USAF Fairford | Base Ops |
| 78.36250 | | NFM | Bovington | Army Camp Ch 6 |
| 78.36750 | | NFM | Portsmouth | RN Police |
| 78.37500 | | NFM | Aldershot | MoD Police and Army Camp Security |
| 78.38750 | | NFM | London | MoD Police |
| 78.38750 | | NFM | Portsmouth | RN Police |
| 78.40000 | | NFM | Nationwide | Army Equipment Channel 1 |
| 78.40000 | 73.12500 | NFM | London | MoD Police |
| 78.41250 | | NFM | Knightsbridge | Bomb Squad |
| 78.41250 | | NFM | London | MoD Police repeater (mainly clear: sometimes DVP) |
| 78.41250 | | NFM | London | MoD Police Chelsea Barracks |
| 78.41250 | | NFM | Middle Wallop | Army Air Corps |
| 78.41250 | | NFM | RAF Northolt | Security |
| 78.42500 | 73.15000 | NFM | Nationwide | Army Equipment Channel 2 |
| 78.43750 | | NFM | Bovington | Army Camp Ch 6 |
| 78.45000 | | NFM | London | Data and tone |
| 78.45000 | | NFM | Middle Wallop | Crash (army) |
| 78.45000 | 73.20000 | NFM | Nationwide | Army Equipment Channel 3 |
| 78.47500 | | NFM | Pembroke | Military Range |
| 78.47500 | 73.22500 | NFM | Nationwide | Army Equipment Channel 4 |
| 78.48750 | | NFM | Aldershot Camp | Army Security |
| 78.48750 | | NFM | Guildford | Military Police |
| 78.48750 | | NFM | RAE Farnborough | Army Police |
| 78.48750 | | NFM | RAF Welford | Fire Brigade |
| 78.48750 | 78.48750 | NFM | Colchester | Military Police |
| 78.50000 | | NFM | Nationwide | Army Equipment Channel 5 |
| 78.52500 | | FM | Northern Ireland | Ulster Defence Regiment Police |
| 78.52500 | | NFM | Welford | USAF Bomb Disposal Units |
| 78.53750 | | NFM | Bovington | Army Camp Ch 1 |
| 78.55000 | | NFM | Middle Wallop | Ops. Ch.1 |
| 78.55000 | | NFM | Shropshire | Army Fire Channel |
| 78.57500 | | NFM | RNAS Culdrose | Base Ops |
| 78.57500 | | NFM | RNAS Yeovilton | Crash Ops Ch 4 |
| 78.57500 | | NFM | USAF Fairford | IAT Tanker Ops |
| 78.60000 | | NFM | RAF Wittering | RAF Police Ch 52 |
| 78.61250 | | NFM | Bovington | Army Camp Ch 2 |
| 78.63750 | | NFM | Hampshire | MoD Police |
| 78.65000 | 73.50000 | NFM | Nationwide | Army Equipment Channel 1 |
| 78.67500 | | NFM | RAF Wittering | RAF Police Ch 53 |
| 78.67500 | 73.25000 | NFM | Nationwide | Army Equipment Channel 8 |
| 78.68750 | | NFM | Portsmouth | RN Security |
| 78.69750 | | NFM | Nationwide | RAF Police |

| Base | Mobile | Mode | Location | User and Notes |
|------|--------|------|----------|----------------|
| 78.70000 | | NFM | USAF Fairford | Base Ops |
| 78.77500 | 73.55000 | NFM | Hampshire | Army |
| 78.77500 | 73.55000 | NFM | London | MoD Police |
| 78.77500 | 73.55000 | NFM | Middle Wallop | Ops. Ch.2 |
| 78.77500 | 73.55000 | NFM | Nationwide | Army Equipment Channel 9 |
| 78.77500 | 73.55000 | NFM | RAF Ternhill | Army Fire Channel |
| 78.77500 | 73.55000 | NFM | RNAS Portland | Tower |
| 78.80000 | | NFM | Great Malvern | RSRE Base Security |
| 78.80000 | | NFM | Hampshire | Army |
| 78.80000 | 73.35000 | NFM | Nationwide | Army Equipment Channel 6 |
| 78.80000 | 73.35000 | NFM | Poole | Royal Marines |
| 78.80000 | 149.50000 | NFM | London | MoD Police |
| 78.81250 | | NFM | Newbury | Army |
| 78.82000 | | NFM | Birmingham | ITV News Talkback |
| 78.82500 | | NFM | AAC Middle Wallop | Tower to ground Ch.3 |
| 78.82500 | | NFM | Donington | Army Ordnance Depot Fire |
| 78.82500 | | NFM | London | MoD Police |
| 78.83750 | | NFM | Kildenhall | MoD police |
| 78.85000 | | NFM | AAC Middle Wallop | Ops |
| 78.85000 | | NFM | Brecon Beacons | Army |
| 78.85000 | | NFM | RAF Wittering | RAF Police Ch 54 |
| 78.87500 | | NFM | Nationwide | MoD Police |
| 78.90000 | | NFM | RNAS Lee-On-Solent | Tower to ground |
| 78.90000 | | NFM | RNAS Yeovilton | Fuel & Maintenance |
| 78.90000 | 73.00000 | NFM | Nationwide | Army Equipment Channel 7 |
| 78.95000 | | NFM | AAC Middle Wallop | Tower-Ground |
| 78.95000 | | NFM | Brampton Barracks | Security |
| 78.95000 | | NFM | RNAS Culdrose | Ops |
| 78.95000 | | NFM | RNAS Merryfield | Ops |
| 78.97500 | | NFM | Cheltenham | GCHQ Security and Transport |

## 79.0000 - 80.0000 MHz    MoD and RAF Ground Services 12.5 kHz

| Base | Mobile | Mode | Location | User and Notes |
|------|--------|------|----------|----------------|
| 79.00000 | | NFM | RAF Coningsby | 56(R) Squadron Ops |
| 79.00000 | | NFM | RAF Leeming | Air Defence Channel |
| 79.00000 | | NFM | RAF Odiham | Ops |
| 79.00000 | | NFM | RAF Uxbridge | Ops |
| 79.00000 | | NFM | RNAS Yeovilton | Tower-Ground Ch 3 |
| 79.02500 | | NFM | Nationwide | RAF Cosford |
| 79.02500 | | NFM | RAF Cottesmore | Tower |
| 79.02500 | | NFM | RAF Lyneham | Military Police |
| 79.02500 | | NFM | RAF Manston | Tower/Ground |
| 79.02500 | | NFM | RAF Valley | Q Control |
| 79.02500 | | NFM | Salisbury Plain | Army |
| 79.05000 | | NFM | Nationwide | RAF Cosford |
| 79.05000 | | NFM | RAF Coningsby | Tower |
| 79.05000 | | NFM | RAF Leuchars | Felix Control |
| 79.05000 | | NFM | RAF Lyneham | Crew Buses |
| 79.05000 | | AM | RAF Machrihanish | Tower |
| 79.05000 | | NFM | RAF Northolt | Paintbox Control |
| 79.07500 | | NFM | RAF Church Fenton | Tower-Ground |
| 79.07500 | | NFM | RAF Cosford | Tower-Ground |
| 79.07500 | | NFM | RAF Northolt | Tower Crash Tenders |
| 79.10000 | | NFM | Nationwide | RAF Police Channel 1 |
| 79.10000 | | NFM | RAF Valley | Tower-Ground |
| 79.12500 | | NFM | RAF Brize Norton | Ground Services |

| Base | Mobile | Mode | Location | User and Notes |
|------|--------|------|----------|----------------|
| 79.12500 | | NFM | RAF Cottesmore | Tower/Ground |
| 79.12500 | | NFM | RAF Manston | Maintenance |
| 79.12500 | | NFM | RAF Manston | RAF Police (PRONTO) |
| 79.12500 | | NFM | RAF Marham | Engineering |
| 79.12500 | | NFM | RAF St Athan | Loadmaster and Ground |
| 79.12500 | | NFM | RAF St Mawgan | Personnel Services |
| 79.13750 | | NFM | RAF Leuchars | Ground Services |
| 79.15000 | | NFM | Nationwide | RAF Police Channel 2 |
| 79.15000 | | NFM | RAF Linton-on-Ouse | Ground Services |
| 79.17500 | | NFM | RAF Lyneham | Tower/Ground |
| 79.17500 | | NFM | RAF Northolt | Forward Control |
| 79.18750 | | NFM | RAF Northolt | Link Repeater |
| 79.20000 | | NFM | Nationwide | RAF Police Channel 3 |
| 79.20000 | | NFM | RAF Coningsby | Ground Services |
| 79.20000 | | NFM | RAF Leeming | Saracen |
| 79.20000 | | NFM | RAF Leuchars | Maintenance |
| 79.20000 | | NFM | RAF Newton | Police Training |
| 79.21250 | | NFM | Manchester | Mould |
| 79.21250 | | NFM | Norfolk | Mould |
| 79.21250 | | NFM | RAE Aberporth | MoD Police |
| 79.21250 | 74.11250 | NFM | Gwent | Mould |
| 79.22500 | | NFM | RAF Kinloss | Ops (MOONSHINE CONTROL) |
| 79.22500 | | NFM | RAF Leuchars | Ops (ZULU CONTROL) |
| 79.22500 | | NFM | RAF Spadeadam | Ops |
| 79.22500 | | NFM | RAF Waddington | RAF Police (WHITECAP CONTROL) |
| 79.22500 | | NFM | RAF Wittering | RAF Police Ch 3/13 |
| 79.22500 | 68.30000 | NFM | Nationwide | Army Channel 1 |
| 79.22500 | 79.22500 | NFM | RAF Cottesmore | Ops (BRAVO) |
| 79.25000 | | NFM | Nationwide | RAF Police Channel 4 |
| 79.25000 | | NFM | RAF Church Fenton | Marshallers |
| 79.25000 | | NFM | RAF Leuchars | Ground Ops |
| 79.25000 | | NFM | RAF Linton-on-Ouse | Ground Services |
| 79.25000 | | NFM | RAF Marham | Security |
| 79.25000 | | NFM | RAF Wattisham | Medics |
| 79.25000 | | NFM | RAF Wittering | RAF Police and ops. |
| 79.25000 | 68.40000 | NFM | Nationwide | Army Channel 2 |
| 79.26250 | | NFM | RAF Leeming | Ground |
| 79.27500 | | NFM | RAF Lyneham | Ground Control |
| 79.27500 | | NFM | RAF Marham | Tower |
| 79.27500 | | NFM | RAF Northolt | Ground Control |
| 79.27500 | | NFM | RAF St Athan | Transport and Ground |
| 79.27500 | | NFM | RAF St Mawgan | RAF Police |
| 79.27500 | | NFM | RAF Valley | RAF Police (Livid Control) |
| 79.27500 | | NFM | RAF Wittering | Ops |
| 79.27500 | 68.42500 | NFM | Nationwide | Army Channel 3 |
| 79.30000 | | NFM | Nationwide | RAF Police Channel 5 |
| 79.30000 | | NFM | RAF Coltishall | RAF Police (WHITECAP CONTROL) |
| 79.30000 | | NFM | RAF Coltishall | Tower |
| 79.30000 | | NFM | RAF Odiham | Tower |
| 79.30000 | | NFM | RAF Wittering | RAF Police |
| 79.32500 | | NFM | Galway | Galway Heating Oil Co. |
| 79.32500 | | NFM | Nationwide | RAF Police |
| 79.32500 | | NFM | RAE Farnborough | Ground Control |
| 79.32500 | | NFM | RAF Cosford | Ground Control |
| 79.32500 | | NFM | RAF Leeming | Ground |
| 79.32500 | | NFM | RAF Linton-on-Ouse | Ground Services |

| Base | Mobile | Mode | Location | User and Notes |
|------|--------|------|----------|----------------|
| 79.32500 | | NFM | RAF Lossiemouth | Tower |
| 79.32500 | | NFM | RAF Waddington | Ground Services |
| 79.35000 | | NFM | Nationwide | RAF Police Channel 6 |
| 79.35000 | | NFM | Nationwide | Royal Signals |
| 79.35000 | | NFM | RAF Coningsby | Ground Services |
| 79.35000 | | NFM | RAF Leuchars | Crash Ops |
| 79.35000 | | NFM | RAF Manston | RAF Police (FLACKMAN) |
| 79.35000 | | NFM | RAF Valley | Military Police |
| 79.35000 | | NFM | RAF Waddington | Channel One |
| 79.35000 | | NFM | RAF Wittering | Ch I/11/51 |
| 79.37500 | | NFM | Gosport | RN Security (TANZY CONTROL) |
| 79.37500 | | NFM | RAF Church Fenton | RAF Police (WHITECAP CONTROL) |
| 79.37500 | | NFM | RAF Leuchars | Crash Ops |
| 79.37500 | | NFM | RAF Marham | Military Police |
| 79.37500 | | NFM | RAF Odiham | Ruler |
| 79.38750 | | NFM | RAF Leuchars | Ground Services |
| 79.40000 | | NFM | Nationwide | Army Channel 4 |
| 79.40000 | | NFM | Nationwide | RAF Police Channel 7 |
| 79.40000 | | NFM | RAF Coningsby | Ground Services |
| 79.40000 | | NFM | RAF Honington | Military Police |
| 79.40000 | | NFM | RAF Leeming | Air Defence Channel |
| 79.40000 | | NFM | RAF Leuchars | Ground Services |
| 79.40000 | | NFM | RAF Lyneham | Ops |
| 79.40000 | | NFM | RAF Northolt | RAF Police (MAYFLY) |
| 79.40000 | | NFM | RAF Wittering | RAF Police Ch 7/17 |
| 79.40000 | | NFM | Tain | Range Control |
| 79.41250 | 74.38750 | NFM | Gwent | Mould |
| 79.42500 | | NFM | RAF Brize Norton | Tower-Ground |
| 79.42500 | | NFM | RAF Kinloss | Tower |
| 79.42500 | | NFM | RAF Waddington | Tower-Ground |
| 79.45000 | | NFM | Nationwide | RAF Police Channel 8 |
| 79.45000 | | NFM | RAF Coltishall | Ops (ZERO) |
| 79.45000 | | NFM | RAF Cosford | Charlie Control |
| 79.45000 | | NFM | RAF Leeming | Air Defence Channel |
| 79.45000 | | NFM | RAF Wittering | RAF Police |
| 79.47500 | | NFM | Lydd | Army Camp Security |
| 79.47500 | | NFM | Nationwide | RAF Police |
| 79.47500 | | NFM | RAF Coningsby | Line |
| 79.47500 | | NFM | RAF Cranwell | Ground Services |
| 79.47500 | | NFM | RAF Northolt | Ops (PAPA) |
| 79.48750 | | NFM | Northern Ireland | RAF Repeater |
| 79.48750 | | NFM | Southend on Sea | MoD Repeater |
| 79.50000 | | NFM | Lydd | Army Camp Security |
| 79.50000 | | NFM | Nationwide | RAF Police Channel 9 |
| 79.50000 | | NFM | RAE Aberporth | MoD Police |
| 79.50000 | | NFM | RAF Neatishead | Security |
| 79.50000 | | NFM | RAF Waddington | Channel Four |
| 79.50000 | | NFM | RAF Wittering | Ops |
| 79.50000 | | NFM | RAF Wittering | RAF Police Ch 9/19 |
| 79.50000 | | NFM | USAF Mildenhall | Security |
| 79.52500 | | NFM | RAF Lossiemouth | Ops |
| 79.52500 | | NFM | RAF Newton | Ops (TEMPO) |
| 79.52500 | | NFM | RAF Wittering | Ops/RAF Police |
| 79.53750 | | NFM | RAE Farnborough | Medical Ops |
| 79.55000 | | NFM | Nationwide | RAF Police Channel 10 |
| 79.55000 | | NFM | RAF Coningsby | Ground Services |

| Base | Mobile | Mode | Location | User and Notes |
| --- | --- | --- | --- | --- |
| 79.56250 | | NFM | RAF Ternhill | Army Staff Cars |
| 79.57500 | | NFM | RAF Leeming | Air Defence Channel |
| 79.57500 | | NFM | RAF Lossiemouth | Ops (EPOCH CONTROL) |
| 79.60000 | | NFM | Nationwide | RAF Police Channel 11 |
| 79.60000 | | NFM | RAF Brize Norton | Ops (BRIZE OPS) |
| 79.60000 | | NFM | RAF Lossiemouth | Ops (OXIDE CONTROL) |
| 79.60000 | | NFM | RAF Manston | RAF Police (SEAGULL) |
| 79.61250 | | NFM | Cambridgeshire | Mould Ch 4 |
| 79.62500 | | NFM | RAF Wittering | Ground Services |
| 79.65000 | | NFM | Nationwide | RAF Police Channel 12 |
| 79.65000 | | NFM | RAF Benson | Tower |
| 79.65000 | | NFM | RAF Brize Norton | Loadmasters/Tower-Ground |
| 79.65000 | | NFM | RAF Coningsby | Ground Services |
| 79.65000 | | NFM | RAF Lyneham | Tower |
| 79.67500 | | NFM | RAF Brize Norton | Loadmaster |
| 79.67500 | | NFM | RAF Newton | Tower |
| 79.67500 | | NFM | RAF Northolt | Ops |
| 79.67500 | | NFM | RAF Valley | Fuel/Maintenance |
| 79.68000 | | NFM | RAF Waddington | Channel Five |
| 79.70000 | | NFM | RAF Coningsby | Ground Services |
| 79.70000 | | NFM | RAF Leeming | Air Defence Channel |
| 79.70000 | | NFM | RAF Marham | Link |
| 79.70000 | 68.15000 | NFM | Nationwide | Army Channel 6 |
| 79.71250 | | NFM | Colchester | Barracks |
| 79.71250 | | NFM | Stanford Battle Area | Stanford Ops |
| 79.71250 | 74.46750 | NFM | Gwent | Mould |
| 79.72500 | 74.72500 | NFM | RAF Cottesmore | Grady Control |
| 79.76250 | | NFM | Derbyshire | Mould |
| 79.76250 | 74.26250 | NFM | Gwent | Mould |
| 79.77500 | | NFM | Colchester | Barracks |
| 79.77500 | | NFM | Nationwide | RAF Fire Channel |
| 79.77500 | | NFM | RAF Leeming | Air Defence Channel |
| 79.77500 | | NFM | RAF Northolt | Ops |
| 79.80000 | | NFM | Nationwide | Army Channel 7 |
| 79.80000 | | NFM | RAF Coningsby | Ground Services |
| 79.82500 | | NFM | Nationwide | RAF Police convoys |
| 79.82500 | | NFM | RAF Wittering | RAF Police |
| 79.82500 | 84.82500 | NFM | Berkshire | Royal Ordnance weapons testing |
| 79.87500 | | NFM | RAF Odiham | 33 Squadron link |
| 79.90000 | 68.52500 | NFM | Nationwide | Army Channel 8 |
| 79.95000 | | NFM | RAF Wittering | Ground Services |
| 79.95000 | 68.60000 | NFM | Nationwide | Army Channel 9 |
| 79.98750 | 79.97500 | NFM | RAF Coningsby | 56(R) Squadron Ops |

**80.0000 - 82.5000 MHz**  RADIO ASTRONOMY

WITHIN 48 KM OF CAMBRIDGE

**81.5000 - 83.5000 MHz**  LOW BAND PMR (SIMPLEX & DUPLEX)

[SPLIT - 10.5 MHz]

| Base | Mobile | Mode | Location | User and Notes |
| --- | --- | --- | --- | --- |
| 81.57500 | 68.07500 | NFM | England & Wales | Police Radio Engineering |
| 81.70000 | 68.20000 | NFM | London, Heathrow | HM Custom & Excise |
| 81.75000 | 68.25000 | NFM | Dover | HM Customs & Excise (DINGO) |
| 81.75000 | 68.25000 | NFM | Suffolk | HM Customs & Excise (IPEX) |
| 81.76250 | 68.26250 | NFM | Nationwide | HM Customs & Excise |
| 81.76250 | 68.26250 | NFM | Newhaven | HM Customs & Excise (SIERRA) |

| Base | Mobile | Mode | Location | User and Notes |
|------|--------|------|----------|----------------|
| 81.77500 | 68.27500 | NFM | East Anglia/Suffolk | HM Customs & Excise (IPEX) |
| 81.77500 | 68.27500 | NFM | Immingham | HM Customs & Excise |
| 81.77500 | 68.27500 | NFM | Nationwide | HM Customs & Excise |
| 81.77500 | 68.27500 | NFM | Nationwide | Network Q RAC Rally Marshall |
| 81.77500 | 68.27500 | NFM | Solent | HM Customs & Excise (SAXON/OSCAR) |
| 81.78750 | 62.28750 | NFM | England (South) | HM Customs & Excise |
| 81.78750 | 68.28750 | NFM | Dartford | HM Customs & Excise |
| 81.78750 | 68.28750 | NFM | Immingham | HM Customs & Excise |
| 81.78750 | 68.28750 | NFM | London | HM Customs & Excise |
| 81.78750 | 68.28750 | NFM | Nationwide | HM Customs & Excise |
| 81.78750 | 68.28750 | NFM | Oban | HM Customs & Excise |
| 81.80000 | 68.30000 | NFM | Poole | Repeater |
| 81.80000 | 68.30000 | NFM | Portsmouth | Council |
| 81.80000 | 68.30000 | NFM | Portsmouth | Red Star Parcels |
| 81.80000 | 68.30000 | NFM | Purbrock | Battmans |
| 81.80000 | 68.30000 | NFM | Ringwood | Hall Aggregates |
| 81.80000 | 68.30000 | NFM | Southampton | Ennimix |
| 81.81250 | 68.31250 | NFM | Melksham | Radio Rentals |
| 81.81250 | 68.31250 | NFM | Weston-Super-Mare | Radio Rentals |
| 81.82500 | 81.82500 | AM | Nationwide | Police Motorway Units |
| 81.85000 | 68.35000 | NFM | Glasgow | Taxis |
| 81.86250 | 68.36250 | NFM | London, Kew Bridge | Tonis Radio Cars |
| 81.88750 | 68.38750 | NFM | Sussex | PMR Repeater |
| 81.91250 | 68.41250 | NFM | Slough | Taxis |
| 81.92500 | 68.42500 | NFM | Birmingham | Taxis |
| 81.92500 | 68.42500 | NFM | Redcar | Taxis |
| 81.93750 | 68.43750 | NFM | Southall | Sky Cars |
| 81.95000 | 81.95000 | NFM | London | Fire Brigade HQ Ops Room |
| 81.96250 | 68.46250 | AM | Plymouth | Plymouth Taxis |
| 81.98750 | 68.48750 | NFM | Grimsby | Marine Gas and Oil |
| 81.98750 | 68.48750 | NFM | Kent | Courier Service |
| 81.98750 | 68.48750 | NFM | Kent | Doctors |
| 81.98750 | 68.48750 | NFM | Portsmouth | PMR |
| 82.00000 | 68.50000 | NFM | Sussex | PMR Repeater |
| 82.02500 | 68.52500 | NFM | Bexley Heath | Taxis |
| 82.03750 | 68.53750 | NFM | London | London Car Hire |
| 82.05000 | 68.55000 | NFM | Liverpool | HM Customs & Excise |
| 82.05000 | 68.55000 | NFM | Manchester | HM Customs & Excise |
| 82.05000 | 68.55000 | NFM | Nationwide | HM Customs & Excise |
| 82.06000 | 68.56250 | NFM | Worcester | Amber Taxis |
| 82.06250 | 68.56250 | NFM | Glasgow | Taxis |
| 82.10000 | 68.60000 | NFM | Glasgow | Taxis |
| 82.10000 | 68.60000 | NFM | London, South Bermondsey | Roadrunner Taxis |
| 82.10000 | 68.60000 | AM | Swansea | Ryan Mining Ch 1 |
| 82.10000 | 71.60000 | AM | Swansea | Council Works Department |
| 82.11250 | 68.61250 | NFM | Edinburgh | Taxis |
| 82.11250 | 68.61250 | NFM | Glasgow | Taxis |
| 82.13750 | 68.63750 | NFM | East Yorkshire | Council roads dept. |
| 82.13750 | 68.63750 | NFM | London | Building Supplier |
| 82.13750 | 68.63750 | NFM | Tonbridge | Medicall |
| 82.17500 | 85.17500 | NFM | Bristol Area | Maintenance Company |
| 82.18750 | 68.68750 | NFM | London | Contract Dustcart |
| 82.21250 | 68.71250 | AM | Swansea | Ryan Mining Ch 2 |
| 82.22500 | 68.72500 | NFM | Newcastle | PMR |
| 82.26500 | 68.76500 | NFM | Ayr | North of Scotland Water Authority |
| 82.30000 | 68.80000 | NFM | Leicester | PMR Repeater |

| Base | Mobile | Mode | Location | User and Notes |
|------|--------|------|----------|----------------|
| 82.30000 | 68.80000 | NFM | Sussex | PMR Repeater |
| 82.30000 | 68.80000 | NFM | Tunbridge Wells | Medicall |
| 82.40000 | 68.90000 | NFM | London | Ambassordor Mini Cabs |
| 82.43750 | 68.93750 | NFM | Glasgow | Taxis |
| 82.43750 | 68.93750 | NFM | Gravesend | Taxis |
| 82.52500 | 69.02500 | NFM | Nationwide | Road Construction Recovery |
| 82.53750 | 69.02500 | NFM | Walsall | Taxi |
| 82.55000 | 69.05000 | NFM | Lincoln | PMR |
| 82.78750 | 69.28750 | NFM | Nationwide | RAC Network Q Rally |
| 82.80000 | 68.50000 | NFM | Bournmouth | Securiguard |
| 82.80000 | 68.50000 | NFM | Nationwide | Nynex Telecoms engineers |
| 82.80000 | 82.80000 | NFM | RAC Network 'Q' Rally | Rally Control |
| 82.80000 | 86.43500 | NFM | Keilder Forrest | RAC Rally |
| 82.81250 | 82.81250 | NFM | RAC Network 'Q' Rally | Rally Channel 3 |
| 82.90000 | 82.90000 | NFM | RAC Network 'Q' Rally | Ford Team |
| 82.92500 | 69.42500 | NFM | RAC Network 'Q' Rally | Subara Team |
| 82.95000 | 69.45000 | NFM | Nationwide | Network Q RAC Rally Recovery |
| 82.98750 | 69.48750 | NFM | RAC Network 'Q' Rally | Toyota Channel 2 |
| 83.06500 | 69.56500 | NFM | Birmingham | Building Suppliers |
| 83.07500 | 69.57500 | NFM | Birmingham | Severn Trent Water - Aqua Base |
| 83.24500 | 69.74500 | NFM | Dublin | Electricity |
| 83.31250 | 69.81250 | NFM | Belfast | Water Board |
| 83.35000 | 69.85000 | NFM | Swansea | Council works dept |

**83.500 - 84.000 MHz**       EMERGENCY SERVICES

**83.996 - 84.004 MHz**       INDUSTRIAL, SCIENTIFIC AND MEDICAL EQUIPMENT

**84.000 - 84.9750 MHz**       MOD COMMUNICATIONS 25 kHz SIMPLEX

| Base | Mobile | Mode | Location | User and Notes |
|------|--------|------|----------|----------------|
| 84.05000 | | NFM | Tweed Valley | Military Police |
| 84.08750 | | NFM | Nationwide | Military Close Protection Ch 3 |
| 84.12500 | | NFM | Imber Range | MoD Police Ch.6 |
| 84.12500 | | NFM | Nationwide | Army Cadet Force |
| 84.15000 | | NFM | Nationwide | Military Close Protection Ch 4 |
| 84.20000 | | NFM | Imber Range | MoD Police Ch.8 |
| 84.22500 | | NFM | Nationwide | RAF |
| 84.26250 | | NFM | Nationwide | Military Close Protection Ch 7 |
| 84.30000 | | NFM | Brecon Beacons | RAF Mountain Rescue Ch1 |
| 84.30000 | | NFM | Nationwide | RAF Mountain Rescue |
| 84.30000 | | NFM | Nationwide | RAF Mountain Rescue Ch.1 |
| 84.31250 | | NFM | Salisbury | MoD Police Larkhill Range |
| 84.32500 | | NFM | Nationwide | RAF Mountain Rescue Ch.2 |
| 84.32500 | | NFM | Wiltshire | MoD Raydex Helicopter downlink |
| 84.33750 | | NFM | Blandford | MoD Police |
| 84.36250 | | NFM | Nationwide | Military Close Protection Ch 6 |
| 84.37500 | | NFM | Nationwide | Military Police |
| 84.38750 | | NFM | Nationwide | Military Police |
| 84.40000 | | NFM | Nationwide | Military Police |
| 84.41250 | | NFM | Nationwide | Military Police |
| 84.41250 | | NFM | Salisbury | Army (T/O) |
| 84.42500 | | NFM | Nationwide | Military Police |
| 84.43750 | | NFM | Nationwide | Military Police |
| 84.45000 | | NFM | Nationwide | Military Police |
| 84.46250 | | NFM | Nationwide | Military Police |

| Base | Mobile | Mode | Location | User and Notes |
|------|--------|------|----------|----------------|
| 84.47500 | | NFM | Castlemartin | RAC Range |
| 84.47500 | | NFM | Nationwide | Military Police |
| 84.48750 | | NFM | England (South West) | MoD Police |
| 84.48750 | | NFM | Nationwide | Military Police Escorts |
| 84.50000 | | NFM | Nationwide | Military Police Escorts |
| 84.51250 | | NFM | Nationwide | Military Police |
| 84.52500 | | NFM | Aldershot | Military Police Data |
| 84.53750 | | NFM | Nationwide | Military Police |
| 84.55000 | | NFM | London | Military Police |
| 84.56250 | | NFM | Nationwide | Military Police |
| 84.57500 | | NFM | Nationwide | Military Police |
| 84.58750 | | NFM | Nationwide | Military Police |
| 84.60000 | | NFM | Nationwide | Military Mountain Rescue |
| 84.60000 | | NFM | Southampton | Royal Navy |
| 84.61250 | | NFM | Southampton | Army Marchwood Camp shipping Office |
| 84.64000 | | NFM | Salisbury Plain | Defence Land Services |
| 84.65000 | 72.85000 | NFM | RN Faslane | Medics |
| 84.71250 | | NFM | Nationwide | Military Close Protection Ch 2 |
| 84.76250 | | NFM | Nationwide | Military Close Protection Ch 1 |
| 84.77500 | | NFM | Southampton | Royal Navy |
| 84.82500 | | NFM | Nationwide | RAF Helicopter Winchmen |
| 84.82500 | 79.82500 | NFM | Nationwide | Royal Ordnance Weapons Transport |
| 84.83750 | | NFM | Nationwide | Military Close Protection Ch 6 |
| 84.83750 | | NFM | Perth | Territorial Army |
| 84.85000 | | NFM | Nationwide | Military Close Protection Ch 5 |
| 84.92500 | | NFM | Southampton | Royal Navy |
| 84.97500 | | NFM | Ludford Cove | Army Range Control Ch 1 |

## 84.35000- 84.55000 MHz    REPUBIC OF IRELAND FIRE BRIGADE AND AMBULANCE SERVICE (DUPLEX)

| Base | Mobile | Mode | Location | User and Notes |
|------|--------|------|----------|----------------|
| 84.350 | 74.125 | NFM | Nationwide | Fire Brigade |
| 84.375 | 74.150 | NFM | Nationwide | Fire Brigade |
| 84.400 | 74.175 | NFM | Nationwide | Fire Brigade |
| 84.425 | 74.200 | NFM | Nationwide | Fire Brigade |
| 84.450 | 74.225 | NFM | Nationwide | Fire Brigade |
| 84.475 | 74.250 | NFM | Nationwide | Fire Brigade |
| 84.500 | 74.275 | NFM | Nationwide | Fire Brigade |
| 84.525 | 74.300 | NFM | Nationwide | Fire Brigade |
| 84.550 | 74.325 | NFM | Nationwide | Fire Brigade |
| 84.575 | 74.350 | NFM | Nationwide | Ambulance Service |
| 84.600 | 74.375 | NFM | Nationwide | Ambulance Service |
| 84.625 | 74.400 | NFM | Nationwide | Ambulance Service |
| 84.650 | 74.425 | NFM | Nationwide | Ambulance Service |
| 84.675 | 74.450 | NFM | Nationwide | Ambulance Service |
| 84.700 | 74.475 | NFM | Nationwide | Ambulance Service |
| 84.725 | 74.500 | NFM | Nationwide | Ambulance Service |
| 84.750 | 74.525 | NFM | Nationwide | Ambulance Service |
| 84.775 | 74.550 | NFM | Nationwide | Ambulance Service |
| 84.800 | 74.575 | NFM | Nationwide | Ambulance Service |
| 84.825 | 74.600 | NFM | Nationwide | Ambulance Service |

## 85.00625 - 87.5000 MHz  PMR Low Band Base Repeaters 12.5 kHz
### [Split - 13.5 MHz]

| Base | Mobile | Mode | Location | User and Notes |
|---|---|---|---|---|
| 85.01250 | 71.51250 | NFM | Birmingham | National Breakdown |
| 85.01250 | 71.51250 | NFM | Brighton | Focsa Street Cleaners |
| 85.01250 | 71.51250 | NFM | Bristol | Severn Trent Water |
| 85.01250 | 71.51250 | NFM | Co. Londonderry | NI Electricity - North coast Ch.2 |
| 85.01250 | 71.51250 | NFM | Ealing | PMR |
| 85.01250 | 71.51250 | NFM | Isle of Man | Isle of Man Water |
| 85.01250 | 71.51250 | AM | Jersey | Jersey Telecom |
| 85.01250 | 71.51250 | NFM | London | Breakdown services |
| 85.01250 | 71.51250 | NFM | Newport, Wales | Cardiff Council technical services/DLO |
| 85.01250 | 71.51250 | NFM | Perth | North of Scotland Water Authority |
| 85.01250 | 71.51250 | NFM | Widnes | Skip Hire |
| 85.02500 | 71.52500 | NFM | Belfast | Water Board |
| 85.02500 | 71.52500 | NFM | Birmingham | Breakdown Company |
| 85.02500 | 71.52500 | NFM | Exeter | National Rivers Authority |
| 85.02500 | 71.52500 | NFM | Gedling | Gedling Borough Council |
| 85.02500 | 71.52500 | NFM | Ipswich | Council |
| 85.02500 | 71.52500 | NFM | Neath | Council |
| 85.02500 | 71.52500 | NFM | Norfolk | County Highways |
| 85.02500 | 71.52500 | NFM | Peterborough | Peterborough Development Corp |
| 85.02500 | 71.52500 | NFM | Pickering | Council |
| 85.02500 | 71.52500 | NFM | Port Talbot | Council Services |
| 85.02500 | 71.52500 | NFM | Southampton | Interlink |
| 85.03750 | 71.53750 | NFM | Aberdeen | Roads Department |
| 85.03750 | 71.53750 | NFM | Ayr | East Ayrshire Road Dept. (Highways) |
| 85.03750 | 71.53750 | NFM | Cambridge | Regency Cars |
| 85.03750 | 71.53750 | NFM | Dumfries | Council Roads Department |
| 85.03750 | 71.53750 | NFM | Easington | Works Dept |
| 85.03750 | 71.53750 | NFM | Exeter | Moorland Garage |
| 85.03750 | 71.53750 | NFM | Hastings | Council |
| 85.03750 | 71.53750 | NFM | Ipswich | Council Repeater |
| 85.03750 | 71.53750 | AM | Killwinning | Roads Department |
| 85.03750 | 71.53750 | AM | Leeds | Gritters/snow ploughs |
| 85.03750 | 71.53750 | NFM | Newport, Wales | Cardiff Council technical services/DLO |
| 85.03750 | 71.53750 | AM | St Austell | Chris Perry Motors |
| 85.03750 | 71.53750 | NFM | Strathclyde | Strathclyde Council |
| 85.05000 | 71.55000 | NFM | Aylsham | East Coast Grain |
| 85.05000 | 71.55000 | NFM | Benington | Braceys |
| 85.05000 | 71.55000 | NFM | Cambridge | Bidwells |
| 85.05000 | 71.55000 | NFM | Cambridge | Trumpington Farms |
| 85.05000 | 71.55000 | NFM | Cleveland | Mastercare |
| 85.05000 | 71.55000 | NFM | Ipswich | Anglian Water |
| 85.05000 | 71.55000 | NFM | Ipswich | Anglia Water |
| 85.05000 | 71.55000 | AM | Jersey | Abbey |
| 85.05000 | 71.55000 | NFM | London | Baron Cars |
| 85.05000 | 71.55000 | NFM | London | Baron Transport |
| 85.05000 | 71.55000 | NFM | Norfolk | Farm Feed Co. |
| 85.05000 | 71.55000 | NFM | Perth | North of Scotland Water Authority |
| 85.05000 | 71.55000 | NFM | Peterborough | Royal Taxis |
| 85.05000 | 71.55000 | NFM | Reepham | Salle Farm Co. |
| 85.05000 | 71.55000 | NFM | Romford | Atlas Minicabs |
| 85.05000 | 71.55000 | NFM | Southampton | Taxis |
| 85.05000 | 71.55000 | NFM | Suffolk | Farm Feed Co. |
| 85.05000 | 71.55000 | NFM | Swanage | Associted Taxis |
| 85.06250 | 71.56250 | NFM | Birmingham | Community ambulance |

| Base | Mobile | Mode | Location | User and Notes |
|------|--------|------|----------|----------------|
| 85.06250 | 71.56250 | NFM | Caerphilly | Coddy Cabs |
| 85.06250 | 71.56250 | NFM | Cleveland | Mastercare |
| 85.06250 | 71.56250 | NFM | Hull | Moss Tyres |
| 85.06250 | 71.56250 | NFM | Kettering | A-Z Taxis |
| 85.06250 | 71.56250 | NFM | London | Diamond Cars |
| 85.06250 | 71.56250 | NFM | London | Lee Vans |
| 85.06250 | 71.56250 | NFM | Norfolk | James Abbotts Ltd |
| 85.06250 | 71.56250 | NFM | Suffolk | James Abbotts Ltd |
| 85.06250 | 71.56250 | NFM | Swansea | Bryan Twyn Taxis |
| 85.06250 | 71.56250 | NFM | West Midlands | Mastercare |
| 85.06250 | 71.56250 | NFM | Winterbourne | Simpson Agricultural |
| 85.06250 | 71.56250 | NFM | Witham | Anglia Land Drainage |
| 85.06350 | 71.56350 | NFM | Birmingham | Ambuline Private Ambulance |
| 85.07500 | 71.57500 | AM | Derbyshire | Tilcon |
| 85.07500 | 71.57500 | NFM | Fordingbridge | Newton Farm |
| 85.07500 | 71.57500 | NFM | Great Yarmouth | Wolsey Taxis |
| 85.07500 | 71.57500 | NFM | Hitchin | Castles Taxis |
| 85.07500 | 71.57500 | NFM | Ipswich | Anglia Water |
| 85.07500 | 71.57500 | NFM | Kendal | Vets |
| 85.07500 | 71.57500 | NFM | Lakenheath | H. Palmer |
| 85.07500 | 71.57500 | AM | Leeds | Gritter/Snow Ploughs |
| 85.07500 | 71.57500 | NFM | Little Downham | W.B. Chambers. |
| 85.07500 | 71.57500 | NFM | London | David Marshall |
| 85.07500 | 71.57500 | AM | Melksham | Dance Taxis |
| 85.07500 | 71.57500 | NFM | Scunthorpe | Taxis |
| 85.07500 | 71.57500 | NFM | Woodchurch | Arrow Park Taxis |
| 85.07500 | 71.57500 | NFM | Wrexham | Trafford Estate |
| 85.08750 | 71.58750 | NFM | Baldock | Winifred Express |
| 85.08750 | 71.58750 | NFM | Cambridge | Regency Cars |
| 85.08750 | 71.58750 | NFM | Colchester | Wooldridge |
| 85.08750 | 71.58750 | AM | Cornwall | County Council |
| 85.08750 | 71.58750 | NFM | Guernsey | Guernsey Gas Co. |
| 85.08750 | 71.58750 | NFM | Hillingdon | Sky Radio Cars |
| 85.08750 | 71.58750 | NFM | Newmarket | Six Mile Bottom Estate |
| 85.10000 | 71.60000 | NFM | Glasgow | Water Department |
| 85.10000 | 71.60000 | NFM | Grampian | North of Scotland Water Authority |
| 85.10000 | 71.60000 | NFM | Ipswich | Anglia Water |
| 85.10000 | 71.60000 | NFM | Neath | Welsh Water control room |
| 85.10000 | 71.60000 | NFM | Nottingham | Trent Water |
| 85.11250 | 71.61250 | NFM | Abergavenny | Welsh Water |
| 85.11250 | 71.61250 | NFM | Colchester | Roadworks Depot |
| 85.11250 | 71.61250 | NFM | Ipswich | Roadworks Depot |
| 85.11250 | 71.61250 | NFM | Manchester | PMR |
| 85.11250 | 71.61250 | NFM | Norwich | Anglian Water |
| 85.11250 | 71.61250 | NFM | Stanway | Roadworks Depot |
| 85.11250 | 71.61250 | NFM | Thames Valley | Thames Valley Water |
| 85.11250 | 71.61250 | NFM | West Yorkshire | British Pipeline |
| 85.12500 | 71.62500 | NFM | Ayr | East Ayrshire Road Dept. (Highways) |
| 85.12500 | 71.62500 | NFM | Belfast | Water Board |
| 85.12500 | 71.62500 | NFM | Brighton | Skip Service |
| 85.12500 | 71.62500 | NFM | Essex | British Pipeline |
| 85.12500 | 71.62500 | NFM | Jersey | Jersey Electricity Company Ch 3 |
| 85.12500 | 71.62500 | NFM | Nationwide | British Pipeline |
| 85.12500 | 71.62500 | NFM | Strathclyde | Strathclyde Council |
| 85.13750 | 71.63750 | NFM | Edinburgh | British Telecom |
| 85.13750 | 71.63750 | NFM | Nationwide | British Telecom Channel 6 |

| Base | Mobile | Mode | Location | User and Notes |
|---|---|---|---|---|
| 85.15000 | 71.65000 | NFM | Nationwide | British Telecom Channel 2 |
| 85.16250 | 71.66250 | NFM | Glasgow | Data Link |
| 85.16250 | 71.66250 | NFM | Lancaster | British Telecom |
| 85.16250 | 71.66250 | NFM | Morecambe | British Telecom |
| 85.16250 | 71.66250 | NFM | Nationwide | British Telecom Channel 4 |
| 85.16250 | 71.66250 | NFM | Perth | British Telecom |
| 85.16250 | 71.66250 | AM | Swansea | British Telecom Base |
| 85.17500 | 71.67500 | NFM | Dundee | BT Data Link |
| 85.17500 | 71.67500 | NFM | Jersey | Jersey Electricity Company Ch 2 |
| 85.17500 | 71.67500 | NFM | Nationwide | British Telecom Channel 1 |
| 85.17500 | 71.67500 | NFM | Perth | British Telecom |
| 85.18750 | 71.68750 | NFM | Edinburgh | British Telecom Voice Link |
| 85.18750 | 71.68750 | NFM | Nationwide | British Telecom Channel 5 |
| 85.18750 | 71.68750 | NFM | Perth | British Telecom Data Link |
| 85.20000 | 71.70000 | AM | Liverpool | Taxis |
| 85.20000 | 71.70000 | NFM | Manchester | Police |
| 85.20000 | 71.70000 | NFM | Nationwide | British Telecom Channel 3 |
| 85.20000 | 71.70000 | AM | York | British Telecom |
| 85.21000 | 71.71000 | NFM | Ayr | North of Scotland Water Authority |
| 85.21250 | 71.71250 | NFM | Bishop Stortford | Thames Water |
| 85.21250 | 71.71250 | NFM | Dundee | North of Scotland Water Authority |
| 85.21250 | 71.71250 | NFM | Folkestone | Southern Water |
| 85.21250 | 71.71250 | NFM | Glossop | Severn Trent Water |
| 85.21250 | 71.71250 | NFM | Gwent | South Wales Water |
| 85.21250 | 71.71250 | NFM | Hampshire | Water Board Ch 2 |
| 85.21250 | 71.71250 | NFM | Ipswich | Anglia Water |
| 85.21250 | 71.71250 | NFM | Lancaster | North West Water |
| 85.21250 | 71.71250 | NFM | Lea Valley | Southern Water Channel 2 |
| 85.21250 | 71.71250 | NFM | Llanelli | Welsh Water |
| 85.21250 | 71.71250 | NFM | Montgomery | Severn Trent Water |
| 85.21250 | 71.71250 | NFM | Morecambe | North West Water |
| 85.21250 | 71.71250 | NFM | Saffron Waldon | Southern Water |
| 85.22500 | 71.72500 | AM | Cardiff | South Glamorgan Council |
| 85.22500 | 71.72500 | NFM | Cardiff Area | Maintenance Company |
| 85.22500 | 71.72500 | AM | Cornwall | County Council |
| 85.22500 | 71.72500 | NFM | Dumbarton | Council |
| 85.22500 | 71.72500 | NFM | Dumfries | West of Scotland Water |
| 85.22500 | 71.72500 | NFM | Lea Valley | Southern Water Channel 4 |
| 85.22500 | 71.72500 | NFM | London | Chelsea Council |
| 85.22500 | 71.72500 | NFM | London | Westminster Council |
| 85.22500 | 71.72500 | NFM | North Wales | Welsh Water |
| 85.22500 | 71.72500 | NFM | Peebles | Scottish Border Council |
| 85.22500 | 71.72500 | NFM | Thames Valley | Thames Valley Water |
| 85.23750 | 71.73750 | NFM | Aberdeen | North of Scotland Water Authority |
| 85.23750 | 71.73750 | NFM | Borders | West of Scotland Water |
| 85.23750 | 71.73750 | NFM | Essex | Wessex Water |
| 85.23750 | 71.73750 | NFM | Gwynedd | Welsh Water |
| 85.23750 | 71.73750 | NFM | Nottingham | Trent Water |
| 85.23750 | 71.73750 | NFM | Perth | North of Scotland Water Authority |
| 85.23750 | 71.73750 | NFM | Suffolk | Suffolk Water |
| 85.23750 | 71.73750 | NFM | Thames Valley | Thames Valley Water |
| 85.23750 | 71.73750 | NFM | Walsall | Severn Trent Water |
| 85.23750 | 71.73750 | NFM | Whitehaven | North West Water |
| 85.25000 | 71.75000 | NFM | Ayr | North of Scotland Water Authority |
| 85.25000 | 71.75000 | NFM | Barrow | North West Water |
| 85.25000 | 71.75000 | NFM | Frimley | Surrey Water |

| Base | Mobile | Mode | Location | User and Notes |
|------|--------|------|----------|----------------|
| 85.25000 | 71.75000 | NFM | Hampshire | Portsmouth Water |
| 85.25000 | 71.75000 | NFM | Jersey | Jersey Milk |
| 85.25000 | 71.75000 | NFM | Lancaster | North West Water |
| 85.25000 | 71.75000 | NFM | Leeds | Automobile Association |
| 85.25000 | 71.75000 | NFM | Letchwood | Thames Water |
| 85.25000 | 71.75000 | NFM | Morecambe | North West Water |
| 85.25000 | 71.75000 | NFM | Newcastle | Northumbrian Water |
| 85.25000 | 71.75000 | NFM | Norfolk | Anglia Water |
| 85.25000 | 71.75000 | NFM | Perth | North of Scotland Water Authority |
| 85.25000 | 71.75000 | NFM | Scarborough | Water Authority |
| 85.25000 | 71.75000 | NFM | Suffolk | Anglia Water |
| 85.25000 | 71.75000 | NFM | Surrey | Thames Water |
| 85.25000 | 71.75000 | NFM | West Yorkshire | Automobile Association |
| 85.26250 | 71.76250 | NFM | Avon | Severn Trent Water |
| 85.26250 | 71.76250 | NFM | Belfast | Water Board |
| 85.26250 | 71.76250 | NFM | Devon, North | South West Water |
| 85.26250 | 71.76250 | NFM | Hampshire | Portsmouth Water |
| 85.26250 | 71.76250 | NFM | Huddersfield | Yorkshire Water |
| 85.26250 | 71.76250 | NFM | Kent | Kent Water |
| 85.26250 | 71.76250 | NFM | Nottinghamshire | Severn Trent Water |
| 85.26250 | 71.76250 | NFM | Taunton | Wessex Water |
| 85.26250 | 71.76250 | NFM | Thames Valley | Thames Valley Water |
| 85.27500 | 71.77500 | NFM | Cornwall | South West Water |
| 85.27500 | 71.77500 | NFM | East Sussex | Southern Water |
| 85.27500 | 71.77500 | NFM | Ipswich | Anglia Water |
| 85.27500 | 71.77500 | NFM | Kent | Kent Water |
| 85.27500 | 71.77500 | NFM | Manchester | North West Water |
| 85.27500 | 71.77500 | NFM | Norfolk | Anglia Water |
| 85.27500 | 71.77500 | NFM | Perth | North of Scotland Water Authority |
| 85.27500 | 71.77500 | NFM | Somerset | Council Housing |
| 85.27500 | 71.77500 | NFM | St. Helens | North West Water |
| 85.27500 | 71.77500 | NFM | Suffolk | Anglia Water |
| 85.27500 | 71.77500 | NFM | Tayside | North of Scotland Water Authority |
| 85.27500 | 71.77500 | NFM | West Yorkshire | Yorkshire Water |
| 85.28750 | 71.78750 | NFM | Anglia | Anglia Water Ch 13 |
| 85.28750 | 71.78750 | NFM | Belfast | Water Board |
| 85.28750 | 71.78750 | NFM | Brighton | Southern Water (Red Base) |
| 85.28750 | 71.78750 | NFM | Peterborough | Anglia Water |
| 85.28750 | 71.78750 | NFM | Tayside | North of Scotland Water Authority |
| 85.28750 | 71.78750 | NFM | Warrington | North West Water |
| 85.28750 | 71.78750 | NFM | Yorkshire | Yorkshire Water |
| 85.30000 | 71.80000 | NFM | Aberdeen | Council Dog Catcher |
| 85.30000 | 71.80000 | NFM | Breckland | Council HQ |
| 85.30000 | 71.80000 | NFM | Hampshire | Council Drainage |
| 85.30000 | 71.80000 | NFM | Ipswich | Community Repeater |
| 85.30000 | 71.80000 | NFM | Isle of Wight | Council Roads Dept. |
| 85.30000 | 71.80000 | NFM | London | Brent Council |
| 85.30000 | 71.80000 | NFM | Thames Valley | Thames Valley Water Ch 5 |
| 85.30000 | 71.80000 | NFM | Trafford | Council Cleansing Dept. |
| 85.31250 | 71.81250 | NFM | Blackburn | North West Water |
| 85.31250 | 71.81250 | NFM | Brighton | Southern Water (Distribution) |
| 85.31250 | 71.81250 | NFM | Bristol | Water Authority |
| 85.31250 | 71.81250 | NFM | Humberside | Council |
| 85.31250 | 71.81250 | NFM | Huntingdon | Anglia Water |
| 85.31250 | 71.81250 | NFM | Newmarket | Anglia Water |
| 85.31250 | 71.81250 | NFM | Sheffield | Yorkshire Water Board |

| Base | Mobile | Mode | Location | User and Notes |
|---|---|---|---|---|
| 85.31250 | 71.81250 | NFM | Tayside | North of Scotland Water Authority |
| 85.31250 | 71.81250 | NFM | West Sussex | Wessex Water Ch 6 |
| 85.31250 | 71.81250 | NFM | Whitehaven | North West Water |
| 85.32500 | 71.82500 | NFM | Aberdeen | British Gas |
| 85.32500 | 71.82500 | NFM | Bournemouth | Dorset Water |
| 85.32500 | 71.82500 | NFM | Brighton | Southern Water (GREEN BASE) |
| 85.32500 | 71.82500 | NFM | Burnley | North West Water |
| 85.32500 | 71.82500 | NFM | Chelmsford | Southern Water |
| 85.32500 | 71.82500 | NFM | Co. Durham | Electricians |
| 85.32500 | 71.82500 | NFM | Doncaster | Yorkshire Water |
| 85.32500 | 71.82500 | NFM | Edinburgh | East of Scotland Water |
| 85.32500 | 71.82500 | NFM | Folkestone | Community Repeater |
| 85.32500 | 71.82500 | NFM | Gloucester | Gloucester Water |
| 85.32500 | 71.82500 | NFM | Ipswich | Anglia Water |
| 85.32500 | 71.82500 | NFM | Merseyside | PMR |
| 85.32500 | 71.82500 | NFM | Northampton | Anglia Water |
| 85.32500 | 71.82500 | NFM | Pendle | Northwest Water |
| 85.32500 | 71.82500 | NFM | Rossendale | Mountain Rescue |
| 85.33750 | 71.83750 | NFM | Belfast | Water Board |
| 85.33750 | 71.83750 | NFM | Carlisle | North West Water |
| 85.33750 | 71.83750 | NFM | Gwent | Severn Trent Water |
| 85.33750 | 71.83750 | NFM | Humberside | Humberside Water |
| 85.33750 | 71.83750 | NFM | Kidderminster | Worcestershire Water |
| 85.33750 | 71.83750 | NFM | Mold | Clwyd Water Board |
| 85.33750 | 71.83750 | NFM | Perth | North of Scotland Water Authority |
| 85.33750 | 71.83750 | NFM | Plymouth | South West Water |
| 85.33750 | 71.83750 | NFM | Sheffield | Yorkshire Water Board |
| 85.33750 | 71.83750 | NFM | Worcester | Severn Trent Water |
| 85.33750 | 75.53750 | NFM | Aberdeen | North of Scotland Water Authority |
| 85.33750 | 75.53750 | NFM | Taunton | Wessex Water |
| 85.35000 | 71.85000 | NFM | Belfast | Water Board |
| 85.35000 | 71.85000 | NFM | Clwyd | Clwyd Council |
| 85.35000 | 71.85000 | NFM | East Sussex | Bottle Bank Clearance |
| 85.35000 | 71.85000 | NFM | Guernsey | Civil Defence |
| 85.35000 | 71.85000 | NFM | Hampshire | Bottle Bank Collection |
| 85.35000 | 71.85000 | NFM | Hawick | Scottish Borders Council Roads Dept. |
| 85.35000 | 71.85000 | NFM | Kent | Kent Water |
| 85.35000 | 71.85000 | NFM | Newcastle, Byker | North East Water |
| 85.35000 | 71.85000 | NFM | Portsmouth | City Council |
| 85.35000 | 71.85000 | NFM | Renfrew | Council |
| 85.35000 | 71.85000 | NFM | Saddleworth | Highways |
| 85.35000 | 71.85000 | NFM | Stowmarket | Council Highways |
| 85.35000 | 71.85000 | NFM | Swansea City | Council |
| 85.35000 | 71.85000 | NFM | Warrington | North West Water |
| 85.36200 | 71.86250 | NFM | Nuneaton | Anglian Water |
| 85.36250 | 71.86250 | NFM | Ayr | District Council |
| 85.36250 | 71.86250 | NFM | Ayrshire | West of Scotland Water |
| 85.36250 | 71.86250 | NFM | Chester | Car Transporters |
| 85.36250 | 71.86250 | NFM | Coventry | Severn Trent Water |
| 85.36250 | 71.86250 | NFM | Essex | Wessex Water |
| 85.36250 | 71.86250 | NFM | Hawick | Scottish Borders Council Water Dept. |
| 85.36250 | 71.86250 | NFM | Huntingdon | Anglia Water |
| 85.36250 | 71.86250 | NFM | Liverpool | North West Water |
| 85.36250 | 71.86250 | NFM | Tayside | North of Scotland Water Authority |
| 85.36250 | 71.86250 | NFM | Warwickshire | Severn Trent Water |
| 85.36250 | 71.86250 | NFM | Wirral | North West Water |

| Base | Mobile | Mode | Location | User and Notes |
|------|--------|------|----------|----------------|
| 85.36250 | 71.86250 | NFM | Yorkshire | Yorkshire Water |
| 85.37500 | 71.87500 | NFM | Barnsley | Yorkshire Water |
| 85.37500 | 71.87500 | NFM | Belfast | NI Electricity Service |
| 85.37500 | 71.87500 | NFM | Bury St Edmunds | Council Highways |
| 85.37500 | 71.87500 | NFM | Hawick | Tween Commission Water Bailiffs (scrambled) (TC) |
| 85.37500 | 71.87500 | NFM | Leicester | Severn Trent Water |
| 85.37500 | 71.87500 | NFM | London | Thames Water Authority |
| 85.37500 | 71.87500 | NFM | West Sussex | Water Board Engineer and Base |
| 85.38750 | 71.88750 | NFM | Belfast | Council |
| 85.38750 | 71.88750 | NFM | Cambridge | Anglia Water |
| 85.38750 | 71.88750 | NFM | Huntingdon | Anglia Water |
| 85.38750 | 71.88750 | NFM | Nottinghamshire | Severn Trent Water |
| 85.38750 | 71.88750 | NFM | Perth | North of Scotland Water Authority |
| 85.38750 | 71.88750 | NFM | West Glasgow | Strathclyde Water |
| 85.38750 | 71.88750 | NFM | Wyre | Council |
| 85.40000 | 71.90000 | AM | Devon, North | District Council (DOLPHIN BASE) |
| 85.40000 | 71.90000 | NFM | Hawick | Tweed Commission Water Bailiffs (scrambled) (TC) |
| 85.40000 | 71.90000 | NFM | Hounslow | Council |
| 85.40000 | 71.90000 | NFM | Kent | Kent Water |
| 85.40000 | 71.90000 | AM | Nationwide | Selective Call |
| 85.40000 | 71.90000 | NFM | Northampton | Social Services |
| 85.40000 | 71.90000 | NFM | Perth | North of Scotland Water Authority |
| 85.40000 | 71.90000 | NFM | Sheffield | County Council |
| 85.40000 | 71.90000 | NFM | Somerset | Tarmac Topmix |
| 85.40000 | 71.90000 | NFM | Yorkshire | Yorkshire Water |
| 85.41250 | 71.91250 | NFM | Brighton | Southern Water (Drainage) |
| 85.41250 | 71.91250 | NFM | Ipswich | Anglia Water |
| 85.41250 | 71.91250 | NFM | Manchester | PMR |
| 85.41250 | 71.91250 | NFM | Newport, Wales | Wessex Water |
| 85.41250 | 71.91250 | NFM | Perth | North of Scotland Water Authority |
| 85.41250 | 71.91250 | NFM | Stoke-on-Trent | Severn Trent Water |
| 85.41250 | 71.91250 | NFM | West Midlands | Midland Water |
| 85.41250 | 71.91250 | NFM | West Sussex | Southern Water |
| 85.41250 | 71.91250 | NFM | Wye | Welsh Water Channel 33 |
| 85.42500 | 71.92500 | NFM | Guernsey | Fire Service |
| 85.42500 | 71.92500 | NFM | Ipswich | Community Repeater |
| 85.42500 | 71.92500 | NFM | Kent | Council |
| 85.42500 | 71.92500 | NFM | Northampton | Al Taxis & Mini Buses |
| 85.42500 | 71.92500 | NFM | Northampton | Social Services |
| 85.42500 | 71.92500 | NFM | Tayside | North of Scotland Water Authority |
| 85.42500 | 71.92500 | NFM | Wales | Council Repeater |
| 85.43750 | 71.93750 | NFM | Alford | Roads Department |
| 85.43750 | 71.93750 | NFM | Cornwall | South West Water |
| 85.43750 | 71.93750 | NFM | Eastbourne | Eastbourne Water |
| 85.43750 | 71.93750 | NFM | Gloucestershire | Cotswolds Water |
| 85.43750 | 71.93750 | NFM | Gowerton | Welsh Water |
| 85.43750 | 71.93750 | NFM | Lea Valley | Southern Water |
| 85.43750 | 71.93750 | NFM | Leeds | Roadworks |
| 85.43750 | 71.93750 | NFM | Liverpool | North West Water |
| 85.43750 | 71.93750 | NFM | Merseyside | PMR |
| 85.43750 | 71.93750 | NFM | Surrey | Thames Water |
| 85.43750 | 71.93750 | NFM | Warrington | North West Water |
| 85.45000 | 71.95000 | NFM | Ayr | Skip Hire |
| 85.45000 | 71.95000 | NFM | Belfast | Water Board |
| 85.45000 | 71.95000 | NFM | Cumnock | Council |
| 85.45000 | 71.95000 | NFM | Gwynedd | Welsh Water |

| Base | Mobile | Mode | Location | User and Notes |
|---|---|---|---|---|
| 85.45000 | 71.95000 | NFM | Kent | Kent Water |
| 85.45000 | 71.95000 | NFM | Minehead | Somerset Water |
| 85.45000 | 71.95000 | NFM | Newport | Council Ch 3 |
| 85.45000 | 71.95000 | NFM | Norfolk | Anglia Water |
| 85.45000 | 71.95000 | NFM | Pitcaple | Roads Department |
| 85.45000 | 71.95000 | NFM | Suffolk | Anglia Water |
| 85.45000 | 71.95000 | NFM | Swansea | Dyfed Council |
| 85.46250 | 71.96250 | AM | Ayr | West of Scotland Water |
| 85.46250 | 71.96250 | NFM | Barrow | PMR |
| 85.46250 | 71.96250 | NFM | Bristol | Severn Trent Water |
| 85.46250 | 71.96250 | NFM | Haverfordwest | Welsh Water |
| 85.46250 | 71.96250 | NFM | Manchester | North West Water |
| 85.46250 | 71.96250 | NFM | Manchester | North West Water |
| 85.46250 | 71.96250 | NFM | Norfolk | Anglia Water |
| 85.46250 | 71.96250 | NFM | Suffolk | Anglia Water |
| 85.46250 | 71.96250 | NFM | Taunton | Wessex Water |
| 85.46250 | 71.96250 | NFM | West Sussex | Southern Water Ch 3 |
| 85.47500 | 71.97500 | NFM | Belfast | Water Board |
| 85.47500 | 71.97500 | NFM | Bristol | Automobile Association |
| 85.47500 | 71.97500 | NFM | Broadstairs | Chauffeur Service |
| 85.47500 | 71.97500 | NFM | Gatwick | Capital Coaches |
| 05.47500 | 71.07600 | NFM | Grampian | Transport |
| 85.47500 | 71.97500 | NFM | Hastings | Hastings Water |
| 85.47500 | 71.97500 | NFM | Kings Lynn | Dow Chemicals |
| 85.48750 | 71.98750 | AM | Dumfries | Automobile Association |
| 85.48750 | 71.98750 | NFM | London | Automobile Association |
| 85.48750 | 71.98750 | NFM | Nationwide | Automobile Association Ch. 6 |
| 85.50000 | 72.00000 | NFM | Cardiff | Automobile Association |
| 85.50000 | 72.00000 | NFM | Dumfries | Automobile Association |
| 85.50000 | 72.00000 | NFM | London | Automobile Association |
| 85.50000 | 72.00000 | NFM | Midlands | Automobile Association |
| 85.50000 | 72.00000 | NFM | Nationwide | Automobile Association Ch. 2 |
| 85.50000 | 72.00000 | NFM | Nottingham | Automobile Association |
| 85.51250 | 72.01250 | NFM | Birmingham | Automobile Association |
| 85.51250 | 72.01250 | NFM | Coniston | Automobile Association |
| 85.51250 | 72.01250 | NFM | Ipswich | Automobile Association |
| 85.51250 | 72.01250 | NFM | London | Automobile Association |
| 85.51250 | 72.01250 | NFM | Nationwide | Automobile Association Ch. 4 |
| 85.51250 | 72.01250 | NFM | Perth | Automobile Association |
| 85.52500 | 72.02500 | NFM | Aberdeen | Automobile Association |
| 85.52500 | 72.02500 | NFM | Anglia | Automobile Association |
| 85.52500 | 72.02500 | NFM | Belfast | Automobile Association Ch 1 |
| 85.52500 | 72.02500 | NFM | Blackpool | Automobile Association |
| 85.52500 | 72.02500 | NFM | Boscombe | Automobile Association |
| 85.52500 | 72.02500 | NFM | Cardiff | Automobile Association |
| 85.52500 | 72.02500 | NFM | Glasgow | Automobile Association |
| 85.52500 | 72.02500 | NFM | Guernsey | Automobile Association |
| 85.52500 | 72.02500 | NFM | London | Automobile Association |
| 85.52500 | 72.02500 | NFM | Nationwide | Automobile Association Ch. 1 |
| 85.52500 | 72.02500 | NFM | Perth | Automobile Association |
| 85.52500 | 72.02500 | NFM | West Midlands | Automobile Association |
| 85.53750 | 72.03750 | NFM | Brighton | Automobile Association |
| 85.53750 | 72.03750 | NFM | Exeter | Automobile Association |
| 85.53750 | 72.03750 | NFM | London | Automobile Association |
| 85.53750 | 72.03750 | NFM | Milton Keynes | Automobile Association |
| 85.53750 | 72.03750 | NFM | Nationwide | Automobile Association Ch. 5 |

| Base | Mobile | Mode | Location | User and Notes |
|------|--------|------|----------|----------------|
| 85.53750 | 72.03750 | NFM | Okekhampton | Automobile Association |
| 85.53750 | 72.03750 | NFM | Perth | Automobile Association |
| 85.53750 | 72.03750 | NFM | Warrington | Automobile Association |
| 85.55000 | 72.05000 | NFM | Aberdeen | Automobile Association |
| 85.55000 | 72.05000 | NFM | Bristol | Automobile Association |
| 85.55000 | 72.05000 | NFM | Ipswich | Automobile Association |
| 85.55000 | 72.05000 | NFM | London | Automobile Association |
| 85.55000 | 72.05000 | NFM | Nationwide | Automobile Association Ch. 3 |
| 85.55000 | 72.05000 | NFM | Norwich | Automobile Association |
| 85.55000 | 72.05000 | NFM | Whitehaven | Automobile Association |
| 85.56250 | 72.06250 | NFM | Edinburgh | Automobile Association |
| 85.56250 | 72.06250 | NFM | Guernsey | Water Board |
| 85.56250 | 72.06250 | NFM | Ipswich | Automobile Association |
| 85.56250 | 72.06250 | NFM | Lancaster | Automobile Association |
| 85.56250 | 72.06250 | NFM | Liverpool | Automobile Association |
| 85.56250 | 72.06250 | NFM | London | Automobile Association |
| 85.56250 | 72.06250 | NFM | Nationwide | Automobile Association Ch. 7 |
| 85.56250 | 72.06250 | NFM | Perth | Automobile Association |
| 85.57500 | 72.07500 | NFM | Belfast | NI Electricity Service |
| 85.57500 | 72.07500 | NFM | Berkshire | Thames Water Ch 3 |
| 85.57500 | 72.07500 | NFM | Jersey | Jersey Electricity Company Ch 1 |
| 85.58750 | 72.08750 | NFM | Cumbria | Automobile Association |
| 85.58750 | 72.08750 | NFM | Ipswich | Automobile Association |
| 85.58750 | 72.08750 | NFM | Lancashire | Automobile Association |
| 85.58750 | 72.08750 | NFM | London | Automobile Association |
| 85.58750 | 72.08750 | NFM | Nationwide | Automobile Association Ch. 8 |
| 85.58750 | 72.08750 | NFM | Perth | Automobile Association Data |
| 85.58750 | 72.08750 | NFM | Whinfell | Automobile Association |
| 85.60000 | 72.10000 | NFM | Ayrshire, south | Council repairs dept. |
| 85.60000 | 72.10000 | NFM | Blackpool | Council Parks |
| 85.60000 | 72.10000 | NFM | Co. Londonderry | NI Electricity Service north coast Ch.1 |
| 85.60000 | 72.10000 | NFM | Exeter | Council |
| 85.60000 | 72.10000 | NFM | Forest Heath | Council |
| 85.60000 | 72.10000 | NFM | Jersey | Civil Defence Link to France |
| 85.60000 | 72.10000 | NFM | Norfolk | Royal Automobile Club |
| 85.60000 | 72.10000 | NFM | Scarborough | Council |
| 85.60000 | 72.10000 | NFM | Suffolk | Royal Automobile Club |
| 85.60000 | 72.10000 | NFM | Wigan | Council plumbers |
| 85.61250 | 72.11250 | NFM | Humberside | Community Repeater |
| 85.61250 | 72.11250 | NFM | Lake District | Lake District National Park |
| 85.61250 | 72.11250 | NFM | London | Concord Ltd |
| 85.61250 | 72.11250 | NFM | Oldham | Courier |
| 85.61250 | 72.11250 | NFM | Poole | Poole Adventure Centre |
| 85.62500 | 72.12500 | NFM | Abbotts Ripton, Cambs | Fellows Estate |
| 85.62500 | 72.12500 | NFM | Bath | Silversails Taxis |
| 85.62500 | 72.12500 | NFM | Birmingham | Poolview Car Sales |
| 85.62500 | 72.12500 | NFM | Colchester | J. Collie Ltd |
| 85.62500 | 72.12500 | NFM | Liverpool | Taxi |
| 85.62500 | 72.12500 | NFM | London | Battersea Cars |
| 85.62500 | 72.12500 | NFM | London | Globe Bikes |
| 85.62500 | 72.12500 | NFM | London | Haden Carriers |
| 85.62500 | 72.12500 | NFM | Norfolk | Automobile Association |
| 85.62500 | 72.12500 | NFM | Suffolk | Automobile Association |
| 85.62500 | 72.12500 | NFM | Uxbridge | Cabline |
| 85.62750 | 72.12750 | NFM | Barrow in Furness | Furness Emergency Doctor Service |
| 85.62750 | 72.12750 | NFM | Salisbury | Defence Land Services |

| Base | Mobile | Mode | Location | User and Notes |
|---|---|---|---|---|
| 85.63750 | 72.13750 | NFM | England (South West) | Defence Land Services |
| 85.63750 | 72.13750 | NFM | Exeter | TNT |
| 85.63750 | 72.13750 | NFM | Guernsey | Fruit Exporters |
| 85.63750 | 72.13750 | NFM | Solent | Solent Waters Rescue |
| 85.63750 | 72.18750 | NFM | Aberdeen | Taxi |
| 85.65000 | 72.15000 | AM | Altringcham | Trafftax |
| 85.65000 | 72.15000 | NFM | Ealing | Trade Centre Ch 1 |
| 85.65000 | 72.15000 | NFM | Jersey | Civil Defence Link to France |
| 85.65000 | 72.15000 | NFM | London | Chequers Transport |
| 85.65000 | 72.15000 | NFM | London | Riva Communications Ltd |
| 85.65000 | 72.15000 | NFM | Mannington | Bascombe Ltd |
| 85.65000 | 72.15000 | NFM | Norfolk | Royal Automobile Club |
| 85.65000 | 72.15000 | AM | Portsmouth | Taxis |
| 85.65000 | 72.15000 | NFM | Seaforth | Taxi |
| 85.65000 | 72.15000 | NFM | St Ives | Tyrell Contractors |
| 85.65000 | 72.15000 | NFM | Suffolk | Royal Automobile Club |
| 85.66250 | 72.16250 | NFM | Gussage St. Michael | Manor Farm |
| 85.66250 | 72.16250 | NFM | Lochaber | Caledonian Canal |
| 85.66250 | 72.16250 | NFM | London | Anderson Young Ltd |
| 85.66250 | 72.16250 | NFM | London | Westland Market Tower |
| 85.66250 | 72.16250 | NFM | London | Wide Fulham |
| 85.66250 | 72.16250 | NFM | Maidenhead | Valley Taxis |
| 85.66250 | 72.16250 | NFM | Norfolk | M. Crouch Ltd |
| 85.66250 | 72.16250 | NFM | Suffolk | M. Crouch Ltd |
| 85.67500 | 72.17500 | NFM | Aberdeen | Taxi |
| 85.67500 | 72.17500 | NFM | Ayr | Taxi |
| 85.67500 | 72.17500 | NFM | Barrow in Furness | Barrow 5 Taxis |
| 85.67500 | 72.17500 | NFM | Brighton | Streamline Taxis |
| 85.67500 | 72.17500 | NFM | Chatteris | Allpress Farms |
| 85.67500 | 72.17500 | NFM | Colchester | Eastern Tractors |
| 85.67500 | 72.17500 | NFM | Gillingham | TA Taxis |
| 85.67500 | 72.17500 | NFM | Jersey | LuxiCabs  Ch 1 |
| 85.67500 | 72.17500 | NFM | London | Petchey & Velite Cars |
| 85.67500 | 72.17500 | NFM | Milton Keynes | Harper Cars |
| 85.67500 | 72.17500 | NFM | Norfolk | Hughes TV Servicing |
| 85.67500 | 72.17500 | NFM | Suffolk | Hughes TV Servicing |
| 85.67500 | 72.17500 | NFM | Thetford | Lloyd & Marriot Vets |
| 85.67500 | 72.17500 | NFM | Walsall Wood | Claridge TV & Radio |
| 85.68750 | 72.18750 | NFM | Exeter | TNT Parcels |
| 85.68750 | 72.18750 | NFM | London | Belsize Ltd |
| 85.68750 | 72.18750 | NFM | Milton Keynes | Skyline Taxis |
| 85.68750 | 72.18750 | NFM | Norfolk | Royal Automobile Club |
| 85.68750 | 72.18750 | NFM | Slough | Castle Radio Cars |
| 85.68750 | 72.18750 | NFM | Suffolk | Royal Automobile Club |
| 85.68750 | 72.18750 | NFM | Wishaw | Myles Taxis |
| 85.70000 | 72.20000 | NFM | Aberdeen | Shanks Transport |
| 85.70000 | 72.20000 | NFM | Grimsby | Stoneledge Haulage |
| 85.70000 | 72.20000 | NFM | Hawick | Eildon Taxis |
| 85.70000 | 72.20000 | AM | Hull | Redune Taxis |
| 85.70000 | 72.20000 | NFM | London | Echo Cars |
| 85.70000 | 72.20000 | NFM | Old Swan | Taxi |
| 85.70000 | 72.20000 | NFM | Scarborough | R&C Company |
| 85.70000 | 72.20000 | NFM | Southampton | Fletchwood Vending |
| 85.70000 | 72.70000 | NFM | Letchworth | B&D Taxis |
| 85.70000 | 72.70000 | NFM | Walthamstow | Advance Cars |
| 85.71250 | 72.21250 | NFM | Isle of Wight | Phonographic Hire Ltd. |

| Base | Mobile | Mode | Location | User and Notes |
|---|---|---|---|---|
| 85.71250 | 72.21250 | NFM | London | Automobile Association M25 Recovery |
| 85.71250 | 74.21250 | NFM | London | Summit Cars |
| 85.71250 | 74.21250 | NFM | Nationwide | Curry's Master Care |
| 85.71250 | 74.21250 | NFM | West Mersea | Grey |
| 85.72500 | 72.22500 | NFM | Bedford | Carlow Radio |
| 85.72500 | 72.22500 | NFM | Brighton | Rediffusion |
| 85.72500 | 72.22500 | NFM | Clackmannan | Council |
| 85.72500 | 72.22500 | NFM | Ipswich | RAC Motor Recovery |
| 85.72500 | 72.22500 | NFM | London | Ascot & Bracknell |
| 85.72500 | 72.22500 | NFM | Nationwide | Sitaclear Technology Ltd |
| 85.72500 | 72.22500 | NFM | Nationwide | BBC/IBA Microwave Links Setup |
| 85.72500 | 72.22500 | NFM | Norfolk | Automobile Association A12 Recovery |
| 85.72500 | 72.22500 | NFM | Shrewsbury | Taxis |
| 85.72500 | 72.22500 | NFM | Suffolk | Automobile Association Recovery (A12) |
| 85.72500 | 72.22500 | NFM | Weasenham | Farms |
| 85.73750 | 72.23750 | NFM | Colchester | Fieldspray Ltd |
| 85.73750 | 72.23750 | NFM | Dundee | Deliveries |
| 85.73750 | 72.23750 | NFM | Eastbourne | Skip Hire |
| 85.73750 | 72.23750 | NFM | Edinburgh | Garage |
| 85.73750 | 72.23750 | NFM | Glasgow | Plant Hire |
| 85.73750 | 72.23750 | NFM | London | Swift & Safe |
| 85.73750 | 72.23750 | NFM | London, North | Network Cars & Courier Service |
| 85.73750 | 72.23750 | NFM | North Yorkshire | Taxis |
| 85.73750 | 72.23750 | NFM | Southampton | Bass Leisure |
| 85.73750 | 72.23750 | AM | St Austell | Haul-U-Waste |
| 85.75000 | 72.25000 | NFM | A55 | Automobile Association |
| 85.75000 | 72.25000 | NFM | Dorchester | Petes Cabs |
| 85.75000 | 72.25000 | NFM | Guernsey | Warry's Bakery |
| 85.75000 | 72.25000 | NFM | Hitchin | Rorall Taxis |
| 85.75000 | 72.25000 | NFM | Lakenheath | Trevor Cobbold |
| 85.75000 | 72.25000 | NFM | London | American Cars |
| 85.75000 | 72.25000 | NFM | London | Putney Cars |
| 85.75000 | 72.25000 | NFM | Manchester | Taxis |
| 85.75000 | 72.25000 | NFM | Oldham | Taxis |
| 85.75000 | 72.25000 | NFM | Royton | Borough Taxis |
| 85.76250 | 72.26250 | NFM | Aberdeen | Port Maintenance |
| 85.76250 | 72.26250 | NFM | Cambridge | Plant Growing Institute |
| 85.76250 | 72.26250 | NFM | Culzean | National Trust for Scotland Rangers |
| 85.76250 | 72.26250 | NFM | Jersey | Regent Radio |
| 85.76250 | 72.26250 | NFM | London | Galaxy Cars |
| 85.76250 | 72.26250 | NFM | Long Stratton | C.P.S Fuels |
| 85.76250 | 72.26250 | NFM | Norfolk | Automobile Association |
| 85.76250 | 72.26250 | NFM | St. Leonards | A E Bartholomew Ltd |
| 85.76250 | 72.26250 | NFM | Suffolk | Automobile Association |
| 85.77500 | 72.27500 | NFM | Alloa | Taxi |
| 85.77500 | 72.27500 | NFM | Blackpool | Red Cabs |
| 85.77500 | 72.27500 | NFM | Guernsey | Le Pelley Taxi |
| 85.77500 | 72.27500 | NFM | Leigh-on-Sea | Taxis |
| 85.77500 | 72.27500 | NFM | Levenshulme | Premier Cars |
| 85.77500 | 72.27500 | NFM | London | Allways Ltd |
| 85.77500 | 72.27500 | NFM | Manchester | Vehicle wheel clampers |
| 85.77500 | 72.27500 | NFM | Norfolk | Automobile Association |
| 85.77500 | 72.27500 | NFM | Norwich | R.C. Snelling |
| 85.77500 | 72.27500 | NFM | Oxford | LuxiCabs |
| 85.77500 | 72.27500 | NFM | Perth | Taxis |
| 85.77500 | 72.27500 | NFM | Preston | Wheel Clampers |

| Base | Mobile | Mode | Location | User and Notes |
|------|--------|------|----------|----------------|
| 85.77500 | 72.27500 | NFM | Sheffield | Hargreaves Clearwaste Co. |
| 85.77500 | 72.27500 | NFM | Slough | Scorpio Radio Cars |
| 85.77500 | 72.27500 | NFM | Stoke on Trent | Lucky Seven Taxis |
| 85.77500 | 72.27500 | NFM | Suffolk | Automobile Association |
| 85.77500 | 72.27500 | NFM | Warrington | Wheel Clampers |
| 85.77500 | 72.27500 | NFM | Weymouth | Portwey Servicing |
| 85.78250 | 72.28750 | AM | Birmingham | Wimply Builders |
| 85.78750 | 72.28750 | NFM | Brighton | Automobile Association |
| 85.78750 | 72.28750 | NFM | Edinburgh | Taxis |
| 85.78750 | 72.28750 | NFM | Ipswich | Automobile Association |
| 85.78750 | 72.28750 | NFM | London | Automobile Association |
| 85.78750 | 72.28750 | NFM | Nationwide | Automobile Association Ch. 9 |
| 85.80000 | 72.30000 | NFM | Aberdeen | City Council |
| 85.80000 | 72.30000 | NFM | Anglia | Parceline Ltd |
| 85.80000 | 72.30000 | NFM | Brighton | Express Security Vans |
| 85.80000 | 72.30000 | NFM | Cardiff | Cardiff Garage Services |
| 85.80000 | 72.30000 | NFM | Hull | Security Express |
| 85.80000 | 72.30000 | NFM | Nationwide | Express Security Vans |
| 85.80000 | 72.30000 | NFM | Nationwide | Parceline Ltd |
| 85.80000 | 72.30000 | NFM | Plymouth | City Council Cleansing Dept |
| 85.80000 | 72.30000 | NFM | Warrington | Parceline |
| 85.81250 | 72.31250 | NFM | Aberdeen | Taxi |
| 85.81250 | 72.31250 | NFM | Chorley | M6 Motorway Maintenance |
| 85.81250 | 72.31250 | NFM | Haverfordwest | Vet Service |
| 85.81250 | 72.31250 | NFM | Nationwide | DTI Channel L0065 |
| 85.81250 | 72.31250 | NFM | Weymouth | Bennet & Escott |
| 85.81250 | 72.31250 | NFM | Weymouth | Gould Electronics |
| 85.81250 | 72.31250 | NFM | Weymouth | J Bentham |
| 85.81250 | 72.31250 | NFM | Weymouth | Wessex Aerials |
| 85.81250 | 72.31250 | NFM | Weymouth | Western Pipe Services |
| 85.82500 | 72.32500 | NFM | Cornwall | Pye Transport |
| 85.82500 | 72.32500 | NFM | Guernsey | Huelin |
| 85.82500 | 72.32500 | NFM | Letchwood | Joe's Taxis |
| 85.82500 | 72.32500 | NFM | London | Kwik Cars |
| 85.82500 | 72.32500 | NFM | Norwich | Beeline Taxis |
| 85.82500 | 72.32500 | NFM | Shoreham | Taxi |
| 85.82500 | 72.32500 | NFM | Soham | P. Lyon |
| 85.82500 | 72.32500 | NFM | Southampton | Streamline Taxis |
| 85.83750 | 72.33750 | NFM | Blantyre | Ariel & Art Cabs |
| 85.83750 | 72.33750 | NFM | Cornwall | English China Clay |
| 85.83750 | 72.33750 | NFM | Guernsey | Falles Hire Cars |
| 85.83750 | 72.33750 | NFM | Jersey | Ideal Cars Channel 1 |
| 85.83750 | 72.33750 | NFM | Jersey | Rank Taxis Channel 3 |
| 85.83750 | 72.33750 | NFM | Littleport | J.C. Rains Ltd |
| 85.83750 | 72.33750 | NFM | London | Belsize Ltd |
| 85.83750 | 72.33750 | NFM | London | Courier 83 Ltd |
| 85.83750 | 72.33750 | NFM | Luton | James Early Ltd |
| 85.83750 | 72.33750 | AM | St Austell | Haul-U-Waste |
| 85.83750 | 72.33750 | NFM | Wareham | Hall Waste |
| 85.85000 | 72.35000 | NFM | Cornwall | English China Clay |
| 85.85000 | 72.35000 | NFM | Kirkby | Taxis |
| 85.85000 | 72.35000 | NFM | Nationwide | Philips Transport Scheme |
| 85.85000 | 72.35000 | NFM | Nationwide | Pye Telecom Channel 2 |
| 85.85000 | 72.35000 | NFM | Newtown | Taxis |
| 85.85000 | 72.35000 | NFM | Oldham | Pest control (WATERHEAD CONTROL) |
| 85.85000 | 72.35000 | NFM | Skelmersdale | Taxis |

| Base | Mobile | Mode | Location | User and Notes |
|------|--------|------|----------|----------------|
| 85.85000 | 72.35000 | NFM | Tyneside | Taxis |
| 85.85000 | 72.35000 | NFM | Widnes | Taxis |
| 85.85000 | 72.35000 | NFM | Wigan | Taxis |
| 85.86250 | 72.36250 | NFM | Guernsey | J.H. Mahy & Sons Ltd |
| 85.86250 | 72.36250 | NFM | Lanarkshire | Doctor deputy service |
| 85.86250 | 72.36250 | NFM | London | Fisher Sylvester Ltd |
| 85.86250 | 72.36250 | NFM | London | G & R Tyres |
| 85.86250 | 72.36250 | NFM | London | Pronto Cars |
| 85.86250 | 72.36250 | NFM | Parkstone | Secure Alarms |
| 85.87500 | 72.37500 | NFM | Nationwide | DTI 28 Day Hire |
| 85.87500 | 72.37500 | NFM | Nationwide | Pye Telecom Channel 1 |
| 85.88750 | 72.38750 | NFM | Aylsham | Aylsham Produce |
| 85.88750 | 72.38750 | NFM | Blackpool | Tower Taxis |
| 85.88750 | 72.38750 | NFM | Burnley | Delta Cabs |
| 85.88750 | 72.38750 | NFM | Coventry | Allens Taxis and Coaches |
| 85.88750 | 72.38750 | NFM | London | Teleportation Ltd |
| 85.88750 | 72.38750 | NFM | Neath | Car Rallying |
| 85.88750 | 72.38750 | NFM | Norfolk | East Coast Grain |
| 85.88750 | 72.38750 | AM | Perth | Tay Transport |
| 85.90000 | 72.40000 | NFM | Burnley | Delta Cabs |
| 85.90000 | 72.40000 | NFM | Cambridge | John's of Cambridge |
| 85.90000 | 72.40000 | NFM | Diss, Norfolk | G.W. Padley |
| 85.90000 | 72.40000 | NFM | Edinburgh | TV Repairs |
| 85.90000 | 72.40000 | NFM | Jersey | Rank Taxis |
| 85.90000 | 72.40000 | AM | Kettering | Headlands Taxis |
| 85.90000 | 72.40000 | NFM | London | Sensechoice |
| 85.90000 | 72.40000 | NFM | Newcastle | Taxis |
| 85.90000 | 72.40000 | NFM | Parkstone | Bourne Plasterers |
| 85.90000 | 72.40000 | NFM | Spalding | Glen Heat and Irrigation |
| 85.91250 | 72.41250 | NFM | Aberdeen | Breakdown Services |
| 85.91250 | 72.41250 | NFM | Brigg | Gallowswood Recovery Service |
| 85.91250 | 72.41250 | NFM | Edinburgh | TV Repairs |
| 85.91250 | 72.41250 | NFM | Ipswich | Taxi |
| 85.91250 | 72.41250 | NFM | Letchworth | Eurocars |
| 85.91250 | 72.41250 | NFM | London | Anglo Spanish |
| 85.91250 | 72.41250 | NFM | London | Arrival Couriers |
| 85.91250 | 72.41250 | NFM | London | Central Motors |
| 85.91250 | 72.41250 | NFM | London | K Cars |
| 85.91250 | 72.41250 | NFM | Perth | Local deliveries |
| 85.91250 | 72.41250 | NFM | Perth | Tay Breakdown Service |
| 85.91250 | 72.41250 | NFM | Weymouth | West Ham Cars |
| 85.92500 | 72.42500 | NFM | Birmingham | Star Cars |
| 85.92500 | 72.42500 | NFM | Blackpool | Radio Cabs |
| 85.92500 | 72.42500 | NFM | Jersey | LuxiCabs Ch 2 |
| 85.92500 | 72.42500 | NFM | London | Laurie Buxton |
| 85.92500 | 72.42500 | NFM | London | Town & Country |
| 85.92500 | 72.42500 | NFM | Newport, Wales | TV rental and repair company |
| 85.92500 | 72.42500 | NFM | Wigan | District Council |
| 85.92500 | 72.42500 | NFM | Wirral | Cleansing Dept |
| 85.92500 | 72.42500 | NFM | Yeovil | Vets |
| 85.93750 | 72.43750 | AM | Blackpool | Progress Taxis |
| 85.93750 | 72.43750 | NFM | Bury | Moorside Taxis |
| 85.93750 | 72.43750 | NFM | Kent | Porlant Car Hire |
| 85.93750 | 72.43750 | NFM | London | Action Cars |
| 85.93750 | 72.43750 | NFM | Luton | Home and Away Car and Bus Service |
| 85.95000 | 72.45000 | AM | Chichester | Taxis |

| Base | Mobile | Mode | Location | User and Notes |
|------|--------|------|----------|----------------|
| 85.95000 | 72.45000 | NFM | Guernsey | Crossways Agricultural |
| 85.95000 | 72.45000 | NFM | Langholm | District Council |
| 85.95000 | 72.45000 | NFM | Leigh-on-Sea | Taxis |
| 85.95000 | 72.45000 | NFM | London | Action Cars |
| 85.95000 | 72.45000 | NFM | London | Galaxy Bikes |
| 85.95000 | 72.45000 | NFM | London | Super Express |
| 85.96250 | 72.46250 | NFM | Great Massingham | Gilman Ltd |
| 85.96250 | 72.46250 | NFM | London | Globe Cars |
| 85.96250 | 72.46250 | NFM | Norfolk | Don Robin Farms |
| 85.96250 | 72.46250 | NFM | Southampton | Currys Mastercare |
| 85.97500 | 72.47500 | NFM | Bristol | Mobile Windscreens |
| 85.97500 | 72.47500 | NFM | Cheddington | Colebird & Sons |
| 85.97500 | 72.47500 | NFM | Guernsey | Stan Brouard Ltd |
| 85.97500 | 72.47500 | NFM | Hamilton | Bridge Cars |
| 85.97500 | 72.47500 | AM | Leeds | Amber Cars |
| 85.97500 | 72.47500 | NFM | Nationwide | Tarmac Roadstone |
| 85.97500 | 72.47500 | NFM | Norfolk | Stanway Taxis |
| 85.97500 | 72.47500 | NFM | Plymouth | Mainline Catering |
| 85.97500 | 72.47500 | NFM | Somerton | Interlink |
| 85.97500 | 72.47500 | NFM | St Austel | Mobile Windscreens |
| 85.97500 | 72.47500 | NFM | Woodbridge | Wm Kerr Farms |
| 85.97500 | 72.47500 | NFM | Yeovil | Douglas Seatons |
| 85.98750 | 72.48750 | NFM | Jersey | Fetch & Carry |
| 85.98750 | 72.48750 | NFM | London | Avery Cars |
| 85.98750 | 72.48750 | NFM | London | City & Suburban |
| 85.98750 | 72.48750 | NFM | London | Commutercars |
| 85.98750 | 72.48750 | NFM | London | Parkward Ltd |
| 85.98750 | 72.48750 | NFM | London | Southampton Way Cars |
| 85.98750 | 72.48750 | NFM | St. Neots | Eynsbury Plant Hire |
| 86.00000 | 72.50000 | NFM | Aberdeen | Oil rig maintenance |
| 86.00000 | 72.50000 | NFM | Irvine | Taxis |
| 86.00000 | 72.50000 | NFM | London | Kilburn Cars |
| 86.00000 | 72.50000 | NFM | London | Windmill Cars |
| 86.00000 | 72.50000 | NFM | Nationwide | Community Repeater |
| 86.01250 | 72.51250 | NFM | Birmingham | Murphy |
| 86.01250 | 72.51250 | NFM | Jersey | Blue Coaches |
| 86.01250 | 72.51250 | NFM | Leeds | Hotpoint |
| 86.01250 | 72.51250 | NFM | Milton Keynes | Hotpoint |
| 86.01250 | 72.51250 | NFM | York | Hotpoint |
| 86.02500 | 72.52500 | NFM | Bedfordshire | Bedford Social Services |
| 86.02500 | 72.52500 | NFM | Humberside | Community Repeater |
| 86.02500 | 75.52500 | NFM | Merthyr | Mountain Rescue (SIERRA) |
| 86.03750 | 72.53750 | NFM | Eastbourne | Downland rangers |
| 86.03750 | 72.53750 | AM | Guernsey | Public Works |
| 86.03750 | 72.53750 | AM | Lincolnshire | Community Repeater |
| 86.03750 | 72.53750 | AM | London | Medicall |
| 86.03750 | 72.53750 | AM | Methley Park | Private Hospital |
| 86.03750 | 72.53750 | AM | Nationwide | Private ambulance services |
| 86.03750 | 72.53750 | AM | Nationwide | St Johns Private Ambulance |
| 86.05000 | 72.55000 | NFM | Lincolnshire | Comunity Repeater |
| 86.05000 | 72.55000 | NFM | London | Medicall |
| 86.05000 | 72.55000 | NFM | Peterborough | Repeater |
| 86.05000 | 72.55000 | NFM | Southampton | Taxis |
| 86.06250 | 72.56250 | NFM | Anglesey | Council |
| 86.06250 | 72.56250 | NFM | Gt. Ashfield | G. Miles |
| 86.06250 | 72.56250 | NFM | Norfolk | Sandringham Estate |

| Base | Mobile | Mode | Location | User and Notes |
|------|--------|------|----------|----------------|
| 86.07500 | 72.57500 | NFM | Annan | District Council |
| 86.07500 | 72.57500 | NFM | Wiltshire | Severn Trent Water Ch 1 |
| 86.08750 | 72.58750 | NFM | Norfolk | Cabban Breeze |
| 86.08750 | 72.58750 | NFM | Norfolk | Douglas Framlingham |
| 86.10000 | 72.60000 | NFM | Hadleigh | Lemon & Sutherland |
| 86.10000 | 72.60000 | NFM | Newmarket | PMR |
| 86.11250 | 72.61250 | NFM | Humberside | Tyre Co. |
| 86.11250 | 72.61250 | NFM | Lincolnshire | Community Repeater |
| 86.12500 | 72.62500 | NFM | Cardiff | F.W. Morgan Builders |
| 86.12500 | 72.62500 | NFM | Cheshire | Courier Service |
| 86.12500 | 72.62500 | NFM | Guernsey | Guernsey Telecoms |
| 86.12500 | 72.62500 | NFM | Norfolk | E.P.H. Radio Repeater |
| 86.12500 | 72.62500 | NFM | Sheffield | Community Repeater |
| 86.13750 | 72.63750 | AM | Jersey | De Gruchy Vets |
| 86.13750 | 72.63750 | NFM | Mid Wales | British Waterways |
| 86.13750 | 72.63750 | NFM | Norfolk | Storno Radio Telephone Co |
| 86.13750 | 72.63750 | NFM | Suffolk | Storno Radio Telephone Co |
| 86.15000 | 72.65000 | NFM | Kent | Tour de France French PMR |
| 86.16250 | 72.66250 | AM | Kent | County Council |
| 86.16250 | 72.66250 | AM | Lancashire | Regional Health Ambulance |
| 86.16250 | 72.66250 | NFM | Nationwide | Radiofone Channel |
| 86.16250 | 72.66250 | AM | Radnor | County Council |
| 86.17500 | 72.67500 | NFM | Newmarket | PMR |
| 86.17500 | 72.67500 | NFM | Newtownabbey | NI Electricity Service (C) |
| 86.17500 | 72.67500 | NFM | Norfolk | Ipswich Transport Ltd |
| 86.17500 | 72.67500 | NFM | Suffolk | Ipswich Transport Ltd |
| 86.18750 | 72.68750 | NFM | Nationwide | Automobile Association Channel 10 |
| 86.20000 | 72.70000 | NFM | Bristol | Automobile Association Channel 11 |
| 86.20000 | 72.70000 | NFM | Ipswich | Automobile Association Channel 11 |
| 86.20000 | 72.70000 | NFM | Nationwide | Automobile Association Channel 11 |
| 86.21250 | 72.71250 | NFM | East Sussex | County Council |
| 86.21250 | 72.71250 | NFM | London | Enterprise Ltd |
| 86.21250 | 72.71250 | NFN | Needham Market | Quinton Skip Hire |
| 86.21250 | 72.71250 | NFM | Norfolk | William Cory Heating |
| 86.22500 | 72.72500 | NFM | Belfast | NI Electricity Service |
| 86.22500 | 72.72500 | NFM | Burnley | Breakdown Recovery |
| 86.22500 | 72.72500 | NFM | Cambridge | Vets |
| 86.22500 | 72.72500 | NFM | Carnforth | PMR |
| 86.22500 | 72.72500 | NFM | Humberside | Motorway Maintenance |
| 86.22500 | 72.72500 | NFM | Ipswich | Biffa Bins (D) |
| 86.22500 | 72.72500 | NFM | Ipswich | Doctors on Call |
| 86.22500 | 72.72500 | NFM | London | RSPCA animal transport |
| 86.22500 | 72.72500 | NFM | Norfolk | Ipswich Transport Ltd |
| 86.22500 | 72.72500 | NFM | Perth | Amtrac Delivery Service |
| 86.22500 | 72.72500 | NFM | Peterborough | Watchdog |
| 86.22500 | 72.72500 | NFM | Portsmouth | Taxis |
| 86.22500 | 72.72500 | NFM | Scunthorpe | Humberside Highways |
| 86.22500 | 72.72500 | NFM | Suffolk | Ipswich Transport Ltd |
| 86.23750 | 72.72500 | NFM | Great Oakley | Oakley Skip Hire |
| 86.23750 | 72.72500 | NFM | Great Yarmouth | Container Depot |
| 86.23750 | 72.72500 | NFM | Ipswich | Deliveries |
| 86.23750 | 72.72500 | NFM | Kettering | Farmers |
| 86.23750 | 72.72500 | NFM | Perth | Deliveries |
| 86.23750 | 72.73750 | NFM | Armagh | Road Construction |
| 86.25000 | 72.75000 | NFM | Aberdeen | Snowploughs |
| 86.25000 | 72.75000 | NFM | East Sussex | County Council |

| Base | Mobile | Mode | Location | User and Notes |
|------|--------|------|----------|----------------|
| 86.25000 | 72.75000 | NFM | Hull | Hotpoint |
| 86.25000 | 72.75000 | NFM | Nationwide | Hotpoint Channel 1 |
| 86.26250 | 72.76250 | AM | Aberdeen | Council |
| 86.26250 | 72.76250 | NFM | Grampian | Taxis |
| 86.26250 | 72.76250 | AM | Humberside | Council |
| 86.26250 | 72.76250 | AM | Nationwide | Hotpoint Channel 2 |
| 86.27500 | 72.77500 | NFM | Belfast | NI Electricity Service |
| 86.27500 | 72.77500 | NFM | Bournemouth | Cryston Communications |
| 86.27500 | 72.77500 | NFM | Dumfries | Council |
| 86.27500 | 72.77500 | NFM | East Sussex | Wealdon |
| 86.27500 | 72.77500 | NFM | Hull | Cryston Communications |
| 86.27500 | 72.77500 | NFM | Leeds | Cryston Communications |
| 86.27500 | 72.77500 | NFM | Nationwide | Cryston Communications |
| 86.28750 | 72.78750 | NFM | Ayrshire, south | Council cleansing dept. |
| 86.28750 | 72.78750 | NFM | Great Yarmouth | Container Depot |
| 86.28750 | 72.78750 | NFM | Ipswich | RSPCA |
| 86.28750 | 72.78750 | NFM | Irvine | North Ayrshire Council |
| 86.28750 | 72.78750 | NFM | Leeds | RSPCA |
| 86.28750 | 72.78750 | NFM | Perth | North of Scotland Water Authority |
| 86.28750 | 72.78750 | NFM | Wilmston | Vets |
| 86.28750 | 75.78750 | NFM | Ashton under Lyme | Satellite Installation |
| 86.30000 | 72.80000 | NFM | East Sussex | County Council |
| 86.30000 | 72.80000 | NFM | Jersey | Jersey Hospital |
| 86.30000 | 72.80000 | NFM | Nationwide | IBA Aerial Riggers |
| 86.30000 | 72.80000 | NFM | Nationwide | Vibroplant Plc |
| 8603750 | 72.53750 | AM | Nationwide | Private ambulance services |

## 86.3125 - 86.7000 MHz    PMR Low Band 12.5 kHz (Simplex)

| Base | Mobile | Mode | Location | User and Notes |
|------|--------|------|----------|----------------|
| 86.31250 | | AM | Nationwide | Park Ranger Service Ch 2 |
| 86.31250 | | AM | Nationwide | St Johns Ambulance Channel 1 |
| 86.31250 | | NFM | Nationwide | Mountain Rescue Ch.1 |
| 86.31250 | | NFM | North Yorkshire Moors | Rangers |
| 86.31250 | | NFM | Oxford | City Council |
| 86.32500 | | AM | Blackpool | Gino's Pizza Deliveries |
| 86.32500 | | NFM | Jersey | Lifeguards |
| 86.32500 | | NFM | Nationwide | Mountain Rescue Ch.2 |
| 86.32500 | | NFM | Nationwide | National Parks Ch 2 |
| 86.32500 | | NFM | Nationwide | Red Cross |
| 86.33750 | | NFM | Cumbria | Lakes Mountain Rescue Ch. 2 |
| 86.33750 | | NFM | Norwich | Sir Robin Lee |
| 86.35000 | | NFM | Cairngorm | Ski Lifts |
| 86.35000 | | NFM | Cumbria | Lakes Mountain Rescue Ch. 3 |
| 86.35000 | | NFM | Edinburgh | The Scottish Office |
| 86.35000 | | NFM | Jersey | D. E. Payn Electrics |
| 86.35000 | | NFM | Leicestershire | Red Cross Ch.1 |
| 86.35000 | | AM | Nationwide | St Johns Ambulance Channel 3 |
| 86.35000 | | NFM | Nationwide | Mountain Rescue Channel 3 |
| 86.35000 | | NFM | Nationwide | Red Cross |
| 86.36250 | | NFM | Nationwide | Boy Scouts Channel 1 |
| 86.37500 | | NFM | Edinburgh | The Scottish Office |
| 86.37500 | | NFM | Jersey | Building firm |
| 86.37500 | | NFM | Nationwide | REACT CB Emergency |
| 86.37500 | | NFM | Wakefield | Stanley Royal Hospital |
| 86.38750 | | NFM | Nationwide | National Parks Ch 1 |
| 86.40000 | | NFM | Felixstowe | Docks |
| 86.40000 | | NFM | Nationwide | National Park Rangers |

| Base | Mobile | Mode | Location | User and Notes |
| --- | --- | --- | --- | --- |
| 86.40000 | | NFM | North Yorkshire Moors | Rangers |
| 86.40000 | | NFM | Yorkshire | Yorkshire Dales Warden |
| 86.41250 | | NFM | Berkshire | Council Ch 3 |
| 86.41250 | | AM | Nationwide | St Johns Ambulance Channel 2 |
| 86.41250 | | NFM | Nationwide | Mountain Rescue Channel 2 |
| 86.41250 | | NFM | Nationwide | Red Cross |
| 86.41250 | | NFM | Peak National Parks | Mountain Rescue |
| 86.42500 | | NFM | Ettrick & Lauderdale | District Council |
| 86.42500 | | NFM | Guernsey | Ambulance Service |
| 86.42500 | | NFM | Nationwide | Forestry Commission Channel 3 |
| 86.42500 | | AM | Neath | Forestry Commission |
| 86.43750 | | NFM | Isle of Man | Tudor Manx Rally |
| 86.43750 | | NFM | Jersey | Jersey Rally Control |
| 86.43750 | | NFM | Nationwide | RAC Rally Medical/Safety |
| 86.45000 | | NFM | Avon | Severn Trent Water |
| 86.45000 | | AM | Blackpool | Private Ambulance |
| 86.45000 | | NFM | Nationwide | Forestry Commission Channel 2 |
| 86.45000 | | NFM | Nationwide | Wimpey Construction Ch. 1 |
| 86.45000 | | NFM | Neath | Forestry Commission |
| 86.46500 | | NFM | Glasgow, west | Skip Hire |
| 86.47500 | | NFM | Cheshire | Gallifords Civil Engineers |
| 86.47500 | | NFM | Jersey | Public Health Ambulance |
| 86.47500 | | NFM | Linton | T.B. Fairy |
| 86.47500 | | NFM | Nationwide | Forestry Commission Channel 1 |
| 86.47500 | | NFM | Nationwide | Railtrack Incidents |
| 86.47500 | | NFM | Neath | Forestry Commission |
| 86.50000 | | NFM | Luton Airport | McAlpine Aviation |
| 86.50000 | | NFM | Nationwide | BNFL Nuclear Incident Ch 1 |
| 86.50000 | | NFM | Nationwide | ITC Aerial Riggers |
| 86.50000 | | NFM | Suffolk | Suffolk County Council |
| 86.50000 | | NFM | Swindon | Radio Taxis |
| 86.51250 | | NFM | Guernsey | St John Ambulance Link |
| 86.52500 | | NFM | Dunstable | Taleds Motors Co |
| 86.52500 | | NFM | Enfield | Weston Ltd |
| 86.52500 | | NFM | Nationwide | BBC O/B Riggers |
| 86.52500 | | NFM | Nationwide | BNFL Nuclear Incident Ch 2 |
| 86.53750 | | NFM | Derbyshire | Middleton Top Rangers |
| 86.53750 | | NFM | North-West | PMR |
| 86.55000 | | NFM | Guernsey | Cobo Surgery |
| 86.55000 | | NFM | Nationwide | BNFL Nuclear Incident Ch. 3 |
| 86.56250 | | NFM | Aberdeen | Robert Gordon Univ. of Tech |
| 86.56250 | | NFM | Nationwide | DHL International |
| 86.62500 | | NFM | Nationwide | Boy Scouts Channel 2 |
| 86.62500 | | NFM | Nationwide | Wimpey Construction Ch. 2 |
| 86.62500 | | NFM | RAF Marham | Wimpey Construction Ch. 2 |
| 86.62500 | | AM | Sheffield | Council Repairs |
| 86.63750 | | NFM | Bedford | RSPB |
| 86.63750 | | NFM | Jersey | Telefitters |
| 86.63750 | | NFM | Nationwide | Wimpey Construction Ch. 3 |
| 86.63750 | | NFM | RAF Marham | Wimpey Construction Ch. 3 |
| 86.66250 | | NFM | Nationwide | Vickers Seismic Surveys |
| 86.67500 | | NFM | England, South West | Studio Link |
| 86.67500 | | NFM | England, West | JFMG Talkback from Wales |
| 86.67500 | | NFM | Jersey | Dinard Emergency Link |
| 86.67500 | | NFM | Nationwide | UKAEA Radiation Survey |
| 86.68750 | | NFM | Chester | King Cabs |

| Base | Mobile | Mode | Location | User and Notes |
|---|---|---|---|---|
| 86.70000 | | NFM | Dungeness | Power Station |
| 86.70000 | | NFM | Nationwide | UK Emergency Channel 999 |
| 86.70000 | | NFM | Nationwide | UKAEA Health Physics Ch 2 |
| 86.70000 | | NFM | Sizewell | Nuclear Power Station |
| 86.70000 | 86.70000 | NFM | Nationwide | Automobile Association Emergency |

## 86.7125 - 87.5000 MHz  PMR Low Band Base Duplex
### (Mobiles - 10.5 MHz)

| Base | Mobile | Mode | Location | User and Notes |
|---|---|---|---|---|
| 86.71250 | 76.21250 | NFM | Renfrewshire | W. of Scotland Water (AS) |
| 86.71250 | 76.71250 | NFM | Nationwide | HM Customs & Excise Ch 1 |
| 86.72500 | 76.22500 | NFM | Nationwide | HM Customs & Excise Ch 2 |
| 86.72500 | 76.22500 | NFM | Swansea Docks | HM Customs & Excise |
| 86.72500 | 76.22500 | NFM | Tayside | North of Scotland Water Authority |
| 86.73750 | 76.23750 | NFM | Ipswich | Repeater |
| 86.73750 | 76.23750 | NFM | London | HM Customs Drugs Squad |
| 86.73750 | 76.23750 | NFM | Nationwide | HM Customs & Excise Ch 9 |
| 86.75000 | 76.25000 | NFM | Burnley | Plant Hire |
| 86.75000 | 76.25000 | NFM | Cwmbran | Gwent Council Ch 8 |
| 86.75000 | 76.25000 | NFM | Hornsea | East Coast Caravan Security |
| 86.75000 | 76.25000 | NFM | Lowestoft | Hughes TV Rentals |
| 86.76250 | 76.76250 | NFM | Llanelli | BT |
| 86.76250 | 76.76250 | NFM | Llanelli | Taxi |
| 86.76250 | 76.76250 | NFM | Tayside | Community Repeater |
| 86.77500 | 76.27500 | NFM | Merseyside | Plant Hire Company |
| 86.77500 | 76.27500 | NFM | Portsmouth | City Council |
| 86.77500 | 76.27500 | NFM | York | Yorkshire Parcels Group |
| 86.80000 | 76.30000 | NFM | Brighton | Community Repeater |
| 86.80000 | 76.30000 | NFM | Dyfed | Vets |
| 86.80000 | 76.30000 | NFM | Hampshire | Council |
| 86.80000 | 76.30000 | NFM | London | Post Office Tower |
| 86.80000 | 76.30000 | NFM | Nationwide | Vibroplant |
| 86.80000 | 76.30000 | NFM | Sussex | Community Repeater |
| 86.80000 | 76.80000 | NFM | Bradford | Community Transport |
| 86.80000 | 76.80000 | NFM | Oldham | Plant Hire |
| 86.80000 | 76.80000 | NFM | West Sussex | West Dock Air Call |
| 86.80625 | 76.30625 | NFM | Nationwide | JFMG Airborne |
| 86.82500 | 76.32500 | NFM | Bristol | ITV Broadcast Link |
| 86.82500 | 76.32500 | NFM | Manchester | Granada TV Talkback |
| 86.82500 | 76.32500 | NFM | Thames Valley | ITN Ch 4 |
| 86.85000 | 76.35000 | NFM | Clwyd | Delivery Company |
| 86.85000 | 76.35000 | NFM | Co Durham | BT Aerial Riggers |
| 86.85000 | 76.35000 | NFM | Perth | North of Scotland Water Authority |
| 86.86250 | 76.36250 | NFM | Manchester | Amtrak Express Parcels |
| 86.86250 | 76.36250 | NFM | Nationwide | RSPCA |
| 86.86250 | 76.36250 | NFM | Plymouth | Plymouth Vets |
| 86.87500 | 76.37500 | NFM | Lochaber | Council Roads Dept |
| 86.87500 | 76.37500 | NFM | Malvern | Abbey Taix |
| 86.88750 | 76.38750 | NFM | Ballachulish | Highland Regional Council Roads/Snow Ploughs |
| 86.88750 | 76.38750 | NFM | Lothian & Borders | East of Scotland Water |
| 86.90000 | 76.40000 | NFM | Merseyside | Transport Company |
| 86.90000 | 76.40000 | NFM | Southwold | Suffolk Traffic |
| 86.91250 | 76.41250 | NFM | Lochaber | Highland Regional Council Roads |
| 86.91250 | 76.41250 | NFM | Wirral | A1 Breakdown |
| 86.93750 | 76.43750 | NFM | London | HM Customs & Excise Drugs Squad |
| 86.93750 | 76.43750 | NFM | Nationwide | HM Customs Ch 3 |

| Base | Mobile | Mode | Location | User and Notes |
|------|--------|------|----------|----------------|
| 86.93750 | 76.43750 | NFM | Perth | North of Scotland Water Authority |
| 86.95000 | 76.45000 | NFM | Dover | HM Customs & Excise |
| 86.95000 | 76.45000 | NFM | Dundee | North of Scotland Water Authority |
| 86.95000 | 76.45000 | NFM | Fishguard Docks | HM Customs & Excise |
| 86.95000 | 76.45000 | NFM | Nationwide | HM Customs Ch 4 |
| 86.96250 | 76.46250 | NFM | Brighton | RSPCA |
| 86.96250 | 76.46250 | NFM | Grizedale Forest Park | Forestry Commission |
| 86.96250 | 76.46250 | NFM | Gwynedd | Forestry Commission |
| 86.96250 | 76.46250 | NFM | Keilder, Border Forest Park | Forestry Commission |
| 86.96250 | 76.46250 | NFM | Lochaber | Forestry Commission |
| 86.96250 | 76.46250 | NFM | Nationwide | Forestry Commission |
| 86.96250 | 76.46250 | NFM | Nationwide | RSPCA Channel |
| 86.96250 | 76.46250 | NFM | Newtown | Wayside Forestry Commission |
| 86.96250 | 76.46250 | NFM | Sherwood Forest | Forestry Commission |
| 86.96250 | 76.46250 | NFM | Thetford Forest | Forestry Commission |
| 86.97500 | 76.47500 | NFM | Bolton | BT |
| 86.97500 | 76.47500 | NFM | Manchester | North West Water |
| 86.98750 | 76.47500 | NFM | Hertfordshire | County Council  (HIGHGROUND) |
| 86.98750 | 76.47500 | NFM | London | Guarda Security |

### 87.000 - 87.900 MHz          PMR (Split -10 MHz)

| Base | Mobile | Mode | Location | User and Notes |
|------|--------|------|----------|----------------|
| 87.00000 | 77.00000 | NFM | Berkshire | Council |
| 87.00000 | 77.00000 | NFM | Cumbria | RAC Data Link |
| 87.00000 | 77.00000 | NFM | Edinburgh | Data Link |
| 87.00000 | 77.00000 | NFM | Guernsey | RAC |
| 87.00000 | 77.00000 | NFM | Lancashire | RAC Data Link |
| 87.00000 | 77.00000 | NFM | Nationwide | RAC Channel 2 |
| 87.00000 | 77.00000 | NFM | Wymondham | Ayton Asphalt |
| 87.01250 | 77.01250 | NFM | Glasgow | RAC Data Link |
| 87.01250 | 77.01250 | NFM | Ipswich | RAC Data Link |
| 87.01250 | 77.01250 | NFM | Nationwide | RAC Channel 4 |
| 87.01250 | 77.01250 | NFM | Newcastle | RAC Data Link |
| 87.01250 | 77.01250 | NFM | Stirling | RAC Data Link |
| 87.01250 | 77.01250 | NFM | York | RAC Data Link |
| 87.02500 | 77.02500 | NFM | Glasgow | Data Link |
| 87.02500 | 77.02500 | NFM | Ipswich | RAC |
| 87.02500 | 77.02500 | NFM | Nationwide | RAC Channel 1 |
| 87.02500 | 77.02500 | NFM | Newmarket | RAC Data Link |
| 87.02500 | 77.02500 | NFM | Perth | RAC Data Link |
| 87.02500 | 77.02500 | NFM | Stirling | RAC |
| 87.03750 | 77.03750 | NFM | East Durham | Private Message |
| 87.03750 | 77.03750 | NFM | Kent (Euro Tunnel) | Trans Manche Ltd |
| 87.03750 | 77.03750 | NFM | Nationwide | RAC Channel 5 |
| 87.04500 | 76.54500 | NFM | Neath | TA Barracks |
| 87.05000 | 77.05000 | NFM | Grimsby | Raylor Ltd |
| 87.05000 | 77.05000 | NFM | Leeds | Armor Guard |
| 87.05000 | 77.05000 | NFM | Leeds | Raylor Ltd |
| 87.05000 | 77.05000 | NFM | Lothian and Borders | RAC |
| 87.05000 | 77.05000 | NFM | Nationwide | RAC Channel 3 |
| 87.05000 | 77.05000 | NFM | Perth | Data Link |
| 87.05000 | 77.05000 | NFM | Skelmersdale | Taxis |
| 87.05000 | 77.05000 | NFM | Teesside | Raylor Ltd |
| 87.05000 | 77.05000 | NFM | York | Raylor Ltd |
| 87.06250 | 77.06250 | NFM | Bishop Stortford | Rougewell Ltd |
| 87.06250 | 77.06250 | NFM | Gwent | Forestry Commission |
| 87.06250 | 77.06250 | NFM | Haywards Heath | Station Taxis |

| Base | Mobile | Mode | Location | User and Notes |
| --- | --- | --- | --- | --- |
| 87.06250 | 77.06250 | NFM | Jersey | RAC |
| 87.06250 | 77.06250 | NFM | London | Statisted Containers Ltd |
| 87.06250 | 77.06250 | NFM | Neath | Forestry Commission |
| 87.06250 | 77.06250 | NFM | Perth | Wilsons Taxis |
| 87.06250 | 77.06250 | NFM | Wrexham | Derek's Taxis |
| 87.07500 | 77.07500 | NFM | Bristol | Ace Taxis |
| 87.07500 | 77.07500 | NFM | Bury | Red Rose Taxis |
| 87.07500 | 77.07500 | NFM | Droitwich | NY Taxis |
| 87.07500 | 77.07500 | NFM | Glasgow | Taxis |
| 87.07500 | 77.07500 | NFM | Ipswich | Council |
| 87.07500 | 77.07500 | AM | Jersey | Taxi Rank |
| 87.07500 | 77.07500 | AM | London | Concorde Minicabs Wembley |
| 87.07500 | 77.07500 | NFM | St Ives | RAC |
| 87.08750 | 77.08750 | NFM | Chichester | Council Refuse |
| 87.08750 | 77.08750 | NFM | Halifax | Halifax Council |
| 87.08750 | 77.08750 | NFM | Jersey | Jersey Evening Post |
| 87.08750 | 77.08750 | NFM | Lancashire | Haulage Contractor |
| 87.08750 | 77.08750 | NFM | London | Savoy Rolls Royce |
| 87.08750 | 77.08750 | NFM | London | Stansted Containers Ltd |
| 87.08750 | 77.08750 | NFM | Nationwide | RSPCA Channel Ch 2 |
| 87.10000 | 77.10000 | NFM | Barrow | PMR |
| 87.10000 | 77.10000 | NFM | Bolton | Road Maintenance |
| 87.10000 | 77.10000 | NFM | Brighton | Taxis |
| 87.10000 | 77.10000 | NFM | Guernsey | Gilroy's |
| 87.10000 | 77.10000 | NFM | Hove | Hove Streamline Taxis |
| 87.10000 | 77.10000 | NFM | Kendal | Builders |
| 87.10000 | 77.10000 | NFM | Lancashire | Kennedy's road contractors |
| 87.10000 | 77.10000 | NFM | Leicester | ABC Taxis |
| 87.10000 | 77.10000 | NFM | London | B.J. Transport |
| 87.10000 | 77.10000 | NFM | London | J.R. Cars |
| 87.10000 | 77.10000 | NFM | Montrose | Council Housing |
| 87.10000 | 77.10000 | NFM | Preston | Taxis |
| 87.10000 | 77.10000 | NFM | Stockport | North West Water |
| 87.12500 | 77.12500 | NFM | Ayr | SRC Building & Works Depart. |
| 87.12500 | 77.12500 | NFM | Hawick | District Council |
| 87.12500 | 77.12500 | NFM | Powys | Forestry Commission |
| 87.12500 | 77.12500 | NFM | Strathclyde | Strathclyde Council |
| 87.13750 | 71.13750 | NFM | Cardiff | Community Repeater |
| 87.13750 | 77.13750 | NFM | Fishguard | Highways Council |
| 87.13750 | 77.13750 | NFM | Hampshire | Council |
| 87.13750 | 77.13750 | NFM | Kent | Kent Council Highways Dept. |
| 87.13750 | 77.13750 | NFM | Leeds | Construction Co. |
| 87.13750 | 77.13750 | NFM | Liverpool | Street Lighting |
| 87.15000 | 77.15000 | NFM | Fishguard | District Council |
| 87.15000 | 77.15000 | NFM | Kent | Tour de France |
| 87.15000 | 77.15000 | NFM | Lancashire | County Highways Ch 1 |
| 87.15000 | 77.15000 | NFM | Nationwide | Radiofone Channel Ch 1 |
| 87.15000 | 77.15000 | NFM | Preston | Council snow ploughs and gritters |
| 87.15000 | 77.15000 | NFM | Stirling | PMR |
| 87.16250 | 77.16250 | NFM | Aberdeen | Council |
| 87.16250 | 77.16250 | NFM | Buckinghamshire | Council |
| 87.16250 | 77.16250 | NFM | Dumfermline | Fife Regional Council |
| 87.16250 | 77.16250 | NFM | Hawick | District Council |
| 87.16250 | 77.16250 | AM | Kent | Kent Council Highways Dept. |
| 87.16250 | 77.16250 | NFM | Lincolnshire | Highways |
| 87.16250 | 77.16250 | NFM | North Yorkshire | Highways |

| Base | Mobile | Mode | Location | User and Notes |
|------|--------|------|----------|----------------|
| 87.16250 | 77.16250 | NFM | Shropshire | County Council Emer. Planning |
| 87.17500 | 77.17500 | NFM | Bristol | Highways |
| 87.17500 | 77.17500 | NFM | Glasgow | Underground Control |
| 87.17500 | 77.17500 | NFM | Lake District | Lake District National Park |
| 87.17500 | 77.17500 | NFM | Lancashire | County Park Rangers |
| 87.17500 | 77.17500 | NFM | Nottinghamshire | Community Repeater |
| 87.18750 | 77.18750 | NFM | Cambridgeshire | Council |
| 87.18750 | 77.18750 | NFM | Chichester | West Sussex Council |
| 87.18750 | 77.18750 | NFM | Fife | Fife Regional Council Roads |
| 87.18750 | 77.18750 | NFM | Lancashire | Snowploughs & Gritters Ch 2 |
| 87.18750 | 77.18750 | NFM | Oxford | Council |
| 87.18750 | 77.18750 | NFM | Radnor | Powys Council Highways |
| 87.18750 | 77.18750 | NFM | Surrey | Council Ch 2 |
| 87.18750 | 77.18750 | AM | West Yorkshire | Highways |
| 87.19000 | 77.19000 | NFM | Burnley | Council maintainance |
| 87.20000 | 77.20000 | NFM | Ballymena | DOE Roads Service |
| 87.20000 | 77.20000 | NFM | Bury | Bury Council |
| 87.20000 | 77.20000 | NFM | County Durham | County Council |
| 87.20000 | 77.20000 | NFM | Cumbria | Quarry |
| 87.20000 | 77.20000 | NFM | Foreham | Council |
| 87.20000 | 77.20000 | NFM | Preston | Council |
| 87.20000 | 77.20000 | NFM | Surrey | Council |
| 87.20000 | 77.20000 | NFM | Warickshire | Council Roads Dept. (SHIPTON BASE) |
| 87.21250 | 77.21250 | NFM | Aberfeldy | Council Gritters |
| 87.21250 | 77.21250 | NFM | Buckinghamshire | Council |
| 87.21250 | 77.21250 | NFM | Hertfordshire | Council |
| 87.21250 | 77.21250 | NFM | Humberside | Council |
| 87.21250 | 77.21250 | NFM | London, Raynes Park | Merton Council road gritters |
| 87.21250 | 77.21250 | NFM | Nationwide | Council Common |
| 87.21250 | 77.21250 | NFM | Rushmoor | Council |
| 87.21250 | 77.21250 | NFM | Sheffield | Council Highways |
| 87.21250 | 77.21250 | NFM | Somerset | Council |
| 87.21250 | 77.21250 | NFM | Staffordshire | Council |
| 87.22500 | 77.22500 | NFM | Bristol Area | Skip Company |
| 87.22500 | 77.22500 | NFM | Kent | Tour de France |
| 87.22500 | 77.22500 | NFM | London | Vehicle Clamping |
| 87.22500 | 77.22500 | NFM | Oxford | City Council Ch 3 |
| 87.23500 | 77.23750 | NFM | St. Annes | Council road maintenance |
| 87.23750 | 77.23750 | NFM | Dundee | North of Scotland Water Authority |
| 87.23750 | 77.23750 | NFM | East Sussex | County Highways |
| 87.23750 | 77.23750 | NFM | Eastbourne | Council |
| 87.23750 | 77.23750 | NFM | Fife | Fife Regional Council |
| 87.23750 | 77.23750 | AM | Gwynedd | Gwynedd Council |
| 87.23750 | 77.23750 | NFM | Heysham | PMR |
| 87.23750 | 77.23750 | NFM | Lancashire | County Council Ch 3 |
| 87.23750 | 77.23750 | NFM | Manchester | Sheltered Housing Wardens |
| 87.23750 | 77.23750 | NFM | North West England | PMR |
| 87.23750 | 77.23750 | NFM | Oxfordshire | County Council Ch 1 |
| 87.23750 | 77.23750 | NFM | Perth | Perth & Kinross Council |
| 87.24000 | 77.24000 | NFM | Gwent Area | Highway Maintenance Company |
| 87.25000 | 77.25000 | NFM | Birmingham | City Council Engineers |
| 87.25000 | 77.25000 | NFM | Brecon | Powys County Highways |
| 87.25000 | 77.25000 | NFM | Congleton | Council |
| 87.25000 | 77.25000 | NFM | East Sussex | Emergency Centre |
| 87.25000 | 77.25000 | NFM | Hampshire | Council |
| 87.25000 | 77.25000 | NFM | Hertfordshire | Council |

| Base | Mobile | Mode | Location | User and Notes |
|---|---|---|---|---|
| 87.25000 | 77.25000 | NFM | Langholm | Dumfries & Galloway Council Roads dept. |
| 87.25000 | 77.25000 | NFM | West Midlands | Snowploughs & Gritters |
| 87.26250 | 77.26250 | NFM | Ayr | Local Council Services |
| 87.26250 | 77.26250 | NFM | England & Wales | Council Common |
| 87.26250 | 77.26250 | NFM | Gwent | Council |
| 87.26250 | 77.26250 | NFM | Leicester | Council |
| 87.26250 | 77.26250 | NFM | Oxfordshire | County Council |
| 87.26250 | 77.26250 | NFM | Perth | Perth & Kinross Council |
| 87.26250 | 77.26250 | NFM | Slough | Council |
| 87.26250 | 77.26250 | NFM | Stockton | CCC Engineers |
| 87.26250 | 77.26250 | AM | West Sussex | County Council |
| 87.26250 | 77.26250 | AM | Yorkshire | Trading Standards Office |
| 87.27500 | 77.27500 | NFM | Blackpool | Illuminations |
| 87.27500 | 77.27500 | NFM | Devon | Highways Dept. |
| 87.27500 | 77.27500 | NFM | Edinburgh | Council |
| 87.27500 | 77.27500 | NFM | Hanley | Security |
| 87.27500 | 77.27500 | NFM | Lothian and Borders | Lothian Regional Council |
| 87.27500 | 77.27500 | NFM | West Yorkshire | Bus Inspectors |
| 87.28750 | 77.28750 | NFM | Fife | Fife Regional Council Drainage |
| 87.30000 | 77.30000 | NFM | Accrington | Town Council base |
| 87.30000 | 77.30000 | NFM | Anglia | Breckland District Council |
| 87.30000 | 77.30000 | NFM | Derbyshire | Derbyshire Council Roads |
| 07.30000 | 77.30000 | AM | Dumfries | Snowploughs & Gritters |
| 87.30000 | 77.30000 | NFM | Hertfordshire | Council |
| 87.30000 | 77.30000 | NFM | Jersey | Waterworks |
| 87.30000 | 77.30000 | NFM | Mold | Clwyd County Council |
| 87.30000 | 77.30000 | NFM | Norfolk | Breckland District Council |
| 87.30000 | 77.30000 | NFM | Perth | North of Scotland Water Authority |
| 87.31250 | 77.31250 | NFM | Cardiff | Parcel Force Ch 2 |
| 87.31250 | 77.31250 | NFM | Perth | Perth & Kinross Council |
| 87.31250 | 77.31250 | NFM | Windsor | Royal Parks |
| 87.32500 | 77.32500 | NFM | Bedfordshire | County Council Highways |
| 87.32500 | 77.32500 | NFM | Derbyshire | Council |
| 87.32500 | 77.32500 | NFM | Perth | Perth & Kinross Council |
| 87.32500 | 77.32500 | NFM | South Yorkshire | Council |
| 87.33750 | 77.33750 | NFM | Cardiff | Parcel Force Ch 1 |
| 87.33750 | 77.33750 | NFM | Edinburgh | Highways Control |
| 87.33750 | 77.33750 | NFM | Lancaster | Vet Service |
| 87.33750 | 77.33750 | NFM | Morecambe | Vet Service |
| 87.35000 | 77.35000 | NFM | Castle Douglas | Stewartry Council |
| 87.35000 | 77.35000 | NFM | Edinburgh | MacGas |
| 87.35000 | 77.35000 | NFM | Guernsey | Gaudion Skip Hire |
| 87.35000 | 77.35000 | NFM | Stoke | Civil Engineers |
| 87.36250 | 77.36250 | NFM | Castle Douglas | Forestry Commission |
| 87.36250 | 77.36250 | NFM | Perth | Perth & Kinross Council |
| 87.36250 | 77.36250 | NFM | Saddleworth | Haulage Firm |
| 87.36250 | 77.36250 | NFM | Strathclyde | Forestry Commission |
| 87.36250 | 77.36250 | NFM | Tayside | Forestry Commission |
| 87.37500 | 77.37500 | AM | Jersey | Dr Scott Warren |
| 87.37500 | 77.37500 | NFM | Linconshire | Community Repeater |
| 87.37500 | 77.37500 | NFM | Oldham | Harris Deliveries |
| 87.37500 | 77.37500 | NFM | Yorkshire | RSPCA |
| 87.38750 | 77.38750 | NFM | Cardiff | Thorn Homeserve TV Repairs |
| 87.38750 | 77.38750 | NFM | Ipswich | Community Repeater |
| 87.38750 | 77.38750 | NFM | Perth | Community Repeater |
| 87.38750 | 77.38750 | NFM | Stoke | Garage |

| Base | Mobile | Mode | Location | User and Notes |
|------|--------|------|----------|----------------|
| 87.40000 | 77.40000 | NFM | Aberdeen | Aberdeen Skip Hire |
| 87.40000 | 77.40000 | NFM | Huntington | Doctors Scheme |
| 87.40000 | 77.40000 | NFM | Nationwide | Doctors Scheme |
| 87.40000 | 77.40000 | NFM | Perth | North of Scotland Water Authority |
| 87.41250 | 77.41250 | NFM | Bournemouth | Beach lifeguards |
| 87.41250 | 77.41250 | NFM | Bristol | Ace Skip Hire |
| 87.41250 | 77.41250 | NFM | Bristol | Magnum Scaffolding |
| 87.41250 | 77.41250 | NFM | Bristol | P.D.G Courier Service |
| 87.41250 | 77.41250 | NFM | Elvington | A1 Haulage |
| 87.41250 | 77.41250 | NFM | Elvington | Elvington Plant Hire |
| 87.41250 | 77.41250 | NFM | Elvington | Silverseal Auto Windscreens |
| 87.41250 | 77.41250 | NFM | Lochaber | Council Roads Dept |
| 87.41250 | 77.41250 | NFM | London | Onyx Cleansing Services |
| 87.41250 | 77.41250 | NFM | Perth | Perth & Kinross Council |
| 87.41250 | 77.41250 | NFM | Scotland | Council Highways Common |
| 87.41250 | 77.41250 | NFM | Staffordshire | JCB Drivers |
| 87.42500 | 77.42500 | NFM | Blackpool | County Highways |
| 87.42500 | 77.42500 | NFM | Guernsey | Remote Gas Detectors |
| 87.42500 | 77.42500 | NFM | Stirling | County Council (B) |
| 87.43750 | 77.43750 | NFM | Bedford | County Surveyors Ch 1 |
| 87.43750 | 77.43750 | NFM | Coris Mid Wales | Forestry Commission |
| 87.43750 | 77.43750 | NFM | London | A3 road repair workers |
| 87.43750 | 77.43750 | NFM | Plymouth | City Engineers |
| 87.43750 | 77.43750 | NFM | Scotland | Council Highways Common |
| 87.43750 | 77.43750 | NFM | Southampton | M27 Motorway Maintenance |
| 87.43750 | 77.43750 | NFM | West Midlands | Council |
| 87.43750 | 77.43750 | NFM | Wigan | North West Water |
| 87.45000 | 77.45000 | NFM | Belfast | Dept. of Environment roads services (AL /D/ DS/ DL/ P/ I) |
| 87.45000 | 77.45000 | NFM | Berkshire | Council Ch I |
| 87.45000 | 77.45000 | AM | Bristol | Sub Council Control |
| 87.45000 | 77.45000 | NFM | Cambridge | Highways Ch 3 |
| 87.45000 | 77.45000 | NFM | Haverfordwest | Preseli Pembroke Council |
| 87.45000 | 77.45000 | NFM | London | Information Service |
| 87.45000 | 77.45000 | NFM | Peterborough | Cotton TV Servicing |
| 87.45000 | 77.45000 | NFM | Wiltshire | Council Roads Dept |
| 87.46000 | 77.46000 | NFM | Pendle | Pendle Council |
| 87.46250 | 77.46250 | NFM | Berkshire | Council Surveyor Ch 2 |
| 87.46250 | 77.46250 | NFM | Essex | Highways Ch 2 |
| 87.46250 | 77.46250 | NFM | Fife | NE Fife Council Road Ch 5 |
| 87.46250 | 77.46250 | NFM | Hereford | Council |
| 87.46250 | 77.46250 | AM | Lincolnshire | Highways |
| 87.46250 | 77.46250 | NFM | Lothian & Borders | Roads Dept |
| 87.46250 | 77.46250 | NFM | Scarborough | Snowploughs |
| 87.46250 | 77.46250 | NFM | West Midlands | Snowploughs & Gritters |
| 87.46250 | 77.46250 | NFM | West Sussex | West Sussex Council |
| 87.46250 | 77.46250 | NFM | Worcester | Council |
| 87.47500 | 77.47500 | NFM | Buckinghamshire | County Council |
| 87.47500 | 77.47500 | NFM | Morecambe | PMR |
| 87.47500 | 77.47500 | NFM | Nottingham | DGA Cars Ch 2 |
| 87.47500 | 77.47500 | NFM | Pembrokeshire | MoD Castlemartin |
| 87.47500 | 77.47500 | NFM | Peterborough | Cotton TV |
| 87.48750 | 77.48750 | NFM | Fife | Council Works Drainage |
| 87.48750 | 77.48750 | NFM | Gainsbrough | Grimsby Council |
| 87.48750 | 77.48750 | NFM | Liverpool | Taxi |
| 87.48750 | 77.48750 | NFM | Nottingham | DGA Cars Ch 1 |

| Base | Mobile | Mode | Location | User and Notes |
|------|--------|------|----------|----------------|
| 87.48750 | 77.48750 | NFM | Peterborough | Royal Taxis |
| 87.50000 | 77.50000 | NFM | Cambridge | John Grieves |
| 87.50000 | 77.50000 | NFM | Guernsey | States Telecom |
| 87.50000 | 77.50000 | NFM | Leeds | Skip Hire |
| 87.52500 | 77.52500 | NFM | Edinburgh | Longstone/Hazelbank (Quarry) |
| 87.52500 | 77.52500 | NFM | Northern Ireland | Ambulance Service |
| 87.55000 | 77.55000 | NFM | Fife | Fife Council Ch 4 |
| 87.55000 | 77.55000 | NFM | Northern Ireland | Ambulance Service |
| 87.57500 | 77.57500 | NFM | Northern Ireland | Ambulance Service |
| 87.62500 | 77.62500 | NFM | Northern Ireland | Ambulance Service |
| 87.65000 | 77.65000 | NFM | Northern Ireland | Ambulance Service |
| 87.67500 | 77.67500 | NFM | Northern Ireland | Ambulance Service |
| 87.70000 | 77.70000 | NFM | London | Middlesex Cars |
| 87.70000 | 77.70000 | WFM | Nationwide | RSL 28 Day Stations |
| 87.70000 | 77.70000 | NFM | Wymondham, Norfolk | Ayton Asphalt |
| 87.71250 | 77.71250 | NFM | London | Reliable Cars |
| 87.72500 | 77.72500 | NFM | Birmingham | Council |
| 87.72500 | 77.72500 | NFM | Guernsey | British Gas |
| 87.72500 | 77.72500 | NFM | London | Camberwell Cars |
| 87.73500 | 87.73500 | NFM | Cardiff Area | Maintenance Company |
| 87.73750 | 77.73750 | NFM | Ipswich | Council |
| 87.75000 | 77.75000 | NFM | Croydon | Metro Cars |
| 87.70250 | 77.76250 | NFM | Nationwide | Forestry Commission Ch 2 |
| 87.80000 | 77.80000 | WFM | Nationwide | RSL 28 Day Stations |
| 87.82500 | 77.82500 | NFM | Nationwide | Forestry Commission Ch 1 |
| 87.87500 | 77.87500 | NFM | Jersey | "Evening Post" |
| 87.90000 | 77.90000 | WFM | London | Energy |
| 87.90000 | 77.90000 | NFM | London | Intercity Couriers |
| 87.90000 | 77.90000 | WFM | Nottingham | Heatwave Radio |
| 87.91250 | 77.91250 | NFM | London | Cheeta Mini Cars |
| 87.92500 | 77.92500 | NFM | Manchester | "Guardian" newspaper |
| 87.92500 | 77.92500 | NFM | Nationwide | Star Sat Racing Results |
| 87.96250 | 77.96250 | NFM | Nationwide | Forestry Commission Ch 3 |

## 88.0000 - 90.2000 MHz    NATIONWIDE BBC RADIO 2, RTE AND LOCAL RADIO

| Base | Mobile | Mode | Location | User and Notes |
|------|--------|------|----------|----------------|
| 88.100 | | WFM | Ballachulish | |
| 88.100 | | WFM | Bowmore | |
| 88.100 | | WFM | Cirencester | |
| 88.100 | | WFM | Clettraval | |
| 88.100 | | WFM | Clyro | |
| 88.100 | | WFM | Deiniolen | |
| 88.100 | | WFM | Ffestiniog | |
| 88.100 | | WFM | Grantham | |
| 88.100 | | WFM | Guildford | |
| 88.100 | | WFM | Llanidloes | |
| 88.100 | | WFM | Mallaig | |
| 88.100 | | WFM | Manningtree | |
| 88.100 | | WFM | North Hessary Tor | |
| 88.100 | | WFM | Penifiler | |
| 88.100 | | WFM | Sundale | |
| 88.200 | | WFM | Betws-Y-Coed | |
| 88.200 | | WFM | Bexhill | |
| 88.200 | | WFM | Calne | |
| 88.200 | | WFM | Crosshaven | RTE Radio 1 |

| Base | Mobile | Mode | Location | User and Notes |
|------|--------|------|----------|----------------|
| 88.200 | | WFM | Knock More | |
| 88.200 | | WFM | Nailsworth | |
| 88.200 | | WFM | Newbury | |
| 88.200 | | WFM | Rheola | |
| 88.200 | | WFM | Truskmore | RTE Radio 1 |
| 88.300 | | WFM | Bressay | |
| 88.300 | | WFM | Castletownbere | RTE Radio 1 |
| 88.300 | | WFM | Clonmel | RTE Radio 1 |
| 88.300 | | WFM | Forfar | |
| 88.300 | | WFM | Lethanhill | |
| 88.300 | | WFM | Llwyn-Onn | |
| 88.300 | | WFM | Lochgilphead | |
| 88.300 | | WFM | Millburn Muir | |
| 88.300 | | WFM | Moville | RTE Radio 1 |
| 88.300 | | WFM | Ness of Lewis | |
| 88.300 | | WFM | Rostrevor Forest | |
| 88.300 | | WFM | Sutton Coldfield | |
| 88.300 | | WFM | Ullapool | |
| 88.300 | | WFM | Wensleydale | |
| 88.300 | | WFM | Westwood | |
| 88.300 | | WFM | Windermere | |
| 88.400 | | WFM | Campbeltown | |
| 88.400 | | WFM | Carmel | |
| 88.400 | | WFM | Douglas, Isle Of Man | |
| 88.400 | | WFM | Ebbw Vale | |
| 88.400 | | WFM | Folkestone | |
| 88.400 | | WFM | Hebden Bridge | |
| 88.400 | | WFM | Kenley | |
| 88.400 | | WFM | Knockmoyle | RTE Radio 1 |
| 88.400 | | WFM | Peebles | |
| 88.400 | | WFM | Penmaen Rhos | |
| 88.400 | | WFM | Porth | |
| 88.400 | | WFM | Walsden South | |
| 88.400 | | WFM | Wharfdale | |
| 88.500 | | WFM | Barnstaple | |
| 88.500 | | WFM | Blaenavon | |
| 88.500 | | WFM | Cwmafan | |
| 88.500 | | WFM | Dungarvan | RTE Radio 1 |
| 88.500 | | WFM | Idle | |
| 88.500 | | WFM | Plympton | |
| 88.500 | | WFM | Pontop Pike | |
| 88.500 | | WFM | Rothesay | |
| 88.500 | | WFM | Rowbridge | |
| 88.500 | | WFM | Skraig | |
| 88.500 | | WFM | Three Rock | RTE Radio 1 |
| 88.600 | | WFM | Berwick On Tweed | |
| 88.600 | | WFM | Bow Brickhall | |
| 88.600 | | WFM | Llangeinor | |
| 88.600 | | WFM | Ridge Hill | |
| 88.600 | | WFM | Sheffield | BBC Radio Sheffield |
| 88.600 | | WFM | Strachur | |
| 88.600 | | WFM | Upperton | |
| 88.600 | | WFM | Winter Hill | |
| 88.700 | | WFM | Abergavenny | |
| 88.700 | | WFM | Ardgour | |
| 88.700 | | WFM | Beacon Hill | |

| Base | Mobile | Mode | Location | User and Notes |
|------|--------|------|----------|----------------|
| 88.700 | | WFM | Ben Gullipen | |
| 88.700 | | WFM | Cambret Hill | |
| 88.700 | | WFM | Camlough | |
| 88.700 | | WFM | Kirkconnel | |
| 88.700 | | WFM | Londonderry | |
| 88.700 | | WFM | Luddenden | |
| 88.700 | | WFM | Meldrum | |
| 88.700 | | WFM | Okehampton | |
| 88.800 | | WFM | Ballycastle | |
| 88.800 | | WFM | Belmont | |
| 88.800 | | WFM | Carnmoney Hill | |
| 88.800 | | WFM | Chippenham | |
| 88.800 | | WFM | County Mayo | RTE Radio 1 |
| 88.800 | | WFM | Crystal Palace | |
| 88.800 | | WFM | Isles of Scilly | |
| 88.800 | | WFM | Jersey | BBC Radio Jersey |
| 88.800 | | WFM | Maghera | RTE Radio 1 |
| 88.800 | | WFM | Penaligon Downs | |
| 88.800 | | WFM | Ton Pentre | |
| 88.900 | | WFM | Brecon | |
| 88.900 | | WFM | Cambridge | |
| 88.900 | | WFM | Carmarthen | |
| 00.900 | | WFM | Chard | |
| 88.900 | | WFM | Girvan | |
| 88.900 | | WFM | Keighley | |
| 88.900 | | WFM | Llangollen | |
| 88.900 | | WFM | Monaghan | RTE Radio 1 |
| 88.900 | | WFM | Northampton | |
| 88.900 | | WFM | Oban | |
| 88.900 | | WFM | Todmorden | |
| 88.900 | | WFM | Varteg Hill | |
| 89.000 | | WFM | Abertillery | |
| 89.000 | | WFM | Bath City | |
| 89.000 | | WFM | Blunsdon | |
| 89.000 | | WFM | Chesterfield | |
| 89.000 | | WFM | Churchdown Hill | |
| 89.000 | | WFM | Croeserw | |
| 89.000 | | WFM | Isle of Man | Manx Radio |
| 89.000 | | WFM | Kendal | |
| 89.000 | | WFM | Kirkton Mailer | |
| 89.000 | | WFM | Minehead | |
| 89.000 | | WFM | Port Ellen | |
| 89.000 | | WFM | St Thomas | |
| 89.000 | | WFM | Suir Valley | RTE Radio 1 |
| 89.100 | | WFM | Ashkirk | |
| 89.100 | | WFM | Brigport | |
| 89.100 | | WFM | Combe Martin | |
| 89.100 | | WFM | Conwy | |
| 89.100 | | WFM | Egford Hill | |
| 89.100 | | WFM | Kingussie | |
| 89.100 | | WFM | Kippure | RTE Radio 1 |
| 89.100 | | WFM | Larne | |
| 89.100 | | WFM | Llandrindod Wells | |
| 89.100 | | WFM | Llanfyllin | |
| 89.100 | | WFM | Melvaig | |
| 89.100 | | WFM | Schull/Skibbereen | RTE Radio 1 |

| Base | Mobile | Mode | Location | User and Notes |
|------|--------|------|----------|----------------|
| 89.100 | | WFM | West Kilbride | |
| 89.100 | | WFM | Wrotham | |
| 89.200 | | WFM | Aberdare | |
| 89.200 | | WFM | Chalford | |
| 89.200 | | WFM | Cork City | RTE Radio 1 |
| 89.200 | | WFM | Holywell Hill | RTE Radio 1 |
| 89.200 | | WFM | Ogmore Vale | |
| 89.200 | | WFM | Pitlochry | |
| 89.200 | | WFM | Pontypool | |
| 89.200 | | WFM | Rosneath | |
| 89.300 | | WFM | Achill | RTE Radio 1 |
| 89.300 | | WFM | County Galway | RTE Radio 1 |
| 89.300 | | WFM | Crieff | |
| 89.300 | | WFM | Daliburg | |
| 89.300 | | WFM | Fort William | |
| 89.300 | | WFM | Haverfordwest | |
| 89.300 | | WFM | Holme Moss | |
| 89.300 | | WFM | Ilchester Cresent | |
| 89.300 | | WFM | Keelylang Hill | |
| 89.300 | | WFM | Rhymney | |
| 89.300 | | WFM | South Khapdale | |
| 89.400 | | WFM | Brougher Mountain | |
| 89.400 | | WFM | Durris | |
| 89.400 | | WFM | Hutton | |
| 89.400 | | WFM | Kikeel | |
| 89.400 | | WFM | Limerick City | RTE Radio 1 |
| 89.400 | | WFM | Llamdecwyn | |
| 89.400 | | WFM | Machynlleth | |
| 89.400 | | WFM | Newton | |
| 89.400 | | WFM | Ventnor | |
| 89.500 | | WFM | Axe Valley | |
| 89.500 | | WFM | Cahirciveen | RTE Radio 1 |
| 89.500 | | WFM | Clifden | RTE Radio 1 |
| 89.500 | | WFM | Darvel | |
| 89.500 | | WFM | Darwen | |
| 89.500 | | WFM | Glengorm | |
| 89.500 | | WFM | Innerleithen | |
| 89.500 | | WFM | Kilvey Hill | |
| 89.500 | | WFM | Oxford | |
| 89.500 | | WFM | Pennar | |
| 89.500 | | WFM | Salcombe | |
| 89.600 | | WFM | Aranmore | RTE Radio 1 |
| 89.600 | | WFM | Channel Islands | |
| 89.600 | | WFM | Fermdale | |
| 89.600 | | WFM | Hastings | |
| 89.600 | | WFM | Keswick Forest | |
| 89.600 | | WFM | Limavady | |
| 89.600 | | WFM | Llyswen | |
| 89.600 | | WFM | Long Mountain | |
| 89.600 | | WFM | Ludlow | |
| 89.600 | | WFM | Mount Leinster | RTE Radio 1 |
| 89.600 | | WFM | Rosemarkie | |
| 89.600 | | WFM | Whalley | |
| 89.600 | | WFM | Whitby | |
| 89.700 | | WFM | Barnoldswick | |
| 89.700 | | WFM | Caterham | |

| Base | Mobile | Mode | Location | User and Notes |
|------|--------|------|----------|----------------|
| 89.700 | | WFM | Cornholme | |
| 89.700 | | WFM | Eyemouth | |
| 89.700 | | WFM | Kinlochleven | |
| 89.700 | | WFM | Lyme Regis | |
| 89.700 | | WFM | Mynydd Pencarreg | |
| 89.700 | | WFM | Newhaven | |
| 89.700 | | WFM | Redruth | |
| 89.700 | | WFM | Stranraer | |
| 89.700 | | WFM | Tacolneston | |
| 89.700 | | WFM | Wearsdale | |
| 89.700 | | WFM | Whitehaven | |
| 89.800 | | WFM | Beecroft Hill | |
| 89.800 | | WFM | Castlebar | RTE Radio 1 |
| 89.800 | | WFM | Croaghmoyle, Mayo | RTE Radio 1 |
| 89.800 | | WFM | Eitshal | |
| 89.800 | | WFM | Fanad | RTE Radio 1 |
| 89.800 | | WFM | Fendale | |
| 89.800 | | WFM | Grantown | |
| 89.800 | | WFM | Hemdean | |
| 89.800 | | WFM | Kingswear | |
| 89.800 | | WFM | Llanddona | |
| 89.800 | | WFM | Llanrhaeadr-ym-M | |
| 89.800 | | WFM | Saddleworth | |
| 89.800 | | WFM | Salisbury | |
| 89.800 | | WFM | Stanton Moor | |
| 89.900 | | WFM | Athlone | RTE Radio 1 |
| 89.900 | | WFM | Black Hill | |
| 89.900 | | WFM | County Mayo | RTE Radio 1 |
| 89.900 | | WFM | Haslingden | |
| 89.900 | | WFM | Ivybridge | |
| 89.900 | | WFM | Oliver's Mount | |
| 89.900 | | WFM | Sheffield | |
| 89.900 | | WFM | Wenvoe | |
| 90.000 | | WFM | Buxton | |
| 90.000 | | WFM | High Wycombe | |
| 90.000 | | WFM | Morecambe Bay | |
| 90.000 | | WFM | Mullaghanish | RTE Radio 1 |
| 90.000 | | WFM | Swingate | |
| 90.000 | | WFM | Weymouth | |
| 90.100 | | WFM | Basingstoke | |
| 90.100 | | WFM | Brighton | |
| 90.100 | | WFM | Chatton | |
| 90.100 | | WFM | Divis | |
| 90.100 | | WFM | Dolgellau | |
| 90.100 | | WFM | Llandinam | |
| 90.100 | | WFM | Llandtfriog | |
| 90.100 | | WFM | Marlborough | |
| 90.100 | | WFM | Peterborough | |
| 90.100 | | WFM | Rumster Forest | |
| 90.100 | | WFM | Tullich | |
| 90.200 | | WFM | Clyro | BBC Radio 3 |
| 90.200 | | WFM | Pendle Forest | |
| 90.200 | | WFM | Woolmoor | |

| Base | Mobile | Mode | Location | User and Notes |
|------|--------|------|----------|----------------|
| 90.3000 - 92.4000 MHz | | | NATIONWIDE BBC RADIO 3, RTE AND LOCAL RADIO | |
| 90.300 | | WFM | Ballachulish | |
| 90.300 | | WFM | Bowmore | |
| 90.300 | | WFM | Cirencester | |
| 90.300 | | WFM | Clettraval | |
| 90.300 | | WFM | Deiniolen | |
| 90.300 | | WFM | Ffestiniog | |
| 90.300 | | WFM | Grantham | |
| 90.300 | | WFM | Guildford | |
| 90.300 | | WFM | Llandloes | |
| 90.300 | | WFM | Mallaig | |
| 90.300 | | WFM | Manningtree | |
| 90.300 | | WFM | North Hessary Tor | |
| 90.300 | | WFM | Penifiler | |
| 90.300 | | WFM | Sandale | |
| 90.400 | | WFM | Aranmore | RTE Radio 3/4 |
| 90.400 | | WFM | Betws-Y-Coed | |
| 90.400 | | WFM | Calne | |
| 90.400 | | WFM | County Mayo | RTE Radio 2 |
| 90.400 | | WFM | Crosshaven | RTE Radio 2 |
| 90.400 | | WFM | Knock More | |
| 90.400 | | WFM | Nailsworth | |
| 90.400 | | WFM | Newbury | |
| 90.400 | | WFM | Rheoloa | |
| 90.400 | | WFM | Truskmore | RTE Radio 2 |
| 90.500 | | WFM | Bressay | |
| 90.500 | | WFM | Castletownbere | RTE Radio 2 |
| 90.500 | | WFM | Clonmel | RTE Radio 2 |
| 90.500 | | WFM | Forfar | |
| 90.500 | | WFM | Lethanhill | |
| 90.500 | | WFM | Llwyn-Onn | |
| 90.500 | | WFM | Lochgilphead | |
| 90.500 | | WFM | Millburn Muir | |
| 90.500 | | WFM | Mt. Leinster | RTE Radio 2 |
| 90.500 | | WFM | Ness of Lewis | |
| 90.500 | | WFM | Rostrevor Forest | |
| 90.500 | | WFM | Sutton Coldfield | |
| 90.500 | | WFM | Ullapool | |
| 90.500 | | WFM | Wensleydale | |
| 90.500 | | WFM | Westwood | |
| 90.500 | | WFM | Windermere | |
| 90.600 | | WFM | Campbeltown | |
| 90.600 | | WFM | Carmel | |
| 90.600 | | WFM | Douglas, Isle Of Man | |
| 90.600 | | WFM | Ebbw Vale | |
| 90.600 | | WFM | Folkestone | |
| 90.600 | | WFM | Hebden Bridge | |
| 90.600 | | WFM | Kenley | |
| 90.600 | | WFM | Knockmoyle | RTE Radio 2 |
| 90.600 | | WFM | Peebles | |
| 90.600 | | WFM | Penmaen Rhos | |
| 90.600 | | WFM | Porth | |
| 90.600 | | WFM | Walsden South | |
| 90.600 | | WFM | Wharfdale | |
| 90.700 | | WFM | Barnstaple | |

| Base | Mobile | Mode | Location | User and Notes |
|---|---|---|---|---|
| 90.700 | | WFM | Blaenavon | |
| 90.700 | | WFM | Cwmafan | |
| 90.700 | | WFM | Dungarvan | RTE Radio 2 |
| 90.700 | | WFM | Idle | |
| 90.700 | | WFM | Plympton | |
| 90.700 | | WFM | Pontop Pike | |
| 90.700 | | WFM | Rothesay | |
| 90.700 | | WFM | Rowbridge | |
| 90.700 | | WFM | Skraig | |
| 90.700 | | WFM | Three Rock | RTE Radio 2 |
| 90.800 | | WFM | Berwick | |
| 90.800 | | WFM | Bow Brickhill | |
| 90.800 | | WFM | Lllangeinor | |
| 90.800 | | WFM | Ridge Hill | |
| 90.800 | | WFM | Strachur | |
| 90.800 | | WFM | Upperton | |
| 90.800 | | WFM | Winter Hill | |
| 90.900 | | WFM | Abergavenny | |
| 90.900 | | WFM | Ardgour | |
| 90.900 | | WFM | Beacon Hill | |
| 90.900 | | WFM | Belmont | |
| 90.900 | | WFM | Ben Gullipen | |
| 90.900 | | WFM | Blaenplwyf | |
| 90.900 | | WFM | Cambret Hill | |
| 90.900 | | WFM | Camlough | |
| 90.900 | | WFM | Kirkconnel | |
| 90.900 | | WFM | Londonderry | |
| 90.900 | | WFM | Luddenden | |
| 90.900 | | WFM | Meldrum | |
| 90.900 | | WFM | Okehampton | |
| 91.000 | | WFM | Ballycastle | |
| 91.000 | | WFM | Belmont | |
| 91.000 | | WFM | Carnmoney Hill | |
| 91.000 | | WFM | Chippenham | |
| 91.000 | | WFM | County Mayo | RTE Radio 2 |
| 91.000 | | WFM | Crystal Palace | |
| 91.000 | | WFM | Galway | RTE Radio 2 |
| 91.000 | | WFM | Isles of Scilly | |
| 91.000 | | WFM | Maghera | RTE Radio 2 |
| 91.000 | | WFM | Penaligon Downs | |
| 91.000 | | WFM | Ton Pentre | |
| 91.100 | | WFM | Brecon | |
| 91.100 | | WFM | Cambridge | |
| 91.100 | | WFM | Carmarthen | |
| 91.100 | | WFM | Chard | |
| 91.100 | | WFM | Girvan | |
| 91.100 | | WFM | Keighley | |
| 91.100 | | WFM | Llangollen | |
| 91.100 | | WFM | Monaghan | RTE Radio 2 |
| 91.100 | | WFM | Northampton | |
| 91.100 | | WFM | Oban | |
| 91.100 | | WFM | Todmorden | |
| 91.100 | | WFM | Varteg Hill | |
| 91.200 | | WFM | Abertillery | |
| 91.200 | | WFM | Bath City | |
| 91.200 | | WFM | Blunsdon | |

| Base | Mobile | Mode | Location | User and Notes |
|------|--------|------|----------|----------------|
| 91.200 | | WFM | Chesterfield | |
| 91.200 | | WFM | Churchdown Hill | |
| 91.200 | | WFM | Croeserw | |
| 91.200 | | WFM | Isle of Man | Manx Radio |
| 91.200 | | WFM | Kendal | |
| 91.200 | | WFM | Kirkton Mailer | |
| 91.200 | | WFM | Minehead | |
| 91.200 | | WFM | Port Ellen | |
| 91.200 | | WFM | St Thomas | |
| 91.200 | | WFM | Suir Valley | RTE Radio 2 |
| 91.300 | | WFM | Ashkirk | |
| 91.300 | | WFM | Brigport | |
| 91.300 | | WFM | Combe Martin | |
| 91.300 | | WFM | Conwy | |
| 91.300 | | WFM | Egford Hill | |
| 91.300 | | WFM | Kingussie | |
| 91.300 | | WFM | Kippure | RTE Radio 2 |
| 91.300 | | WFM | Larne | |
| 91.300 | | WFM | Llandrindod Wells | |
| 91.300 | | WFM | Llanfyllin | |
| 91.300 | | WFM | Melvaig | |
| 91.300 | | WFM | Schull/Skibbereen | RTE Radio 2 |
| 91.300 | | WFM | West Kilbride | |
| 91.300 | | WFM | Wrotham | |
| 91.400 | | WFM | Aberdare | |
| 91.400 | | WFM | Chalford | |
| 91.400 | | WFM | Cork City | RTE Radio 2 |
| 91.400 | | WFM | Holywell Hill | RTE Radio 2 |
| 91.400 | | WFM | Ogmore Vale | |
| 91.400 | | WFM | Pitlochry | |
| 91.400 | | WFM | Pontypool | |
| 91.400 | | WFM | Rosneath | |
| 91.500 | | WFM | Achill | RTE Radio 2 |
| 91.500 | | WFM | Crieff | |
| 91.500 | | WFM | Daliburg | |
| 91.500 | | WFM | Fort William | |
| 91.500 | | WFM | Haverfordwest | |
| 91.500 | | WFM | Holme Moss | |
| 91.500 | | WFM | Ilchester Cresent | |
| 91.500 | | WFM | Keelylang Hill | |
| 91.500 | | WFM | Rhymney | |
| 91.500 | | WFM | South Khapdale | |
| 91.600 | | WFM | Brougher Mountain | |
| 91.600 | | WFM | Durris | |
| 91.600 | | WFM | Hutton | |
| 91.600 | | WFM | Kikeel | |
| 91.600 | | WFM | Limerick City | RTE Radio 2 |
| 91.600 | | WFM | Llamdecwyn | |
| 91.600 | | WFM | Machynlleth | |
| 91.600 | | WFM | Newton | |
| 91.600 | | WFM | Ventnor | |
| 91.700 | | WFM | Axe Valley | |
| 91.700 | | WFM | Cahirciveen | RTE Radio 2 |
| 91.700 | | WFM | Clifden | RTE Radio 2 |
| 91.700 | | WFM | Darvel | |
| 91.700 | | WFM | Darwen | |

| Base | Mobile | Mode | Location | User and Notes |
|------|--------|------|----------|----------------|
| 91.700 | | WFM | Glengorm | |
| 91.700 | | WFM | Innerleithin | |
| 91.700 | | WFM | Kilvey Hill | |
| 91.700 | | WFM | Oxford | |
| 91.700 | | WFM | Pennar | |
| 91.700 | | WFM | Salcombe | |
| 91.800 | | WFM | Aranmore | RTE Radio 2 |
| 91.800 | | WFM | Fermdale | |
| 91.800 | | WFM | Hastings | |
| 91.800 | | WFM | Keswick Forest | |
| 91.800 | | WFM | Limavady | |
| 91.800 | | WFM | Llyswen | |
| 91.800 | | WFM | Long Mountain | |
| 91.800 | | WFM | Ludlow | |
| 91.800 | | WFM | Mount Leinster | RTE Radio 2 |
| 91.800 | | WFM | Rosemarkie | |
| 91.800 | | WFM | Whalley | |
| 91.800 | | WFM | Whitby | |
| 91.900 | | WFM | Barnoldswick | |
| 91.900 | | WFM | Caterham | |
| 91.900 | | WFM | Cornholme | |
| 91.900 | | WFM | Eyemouth | |
| 91.900 | | WFM | Kinlochleven | |
| 91.900 | | WFM | Lyme Regis | |
| 91.900 | | WFM | Mynydd Pencarreg | |
| 91.900 | | WFM | Newhaven | |
| 91.900 | | WFM | Redruth | |
| 91.900 | | WFM | Stranraer | |
| 91.900 | | WFM | Tacolneston | |
| 91.900 | | WFM | Wearsdale | |
| 91.900 | | WFM | Whitehaven | |
| 92.000 | | WFM | Beecroft Hill | |
| 92.000 | | WFM | Castlebar | RTE Radio 2 |
| 92.000 | | WFM | Croaghmoyle, Mayo | RTE Radio 2 |
| 92.000 | | WFM | Eitshal | |
| 92.000 | | WFM | Fanad | RTE Radio 2 |
| 92.000 | | WFM | Fendale | |
| 92.000 | | WFM | Grantown | |
| 92.000 | | WFM | Hemdean | |
| 92.000 | | WFM | Kingswear | |
| 92.000 | | WFM | Llanddona | |
| 92.000 | | WFM | Llanrhaeadr-ym-M | |
| 92.000 | | WFM | Saddleworth | |
| 92.000 | | WFM | Salisbury | |
| 92.000 | | WFM | Stanton Moor | |
| 92.100 | | WFM | Athlone | RTE Radio 2 |
| 92.100 | | WFM | Black Hill | |
| 92.100 | | WFM | County Mayo | RTE Radio 2 |
| 92.100 | | WFM | Haslingden | |
| 92.100 | | WFM | Ivybridge | |
| 92.100 | | WFM | Oliver's Mount | |
| 92.100 | | WFM | Sheffield | |
| 92.100 | | WFM | Wenvoe | |
| 92.200 | | WFM | Bexhill | |
| 92.200 | | WFM | Buxton | |
| 92.200 | | WFM | High Wycombe | |

| Base | Mobile | Mode | Location | User and Notes |
|---|---|---|---|---|
| 92.200 | | WFM | Morecambe Bay | |
| 92.200 | | WFM | Mullaghanish | RTE Radio 2 |
| 92.200 | | WFM | Weymouth | |
| 92.200 | | WFM | Woolmoor | |
| 92.300 | | WFM | Basingstoke | |
| 92.300 | | WFM | Brighton | |
| 92.300 | | WFM | Chatton | |
| 92.300 | | WFM | Divis | |
| 92.300 | | WFM | Dolgellau | |
| 92.300 | | WFM | Llandinam | |
| 92.300 | | WFM | Llandtfriog | |
| 92.300 | | WFM | Marlborough | |
| 92.300 | | WFM | Peterborough | |
| 92.300 | | WFM | Rumster Forest | |
| 92.300 | | WFM | Tullich | |

## 92.4000 -94.6000 MHz  NATIONWIDE BBC RADIO 4, RTE AND LOCAL RADIO

| Base | Mobile | Mode | Location | User and Notes |
|---|---|---|---|---|
| 92.400 | | WFM | Clyro | BBC Radio Cymru |
| 92.400 | | WFM | Holme Moss | BBC Radio Leeds |
| 92.400 | | WFM | Swingate | BBC Radio 3 |
| 92.500 | | WFM | Ballachulish | BBC Radio Scotland |
| 92.500 | | WFM | Bowmore | BBC Radio Scotland |
| 92.500 | | WFM | Cirencester | |
| 92.500 | | WFM | Clettral | BBC Radio Scotland |
| 92.500 | | WFM | Deiniolen | BBC Radio Cymru |
| 92.500 | | WFM | Ffestiniog | BBC Radio Cymru |
| 92.500 | | WFM | Grantham | |
| 92.500 | | WFM | Guildford | |
| 92.500 | | WFM | Llanidloes | BBC Radio Cymru |
| 92.500 | | WFM | Mallaig | BBC Radio Scotland |
| 92.500 | | WFM | Manningtree | |
| 92.500 | | WFM | North Hessary Tor | |
| 92.500 | | WFM | Penifiler | BBC Radio Scotland |
| 92.500 | | WFM | Sundale | |
| 92.600 | | WFM | Betws-y-Coed | BBC Radio Cymru |
| 92.600 | | WFM | Calne | |
| 92.600 | | WFM | County Mayo | RTE Radio 3 |
| 92.600 | | WFM | Crosshaven | RTE Radio 3/4 |
| 92.600 | | WFM | Galway | RTE Radio 3 |
| 92.600 | | WFM | Knock More | BBC Radio Scotland |
| 92.600 | | WFM | Nailsworth | |
| 92.600 | | WFM | Newbury | |
| 92.600 | | WFM | Rheola | BBC Radio Cymru |
| 92.600 | | WFM | Truskmore | Raidio Na Gaeltachta |
| 92.700 | | WFM | Castletownbere | Raidio Na Gaeltachta |
| 92.700 | | WFM | Clonmel | RTE Radio 3/4 |
| 92.700 | | WMF | Edinburgh | BBC Radio Scotland |
| 92.700 | | WFM | Forfar | BBC Radio Scotland |
| 92.700 | | WFM | Kilmarnock | BBC Radio Scotland |
| 92.700 | | WFM | Leicestershire | |
| 92.700 | | WFM | Leven & Renton | BBC Radio Scotland |
| 92.700 | | WFM | Lochgilphead | BBC Radio Scotland |
| 92.700 | | WFM | Midland Counties | |
| 92.700 | | WFM | Ness of Lewis | BBC Radio Scotland |

| Base | Mobile | Mode | Location | User and Notes |
|------|--------|------|----------|----------------|
| 92.700 | | WFM | Nottinghamshire | |
| 92.700 | | WFM | Shetland Isl | BBC Radio Scotland |
| 92.700 | | WFM | Staffordshire & Shorpshire | |
| 92.700 | | WFM | Trowbridge | |
| 92.700 | | WFM | Wensleydale | |
| 92.700 | | WFM | Westwood | |
| 92.700 | | WFM | Windermere | |
| 92.800 | | WFM | Campbeltown | BBC Radio Scotland |
| 92.800 | | WFM | Clwyd | BBC Radio Cymru |
| 92.800 | | WFM | Eastbourne | |
| 92.800 | | WFM | Ebbw Vale | |
| 92.800 | | WFM | Hebden Bridge | |
| 92.800 | | WFM | Isle of Man | |
| 92.800 | | WFM | Knockmoyle | RTE Radio 3/4 |
| 92.800 | | WFM | Mid Glamorgan | |
| 92.800 | | WFM | Peebles | BBC Radio Scotland |
| 92.800 | | WFM | South London | |
| 92.800 | | WFM | Surrey | |
| 92.800 | | WFM | Walsden | |
| 92.800 | | WFM | Wharfdale | |
| 92.900 | | WFM | Central South of England | |
| 92.900 | | WFM | Cowal Peninsular | BBC Radio Scotland |
| 92.900 | | WFM | Croaghmoyle, Mayo | Raidio Na Gaeltachta |
| 92.900 | | WFM | Devon | |
| 92.900 | | WFM | Dungarvan | RTE Radio 3/4 |
| 92.900 | | WFM | Gwent | |
| 92.900 | | WFM | Isle of Wight | |
| 92.900 | | WFM | Moville | Raidio Na Gaeltachta |
| 92.900 | | WFM | North Eastern Counties | |
| 92.900 | | WFM | Three Rock | Raidio Na Gaeltachta |
| 92.900 | | WFM | West Glamorgan | |
| 92.900 | | WFM | West Skye | BBC Radio Scotland |
| 92.900 | | WFM | West Yorkshire | |
| 93.000 | | WFM | Bedford | |
| 93.000 | | WFM | Berwick | |
| 93.000 | | WFM | Derrybeg | RTE Radio 3/4 |
| 93.000 | | WFM | Hereford & Welsh Borders | |
| 93.000 | | WFM | Inveraray | BBC Radio Scotland |
| 93.000 | | WFM | Mid Glamorgan | |
| 93.000 | | WFM | North West Lancashire | |
| 93.000 | | WFM | Ross On Wye | |
| 93.000 | | WFM | Warrenpoint | Radio Ulster |
| 93.100 | | WFM | Aberystwyth | BBC Radio Cymru |
| 93.100 | | WFM | Ayr | BBC Radio Scotland |
| 93.100 | | WFM | Cambridgeshire | |
| 93.100 | | WFM | Edinburgh | BBC Radio Scotland |
| 93.100 | | WFM | Folkestone | |
| 93.100 | | WFM | Grampian | BBC Radio Scotland |
| 93.100 | | WFM | Gwent | |
| 93.100 | | WFM | Kirkconnel | BBC Radio Scotland |
| 93.100 | | WFM | Lincolnshire | |
| 93.100 | | WFM | Londonderry | Radio Foyle |
| 93.100 | | WFM | Newark | |
| 93.100 | | WFM | Okehampton | |
| 93.200 | | WFM | Ballycastle | |
| 93.200 | | WFM | Chippenham | |

| Base | Mobile | Mode | Location | User and Notes |
|------|--------|------|----------|----------------|
| 93.200 | | WFM | Co Antrim | |
| 93.200 | | WFM | Cornwall | |
| 93.200 | | WFM | County Mayo | RTE Radio 3 |
| 93.200 | | WFM | Crystal Palace | |
| 93.200 | | WFM | Galway | RTE Radio 3 |
| 93.200 | | WFM | Guernsey | BBC Radio Guernsey |
| 93.200 | | WFM | Isles of Scilly | |
| 93.200 | | WFM | Maghera | Raidio Na Gaeltachta |
| 93.200 | | WFM | Penaligon Downs | |
| 93.200 | | WFM | Ton Petre | BBC Radio Cymru |
| 93.300 | | WFM | Brecon | BBC Radio Cymru |
| 93.300 | | WFM | Cambridge | |
| 93.300 | | WFM | Carmarthen | BBC Radio Cymru |
| 93.300 | | WFM | Chard | |
| 93.300 | | WFM | Girvan | BBC Radio Scotland |
| 93.300 | | WFM | Gwent | BBC Radio Cymru |
| 93.300 | | WFM | Keighley | |
| 93.300 | | WFM | Kinross | BBC Radio Scotland |
| 93.300 | | WFM | Llangollen | |
| 93.300 | | WFM | Monaghan | RTE Radio 3/4 |
| 93.300 | | WFM | Northampton | |
| 93.300 | | WFM | Oban | BBC Radio Scotland |
| 93.300 | | WFM | Todmorden | |
| 93.400 | | WFM | Abertillery | |
| 93.400 | | WFM | Bath City | |
| 93.400 | | WFM | Chesterfield | |
| 93.400 | | WFM | Exeter | |
| 93.400 | | WFM | Kendal | |
| 93.400 | | WFM | Kinsale | RTE Radio 3/4 |
| 93.400 | | WFM | Minehead | |
| 93.400 | | WFM | North Gloucestershire | |
| 93.400 | | WFM | Perth | BBC Radio Scotland |
| 93.400 | | WFM | South Glamorgan | BBC Radio Cymru |
| 93.400 | | WFM | South Islay | BBC Radio Scotland |
| 93.400 | | WFM | Suir Valley | RTE Radio 3/4 |
| 93.400 | | WFM | Swindon | |
| 93.500 | | WFM | Border Counties | BBC Radio Scotland |
| 93.500 | | WFM | Brigport | |
| 93.500 | | WFM | Bristol City | |
| 93.500 | | WFM | Conwy | BBC Radio Cymru |
| 93.500 | | WFM | Devon | |
| 93.500 | | WFM | Dorset | |
| 93.500 | | WFM | Home Counties | |
| 93.500 | | WFM | Kent | |
| 93.500 | | WFM | Kingussie | BBC Radio Scotland |
| 93.500 | | WFM | Kippure | Raidio Na Gaeltachta |
| 93.500 | | WFM | Larne | Radio Ulster |
| 93.500 | | WFM | Llandrindod Wells | BBC Radio Cymru |
| 93.500 | | WFM | London | |
| 93.500 | | WFM | Poseys | |
| 93.500 | | WFM | Scull/Skibbereen | RTE Radio 3/4 |
| 93.500 | | WFM | Somerset | |
| 93.500 | | WFM | Ullapool & Lewis | BBC Radio Scotland |
| 93.500 | | WFM | West Kilbride | BBC Radio Scotland |
| 93.600 | | WFM | Aberdare | BBC Radio Cymru |
| 93.600 | | WFM | Cork City | Raidio Na Gaeltachta |

| Base | Mobile | Mode | Location | User and Notes |
|------|--------|------|----------|----------------|
| 93.600 | | WFM | Holywell Hill | Raidio Na Gaeltachta |
| 93.600 | | WFM | Mid Glamorgan | |
| 93.600 | | WFM | Pitlochry | BBC Radio Scotland |
| 93.600 | | WFM | Pontypool | BBC Radio Cymru |
| 93.600 | | WFM | Rosneath | BBC Radio Scotland |
| 93.600 | | WFM | Stroud | |
| 93.700 | | WFM | Achill | Raidio Na Gaeltachta |
| 93.700 | | WFM | Alderney | 104.7 Island FM |
| 93.700 | | WFM | Bristol | BBC Radio 4 |
| 93.700 | | WFM | Bristol | BBC Radio 4 |
| 93.700 | | WFM | Cheshire | |
| 93.700 | | WFM | County Galway | RTE Radio 3 |
| 93.700 | | WFM | Daliburgh | BBC Radio Scotland/Highland |
| 93.700 | | WFM | Derbyshire | |
| 93.700 | | WFM | Fort William | BBC Radio Scotland |
| 93.700 | | WFM | Galway | RTE Radio 3 |
| 93.700 | | WFM | Greater Manchester | |
| 93.700 | | WFM | Gwent | |
| 93.700 | | WFM | Humberside | |
| 93.700 | | WFM | Lancashire | |
| 93.700 | | WFM | Merseyside | |
| 93.700 | | WFM | Nottinghamshire | |
| 93.700 | | WFM | Orkney Isl | BBC Radio Scotland |
| 93.700 | | WFM | Perthshire | BBC Radio Scotland |
| 93.700 | | WFM | South Knapdale | BBC Radio Scotland |
| 93.700 | | WFM | Wrexham & Deeside | |
| 93.700 | | WFM | Yorkshire | |
| 93.800 | | WFM | Avon | |
| 93.800 | | WFM | Enniskillen | Radio Ulster |
| 93.800 | | WFM | Gwynedd | |
| 93.800 | | WFM | Kincardine | BBC Radio Scotland |
| 93.800 | | WFM | Limerick City | RTE Radio 3/4 |
| 93.800 | | WFM | London | Vibes FM |
| 93.800 | | WFM | Newry | BBC Radio Ulster |
| 93.800 | | WFM | Northumberland | |
| 93.800 | | WFM | Poseys | BBC Radio Cymru |
| 93.800 | | WFM | Ventnor | |
| 93.900 | | WFM | Cahirciveen | Raidio Na Gaeltachta |
| 93.900 | | WFM | Clifden | RTE Radio 3/4 |
| 93.900 | | WFM | Devon | |
| 93.900 | | WFM | East Skye | BBC Radio Scotland |
| 93.900 | | WFM | Grantham | |
| 93.900 | | WFM | Greenholm & Darvel | BBC Radio Scotland |
| 93.900 | | WFM | Innerleithen | BBC Radio Scotland |
| 93.900 | | WFM | Oxfordshire & Wiltshire | |
| 93.900 | | WFM | Pennar | |
| 93.900 | | WFM | Swansea | BBC Radio Cymru |
| 93.900 | | WFM | Tobermoray & Mull | BBC Radio Scotland |
| 93.900 | | WFM | Todmorden | |
| 93.900 | | WFM | Welshpool | |
| 94.000 | | WFM | Fermdale | |
| 94.000 | | WFM | Inverness | BBC Radio Scotland |
| 94.000 | | WFM | Keswick Forest | |
| 94.000 | | WFM | Lancashire | |
| 94.000 | | WFM | Limavady | |
| 94.000 | | WFM | Ludlow | |

| Base | Mobile | Mode | Location | User and Notes |
|------|--------|------|----------|----------------|
| 94.000 | | WFM | Mid Glamorgan | |
| 94.000 | | WFM | Mount Leinster | Raidio Na Gaeltachta |
| 94.000 | | WFM | North East Scotland | BBC Radio Scotland |
| 94.000 | | WFM | W. Midlands | Black County Sounds |
| 94.000 | | WFM | Whitby | |
| 94.100 | | WFM | Berwickshire | BBC Radio Scotland |
| 94.100 | | WFM | Cornholme | |
| 94.100 | | WFM | Kinlochleven | BBC Radio Scotland |
| 94.100 | | WFM | Lyme Regis | |
| 94.100 | | WFM | Newhaven | |
| 94.100 | | WFM | Norfolk | |
| 94.100 | | WFM | Redruth | |
| 94.100 | | WFM | Saddleworth | |
| 94.100 | | WFM | South East London | |
| 94.100 | | WFM | Stranraer | BBC Radio Scotland |
| 94.100 | | WFM | Suffolk | |
| 94.100 | | WFM | Surrey | |
| 94.100 | | WFM | Wearsdale | |
| 94.100 | | WFM | West Cornwall | |
| 94.100 | | WFM | Whitehaven | |
| 94.200 | | WFM | Anglesey | BBC Radio Cymru |
| 94.200 | | WFM | Castlebar | RTE Radio 3/4 |
| 94.200 | | WFM | Caversham | |
| 94.200 | | WFM | Clwyd | |
| 94.200 | | WFM | County Mayo | RTE Radio 3 |
| 94.200 | | WFM | Derby | BBC Radio Derby |
| 94.200 | | WFM | Fanad | Raidio Na Gaeltachta |
| 94.200 | | WFM | Galway | RTE Radio 3 |
| 94.200 | | WFM | Hastings | |
| 94.200 | | WFM | Matlock | |
| 94.200 | | WFM | Newcastle | |
| 94.200 | | WFM | Pudsey | |
| 94.200 | | WFM | Salisbury | |
| 94.200 | | WFM | South Devon | |
| 94.200 | | WFM | Stornaway | BBC Radio Scotland |
| 94.300 | | WFM | Bristol | |
| 94.300 | | WFM | Edinburgh | BBC Radio Scotland |
| 94.300 | | WFM | Forth Valley | BBC Radio Scotland |
| 94.300 | | WFM | Gloucester & Somerset | |
| 94.300 | | WFM | Haslingden | |
| 94.300 | | WFM | High Wycombe | |
| 94.300 | | WFM | Lowland Scotland | BBC Radio Scotland |
| 94.300 | | WFM | Scarborough | |
| 94.300 | | WFM | Sheffield | |
| 94.300 | | WFM | Somerset & North Devon | |
| 94.300 | | WFM | South & East Wales | |
| 94.400 | | WFM | Buxton | |
| 94.400 | | WFM | High Wycombe | |
| 94.400 | | WFM | Morecambe Bay | |
| 94.400 | | WFM | Mullaghanish | Raidio Na Gaeltachta |
| 94.400 | | WFM | North Yorkshire | |
| 94.400 | | WFM | South Cumbria | |
| 94.400 | | WFM | South East Kent | |
| 94.400 | | WFM | Weymouth | |
| 94.500 | | WFM | Basingstoke | |
| 94.500 | | WFM | Belfast & East Counties | Radio Ulster |

| Base | Mobile | Mode | Location | User and Notes |
|------|--------|------|----------|----------------|
| 94.500 | | WFM | Berwick & Borders | |
| 94.500 | | WFM | Brighton | |
| 94.500 | | WFM | Chatton | |
| 94.500 | | WFM | Deeside | BBC Radio Scotland |
| 94.500 | | WFM | Dolgellau | BBC Radio Cymru |
| 94.500 | | WFM | Llandyfriod | BBC Radio Cymru |
| 94.500 | | WFM | Marlborough | |
| 94.500 | | WFM | Peterborough | |
| 94.500 | | WFM | Poseys | |
| 94.500 | | WFM | Wick | BBC Radio Scotland |

| Base | Mobile | Mode | Location | User and Notes |
|------|--------|------|----------|----------------|
| 94.6000 -97.6000 MHz | | | NATIONWIDE INDEPENDENT RADIO RTE AND LOCAL RADIO | |
| 94.600 | | WFM | Bexhill | BBC Radio 4 |
| 94.600 | | WFM | Cheshire | BBC Radio Stoke On Trent |
| 94.600 | | WFM | Granton | BBC Radio Scotland |
| 94.600 | | WFM | Henley | BBC Thames Valley FM |
| 94.600 | | WFM | Pendle Forest | BBC Radio 4 |
| 94.700 | | WFM | Argyll | BBC Radio 4 |
| 94.700 | | WFM | Ballybofey | Highland Radio |
| 04.700 | | WFM | Chesterfield | BBC Radio Sheffield |
| 94.700 | | WFM | Glasgow | BBC Radio Scotland |
| 94.700 | | WFM | Hereford | BBC Radio Hereford & Worcestershire |
| 94.700 | | WFM | Invernessshire | BBC Radio 4 |
| 94.700 | | WFM | Isle of Islay | BBC Radio 4 |
| 94.700 | | WFM | Solway | BBC Radio Solway |
| 94.800 | | WFM | Huntshaw Cross | BBC Radio Devon |
| 94.800 | | WFM | Isle of Skye | BBC Radio 4 |
| 94.800 | | WFM | Jersey | BBC Radio 4 |
| 94.800 | | WFM | Knock More | BBC Radio 4 |
| 94.800 | | WFM | Meridan | BBC Coventry and Warwickshire |
| 94.800 | | WFM | Slieve Glah | Northern Sound |
| 94.900 | | WFM | Ayrshire | BBC Radio 4 |
| 94.900 | | WFM | Bristol City | BBC Radio Bristol |
| 94.900 | | WFM | Crystal Palace | BBC GLR |
| 94.900 | | WFM | Edinburgh | BBC Radio 4 |
| 94.900 | | WFM | Forfar | BBC Radio 4 |
| 94.900 | | WFM | Lincolnshire | BBC Radio Lincolnshire |
| 94.900 | | WFM | Londonderry | BBC Radio 4 |
| 94.900 | | WFM | Perth | BBC Radio Scotland |
| 94.900 | | WFM | Shetland | BBC Radio 4 |
| 94.900 | | WFM | Windgates | East Coast Radio |
| 95.000 | | WFM | Leicester | BBC Radio Leicestershire |
| 95.000 | | WFM | Limerick | Limerick 2000 |
| 95.000 | | WFM | Ludlow | BBC Radio Shropshire |
| 95.000 | | WFM | Newhaven | BBC Radio Sussex |
| 95.000 | | WFM | Newhaven | BBC SCR |
| 95.000 | | WFM | Peebles | BBC Radio 4 |
| 95.000 | | WFM | Stroud | BBC Radio Gloucestershire |
| 95.000 | | WFM | Teesside | BBC Radio Cleveland |
| 95.100 | | WFM | Argyll | BBC Radio 4 |
| 95.100 | | WFM | Ballycastle | Radio Ulster |
| 95.100 | | WFM | Faha | WLR FM |
| 95.100 | | WFM | Gwent | BBC Radio Wales |
| 95.100 | | WFM | Holme Moss | BBC GMR |
| 95.100 | | WFM | Horsham | BBC Radio Sussex |

| Base | Mobile | Mode | Location | User and Notes |
|------|--------|------|----------|----------------|
| 95.100 | | WFM | Horsham | BBC SCR |
| 95.100 | | WFM | Isle of Lewis | BBC Radio 4 |
| 95.100 | | WFM | Norfolk | BBC Radio Norfolk |
| 95.100 | | WFM | South Wales | BBC Radio Gwent |
| 95.100 | | WFM | Western Isles | BBC Radio 4 |
| 95.200 | | WFM | Argyll | BBC Radio 4 |
| 95.200 | | WFM | Arranmore | Highland Radio |
| 95.200 | | WFM | Clermont Carn | RTE Radio 1 |
| 95.200 | | WFM | Dingle | Radio Kerry |
| 95.200 | | WFM | E Cornwall | BBC Radio Cornwall |
| 95.200 | | WFM | Kendal | BBC Radio Cumbria |
| 95.200 | | WFM | Markinch | Kingdom FM |
| 95.200 | | WFM | Oxfordshire | BBC Thames Valley FM |
| 95.300 | | WFM | Aberdeenshire | BBC Radio 4 |
| 95.300 | | WFM | Argyll | BBC Radio 4 |
| 95.300 | | WFM | Ayrshire | BBC Radio 4 |
| 95.300 | | WFM | Brighton | BBC Radio Sussex |
| 95.300 | | WFM | Dumfriesshire | BBC Radio 4 |
| 95.300 | | WFM | Kirkcudbrightshire | BBC Radio 4 |
| 95.300 | | WFM | Matlock | BBC Radio Derby |
| 95.300 | | WFM | Perthshire | BBC Radio 4 |
| 95.300 | | WFM | Southend | BBC Radio Essex |
| 95.300 | | WFM | Wharfdale | BBC Radio Leeds |
| 95.300 | | WFM | Whitehawk Hill | BBC SCR |
| 95.400 | | WFM | Limavady | Radio Ulster |
| 95.400 | | WFM | Tyneside | BBC Radio Newcastle |
| 95.400 | | WFM | Westpoint | MWR FM |
| 95.400 | | WFM | Windsor | BBC Thames Valley FM |
| 95.500 | | WFM | Bedford | BBC Radio Bedfordshire |
| 95.500 | | WFM | Bristol | BBC Radio Bristol |
| 95.500 | | WFM | Carmarthen | BBC Radio 4 |
| 95.500 | | WFM | Co. Meath | LM FM |
| 95.500 | | WFM | E Lancashire | BBC Radio Lancashire |
| 95.500 | | WFM | Kilrush | Clare FM |
| 95.500 | | WFM | Lowestoft | BBC Suffolk |
| 95.500 | | WFM | Mansfield | BBC Radio Nottingham |
| 95.500 | | WFM | Sandy Heath | BBC 3CR |
| 95.500 | | WFM | Scarborough | BBC Radio York |
| 95.500 | | WFM | Somerset | Somerset Sound |
| 95.500 | | WFM | Taunton | BBC Radio Bristol |
| 95.500 | | WFM | Tayside | BBC Radio 4 |
| 95.600 | | WFM | Argyll | BBC Radio 4 |
| 95.600 | | WFM | Co Fermanagh | BBC Radio 4 |
| 95.600 | | WFM | Cumbria | BBC Radio Cumbria |
| 95.600 | | WFM | W Midlands | BBC Radio West Midlands |
| 95.700 | | WFM | Boyle | Shannonside 104FM |
| 95.700 | | WFM | Dorset | BBC Radio Dorset |
| 95.700 | | WFM | Invernessshire | BBC Radio 4 |
| 95.700 | | WFM | Isle of Islay | BBC Radio 4 |
| 95.700 | | WFM | Peterborough | BBC Radio Cambridge |
| 95.800 | | WFM | Circencester | BBC Radio Gloucestershire |
| 95.800 | | WFM | Edinburgh | BBC Radio 4 |
| 95.800 | | WFM | Exeter | BBC Radio Devon |
| 95.800 | | WFM | Galway | Galway Bay FM |
| 95.800 | | WFM | Glasgow | BBC Radio 4 |
| 95.800 | | WFM | Lanarkshire | BBC Radio 4 |

| Base | Mobile | Mode | Location | User and Notes |
|---|---|---|---|---|
| 95.800 | | WFM | London | 95.8 Capital FM |
| 95.800 | | WFM | Merseyside | BBC Radio Merseyside |
| 95.800 | | WFM | Mt. Oriel | LM FM |
| 95.800 | | WFM | Whitby | BBC Radio Cleveland |
| 95.900 | | WFM | Aberdeenshire | BBC Radio 4 |
| 95.900 | | WFM | Borders | BBC Radio Newcastle |
| 95.900 | | WFM | East Clare | Clare FM |
| 95.900 | | WFM | Fort William | BBC Radio 4 |
| 95.900 | | WFM | Orkney | BBC Radio 4 |
| 95.900 | | WFM | South Wales | BBC Radio Gwent |
| 95.900 | | WFM | SW Wales | BBC Radio 4 |
| 95.900 | | WFM | Thanet | Invicta FM |
| 95.900 | | WFM | Western Isles | BBC Radio 4 |
| 95.900 | | WFM | Yorkshire | BBC Radio Humberside |
| 96.000 | | WFM | Belfast | BBC Radio 4 |
| 96.000 | | WFM | Belfast | Radio Ulster |
| 96.000 | | WFM | Cambridgeshire | BBC Radio Cambridge |
| 96.000 | | WFM | Chatton | BBC Radio Newcastle |
| 96.000 | | WFM | Corbally Wood | Radio Kilkenny |
| 96.000 | | WFM | Okehampton | BBC Radio Devon |
| 96.000 | | WFM | Scillies | BBC Radio Cornwall |
| 96.000 | | WFM | Shropshire | BBC Radio Shropshire |
| 96.000 | | WFM | Weymouth | Wessex FM |
| 96.100 | | WFM | Ashford | Invicta FM |
| 96.100 | | WFM | Colchester | SGR Colchester |
| 96.100 | | WFM | County Mayo | MWR FM |
| 96.100 | | WFM | Innerleithen | BBC Radio 4 |
| 96.100 | | WFM | Isle of Lewis | BBC Radio 4 |
| 96.100 | | WFM | Isle of Mull | BBC Radio 4 |
| 96.100 | | WFM | Isle of Skye | BBC Radio 4 |
| 96.100 | | WFM | Kiltimagh | MWR FM |
| 96.100 | | WFM | Markinch | Kingdom FM |
| 96.100 | | WFM | Morecambe Bay | BBC Radio Cumbria |
| 96.100 | | WFM | Poseys | BBC Radio Cymru |
| 96.100 | | WFM | S Hampshire | BBC Radio Solent |
| 96.100 | | WFM | SW Cumbria | BBC Radio Furness |
| 96.100 | | WFM | Ullapool | BBC Radio 4 |
| 96.200 | | WFM | Aylesbury | Mix 96 |
| 96.200 | | WFM | Barnstaple | Lantern FM |
| 96.200 | | WFM | Bray | East Coast Radio |
| 96.200 | | WFM | Cahirciveen | Radio Kerry |
| 96.200 | | WFM | Coventry | Kix 96 |
| 96.200 | | WFM | Gorey | South East Radio |
| 96.200 | | WFM | Nottingham | 96 Trent FM |
| 96.200 | | WFM | Oldham | Revolution |
| 96.200 | | WFM | Scarborough | Yorkshire Coast Radio |
| 96.200 | | WFM | Shetland | SIBC |
| 96.200 | | WFM | Tunbridge | KFM |
| 96.200 | | WFM | Tyneside | Century Radio |
| 96.300 | | WFM | Bristol | GWR FM |
| 96.300 | | WFM | Corcaghan | Northern Sound |
| 96.300 | | WFM | Leeds | 96.3 Aire FM |
| 96.300 | | WFM | Mt. Charles | North West Radio |
| 96.300 | | WFM | North Wales | Coast FM |
| 96.300 | | WFM | Paisley | 96.3 QFM |
| 96.300 | | WFM | Southend | Essex FM |

| Base | Mobile | Mode | Location | User and Notes |
|---|---|---|---|---|
| 96.400 | | WFM | Birmingham | 96.4 FM BRMB |
| 96.400 | | WFM | Bury St Edmonds | SGR-FM |
| 96.400 | | WFM | Cheshire | Signal FM |
| 96.400 | | WFM | Cork City | Cork's 96 FM |
| 96.400 | | WFM | County Mayo | RTE 3 |
| 96.400 | | WFM | Folkestone | Neptune Radio |
| 96.400 | | WFM | Galway | County Clare Radio |
| 96.400 | | WFM | Guildford | 96.4 The Eagle |
| 96.400 | | WFM | Limavady | Downtown Radio |
| 96.400 | | WFM | Maghera | Clare FM |
| 96.400 | | WFM | Newton | Century Radio |
| 96.400 | | WFM | Penrith | CFM |
| 96.400 | | WFM | Perth | Tay FM |
| 96.400 | | WFM | Swansea | 96.4 FM The Wave |
| 96.400 | | WFM | Torbay | Gemini FM |
| 96.500 | | WFM | Blackpool | The Wave 96.5 |
| 96.500 | | WFM | Dumfries | South West Sound |
| 96.500 | | WFM | Marlborough | GWR FM |
| 96.500 | | WFM | Nottingham | 96 Trent FM |
| 96.500 | | WFM | Taunton | Orchard FM |
| 96.600 | | WFM | Aberystwyth | Radio Ceredigion |
| 96.600 | | WFM | Arbroath | RNA FM |
| 96.600 | | WFM | Chichester | Spirit FM |
| 96.600 | | WFM | Enniskillen | Downtown Radio |
| 96.600 | | WFM | Fort William | Nevis Radio |
| 96.600 | | WFM | Johnswell | Radio Kilkenny |
| 96.600 | | WFM | Northampton | Northants 96 |
| 96.600 | | WFM | Plymouth | 97 FM Plymouth Sound |
| 96.600 | | WFM | St Albans | Oasis FM |
| 96.600 | | WFM | Strathspey | Moray Firth Radio Speysound |
| 96.600 | | WFM | Teesside | TFM |
| 96.700 | | WFM | Ayr | West FM |
| 96.700 | | WFM | Belfast | City Beat 96.7 |
| 96.700 | | WFM | Fraserburgh | MFR Kinnaird Radio |
| 96.700 | | WFM | Grantham | Lincs FM |
| 96.700 | | WFM | Kidderminster | Wyvern FM |
| 96.700 | | WFM | Kings Lynn | KL.FM 96.7 |
| 96.700 | | WFM | Liverpool | Radio City 96.7 |
| 96.700 | | WFM | Monatrea | Cork's 96 FM |
| 96.700 | | WFM | North Kent | BBC Radio Kent |
| 96.700 | | WFM | South Hampshire | Ocean FM |
| 96.800 | | WFM | Abbeyknockmoy | Galway Bay FM |
| 96.800 | | WFM | Bristol | BBC Radio Cymru |
| 96.800 | | WFM | County Mayo | Galway Bay Radio |
| 96.800 | | WFM | Selkirk | Radio Borders |
| 96.800 | | WFM | Wenvoe | BBC Radio Cymru |
| 96.900 | | WFM | Aberdeen | NorthSound One |
| 96.900 | | WFM | Bedford | B97 Chiltern FM |
| 96.900 | | WFM | Brixton | Choice FM |
| 96.900 | | WFM | Humberside | 96.9 Viking FM |
| 96.900 | | WFM | Isle of Man | Manx Radio |
| 96.900 | | WFM | Morecambe Bay | The Bay |
| 96.900 | | WFM | Newhaven | Southern FM |
| 96.900 | | WFM | Stoke-on-Trent | Signal 1 |
| 97.000 | | WFM | Clermont Carn | RTE Radio 2 |
| 97.000 | | WFM | Coventry | Mercia FM |

| Base | Mobile | Mode | Location | User and Notes |
|------|--------|------|----------|----------------|
| 97.000 | | WFM | Dover | Invicta FM |
| 97.000 | | WFM | Dumfries | South West Sound |
| 97.000 | | WFM | Exeter | Gemini FM |
| 97.000 | | WFM | Glasgow | Clyde 1 FM |
| 97.000 | | WFM | Glencoe | Nevis Radio |
| 97.000 | | WFM | Mullaghanish | Radio Kerry |
| 97.000 | | WFM | Plymouth | 97 FM Plymouth Sound |
| 97.000 | | WFM | Reading | 2-TEN FM |
| 97.100 | | WFM | Achill | MWR FM |
| 97.100 | | WFM | Braemar | North East Community Radio |
| 97.100 | | WFM | Galway | MWR FM |
| 97.100 | | WFM | Haslemere | Delta Radio |
| 97.100 | | WFM | Ipswich | SGR-FM |
| 97.100 | | WFM | Jersey | BBC Radio 1 |
| 97.100 | | WFM | Larne | Downtown Radio |
| 97.100 | | WFM | Stockport | Signal FM |
| 97.100 | | WFM | Tyneside | Metro FM |
| 97.100 | | WFM | Wirral | The Buzz 97.1 |
| 97.100 | | WFM | Wooddruff | Tipp FM |
| 97.100 | | WFM | Yeovil | Orchard FM |
| 97.200 | | WFM | Ballina | MWR FM |
| 97.200 | | WFM | Bristol | Galaxy 101 |
| 97.200 | | WFM | Dorchester | Wessex FM |
| 97.200 | | WFM | Harrogate | 97.2 Stray FM |
| 97.200 | | WFM | Isle of Man | Manx Radio |
| 97.200 | | WFM | Swindon | GWR FM |
| 97.200 | | WFM | Wellingborough | Connect FM |
| 97.200 | | WFM | Wolverhampton | Beacon FM |
| 97.300 | | WFM | Edinburgh | Radio Forth FM |
| 97.300 | | WFM | Kileshin | CKR |
| 97.300 | | WFM | London | News Direct 97.3 FM |
| 97.400 | | WFM | Ballinasloe | Galway Bay FM |
| 97.400 | | WFM | Banbury | Fox FM |
| 97.400 | | WFM | Belfast | Cool FM |
| 97.400 | | WFM | Ceredigion | Radio Ceredigion |
| 97.400 | | WFM | Inverness | Moray Firth Radio |
| 97.400 | | WFM | Newmarket | Q103 FM |
| 97.400 | | WFM | Newport | Red Dragon Radio |
| 97.400 | | WFM | Preston | Rock FM |
| 97.400 | | WFM | Shaftesbury | 97.4 Vale FM |
| 97.400 | | WFM | Sheffield | Hallam FM |
| 97.400 | | WFM | Stamford | Rutland Radio |
| 97.500 | | WFM | Berwick | Radio Borders |
| 97.500 | | WFM | Bradford | The Pulse |
| 97.500 | | WFM | Carrickmacross | Northern Sound |
| 97.500 | | WFM | Carrickpherish | WLR FM |
| 97.500 | | WFM | Crawley | Murcury FM |
| 97.500 | | WFM | Girvan | West FM |
| 97.500 | | WFM | Pitlochry | Heartland FM |
| 97.500 | | WFM | South Hampshire | Ocean FM |
| 97.500 | | WFM | Southend on Sea | Essex FM |

| Base | Mobile | Mode | Location | User and Notes |
|---|---|---|---|---|
| **97.60 -107.90 MHz** | | | NATIONWIDE BBC RADIO , RTE AND INDEPENDENT LOCAL RADIO | |
| 97.600 | | WFM | Aberdeen | NorthSound One |
| 97.600 | | WFM | Edinburgh | Forth FM |
| 97.600 | | WFM | Folkestone | BBC Radio Kent |
| 97.600 | | WFM | Hereford | Wyvern FM |
| 97.600 | | WFM | Kent | BBC Kent |
| 97.600 | | WFM | Knockanore | Radio Kerry |
| 97.600 | | WFM | Luton | Chiltern FM |
| 97.600 | | WFM | Red Gap | CKR |
| 97.600 | | WFM | Scunthorpe | Lincs FM |
| 97.700 | | WFM | Ballachulish | |
| 97.700 | | WFM | Bowmore | |
| 97.700 | | WFM | Cirencester | |
| 97.700 | | WFM | Clettraval | |
| 97.700 | | WFM | Clyro | |
| 97.700 | | WFM | Deiniolen | |
| 97.700 | | WFM | Ffestiniog | |
| 97.700 | | WFM | Grantham | |
| 97.700 | | WFM | Guildford | |
| 97.700 | | WFM | Llanidloes | |
| 97.700 | | WFM | Mallaig | |
| 97.700 | | WFM | Manningtree | |
| 97.700 | | WFM | North Hessary Tor | |
| 97.700 | | WFM | Penifiler | |
| 97.700 | | WFM | Sundale | |
| 97.800 | | WFM | Betws-y-Coed | |
| 97.800 | | WFM | Bexhill | |
| 97.800 | | WFM | Calne | |
| 97.800 | | WFM | Knock More | |
| 97.800 | | WFM | Nailsworth | |
| 97.800 | | WFM | Newbury | |
| 97.800 | | WFM | Rheola | |
| 97.900 | | WFM | Bressay | |
| 97.900 | | WFM | Forfar | |
| 97.900 | | WFM | Lethanhill | |
| 97.900 | | WFM | Llwyn-Onn | |
| 97.900 | | WFM | Lochgilphead | |
| 97.900 | | WFM | Millburn Muir | |
| 97.900 | | WFM | Ness of Lewis | |
| 97.900 | | WFM | Rostrevor Forest | |
| 97.900 | | WFM | Sutton Coldfield | |
| 97.900 | | WFM | Ullapool | |
| 97.900 | | WFM | Wensleydale | |
| 97.900 | | WFM | Westwood | |
| 97.900 | | WFM | Windermere | |
| 98.000 | | WFM | Campbeltown | |
| 98.000 | | WFM | Carmel | |
| 98.000 | | WFM | Douglas, Isle Of Man | |
| 98.000 | | WFM | Ebbw Vale | |
| 98.000 | | WFM | Folkestone | |
| 98.000 | | WFM | Hebden Bridge | |
| 98.000 | | WFM | Kenley | |
| 98.000 | | WFM | London | Unity FM |
| 98.000 | | WFM | Peebles | |
| 98.000 | | WFM | Penmaen Rhos | |

| Base | Mobile | Mode | Location | User and Notes |
|------|--------|------|----------|----------------|
| 98.000 | | WFM | Porth | |
| 98.000 | | WFM | Walsden South | |
| 98.000 | | WFM | Wharfdale | |
| 98.100 | | WFM | Barnstaple | |
| 98.100 | | WFM | Blaenavon | |
| 98.100 | | WFM | Cwmafan | |
| 98.100 | | WFM | Dublin | 98 FM |
| 98.100 | | WFM | Idle | |
| 98.100 | | WFM | Plympton | |
| 98.100 | | WFM | Pontop Pike | |
| 98.100 | | WFM | Rothesay | |
| 98.100 | | WFM | Rowbridge | |
| 98.100 | | WFM | Skraig | |
| 98.200 | | WFM | Berwick On Tweed | |
| 98.200 | | WFM | Bow Brickhall | |
| 98.200 | | WFM | Llangeinor | |
| 98.200 | | WFM | Ridge Hill | |
| 98.200 | | WFM | Strachur | |
| 98.200 | | WFM | Upperton | |
| 98.200 | | WFM | Winter Hill | |
| 98.300 | | WFM | Abergavenny | |
| 98.300 | | WFM | Ardgour | |
| 98.300 | | WFM | Beacon Hill | |
| 98.300 | | WFM | Ben Gullipen | |
| 98.300 | | WFM | Cambret Hill | |
| 98.300 | | WFM | Camlough | |
| 98.300 | | WFM | Kirkconnel | |
| 98.300 | | WFM | Londonderry | |
| 98.300 | | WFM | Luddenden | |
| 98.300 | | WFM | Meldrum | |
| 98.300 | | WFM | Okehampton | |
| 98.400 | | WFM | Ballycastle | |
| 98.400 | | WFM | Belmont | |
| 98.400 | | WFM | Carnmoney Hill | |
| 98.400 | | WFM | Chippenham | |
| 98.400 | | WFM | Crystal Palace | |
| 98.400 | | WFM | Isles of Scilly | |
| 98.400 | | WFM | Penaligon Downs | |
| 98.400 | | WFM | Ton Pentre | |
| 98.500 | | WFM | Brecon | |
| 98.500 | | WFM | Cambridge | |
| 98.500 | | WFM | Carmarthen | |
| 98.500 | | WFM | Chard | |
| 98.500 | | WFM | Crystal Palace | |
| 98.500 | | WFM | Girvan | |
| 98.500 | | WFM | Gwent | |
| 98.500 | | WFM | Keighley | |
| 98.500 | | WFM | Llangollen | |
| 98.500 | | WFM | Northampton | |
| 98.500 | | WFM | Oban | |
| 98.500 | | WFM | Todmorden | |
| 98.600 | | WFM | Abertillery | |
| 98.600 | | WFM | Bath City | |
| 98.600 | | WFM | Blunsdon | |
| 98.600 | | WFM | Chesterfield | |
| 98.600 | | WFM | Churchdown Hill | |

| Base | Mobile | Mode | Location | User and Notes |
|------|--------|------|----------|----------------|
| 98.600 | | WFM | Croeserw | |
| 98.600 | | WFM | Isle of Man | Manx Radio |
| 98.600 | | WFM | Kendal | |
| 98.600 | | WFM | Kirkton Mailer | |
| 98.600 | | WFM | Minehead | |
| 98.600 | | WFM | Port Ellen | |
| 98.600 | | WFM | St Thomas | |
| 98.700 | | WFM | Ashkirk | |
| 98.700 | | WFM | Brigport | |
| 98.700 | | WFM | Combe Martin | |
| 98.700 | | WFM | Conwy | |
| 98.700 | | WFM | Egford Hill | |
| 98.700 | | WFM | Kingussie | |
| 98.700 | | WFM | Larne | |
| 98.700 | | WFM | Llandrindod Wells | |
| 98.700 | | WFM | Llanfyllin | |
| 98.700 | | WFM | Melvaig | |
| 98.700 | | WFM | West Kilbride | |
| 98.800 | | WFM | Aberdare | |
| 98.800 | | WFM | Chalford | |
| 98.800 | | WFM | Ogmore Vale | |
| 98.800 | | WFM | Pitlochry | |
| 98.800 | | WFM | Pontypool | |
| 98.800 | | WFM | Rosneath | |
| 98.900 | | WFM | Crieff | |
| 98.900 | | WFM | Daliburg | |
| 98.900 | | WFM | Fort William | |
| 98.900 | | WFM | Haverfordwest | |
| 98.900 | | WFM | Holme Moss | |
| 98.900 | | WFM | Ilchester Crescent | |
| 98.900 | | WFM | Keelylang Hill | |
| 98.900 | | WFM | Rhymney | |
| 98.900 | | WFM | South Khapdale | |
| 99.000 | | WFM | Brougher Mountain | |
| 99.000 | | WFM | Durris | |
| 99.000 | | WFM | Hutton | |
| 99.000 | | WFM | Kikeel | |
| 99.000 | | WFM | Llamdecwyn | |
| 99.000 | | WFM | Machynlleth | |
| 99.000 | | WFM | Newton | |
| 99.000 | | WFM | Ventnor | |
| 99.100 | | WFM | Axe Valley | |
| 99.100 | | WFM | Darvel | |
| 99.100 | | WFM | Darwen | |
| 99.100 | | WFM | Glengorm | |
| 99.100 | | WFM | Innerleithen | |
| 99.100 | | WFM | Kilvey Hill | |
| 99.100 | | WFM | Oxford | |
| 99.100 | | WFM | Pennar | |
| 99.100 | | WFM | Salcombe | |
| 99.200 | | WFM | Bexhill | |
| 99.200 | | WFM | Fermdale | |
| 99.200 | | WFM | Hastings | |
| 99.200 | | WFM | Keswick Forest | |
| 99.200 | | WFM | Limavady | |
| 99.200 | | WFM | Llyswen | |

| Base | Mobile | Mode | Location | User and Notes |
|------|--------|------|----------|----------------|
| 99.200 | | WFM | Long Mountain | |
| 99.200 | | WFM | Ludlow | |
| 99.200 | | WFM | Mt. Leinster | South East Radio |
| 99.200 | | WFM | Rosemarkie | |
| 99.200 | | WFM | Whalley | |
| 99.200 | | WFM | Whitby | |
| 99.300 | | WFM | Barnoldswick | |
| 99.300 | | WFM | Caterham | |
| 99.300 | | WFM | Cornholme | |
| 99.300 | | WFM | Eyemouth | |
| 99.300 | | WFM | Kinlochleven | |
| 99.300 | | WFM | Lyme Regis | |
| 99.300 | | WFM | Mynydd Pencarreg | |
| 99.300 | | WFM | Newhaven | |
| 99.300 | | WFM | Redruth | |
| 99.300 | | WFM | Stranraer | |
| 99.300 | | WFM | Tacolneston | |
| 99.300 | | WFM | Wearsdale | |
| 99.300 | | WFM | Whitehaven | |
| 99.400 | | WFM | Beecroft Hill | |
| 99.400 | | WFM | Eitshal | |
| 99.400 | | WFM | Fendale | |
| 99.400 | | WFM | Grantown | |
| 99.400 | | WFM | Hemdean | |
| 99.400 | | WFM | Kingswear | |
| 99.400 | | WFM | Llanddona | |
| 99.400 | | WFM | Llanrhaeadr-ym-M | |
| 99.400 | | WFM | Saddleworth | |
| 99.400 | | WFM | Salisbury | |
| 99.400 | | WFM | Stanton Moor | |
| 99.500 | | WFM | Black Hill | |
| 99.500 | | WFM | Haslingden | |
| 99.500 | | WFM | Ivybridge | |
| 99.500 | | WFM | Oliver's Mount | |
| 99.500 | | WFM | Sheffield | |
| 99.500 | | WFM | Wenvoe | |
| 99.600 | | WFM | Buxton | |
| 99.600 | | WFM | High Wycombe | |
| 99.600 | | WFM | Morecambe Bay | |
| 99.600 | | WFM | Swingate | |
| 99.600 | | WFM | Weymonth | |
| 99.600 | | WFM | Woolmoor | |
| 99.700 | | WFM | Basingstoke | |
| 99.700 | | WFM | Brighton | |
| 99.700 | | WFM | Chatton | |
| 99.700 | | WFM | Divis | |
| 99.700 | | WFM | Dolgellau | |
| 99.700 | | WFM | Llandinam | |
| 99.700 | | WFM | Llandtfriog | |
| 99.700 | | WFM | Marlborough | |
| 99.700 | | WFM | Peterborough | |
| 99.700 | | WFM | Rumster Forest | |
| 99.700 | | WFM | Tullich | |
| 99.800 | | WFM | Clyro | |
| 100.000 | | WFM | Crosshaven | Radio Ireland |
| 100.000 | | WFM | London | Kiss FM |

| Base | Mobile | Mode | Location | User and Notes |
|---|---|---|---|---|
| 100.000 | | WFM | North Hessary Tor | Classic FM |
| 100.000 | | WFM | Truskmore | Radio Ireland |
| 100.100 | | WFM | Angus | Classic FM |
| 100.100 | | WFM | Clonmel | Radio Ireland |
| 100.100 | | WFM | Manchester | Classic FM |
| 100.100 | | WFM | Sutton Coldfield | Classic FM |
| 100.200 | | WFM | Knockmoyle | Radio Ireland |
| 100.200 | | WFM | Tendring | Dream 100 FM |
| 100.300 | | WFM | Cappowuin | Radio Ireland |
| 100.300 | | WFM | Central Scotland | Scot FM |
| 100.300 | | WFM | Gosport | Classic FM |
| 100.300 | | WFM | Isle of Wight | Classic FM |
| 100.300 | | WFM | Three Rock | Radio Ireland |
| 100.300 | | WFM | Tyneside | Classic FM |
| 100.400 | | WFM | Medway | Medway FM |
| 100.400 | | WFM | North West England | Jazz FM 100.4 |
| 100.500 | | WFM | Lincolnshire | Classic FM |
| 100.500 | | WFM | Londonderry | Classic FM |
| 100.500 | | WFM | Meldrum | Classic FM |
| 100.500 | | WFM | Nationwide | RSL 28 Day stations |
| 100.600 | | WFM | Crystal Palace | Classic FM |
| 100.600 | | WFM | Maghera | Radio Ireland |
| 100.700 | | WFM | Gwynedd | Classic FM |
| 100.700 | | WFM | Monaghan | Radio Ireland |
| 100.700 | | WFM | North East | Century Radio |
| 100.700 | | WFM | West Midlands | 100.7 Heart FM |
| 100.800 | | WFM | Berkshire | Classic FM |
| 100.800 | | WFM | Buckinghamshire | Classic FM |
| 100.800 | | WFM | Mullaghanish | Radio Ireland |
| 100.800 | | WFM | Oxfordshire | Classic FM |
| 100.800 | | WFM | Suir Valley | Radio Ireland |
| 100.900 | | WFM | Kent | Classic FM |
| 100.900 | | WFM | Kippure | Radio Ireland |
| 100.900 | | WFM | London | Classic FM |
| 101.000 | | WFM | Holywell Hill | Radio Ireland |
| 101.000 | | WFM | Seven Estuary | Galaxy 101 |
| 101.000 | | WFM | Spur Hill | Radio Ireland |
| 101.100 | | WFM | Achill | Radio Ireland |
| 101.100 | | WFM | Edinburgh | Scot FM |
| 101.100 | | WFM | Holme Moss | Classic FM |
| 101.200 | | WFM | Kingbridge | South Ham Radio |
| 101.200 | | WFM | Peterhead | Waves Radio Peterhead |
| 101.200 | | WFM | Woodcock Hill | Radio Ireland |
| 101.300 | | WFM | Ayrshire | Classic FM |
| 101.300 | | WFM | Oxford | Classic FM |
| 101.300 | | WFM | Swansea | Classic FM |
| 101.400 | | WFM | Mt. Leinster | Radio Ireland |
| 101.500 | | WFM | Norwich | Classic FM |
| 101.600 | | WFM | Alton | Delta FM 102 |
| 101.600 | | WFM | Anglesey | Classic FM |
| 101.600 | | WFM | Castlebar | Radio Ireland |
| 101.600 | | WFM | Fanad | Radio Ireland |
| 101.600 | | WFM | Gwynedd | Classic FM |
| 101.600 | | WFM | SE Staffordshire | Centre FM |
| 101.600 | | WFM | Tunbridge | KFM |
| 101.700 | | WFM | Bristol | Classic FM |

| Base | Mobile | Mode | Location | User and Notes |
|---|---|---|---|---|
| 101.700 | | WFM | Central Scotland | Classic FM |
| 101.700 | | WFM | Harlow | Ten 17 FM |
| 101.700 | | WFM | Sheffield | Classic FM |
| 101.700 | | WFM | Wenvoe | Classic FM |
| 101.800 | | WFM | Dover | Classic FM |
| 101.800 | | WFM | Mullaghanish | Radio Ireland |
| 101.800 | | WFM | North East | Century Radio |
| 101.900 | | WFM | Belfast | Classic FM |
| 101.900 | | WFM | Peterborough | Classic FM |
| 102.000 | | WFM | Alton | Delta FM 102 |
| 102.000 | | WFM | Dundee | Discovery 102 |
| 102.000 | | WFM | Hastings | Southern FM |
| 102.000 | | WFM | Isle of Woght | Isle of Wight Radio |
| 102.000 | | WFM | Manchester | Galaxy 102 |
| 102.000 | | WFM | Matlock | Peak 107 FM |
| 102.000 | | WFM | Salisbury | Spire FM |
| 102.000 | | WFM | Stratford Upon Avon | FM 102 The Bear |
| 102.100 | | WFM | Athlone | Midlands Radio 3 |
| 102.100 | | WFM | Inverurie | North East Community Radio |
| 102.200 | | WFM | Birmingham | Galaxy 102.2 |
| 102.200 | | WFM | Dublin | Radio Na Life |
| 102.200 | | WFM | East Cornwall | Pirate FM |
| 102.200 | | WFM | Edinburgh | Forth FM |
| 102.200 | | WFM | Lincoln | Lincs FM |
| 102.200 | | WFM | London | Jazz FM 102.2 |
| 102.200 | | WFM | Shetland | SIBC |
| 102.200 | | WFM | Ullapool | Lochbroom FM |
| 102.200 | | WFM | Wiltshire | GWR FM |
| 102.200 | | WFM | Workington | CFM |
| 102.300 | | WFM | Ballymena | Downtown Radio |
| 102.300 | | WFM | Bournemouth | 2CR FM |
| 102.300 | | WFM | Littlehampton | Spirit FM |
| 102.300 | | WFM | Morecambe Bay | The Bay |
| 102.300 | | WFM | Skye | Nevis Radio |
| 102.300 | | WFM | Thirsk | Minster FM |
| 102.300 | | WFM | Windermere | The Bay |
| 102.400 | | WFM | Cheltenham | 102.4 Severn Sound FM |
| 102.400 | | WFM | Eastbourne | Southern FM |
| 102.400 | | WFM | Loch Leven | Nevis Radio |
| 102.400 | | WFM | Londonderry | Downtown Radio |
| 102.400 | | WFM | Norwich | Broadland 102 |
| 102.400 | | WFM | SE Staffordshire | Centre FM |
| 102.400 | | WFM | West Somerset | Quay West Radio |
| 102.400 | | WFM | Wigan | Wish 102.4 FM |
| 102.500 | | WFM | Caithness | MFR Caithness FM |
| 102.500 | | WFM | Carlisle | CFM |
| 102.500 | | WFM | County Mayo | MWR FM |
| 102.500 | | WFM | Glasgow | Clyde 1 FM |
| 102.500 | | WFM | Huddersfield | The Pulse |
| 102.500 | | WFM | Truskmore | North West Radio |
| 102.600 | | WFM | Alnwick | Metro FM |
| 102.600 | | WFM | Chelmsford | Essex FM |
| 102.600 | | WFM | Kildrummy | North East Community Radio |
| 102.600 | | WFM | Oxford | Fox FM |
| 102.600 | | WFM | Somerset | Orchard FM |
| 102.600 | | WFM | Staffordshire | Signal 1 |

| Base | Mobile | Mode | Location | User and Notes |
|------|--------|------|----------|----------------|
| 102.700 | | WFM | Clermont Carn | Raidio Na Gaeltachta |
| 102.700 | | WFM | Keighley | BBC Radio Leeds |
| 102.700 | | WFM | Peterborough | 102.7 Hereward FM |
| 102.700 | | WFM | Reigate | Mercury FM |
| 102.800 | | WFM | Canterbury | Invicta FM |
| 102.800 | | WFM | Derby | Ram FM |
| 102.800 | | WFM | Dundee | Tay FM |
| 102.800 | | WFM | Keith | MFM Keith Community Radio |
| 102.800 | | WFM | West Cornwall | Pirate FM |
| 102.800 | | WFM | Worcester | Wyvern FM |
| 102.900 | | WFM | Ballyguille | East Coast Radio |
| 102.900 | | WFM | Barnsley | Hallam FM |
| 102.900 | | WFM | Basingstoke | 2-TEN FM |
| 102.900 | | WFM | Leamington Spa | Mercia FM |
| 102.900 | | WFM | Londonderry | Q102.9 FM |
| 103.000 | | WFM | Bath | GWR FM |
| 103.000 | | WFM | Caernarfon | Champion FM |
| 103.000 | | WFM | Cambridge | Q103 FM |
| 103.000 | | WFM | Dumfries | South West Sound |
| 103.000 | | WFM | Isle of Wight | Classic FM |
| 103.000 | | WFM | Manchester | Key 103 |
| 103.000 | | WFM | Peterhead | Northsound One |
| 103.000 | | WFM | Stornoway | Isles FM |
| 103.000 | | WFM | Stroud | 102.4 Severn Sound FM |
| 103.000 | | WFM | Torbay | Gemini FM |
| 103.000 | | WFM | Tyne Valley | Metro FM |
| 103.100 | | WFM | Maidstone | Invicta FM |
| 103.100 | | WFM | Peebles | Radio Borders |
| 103.100 | | WFM | Scarborough | Yorkshire Coast Radio |
| 103.100 | | WFM | Shrewsbury | Beacon Radio |
| 103.100 | | WFM | Stirling | Central FM |
| 103.200 | | WFM | Bradford | Sunrise FM |
| 103.200 | | WFM | Cardiff | Red Dragon Radio |
| 103.200 | | WFM | Colpy | North East Community Radio |
| 103.200 | | WFM | Darlington | Alpha 103.2 |
| 103.200 | | WFM | Hexham | Metro FM |
| 103.200 | | WFM | Mansfield | Mansfield 103.2 |
| 103.200 | | WFM | Morecambe Bay | The Bay |
| 103.200 | | WFM | Solent | Power FM |
| 103.300 | | WFM | Aberystwyth | Radio Ceredigion |
| 103.300 | | WFM | Brunfoot | Highland Radio |
| 103.300 | | WFM | Donegal | Hi-Land Radio |
| 103.300 | | WFM | Haringay | London Greek Radio |
| 103.300 | | WFM | Milton Keynes | FM 103 Horizon |
| 103.300 | | WFM | Nowen Hill | 103 FM County Sound Radio |
| 103.300 | | WFM | Oban | Oban FM |
| 103.300 | | WFM | Roseneath | Clyde 1 FM |
| 103.400 | | WFM | Basingstoke | 2-Ten FM |
| 103.400 | | WFM | Devon | BBC Radio Devon |
| 103.400 | | WFM | Doncaster | Hallam FM |
| 103.400 | | WFM | Eyemouth | Radio Borders |
| 103.400 | | WFM | Great Yarmouth | 103.4 The Beach |
| 103.400 | | WFM | Kingscourt | Northern Sound |
| 103.400 | | WFM | Newcastle, NI | Downtown Radio |
| 103.400 | | WFM | Sunderland | Sun FM |
| 103.400 | | WFM | Whitehaven | CFM |

| Base | Mobile | Mode | Location | User and Notes |
|------|--------|------|----------|----------------|
| 103.400 | | WFM | Wrexham | MFM |
| 103.500 | | WFM | Abergavenny | Radio Cymru |
| 103.500 | | WFM | Brighton | Southern FM |
| 103.500 | | WFM | Ffestiniog | BBC Radio 4 |
| 103.500 | | WFM | Great Bransted | BBC Radio Essex |
| 103.500 | | WFM | Isle of Mull | BBC Radio Nan Gaidheal |
| 103.500 | | WFM | Larne | BBC Radio 4 |
| 103.500 | | WFM | Newton Barrow | BBC Wiltshire Sounds |
| 103.500 | | WFM | Slieve Bloom | Madlands Radio 3 |
| 103.500 | | WFM | Verteg Hill | BBC Radio 4 |
| 103.500 | | WFM | West Kilbride | BBC Radio 4 |
| 103.600 | | WFM | Bowmore | BBC Radio Nan Gaidheal |
| 103.600 | | WFM | Croeserw | BBC Radio 4 |
| 103.600 | | WFM | Dolgellau | BBC Radio 4 |
| 103.600 | | WFM | Geddington | BBC Radio Northampton |
| 103.600 | | WFM | Llanddona | BBC Radio 4 |
| 103.600 | | WFM | Long Mountain | BBC Radio Cymru |
| 103.600 | | WFM | Machynlleth | BBC Radio 4 |
| 103.600 | | WFM | Rosemarkie | BBC Radio 4 |
| 103.600 | | WFM | Stranraer | BBC Radio 4 |
| 103.700 | | WFM | Aklam Wood | BBC Radio York |
| 103.700 | | WFM | Ballachulish | BBC Radio Nan Gaidheal |
| 103.700 | | WFM | Clettraval | BBC Radio Nan Gaidheal |
| 103.700 | | WFM | Jersey | Channel 103 |
| 103.700 | | WFM | Jurby | Manx Radio |
| 103.700 | | WFM | Lark Stoke | BBC Coventry and Warwichshire |
| 103.700 | | WFM | Mt. Hillery | 103 FM County Sound North |
| 103.700 | | WFM | Mynydd Pencarreg | BBC Radio Cymru |
| 103.700 | | WFM | Ogmore Vale | BBC Radio Cymru |
| 103.700 | | WFM | Pennar | BBC Radio Cymru |
| 103.800 | | WFM | Bincombe Hill | BBC Dorset FM |
| 103.800 | | WFM | Donegal | North Atlantic Radio |
| 103.800 | | WFM | Dublin | Anna Livia 103 FM |
| 103.800 | | WFM | Llandrindod Wells | BBC Radio 4 |
| 103.800 | | WFM | Llanrhaeadr-ym-M | BBC Radio Cymru |
| 103.800 | | WFM | Mapperley Ridge | BBC Radio Nottingham |
| 103.800 | | WFM | Roseneath | BBC Radio 4 |
| 103.800 | | WFM | Zouches Farm | BBC 3CR |
| 103.900 | | WFM | Ashkirk | BBC Radio 4 |
| 103.900 | | WFM | Beecroft Hill | BBC Radio Leeds |
| 103.900 | | WFM | Blunsdon | BBC Wiltshire Sounds |
| 103.900 | | WFM | Devils Bit | Tipp FM |
| 103.900 | | WFM | Kilkeel | BBC Radio 4 |
| 103.900 | | WFM | Mannongtree | BBC Radio Suffolk |
| 103.900 | | WFM | Melvaig | BBC Radio Nan Gaidheal |
| 103.900 | | WFM | Pitlochry | BBC Radio 4 |
| 103.900 | | WFM | Redruth | BBC Radio Cornwall |
| 103.900 | | WFM | Rostrevor Forest | BBC Radio 4 |
| 103.900 | | WFM | Winter Hill | BBC Radio Lancashire |
| 104.000 | | WFM | Blaenavon | BBC Radio Cymru |
| 104.000 | | WFM | Blaenplwyf | BBC Radio 4 |
| 104.000 | | WFM | Great Malvern | BBC Hereford & Worcester |
| 104.000 | | WFM | Nuneaton | BBC Coventry and Warwickshire |
| 104.000 | | WFM | Reigate | BBC SCR |
| 104.100 | | WFM | Deiniolen | BBC Radio 4 |
| 104.100 | | WFM | Edinburgh | BBC Gaelic |

| Base | Mobile | Mode | Location | User and Notes |
|------|--------|------|----------|----------------|
| 104.100 | | WFM | Hannington | BBC Thames Valley FM |
| 104.100 | | WFM | Holme Moss | BBC Radio Sheffield |
| 104.100 | | WFM | Millburn Muir | BBC Radio 4 |
| 104.100 | | WFM | Slieve Bawn | Shannonside 104 FM |
| 104.100 | | WFM | Stafford | BBC Radio Stoke |
| 104.100 | | WFM | Whitehaven | BBC Radio Cumbria |
| 104.200 | | WFM | Daliburgh | BBC Radio Nan Gaidheal |
| 104.200 | | WFM | Fort William | BBC Radio Nan Gaidheal |
| 104.200 | | WFM | Grantown | BBC Radio 4 |
| 104.200 | | WFM | Kilvey Hill | BBC Radio 4 |
| 104.200 | | WFM | Northampton | BBC Radio Northampton |
| 104.200 | | WFM | Strachur | BBC Radio Nan Gaidheal |
| 104.200 | | WFM | Swingate | BBC Radio Kent |
| 104.200 | | WFM | Windermere | BBC Radio Cumbria |
| 104.300 | | WFM | Abertillery | BBC Radio Cymru |
| 104.300 | | WFM | Darvel | BBC Radio 4 |
| 104.300 | | WFM | Eitshal | BBC Radio Nan Gaidheal |
| 104.300 | | WFM | Llangollen | BBC Radio Cymru |
| 104.300 | | FM | Mallaig | BBC Radio Nan Gaidheal |
| 104.300 | | WFM | Naish Hill | BBC Wiltshire Sound |
| 104.300 | | WFM | Penifiler | BBC Radio Nan Gaidheal |
| 104.300 | | WFM | Ton Petre | BBC Radio 4 |
| 104.300 | | WFM | Woolmoor | BBC Radio York |
| 104.400 | | WFM | Arklow | East Coast Radio |
| 104.400 | | WFM | Conwy | BBC Radio 4 |
| 104.400 | | WFM | Dublin | FM 104 |
| 104.400 | | WFM | Fenham | BBC Radio Newcastle |
| 104.400 | | WFM | Great Massingham | BBC Radio Norfolk |
| 104.400 | | WFM | Kinlochleven | BBC Radio Nan Gaidheal |
| 104.400 | | WFM | Llandyfriog | BBC Radio 4 |
| 104.400 | | WFM | Llyswen | BBC Radio 4 |
| 104.400 | | WFM | Reading | BBC Thames Valley FM |
| 104.500 | | WFM | Bow Brickhill | BBC 3CR |
| 104.500 | | WFM | Cwmafan | BBC Radio Cymru |
| 104.500 | | WFM | Heathfield | BBC Southern Counties Radio |
| 104.500 | | WFM | Kirkton Mailer | BBC Radio 4 |
| 104.500 | | WFM | Lancaster | BBC Radio Lancashire |
| 104.500 | | WFM | Porth | BBC Radio Cymru |
| 104.500 | | WFM | Rumster Forest | BBC Radio 4 |
| 104.500 | | WFM | Sutton Coldfield | BBC Radio Derby |
| 104.500 | | WFM | Tullich | BBC Radio 4 |
| 104.600 | | WFM | Bath | BBC Radio Bristol |
| 104.600 | | WFM | Camlough | BBC Radio 4 |
| 104.600 | | WFM | Carmel | BBC Radio 4 |
| 104.600 | | WFM | Ebbw Vale | BBC Radio Cymru |
| 104.600 | | WFM | Eyemouth | BBC Radio 4 |
| 104.600 | | WFM | Great Barton | BBC Radio Suffolk |
| 104.600 | | WFM | Guildford | BBC Southern Counties Radio |
| 104.600 | | WFM | Kidderminster | BBC Hereford & Worcester |
| 104.600 | | WFM | Llangeinor | BBC Radio Cymru |
| 104.600 | | WFM | Oban | BBC Radio Nan Gaidheal |
| 104.600 | | WFM | Penmaen Rhos | BBC Radio 4 |
| 104.600 | | WFM | Saddleworth | BBC GMR |
| 104.700 | | WFM | Aberdare | BBC Radio 4 |
| 104.700 | | WFM | Brecon | BBC Radio 4 |
| 104.700 | | WFM | Churchdown Hill | BBC Radio Gloucestershire |

| Base | Mobile | Mode | Location | User and Notes |
|------|--------|------|----------|----------------|
| 104.700 | | WFM | Edinburgh | BBC Gaelic |
| 104.700 | | WFM | Grantham | BBC Radio Lincoinshire |
| 104.700 | | WFM | Guernsey | 104.7 Island FM |
| 104.700 | | WFM | Skraig | BBC Radio Nan Gaidheal |
| 104.700 | | WFM | York | Minster FM |
| 104.800 | | WFM | Burton Down | BBC Southern Counties Radio |
| 104.800 | | WFM | Dangandargan | Tipperary Mid-West Radio |
| 104.800 | | WFM | Llanidloes | BBC Radio 4 |
| 104.800 | | WFM | Llwyn-Onn | BBC Radio 4 |
| 104.800 | | WFM | Pontypool | BBC Radio 4 |
| 104.800 | | WFM | Rheola | BBC Radio 4 |
| 104.800 | | WFM | South Knapdale | BBC Radio Nan Gaidheal |
| 104.900 | | WFM | Ardgour | BBC Radio Nan Gaidheal |
| 104.900 | | WFM | Ben Gullipen | BBC Radio 4 |
| 104.900 | | WFM | Betws-y-Coed | BBC Radio 4 |
| 104.900 | | WFM | Clyro | BBC Radio 4 |
| 104.900 | | WFM | Copt Oak | BBC Radio Leicester |
| 104.900 | | WFM | Dundalk | LM FM |
| 104.900 | | WFM | Edinburgh | BBC Radio 4 |
| 104.900 | | WFM | Ferndale | BBC Radio Cymru |
| 104.900 | | WFM | Haverfordwoet | BBC Radio 4 |
| 104.900 | | WFM | Llandecwyn | BBC Radio Cymru |
| 104.900 | | WFM | London | Xfm |
| 104.900 | | WFM | Marlborough | BBC Wiltshire Sound |
| 104.900 | | WFM | Ness of Lewis | BBC Radio Nan Gaidheal |
| 104.900 | | WFM | Port Ellen | BBC Radio Nan Gaidheal |
| 104.900 | | WFM | Rhymney | BBC Radio Cymru |
| 104.900 | | WFM | Rosemarkie | BBC Radio Nan Gaidheal |
| 104.900 | | WFM | Stockport | Signal Cheshire |
| 104.900 | | WFM | Ullapool | BBC Radio Nan Gaidheal |
| 105.000 | | WFM | Oughtdarnid | North West Radio |
| 105.100 | | WFM | Leeds | Galaxy 105 |
| 105.200 | | WFM | Bournemouth | Wave 105 FM |
| 105.200 | | WFM | Nationwide | RSL 28 Day stations |
| 105.300 | | WFM | NE England | Galaxy 105-106 |
| 105.400 | | WFM | Campbeltown | Kintyre Community Radio Weekends Only |
| 105.400 | | WFM | Leicester | Leicester Sound |
| 105.400 | | WFM | London | Magic 105.4 |
| 105.400 | | WFM | Manchester | Century 105 |
| 105.400 | | WFM | Nationwide | RSL 28 Day stations |
| 105.500 | | WFM | Clermont Carn | Radio Ireland |
| 105.600 | | WFM | Bradford | Galaxy 105 |
| 105.600 | | WFM | Cambridge | Vibe FM |
| 105.600 | | WFM | Nationwide | RSL 28 Day stations |
| 105.600 | | WFM | NE England | Galaxy 105-106 |
| 105.800 | | WFM | Hull | Galaxy 105 |
| 105.800 | | WFM | London | Virgin 105.8 |
| 105.800 | | WFM | Nationwide | RSL 28 Day stations |
| 105.800 | | WFM | Poole | Wave 105 FM |
| 106.000 | | WFM | Canterbury | 106 CTFM Radio |
| 106.000 | | WFM | East Midlands | Century 106 |
| 106.000 | | WFM | Nationwide | RSL 28 Day stations |
| 106.100 | | WFM | Norwich | Vibe FM |
| 106.200 | | WFM | London | Heart 106.2 |
| 106.200 | | WFM | Nationwide | RSL 28 Day stations |
| 106.400 | | WFM | Ipswich | Vibe FM |

| Base | Mobile | Mode | Location | User and Notes |
|---|---|---|---|---|
| 106.400 | | WFM | NE England | Galaxy 105-106 |
| 106.600 | | WFM | Nationwide | RSL 28 Day stations |
| 106.600 | | WFM | Slough | Star FM |
| 106.800 | | WFM | Dover | Neptune Radio |
| 106.800 | | WFM | Peterborough | Lite FM |
| 106.800 | | WFM | Thamesmead | Melenium Radio |
| 106.800 | | WFM | Wakefield | Ridings FM |
| 106.900 | | WFM | Macclesfield | 106.9 Silk FM |
| 107.000 | | WFM | Isle of Wight | Isle of Wight Radio |
| 107.000 | | WFM | Loughborough | 107 Oak FM |
| 107.000 | | WFM | Nationwide | RSL 28 Day stations |
| 107.100 | | WFM | Doncaster | Trax FM |
| 107.100 | | WFM | Fenland | X-Cel FM |
| 107.200 | | WFM | Brighton | Surf 107.2 |
| 107.200 | | WFM | Rutland | Rutland Radio |
| 107.200 | | WFM | Stroud | FM 107 The Falcon |
| 107.200 | | WFM | Thanet | TLR |
| 107.200 | | WFM | Warrington | 107.2 Wire FM |
| 107.200 | | WFM | Winchester | Win 107.2 |
| 107.300 | | WFM | Lewisham | FLR 107.3 |
| 107.400 | | WFM | Bolton | Tower FM |
| 107.400 | | WFM | Chesterfield | Peak 107 FM |
| 107.400 | | WFM | Kettering | KCBC |
| 107.400 | | WFM | Nationwide | RSL 28 Day stations |
| 107.400 | | WFM | Portsmouth | Radio Victory |
| 107.400 | | WFM | Telford | 107.4 Telford FM |
| 107.500 | | WFM | Cheltenham | Cat FM |
| 107.500 | | WFM | Eastbourne | Sovereign Radio |
| 107.500 | | WFM | Fenland | X-Cel FM |
| 107.500 | | WFM | Havering | Active 107.5 |
| 107.600 | | WFM | Basingstoke | 107.6 Kestrel FM |
| 107.600 | | WFM | Bournemouth | The NRG |
| 107.600 | | WFM | M20/Channel Ports | Channel Travel Radio |
| 107.700 | | WFM | Chelmsford | 107.7 Chelmer FM |
| 107.700 | | WFM | Peterborough | Vibe FM |
| 107.700 | | WFM | Wolverhampton | 107.7 The Wolf |
| 107.800 | | WFM | Hastings | 107.8 Arrow FM |
| 107.800 | | WFM | Kingston-Upon-Thames | 107.8 FM Thames Radio |
| 107.800 | | WFM | Nationwide | RSL 28 Day stations |
| 107.800 | | WFM | Southampton | SouthCity FM |
| 107.900 | | WFM | Bassetlaw | Trax FM |
| 107.900 | | WFM | Cambridge | Cambridge Red Rose |
| 107.900 | | WFM | Hinckley | Fosseway Radio |
| 107.900 | | WFM | Huddersfield | Huddersfield FM |
| 107.900 | | WFM | Medway | Medway FM |
| 107.900 | | WFM | Oxford | Oxygen 107.9 FM |
| 107.900 | | WFM | Southport | Dune FM |
| 107.900 | | WFM | Stroud | FM 107 The Falcon |

| Base | Mobile | Mode | Location | User and Notes |
|------|--------|------|----------|----------------|

**108.0000 - 112.0000 MHz   TACAN AND DME IDENTS, ILS LOCALISERS AND ILS LOCALISERS**

| Base | Mode | Location | User and Notes |
|------|------|----------|----------------|
| 108.000 | AM | Belfast | DME (I-BFH) |
| 108.000 | AM | Dundee Airport | DME Ident (DDE) |
| 108.000 | AM | Guernsey | ILS Localiser Runway 09 (I-UY) |
| 108.000 | AM | Guernsey | ILS Localiser Runway 27 (I-GH) |
| 108.000 | AM | RAF Chivenor | ILS Localiser Runway 28 (CV) |
| 108.000 | AM | RAF Cottesmore | TACAN Ident (CTM) |
| 108.000 | AM | USAF Mildenhall | ILS Localiser Runway 11 (I-MIL) |
| 108.000 | AM | USAF Mildenhall | ILS Localiser Runway 29 (I-MLD) |
| 108.150 | AM | Blackpool | DME Ident |
| 108.150 | AM | Blackpool | ILS Localiser Runway 28 (I-BPL) |
| 108.150 | AM | Lydd Airport | DME Ident |
| 108.150 | AM | Lydd Airport | ILS Localiser Runway 22 (I-LYX) |
| 108.200 | AM | Boscombe Down (MoD) | TACAN Ident (BDN) |
| 108.300 | AM | Londonderry | ILS/DME Rwy 26 (EGT) |
| 108.300 | AM | USAF Lakenheath | ILS Localiser Runway 24 (I-LKH) |
| 108.400 | AM | RAF Valley | TACAN Ident (VYL) |
| 108.500 | AM | RAF Benson | ILS Localiser Runway 19 (BO) |
| 100.500 | AM | Sumburgh Airport | DME Ident |
| 108.500 | AM | Sumburgh Airport | ILS Localiser Runway 09 (SUB) |
| 108.500 | AM | Sumburgh Airport | ILS Localiser Runway 27 (I SG) |
| 108.500 | AM | Teesside Airport | DME Ident |
| 108.500 | AM | Teesside Airport | ILS Localiser Runway 05 (I-TSE) |
| 108.500 | AM | Teesside Airport | ILS Localiser Runway 23 (I-TD) |
| 108.600 | AM | Kirkwall Airport | VOR/DME Ident (KWL) |
| 108.700 | AM | Newton Point | TACAN Ident (NTP) |
| 108.700 | AM | RAF Leuchars | ILS Localiser Runway 27 (LU) |
| 108.700 | AM | RAF Shawbury | ILS Localiser Runway 19 (SY) |
| 108.700 | AM | RAF St Mawgan | ILS Localiser Runway 31 (SM) |
| 108.750 | AM | Humberside Airport | DME Ident |
| 108.750 | AM | Humberside Airport | ILS Localiser Runway 21 (I-HS) |
| 108.800 | AM | Weathersfield | TACAN Ident (WET) |
| 108.900 | AM | Cranfield | ILS Localiser Runway 22 (I-CR) |
| 108.900 | AM | Dublin | ILS/DME Rwy 10 |
| 108.900 | AM | Dublin | ILS/DME Rwy 28 |
| 108.900 | AM | Edinburgh Airport | DME Ident |
| 108.900 | AM | Edinburgh Airport | ILS Localiser Runway 07 (I-VG) |
| 108.900 | AM | Edinburgh Airport | ILS Localiser Runway 25 (I-TH) |
| 108.900 | AM | Kerry | DME/ILS R25 KER |
| 108.900 | AM | Ventnor | TACAN Ident (VNR) |
| 108.950 | AM | Woodford | DME Ident (I-WU) |
| 108.950 | AM | Woodford | ILS Localiser Runway 25 (I-WU) |
| 109.050 | AM | Yeovil Aerodrome | DME Ident (YVL) |
| 109.100 | AM | Southampton Airport | ILS Localiser Runway 20 (I-SN) |
| 109.150 | AM | Luton Airport | DME Ident |
| 109.150 | AM | Luton Airport | ILS Localiser Runway 26 (I-LJ) |
| 109.150 | AM | Luton Airport | ILS Localiser Rwy 08 (I-LTN) |
| 109.200 | AM | Inverness Airport | VOR/DME Ident (INS) |
| 109.200 | AM | Swansea Aerodrome | DME Ident (SWZ) |
| 109.300 | AM | Glasgow | ILS Localiser Runway 23 (I-OO) |
| 109.350 | AM | Biggin Hill | ILS Localiser Runway 21 (I-BGH) |
| 109.350 | AM | East Midlands | ILS Localiser Runway 09 (I-EMW) |
| 109.350 | AM | East Midlands | ILS Localiser Runway 27 (I-EME) |
| 109.400 | AM | Barrow Airport | DME Ident (WL) |

| Base | Mobile | Mode | Location | User and Notes |
|------|--------|------|----------|----------------|
| 109.400 | | AM | Guernsey | ATIS |
| 109.400 | | AM | Guernsey | VOR/ATIS (GUR) |
| 109.500 | | AM | London, Heathrow | DME Ident |
| 109.500 | | AM | London, Heathrow | ILS Localiser Runway 09R (I-BB) |
| 109.500 | | AM | London, Heathrow | ILS Localiser Runway 27L (I-LL) |
| 109.500 | | AM | Manchester Airport | DME Ident |
| 109.500 | | AM | Manchester Airport | ILS Localiser Runway 06 (I-MM) |
| 109.500 | | AM | Manchester Airport | ILS Localiser Runway 24 (I-NN) |
| 109.500 | | AM | Plymouth Airport | DME Ident |
| 109.500 | | AM | Plymouth Airport | ILS Localiser Runway 31 (I-PLY) |
| 109.500 | | AM | Shannon Airport | ILS Runway 24 (SA) |
| 109.600 | | AM | RAF Linton-on-Ouse | TACAN Ident (LOZ) |
| 109.600 | | AM | RAF Odiham | TACAN Ident (ODH) |
| 109.700 | | AM | Belfast (Aldergrove) | ILS Localiser Runway 25 (I-AG) |
| 109.700 | | AM | RAF Cranwell | ILS Localiser Runway 26 (CW) |
| 109.700 | | AM | RAF Kinloss | ILS Localiser Runway 26 (KS) |
| 109.700 | | AM | RAF Lyneham | ILS Localiser Runway (LA) |
| 109.700 | | AM | RAF Valley | ILS Localiser Runway 14 (VY) |
| 109.750 | | AM | Coventry Airport | ILS Localiser Runway 23 (I-CT) |
| 109.800 | | AM | RAF Kinloss | TACAN Ident (KSS) |
| 109.800 | | AM | RAF Lyneham | TACAN (LYE) |
| 109.850 | | AM | Fair Oaks Aerodrome | DME Ident (FRK) |
| 109.900 | | AM | Aberdeen (Dyce Airport) | ILS Localiser Runway 16 (I-AX) |
| 109.900 | | AM | Aberdeen (Dyce Airport) | ILS Localiser Runway 34 (I-ABD) |
| 109.900 | | AM | Cork Airport | ILS Runway 17 (ICA) |
| 109.900 | | AM | Cork Airport | ILS Runway 35 (ICN) |
| 109.900 | | AM | East Midlands Airport | ILS Localiser Runway 09 (I-EMW) |
| 109.900 | | AM | East Midlands Airport | ILS Localsier Runway 27 (I-EME) |
| 109.900 | | AM | Exeter Airport | ILS Localiser Runway 26 (I-XR) |
| 109.900 | | AM | Stornoway Airport | ILS Localiser Runway 18 (I-SV) |
| 109.900 | | AM | Warton (MoD) | DME Ident |
| 109.900 | | AM | Warton (MoD) | ILS Localiser Runway 26 (WQ) |
| 110.000 | | AM | Galway | DME (CRN) |
| 110.100 | | AM | Birmingham International | DME Ident |
| 110.100 | | AM | Birmingham International | ILS Localiser Runway 15 (I-BIR) |
| 110.100 | | AM | Birmingham International | ILS Localiser Runway 33 (I-BM) |
| 110.100 | | AM | Glasgow | ILS Localiser Runway 05 (I-UU) |
| 110.100 | | AM | RAF Marham | ILS Localiser Runway 24 (MR) |
| 110.150 | | AM | Bristol Airport | ILS Localiser Runway 09 (I-BON) |
| 110.150 | | AM | Bristol Airport | ILS Localiser Runway 27 (I-BTS) |
| 110.200 | | AM | USAF Lakenheath | TACAN Ident (LKH) |
| 110.300 | | AM | Jersey Airport | ILS Localiser Runway 27 (I-DD) |
| 110.300 | | AM | London, Heathrow | DME Ident |
| 110.300 | | AM | London, Heathrow | ILS Localiser Runway 09L (I-AA) |
| 110.300 | | AM | London, Heathrow | ILS Localiser Runway 27R (I-RR) |
| 110.300 | | AM | Prestwick Airport | ILS Localiser Runway 13 (I-PP) |
| 110.300 | | AM | Prestwick Airport | ILS Localiser Runway 31 (I-KK) |
| 110.300 | | AM | RAF Cottesmore | ILS Localiser Runway 23 (CM) |
| 110.300 | | AM | RAF Leeming | ILS Localiser Runway 16 (LI) |
| 110.400 | | AM | Perth Aerodrome | VOR (PTH) |
| 110.500 | | AM | Bournemouth (Hurn) | DME Ident |
| 110.500 | | AM | Bournemouth (Hurn) | ILS Localiser Runway 08 (I-BMH) |
| 110.500 | | AM | Bournemouth (Hurn) | ILS Localiser Runway 26 (I-BH) |
| 110.500 | | AM | RAF Leuchars | TACAN Ident (LUK) |
| 110.500 | | AM | Stansted | DME Ident |
| 110.500 | | AM | Stansted | ILS Localiser Runway 05 (I-SED) |

| Base | Mobile | Mode | Location | User and Notes |
|------|--------|------|----------|----------------|
| 110.500 | | AM | Stansted | ILS Localiser Runway 23 (I-SX) |
| 110.550 | | AM | Filton (BAe), Bristol | ILS Localiser Runway 10 (I-BRF) |
| 110.550 | | AM | Filton (BAe), Bristol | ILS Localiser Runway 28 (I-FB) |
| 110.700 | | AM | Cardiff Airport | DME Ident |
| 110.700 | | AM | Cardiff Airport | ILS Localiser Runway 12 (I-CDF |
| 110.700 | | AM | Cardiff Airport | ILS Localiser Runway 30 (I-CWA) |
| 110.700 | | AM | Carlisle Airport | DME Ident (CO) |
| 110.700 | | AM | Connaught (Knock) | ILS Localsier Rwy 27 (I-CK) |
| 110.700 | | AM | London, Heathrow | DME Ident (HHT) |
| 110.700 | | AM | London, Heathrow | ILS Localiser Runway 23 (I-CC) |
| 110.700 | | AM | RAF Coningsby | ILS Localiser Runway 26 (CY) |
| 110.700 | | AM | RAF Linton-on-Ouse | ILS Localsier Runway 22 (LO) |
| 110.900 | | AM | Belfast (Aldergrove) | ILS Runway 17 (I-FT) |
| 110.900 | | AM | Jersey Airport | DME Ident (I-JJ) |
| 110.900 | | AM | Jersey Airport | ILS Localiser Runway 09 (I-JJ) |
| 110.900 | | AM | Leeds/Bradford Airport | ILS Localiser Runway 09 (I-LBF) |
| 110.900 | | AM | Leeds/Bradford Airport | ILS Localiser Runway 32 (I-LF) |
| 110.900 | | AM | London, Gatwick | DME Ident |
| 110.900 | | AM | London, Gatwick | ILS Localiser Runway 08R (I-GG) |
| 110.900 | | AM | London, Gatwick | ILS Localiser Runway 26L (I-WW) |
| 110.900 | | AM | Norwich Airport | ILS Localiser Runway 14 (I-NH) |
| 110.900 | | AM | Ronaldsway, Isle of Man | DME Ident |
| 110.900 | | AM | Ronaldsway, Isle of Man | ILS Localiser Runway 27 (I-RY) |
| 111.000 | | AM | RNAS Yeovilton | TACAN Ident (VLN) |
| 111.100 | | AM | RAF Coningsby | TACAN Ident (CGY) |
| 111.100 | | AM | RAF Lossiemouth | ILS Localiser Runway 23 (LM) |
| 111.100 | | AM | RAF Waddington | ILS Localiser Runway 21 (WA) |
| 111.100 | | AM | USAF Fairford | ILS Localiser Runway 09 (I-FFA) |
| 111.100 | | AM | USAF Fairford | ILS Localiser Runway 27 (I-FFD) |
| 111.200 | | NFM | Nationwide | Illegal Bugging Device |
| 111.300 | | AM | Hatfield Aerodrome | ILS Localiser Runway 24 (I-HD) |
| 111.350 | | AM | Southend Airport | DME Ident |
| 111.350 | | AM | Southend Airport | ILS Localiser Runway 24 (I-ND) |
| 111.500 | | AM | Dublin | ILS/DME Rwy 16 |
| 111.500 | | AM | London, City Airport | DME Ident |
| 111.500 | | AM | London, City Airport | ILS Localiser Runway 10 (LST) |
| 111.500 | | AM | London, City Airport | ILS Localiser Runway 28 (LST) |
| 111.500 | | AM | Newcastle Airport | DME Ident |
| 111.500 | | AM | Newcastle Airport | ILS Localiser Runway 07 (I-NC) |
| 111.500 | | AM | Newcastle Airport | ILS Localiser Runway 25 (I-NWC) |
| 111.500 | | AM | RAF Coltishall | ILS Localiser Runway 22 (CS) |
| 111.500 | | AM | USAF Fairford | TACAN Ident (FFA) |
| 111.600 | | AM | RAF Chivenor | TACAN Ident (CVR) |
| 111.700 | | AM | Boscombe Down (MoD) | ILS Localiser Runway 24 (BD) |
| 111.750 | | AM | Liverpool Airport | DME Ident |
| 111.750 | | AM | Liverpool Airport | ILS Localiser Runway 09 (LVR) |
| 111.750 | | AM | Liverpool Airport | ILS Localiser Runway 27 (I-LQ) |
| 111.900 | | AM | RAF Brize Norton | ILS Localiser Runway 08 (BZA) |
| 111.900 | | AM | RAF Brize Norton | ILS Localiser Runway 26 (BZB) |
| 111.900 | | AM | RAF Brize Norton | TACAN Ident (BZN) |
| 111.900 | | AM | RAF Honington | ILS Localiser Runway 27 (HT) |

| Base | Mobile | Mode | Location | User and Notes |
|------|--------|------|----------|----------------|

**112.0000 - 117.9750 MHz**     TACAN and DME Idents, ATIS and VOR Aero

| Base | Mobile | Mode | Location | User and Notes |
|------|--------|------|----------|----------------|
| 112.100 | | AM | Pole Hill | VOR/DME Ident (POL) |
| 112.200 | | AM | Jersey Airport | VOR/ATIS (JSY) |
| 112.200 | | AM | Ronaldsway, Isle of Man | VOR/DME Ident (IOM) |
| 112.500 | | AM | St Abbs | VOR/DME Ident (SAB) |
| 112.600 | | AM | RAF St Mawgan | TACAN Ident (SMG) |
| 112.700 | | AM | Berry Head | VOR/DME Ident (BHD) |
| 112.700 | | AM | Donegal Aerodrome | DME Ident (CFN) |
| 112.800 | | AM | Gamston Aerodrome | VOR/DME Ident (GAM) |
| 112.800 | | AM | Rennes Airport | VOR (RNE) France |
| 113.100 | | AM | Strumble | VOR/DME Ident (STU) |
| 113.200 | | AM | Warton (MoD) | TACAN Ident (WTN) |
| 113.300 | | AM | Shannon Airport | DVOR/DME (SHA) |
| 113.350 | | AM | Southampton Airport | VOR/ATIS (SAM) |
| 113.550 | | AM | Manchester Airport | VOR/DME Ident (MCT) |
| 113.600 | | AM | London, Heathrow | VOR/DME Ident (LON) |
| 113.600 | | AM | Wick Aerodrome | TACAN Ident (WIZ) |
| 113.600 | | AM | Wick Aerodrome | VOR (WIK) |
| 113.650 | | AM | Honiley | VOR/DME Ident (HON) |
| 113.750 | | AM | Bovingdon | VOR/DME Ident (BNN) |
| 113.900 | | AM | Ottringham | VOR/DME Ident (OTR) |
| 114.000 | | AM | Midhurst | VOR/DME Ident (MID) |
| 114.050 | | AM | Lydd Airport | VOR (LYD) |
| 114.100 | | AM | Wallasey | VOR/DME Ident (WAL) |
| 114.200 | | AM | Land's End Airport | VOR/DME Ident (LND) |
| 114.250 | | AM | Newcastle Airport | VOR/ATIS (NEW) |
| 114.300 | | AM | Aberdeen (Dyce Airport) | ATIS |
| 114.300 | | AM | Aberdeen (Dyce Airport) | VOR/DME Ident (ADN) |
| 114.350 | | AM | Compton | VOR/DME Ident (CPT) |
| 114.400 | | AM | Benbecula Airport | TACAN Ident (BEZ) |
| 114.400 | | AM | Benbecula Airport | VOR (BEN) |
| 114.550 | | AM | Clacton Aerodrome | VOR/DME Ident (CLN) |
| 114.600 | | AM | Cork Airport | DVOR/DME Ident (CRK) |
| 114.750 | | AM | Chichester/Goodwood | VOR (GWC) |
| 114.900 | | AM | Dublin | VOR/DME Ident (DUB) |
| 114.900 | | AM | Vallafield | TACAN Ident (VFD) |
| 114.950 | | AM | Dover | VOR/DME Ident (DVR) |
| 115.100 | | AM | Biggin Hill | VOR/DME Ident (BIG) |
| 115.100 | | AM | Stornoway Airport | TACAN Ident (STZ) |
| 115.100 | | AM | Stornoway Airport | VOR (STN) |
| 115.200 | | AM | Dean Cross | VOR/DME Ident (DCS) |
| 115.300 | | AM | Ockham | VOR/DME Ident (OCK) |
| 115.400 | | AM | Glasgow | VOR/ATIS/DME Ident (GOW) |
| 115.550 | | AM | Gloucestershire Airport | DME Ident (GOS) |
| 115.600 | | AM | Lambourne | VOR/DME Ident (LAM) |
| 115.700 | | AM | Stoke on Trent | VOR/DME Ident (TNT) |
| 115.800 | | AM | Baldonnel, Eire | VOR Ident (BAL) |
| 115.900 | | AM | USAF Mildenhall | TACAN Ident (MLD) |
| 116.000 | | AM | RAF Machrihanish | DVOR (MAC) |
| 116.200 | | AM | Blackbushe | DME Ident (BLC) |
| 116.250 | | AM | Barkway | VOR/DME Ident (BKY) |
| 116.400 | | AM | Daventry | VOR/DME Ident (DTY) |
| 116.500 | | AM | Cranfield | VOR Ident (CFD) |
| 116.500 | | AM | RAF Coltishall | TACAN Ident (CSL) |

| Base | Mobile | Mode | Location | User and Notes |
|------|--------|------|----------|----------------|
| 116.750 | | AM | Cambridge Airport | DME Ident (CAB) |
| 117.000 | | AM | Seaford | VOR/DME Ident (SFD) |
| 117.100 | | AM | Burnham | VOR (BUR) |
| 117.200 | | AM | Belfast | VOR/DME Ident (BEL) |
| 117.300 | | AM | Detling | VOR/DME Ident (DET) |
| 117.350 | | AM | Sumburgh Airport | VOR/DME Ident (SUM) |
| 117.400 | | AM | Connaught (Knock) | VOR/DME Ident (CON) |
| 117.400 | | AM | RAF Cranwell | TACAN Ident (CWZ) |
| 117.450 | | AM | Brecon | VOR/DME Ident (BCN) |
| 117.500 | | AM | Brookmans Park | VOR/DME Ident (BPK) |
| 117.500 | | AM | Turnberry | VOR/DME Ident (TRN) |
| 117.600 | | AM | RAF Wittering | TACAN Ident (WIT) |
| 117.700 | | AM | Oxford/Kidlington Airport | DME Ident (OX) |
| 117.700 | | AM | Tiree | VOR/DME Ident (TIR) |
| 117.900 | | AM | Mayfield | VOR/DME Ident (MAY) |

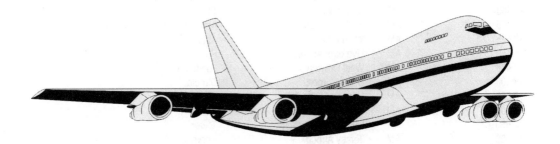

117.9750 - 136.0000 MHz    INTERNATIONAL CIVIL AVIATION BAND 50 kHz

| Base | Mobile | Mode | Location | User and Notes |
|------|--------|------|----------|----------------|
| 118.000 | | AM | Nationwide | Air-Air Display Coordination |
| 118.000 | | AM | Nationwide | Crunchie Flight Team |
| 118.000 | | AM | Nationwide | Marlboro Aerobatic Display |
| 118.000 | | AM. | Natiownide | Civilian Air-Air |
| 118.000 | | AM | RAF Mildenhall | 100th Refuelling Wing |
| 118.000 | | AM | Yeovil | Westland Helicopter Tests |
| 118.025 | | AM | Leeds/Bradford Airport | ATIS |
| 118.050 | | AM | Birmingham International | Radar/Approach |
| 118.050 | | AM | North Sea | Frigg Oil Field deck |
| 118.075 | | AM | Barra, Scotland | AFIS |
| 118.075 | | AM | London, City Airport | Tower |
| 118.100 | | AM | Aberdeen (Dyce Airport) | Tower |
| 118.100 | | AM | Farnborough | Air Show Tower |
| 118.100 | | AM | Liverpool Airport | Tower |
| 118.100 | | AM | Penzance Heliport | Tower |
| 118.150 | | AM | Prestwick Airport | Tower |
| 118.150 | | AM | RAF Wittering | Tower |
| 118.200 | | AM | Ronaldsway, Isle of Man | Radar |
| 118.200 | | AM | Southampton Airport | Tower |
| 118.250 | | AM | Brittas Bay, Eire | Air/Ground (Brittas Bay Radio) |
| 118.250 | | AM | Sumburgh Airport | Tower |
| 118.275 | | AM | Fishburn | Air/Ground |
| 118.300 | | AM | Belfast (Aldergrove) | Tower |
| 118.300 | | AM | Birmingham International | Tower |
| 118.300 | | AM | Kirkwall Airport | Tower/Approach |
| 118.325 | | AM | Ipswich Airport | AFIS |
| 118.350 | | AM | Derby | Air/Ground |
| 118.375 | | AM | RAF West Drayton | Air Traffic Control |
| 118.400 | | AM | Blackpool | Tower |
| 118.425 | | AM | RAF Lyneham | Approach/Radar (Director) |
| 118.425 | | AM | Wroughton | Approach |
| 118.450 | | AM | Liverpool Airport | Radar |
| 118.475 | | AM | West Drayton | London ATC |
| 118.500 | | AM | Dublin Airport | Director |
| 118.500 | | AM | London, Heathrow | Tower |
| 118.500 | | AM | Newcastle Airport | Radar |
| 118.550 | | AM | Humberside Airport | Tower |
| 118.550 | | AM | Jersey Airport | Approach |
| 118.550 | | AM | Jersey Airport | Radar |
| 118.575 | | AM | Manchester Airport | ATC arrivals |
| 118.575 | | AM | Manchester Airport | Radar Standby |
| 118.600 | | AM | Dublin Airport | Tower |
| 118.625 | | AM | Manchester Airport | Tower |
| 118.650 | | AM | Bournemouth (Hurn) | Radar |
| 118.700 | | AM | Edinburgh Airport | Tower |
| 118.700 | | AM | London, Heathrow | Tower |
| 118.700 | | AM | Shannon Airport | Tower |
| 118.800 | | AM | Cork Airport | Radar |
| 118.800 | | AM | Glasgow | Tower |
| 118.825 | | AM | West Drayton | London Control ACC |
| 118.850 | | AM | Teesside Airport | Approach/Radar |
| 118.875 | | AM | Oxford (Kidlington Airport) | Tower/AFIS |
| 118.900 | | AM | Guernsey | Radar |
| 118.900 | | AM | Kemble | Air/Ground |
| 118.900 | | AM | RAF Lossiemouth | Tower |

| Base | Mobile | Mode | Location | User and Notes |
|------|--------|------|----------|----------------|
| 118.900 | | AM | Ronaldsway, Isle of Man | Tower |
| 118.925 | | AM | RAF Cosford | Approach/Tower |
| 118.950 | | AM | London, Gatwick | Radar |
| 119.000 | | AM | Nationwide | RAF Common |
| 119.000 | | AM | RAF Brize Norton | Zone |
| 119.000 | | AM | RAF Fairford | Approach |
| 119.000 | | AM | RAF Mildenhall | 100th Refuelling Wing |
| 119.000 | | AM | Shetlands | East Shetland Information |
| 119.050 | | AM | Exeter Airport | Radar |
| 119.100 | | AM | Glasgow | Approach/Radar |
| 119.120 | | AM | Newton | Approach/Tower |
| 119.125 | | AM | RAF Newton | Tower |
| 119.150 | | AM | RAF Fairford | Tower |
| 119.200 | | AM | Benbecula | Approach/Tower and FIS |
| 119.225 | | AM | RAF Lyneham | Tower |
| 119.250 | | AM | Coventry Airport | Approach |
| 119.275 | | AM | Manston | Talkdown |
| 119.300 | | AM | Cork Airport | Tower |
| 119.300 | | AM | Glasgow | Radar |
| 119.300 | | AM | Hatfield Aerodrome | Radar |
| 119.350 | | AM | Dornoch Aerodrome | Approach (Lossiemouth) |
| 119.350 | | AM | Norwich Airport | Approach/Radar |
| 119.350 | | AM | RAF Kinloss | Approach |
| 119.350 | | AM | RAF Lossiemouth | Approach (LARS/MATZ) |
| 119.375 | | AM | RAF Cranwell | Approach |
| 119.400 | | AM | Haydock Park | Approach |
| 119.400 | | AM | Manchester Airport | Approach/Radar (Director) |
| 119.425 | | AM | Stubton Park | Air/Ground |
| 119.450 | | AM | Hinton in the Hedges | Air/Ground |
| 119.450 | | AM | Jersey Airport | Tower |
| 119.450 | | AM | Prestwick Airport | Radar |
| 119.475 | | AM | Cardiff Airport | ATIS |
| 119.475 | | AM | RAF St Athan | Cardiff Information |
| 119.550 | | AM | Dublin Airport | Radar |
| 119.550 | | AM | Shipdam | Air/Ground and AFIS |
| 119.625 | | AM | Bournemouth (Hurn) | Approach/Radar |
| 119.650 | | AM | Derby | Approach (East Midlands) |
| 119.650 | | AM | East Midlands Airport | Approach |
| 119.700 | | AM | Newcastle Airport | Tower |
| 119.700 | | AM | Swansea Airport | Air/Ground |
| 119.700 | | AM | Wick | Air/Ground |
| 119.725 | | AM | London, Heathrow | Approach (Director) |
| 119.750 | | AM | Perranporth | Air/Ground |
| 119.750 | | AM | RAF Woodvale | Tower |
| 119.775 | | AM | West Drayton | London Control |
| 119.800 | | AM | Exeter Airport | Tower |
| 119.800 | | AM | London, Gatwick | Police Helicopter Ops |
| 119.800 | | AM | Perth (Scone) | Air/Ground and AFIS |
| 119.800 | | AM | Teesside Airport | Tower |
| 119.850 | | AM | Burtonwood | US Army Helicopter Ops |
| 119.850 | | AM | Liverpool Airport | Approach/Radar |
| 119.875 | | AM | Prestwick | Scottish ACC (Information) |
| 119.900 | | AM | Cork Airport | Approach |
| 119.900 | | AM | London, Heathrow | Radar |
| 119.900 | | AM | RAF Odiham | Helicopter Ops |
| 119.950 | | AM | Blackpool | Approach |

| Base | Mobile | Mode | Location | User and Notes |
|------|--------|------|----------|----------------|
| 119.950 | | AM | Guernsey | Tower |
| 119.975 | | AM | RAF Coningsby | Tower |
| 120.000 | | AM | Belfast (Aldergrove) | Radar |
| 120.025 | | AM | West Drayton | London Control |
| 120.075 | | AM | North Sea | Pickerill Oil Field deck |
| 120.075 | | AM | North Sea | Trent Oil Field deck |
| 120.075 | | AM | North Sea | Tyne Oil Field deck |
| 120.075 | | AM | North Sea | Viking Oil Field log |
| 120.125 | | AM | East Midlands Airport | Radar |
| 120.150 | | AM | North Coates | Air/Ground |
| 120.175 | | AM | West Drayton | London Control Inbound |
| 120.200 | | AM | Shannon Airport | Approach |
| 120.225 | | AM | Southampton Airport | Approach Solent |
| 120.250 | | AM | Panshanger | Air/Ground |
| 120.255 | | AM | Solent | Interial contact frequency |
| 120.275 | | AM | Redhill Aerodrome | Tower/AFIS |
| 120.300 | | AM | Jersey Airport | Approach/Radar |
| 120.300 | | AM | Leeds/Bradford Airport | Tower |
| 120.325 | | AM | RAF Northolt | Departure |
| 120.400 | | AM | Aberdeen (Dyce Airport) | Approach/Radar |
| 120.400 | | AM | London, Heathrow | Approach |
| 120.425 | | AM | RAF Barkston Heath | Tower |
| 120.450 | | AM | Jersey Airport | Air Traffic Control (Zone)/Radar |
| 120.450 | | AM | North Sea | Oil Rig Heliport Common |
| 120.475 | | AM | West Drayton | London Control SIDs |
| 120.500 | | AM | RAF Leeming | Tower |
| 120.525 | | AM | Biggin Hill | Speedbird Ops |
| 120.525 | | AM | West Drayton | London Control ACC |
| 120.550 | | AM | Prestwick Airport | Approach/Radar |
| 120.575 | | AM | Luton Airport | ATIS |
| 120.600 | | AM | Cumbernauld Airport | AFIS |
| 120.625 | | AM | Andrewsfield | Radar (Stansted) |
| 120.625 | | AM | High Easter Aerodrome | Approach (Stansted) |
| 120.625 | | AM | Stansted | Approach/Radar |
| 120.675 | | AM | RAF Northolt | Tower |
| 120.700 | | AM | Lydd Airport | AFIS |
| 120.775 | | AM | RAF Shawbury | Approach/Tower (LARS and MATZ) |
| 120.800 | | AM | Nationwide | Battle of Britain Flight (discrete) |
| 120.800 | | AM | RAF Coningsby | Approach (LARS and MATZ) |
| 120.850 | | AM | Ronaldsway, Isle of Man | Approach/Radar |
| 120.900 | | AM | Belfast (Aldergrove) | Approach/Radar |
| 120.900 | | AM | RAF Benson | Zone |
| 120.925 | | AM | Cork Airport | ATIS |
| 120.925 | | AM | Fowlemere | Air/Ground |
| 120.975 | | AM | Gloucestershire Airport | Radar |
| 121.000 | | AM | RAF Woodvale | Approach |
| 121.025 | | AM | London, Gatwick | ATIS |
| 121.050 | | AM | Leeds/Bradford Airport | Radar |
| 121.075 | | AM | Cheltenham Racecourse | Heliport |
| 121.075 | | AM | Duxford | Air Display Channel |
| 121.075 | | AM | North Weald | Fighter Grouping meet |
| 121.075 | | AM | Silverstone | Air/Ground |
| 121.100 | | AM | Dublin Airport | Approach |
| 121.100 | | AM | Henlow | Air/Ground |
| 121.125 | | AM | RAF Mildenhall | Air to air tanker flights |
| 121.175 | | AM | Farnborough Airshow | CAA Event Special use |

| Base | Mobile | Mode | Location | User and Notes |
|------|--------|------|----------|----------------|
| 121.175 | | AM | Nationwide | CAA events air to ground |
| 121.175 | | AM | North Weald | Display Frequency |
| 121.200 | | AM | Edinburgh Airport | Approach/Radar |
| 121.225 | | AM | West Drayton | London Control |
| 121.250 | | AM | Aberdeen (Dyce Airport) | Radar |
| 121.275 | | AM | West Drayton | London Control |
| 121.300 | | AM | Glasgow | Radar |
| 121.300 | | AM | Lochaber | Air Ambulance |
| 121.325 | | AM | West Drayton | London Control TMA |
| 121.350 | | AM | Manchester Airport | Radar |
| 121.400 | | AM | Shannon Airport | Approach |
| 121.500 | | AM | Nationwide | Civil Aviation Distress Channel |
| 121.500 | | AM | Nationwide | Maritime Emergency Position Indicating Radio Beacons |
| 121.600 | | AM | Aberdeen (Dyce Airport) | Fire Channel |
| 121.600 | | AM | Birmingham International | Fire Service |
| 121.600 | | AM | East Midlands Airport | Fire Service |
| 121.600 | | AM | Manchester Airport | Fire Service |
| 121.600 | | AM | Nationwide | Airfield Fire & Rescue |
| 121.700 | | AM | Aberdeen (Dyce Airport) | Ground |
| 121.700 | | AM | Bournemouth (Hurn) | Ground |
| 121.700 | | AM | Cork Airport | Tower |
| 121.700 | | AM | Coventry Airport | Ground |
| 121.700 | | AM | Glasgow | Ground |
| 121.700 | | AM | Manchester Airport | Delivery/Ground |
| 121.700 | | AM | Nationwide | CAA events (rarely used) |
| 121.700 | | AM | Shannon | Clearance Delivery |
| 121.725 | | AM | RAF Brize Norton | Ground |
| 121.725 | | AM | Stansted | Ground |
| 121.750 | | AM | Belfast (Aldergrove) | Ground |
| 121.750 | | AM | Blackpool | ATIS |
| 121.750 | | AM | Edinburgh Airport | Ground |
| 121.750 | | AM | Luton Airport | Ground |
| 121.750 | | AM | Oxford (Kidlington Airport) | ATIS |
| 121.775 | | AM | Wycombe Air Park (Booker) | Ground |
| 121.800 | | AM | Birmingham International | Ground |
| 121.800 | | AM | Cork Airport | Ground |
| 121.800 | | AM | Dublin Airport | Ground |
| 121.800 | | AM | Guernsey | Ground |
| 121.800 | | AM | London, Gatwick | Ground |
| 121.800 | | AM | Prestwick Airport | Tower |
| 121.800 | | AM | Shannon Airport | Ground |
| 121.800 | | AM | Southend Airport | ATIS |
| 121.825 | | AM | Teesside Airport | Teesside Information |
| 121.850 | | AM | Aberdeen (Dyce Airport) | ATIS |
| 121.850 | | AM | Wroughton | PFA Delivery |
| 121.875 | | AM | Biggin Hill | ATIS |
| 121.875 | | AM | Cranfield | Approach/ATIS |
| 121.875 | | AM | Dublin Airport | Delivery |
| 121.900 | | AM | Connaught (Knock) Airport | Ground |
| 121.900 | | AM | East Midlands Airport | Ground |
| 121.900 | | AM | Jersey Airport | Ground |
| 121.900 | | AM | London, Heathrow | Ground |
| 121.925 | | AM | Redhill Aerodrome | Ground (Airshows Only) |
| 121.925 | | AM | Wroughton | PFA Ground |
| 121.950 | | AM | Bournemouth (Hurn) | ATIS |

| Base | Mobile | Mode | Location | User and Notes |
|------|--------|------|----------|----------------|
| 121.950 | | AM | London, Gatwick | Delivery |
| 121.950 | | AM | Oxford (Kidlington Airport) | Ground |
| 121.950 | | AM | RAF Cosford | Ground |
| 121.975 | | AM | London, Heathrow | Delivery |
| 122.000 | | AM | Baldonnel, Eire | Approach |
| 122.000 | | AM | Coventry Airport | Radar |
| 122.000 | | AM | Lashenden (Headcorn) | Air/Ground |
| 122.000 | | AM | North Sea | BP Buchan Field |
| 122.000 | | AM | North Sea | BP Cyprus Field |
| 122.000 | | AM | North Sea | BP Forties Field |
| 122.000 | | AM | North Sea | BP Gyda Field |
| 122.000 | | AM | North Sea | Caister Oil Field deck |
| 122.000 | | AM | North Sea | Unity Oil Field deck |
| 122.000 | | AM | RAF Mona | Air/Ground (weekends only) |
| 122.025 | | AM | North Sea | Murdoch Oil Field deck |
| 122.050 | | AM | Aberdeen (Dyce Airport) | British Airways |
| 122.050 | | AM | Liverpool Airport | Keenair Ops |
| 122.050 | | AM | London | Jersey Air Ops |
| 122.050 | | AM | Nationwide | Brymon Airways |
| 122.050 | | AM | North Sea | Chevron Ninian Field log |
| 122.050 | | AM | North Sea | Conoco Murchison Field Deck |
| 122.050 | | AM | North Sea | Ninian Field |
| 122.050 | | AM | North Sea | Shell/Esso Auk Field |
| 122.050 | | AM | North Sea | Shell/Esso Fulmar Field |
| 122.050 | | AM | North Sea | Shell/Esso Kittiwake Field |
| 122.050 | | AM | North Sea | Thistle Field Deck |
| 122.050 | | AM | Nottingham Aerodrome | Hutchins Crop Sprayers |
| 122.050 | | AM | Southend Airport | Heavilift Ops |
| 122.050 | | AM | Stapleford | Aeromega Ops. (Helicopter ops) |
| 122.075 | | AM | Duxford | Information |
| 122.075 | | AM | Whitchurch (Tilstock) | Air/Ground |
| 122.100 | | AM | Dishforth | Approach |
| 122.100 | | AM | Middle Wallop Army Airfield | Tower/Approach |
| 122.100 | | AM | N of 56N | Fisheries Protection |
| 122.100 | | AM | Nationwide | Military Tower Common |
| 122.100 | | AM | RAF Benson | Approach |
| 122.100 | | AM | RAF Church Fenton | Tower/Ground |
| 122.100 | | AM | RAF Colerne | Approach/Tower |
| 122.100 | | AM | RAF Coltishall | Approach/Tower |
| 122.100 | | AM | RAF Coningsby | Approach/Tower and Ground |
| 122.100 | | AM | RAF Cottesmore | Tower/Ground |
| 122.100 | | AM | RAF Cranwell | Tower |
| 122.100 | | AM | RAF Dishforth (also Army) | Approach/Tower |
| 122.100 | | AM | RAF Fairford | Approach |
| 122.100 | | AM | RAF Honington | Tower |
| 122.100 | | AM | RAF Kinloss | Tower |
| 122.100 | | AM | RAF Lakenheath | Tower |
| 122.100 | | AM | RAF Leeming | Tower |
| 122.100 | | AM | RAF Leuchars | Tower/Ground |
| 122.100 | | AM | RAF Linton-On-Ouse | Tower/Ground |
| 122.100 | | AM | RAF Lossiemouth | Tower |
| 122.100 | | AM | RAF Lyneham | Tower/Ground |
| 122.100 | | AM | RAF Marham | Tower |
| 122.100 | | AM | RAF Newton | Tower |
| 122.100 | | AM | RAF Odiham | Tower/Odiham Information |
| 122.100 | | AM | RAF Shawbury | Tower |

| Base | Mobile | Mode | Location | User and Notes |
|------|--------|------|----------|----------------|
| 122.100 | | AM | RAF Spadeadam | SRE |
| 122.100 | | AM | RAF St Athan | Tower |
| 122.100 | | AM | RAF St Mawgan | Approach/Tower |
| 122.100 | | AM | RAF Ternhill | Approach |
| 122.100 | | AM | RAF Topcliffe | Approach/Tower |
| 122.100 | | AM | RAF Valley | Tower          /Ground |
| 122.100 | | AM | RAF Wyton | Tower |
| 122.100 | | AM | RNAS Culdrose | Tower |
| 122.100 | | AM | RNAS Merryfield | Tower |
| 122.100 | | AM | RNAS Predannack | Tower |
| 122.100 | | AM | RNAS Yeovilton | Tower |
| 122.100 | | AM | Sligo | Tower/AFIS |
| 122.100 | | AM | Wattisham (Army Airfield) | Tower |
| 122.125 | | AM | Flotta Airfield | Tower |
| 122.125 | | AM | Leicester Aerodrome | Air/Ground |
| 122.125 | | AM | North Sea | Hamilton Argyll Field |
| 122.150 | | AM | Aberporth (MoD) | AFIS |
| 122.175 | | AM | North Sea | Mobil Beryl Field |
| 122.175 | | AM | Turweston Aerodrome | Air/Ground |
| 122.200 | | AM | Cambridge Airport | Tower |
| 122.200 | | AM | Gormanston, Eire | IAC Military Approach |
| 122.200 | | AM | Haverfordwest Aerodrome | Air/Ground |
| 122.200 | | AM | Huddersfield (Crossland Moor) | Air/Ground |
| 122.250 | | AM | Caernarfon Aerodrome | Tower |
| 122.250 | | AM | North Sea | Shell/Esso Brent Field |
| 122.250 | | AM | Rochester Aerodrome | AFIS |
| 122.275 | | AM | Nationwide | CAA Calibrator Aircraft |
| 122.275 | | AM | Nationwide | Dutch F-16 Team Air/Ground |
| 122.300 | | AM | Alderney | Aurigny Airlines |
| 122.300 | | AM | Baldonnel, Eire | IAC Military Radar |
| 122.300 | | AM | Blackbushe | AFIS and Air/Ground |
| 122.300 | | AM | Nationwide | Aircraft Exercise Frequency |
| 122.300 | | AM | Peterborough (Sibson) | Approach/Radar |
| 122.325 | | AM | North Sea | Hamilton Esmond Field |
| 122.325 | | AM | North Sea | Hamilton Forbes Field |
| 122.325 | | AM | North Sea | Hamilton Gordon Field |
| 122.350 | | AM | Audley End | Air/Ground |
| 122.350 | | AM | Brooklands | Air/Ground |
| 122.350 | | AM | Cardiff Airport | Operations |
| 122.350 | | AM | East Midlands Airport | Air Bridge Carriers Ops |
| 122.350 | | AM | Edinburgh Airport | Execair Operations |
| 122.350 | | AM | Glasgow | Execair |
| 122.350 | | AM | Grimsby (Cuxwold) | Air/Ground |
| 122.350 | | AM | Guernsey | Aurigny Air Services |
| 122.350 | | AM | Hethel | Air/Ground |
| 122.350 | | AM | Hitchin (Rush Green) | Air/Ground |
| 122.350 | | AM | Liverpool Airport | Cheshire Air Training Ops |
| 122.350 | | AM | Lochaber | PLM Helicopters |
| 122.350 | | AM | London, Heathrow | Gulf Air Terminal 3 |
| 122.350 | | AM | Luton Airport | Reed Aviation |
| 122.350 | | AM | Manchester Airport | Air Kilroe Ops |
| 122.350 | | AM | North Sea | Total Alwyn Field |
| 122.350 | | AM | Teesside Airport | Air Cam |
| 122.375 | | AM | Humberside | Bond Helicopters |
| 122.375 | | AM | Morecambe Bay BP Field | Helicopters |
| 122.375 | | AM | North Sea | BP Magnus Field Deck |

| Base | Mobile | Mode | Location | User and Notes |
|------|--------|------|----------|----------------|
| 122.375 | | AM | Peterhead/Longside | Air/Ground Bond Helicopters |
| 122.375 | | AM | Plockton Airfield | Air/Ground |
| 122.375 | | AM | Strubby Heliport | Air/Ground |
| 122.395 | | AM | North Sea | Magnus BP |
| 122.400 | | AM | Bantry, Eire | Air/Ground |
| 122.400 | | AM | Dounreay Aerodrome | Tower |
| 122.400 | | AM | Elstree Aerodrome | Air/Ground/AFIS |
| 122.400 | | AM | Scatsa Aerodrome | Radar |
| 122.400 | | AM | Weston (Dublin) | Air/Ground |
| 122.425 | | AM | Earls Colne | Air/Ground |
| 122.450 | | AM | Chichester | Military Police Helicopter Ops |
| 122.450 | | AM | Chichester (Goodwood) | AFIS |
| 122.450 | | AM | North Sea | Claymore & Tartan |
| 122.450 | | AM | North Sea | Occidental Claymore Field |
| 122.450 | | AM | North Sea | Piper Oil Field deck |
| 122.450 | | AM | North Sea | Saltire Oil Field deck |
| 122.450 | | AM | North Sea | Texaco Tartan Field |
| 122.450 | | AM | Sleap Aerodrome | Air/Ground |
| 122.450 | | AM | Wickenby Aerodrome | Air/Ground |
| 122.475 | | AM | Nationwide | Aero Stars formerly Red Stars Aerobatic Team Manual 2 |
| 122.475 | | AM | Nationwide | Hot Air Ballooning |
| 122.500 | | AM | Bitteswell Aerodrome | Air/Ground |
| 122.500 | | AM | Farnborough (RAE Airfield) | Tower |
| 122.500 | | AM | Galway | A/G and AFIS |
| 122.500 | | AM | Llanbedr (MoD) | Tower/Radar |
| 122.500 | | AM | Weston-super-Mare | Tower |
| 122.525 | | AM | Ashcroft Farm | Air/Ground |
| 122.525 | | AM | North Sea | Clyde Oil Field deck |
| 122.525 | | AM | North Sea | Hamilton Pipe Field |
| 122.525 | | AM | North Sea | Judy Oil Field deck |
| 122.550 | | AM | Dunsfold Aerodrome | Radar |
| 122.550 | | AM | RAF Mildenhall | Tower |
| 122.550 | | AM | West Freugh (MoD) | Tower |
| 122.600 | | AM | Abbeyshrule, Eire | Air/Ground |
| 122.600 | | AM | Castlebar, Eire | Air/Ground |
| 122.600 | | AM | Inverness Airport | Approach/Tower |
| 122.600 | | AM | Lerwick (Tingwall) | Air/Ground and Air Ambulance |
| 122.600 | | AM | Plymouth City Airport | Tower |
| 122.600 | | AM | Seething Aerodrome | Air/Ground |
| 122.600 | | AM | Sherburn-in-Elmet Aerodrome | Tower |
| 122.600 | | AM | White Waltham Aerodrome | Air/Ground |
| 122.625 | | AM | North Sea | Conoco Viking Field |
| 122.650 | | AM | North Sea | Nelson Oil Field deck |
| 122.675 | | AM | Duxford | Ops |
| 122.675 | | AM | Scotland | Bonzai Sqn Air-Air |
| 122.700 | | AM | Barton Aerodrome, Manchester | Air/Ground |
| 122.700 | | AM | Bodmin | Tower |
| 122.700 | | AM | Compton Abbas Aerodrome | Air/Ground |
| 122.700 | | AM | Gormanston, Eire | IAC Military Tower |
| 122.700 | | AM | Northampton (Sywell) | AFIS |
| 122.700 | | AM | Silverstone | Tower |
| 122.700 | | AM | Tiree | AFIS |
| 122.725 | | AM | Filton (BAe), Bristol | Approach/Radar |
| 122.750 | | AM | Cowden Range | Range Control |
| 122.750 | | AM | Netheravon (Army) | Air/Ground (Salisbury Plain) |

| Base | Mobile | Mode | Location | User and Notes |
|---|---|---|---|---|
| 122.750 | | AM | North Coates | Air/Ground Donna Nook Range |
| 122.750 | | AM | Salisbury Plain (Army) | Ops |
| 122.775 | | AM | Crowfield Aerodrome | Air/Ground |
| 122.775 | | AM | North Sea | Scott Oil Field deck |
| 122.775 | | AM | Oaksey Park | Air/Ground |
| 122.800 | | AM | Baldonnel, Eire | Area Control |
| 122.800 | | AM | North Sea | Unionoil Heather Field |
| 122.800 | | AM | Nottingham Aerodrome | Air/Ground |
| 122.800 | | AM | Stapleford | Air/Ground |
| 122.825 | | AM | Bruntingthorpe | Air/Ground |
| 122.850 | | AM | Cranfield | Approach |
| 122.875 | | AM | North Sea | Excalibur Oil Field deck |
| 122.875 | | AM | North Sea | Galahad Oil Field deck |
| 122.875 | | AM | North Sea | Guinevere Oil Field deck |
| 122.875 | | AM | North Sea | Lancelot Oil Field deck |
| 122.875 | | AM | North Sea | Phillips Hewett Field |
| 122.900 | | AM | Dundee | Approach Tower |
| 122.900 | | AM | Gloucestershire Airport | Tower |
| 122.900 | | AM | Kilkenny | Air/Ground |
| 122.900 | | AM | London, Westland Heliport | Tower (Battersea) |
| 122.900 | | AM | Long Marston Aerodrome | Tower |
| 122.925 | | AM | Fenland | Air/Ground and AFIS |
| 122.925 | | AM | North Sea | Phillip Ekofisk Field |
| 122.950 | | AM | Aberdeen (Dyce Airport) | Bristow Helicopters |
| 122.950 | | AM | Birr Aerodrome, Eire | Air/Ground (Birr Radio) |
| 122.950 | | AM | London | Air Ambulance G-HEMS |
| 122.950 | | AM | Nationwide | Freemans Aviation |
| 122.950 | | AM | Nationwide | Helicopter DEPCON (deparature comms.) |
| 122.950 | | AM | North Sea | Eko/Tees Pip Oil Field deck |
| 122.950 | | AM | North Sea | Kotter Oil Field deck |
| 122.950 | | AM | North Sea | Logger Oil Field deck |
| 122.950 | | AM | North Sea | Nam Nam Field |
| 122.950 | | AM | North Sea | Nam Noordwinning |
| 122.950 | | AM | North Sea | Penzoil Noordwinning |
| 122.950 | | AM | North Sea | Petroland Petroland Field |
| 122.950 | | AM | North Sea | Placid Placid Field |
| 122.950 | | AM | North Sea | Zanddijk |
| 122.975 | | AM | Marston Moor Aerodrome | Tower |
| 123.000 | | AM | Connemara, Eire | Air/Ground |
| 123.000 | | AM | Eaglescott | Air/Ground |
| 123.000 | | AM | Halfpenny Green Aerodrome | FIS |
| 123.000 | | AM | Inisheer, Eire | Air/Ground |
| 123.000 | | AM | Inishman, Eire | Air/Ground |
| 123.000 | | AM | Inishmore, Eire | Air/Ground |
| 123.000 | | AM | North Sea | Ivanhoe Oil Field deck |
| 123.025 | | AM | North Sea | Gryphon Oil Field deck |
| 123.025 | | AM | North Sea | Hamilton Ravenspurnn North |
| 123.050 | | AM | Beverley (Linley Hill) | Tower |
| 123.050 | | AM | North Sea | Brent Oil Field log |
| 123.050 | | AM | North Sea | North Cormorant log |
| 123.050 | | AM | North Sea | Shell/Esso Eider Field log |
| 123.050 | | AM | North Sea | Shell/Esso Tern Field log |
| 123.050 | | AM | North Sea | South Cormorant log |
| 123.050 | | AM | Nuthampstead, Royston | Air/Ground |
| 123.050 | | AM | Old Warden (Biggleswade) | Tower (Display days only) |
| 123.050 | | AM | RAF Leconfield | Leconfield Rescue |

| Base | Mobile | Mode | Location | User and Notes |
|---|---|---|---|---|
| 123.050 | | AM | Stevenage Aerodrome | British Aerospace |
| 123.050 | | AM | Wigtown | Tower |
| 123.100 | | AM | Baldonnel, Eire | Ground |
| 123.100 | | AM | London | Special Flypasts Air/Ground (Trooping the Colours etc) |
| 123.100 | | AM | Nationwide | Search & Rescue scene co-ordination |
| 123.100 | | AM | Nationwide | Search and Rescue |
| 123.100 | | AM | RAF Boulmer | Boulmer Rescue |
| 123.100 | | AM | Scotland | Air Mountain Rescue |
| 123.150 | | AM | Fair Isle | Approach (Sumburgh) |
| 123.150 | | AM | Humberside Airport | Radar |
| 123.150 | | AM | Islay Airport | AFIS |
| 123.150 | | AM | Scilly Isles (St. Marys) | Approach/Tower |
| 123.150 | | AM | Shoreham Aerodrome | Approach/Tower |
| 123.150 | | AM | Sumburgh Airport | Approach/Radar |
| 123.175 | | AM | Badminton | Air/Ground |
| 123.200 | | AM | Barrow (Walney Island) | Air/Ground |
| 123.200 | | AM | Enniskillen (St. Angelo) | Air/Ground |
| 123.200 | | AM | Old Sarum | Air/Ground |
| 123.200 | | AM | St Angelo | Tower |
| 123.220 | | AM | Fadmoor Aerodrome | Air/Ground |
| 123.225 | | AM | North Sea | Arco Thames Field |
| 123.225 | | AM | North Sea | Bruce Oil Field deck |
| 123.250 | | AM | Bagby (Thirsk) | Air/Ground |
| 123.250 | | AM | Bembridge, Isle of Wight | AFIS and Air/Ground |
| 123.250 | | AM | Welshpool | Air/Ground |
| 123.275 | | AM | Netherthorpe | Air/Ground |
| 123.300 | | AM | Dublin Airport | Dublin Military ATC |
| 123.300 | | AM | Manchester Airport | ATC |
| 123.300 | | AM | Nationwide | Military Airfield Radar |
| 123.300 | | AM | RAF Benson | Radar |
| 123.300 | | AM | RAF Church Fenton | Talkdown |
| 123.300 | | AM | RAF Coltishall | Radar |
| 123.300 | | AM | RAF Coningsby | Radar |
| 123.300 | | AM | RAF Cottesmore | Talkdown |
| 123.300 | | AM | RAF Cranwell | Talkdown |
| 123.300 | | AM | RAF Honington | Approach |
| 123.300 | | AM | RAF Kinloss | Radar |
| 123.300 | | AM | RAF Lakenheath | Radar |
| 123.300 | | AM | RAF Leeming | Approach |
| 123.300 | | AM | RAF Leuchars | Tower/Radar |
| 123.300 | | AM | RAF Linton-On-Ouse | Radar |
| 123.300 | | AM | RAF Lossiemouth | Director |
| 123.300 | | AM | RAF Lyneham | Talkdown |
| 123.300 | | AM | RAF Marham | Radar |
| 123.300 | | AM | RAF Odiham | Talkdown |
| 123.300 | | AM | RAF Shawbury | Talkdown |
| 123.300 | | AM | RAF St Athan | Talkdown |
| 123.300 | | AM | RAF St Mawgan | Radar |
| 123.300 | | AM | RAF Topcliffe | Talkdown |
| 123.300 | | AM | RAF Valley | Director/Talkdown |
| 123.300 | | AM | RAF Waddington | Director |
| 123.300 | | AM | RAF Wittering | Radar |
| 123.300 | | AM | RNAS Culdrose | Tower/Talkdown |
| 123.300 | | AM | RNAS Yeovilton | Director/Talkdown |
| 123.300 | | AM | Spanish Point, Eire | Air/Ground |

| Base | Mobile | Mode | Location | User and Notes |
|------|--------|------|----------|----------------|
| 123.300 | | AM | Trim, Eire | Air/Ground |
| 123.300 | | AM | Wattishan (Army Airfield) | Approach |
| 123.325 | | AM | Kerry | Tower |
| 123.350 | | AM | Hatfield Aerodrome | Approach |
| 123.350 | | AM | Hawarden Aerodrome | Approach |
| 123.350 | | AM | Nationwide | CAA events (rearly used) |
| 123.350 | | AM | Nationwide | Red Star Racing Yaks Team |
| 123.375 | | AM | Morecambe Bay | British Gas Helicopters |
| 123.375 | | AM | Prestwick | Scottish Control TMA |
| 123.400 | | AM | Great Yarmouth (North Denes) | Approach, Tower and Air/Ground |
| 123.400 | | AM | North Sea | Dab Duc Skjold Field |
| 123.400 | | AM | RAF Lyneham | Radar (Zone) |
| 123.400 | | AM | RAF St Mawgan | Tower |
| 123.425 | | AM | Fairoaks | Tower and AFIS |
| 123.450 | | AM | Cark | Cark Radio |
| 123.450 | | AM | Errol Aerodrome | Drop Zone Control |
| 123.450 | | AM | Mull | Mull Traffic |
| 123.450 | | AM | Nationwide | 100 Sqd. Air to Air |
| 123.450 | | AM | Nationwide | Air-Air Common |
| 123.450 | | AM | Nationwide | US Navy C-12 Air to Air |
| 123.450 | | AM | North Sea | Amoco Indefatigable Field |
| 123.450 | | AM | North Sea | Dab Duc Dan Field |
| 123.450 | | AM | North Sea | Dab Duc Gorm Field |
| 123.450 | | AM | North Sea | Marathon East Kinsale |
| 123.450 | | AM | North Sea | Marathon West Kinsale |
| 123.450 | | AM | North Sea | Rolf Oil Field deck |
| 123.450 | | AM | Unst (Saxa Vord) | Ops |
| 123.475 | | AM | Dunkeswell Aerodrome | Air/Ground |
| 123.475 | | AM | Nationwide | Air Display Team Frecce Tricolori |
| 123.500 | | AM | Baldonnel, Eire | Tower |
| 123.500 | | AM | Berwick-on-Tweed (Winfield) | Winfield Radio |
| 123.500 | | AM | Eggesford Aerodrome | Tower |
| 123.500 | | AM | Felthorpe Aerodrome | Tower |
| 123.500 | | AM | Newtownards | Air/Ground |
| 123.500 | | AM | Sandown, Isle of Wight | Air/Ground |
| 123.500 | | AM | Shobdon Aerodrome | Air/Ground |
| 123.500 | | AM | Stornoway Airport | Approach/Tower and AFIS |
| 123.500 | | AM | Swanton Morley Aerodrome | Air/Ground |
| 123.525 | | AM | North Weald | Air/Ground |
| 123.550 | | AM | North Sea | Captian Oil Field deck |
| 123.550 | | AM | North Sea | Sun Balmoral Field |
| 123.550 | | AM | RAF Brize Norton | ATC |
| 123.575 | | AM | North Sea | Tiffany Oil Field deck |
| 123.600 | | AM | Belmullet, Eire | AFIS and Air/Ground |
| 123.600 | | AM | Cambridge Airport | Approach |
| 123.600 | | AM | Carlisle Airport | Approach/Tower and Air/Ground |
| 123.600 | | AM | Rathkenny | Air/Ground (Rathkenny Radio) |
| 123.600 | | AM | Scatsa Aerodrome | Approach/Tower |
| 123.625 | | AM | Ballykelly | Approach (Eglinton) ATZ |
| 123.625 | | AM | Londonderry | Approach |
| 123.625 | | AM | North Sea | Amoco Indefatigable Field |
| 123.625 | | AM | North Sea | Amoco Leman Field |
| 123.625 | | AM | North Sea | Bessemer Oil Field deck |
| 123.625 | | AM | North Sea | Camelott Oil Field deck |
| 123.625 | | AM | North Sea | Davey Oil Field deck |
| 123.625 | | AM | North Sea | Shell/Esso Indefatigable |

| Base | Mobile | Mode | Location | User and Notes |
|------|--------|------|----------|----------------|
| 123.625 | | AM | North Sea | Shell/Esso Leman Field |
| 123.625 | | AM | North Sea | Shell/Esso Sean Field |
| 123.625 | | AM | North Sea | Thames Oil Field deck |
| 123.625 | | AM | Walton Wood | Air/Ground |
| 123.650 | | AM | Bournemouth | FRADU FR Aviation (Broadway ops.) |
| 123.650 | | AM | Hatfield Aerodrome | Hatair Ops |
| 123.650 | | AM | Hayes Heliport | A/G (Macline Hayes) |
| 123.650 | | AM | London, Heathrow | British Airways |
| 123.650 | | AM | Nationwide | Brymon Airways |
| 123.650 | | AM | North Sea | Beatrice Field deck |
| 123.650 | | AM | North Sea | Brae Oil Field deck |
| 123.650 | | AM | North Sea | East Brae Oil Field deck |
| 123.650 | | AM | S of 56N | Fisheries Protection |
| 123.725 | | AM | Epson Aerodrome | Tower |
| 123.725 | | AM | RAF Brize Norton | Brize Talkdown/Tower |
| 123.750 | | AM | Leeds/Bradford Airport | Approach |
| 123.775 | | AM | Natinwide | CAA Events (rarely used) |
| 123.775 | | AM | Prestwick | Scottish Control |
| 123.800 | | AM | Stansted | Tower |
| 123.875 | | AM | North Sea | Maureen Oil Field deck |
| 123.900 | | AM | London, Heathrow | ATIS |
| 123.925 | | AM | Little Staughton | Air/Ground |
| 123.950 | | AM | Shannon | Shanwick Oceanic ACC |
| 124.000 | | AM | East Midlands Airport | Tower |
| 124.025 | | AM | Wellesbourne Mountford | Air/Ground |
| 124.050 | | AM | Prestwick | Scottish Control |
| 124.075 | | AM | Tatenhill Aerodrome | Air/Ground |
| 124.100 | | AM | Cardiff Airport | Radar |
| 124.125 | | AM | Humberside Airport | ATIS |
| 124.150 | | AM | Little Snoring Aerodrome | Air/Ground |
| 124.150 | | AM | Nationwide | Army Helicopter Common |
| 124.150 | | AM | RAF Marham | Approach |
| 124.200 | | AM | Manchester Airport | Manchester Air Traffic Control |
| 124.225 | | AM | London, Gatwick | Tower |
| 124.250 | | AM | Norwich Airport | Tower |
| 124.275 | | AM | RAF Brize Norton | Brize Director |
| 124.275 | | AM | West Drayton | London Control |
| 124.325 | | AM | Dunsfold Aerodrome | Tower |
| 124.350 | | AM | Bristol Airport | Radar |
| 124.375 | | AM | Newcastle Airport | Approach/Radar |
| 124.450 | | AM | North Sea | Tyra Oil Field deck |
| 124.450 | | AM | Warton (BAe) | Radar |
| 124.475 | | AM | London, Heathrow | Stand-by Tower |
| 124.500 | | AM | Guernsey | Radar |
| 124.500 | | AM | Prestwick | Scottish Control |
| 124.525 | | AM | Dublin | ATIS |
| 124.600 | | AM | West Drayton | London Control FIR Information |
| 124.650 | | AM | Dublin Airport | Area Control Centre (South Sector) & Radar |
| 124.670 | | AM | Hull (Mount Airy) | Approach (Humberside) |
| 124.675 | | AM | Humberside Airport | Approach/Radar |
| 124.700 | | AM | Shannon | Shannon Control |
| 124.750 | | AM | West Drayton | London Control Information |
| 124.800 | | AM | Coventry Airport | Tower |
| 124.825 | | AM | Prestwick | Scottish Control (0700-2145) |
| 124.950 | | AM | Chester Garrison | Army Helicopter |
| 124.950 | | AM | Filton (BAe), Bristol | Approach/Radar |

| Base | Mobile | Mode | Location | User and Notes |
|---|---|---|---|---|
| 124.950 | | AM | Hawarden Aerodrome | Tower |
| 124.975 | | AM | RAF Northolt | Radar |
| 125.000 | | AM | Cardiff Airport | Tower |
| 125.000 | | AM | Dishforth | Approach |
| 125.000 | | AM | RAF Topcliffe | Director |
| 125.050 | | AM | Southend Airport | Radar |
| 125.100 | | AM | Manchester Airport | Manchester Air Traffic Control |
| 125.125 | | AM | RAF Northolt | ATIS |
| 125.175 | | AM | North Sea | Markham Oil Field deck |
| 125.175 | | AM | North Sea | Noordwinning Oil Field deck |
| 125.175 | | AM | North Sea | Noordwinning/Zanddijk Oil Field deck |
| 125.175 | | AM | North Sea | Petroland Oil Field deck |
| 125.175 | | AM | North Sea | Placid Oil Field deck |
| 125.200 | | AM | Jersey Airport | Air Traffic Control (Zone)/Radar |
| 125.250 | | AM | Farnborough (RAE Airfield) | Radar |
| 125.250 | | AM | Lasham | Approach (Farnborough) |
| 125.250 | | AM | RAF Odiham | Approach |
| 125.300 | | AM | Ronaldsway, Isle of Man | Radar |
| 125.325 | | AM | Oxford (Kidlington Airport) | Approach |
| 125.350 | | AM | Alderney | Tower |
| 125.350 | | AM | RAF Waddington | Zone |
| 125.400 | | AM | Shoreham Aerodrome | Tower (when directed) |
| 125.400 | | AM | Yeovil (Westland) | Tower and Air/Ground (Judwin Radio) |
| 125.475 | | AM | West Drayton | London Control Information |
| 125.500 | | AM | RAF Fairford | International Air Tattoo Base Ops |
| 125.550 | | AM | RAF St Mawgan | Approach |
| 125.550 | | AM | Stansted | Tower |
| 125.600 | | AM | Bournemouth (Hurn) | Tower |
| 125.625 | | AM | London, Heathrow | Radar |
| 125.650 | | AM | Gloucestershire Airport | Approach |
| 125.675 | | AM | Prestwick | Scottish Control |
| 125.725 | | AM | Prestwick Airport | Scottish VOLMET |
| 125.800 | | AM | Wattisham (Army Airfield) | Approach |
| 125.800 | | AM | West Drayton | London Control Radar Departure |
| 125.850 | | AM | Cardiff Airport | Approach/Radar |
| 125.850 | | AM | RAF St Athan | Approach |
| 125.850 | | AM | Sumburgh Airport | ATIS |
| 125.875 | | AM | RAF Northolt | Talkdown |
| 125.900 | | AM | Campbeltown | Flight Information |
| 125.900 | | AM | RAF Coltishall | Director |
| 125.950 | | AM | Manchester Airport | Manchester Air Traffic Control |
| 126.025 | | AM | Bristol Airport | ATIS |
| 126.050 | | AM | Coventry Airport | ATIS |
| 126.075 | | AM | West Drayton | London Control |
| 126.100 | | AM | Prestwick | Highland Radar |
| 126.150 | | AM | Nationwide | RAF Flight Checker |
| 126.250 | | AM | Prestwick | Scottish Control (Information) |
| 126.275 | | AM | Birmingham International | ATIS |
| 126.300 | | AM | Prestwick | Scottish Control (2145-0700 Hrs) |
| 126.300 | | AM | West Drayton | London Control Inbound |
| 126.350 | | AM | Canterbury | Traffic information (Manston) |
| 126.350 | | AM | Manston | Approach/Radar (LARS/MATZ) |
| 126.450 | | AM | RAF Northolt | Approach |
| 126.500 | | AM | RAF Church Fenton | Approach (MATZ) |
| 126.500 | | AM | RAF Fairford | Tower (Airshows Only) |
| 126.500 | | AM | RAF Leuchars | Approach (LARS and MATZ) |

| Base | Mobile | Mode | Location | User and Notes |
|------|--------|------|----------|----------------|
| 126.500 | | AM | RAF St Mawgan | Approach (LARS and MATZ) |
| 126.550 | | AM | Wycombe Air Park (Booker) | Tower/AFIS |
| 126.600 | | AM | Manchester Airport | London VOLMET (North) |
| 126.650 | | AM | Manchester Airport | Manchester Air Traffic Control |
| 126.700 | | AM | Boscombe Down (MoD) | Radar |
| 126.700 | | AM | Middle Wallop Army Airfield | Army Air/Ground |
| 126.725 | | AM | Luton Airport | Approach/Radar |
| 126.825 | | AM | London, Gatwick | Approach (Director) |
| 126.850 | | AM | Prestwick | Scottish Control |
| 126.875 | | AM | West Drayton | London Control Inbound |
| 126.925 | | AM | Woodford | Approach/Tower |
| 126.950 | | AM | Stansted | Radar |
| 127.000 | | AM | Dublin Airport | Dublin VOLMET |
| 127.050 | | AM | Nationwide | CAA Test Flights |
| 127.100 | | AM | West Drayton | London Control |
| 127.125 | | AM | Prestwick Airport | ATIS (Information) |
| 127.150 | | AM | RAF Benson | Approach |
| 127.275 | | AM | Prestwick | Scottish ACC (Information) |
| 127.350 | | AM | RAF Waddington | Radar (LARS and MATZ) |
| 127.350 | | AM | RNAS Yeovilton | Approach/Radar |
| 127.350 | | AM | Yeovil | Radar (LAKS) |
| 127.425 | | AM | West Drayton | London Control Upper Sector East |
| 127.450 | | AM | West Drayton | London Military Northwest |
| 127.475 | | AM | Gloucestershire Airport | ATIS |
| 127.500 | | AM | Shannon Airport | ACC |
| 127.525 | | AM | London, Heathrow | Approach |
| 127.575 | | AM | Deanethorpe | Approach |
| 127.650 | | AM | Shannon Airport | Shanwick Oceanic ACC |
| 127.650 | | AM | West Drayton | Oceanic Clearance (E of 30°W) |
| 127.700 | | AM | West Drayton | London Control |
| 127.725 | | AM | Southend Airport | Approach/Tower |
| 127.750 | | AM | Nationwide | Air UK Company Channel |
| 127.750 | | AM | RAF Leeming | Approach/Director |
| 127.875 | | AM | West Drayton | London Control |
| 127.900 | | AM | Shannon | Shanwick Oceanic ACC (Shanwick Radio) |
| 127.900 | | AM | West Midlands | Air Ambulance |
| 127.950 | | AM | London, City Airport | Tower/ATIS |
| 127.975 | | AM | Warton (BAe) | Ops |
| 128.025 | | AM | London, City Airport | Radar/City Radar |
| 128.100 | | AM | St Kilda | Tower |
| 128.125 | | AM | West Drayton | London Control North Sea |
| 128.150 | | AM | Exeter Airport | Tower/Radar |
| 128.175 | | AM | Manchester Airport | ATIS |
| 128.200 | | AM | Belfast (Aldergrove) | ATIS |
| 128.225 | | AM | East Midlands Airport | ATIS |
| 128.250 | | AM | Southampton Airport | Radar |
| 128.250 | | AM | West Drayton | London Military |
| 128.300 | | AM | Aberdeen (Dyce Airport) | Radar |
| 128.300 | | AM | Netheravon (Army) | Drop Zone Radio |
| 128.300 | | AM | Netheravon (Army) | Information |
| 128.325 | | AM | Norwich Airport | Radar |
| 128.350 | | AM | Newcastle Airport | Army Tower |
| 128.425 | | AM | West Drayton | London Control |
| 128.500 | | AM | Duxford | Air Display Channel |
| 128.500 | | AM | Fairford | IAT Ukraine Team SU-27 ops. |
| 128.500 | | AM | Prestwick | Scottish Control (TMA) |

| Base | Mobile | Mode | Location | User and Notes |
|---|---|---|---|---|
| 128.525 | | AM | Sheffield City | AFIS |
| 128.525 | | AM | Sheffield City | Tower/Approach |
| 128.550 | | AM | Bristol Airport | Approach |
| 128.550 | | AM | Clonbullogue, Eire | Air/Ground |
| 128.600 | | AM | West Drayton | London VOLMET (South) |
| 128.625 | | AM | Norwich Airport | ATIS |
| 128.650 | | AM | Alderney | Approach (Guernsey) |
| 128.650 | | AM | Guernsey | Approach |
| 128.675 | | AM | Manchester Airport | Pennine Radar |
| 128.700 | | AM | West Drayton | London Military Radar |
| 128.750 | | AM | Luton Airport | Approach/Radar |
| 128.850 | | AM | Nationwide | Eastern Airlines Packet Ch |
| 128.850 | | AM | Southampton Airport | Approach (as directed)/Radar |
| 128.850 | | AM | Teesside Airport | Radar |
| 128.900 | | AM | RAF Lakenheath | MATZ |
| 128.950 | | AM | Southend Airport | Approach/Radar |
| 128.975 | | AM | Edinburgh Airport | Radar |
| 129.000 | | AM | Nationwide | Hang Gliders & Balloons |
| 129.025 | | AM | London, Gatwick | Radar Standby |
| 129.025 | | AM | Nationwide | Air France Company Chan |
| 129.075 | | AM | West Drayton | London Control |
| 129.100 | | AM | West Drayton | London Control |
| 129.150 | | AM | RAF Linton-On-Ouse | Director/Radar and Departures |
| 129.175 | | AM | Dublin | Area Control Centre (North Sector) |
| 129.200 | | AM | Nationwide | American Airlines Packet |
| 129.200 | | AM | West Drayton | London Control |
| 129.225 | | AM | Prestwick | Scottish Control |
| 129.225 | | AM | Wroughton | PFA Circuit |
| 129.250 | | AM | Nationwide | CAA Special Events |
| 129.250 | | AM | RAF Fairford | Tower (Airshows Only) |
| 129.375 | | AM | West Drayton | London Control |
| 129.400 | | AM | Biggin Hill | Approach |
| 129.425 | | AM | West Drayton | London Control |
| 129.450 | | AM | Manston | Director |
| 129.475 | | AM | RAF Lyneham | Ground |
| 129.500 | | AM | Nationwide | Delta Airlines Packet Channel |
| 129.550 | | AM | Luton Airport | Approach/Radar |
| 129.575 | | AM | Glasgow | ATIS |
| 129.600 | | AM | Nationwide | Delta Airlines Packet Channel |
| 129.600 | | AM | West Drayton | London Control |
| 129.625 | | AM | Nationwide | TWA Packet Frequency |
| 129.650 | | AM | North Sea | Statfjord Oil Field deck |
| 129.700 | | AM | Alderney | Trinity Lightship Heliport |
| 129.700 | | AM | Baldonnel, Eire | IAC Military Radar |
| 129.700 | | AM | Baldonnel, Eire | Radar |
| 129.700 | | AM | Blackbushe | A.T.S. |
| 129.700 | | AM | English Channel | Bishops Rock Trinity Lightship |
| 129.700 | | AM | English Channel | Casquets Trinity Lightship |
| 129.700 | | AM | English Channel | Flatholm Trinity Lightship |
| 129.700 | | AM | English Channel | Hanois Trinity Lightship |
| 129.700 | | AM | English Channel | Inner Dowsing Trinity Lightship |
| 129.700 | | AM | English Channel | Longships Trinity Lightship |
| 129.700 | | AM | English Channel | Lundy South Trinity Lightship |
| 129.700 | | AM | English Channel | Round Island Trinity Lightship |
| 129.700 | | AM | English Channel | Royal Sovereign Trinity Lightship |
| 129.700 | | AM | English Channel | Skerries Trinity Lightship |

| Base | Mobile | Mode | Location | User and Notes |
|---|---|---|---|---|
| 129.700 | | AM | English Channel | Skokholm Trinity Lightship |
| 129.700 | | AM | English Channel | Smalls Trinity Lightship |
| 129.700 | | AM | English Channel | South Bishop Trinity Lightship |
| 129.700 | | AM | English Channel | St Anns Head Trinity Lightship |
| 129.700 | | AM | Glasgow | Northwest |
| 129.700 | | AM | Jersey Airport | Aviation Beauport Ops |
| 129.700 | | AM | London, Heathrow | Mam Aviation |
| 129.700 | | AM | Nationwide | Britannia Ops |
| 129.700 | | AM | Nationwide | Helicopters Air/Air & Air/Ground (temp helipads for BBC O/B) |
| 129.700 | | AM | Nationwide | Trinity House Helicopters |
| 129.700 | | AM | North Sea | Amoco Arbroath Field |
| 129.700 | | AM | North Sea | Amoco Montrose Field |
| 129.700 | | AM | North Sea | Everest Oil Field deck |
| 129.700 | | AM | North Sea | Gannet Oil Field deck |
| 129.700 | | AM | North Sea | Lomond Oil Field deck |
| 129.700 | | AM | Prestwick | Flight handling |
| 129.700 | | AM | Prestwick Airport | Ogden Aviation |
| 129.700 | | AM | Southend Airport | Express Flight |
| 129.725 | | AM | Jersey Airport | Information |
| 129.725 | | AM | Lewes (Deanland) | Air/Ground |
| 129.725 | | AM | Peterborough (Conington) | Air/Ground |
| 129.725 | | AM | Warton (BAe) | Radar |
| 129.750 | | AM | Filton (BAe), Bristol | Rolls Royce Ops |
| 129.750 | | AM | Nationwide | Air Express Ops |
| 129.750 | | AM | Nationwide | BMA Ops |
| 129.750 | | AM | Nationwide | Brymon Airways |
| 129.750 | | AM | Nationwide | Loganair Ops |
| 129.750 | | AM | Nationwide | Manx Ops |
| 129.750 | | AM | North Sea | Elf Aquataine Norge Frigg |
| 129.750 | | AM | North Sea | Kewanee Nordsee Field |
| 129.750 | | AM | North Sea | Total/Elf Frigg Field |
| 129.750 | | AM | Norwich Airport | Air UK Ops |
| 129.750 | | AM | Stansted | Servisair Ops |
| 129.775 | | AM | North Sea | Lennox Oil Field deck |
| 129.775 | | AM | North Sea | North Hamilton Oil Field deck |
| 129.800 | | AM | Bourn Aerodrome | Air/Ground |
| 129.800 | | AM | Breighton | Air/Ground |
| 129.800 | | AM | Donegal (Carrickfinn),Eire | Tower/AFIS |
| 129.800 | | AM | Popham Aerodrome | Popham Radio |
| 129.800 | | AM | Truro Aerodrome | Air/Ground |
| 129.820 | | AM | Esholt | Air/Ground (Esholt Radio Weekends) |
| 129.825 | | AM | Cromer (Northrepps) | Air/Ground (Micro) |
| 129.825 | | AM | Insch Airfield | Air/Ground |
| 129.825 | | AM | Nationwide | Microlight Common |
| 129.825 | | AM | Swindon (Draycott) | Air/Ground |
| 129.850 | | AM | Chester Garrison | Army Helicopter Tower |
| 129.850 | | AM | Waterford | Tower and AFIS |
| 129.875 | | AM | Enstone Aerodrome | Air/Ground |
| 129.875 | | AM | Hethersett Aerodrome | Hethersett Radio |
| 129.875 | | AM | North Sea | Amethyst Field deck |
| 129.875 | | AM | North Sea | BP Cleeton Field deck |
| 129.875 | | AM | North Sea | BP Ravenspurn North Field deck |
| 129.875 | | AM | North Sea | BP West Sole Field deck |
| 129.875 | | AM | North Sea | British Gas Rough Field deck |
| 129.875 | | AM | North Sea | West Sole Oil Field deck |

| Base | Mobile | Mode | Location | User and Notes |
|------|--------|------|----------|----------------|
| 129.900 | | AM | Cardiff | Tremorfa Heliport |
| 129.900 | | NFM | Cockerham | Parachuting |
| 129.900 | | AM | Colerne | AFIS |
| 129.900 | | AM | Coonagh, Eire | Air/Ground |
| 129.900 | | AM | Langar Airfield | Drop Zone |
| 129.900 | | AM | Lasham Aerodrome | Glider Ops |
| 129.900 | | AM | Limerick (Coonagh) | Air/Ground |
| 129.900 | | AM | Liskeard | Civil Heliport |
| 129.900 | | AM | Nationwide | Air Ambulance |
| 129.900 | | AM | Nationwide | Hang Gliding |
| 129.900 | | AM | Nationwide | Hot Air Ballooning |
| 129.900 | | AM | Nationwide | RAF Formation Air/Air |
| 129.900 | | NFM | Nationwide | RAC Network Q Medivac Helo |
| 129.900 | | AM | North Sea | Eider Oil Field deck |
| 129.900 | | AM | North Sea | Phillips Eko/EMB pipe oil field deck |
| 129.900 | | AM | Pocklington | Base |
| 129.900 | | AM | Strathallan Aerodrome | Air/Ground |
| 129.950 | | AM | North Sea | North Cormorant deck |
| 129.950 | | AM | North Sea | Shell/Esso Dunlin field deck |
| 129.950 | | AM | North Sea | Shell/Esso Tern field deck |
| 129.950 | | AM | North Sea | South Cormorant oil field deck |
| 129.950 | | NFM | North Sea | Conooo oil rig |
| 129.950 | | AM | Shetland Basin | Viking Approach |
| 129.950 | | AM | Sumburgh Airport | Helicopter Information |
| 129.970 | | AM | Tibenham | Air/Ground |
| 129.975 | | AM | Nationwide | Gliding |
| 129.975 | | AM | North Sea | Helicopter Common |
| 129.975 | | AM | North Weald | Gliders |
| 129.975 | | AM | Rufforth, York | Air/Ground |
| 129.975 | | AM | Swansea Airport | ATC Glider Training |
| 130.000 | | AM | Boscombe Down (MoD) | Radar |
| 130.025 | | AM | Biggin Hill | Srikair |
| 130.025 | | AM | London | Capital Radio Flying Eye Ops |
| 130.025 | | AM | Nationwide | Dollar Air Metro |
| 130.025 | | AM | Southend Airport | British World Ops |
| 130.025 | | AM | Woodford | BAe Ops |
| 130.050 | | AM | Aberdeen (Dyce Airport) | Ground Staff |
| 130.050 | | AM | Farnborough (RAE Airfield) | Precision Approach Radar |
| 130.050 | | AM | Sumburgh | Radar |
| 130.050 | | AM | West Freugh (MoD) | Approach |
| 130.050 | | AM | Woodford | Tower |
| 130.075 | | AM | London, Gatwick | Servisair Ops |
| 130.075 | | AM | London, Heathrow | Air Malta Ops |
| 130.075 | | AM | RAF Brize Norton | Brize Ops |
| 130.100 | | AM | Bellarena | Air/Ground Gliders |
| 130.100 | | AM | Dishforth | Air/Ground Gliders |
| 130.100 | | AM | Long Marston Aerodrome | Tower |
| 130.100 | | AM | Nationwide | Gliders |
| 130.100 | | AM | Oban | Air/Ground |
| 130.100 | | AM | Perranporth | Glider Ops |
| 130.100 | | AM | Pocklington | Air/Ground Glider Ops |
| 130.100 | | AM | RAF Dishforth (also Army) | Air/Ground |
| 130.100 | | AM | Spalding (Crowland) | Tower |
| 130.100 | | AM | Strubby Aerodrome | Air/Ground (Strubby Base) gliders |
| 130.100 | | AM | Tibenham | Air/Ground (Gliders) |
| 130.125 | | AM | Nationwide | Glider Training |

| Base | Mobile | Mode | Location | User and Notes |
|------|--------|------|----------|----------------|
| 130.125 | | AM | Scarborough | Air/Ground Glider Ops |
| 130.150 | | AM | London, Heathrow | Emirates Ops |
| 130.175 | | AM | Blackbushe | Air Lynton Ops |
| 130.175 | | AM | Blackpool | Janes Ops |
| 130.175 | | AM | Blackpool | Lynton Ops |
| 130.175 | | AM | Cambridge | Suckling Ops |
| 130.175 | | AM | Cambridge Airport | Magnet Air |
| 130.175 | | AM | Exeter Airport | Handling |
| 130.175 | | AM | Exeter Airport | Markair Ops |
| 130.175 | | AM | Liverpool Airport | Emerald Ops |
| 130.175 | | AM | Liverpool Airport | Royal Mail Ops |
| 130.175 | | AM | London, Heathrow | Ambassador Ops |
| 130.175 | | AM | London, Heathrow | Corporate Jet Ops |
| 130.175 | | AM | London, Heathrow | Gama Ops |
| 130.175 | | AM | Luton Airport | Magec Ops |
| 130.175 | | AM | Manchester Airport | Ryan Air Ops |
| 130.175 | | AM | North Weald | Aceair Company channel |
| 130.200 | | AM | Cottesmore | Approach (LARS and MATZ) |
| 130.200 | | AM | Langar Airfield | Approach |
| 130.200 | | AM | North Sea | Alwyn North Oil Field log |
| 130.200 | | AM | North Sea | Dunbar Oil Field deck |
| 130.200 | | AM | Peterborough (Sibson) | MATZ and LARS |
| 130.200 | | AM | RAF Chivenor | Air/Ground |
| 130.200 | | AM | RAF Cottesmore | Approach/Director |
| 130.200 | | AM | RAF Wittering | Radar |
| 130.250 | | AM | East Midlands Airport | Donington Aviation |
| 130.250 | | AM | Hawarden Aerodrome | Radar |
| 130.250 | | AM | Henstridge | Tower |
| 130.250 | | AM | Nationwide | American Airlines Packet |
| 130.250 | | AM | RAF Benson | Tower/Zone |
| 130.250 | | AM | Tresco | Civil Heliport |
| 130.300 | | AM | Nationwide | Aquilla Spanish Display Team Air/Air (if 130.500 in use) |
| 130.300 | | AM | Sturgate Aerodrome | Air/Ground |
| 130.350 | | AM | RAF Northolt | Radar (Director) |
| 130.350 | | AM | Unst (Saxa Vord) | Air/Ground |
| 130.370 | | AM | Blackbushe | Air Hanson Ops |
| 130.375 | | AM | Farnborough | Executive Ops |
| 130.375 | | AM | Manchester Airport | FLS Engineering Ops |
| 130.375 | | AM | Wick | Fuellers (FarNor) |
| 130.400 | | AM | Edinburgh Airport | Approach (gliders) |
| 130.400 | | AM | Kilkenny | Air/Ground (Weekends) |
| 130.400 | | AM | Nationwide | Gliders |
| 130.400 | | AM | Nationwide | Gliders Channel |
| 130.400 | | AM | Punchestown | Air/Ground (Parachute & Glider OPs) |
| 130.400 | | AM | Spalding (Crowland) | Tower (Gliders) |
| 130.400 | | AM | Thirsk (Sutton Bank) | Air/Ground gliders |
| 130.425 | | AM | Elmsett | Air/Ground (Elmsett Radio) |
| 130.425 | | AM | Halton Aerodrome | Air/Ground |
| 130.425 | | AM | Nationwide | Gliders |
| 130.425 | | AM | Nationwide | SAR Incident |
| 130.425 | | AM | Sandtoft Aerodrome | Tower |
| 130.450 | | AM | Glenrothes | Air/Ground |
| 130.450 | | AM | Skegness Aerodrome | Tower |
| 130.450 | | AM | Thruxton Aerodrome | Air/Ground |
| 130.475 | | AM | London, Lippits Hill | Met Police Helicopter Air/Ground |

| Base | Mobile | Mode | Location | User and Notes |
|------|--------|------|----------|----------------|
| 130.475 | | AM | Retford | Air/Ground |
| 130.500 | | AM | Castleforbes, Eire | Air/Ground |
| 130.500 | | AM | Farnborough Airshow | HeliPad |
| 130.500 | | AM | Nationwide | Aquilla Spanish air display team Air-to-Air |
| 130.500 | | AM | Nationwide | CAA Events Air/Ground |
| 130.525 | | AM | RAF Henlow | Para drop zone |
| 130.550 | | AM | Andrewsfield | Air/Ground |
| 130.550 | | AM | Brough Aerodrome | Tower and Air/Ground |
| 130.550 | | AM | North Sea | Amoco Vauxhall Field |
| 130.550 | | AM | North Sea | Phillips Albuskjell Field |
| 130.550 | | AM | North Sea | Phillips Cod Field |
| 130.550 | | AM | North Sea | Phillips Edda Field |
| 130.550 | | AM | North Sea | Phillips Ekofisk Field |
| 130.550 | | AM | North Sea | Phillips Eldfisk Field |
| 130.550 | | AM | North Sea | Phillips Tor Field |
| 130.550 | | AM | North Sea | Valhall Oil Field deck |
| 130.575 | | AM | London, Gatwick | Interflight Ops |
| 130.575 | | AM | London, Heathrow | Shell Ops |
| 130.575 | | FM | Nationwide | Philips Airship Air to Ground |
| 130.575 | | AM | Stansted | Universal Air Handling |
| 130.000 | | AM | Aberdeen (Dyce Airport) | Air UK |
| 130.600 | | AM | Aberdeen (Dyce Airport) | Sorvisair |
| 130.600 | | AM | Belfast (Aldergrove) | Servisair |
| 130.600 | | AM | Birmingham International | Servisair |
| 130.600 | | AM | Blackpool | Servisair |
| 130.600 | | AM | Bournemouth (Hurn) | Channel Express |
| 130.600 | | AM | Bristol Airport | Servisair |
| 130.600 | | AM | Cardiff Airport | Servisair |
| 130.600 | | AM | Edinburgh Airport | Servisair |
| 130.600 | | AM | Guernsey | Servisair |
| 130.600 | | AM | Jersey Airport | Servisair |
| 130.600 | | AM | London, Gatwick | British Caledonian |
| 130.600 | | AM | London, Heathrow | Fields Aviation Ops |
| 130.600 | | AM | London, Heathrow | Huntair |
| 130.600 | | AM | Manchester Airport | Servisair |
| 130.600 | | AM | Manston | KIA Ops |
| 130.600 | | AM | Nationwide | Brymon Airways Ops |
| 130.600 | | AM | Nationwide | Delta Airlines Ops |
| 130.600 | | AM | Nationwide | Servisair |
| 130.600 | | AM | Newcastle Airport | Servisair |
| 130.600 | | AM | Stansted | Air UK Leisure Ops |
| 130.620 | | AM | Stapleford | Stapleford Ops |
| 130.625 | | AM | Aberdeen (Dyce Airport) | Granite Ops |
| 130.625 | | AM | Bristol Airport | Clifton Ops |
| 130.625 | | AM | East Midlands Airport | Donington Aviation Ops |
| 130.625 | | AM | Ronaldsway, Isle of Man | Island Aviation |
| 130.625 | | AM | Southend Airport | British Air Ferries Ops |
| 130.650 | | AM | Bournemouth (Hurn) | Services |
| 130.650 | | AM | Foulsham Aerodrome | Tower |
| 130.650 | | AM | Glasgow | Loganair Ops |
| 130.650 | | AM | Glasgow | Maersk Ops |
| 130.650 | | AM | Jersey Airport | Company Ops |
| 130.650 | | AM | Kyle of Lochalsh | RN Heliport |
| 130.650 | | AM | London, Gatwick | American Airlines |
| 130.650 | | AM | London, Gatwick | China Airlines |
| 130.650 | | AM | London, Gatwick | Handling |

| Base | Mobile | Mode | Location | User and Notes |
|------|--------|------|----------|----------------|
| 130.650 | | AM | London, Gatwick | Korean Airlines |
| 130.650 | | AM | London, Gatwick | Northwest Orient |
| 130.650 | | AM | Luton Airport | Thames Valley Police Operations |
| 130.650 | | AM | Manchester Airport | Aer Lingus Ops |
| 130.650 | | AM | Manchester Airport | Handling |
| 130.650 | | AM | Manchester Airport | LTU Ops |
| 130.650 | | AM | Manchester Airport | Northern Executive |
| 130.650 | | AM | Newcastle Airport | Samson Ops |
| 130.650 | | AM | Skye | Tower |
| 130.650 | | AM | Southampton Airport | Ops |
| 130.675 | | AM | Duxford | Air Display Channel |
| 130.675 | | AM | Nationwide | CAA Events Approach/Tower |
| 130.700 | | AM | Connaught (Knock) Airport | Tower |
| 130.700 | | AM | Land's End (St Just) | Tower/Approach and Air/Ground |
| 130.700 | | AM | Wroughton | Tower |
| 130.725 | | AM | Denham | Air/Ground and AFIS |
| 130.725 | | AM | North Sea | FRG/STFS Pipe |
| 130.725 | | AM | West Freugh (MoD) | Radar |
| 130.750 | | AM | Belfast (City) | Tower |
| 130.750 | | AM | Boscombe Down (MoD) | Tower/Ground |
| 130.750 | | AM | Cambridge Airport | Radar |
| 130.750 | | AM | Manchester Airport | Aer Lingus Ops |
| 130.750 | | AM | Woodford | Approach |
| 130.775 | | AM | Braintree Airfield | Air/Ground |
| 130.800 | | AM | English Channel | Fisheries Protection |
| 130.800 | | AM | Hatfield Aerodrome | Tower |
| 130.800 | | AM | Hucknall Aerodrome | Air/Ground |
| 130.800 | | AM | North Sea | Amoco NW Hutton Deck |
| 130.800 | | AM | North Sea | Conoco Hutton Deck |
| 130.800 | | AM | Warton (BAe) | Tower |
| 130.800 | | AM | Yeovil (Westland) | Approach/Radar (Judwin) |
| 130.825 | | AM | Nationwide | CAA Events (rarely used) |
| 130.850 | | AM | Belfast (City) | Approach/Radar |
| 130.850 | | AM | Little Gransden Aerodrome | Air/Ground |
| 130.870 | | AM | North Sea | Kittiwake Oil Field deck |
| 130.875 | | AM | Nationwide | CAA Events Approach |
| 130.875 | | AM | North Sea | Alba Oil Field deck |
| 130.875 | | AM | North Sea | Andrew Oil Field deck |
| 130.900 | | AM | Nationwide | Dutch F-16 Display Team Air/Air |
| 130.925 | | AM | West Drayton | London Control TMA |
| 130.950 | | AM | Shannon Airport | ATIS |
| 131.050 | | AM | West Drayton | London Control North East UIR |
| 131.075 | | AM | London, Gatwick | Servisair |
| 131.100 | | AM | Nationwide | British Airways Packet |
| 131.125 | | AM | West Drayton | London Control |
| 131.150 | | AM | Shannon | Shannon Control ACC (Cork sector) |
| 131.300 | | AM | Lydd Airport | AFIS |
| 131.300 | | AM | Prestwick | Scottish Control (Stornoway) |
| 131.300 | | AM | Sumburgh Airport | Radar (N. Sea Offshore Advisory) |
| 131.325 | | AM | Birmingham International | Radar |
| 131.375 | | AM | Glasgow | Air Canada |
| 131.400 | | AM | London, Heathrow | Bangladesh Biman |
| 131.400 | | AM | London, Heathrow | CSA |
| 131.400 | | AM | London, Heathrow | Kenya Airways |
| 131.400 | | AM | London, Heathrow | Trans Mediterranean |
| 131.400 | | AM | London, Heathrow | Zambian Airlines |

| Base | Mobile | Mode | Location | User and Notes |
|------|--------|------|----------|----------------|
| 131.425 | | AM | Birmingham International | Allied |
| 131.425 | | AM | Birmingham International | Ogden Aviation |
| 131.425 | | AM | Dublin | British Midlands Ops |
| 131.425 | | AM | London, Gatwick | Air New Zealand Ops |
| 131.425 | | AM | London, Gatwick | Ogden Aviation Ops |
| 131.425 | | AM | London, Gatwick | Virgin Ops |
| 131.425 | | AM | London, Heathrow | British Midlands Ops |
| 131.425 | | AM | London, Heathrow | Royal Jordanian Ops |
| 131.425 | | AM | London, Heathrow | Saudia Ops |
| 131.425 | | AM | Manchester Airport | Cathay Pacific Ops |
| 131.450 | | AM | London, Heathrow | Aer Lingus Ops |
| 131.450 | | AM | London, Heathrow | Air Canada Ops |
| 131.450 | | AM | London, Heathrow | Air Malta Ops |
| 131.450 | | AM | London, Heathrow | Alitalia Ops |
| 131.450 | | AM | London, Heathrow | BWIA Ops |
| 131.450 | | AM | London, Heathrow | Cathay Pacific Ops |
| 131.450 | | AM | London, Heathrow | KLM Ops |
| 131.450 | | AM | London, Heathrow | Pakistan International Ops |
| 131.450 | | AM | London, Heathrow | Thai Airways Ops |
| 131.450 | | AM | Prestwick Airport | Air Canada Ops |
| 131.450 | | AM | Shannon | Servisair |
| 131.475 | | AM | Dublin | Translift Ops |
| 131.475 | | AM | London, Gatwick | British Airways Maintence. |
| 131.475 | | AM | London, Gatwick | Caledonian Ops |
| 131.475 | | AM | London, Heathrow | All Nippon Ops |
| 131.475 | | AM | London, Heathrow | GB Airways Ops |
| 131.475 | | AM | London, Heathrow | Maersk Ops |
| 131.475 | | AM | London, Heathrow | Sabena |
| 131.475 | | AM | London, Heathrow | Speedbird Control North |
| 131.475 | | AM | London, Heathrow | TAT Ops |
| 131.475 | | AM | Nationwide | Canadian Armed Forces |
| 131.500 | | AM | Cork Airport | Aer Lingus Ops |
| 131.500 | | AM | Dublin Airport | Aer Lingus |
| 131.500 | | AM | London, Heathrow | Air France Ops |
| 131.500 | | AM | London, Heathrow | British Airways Ops |
| 131.500 | | AM | London, Heathrow | Kuwait Airways Ops |
| 131.525 | | AM | Luton Airport | London European Airways |
| 131.525 | | AM | Luton Airport | Monarch Airlines |
| 131.525 | | AM | Luton Airport | Ryan Air |
| 131.525 | | AM | Manchester Airport | American Ops |
| 131.550 | | AM | Dublin | Ryanair Ops |
| 131.550 | | AM | London, Heathrow | British Airways Parking |
| 131.550 | | AM | London, Heathrow | Luxair Ops |
| 131.550 | | AM | London, Heathrow | Ryanair Ops |
| 131.550 | | AM | London, Heathrow | Springbok Ops |
| 131.575 | | AM | Belfast (Aldergrove) | British Midland |
| 131.575 | | AM | Birmingham International | Loganair |
| 131.575 | | AM | Birmingham International | TEA Operations |
| 131.575 | | AM | East Midlands Airport | British Midland |
| 131.575 | | AM | East Midlands Airport | Excalibur Ops |
| 131.575 | | AM | Edinburgh Airport | British Midland |
| 131.575 | | AM | Guernsey | British Midland Ops |
| 131.575 | | AM | Jersey Airport | British Midland Jersey Ops |
| 131.575 | | AM | London, Heathrow | Channnel Express Ops |
| 131.575 | | AM | London, Heathrow | El Al |
| 131.575 | | AM | London, Heathrow | Iran Air Ops |

| Base | Mobile | Mode | Location | User and Notes |
|---|---|---|---|---|
| 131.575 | | AM | London, Heathrow | Manx Ops |
| 131.575 | | AM | Plymouth City Airport | Brymon |
| 131.600 | | AM | East Midlands Airport | UPS Ops |
| 131.600 | | AM | London, Gatwick | City Flyer Ops |
| 131.600 | | AM | London, Gatwick | TWA Ops |
| 131.600 | | AM | London, Heathrow | Air Lines Ops |
| 131.600 | | AM | London, Heathrow | Fields Ops |
| 131.600 | | AM | London, Heathrow | TWA Ops |
| 131.625 | | AM | London, Gatwick | British Caledonian |
| 131.625 | | AM | London, Gatwick | Canadian Pacific Ops |
| 131.625 | | AM | London, Gatwick (S. Terminal) | British Airways |
| 131.625 | | AM | London, Heathrow | Royal Jordanian Ops |
| 131.625 | | AM | London, Heathrow | Sabena |
| 131.625 | | AM | Portishead | Aero Radio Telephones |
| 131.625 | | AM | Shannon | Aerofolt Ops |
| 131.650 | | AM | London, Heathrow | Air Malta Ops |
| 131.650 | | AM | London, Heathrow | Japan Airlines Ops |
| 131.650 | | AM | London, Heathrow | KLM Ops Terminal 4 |
| 131.675 | | AM | Luton Airport | Britannia Airways |
| 131.700 | | AM | Birmingham International | Air 2000 Ops |
| 131.700 | | AM | Glasgow | Air 2000 Ops |
| 131.700 | | AM | London, Gatwick | Jetset Ops |
| 131.700 | | AM | London, Heathrow | Air 2000 Ops |
| 131.700 | | AM | London, Heathrow | Crossair Ops |
| 131.700 | | AM | London, Heathrow | Delta Ops |
| 131.700 | | AM | London, Heathrow | KLM |
| 131.700 | | AM | London, Heathrow | Sabena |
| 131.700 | | AM | London, Heathrow | SAS Ops |
| 131.700 | | AM | London, Heathrow | Swissair Ops |
| 131.700 | | AM | Manchester Airport | Air 2000 Ops |
| 131.700 | | AM | Manchester Airport | SAS Ops |
| 131.700 | | AM | Manchester Airport | Swissair Ops |
| 131.725 | | AM | Nationwide | ACARS frequency |
| 131.750 | | AM | London, Gatwick | Continental |
| 131.750 | | AM | London, Heathrow | Aer Lingus Ops |
| 131.750 | | AM | London, Heathrow | Air UK |
| 131.750 | | AM | London, Heathrow | Kenya Airways |
| 131.750 | | AM | London, Heathrow | Lufthansa Ops |
| 131.750 | | AM | London, Heathrow | TAP Air Portugal |
| 131.750 | | AM | Manchester Airport | Aer Lingus Ops |
| 131.775 | | AM | Birmingham International | Air Foyle |
| 131.775 | | AM | London, Heathrow | Aeroflot |
| 131.775 | | AM | London, Heathrow | British Airways Ops |
| 131.775 | | AM | London, Heathrow | CSA |
| 131.775 | | AM | London, Heathrow | Icelandair |
| 131.775 | | AM | London, Heathrow | JAT |
| 131.775 | | AM | London, Heathrow | Korean Air Ops |
| 131.775 | | AM | London, Heathrow | LOT |
| 131.775 | | AM | London, Heathrow | Malev |
| 131.775 | | AM | London, Heathrow | Olympic |
| 131.775 | | AM | London, Heathrow | Sabena |
| 131.775 | | AM | Luton Airport | Air Foyle |
| 131.775 | | AM | Luton Airport | BA Maintence |
| 131.775 | | AM | Stansted | Air Foyle |
| 131.800 | | AM | Edinburgh Airport | British Airways |
| 131.800 | | AM | London, Heathrow | British Airways |

| Base | Mobile | Mode | Location | User and Notes |
| --- | --- | --- | --- | --- |
| 131.800 | | AM | Nationwide | Air to Air Common |
| 131.800 | | AM | Nationwide | Fisheries Protection |
| 131.825 | | AM | Dublin | Park Aviation |
| 131.825 | | AM | Jersey Airport | Company Ops |
| 131.825 | | AM | London, Heathrow | Cathay Pacific Ops |
| 131.825 | | AM | London, Heathrow | Federal Express Ops |
| 131.825 | | AM | London, Heathrow | Gibair Ops |
| 131.850 | | AM | Aberdeen (Dyce Airport) | British Airways Ops |
| 131.850 | | AM | Belfast (Aldergrove) | British Airways Ops |
| 131.850 | | AM | Benbecula | British Airways Ops |
| 131.850 | | AM | Birmingham International | Birmingham Executive |
| 131.850 | | AM | Birmingham International | British Airways Ops |
| 131.850 | | AM | Cork Airport | Aer Lingus Company Channel |
| 131.850 | | AM | Inverness Airport | British Airways Ops |
| 131.850 | | AM | Jersey Airport | British Airways Jersey Ops |
| 131.850 | | AM | London, Heathrow | Emirates Ops |
| 131.850 | | AM | London, Heathrow | Malaysian Airlines |
| 131.850 | | AM | London, Heathrow | United Ops |
| 131.850 | | AM | London, Heathrow | Zambian Airlines |
| 131.850 | | AM | Manchester Airport | British Airways Ops |
| 131.050 | | AM | Nationwide | British Airways Ops |
| 131.875 | | AM | London, Heathrow | Quantas Ops |
| 131.875 | | AM | Manchester Airport | Euro Manx Ops |
| 131.900 | | AM | London, Gatwick | Air 2000 |
| 131.900 | | AM | London, Heathrow | British Airways Speedbird Ops |
| 131.900 | | AM | London, Heathrow | Conair Ops |
| 131.900 | | AM | London, Heathrow | South African Airlines |
| 131.900 | | AM | London, Heathrow | TAT Ops |
| 131.900 | | AM | Prestwick Airport | Eastern Airlines Ops |
| 131.925 | | AM | Birmingham International | Lufthansa |
| 131.925 | | AM | London, Gatwick | American Airlines |
| 131.925 | | AM | London, Heathrow | Air India Ops |
| 131.925 | | AM | London, Heathrow | American Airlines Maintenance |
| 131.925 | | AM | London, Heathrow | American Ops |
| 131.925 | | AM | London, Heathrow | Lufthansa |
| 131.925 | | AM | Manchester Airport | Lufthansa |
| 131.950 | | AM | Dublin | Aer Turas Ops |
| 131.950 | | AM | London, Heathrow | El Al |
| 131.950 | | AM | London, Heathrow | Federal Express |
| 131.950 | | AM | London, Heathrow | Iberia Airlines Ops |
| 131.950 | | AM | London, Heathrow | MEA Ops |
| 131.950 | | AM | London, Heathrow | Nigerian Airlines Ops |
| 131.950 | | AM | London, Heathrow | Olympic Airways Ops |
| 131.950 | | AM | London, Heathrow | Singapore Airlines Ops |
| 131.950 | | AM | London, Heathrow | Viva Ops |
| 131.950 | | AM | Manchester Airport | Federal Express |
| 131.950 | | AM | Nationwide | AAC Eagles Air to Air Secondary |
| 131.950 | | AM | Nationwide | Air France Company Channel |
| 131.975 | | AM | Glasgow | British Airways |
| 131.975 | | AM | London, Heathrow | El Al |
| 131.975 | | AM | London, Heathrow | Nigerian Airlines Ops |
| 131.975 | | AM | London, Heathrow | United Ops |
| 132.050 | | AM | London, Heathrow | Departure/TMA |
| 132.075 | | AM | Edinburgh Airport | ATIS |
| 132.150 | | AM | Shannon | Shannon Control ACC |
| 132.200 | | AM | Reykjavik | Reykjavik Oceanic (Polar Tracks) |

| Base | Mobile | Mode | Location | User and Notes |
|------|--------|------|----------|----------------|
| 132.325 | | AM | Full Sutton | Air/Ground |
| 132.350 | | AM | Filton (BAe), Bristol | Tower |
| 132.400 | | AM | Shoreham Aerodrome | ATIS |
| 132.450 | | AM | West Drayton | London Control |
| 132.550 | | AM | Luton Airport | Tower |
| 132.600 | | AM | West Drayton | London Control SW Approach |
| 132.650 | | AM | Kent | Air Ambulance |
| 132.650 | | AM | London, Heathrow | Medivac |
| 132.650 | | AM | Nationwide | Coastguard standby (mainly used for pollution reporting) |
| 132.650 | | AM | Nationwide | Royal Flights |
| 132.650 | | AM | Oxford | Churchill Hospital Helicopter |
| 132.650 | | AM | RAF Northolt | Queen's Flight Ops (D) |
| 132.650 | | AM | Swansea Airport | Air Sea Rescue |
| 132.700 | | AM | London, City Airport | Approach/Thames Radar |
| 132.700 | | AM | London, Heathrow | Thames Radar |
| 132.725 | | AM | Prestwick | Scottish Control |
| 132.800 | | AM | West Drayton | London Control (Bristol) |
| 132.900 | | AM | Manchester Airport | Pennine Radar |
| 132.900 | | AM | Nationwide | CAA Events Approach/Tower |
| 132.900 | | AM | RNAS Yeovilton | Display director |
| 132.900 | | AM | Wroughton | PFA Arrivals |
| 132.950 | | AM | West Drayton | London Control |
| 133.000 | | AM | RAF Mildenhall | 100th Refuelling Wing |
| 133.050 | | AM | Manchester Airport | Manchester Air Traffic Control |
| 133.175 | | AM | West Drayton | London Control |
| 133.200 | | AM | Prestwick | Scottish Information |
| 133.300 | | AM | West Drayton | London Military Radar |
| 133.400 | | AM | Manchester Airport | Manchester Air Traffic Control |
| 133.450 | | AM | West Drayton | London Control |
| 133.525 | | AM | West Drayton | London Control North Sea |
| 133.550 | | AM | Plymouth City Airport | Approach |
| 133.575 | | AM | North Sea | Clipper Oil Field deck |
| 133.575 | | AM | North Sea | Galleon Oil Field deck |
| 133.600 | | AM | West Drayton | London Control |
| 133.650 | | AM | Weston on the Green | Weston Radio |
| 133.650 | | AM | Wroughton | Tower |
| 133.675 | | AM | Prestwick | Scottish ACC (Entire Route) |
| 133.700 | | AM | West Drayton | London Control |
| 133.750 | | AM | RAF Brize Norton | Brize Director |
| 133.800 | | AM | Shannon Airport | N Altantic Track Broadcasts |
| 133.800 | | AM | West Drayton | Oceanic Track Broadcasts |
| 133.850 | | AM | Bristol Airport | Tower |
| 133.875 | | AM | North Sea | Barque Oil Field deck |
| 133.900 | | AM | West Drayton | London Military Brize Radar |
| 134.025 | | AM | Farnborough Airshow | Farnborough Tower |
| 134.050 | | AM | RAF Wyton | Approach |
| 134.050 | | AM | RNAS Culdrose | Approach/Radar |
| 134.050 | | AM | RNAS Predannack | Culdrose Approach |
| 134.100 | | AM | Aberdeen (Dyce) | Radar |
| 134.100 | | AM | Prestwick | Highland Radar |
| 134.125 | | AM | West Drayton | London Control |
| 134.150 | | AM | Londonderry | Tower |
| 134.150 | | AM | Shetland | Radar |
| 134.225 | | AM | London, Gatwick | Aproach/Radar |
| 134.250 | | AM | West Drayton | London Control North Sea |

| Base | Mobile | Mode | Location | User and Notes |
|------|--------|------|----------|----------------|
| 134.275 | | AM | Shannon | ACC |
| 134.300 | | AM | Kemble | Radar (Brize) |
| 134.300 | | AM | Prestwick | Scottish Military |
| 134.300 | | AM | RAF Benson | Centralised Approach Control |
| 134.300 | | AM | RAF Brize Norton | Brize Radar |
| 134.300 | | AM | RAF Fairford | Centralised Approach Control |
| 134.350 | | AM | Farnborough (RAE Airfield) | Approach |
| 134.350 | | AM | RAF Mona | Radar |
| 134.350 | | AM | RAF Valley | Radar (LARS and MATZ) |
| 134.425 | | AM | West Drayton | London Control Irish Sea |
| 134.450 | | AM | London, Heathrow | London Zone |
| 134.450 | | AM | West Drayton | London Control (Hurn) |
| 134.475 | | AM | Prestwick | Scottish Military |
| 134.475 | | AM | RAF Mildenhall | Tanker flights Air/Air (discreet) |
| 134.500 | | AM | Filton (BAe), Bristol | Filton Ops |
| 134.500 | | AM | Nationwide | CAA Events (rarely used) |
| 134.600 | | AM | Beccles Heliport | Air/Ground |
| 134.650 | | AM | Nationwide | RAF Flight Checker |
| 134.750 | | AM | West Drayton | London Control Upper Sector West |
| 134.775 | | AM | Prestwick | Scottish Control |
| 134.800 | | AM | Biggin Hill | Tower |
| 134.850 | | AM | Duxford | Air Display Channel |
| 134.850 | | AM | Prestwick | Scottish Air Traffic Control |
| 134.900 | | AM | West Drayton | London Control |
| 134.925 | | AM | Cranfield | Tower |
| 134.975 | | AM | London, Heathrow | Approach |
| 134.975 | | AM | Nationwide | CAA Tests Flight |
| 135.000 | | AM | Nationwide | CAA Tests Flight |
| 135.050 | | AM | West Drayton | London Control |
| 135.150 | | AM | RAF West Drayton | London Military Radar |
| 135.175 | | AM | Aberdeen (Dyce Airport) | Information |
| 135.175 | | AM | Dunsfold Aerodrome | Approach/Radar |
| 135.225 | | AM | Shannon | Shannon Control Southern Sector |
| 135.250 | | AM | West Drayton | London Control (Cardiff) |
| 135.275 | | AM | RAF West Drayton | London Military Radar |
| 135.325 | | AM | West Drayton | London Control (Cardiff) |
| 135.375 | | AM | London, Gatwick | London VOLMET (Main) |
| 135.375 | | AM | London, Heathrow | London VOLMET (Main) |
| 135.375 | | AM | Manchester Airport | London VOLMET (Main) |
| 135.375 | | AM | Stansted | London VOLMET (Main) |
| 135.375 | | AM | West Drayton | London VOLMET (Main) |
| 135.400 | | AM | Clacton Aerodrome | Air/Ground |
| 135.425 | | AM | West Drayton | London Control |
| 135.475 | | AM | Nationwide | CAA Tests Flight |
| 135.525 | | AM | Prestwick | Shanwick Oceanic (Clearances) |
| 135.525 | | AM | Shannon Airport | Shanwick Oceanic ACC (Clearances) |
| 135.575 | | AM | London, Gatwick | Radar Standby |
| 135.600 | | AM | Shannon Airport | ACC |
| 135.675 | | AM | Prestwick | Scottish Air Traffic Control |
| 135.700 | | AM | Lee-on-Solent | Tower (Fleatlands) |
| 135.750 | | AM | Farnborough | Air Show Approach |
| 135.750 | | AM | Nationwide | CAA Tests Flight |
| 135.850 | | AM | Prestwick | Scottish Control UIR |
| 135.925 | | AM | Nationwide | Green March Moroccan Display Team |
| 135.950 | | AM | Blackpool | Radar |
| 135.950 | | AM | Nationwide | Army Air Corps Blue Eagles Display Team |

| Base | Mobile | Mode | Location | User and Notes |
|------|--------|------|----------|----------------|
| 135.975 | | AM | Liverpool Airport | Mail Flights (Air-Air) |
| 135.975 | | AM | Nationwide | Army Air Corps Blue Eagles Display Team |
| 135.975 | | AM | Nationwide | Army Air-Air |
| 135.975 | | AM | Nationwide | Green March Moroccan Display Team |
| 135.975 | | AM | Nationwide | Ryanair (Air-Air) |
| 135.975 | | NFM | RAF Fairford | Silver Eagles Display Team |
| 136.050 | | AM | Dublin Airport | Radar |

136.0000 - 138.0000 MHz   NATIONAL & INTERNATIONAL AIR TRAFFIC
CONTROL CENTRES (UPTO 137.00 MHz)
25 kHz, SPACE OPERATIONS AND RESEARCH,
METEOROLOGICTES

THESE SATELLITES OPERATE IN THE SPACE-TO-EARTH DIRECTION

| Base | Mobile | Mode | Location | User and Notes |
|------|--------|------|----------|----------------|
| 136.050 | | NFM | Nongeostationary | Canada Isis 1 |
| 136.080 | | NFM | Nongeostationary | Canada Isis 2 |
| 136.100 | | NFM | Nongeostationary | NASA Explorer 15 |
| 136.110 | | NFM | Nongeostationary | NASA Explorer 35 |
| 136.111 | | NFM | Nongeostationary | NASA Explorer 18 |
| 136.112 | | NFM | Nongeostationary | France/US Ayame 2 |
| 136.112 | | NFM | Nongeostationary | Japan MOS-1 |
| 136.125 | | NFM | Nongeostationary | NASA Explorer 28 |
| 136.141 | | NFM | Nongeostationary | NASA Explorer 34 |
| 136.142 | | NFM | Nongeostationary | NASA Explorer 21 |
| 136.145 | | NFM | Nongeostationary | NASA Explorer Series |
| 136.150 | | AM | Dublin Airport | Radar |
| 136.159 | | NFM | Nongeostationary | Japan Ohsumi 1 |
| 136.160 | | NFM | Nongeostationary | ESRO Aurorae |
| 136.170 | | NFM | Nongeostationary | NASA Explorer 42 |
| 136.170 | | NFM | Nongeostationary | US Echo 2 |
| 136.171 | | NFM | Nongeostationary | NASA Explorer 22 |
| 136.175 | | NFM | RAF Fairford | Chilean Air Force Display Team |
| 136.200 | | NFM | Nongeostationary | US Cameo 1 |
| 136.200 | | NFM | Nongeostationary | US ERS 20 |
| 136.200 | | NFM | Nongeostationary | US Injun SR3 |
| 136.200 | | NFM | Nongeostationary | US Nimbus 2 |
| 136.200 | | NFM | Nongeostationary | US SERT 2 |
| 136.220 | | NFM | Nongeostationary | US OAO 1 |
| 136.230 | | NFM | Nongeostationary | US ESSA 1 |
| 136.231 | | NFM | Nongeostationary | US Tiros 9 |
| 136.233 | | NFM | Nongeostationary | US Tiros 8 |
| 136.234 | | NFM | Nongeostationary | US Tiros 7 |
| 136.250 | | NFM | Nongeostationary | France Castor |
| 136.260 | | NFM | Nongeostationary | NASA OV5-3 |
| 136.273 | | NFM | Nongeostationary | NASA Explorer Series |
| 136.275 | | NFM | Nongeostationary | NASA Explorer 26 |
| 136.290 | | NFM | Nongeostationary | NASA Explorer 40 |
| 136.290 | | NFM | Nongeostationary | NASA Hawkeye |
| 136.293 | | NFM | Nongeostationary | NASA Explorer 25 |
| 136.300 | | NFM | Nongeostationary | NASA SMS 1 |
| 136.319 | | NFM | Nongeostationary | USAF GGSE 1 |
| 136.320 | | NFM | Nongeostationary | NASA GEOS 3 |
| 136.320 | | NFM | Nongeostationary | USAF Ferret |
| 136.348 | | NFM | Nongeostationary | Australia WRESAT 1 |
| 136.350 | | NFM | Nongeostationary | France EOLE 1 |
| 136.350 | | NFM | Nongeostationary | France FR 1 |

| Base | Mobile | Mode | Location | User and Notes |
|------|--------|------|----------|----------------|
| 136.350 | | NFM | Nongeostationary | USAF SR 11B |
| 136.380 | | NFM | Nongeostationary | US ERS 27 |
| 136.410 | | NFM | Nongeostationary | Canada Isis 1 |
| 136.410 | | NFM | Nongeostationary | ITSO Intelsat |
| 136.415 | | NFM | Nongeostationary | USAF ERS 6 |
| 136.430 | | NFM | Nongeostationary | India Bhaskara |
| 136.440 | | NFM | Nongeostationary | USAF ERS 15 |
| 136.468 | | NFM | Nongeostationary | NASA SYNCOM 2 |
| 136.500 | | NFM | Nongeostationary | NASA ATS Series |
| 136.500 | | NFM | Nongeostationary | NASA Injun |
| 136.500 | | NFM | Nongeostationary | NASA SR 3 |
| 136.500 | | NFM | Nongeostationary | US NOAA 10 |
| 136.510 | | NFM | Nongeostationary | NASA OVS 9 |
| 136.521 | | NFM | Nongeostationary | US SOLRAD 11B |
| 136.525 | | AM | London, Gatwick | Information |
| 136.530 | | NFM | Nongeostationary | US OV 5-9 |
| 136.530 | | NFM | Nongeostationary | US SOLRAD 11B |
| 136.530 | | NFM | Nongeostationary | US Vela Hotel 8 |
| 136.560 | | NFM | Nongeostationary | Germany GRS-A |
| 136.563 | | NFM | Nongeostationary | US RADSAT 43 |
| 136.590 | | NFM | Nongeostationary | Canada Alouette 1 |
| 136.590 | | NFM | Nongeostationary | Canada Isis 1 & 2 |
| 136.600 | | AM | West Drayton | London Air Traffic Control (standby) |
| 136.610 | | NFM | Nongeostationary | ESA Arian LO3 |
| 136.610 | | NFM | Nongeostationary | ESA CAT 1 |
| 136.620 | | NFM | Nongeostationary | Italy Sirio 1 |
| 136.620 | | NFM | Nongeostationary | USAF OV 5 |
| 136.625 | | AM | Belfast (City) | AFIS |
| 136.630 | | NFM | Nongeostationary | France Signe 3 |
| 136.650 | | AM | Manchester Airport | Ringway Handling |
| 136.650 | | NFM | Nongeostationary | US TRAAC |
| 136.650 | | NFM | Nongeostationary | US Transit 5B5 |
| 136.650 | | NFM | Nongeostationary | USAF OV 5-5 |
| 136.651 | | NFM | Nongeostationary | USAF SN-43 |
| 136.678 | | NFM | Nongeostationary | US SMS |
| 136.694 | | NFM | Nongeostationary | Japan Shinsei |
| 136.695 | | NFM | Nongeostationary | Japan Jiki'ken |
| 136.710 | | NFM | Nongeostationary | US OSO-4 |
| 136.712 | | NFM | Nongeostationary | US OGO-2 |
| 136.713 | | NFM | Nongeostationary | Japan Tansei |
| 136.713 | | NFM | Nongeostationary | NASA OSO-2 |
| 136.725 | | NFM | Nongeostationary | Japan CORSA B |
| 136.740 | | NFM | Nongeostationary | France ERS-A |
| 136.768 | | NFM | Nongeostationary | ESA ERS-17 ORS3 |
| 136.770 | | NFM | Nongeostationary | US NOAA 6 |
| 136.770 | | NFM | Nongeostationary | US NOAA 8 |
| 136.770 | | NFM | Nongeostationary | US NOAA 9 |
| 136.771 | | NFM | Nongeostationary | USAF ERS-13 TRS6 |
| 136.800 | | AM | Manchester Airport | Airtours Ops |
| 136.800 | | AM | Manchester Airport | Tourjet Ops |
| 136.800 | | AM | Nationwide | Kestrel Ops |
| 136.801 | | NFM | Nongeostationary | USAF SOLRAD 7B |
| 136.804 | | NFM | Nongeostationary | US EGRS SECOR |
| 136.809 | | NFM | Nongeostationary | Japan UME 1 & 2 |
| 136.810 | | NFM | Nongeostationary | Japan ETS-1 KIKU |
| 136.825 | | AM | Dublin | City Jet Ops |

| Base | Mobile | Mode | Location | User and Notes |
|------|--------|------|----------|----------------|
| 136.825 | | AM | London, City Airport | City Jet Ops |
| 136.825 | | AM | Manchester Airport | American Airlines Ops |
| 136.830 | | NFM | Nongeostationary | USAF EGRS 8 |
| 136.830 | | NFM | Nongeostationary | USAF ERS 28 |
| 136.840 | | NFM | Nongeostationary | USAF EGRS 9 |
| 136.840 | | NFM | Nongeostationary | USAF TOPO 1 |
| 136.850 | | AM | East Midlands Airport | UPS Ops |
| 136.860 | | NFM | Nongeostationary | NASA IUE TETR 2 |
| 136.860 | | NFM | Nongeostationary | NASA RMS |
| 136.860 | | NFM | Nongeostationary | US ERS 21 |
| 136.860 | | NFM | Nongeostationary | USA Landsat 2 |
| 136.860 | | NFM | Nongeostationary | USAF Cannonball 2 |
| 136.860 | | NFM | Nongeostationary | USAF OV5-4 |
| 136.870 | | NFM | Nongeostationary | US Injun 3 |
| 136.875 | | AM | London, Gatwick | Monarch Airlines Ops |
| 136.875 | | AM | Luton Airport | Monarch Airlines Ops |
| 136.875 | | AM | Manchester Airport | Airport Monarch Airlines Ops |
| 136.875 | | AM | Nationwide | Monarch Airlines Ops |
| 136.887 | | NFM | Nongeostationary | USAF SOLRAD 7A |
| 136.890 | | NFM | Nongeostationary | NASA Explorer 47 |
| 136.890 | | NFM | Nongeostationary | USAF ERS 9 TRS4 |
| 136.890 | | NFM | Nongeostationary | USAF SOLRAD 6 |
| 136.891 | | NFM | Nongeostationary | USAF ERS 9 |
| 136.892 | | NFM | Nongeostationary | USAF ERS 5 |
| 136.919 | | NFM | Nongeostationary | US Tiros 9 |
| 136.920 | | NFM | Nongeostationary | USAF OSO 8 |
| 136.920 | | NFM | Nongeostationary | USAF SERT 28 |
| 136.950 | | AM | Nationwide | Royal Navy Pussers Pair |
| 136.950 | | NFM | Nongeostationary | ESA COS B1 |
| 136.975 | | AM | London, Heathrow | British Airways Speedbird Ops |
| 136.975 | | AM | London, Heathrow | Conair Ops |
| 136.975 | | AM | London, Heathrow | South African Airlines |
| 136.975 | | AM | London, Heathrow | TAT Ops |
| 136.975 | | AM | Nationwide | Blue Eagles Ch.1 |
| 136.975 | | AM | Nationwide | Navy Gazelle Duo Air/Air |
| 136.975 | | AM | Nationwide | Sharks Helicopter Displays |
| 137.040 | | NFM | Nongeostationary | USAF Ferret |
| 137.080 | | NFM | Nongeostationary | ESA Meteorsat 1/2 |
| 137.110 | | NFM | Nongeostationary | US ATS 6 |
| 137.140 | | NFM | Nongeostationary | ERS ECS 2 |
| 137.150 | | NFM | Nongeostationary | USSR Meteor |
| 137.170 | | NFM | Nongeostationary | ERS MARECS A |
| 137.170 | | NFM | Nongeostationary | France MAROTS |
| 137.190 | | NFM | Nongeostationary | US GEOS 3 |
| 137.200 | | NFM | Nongeostationary | USSR Meteor |
| 137.200 | | AM | USAF Lakenheath | Dep Con |
| 137.230 | | NFM | Nongeostationary | India/USSR Bhaskara 2 |
| 137.230 | | NFM | Nongeostationary | US NOAA 61 |
| 137.260 | | NFM | Nongeostationary | US OAO-A2 |
| 137.300 | | NFM | Nongeostationary | US Meteor 2-17 |
| 137.300 | | NFM | Nongeostationary | US Meteor 3-2 |
| 137.300 | | NFM | Nongeostationary | US Timation 2 |
| 137.300 | | NFM | Nongeostationary | USSR Meteor 2-18 |
| 137.300 | | NFM | Nongeostationary | USSR Meteor 2-5 |
| 137.380 | | NFM | Nongeostationary | USAF OVS 3 |
| 137.400 | | NFM | Nongeostationary | USAF SMS-2 |

| Base | Mobile | Mode | Location | User and Notes |
|------|--------|------|----------|----------------|
| 137.400 | | NFM | Nongeostationary | USSR Meteor 2-16/17 |
| 137.410 | | NFM | Nongeostationary | USAF Explorer 30 |
| 137.410 | | NFM | Nongeostationary | USSR Meteor 3-1 |
| 137.420 | | NFM | Nongeostationary | India Rohini |
| 137.440 | | NFM | Nongeostationary | India Aryabhata |
| 137.440 | | NFM | Nongeostationary | India Bhaskari 3 |
| 137.450 | | AM | Nationwide | 100 Sqdn. Air/Air |
| 137.500 | | AM | Nationwide | 56R Sqdn. Air/Air |
| 137.500 | | NFM | Nongeostationary | US NOAA 10 |
| 137.500 | | NFM | Nongeostationary | US NOAA 6 |
| 137.500 | | NFM | Nongeostationary | USSR Meteor 3-1 |
| 137.560 | | NFM | Nongeostationary | UK UK 6 |
| 137.570 | | NFM | Nongeostationary | NASA Explorer Series |
| 137.620 | | NFM | Nongeostationary | NASA NOAA 11 |
| 137.620 | | NFM | Nongeostationary | NASA NOAA.9 |
| 137.675 | | NFM | Nongeostationary | US P76-5 |
| 137.770 | | NFM | Nongeostationary | US NOAA 9 |
| 137.800 | | NFM | Nongeostationary | USAF SOLRAD 11 |
| 137.850 | | NFM | Nongeostationary | USSR Intercosmos 18 |
| 137.850 | | NFM | Nongeostationary | USSR Meteor 2-15 |
| 137.850 | | NFM | Nongeostationary | USSR Meteor 2-16 |
| 137.850 | | NFM | Nongeostationary | USSR Meteor 2-19 |
| 137.850 | | NFM | Nongeostationary | USSR Meteor 3-3 |
| 137.860 | | NFM | Nongeostationary | US Landsat 2 |
| 137.890 | | NFM | Nongeostationary | NASA RMS |
| 137.890 | | NFM | Nongeostationary | US ANS-1 |
| 137.950 | | NFM | Nongeostationary | Canada Isis |
| 137.950 | | NFM | Nongeostationary | NASA Explorer 45 |
| 137.980 | | NFM | Nongeostationary | NASA Explorer 50 |
| 138.000 | | NFM | Nongeostationary | USAF Hilat 1 |
| 138.500 | | AM | Nationwide | Military Test Flights |

### 138.0000 - 138.2125 MHz    NATIONWIDE PAGING 12.5 kHz

| Base | Mobile | Mode | Location | User and Notes |
|------|--------|------|----------|----------------|
| 138.07500 | | NFM | Nationwide | Vodapage |
| 138.07500 | | NFM | Newmarket | Hospital Paging (LCD Pagers) |
| 138.15000 | | NFM | Nationwide | Vodafone Paging |
| 138.17500 | | NFM | Nationwide | Mercury Personal Pagers |

### 138.01675 - 138.30625 MHz    POLICE AIR TO GROUND

| Base | Mobile | Mode | Location | User and Notes |
|------|--------|------|----------|----------------|
| 138.01625 | | NFM | London | Police helicopter |
| 138.08750 | | NFM | Nationwide | Police Helicopter Ch. 41 |
| 138.09375 | | NFM | England & Wales | Police Helicopter Ch. 1 |
| 138.09375 | | NFM | Humberside | Police Helicopter Air/Ground |
| 138.09375 | | NFM | London | Police Helicopter Ch.1 |
| 138.09375 | | NFM | Merseyside | Police Air Support Grp (M1) |
| 138.09375 | | NFM | Thames Valley | Police Helicopter Ch.1 |
| 138.09380 | | NFM | Nationwide | Police Helicopters |
| 138.10000 | | NFM | London | Police Metropolitan Helicopter |
| 138.10500 | | NFM | Great Lippits Hill | Police Helicopter Ch. 40 |
| 138.10500 | | NFM | Manchester | Police Air Support Unit (I99) |
| 138.10500 | | NFM | Merseyside | Police Air Support Unit (I99) |
| 138.10625 | | NFM | England & Wales | Police Helicopter Ch.2 |
| 138.10625 | | NFM | London | Police Helicopter Ch.2 |
| 138.10625 | | NFM | Manchester | Police Helicopter |
| 138.10625 | | NFM | Thames Valley | Police Helicopter Ch.2 |

| Base | Mobile | Mode | Location | User and Notes |
|------|--------|------|----------|----------------|
| 138.10625 | | NFM | West Midlands | Police Helicopter Ch.2 |
| 138.29375 | | NFM | Cheshire | Police Helicopter |
| 138.29375 | | NFM | England & Wales | Police Helicopter Ch.3 |
| 138.29375 | | NFM | London | Police Helicopter Ch.3 |
| 138.29375 | | NFM | Thames Valley | Police Helicopter Ch.3 |
| 138.30625 | | NFM | England & Wales | Police Helicopter Ch.4 |
| 138.30625 | | NFM | Lancashire | Police Helicopter |
| 138.30625 | | NFM | London | Police Helicopter Ch.4 |

## 138.00625 - 140.96875 MHz — VHF HIGH BAND PUBLIC UTILITIES AND TRANSPORT 12.5 kHz

| Base | Mobile | Mode | Location | User and Notes |
|------|--------|------|----------|----------------|
| 138.02500 | | NFM | Kent | Southern Gas |
| 138.02500 | | NFM | York | North East Gas |
| 138.16125 | | NFM | Windermere | Data Link |
| 138.20000 | | NFM | Gloucester | British Gas |
| 138.25625 | | NFM | Perth | Data Link |
| 138.30000 | | AM | Nationwide | USAF Air to Air |
| 138.32500 | | AM | Nationwide | Team Apache |
| 138.32500 | | NFM | Nationwide | Railtrack |
| 138.32500 | | NFM | Woodbridge | East Suffolk Line |
| 138.33125 | | NFM | Tayside | Data Link |
| 138.33750 | | NFM | Newmarket | Data Link |
| 138.36875 | | NFM | Norfolk | Data Link |
| 138.36875 | | NFM | Suffolk | Data Link |
| 138.38750 | | AM | Halifax | North East Gas |
| 138.39375 | | AM | Holdengate, Keighley | British Gas |
| 138.39375 | | AM | Southowram, Halifax | British Gas |
| 138.40000 | | AM | Bradford | British Gas |
| 138.40625 | | AM | Holdengate, Keighley | British Gas |
| 138.40625 | | AM | Southowram, Halifax | British Gas |
| 138.41250 | | AM | Keighley | British Gas |
| 138.41875 | | AM | Tingley, Leeds | British Gas |
| 138.41875 | | AM | Wetherby | British Gas |
| 138.43125 | | AM | Moortop, Horsforth | British Gas |
| 138.44000 | | AM | Swindon | British Gas |
| 138.44375 | | AM | Queensbury, Bradford | British Gas |
| 138.45625 | | AM | Moortop, Leeds | British Gas |
| 138.45625 | | AM | Tingley, Leeds | British Gas |
| 138.45625 | | AM | Wetherby | British Gas |
| 138.46250 | | AM | Skipton | British Gas |
| 138.46875 | | AM | Brighouse, Halifax | British Gas |
| 138.46875 | | AM | Heyshaw, Harrogate | British Gas |
| 138.46875 | | AM | Moortop, Ilkley | British Gas |
| 138.46875 | | AM | Nappa, Keighley | British Gas |
| 138.46875 | | AM | Todmorden, Halifax | British Gas |
| 138.47500 | | AM | Otley | British Gas |
| 138.48125 | | AM | Moortop, Horseforth | British Gas |
| 138.48125 | | AM | Tingley, Leeds | British Gas |
| 138.54375 | | AM | Essex | Eastern Gas |
| 138.63135 | | AM | Luton | British Gas Ch2 |
| 138.66250 | | NFM | Barrow in Furness | Norweb Electricity |
| 138.75625 | | AM | Brecon | Welsh Gas |
| 138.75625 | | AM | Suffolk | British Gas |
| 138.82000 | | AM | Manchester | British Gas |
| 138.83125 | | AM | Brecknock East | Welsh Gas |

| Base | Mobile | Mode | Location | User and Notes |
|---|---|---|---|---|
| 138.83125 | | AM | Bury St Edmonds | British Gas |
| 138.83125 | | AM | Luton | British Gas |
| 138.84000 | | AM | Falkirk | Scottish Gas |
| 138.84375 | | AM | Peterborough | British Gas Ch 1 |
| 138.85200 | | AM | Yorkshire | British Gas |
| 138.85625 | | AM | Brecon | Welsh Gas |
| 138.85625 | | AM | Norfolk | Eastern Gas |
| 138.85625 | | AM | Suffolk | Eastern Gas |
| 138.86635 | | AM | Norwich | British Gas Ch 2 |
| 138.86875 | | AM | Norwich | British Gas |
| 138.88755 | | NFM | Belfast | Data Link |
| 138.95625 | | AM | Nationwide | PLC Plant Hire |
| 138.96875 | 148.46875 | NFM | Yorkshire | British Coal Security |
| 138.97500 | | AM | Glasgow | Scottish Power |
| 138.98000 | | AM | Aberdeen | British Gas |
| 138.98000 | | AM | Edinburgh | British Gas |
| 138.98125 | | AM | Brecon | Welsh Gas |
| 138.98125 | | AM | Keighly | British Gas |
| 138.98125 | | AM | Peterborough | British Gas Ch 2 |
| 138.99375 | | AM | Brecknock East | Welsh Gas |
| 138.99375 | | AM | Lincolnshire | British Gas |
| 138.99375 | | AM | Luton | British Gas Ch 1 |
| 139.00000 | | AM | Glasgow | Scottish Power |
| 139.00000 | | AM | Hull | Eastern British Gas |
| 139.00000 | | NFM | Nationwide | Illegal Bugging Devices |
| 139.00625 | | AM | Derbyshire | British Gas |
| 139.00625 | | AM | Humberside | North East Gas |
| 139.00625 | | AM | Ipswich | British Gas |
| 139.00625 | | AM | Norwich | British Gas |
| 139.01250 | | AM | Barrow | British Gas |
| 139.01250 | | AM | Cumbria | British Gas |
| 139.01250 | | AM | Oxford | British Gas |
| 139.01250 | | AM | Truro | British Gas |
| 139.01875 | | AM | Oxfordshire | British Gas |
| 139.03125 | | AM | Bradford | British Gas |
| 139.03125 | | NFM | Lancaster | British Gas |
| 139.03125 | | AM | Luton | British Gas |
| 139.03125 | | NFM | Morecambe | British Gas |
| 139.03125 | | AM | Norwich | British Gas |
| 139.03125 | | AM | Peterborough | British Gas |
| 139.03375 | | AM | Kent | Southern Gas |
| 139.04375 | | AM | Bradford | North East Gas |
| 139.05626 | | AM | Bradford | North East Gas |
| 139.06250 | | AM | Bradford | British Gas |
| 139.06250 | | AM | Edinburgh | British Gas |
| 139.06875 | | NFM | Nationwide | Press Construction Ltd |
| 139.06875 | | AM | Suffolk | British Gas |
| 139.08125 | | AM | Essex | Essex Gas |
| 139.08125 | | AM | Radnor | Welsh Gas Channel 3 |
| 139.08125 | | AM | Reading | British Gas |
| 139.10000 | | AM | Oxford | British Gas |
| 139.10625 | | AM | Balshall | British Gas |
| 139.10625 | | AM | Grimsby | British Gas |
| 139.10625 | | AM | Ipswich | British Gas |
| 139.10625 | | AM | Kings Heath | British Gas |
| 139.11575 | | AM | Kent | Southern Gas |

| Base | Mobile | Mode | Location | User and Notes |
|------|--------|------|----------|----------------|
| 139.11875 | | AM | Oxford | British Gas |
| 139.12250 | | AM | Bath | British Gas |
| 139.12500 | | AM | Kent | British Gas |
| 139.13000 | | AM | Milton Keynes | British Gas |
| 139.13125 | | AM | Bath | British Gas |
| 139.13125 | | AM | Brecon | South Wales Electric |
| 139.13125 | | AM | Milton Keynes | British Gas |
| 139.13750 | | AM | East Sussex | British Gas |
| 139.13750 | | AM | London | British Gas |
| 139.14000 | | AM | Truro | British Gas |
| 139.14375 | | AM | Kent | Southern Gas |
| 139.15000 | | AM | Leicester | British Gas |
| 139.15000 | | AM | Manchester | British Gas |
| 139.15500 | | AM | Crewe | British Gas |
| 139.16250 | | AM | Surrey | British Gas |
| 139.16250 | | AM | Yorkshire | Yorkshire Electric |
| 139.16275 | | NFM | Essex | North Thames Gas |
| 139.17000 | | AM | Farnborough | British Gas |
| 139.17000 | | NFM | Scarborough | British Gas |
| 139.17500 | | AM | Halifax | British Gas |
| 139.17625 | | AM | Essex | Seeboard |
| 139.18130 | | AM | Hull | British Gas |
| 139.19375 | | NFM | Essex | North Thames Gas |
| 139.19500 | | NFM | Lancaster | British Gas |
| 139.19500 | | NFM | Morecambe | British Gas |
| 139.19500 | | AM | South Yorkshire | British Gas |
| 139.19500 | | AM | Swindon | British Gas |
| 139.20000 | | AM | Yorkshire | Emergency Gas Call Outs |
| 139.20625 | | AM | Kent | Southern Gas |
| 139.21000 | | AM | London | British Gas |
| 139.24375 | 147.74375 | AM | Nationwide | New Power and Fuel Ch |
| 139.25000 | | AM | Leeds | British Gas |
| 139.25625 | 147.75625 | AM | Clacton | British Gas |
| 139.25625 | 147.75625 | AM | Nationwide | New Power and Fuel Ch 1 |
| 139.25625 | 147.75625 | AM | Oxford | Western Gas |
| 139.26250 | | AM | Yorkshire | British Gas |
| 139.26575 | | NFM | Kent | Southern Gas |
| 139.26875 | 147.76875 | AM | Nationwide | New Power and Fuel Ch 2 |
| 139.26875 | 147.76875 | AM | West Midlands | Electric Company |
| 139.27500 | | AM | London | British Gas |
| 139.28125 | 147.78125 | AM | Kent | Southern Gas |
| 139.28125 | 147.78125 | AM | Nationwide | New Power and Fuel Ch 3 |
| 139.28750 | | AM | London | British Gas |
| 139.29375 | 147.79375 | AM | Kent | Southern Gas |
| 139.29375 | 147.79375 | AM | Nationwide | New Power and Fuel Ch |
| 139.30000 | | NFM | Space | Shuttle to Mix link |
| 139.30625 | 147.80625 | AM | Essex | Seeboard |
| 139.30625 | 147.80625 | AM | Nationwide | New Power and Fuel Ch 5 |
| 139.31250 | 147.81250 | AM | Staines | North Thames Gas |
| 139.31250 | 147.81250 | AM | Wakefield | British Gas |
| 139.31875 | 147.81875 | AM | Brecon | SWALEC |
| 139.31875 | 147.81875 | AM | Nationwide | New Power and Fuel Ch 6 |
| 139.33125 | 147.83125 | AM | Kent | Southern Gas |
| 139.33125 | 147.83125 | AM | Manchester | British Gas |
| 139.33125 | 147.83125 | AM | Nationwide | New Power and Fuel Ch 7 |
| 139.34375 | 147.84375 | AM | Kent | Southern Gas |

| Base | Mobile | Mode | Location | User and Notes |
|------|--------|------|----------|----------------|
| 139.34375 | 147.84375 | AM | Nationwide | New Power and Fuel Ch 8 |
| 139.35000 | | AM | London | British Gas |
| 139.35625 | 147.85625 | AM | Nationwide | New Power and Fuel Ch 9 |
| 139.35625 | 147.85625 | AM | Walton-on-Thames | Southern Gas |
| 139.35875 | 147.85875 | AM | Walton-on-Thames | Southern Gas |
| 139.36250 | | AM | Surrey | British Gas |
| 139.36875 | 147.86875 | AM | Nationwide | New Power and Fuel Ch 10 |
| 139.36875 | 147.86875 | AM | Woodbridge | British Gas |
| 139.38125 | 147.88125 | AM | Nationwide | New Power and Fuel Ch 11 |
| 139.39375 | 147.89375 | AM | Nationwide | New Power and Fuel Ch 12 |
| 139.39375 | 147.89375 | AM | Norfolk | Eastern Gas |
| 139.39375 | 147.89375 | AM | Suffolk | British Gas |
| 139.40625 | 147.90625 | AM | Nationwide | New Power and Fuel Ch 13 |
| 139.41675 | 147.91875 | AM | Nationwide | New Power and Fuel Ch 14 |
| 139.42500 | | AM | Barrow | British Gas |
| 139.42500 | | AM | Cumbria | British Gas |
| 139.43125 | | AM | Kent | Southern Gas |
| 139.43125 | 147.93125 | AM | Nationwide | New Power and Fuel Ch 15 |
| 139.43750 | | AM | Shipley | Yorkshire Electricity |
| 139.44375 | 147.94375 | AM | Nationwide | New Power and Fuel Ch 16 |
| 139.45500 | | AM | Swindon | British Gas |
| 139.45625 | 147.95625 | AM | Nationwide | New Power and Fuel Ch 17 |
| 139.46875 | | AM | Oxford | Southern Electricity |
| 139.51250 | 148.01250 | NFM | Newport | British Gas |
| 139.51875 | 148.01875 | AM | Kent | Seeboard |
| 139.51875 | 148.01875 | NFM | Nationwide | Electricity Ch J22 |
| 139.52500 | | AM | Cumbria | Norweb |
| 139.52500 | | NFM | Shrewsbury | East Midlands Electricity |
| 139.53000 | | NFM | Manchester | Norweb |
| 139.53125 | 148.03125 | NFM | Nationwide | Electricity Ch J23 |
| 139.53125 | 148.03125 | NFM | West Midlands | East Midlands Electricity |
| 139.54375 | 148.04375 | AM | Highlands | Scottish Hydro Electric |
| 139.54375 | 148.04375 | NFM | Nationwide | Electricity Ch J24 |
| 139.54375 | 148.04375 | AM | Windsor | Eastern Electric |
| 139.55000 | 148.05500 | NFM | Channel Islands | JFMG Radio Mic |
| 139.55000 | 148.05500 | NFM | Leeds | Yorkshire Electricity |
| 139.55000 | 148.05500 | NFM | Plymouth | Parcel Delivery |
| 139.55000 | 148.05500 | NFM | Somerset | SWEB |
| 139.55000 | 148.05500 | AM | Tunbridge Wells | Seeboard Power Care (TANGO) |
| 139.55625 | 148.05625 | AM | Abingdon | Seeboard |
| 139.55625 | 148.05625 | NFM | Nationwide | Electricity Ch J25 |
| 139.55625 | 148.05625 | NFM | West Sussex | Seeboard |
| 139.56250 | 148.06250 | NFM | Arnside | Voice Link |
| 139.56250 | 148.06250 | NFM | Devon | South West Electricity VHF phone link |
| 139.56250 | 148.06250 | AM | Hampshire | Southern Electric |
| 139.56250 | 148.06250 | AM | Hull | Yorkshire Electricity |
| 139.56250 | 148.06250 | AM | Milton Keynes | Eastern Electric |
| 139.56250 | 148.06250 | NFM | Newmarket | Data Link [Multi-Station] |
| 139.56250 | 148.06250 | AM | Tunbridge Wells | Seeboard Power Care (TANGO) |
| 139.56875 | 148.06875 | AM | Argyll | Scottish Hydro Electric |
| 139.56875 | 148.06875 | NFM | Nationwide | Electricity Ch J26 |
| 139.56875 | 148.06875 | AM | Perth | Scottish Hydro Electric |
| 139.56875 | 148.06875 | NFM | West Midlands | MEB |
| 139.57000 | 148.07000 | NFM | Lancaster | ManWeb |
| 139.57000 | 148.07000 | NFM | Morecambe | Northern Electric |
| 139.57000 | 148.07000 | NFM | Newmarket | Data Link |

| Base | Mobile | Mode | Location | User and Notes |
|---|---|---|---|---|
| 139.57500 | 148.07000 | AM | Bradford | Yorkshire Electricity |
| 139.57500 | 148.07000 | NFM | Channel Islands | JFMG Radio Mic |
| 139.57500 | 148.07000 | NFM | Cheshire | MEB |
| 139.57500 | 148.07000 | NFM | Jersey | Electric Board |
| 139.58000 | 139.58000 | NFM | Staffs | East Midland Electricity |
| 139.58000 | 148.01250 | NFM | Burnley | Norweb |
| 139.58000 | 148.01250 | AM | Cornwall | South West Electricity |
| 139.58000 | 148.01250 | NFM | Glenrothes | Scottish Hydro Electric |
| 139.58000 | 148.08000 | NFM | Somerset | SWEB |
| 139.58125 | 148.08125 | NFM | Ipswich | Eastern Electricity |
| 139.58125 | 148.08125 | NFM | Nationwide | Electricity Ch J27 |
| 139.58125 | 148.08125 | AM | Thames Valley | Eastern Electric |
| 139.58500 | 148.08500 | NFM | Glenrothes | Scottish Hydro Electric |
| 139.58750 | | NFM | Glasgow | Data Link |
| 139.59375 | 148.09375 | NFM | Nationwide | Electricity Ch J28 |
| 139.60000 | | NFM | Devon | South West Electricity ground workers |
| 139.60000 | | NFM | Lauder | Data Link |
| 139.60000 | | NFM | Nationwide | Illegal Bugging Devices |
| 139.60500 | | NFM | Manchester | Manweb |
| 139.60625 | 148.10625 | NFM | Nationwide | Electricity Ch J29 |
| 139.61250 | | AM | Morecambe | North West Electricity |
| 139.61375 | 148.11375 | NFM | Stirling | Data Link |
| 139.61875 | 148.11875 | NFM | Nationwide | Electricity Ch J30 |
| 139.62375 | 148.12375 | AM | Stirling | Scottish Hydro Electric |
| 139.62500 | 148.12500 | NFM | Alnwick | Data Link |
| 139.62500 | 148.12500 | NFM | Newport | SWALAC |
| 139.62500 | 148.12500 | AM | Perth | Scottish Hydro Electric |
| 139.63000 | | AM | Rayleigh | Eastern Electricity |
| 139.63125 | 148.13125 | AM | Harold Hill | Eastern Electric |
| 139.63125 | 148.13125 | NFM | Nationwide | Electricity Ch J31 |
| 139.63125 | 148.13125 | AM | Thames Valley | Eastern Electric |
| 139.63125 | 148.13125 | NFM | West Midlands | Midlands Electricity |
| 139.63125 | 148.13125 | NFM | West Sussex | Southern Electric |
| 139.63750 | 148.13750 | AM | Aberdeen | Scottish Hydro Electric |
| 139.63750 | 148.13750 | AM | Gloucester | MEB |
| 139.63750 | 148.13750 | AM | Kent | Seeboard |
| 139.63750 | 148.13750 | AM | Morecambe | North West Electricity |
| 139.63750 | 148.13750 | AM | Newmarket | Eastern Electricity |
| 139.63750 | 148.13750 | AM | Portsmouth | Southern Electric |
| 139.64375 | 148.14375 | AM | Cambridge | Eastern Electricity |
| 139.64375 | 148.14375 | NFM | Chesterfield | East Midlands Electricity |
| 139.64375 | 148.14375 | AM | Highlands | Scottish Hydro Electric |
| 139.64375 | 148.14375 | NFM | Nationwide | Electricity Ch J32 |
| 139.64375 | 148.14375 | NFM | West Midlands | Midlands Electricity |
| 139.64500 | | NFM | Burnley | Norweb |
| 139.64500 | | NFM | Manchester | Norweb |
| 139.65000 | | NFM | Channel Islands | JFMG Radio Mic |
| 139.65000 | | NFM | Harlow | Eastern Electricity |
| 139.65000 | | AM | Immingham | Yorkshire Electricity |
| 139.65000 | | NFM | Manchester | Norweb |
| 139.65625 | | AM | Kent | Southern Electric |
| 139.65625 | 148.15625 | NFM | Nationwide | Electricity Ch J33 |
| 139.65625 | 148.15625 | AM | Norwich | Eastern Electric |
| 139.66875 | 148.16875 | AM | Clacton-on-Sea | Eastern Electricity |
| 139.66875 | 148.16875 | NFM | Nationwide | Electricity Ch J34 |
| 139.66875 | 148.16875 | NFM | West Sussex | Southern Electric |

| Base | Mobile | Mode | Location | User and Notes |
|---|---|---|---|---|
| 139.67500 | | NFM | Devon | South West Electricity |
| 139.67500 | | NFM | Dyfed | SWEB |
| 139.67500 | | AM | Newmarket | Eastern Electricity |
| 139.67500 | | AM | Perth | Scottish Hydro Electric |
| 139.67500 | | AM | Surrey | Seeboard |
| 139.68000 | | AM | Aberdeen | Scottish Hydro Electric |
| 139.68000 | | NFM | Normanton, West Yorkshire | Cable & Wireless |
| 139.68125 | 148.18125 | NFM | Nationwide | Electricity Ch J35 |
| 139.68125 | 148.18125 | AM | Norfolk | Eastern Electric |
| 139.68200 | | AM | Perth | Scottish Hydro Electric |
| 139.68500 | | AM | Aberdeen | Scottish Hydro Electric |
| 139.68750 | | AM | East Sussex | Seeboard |
| 139.69000 | | NFM | Burnley | Norweb |
| 139.69375 | 148.19375 | NFM | Ayr | Scottish Power |
| 139.69375 | 148.19375 | AM | Highlands | Scottish Hydro Electric |
| 139.69375 | 148.19375 | NFM | Nationwide | Electricity Ch J36 |
| 139.69375 | 148.19375 | AM | Norwich | Eastern Electric |
| 139.69375 | 148.19375 | NFM | West Midlands | East Midlands Electricity |
| 139.69500 | | NFM | Glenrothes | Scottish Hydro Electric |
| 139.69500 | | NFM | Tyne & Wear | Northern Electricity |
| 139.70000 | | AM | Kent | Seeboard |
| 139.70000 | | NFM | Lothian & Borders | Scottish Power |
| 139.70500 | | NFM | Bolton | Electric Company |
| 139.70500 | | NFM | Norfolk | Street Lighting |
| 139.70625 | | AM | Chelmsford | Seeboard |
| 139.70625 | | AM | Dundee | Scottish Hydro Electric |
| 139.70625 | 148.20625 | NFM | Ipswich | Eastern Electricity |
| 139.70625 | 148.20625 | NFM | Nationwide | Electricity Ch J37 |
| 139.71250 | | AM | Aberdeen | Scottish Hydro Electric |
| 139.71250 | | NFM | Glasgow | Scottish Power |
| 139.71625 | | AM | Perth | Scottish Hydro Electric |
| 139.71875 | 148.21875 | AM | Harlow | Southern Electric |
| 139.71875 | 148.21875 | NFM | Nationwide | Electricity Ch J38 |
| 139.72000 | | AM | Glasgow | Scottish Power |
| 139.72000 | | AM | Swindon | Southern Electricity |
| 139.72375 | | AM | Stirling | Scottish Hydro Electric |
| 139.72500 | | AM | Hampshire | Southern Electricity |
| 139.72500 | | AM | London | London Electricity |
| 139.72500 | | NFM | South Wales | SWALEC |
| 139.73000 | | NFM | Blackpool | Norweb |
| 139.73000 | | AM | Folkestone | Seeboard |
| 139.73000 | | AM | South Yorkshire | Yorkshire Electricity |
| 139.73125 | 148.23125 | AM | Andover | Electric Line Faults |
| 139.73125 | 148.23125 | AM | Essex | Eastern Electric |
| 139.73125 | 148.23125 | AM | Highlands | Scottish Hydro Electric |
| 139.73125 | 148.23125 | AM | Kings Lynn | Eastern Electric |
| 139.73125 | 148.23125 | NFM | Nationwide | Electricity Ch J39 |
| 139.73125 | 148.23125 | NFM | Whitehaven | Norweb |
| 139.73750 | 148.23750 | AM | Leeds | Yorkshire Electricity |
| 139.73750 | 148.23750 | AM | Portsmouth | Southern Electric |
| 139.73750 | 148.23750 | AM | Slough | Southern Electric |
| 139.73750 | 148.23750 | AM | Surrey | Seeboard |
| 139.74375 | 148.24375 | AM | Essex | Eastern Electric |
| 139.74375 | 148.24375 | NFM | Nationwide | Electricity Ch J40 |
| 139.74375 | 148.24375 | NFM | West Midlands | East Midlands Electricity |
| 139.74375 | 148.24375 | NFM | West Sussex | Southern Electric |

| Base | Mobile | Mode | Location | User and Notes |
|---|---|---|---|---|
| 139.74375 | 148.24375 | AM | West Yorkshire | Yorkshire Electricity |
| 139.74500 | | NFM | Glossop | East Midlands Electricity |
| 139.75000 | | AM | Hertfordshire | East Midlands Electricity |
| 139.75000 | | NFM | South Wales | SWALEC |
| 139.75500 | | AM | Rayleigh | Eastern Electricity |
| 139.75625 | 148.26625 | AM | Essex | Eastern Electric |
| 139.75625 | 148.26625 | NFM | Nationwide | Electricity Ch J41 |
| 139.76250 | 148.25000 | NFM | Cardiff | S Wales Electricity |
| 139.76250 | 148.25000 | AM | Edinburgh | Scottish Power |
| 139.76250 | 148.25000 | AM | Perth | Scottish Hydro Electric |
| 139.76250 | 148.25000 | AM | Shepway | Seeboard |
| 139.76875 | 148.26875 | AM | Humberside | Northern Electric |
| 139.76875 | 148.26875 | NFM | Lancaster | Norweb |
| 139.76875 | 148.26875 | NFM | Morecambe | Northern Electricity |
| 139.76875 | 148.26875 | NFM | Nationwide | Electricity Ch J42 |
| 139.77500 | | NFM | Cardiff | SWALEC |
| 139.77500 | | AM | Halifax | Yorkshire Electricity |
| 139.77500 | | NFM | Harlow | Eastern Electricity |
| 139.77500 | | NFM | Huddersfield | Yorkshire Electricity |
| 139.77500 | 148.28150 | NFM | Glasgow | Celtic Football Club |
| 139.78125 | 148.28125 | NFM | Nationwide | Electricity Ch J43 |
| 139.78125 | 148.28125 | AM | Reading | Electric Company |
| 139.78125 | 148.28125 | NFM | West Midlands | MEB |
| 139.78125 | 148.28125 | NFM | West Sussex | Southern Electric |
| 139.78500 | | AM | Leicester | Seeboard |
| 139.78750 | | AM | Aberdeen | Scottish Hydro Electric |
| 139.78750 | | AM | Keighley | Yorkshire Electricity |
| 139.78750 | | AM | Loughborough | MEB |
| 139.78750 | | NFM | Manchester | MEB |
| 139.79000 | 148.29000 | NFM | Peterborough | Eastern Electric |
| 139.79375 | 148.29375 | AM | Aldershot | Electric Company |
| 139.79375 | 148.29375 | AM | Argyll | Scottish Hydro Electric |
| 139.79375 | 148.29375 | AM | Buckinghamshire | Eastern Electric |
| 139.79375 | 148.29375 | AM | Montgomery | ManWeb |
| 139.79375 | 148.29375 | NFM | Nationwide | Electricity Ch J44 |
| 139.79375 | 148.29375 | AM | Salisbury | Southern Electric |
| 139.79375 | 148.29375 | NFM | West Midlands | Manweb |
| 139.79500 | | NFM | Barrow in Furness | Norweb |
| 139.79775 | | AM | Thames | Eastern Electric |
| 139.80000 | | AM | Ipswich | Eastern Electricity |
| 139.80000 | | NFM | Nationwide | Illegal Bugging Devices |
| 139.80000 | | NFM | South Wales | SWALEC |
| 139.80500 | | NFM | Glenrothes | Scottish Hydro Electric |
| 139.80500 | | NFM | Stoke-on-Trent | MEB |
| 139.80625 | 148.30625 | NFM | Nationwide | Electricity Ch J45 |
| 139.80625 | 148.30625 | NFM | West Midlands | MEB |
| 139.81250 | | AM | Newmarket | Eastern Electricity |
| 139.81250 | | AM | Tunbridge Wells | Seeboard |
| 139.81500 | 139.81500 | NFM | Scarborough | Northern Electric |
| 139.81825 | 148.31825 | NFM | Nationwide | Electricity Ch J46 |
| 139.81875 | 148.31825 | AM | Buckinghamshire | Eastern Electric |
| 139.82000 | | NFM | Manchester | Norweb |
| 139.82000 | | NFM | Southampton | Southern Electric |
| 139.82000 | | NFM | Wigan | Electricity |
| 139.82500 | | NFM | Devon | South West Electricity |
| 139.82500 | | NFM | Glasgow | Scottish Power |

| Base | Mobile | Mode | Location | User and Notes |
|------|--------|------|----------|----------------|
| 139.82500 | | AM | Swindon | MEB |
| 139.82500 | | NFM | West Yorkshire | Yorkshire Electricity |
| 139.83125 | 148.33125 | AM | Humberside | East Midlands Electric |
| 139.83125 | 148.33125 | NFM | Nationwide | Electricity Ch J47 |
| 139.83625 | | AM | London | London Electric |
| 139.83750 | | AM | East Sussex | Seeboard |
| 139.84375 | 148.34375 | AM | Bury St. Edmunds | Eastern Electricity |
| 139.84375 | 148.34375 | NFM | Carlisle | Norweb |
| 139.84375 | 148.34375 | AM | London | London Electric |
| 139.84375 | 148.34375 | NFM | Nationwide | Electricity Ch J48 |
| 139.84375 | 148.34375 | NFM | Sheffield | Yorkshire Electricity |
| 139.84375 | 148.34375 | AM | Surrey | Southern Electric |
| 139.84500 | | NFM | Central Scotland | Scottish Power |
| 139.84500 | | AM | Cornwall | SWEB |
| 139.84500 | | NFM | Glossop | Electric Board |
| 139.85000 | | AM | Gwynedd | MANWEB |
| 139.85000 | | AM | Kent | Seeboard |
| 139.85000 | | AM | Leicester | East Midlands Electricity |
| 139.85000 | | NFM | Merseyside | Manweb |
| 139.85000 | | AM | Plymouth | SWEB |
| 139.85500 | | NFM | Maidstone | Maidstone Power Care (Mike) |
| 139.85500 | | NFM | Newcastle | Northern Electric |
| 139.85625 | 148.35625 | NFM | Nationwide | Electricity Ch J49 |
| 139.85625 | 148.35625 | NFM | West Sussex | Southern Electric |
| 139.86375 | | AM | Stirling | Scottish Hydro Electric |
| 139.86500 | | NFM | Manchester | Manweb |
| 139.86875 | 148.36875 | AM | Argyll | Scottish Hydro Electric |
| 139.86875 | 148.36875 | AM | Kings Lynn | Eastern Electric |
| 139.86875 | 148.36875 | NFM | Lancaster | Norweb |
| 139.86875 | 148.36875 | NFM | Morecambe | Northern Electricity |
| 139.86875 | 148.36875 | NFM | Nationwide | Electricity Ch J50 |
| 139.86875 | 148.36875 | AM | Perth | Scottish Hydro Electric |
| 139.86875 | 148.36875 | NFM | West Midlands | MEB |
| 139.87000 | 139.87000 | NFM | Cheshire | East Midland Electricity |
| 139.87250 | 139.87250 | AM | Nationwide | USAF Air-Air |
| 139.87500 | | AM | Bradford | Yorkshire Electricity |
| 139.88125 | 148.38125 | AM | Essex | Eastern Electric |
| 139.88125 | 148.38125 | NFM | Nationwide | Electricity Ch 51 |
| 139.88250 | | NFM | Essex | Eastern Electric |
| 139.88750 | | NFM | Lauder | Data Link |
| 139.89375 | 148.38125 | AM | West Midlands | MEB |
| 139.89375 | 148.39375 | NFM | Nationwide | Electricity Ch J52 |
| 139.90000 | | NFM | Newport, Wales | SWALEC |
| 139.90125 | | NFM | Ferrybridge | Data Link |
| 139.90125 | | NFM | Lauder | Data Link |
| 139.90125 | | NFM | Stirling | Data Link |
| 139.90625 | 148.40625 | NFM | Nationwide | Electricity Ch J53 |
| 139.91875 | 148.41875 | NFM | Nationwide | Electricity Ch J54 |
| 139.92000 | 148.42000 | NFM | Somerset | SWEB |
| 139.93000 | 148.43000 | NFM | Norfolk | Eastern Electricity |
| 139.93125 | 148.43125 | AM | Essex | Eastern Electric |
| 139.93125 | 148.43125 | AM | Hertfordshire | Electric Company |
| 139.93125 | 148.43125 | NFM | Nationwide | Electricity Ch J55 |
| 139.93125 | 148.43125 | NFM | West Midlands | MEB |
| 139.93750 | | NFM | Cheshire | Electricity Co. Data Link |
| 139.93750 | | AM | Glasgow | Scottish Power |

| Base | Mobile | Mode | Location | User and Notes |
|---|---|---|---|---|
| 139.93750 | | NFM | London, Raynes Park | London Electric |
| 139.94375 | 148.44375 | NFM | London | North Thames Gas |
| 139.94375 | 148.44375 | NFM | Nationwide | Electricity Ch J56 |
| 139.94375 | 148.44375 | NFM | West Midlands | MEB |
| 139.95000 | | NFM | Manchester | Norweb |
| 139.95000 | | NFM | South Wales | SWALEC |
| 139.95000 | | NFM | Sussex | Seeboard Electricity |
| 139.95500 | | NFM | Preston | Norweb |
| 139.95600 | | AM | Berkshire | Southern Electric |
| 139.95625 | 148.45625 | AM | Henley-on-Thames | Southern Electric |
| 139.95625 | 148.45625 | NFM | Nationwide | Electricity Ch J57 |
| 139.95625 | 148.45625 | NFM | Sheffield | Yorkshire Electricity |
| 139.95625 | 148.45625 | NFM | West Midlands | MEB |
| 139.96875 | 148.96875 | NFM | Nationwide | Electricity Ch J58 |
| 139.97500 | | NFM | Devon | South West Electricity |
| 139.97500 | | NFM | Newmarket | Data Link |
| 139.97500 | | AM | Sheffield | Yorkshire Electricity |
| 139.97500 | | NFM | South Wales | SWALEC |
| 139.98125 | 148.48125 | NFM | Nationwide | Electricity Ch J59 |
| 139.98125 | 148.48125 | AM | Perth | Scottish Hydro Electric Data Link |
| 139.98750 | | NFM | Swansea | SWALEC |
| 139.99000 | | NFM | Somerset | British Gas |
| 139.99375 | 148.49375 | NFM | Ayr | Scottish Power |
| 139.99375 | 148.49375 | NFM | Nationwide | Electricity Ch J60 |
| 140.00000 | | NFM | Alnwick | Data Link |
| 140.00000 | | NFM | Nationwide | Illegal Bugging Devices |
| 140.00000 | 140.00000 | AM | Nationwide | USAF Air-Air |
| 140.00625 | 148.50625 | NFM | Nationwide | Electricity Ch J61 |
| 140.01250 | | NFM | Cumbria | Data Link |
| 140.01250 | | NFM | Lancashire | Data Link |
| 140.01875 | 148.51875 | NFM | Nationwide | Electricity Ch J62 |
| 140.02000 | | NFM | Durham | Data Link |
| 140.02500 | | NFM | Alnwick | Data Link |
| 140.03125 | 148.53125 | NFM | Nationwide | Electricity Ch J63 |
| 140.03750 | | NFM | Leeds | British Gas |
| 140.04375 | 148.54375 | NFM | Nationwide | Electricity Ch J64 |
| 140.04400 | | AM | Perth | Data Link |
| 140.05000 | | NFM | Bradford | British Gas |
| 140.05000 | | NFM | Cumbria | Data Link |
| 140.05000 | | NFM | Dundee | Data Link |
| 140.05000 | | NFM | Lancashire | Data Link |
| 140.05000 | | NFM | Lauder | Data Link |
| 140.05000 | | NFM | Nationwide | Mine Rescue Channel |
| 140.05500 | | NFM | Lancaster | Red Rose Radio Link |
| 140.05625 | 148.55625 | NFM | Braintree | Eastern Gas |
| 140.05625 | 148.55625 | AM | Nationwide | NCB Mine Rescue |
| 140.05625 | 148.55625 | NFM | Nationwide | Electricity Ch J65 |
| 140.06250 | | NFM | Glasgow | Data Link |
| 140.07500 | | AM | County Durham | British Gas |
| 140.07500 | | NFM | Newmarket | Data Link |
| 140.08125 | 148.58125 | NFM | West Sussex | British Gas Southern |
| 140.10000 | | NFM | Haggerston | Data Link |
| 140.10000 | | NFM | W Yorkshire | British Gas |
| 140.10625 | | NFM | Ferrybridge | British Gas |
| 140.10625 | 148.60625 | NFM | Nationwide | British Gas Trunked System |
| 140.10625 | 148.60625 | NFM | West Midlands | British Gas |

| Base | Mobile | Mode | Location | User and Notes |
|------|--------|------|----------|----------------|
| 140.11250 | | NFM | Cheshire | British Gas |
| 140.11250 | | AM | County Durham | British Gas |
| 140.11250 | | AM | Selby | North East Gas |
| 140.11875 | 148.61875 | NFM | Nationwide | British Gas Trunked System |
| 140.11875 | 148.61875 | NFM | Stirling | Data Link |
| 140.11875 | 148.61875 | NFM | West Midlands | British Gas |
| 140.12000 | 148.61875 | NFM | Burnley | British Gas |
| 140.12000 | 148.61875 | NFM | Stockport | British Gas |
| 140.12500 | 140.12500 | NFM | Eastham | British Gas |
| 140.12500 | 140.12500 | NFM | Glasgow | British Gas |
| 140.13125 | 148.63125 | NFM | Nationwide | British Gas Trunked System |
| 140.13125 | 148.63125 | NFM | West Midlands | British Gas |
| 140.13750 | | AM | Leeds | North East Gas |
| 140.13875 | | NFM | Stirling | Data Link |
| 140.14375 | 148.64375 | NFM | Colchester | Eastern Gas |
| 140.14375 | 148.64375 | AM | London | London Electric |
| 140.14375 | 148.64375 | NFM | Nationwide | British Gas Trunked System |
| 140.14375 | 148.64375 | NFM | West Midlands | British Gas |
| 140.15000 | | AM | County Durham | British Gas |
| 140.15000 | | NFM | London, Raynes Park | British Gas meter readers |
| 140.15625 | | AM | Cleveland | British Gas |
| 140.15625 | | AM | West Midlands | Bus Company |
| 140.16500 | | NFM | Bradford | British Gas |
| 140.16875 | 140.10625 | AM | Perth | Scottish Hydro Electric |
| 140.16875 | 148.66875 | NFM | Nationwide | British Gas Trunked System |
| 140.16875 | 148.68750 | NFM | West Midlands | British Gas |
| 140.16875 | 148.68750 | NFM | West Sussex | British Gas Southern |
| 140.17500 | | AM | Bolton | British Gas |
| 140.17500 | | NFM | Glasgow | British Gas |
| 140.17500 | | AM | Manchester | British Gas |
| 140.19500 | | AM | Hull | British Gas |
| 140.20000 | | NFM | Dundee | Data Link |
| 140.20000 | | NFM | Leeds | British Gas |
| 140.20500 | | NFM | London, south east | Council schools |
| 140.20500 | 148.70500 | NFM | Portsmouth | Wessex Water |
| 140.20500 | 148.70500 | NFM | Somerset | British Gas |
| 140.20625 | | NFM | Clacton | Eastern Electric |
| 140.21125 | 148.71125 | NFM | London | British Gas |
| 140.21250 | | AM | Fareham | Southern Gas |
| 140.21250 | | AM | Gosport | Southern Gas |
| 140.21250 | | AM | Portsmouth | Southern Gas |
| 140.21875 | | AM | Surrey | Southern Electric |
| 140.22000 | | NFM | Glossop | British Gas |
| 140.22000 | | AM | Rainham | Seeboard Power Care |
| 140.22000 | 148.72000 | NFM | Somerset | SWEB |
| 140.22500 | | AM | Tayside | Scottish Hydro Electric |
| 140.22500 | | NFM | Wakefield | British Gas |
| 140.23125 | | NFM | Lancaster | British Gas |
| 140.23750 | | AM | Newcastle | British Gas Repairs |
| 140.24375 | | AM | Colchester | Eastern Gas |
| 140.24375 | | NFM | West Midlands | British Gas |
| 140.24375 | 148.74375 | NFM | Nationwide | British Gas Trunked System |
| 140.24500 | | NFM | Avon | British Gas |
| 140.24500 | 148.70000 | NFM | Burnley | British Gas |
| 140.25000 | | NFM | Leeds | British Gas |
| 140.25625 | | AM | Ipswich | British Gas Repairs |

| Base | Mobile | Mode | Location | User and Notes |
|------|--------|------|----------|----------------|
| 140.25625 | | NFM | West Midlands | British Gas |
| 140.25625 | 148.75625 | NFM | Nationwide | British Gas Trunked System |
| 140.26125 | | NFM | Stirling | Data Link |
| 140.26250 | 140.26250 | NFM | Neston | British Gas |
| 140.26875 | | NFM | West Midlands | British Gas |
| 140.26875 | 148.76875 | NFM | Nationwide | British Gas Trunked System |
| 140.27000 | | NFM | Runcorn | British Gas |
| 140.28750 | | NFM | Manchester | British Gas |
| 140.29375 | 148.79375 | NFM | Nationwide | British Gas Trunked System |
| 140.29375 | 148.79375 | NFM | West Midlands | British Gas |
| 140.29375 | 148.79375 | NFM | West Sussex | British Gas Southern |
| 140.30000 | | NFM | Glasgow | British Gas |
| 140.30000 | | NFM | Keighley | British Gas |
| 140.30625 | 148.80625 | NFM | Nationwide | British Gas Trunked System |
| 140.30625 | 148.80625 | NFM | West Midlands | British Gas |
| 140.31250 | | NFM | Dewsbury | British Gas |
| 140.32500 | | NFM | Glasgow | British Gas |
| 140.32500 | | NFM | London, South | British Gas |
| 140.33125 | 148.83125 | NFM | Surrey | Southern Gas |
| 140.33125 | 148.83125 | NFM | West Sussex | British Gas Southern |
| 140.33750 | | AM | Fareham | Southern Gas |
| 140.33750 | | AM | Gosport | Southern Gas |
| 140.33750 | | AM | Portmouth | Southern Gas |
| 140.34500 | | NFM | West Midlands | British Gas |
| 140.35000 | | NFM | Ferrybridge | British Gas |
| 140.35000 | | NFM | Lancaster | British Gas |
| 140.35000 | | AM | Plymouth | SWEB |
| 140.35000 | | NFM | Pontefract | British Gas |
| 140.35125 | | NFM | Surrey | Southern Gas |
| 140.35625 | 140.10625 | AM | Perth | Scottish Hydro Electric |
| 140.36250 | | AM | Pontefract | North East Gas |
| 140.37500 | | NFM | Wiltshire | Electricity |
| 140.38750 | | AM | County Durham | Northern Electric |
| 140.38750 | | NFM | Tyne & Wear | Metro Controller |
| 140.39375 | 148.89375 | NFM | Nationwide | British Gas Trunked System |
| 140.39375 | 148.89375 | NFM | West Midlands | British Gas |
| 140.40000 | 148.80000 | AM | London, Croydon | British Gas |
| 140.40000 | 148.80000 | NFM | North West | British Gas |
| 140.41250 | 140.41250 | NFM | Edinburgh | British Gas |
| 140.41250 | 140.41250 | NFM | Swansea | British Gas |
| 140.41875 | 148.91875 | NFM | Nationwide | British Gas Trunked System |
| 140.41875 | 148.91875 | NFM | Surrey | Southern Gas |
| 140.41875 | 148.91875 | NFM | West Midlands | British Gas |
| 140.42500 | 148.82500 | NFM | Bradford | British Gas |
| 140.42500 | 148.82500 | NFM | Devon | South West Electricity |
| 140.42500 | 148.82500 | NFM | Lauder | Data Link |
| 140.42500 | 148.82500 | AM | Newcastle | British Gas |
| 140.43125 | 148.93125 | NFM | Nationwide | British Gas Trunked System |
| 140.43125 | 148.93125 | NFM | West Midlands | British Gas |
| 140.43750 | | AM | Fife | British Gas |
| 140.44000 | | NFM | Manchester | MEB |
| 140.45000 | | NFM | London, SW | British Gas |
| 140.45000 | | AM | Newmarket | Telephone Link |
| 140.45000 | | AM | Plymouth | SWEB |
| 140.45600 | 148.45000 | NFM | Tamworth | British Gas |
| 140.45625 | 148.95625 | NFM | Nationwide | British Gas Trunked System |

| Base | Mobile | Mode | Location | User and Notes |
|------|--------|------|----------|----------------|
| 140.46250 | | AM | Glasgow | Scottish Power |
| 140.46875 | 148.96875 | NFM | Nationwide | British Gas Trunked System |
| 140.46875 | 148.96875 | NFM | West Midlands | British Gas |
| 140.47500 | | NFM | Glasgow | British Gas |
| 140.48000 | 148.88000 | NFM | Barrow | British Gas |
| 140.48125 | 148.98125 | NFM | Barrow in Furness | British Gas |
| 140.48125 | 148.98125 | NFM | Nationwide | British Gas Trunked System |
| 140.48125 | 148.98125 | NFM | Surrey | British Gas |
| 140.48125 | 148.98125 | NFM | West Midlands | British Gas |
| 140.58175 | | AM | London | London Electricity |
| 140.67500 | | NFM | North London | North Thames Gas |
| 140.70625 | | NFM | South Yorkshire | South Yorkshire Bus Company |
| 140.76250 | | AM | Goole | North East Gas |
| 140.83000 | | NFM | Burnley | British Gas |
| 140.83750 | | AM | Pontefract | North East Gas |
| 140.87500 | | AM | Hull | British Gas |
| 140.87500 | | NFM | Isle of Man | Manx Electricity |
| 140.90500 | | NFM | Burnley | British Gas |
| 140.90625 | | NFM | South London | North Thames Gas |
| 140.93125 | | NFM | Kent | Southern Gas |
| 140.94375 | | NFM | Nationwide | LWT Engineering Talkback |
| 140.96875 | | NFM | Nationwide | DTI Short Term 28 Day Hire |

### 141.0000 - 141.2000 MHz    ILR, BBC AND LOCAL RADIO TALKBACK

| Base | Mobile | Mode | Location | User and Notes |
|------|--------|------|----------|----------------|
| 140.99375 | | NFM | London | ITN 6 O'clock News |
| 140.99375 | | NFM | London | LWT TV O/B |
| 140.99375 | | NFM | London | Screen TV O/B |
| 140.99500 | | NFM | Leeds | ITV Studio Maintenance |
| 140.99500 | | NFM | London | GMTV studio direction |
| 140.99575 | | NFM | London | ITV Studio relay for "London Today" |
| 141.01250 | | NFM | Nationwide | ILR Talkback Channel 1 |
| 141.01875 | | NFM | Inverness | Moray Firth Radio O/B |
| 141.02500 | | NFM | Humberside | Viking Radio Links |
| 141.02500 | | NFM | Nationwide | ILR Common Talkback Ch 5 |
| 141.03125 | | NFM | Leeds | Flying Eye for Magic 828, Hallam FM & Viking AM |
| 141.03125 | | NFM | Stoke on Trent | Signal Radio |
| 141.03750 | | NFM | Nationwide | Ch4 TV Engineering /News |
| 141.03750 | | NFM | Nationwide | ILR Engineering Ch 4 |
| 141.03750 | | NFM | Nationwide | ILR Primary O/B Channel 2 |
| 141.04375 | | NFM | Hampshire | Radio 210 |
| 141.04375 | | NFM | Wolverhampton | Beacon Radio O/B |
| 141.04375 | 141.04375 | NFM | Berkshire | Radio 210 |
| 141.05000 | | NFM | Basingstoke | Independent Local Radio |
| 141.05000 | 141.18750 | NFM | Andover | Independent Local Radio |
| 141.05000 | 141.18750 | NFM | Bristol | Independent Local Radio |
| 141.05000 | 141.18750 | NFM | Chelmsford | Independent Local Radio |
| 141.05000 | 141.18750 | NFM | Cornwall | Independent Local Radio |
| 141.05000 | 141.18750 | NFM | Hereward | Independent Local Radio |
| 141.05000 | 141.18750 | NFM | Inverness | Independent Local Radio |
| 141.05000 | 141.18750 | NFM | Liverpool | Independent Local Radio |
| 141.05000 | 141.18750 | NFM | Newcastle | Independent Local Radio |
| 141.05000 | 141.18750 | NFM | Oxford | Independent Local Radio |
| 141.05000 | 141.18750 | NFM | Peterborough | Independent Local Radio |
| 141.05000 | 141.18750 | NFM | Reigate | Independent Local Radio |
| 141.05000 | 141.18750 | NFM | Sheffield | Independent Local Radio |

| Base | Mobile | Mode | Location | User and Notes |
|------|--------|------|----------|----------------|
| 141.05000 | 141.18750 | NFM | Wolverhampton | Independent Local Radio |
| 141.05500 | 141.05500 | NFM | Leeds | Radio Air Talk Back |
| 141.05600 | | NFM | Nongeostationary | US ATS 6 |
| 141.05625 | 141.11250 | NFM | Preston | Red Rose Radio |
| 141.06250 | 141.11250 | NFM | Exeter | Independent Local Radio |
| 141.06250 | 141.11250 | NFM | Gloucester | Independent Local Radio |
| 141.06250 | 141.11250 | NFM | Great Yarmouth | Independent Local Radio |
| 141.06250 | 141.11250 | NFM | Gwynedd | Independent Local Radio |
| 141.06250 | 141.11250 | NFM | Hereford | Independent Local Radio |
| 141.06250 | 141.11250 | NFM | Huddersfield | Independent Local Radio |
| 141.06250 | 141.11250 | NFM | Leicester | Independent Local Radio |
| 141.06250 | 141.11250 | NFM | Maidstone | Independent Local Radio |
| 141.06250 | 141.11250 | NFM | Nationwide | 2CR Eye in the Sky |
| 141.06250 | 141.11250 | NFM | Reading | Independent Local Radio |
| 141.06250 | 141.11250 | NFM | Shrewsbury | Independent Local Radio |
| 141.06875 | | NFM | Liverpool | Radio City |
| 141.07500 | | NFM | Aberdeen | Independent Local Radio |
| 141.07500 | | NFM | Barnsley | Independent Local Radio |
| 141.07500 | | NFM | Berwick-upon-Tweed | Independent Local Radio |
| 141.07500 | | NFM | Cardiff | Independent Local Radio |
| 141.07500 | | NFM | Coventry | Independent Local Radio |
| 141.07500 | | NFM | Glasgow | Independent Local Radio |
| 141.07500 | | NFM | London | Independent Local Radio |
| 141.07500 | | NFM | Manchester | Independent Local Radio |
| 141.07500 | | NFM | Portsmouth | Independent Local Radio |
| 141.07500 | | NFM | Stoke on Trent | Independent Local Radio |
| 141.07500 | | NFM | Swindon | Independent Local Radio |
| 141.08125 | | NFM | Manchester | Piccadilly Radio |
| 141.08750 | 141.15000 | NFM | Bedford | Independent Local Radio |
| 141.08750 | 141.15000 | NFM | Bournemouth | Independent Local Radio |
| 141.08750 | 141.15000 | NFM | Eastbourne | Independent Local Radio |
| 141.08750 | 141.15000 | NFM | Edinburgh | Independent Local Radio |
| 141.08750 | 141.15000 | NFM | Guildford | Independent Local Radio |
| 141.08750 | 141.15000 | NFM | Hereford | Independent Local Radio |
| 141.08750 | 141.15000 | NFM | Humberside | Independent Local Radio |
| 141.08750 | 141.15000 | NFM | Ipswich | Independent Local Radio |
| 141.08750 | 141.15000 | NFM | Manchester | Independent Local Radio |
| 141.08750 | 141.15000 | NFM | Nottingham | Independent Local Radio |
| 141.08750 | 141.15000 | NFM | Plymouth | Independent Local Radio |
| 141.08750 | 141.15000 | NFM | Swansea | Independent Local Radio |
| 141.08750 | 141.15000 | NFM | Trent | Independent Local Radio |
| 141.08750 | 141.15000 | NFM | Whitehaven | Independent Local Radio |
| 141.10000 | 141.20000 | NFM | Aylesbury | Independent Local Radio |
| 141.10000 | 141.20000 | NFM | Belfast | Independent Local Radio |
| 141.10000 | 141.20000 | NFM | Birmingham | Independent Local Radio |
| 141.10000 | 141.20000 | NFM | Blackpool | Independent Local Radio |
| 141.10000 | 141.20000 | NFM | Bognor Regis | Independent Local Radio |
| 141.10000 | 141.20000 | NFM | Bradford | Independent Local Radio |
| 141.10000 | 141.20000 | NFM | Bury St Edmunds | Independent Local Radio |
| 141.10000 | 141.20000 | NFM | Cambridge | Independent Local Radio |
| 141.10000 | 141.20000 | NFM | Canterbury | Independent Local Radio |
| 141.10000 | 141.20000 | NFM | Derby | Independent Local Radio |
| 141.10000 | 141.20000 | NFM | Dorchester | Independent Local Radio |
| 141.10000 | 141.20000 | NFM | Dover | Independent Local Radio |
| 141.10000 | 141.20000 | NFM | Dumfries | Independent Local Radio |
| 141.10000 | 141.20000 | NFM | Dundee | Independent Local Radio |

| Base | Mobile | Mode | Location | User and Notes |
|------|--------|------|----------|----------------|
| 141.10000 | 141.20000 | NFM | Gwent | Independent Local Radio |
| 141.10000 | 141.20000 | NFM | Leeds | Independent Local Radio |
| 141.10000 | 141.20000 | NFM | London | Capitol Radio Link |
| 141.10000 | 141.20000 | NFM | London | Independent Local Radio |
| 141.10000 | 141.20000 | NFM | Londonderry | Independent Local Radio |
| 141.10000 | 141.20000 | NFM | Middlesborough | Independent Local Radio |
| 141.10000 | 141.20000 | NFM | Milton Keynes | Independent Local Radio |
| 141.10000 | 141.20000 | NFM | Newmarket | Independent Local Radio |
| 141.10000 | 141.20000 | NFM | Newport | Independent Local Radio |
| 141.10000 | 141.20000 | NFM | Northampton | Independent Local Radio |
| 141.10000 | 141.20000 | NFM | Perth | Independent Local Radio |
| 141.10000 | 141.20000 | NFM | Preston | Independent Local Radio |
| 141.10000 | 141.20000 | NFM | Southampton | Independent Local Radio |
| 141.10000 | 141.20000 | NFM | Stranraer | Independent Local Radio |
| 141.10000 | 141.20000 | NFM | Taunton | BBC |
| 141.10000 | 141.20000 | NFM | Weymouth | Independent Local Radio |
| 141.10000 | 141.20000 | NFM | Wrexham | Independent Local Radio |
| 141.10000 | 141.20000 | NFM | Yeovil | Independent Local Radio |
| 141.11875 | 468.84375 | NFM | Derby | GEM AM 945/999 |
| 141.11875 | 468.84375 | NFM | Derby | Trent FM 96.2 |
| 141.12500 | 141.17500 | NFM | Birmingham | 96.4 FM BRMB Radio Talkback |
| 141.13125 | | NFM | Manchester | BBC GMR |
| 141.13750 | | NFM | Nationwide | IBA Local Radio Engineers |
| 141.13750 | | NFM | West of England | HTV Clean Feed |
| 141.14000 | | NFM | Tyneside | Metro Radio O/B and helicopter uplink |
| 141.14375 | | NFM | Kent | Invicta FM |
| 141.15000 | | NFM | Humberside | Viking Radio O/B |
| 141.15000 | | NFM | Nationwide | IBA Local Radio Engineers |
| 141.15000 | | NFM | Trent | Independent Local Radio Talkback |
| 141.15500 | | NFM | Birmingham | Birmingham O/B |
| 141.15625 | 469.26250 | NFM | London | LBC Radio Flying Eye |
| 141.16250 | | NFM | Dorset | 2CR Studio Talkback |
| 141.16875 | | NFM | Coventry | Mercia Sound |
| 141.18000 | | NFM | Leicester | Sunrise Radio O/B |
| 141.18000 | | NFM | Manchester | Piccadilly Radio Studio Link |
| 141.18125 | | NFM | London | Independent Radio O/B |
| 141.18750 | | NFM | Humberside | Viking Radio O/B |
| 141.18750 | 469.46250 | NFM | Cowley | Fox FM Flying Eye Uplink |
| 141.19375 | | NFM | Birmingham | Railtrack MB/Xtra AM |
| 141.19375 | | NFM | London | LBC |
| 141.19500 | | NFM | London | LBC Production/Control Room |
| 141.19500 | | NFM | London | Radio Piccadilly Studio Link |
| 141.20000 | | NFM | Hampshire | BBC Radio Solent |
| 141.20500 | | NFM | York | BBC Radio York Talkback |
| 141.20625 | 224.11875 | NFM | Birmingham | BBC Radio West Midlands |
| 141.20625 | 224.11875 | NFM | Northamptonshire | BBC Radio Northants |
| 141.21750 | | NFM | Derby | BBC Radio Derby |
| 141.21875 | | NFM | Hereford & Worcester | BBC Radio Worcester |
| 141.21875 | | NFM | London | BBC Radio Car O/B |
| 141.22000 | | NFM | Lincoln | BBC Radio Lincs Talkback |
| 141.22500 | | NFM | Leicester | BBC O/B Cricket Commentary |
| 141.23125 | | NFM | Surrey | BBC Radio Surrey |
| 141.23750 | | NFM | Taunton | BBC Talkback |
| 141.24300 | | NFM | Berkshire | BBC Radio Berkshire |
| 141.24375 | | NFM | Berkshire | BBC Radio Surrey & Berkshire |
| 141.24375 | | NFM | London | BBC Radio Car O/B |

| Base | Mobile | Mode | Location | User and Notes |
|------|--------|------|----------|----------------|
| 141.24375 | | NFM | Norfolk | ITN |
| 141.24375 | 224.01875 | NFM | Channel Islands | ITN |
| 141.24375 | 224.10625 | NFM | Cornwall | ITN |
| 141.24375 | 224.16875 | NFM | Coventry | BBC CWR |
| 141.25000 | | NFM | London | ITN Music Link |
| 141.25500 | | NFM | Stoke on Trent | Radio Stoke Engineering |
| 141.25625 | 224.10625 | NFM | London | BBC Radio Car O/B |
| 141.25625 | 224.10625 | NFM | Stoke on Trent | BBC Radio Stoke |
| 141.25625 | 224.10625 | NFM | West Sussex | BBC Radio Sussex |
| 141.25630 | 213.73750 | NFM | Sussex | ITN |
| 141.25630 | 213.73750 | NFM | Wiltshire | ITN |
| 141.25630 | 224.09375 | NFM | Leeds | ITN |
| 141.25630 | 224.10625 | NFM | Stoke | ITN |
| 141.25630 | 224.10875 | NFM | Cambridge | ITN |
| 141.25630 | 224.10875 | NFM | Devon | ITN |
| 141.25680 | 224.16750 | NFM | Channel Islands | ITN |
| 141.28750 | | NFM | London Ealing | Five Line O/B |
| 141.29000 | | NFM | Hull | BBC Radio Humberside Talkback |
| 141.29350 | 224.15625 | NFM | Shropshire | ITN |
| 141.29375 | | NFM | London | BBC Radio Car O/B |
| 141.29375 | 224.15625 | NFM | Shrewsbury | BBC Radio Shrewsbury |
| 141.29380 | 224.10875 | NFM | Newcastle | ITN |
| 141.29380 | 224.13125 | NFM | Humberside | ITN |
| 141.29500 | | NFM | London | BBC Radio news studio |
| 141.29750 | | NFM | York | Radio York O/B |
| 141.30625 | 224.13125 | NFM | Leicester | BBC Radio Leicester |
| 141.30630 | 213.76250 | NFM | Bedfordshire | ITN |
| 141.30630 | 224.11875 | NFM | Cleveland | ITN |
| 141.30630 | 224.13125 | NFM | Leicester | ITN |
| 141.30630 | 224.14375 | NFM | Gloucester | ITN |
| 141.31825 | | NFM | London | BBC Radio Car O/B |
| 141.32000 | | NFM | Nationwide | BBC O/B Link |
| 141.35000 | | NFM | Belfast | Data Link |
| 141.35000 | | NFM | London | BBC1 Clean Feed |
| 141.35000 | | NFM | London | ITN Music Links |
| 141.35000 | | NFM | Nationwide | BBC Radio 2 Engineering |
| 141.35000 | | NFM | Yorkshire | IBC Talkback |
| 141.37500 | | NFM | Ayr | Racecourse BBC Outside Broadcasts |
| 141.37500 | | NFM | London | BBC1 TV Studio Sound Link |
| 141.37500 | 224.23350 | NFM | Bristol | BBC Points West Talkback |
| 141.37500 | 224.23350 | NFM | Ipswich | Local Radio |
| 141.37500 | 224.23350 | NFM | Nationwide | BBC O/B Talkback |
| 141.38000 | | WFM | West Midlands | Pebblemill |
| 141.38750 | 468.13750 | NFM | Manchester | Key 103 O/B |
| 141.42650 | | NFM | Newbury | BBC South Talkback |
| 141.42650 | | NFM | Southampton | BBC South Talkback |
| 141.44500 | | NFM | London | BBC2 TV Studio Sound Link |
| 141.45000 | | NFM | London | ITN Music Link |
| 141.46000 | | NFM | Cardiff | BBC O/B |
| 141.46200 | | NFM | Birmingham | BBC Pebble Mill O/B |
| 141.46250 | | NFM | Leicester | BBC1 West Midlands Link |
| 141.46250 | | NFM | London | BBC TV O/B |
| 141.46250 | | NFM | London | BBC1 Link |
| 141.46250 | | NFM | Manchester | BBC TV |
| 141.46250 | | NFM | Nottingham | BBC1 Nottingham Clean Feed |
| 141.47500 | | WFM | Southampton | BBC TV South Feed to OB |

| Base | Mobile | Mode | Location | User and Notes |
|------|--------|------|----------|----------------|
| 141.55000 | | NFM | Nationwide | BBC Radio 2 O/B |
| 141.61875 | | NFM | Cornwall | BBC |
| 141.61875 | | NFM | Essex | BBC |
| 141.61875 | | NFM | Nottingham | BBC |
| 141.61875 | | NFM | Surrey | BBC |
| 141.61875 | | NFM | Trent | BBC Radio Trent O/B |
| 141.63125 | | NFM | Bedford | BBC |
| 141.63125 | | NFM | Chrewsbury | BBC |
| 141.63125 | | NFM | Norfolk | BBC |
| 141.64375 | | NFM | Nationwide | BBC Outside Broadcasts |
| 141.65625 | | NFM | Brighton | BBC |
| 141.65625 | | NFM | Northampton | BBC |
| 141.65625 | | NFM | York | BBC |
| 141.66825 | | NFM | Sussex | BBC |
| 141.66875 | | NFM | Hereford | BBC |
| 141.66875 | | NFM | Lancashire | BBC |
| 141.66875 | | NFM | London | Electronic News Gathering |
| 141.66875 | | NFM | Nationwide | BBC Engineering Talkback |
| 141.67000 | | NFM | Lancaster | Radio Lancashire |
| 141.67000 | | NFM | Nationwide | TV News ENG |
| 141.67500 | | NFM | London | Breakfast Time News |
| 141.68125 | | NFM | Bedford | BBC |
| 141.68125 | | NFM | Lincolnshire | BBC TV O/B |
| 141.69375 | | NFM | Bangor | BBC |
| 141.69375 | | NFM | Gloucester | BBC |
| 141.69375 | | NFM | Nationwide | GLR Talkback |
| 141.69790 | | NFM | London | Radio London. |
| 141.70625 | | NFM | Devon | BBC |
| 141.70625 | | NFM | Leicester | BBC |
| 141.71350 | | NFM | Merseyside | BBC |
| 141.71625 | | NFM | Glasgow | BBC |
| 141.71875 | | NFM | Solent | BBC |
| 141.72500 | | NFM | Northampton | BBC |
| 141.72500 | | NFM | Sheffield | BBC Radio Sheffield O/B |
| 141.73125 | | NFM | Cambridge | BBC |
| 141.73125 | | NFM | Newcastle | BBC |
| 141.73125 | | NFM | Sheffield | BBC |
| 141.73125 | | NFM | West Midlands | BBC |
| 141.73125 | | NFM | Wiltshire | BBC |
| 141.74375 | | NFM | London | Radio News |
| 141.74375 | | NFM | Nationwide | BBC Radio Cue |
| 141.75500 | | NFM | Stoke on Trent | Radio Stoke Engineering |
| 141.75625 | | NFM | Cardiff | BBC |
| 141.75625 | | NFM | Humberside | BBC |
| 141.75625 | | NFM | Stoke-on-Trent | BBC |
| 141.75625 | | NFM | Suffolk | BBC |
| 141.76625 | | NFM | Foyle | BBC |
| 141.76875 | | NFM | Crystal Palace | BBC Radio News |
| 141.76875 | | NFM | Edinburgh | BBC |
| 141.76875 | | NFM | Nationwide | BBC Radio Cue |
| 141.77500 | | NFM | Nationwide | BBC Radio OB (20kHz Audio Ch) |
| 141.77500 | | NFM | Sheffield | BBC Radio Sheffield O/B |
| 141.78125 | | NFM | Bristol | BBC |
| 141.78125 | | NFM | Cumbria | BBC |
| 141.78125 | | NFM | Derby | BBC |
| 141.78125 | | NFM | Leeds | BBC |

| Base | Mobile | Mode | Location | User and Notes |
| --- | --- | --- | --- | --- |
| 141.78750 | | NFM | Manchester | Radio Manchester O/B |
| 141.79375 | | NFM | Cambridge | BBC |
| 141.79375 | | NFM | Cleveland | BBC |
| 141.79375 | | NFM | Kent | BBC |
| 141.79375 | | NFM | Manchester | BBC |
| 141.79375 | | AM | Thames Valley | BBC |
| 141.79375 | | NFM | Warwickshire | BBC |
| 141.79500 | | NFM | Manchester | Radio Manchester O/B |
| 141.80000 | | NFM | Lincolnshire | BBC TV O/B |
| 141.81875 | | NFM | Nationwide | BBC News ENG |
| 141.82500 | | AM | Nationwide | Patroulle de Francais air display team |
| 141.82500 | | NFM | Nationwide | BBC News DB Link |
| 141.83875 | | NFM | Nationwide | BBC O/B Camera Data |
| 141.83875 | | NFM | Nationwide | BBC TV O/B's Data |
| 141.84750 | | NFM | Nationwide | JFMG Airborne |
| 141.85750 | | NFM | Brookman Park | BBC TX Group |
| 141.85750 | | NFM | Nationwide | BBC Transmitter Group |
| 141.86000 | | NFM | Holme Moss | BBC Maintenance |
| 141.86250 | | NFM | Crystal Palace | BBC ENG |
| 141.86250 | | NFM | Dorset | 2CR Eye-In-The-Sky |
| 141.87500 | 141.87500 | AM | Nationwide | BBC TV O/B's Data |
| 141.88750 | 141.88750 | AM | Nationwide | BBC TV Air to Ground |
| 141.89250 | 141.89250 | AM | Nationwide | BBC TFS Air to Ground |

**141.9000 - 142.0000 MHz    GOVERNMENT AGENCIES NFM**

| Base | Mobile | Mode | Location | User and Notes |
| --- | --- | --- | --- | --- |
| 141.91250 | | NFM | Nationwide | Army |
| 141.91250 | | NFM | RAF Chicksands | British Intelligence Centre (DVP and Mould) |
| 141.91250 | | NFM | Sandfield Base | Territorial Army |
| 141.91250 | | NFM | Swansea | Government Surveillance Teams   (D) |
| 141.93750 | | NFM | England, North West | Mould |
| 141.93750 | | NFM | London | MI5/Anti Terrorist Branch IRA op. (OPERATION RESOLVE) |
| 141.93750 | | NFM | Winter Hill-Isle of Man | Mould Link |
| 141.96250 | | NFM | Berkshire | Mould |
| 141.96250 | | NFM | Nationwide | Army |
| 141.98750 | | NFM | Berkshire | Mould |
| 141.98750 | | NFM | England, North West | Government agency |
| 141.98750 | | NFM | London | Police Wembley Relay Transmitter |
| 141.98750 | | NFM | Newhaven | Government agency |
| 141.98750 | | NFM | Sandfields Base | Territorial Army |
| 141.98750 | | NFM | Swansea | Government Surveillance Teams |

**142.0000 - 142.9750 MHz    MoD, USAF & SOVIET SPACE COMMUNICATIONS**

| Base | Mobile | Mode | Location | User and Notes |
| --- | --- | --- | --- | --- |
| 142.01250 | | NFM | Stanford | Battle Training Ground (mainly scrambled) |
| 142.02500 | | NFM | Stanford | Battle Training Ground (mainly scrambled) |
| 142.02500 | 142.02500 | AM | Nationwide | MoD Aircraft |
| 142.02500 | 142.72500 | AM | Nationwide | USAF Air to Air |
| 142.05000 | | AM | Nationwide | 100 Sqdn. Air to Air CH.V04 |
| 142.05000 | | AM | Nationwide | USAF Air to Air |
| 142.05000 | | NFM | Nationwide | USAF Air to Air |
| 142.05000 | | NFM | Thetford | Army Stanford exercise area |
| 142.07500 | | AM | Nationwide | USAF Air to Air |
| 142.07500 | | AM | USAF Mildenhall | Dep Con |
| 142.08750 | | NFM | North Yorkshire | Army |

| Base | Mobile | Mode | Location | User and Notes |
|------|--------|------|----------|----------------|
| 142.08750 | | NFM | Strathclyde | Mould |
| 142.08750 | 149.08750 | NFM | South Wales | Mould |
| 142.10000 | | NFM | England, North West | Government agency Cougarnet/DVP |
| 142.10000 | | AM | Nationwide | USAF Air to Air |
| 142.11250 | | NFM | London | Mould linked to 74.425 MHz |
| 142.11250 | | NFM | South Wales | Mould |
| 142.12500 | | NFM | London | Police Wembley Relay Transmitter |
| 142.15000 | | NFM | Humberside | USAF |
| 142.15000 | | AM | Nationwide | 150 USAF |
| 142.15000 | | NFM | RAF Chicksands | British Intelligence Centre (DVP) |
| 142.17500 | | NFM | London | Police Wembley Relay Transmitter |
| 142.20000 | | AM | Nationwide | USAF 31st FW Ch.V18 |
| 142.21250 | | NFM | London | Police Wembley Relay Transmitter |
| 142.22500 | | AM | USAF Fairford | Tower |
| 142.25000 | | AM | RAF Manston | Ground |
| 142.27500 | | NFM | Belfast | Army Cougar |
| 142.27500 | | AM | USAF Mildenhall | ATIS |
| 142.28750 | | NFM | London | Police Wembley Relay Transmitter |
| 142.29500 | | AM | RAF Coltishall | Tower/Approach |
| 142.29500 | | AM | RAF Wittering | Approach |
| 142.30000 | | AM | RAF Chicksands | British Intelligence Centre (DVP) |
| 142.31250 | | NFM | London | Police Wembley Relay Transmitter |
| 142.32500 | | AM | Nationwide | 100 Sqdn. Air to Air Ch.V03 |
| 142.33750 | | NFM | Humberside | USAF |
| 142.36875 | | NFM | London, Ealing | Police (XD) |
| 142.37500 | | NFM | Chepstow | Mould |
| 142.37500 | | AM | Coningsby | RAF 56 (R) 5QN |
| 142.37500 | | AM | Mildenhall | Black Cat ops. |
| 142.37500 | | AM | Nationwide | 100 Sqdn. Air to Air Ch. V02 |
| 142.40000 | | NFM | Space | Soviet Myr Space Station |
| 142.41250 | | NFM | Nationwide | Mould |
| 142.41250 | | NFM | RAF Welford | Munitions Dump |
| 142.41250 | | NFM | South Wales | Mould |
| 142.41700 | | NFM | Space | Salyut 7 Space Station |
| 142.42500 | | NFM | Dover | Government agency surveillance |
| 142.42500 | | NFM | Gosport | Fort Monkton Camp |
| 142.42500 | | NFM | Stanford | Army |
| 142.42500 | | NFM | Sussex | Royal Sigs Exercise |
| 142.42500 | | NFM | Thetford | Army Stanford exercise area |
| 142.47500 | | AM | Nationwide | Dutch Air Force Display Team Air/Ground crew |
| 142.47500 | | AM | USAF Lakenheath | Approach |
| 142.47500 | 149.17500 | NFM | RAF Chicksands | British Intelligence Centre (DVP/Voice) |
| 142.48750 | | NFM | Strathclyde | Mould |
| 142.50000 | | NFM | Brighton | Lancer Minicabs Encrypted |
| 142.50000 | | NFM | Coulport | MoD Police |
| 142.50000 | | NFM | London | High Speed Computer Link |
| 142.50000 | | NFM | London | Rimington Minicabs Encrypted |
| 142.55000 | | AM | Nationwide | USAF 52 FW Air to Air |
| 142.58750 | | NFM | RAF Chicksands | British Intelligence Centre (Voice/DVP) |
| 142.60000 | | NFM | Stanford | Army |
| 142.60000 | | NFM | Thetford | Army Stanford exercise area |
| 142.61250 | | NFM | Dorset | Mould |
| 142.61250 | | NFM | England, South West | Mould |
| 142.61250 | | NFM | Salisbury | Mould |
| 142.61250 | 149.86750 | NFM | Cranmore | Mould |
| 142.67500 | | NFM | Nationwide | MoD Paging |

| Base | Mobile | Mode | Location | User and Notes |
|------|--------|------|----------|----------------|
| 142.67500 | 149.82500 | NFM | Nationwide | National MoD Radiopaging |
| 142.70000 | | AM | Nationwide | USAF Air to Air |
| 142.70500 | | NFM | Nationwide | BBC Radio 1 Roadshow Talkback |
| 142.72000 | | AM | Nationwide | USAF Air to Air |
| 142.72500 | | AM | Nationwide | USAF Air to Air |
| 142.72500 | | AM | Nationwide | USAF Air to Air |
| 142.72500 | | AM | RAF Brize Norton | 101 Sqn Air to Air |
| 142.77500 | | AM | Doncaster | RAF |
| 142.77500 | | AM | RAF Valley | Air to Air |
| 142.78750 | | FM | England, South West | Military |
| 142.78750 | 149.71250 | NFM | Newton/Morgans | Mould |
| 142.78750 | 149.78750 | NFM | Dorset | Mould Links |
| 142.80000 | | NFM | Belfast | Army Cougar |
| 142.80000 | | NFM | Stanford | Army |
| 142.80000 | | NFM | Thetford | Army Stanford exercise area |
| 142.82500 | | AM | Nationwide | USAF Air to Air |
| 142.82500 | | NFM | Stanford | Battle Ground Scrambled |
| 142.83750 | | NFM | Lochaber | Fire Brigade |
| 142.85000 | | AM | USAF Mildenhall | Command Post |
| 142.87500 | | AM | Coningsby | RAF 56 (R) 5QN |
| 142.87500 | | AM | Nationwide | 100 Sqdn. Air to Air Ch.V01 |
| 142.87500 | | NFM | RAF Chicksands | British Intelligence Centre (DVP & Voice) |
| 142.89750 | | NFM | Nationwide | Mould |
| 142.90000 | | NFM | England, North West | Government agency (DVP) |
| 142.90000 | | AM | RAF Coltishall | Ops |
| 142.91250 | | NFM | Leicester | Mould |
| 142.91250 | | NFM | Strathclyde | Mould |
| 142.93750 | | NFM | Cornwall | Mould |
| 142.93750 | | NFM | Dorset | Mould |
| 142.93750 | | NFM | Suffolk | Mould |
| 142.95000 | | AM | Nationwide | USAF Air to Air |
| 142.96250 | | NFM | Ramsgate | Government agency (DVP) |
| 142.97500 | | NFM | Belfast | Army Cougar |
| 142.97500 | 142.85000 | AM | USAF Mildenhall | US Navy Duty Air to Gnd |
| 143.00000 | | AM | Nationwide | USAF Air to Air |

### 143.0000 - 144.0000 MHz   METROPOLITAN AND
### SW SCOTTISH POLICE MOBILES

| Base | Mobile | Mode | Location | User and Notes |
|------|--------|------|----------|----------------|
| 143.01250 | | NFM | Strathclyde | Police |
| 143.07500 | | NFM | Strathclyde | Police |
| 143.10000 | | AM | Nationwide | Patroille de France Display Team |
| 143.10000 | | NFM | Nationwide | Air Display Team Patroille de France |
| 143.11250 | | NFM | Strathclyde | Police |
| 143.12500 | | NFM | Dumfries and Galloway | Police |
| 143.14400 | | NFM | Nongeostationary | Soviet Voice Channel |
| 143.15000 | | NFM | Strathclyde | Police |
| 143.16000 | | NFM | Dumfries and Galloway | Police |
| 143.21250 | | NFM | Strathclyde | Police |
| 143.23750 | | NFM | Kilmarnock | Police at rugby ground |
| 143.25000 | | NFM | Dumfries and Galloway | Police |
| 143.27500 | | AM | Midlands | USAF |
| 143.27500 | | AM | Nationwide | Dutch F-16 Display Team Air to Air |
| 143.30000 | | NFM | Strathclyde | Police |
| 143.32500 | | NFM | Nationwide | Special Branch |
| 143.35000 | | NFM | Strathclyde | Police |
| 143.37500 | | NFM | Dumfries and Galloway | Police |

| Base | Mobile | Mode | Location | User and Notes |
|------|--------|------|----------|----------------|
| 143.39000 | | NFM | Dumfries and Galloway | Police |
| 143.42500 | | NFM | Strathclyde | Police |
| 143.55000 | | NFM | Strathclyde | Police |
| 143.56250 | | NFM | Strathclyde | Police |
| 143.60000 | | AM | Nationwide | USAF Air to Air |
| 143.61250 | | NFM | Strathclyde | Police |
| 143.62500 | | NFM | Strathclyde | Police |
| 143.63750 | | NFM | Strathclyde | Police |
| 143.80000 | | AM | Nationwide | USAF Air to Air |
| 143.82500 | | NFM | Nongeostationary | Soviet Military Coded Channel |
| 143.88750 | | NFM | Belfast | Data link |
| 143.90000 | | NFM | London | Irish Guards Bomb Jammers in use with 154.60 |
| 143.90000 | | NFM | London | Police Bomb Jamming Van in use with 154.600 |
| 143.90000 | | AM | Nationwide | USAF Air to Air |
| 143.93750 | | NFM | London | National Football Intelligence Unit (DVP/Couganet) |
| 143.93750 | | NFM | Manchester | National Football Intelligence Unit (DVP/Couganet) |

### 144.0000 - 146.0000 MHz   2M AMATEUR RADIO

| Base | Mobile | Mode | Location | User and Notes |
|------|--------|------|----------|----------------|
| 144.00000 | | SSB | Nationwide | Moonbounce |
| 144.05000 | | CW | Nationwide | CW calling Frequency |
| 144.17500 | | NFM | Nationwide | Microwave talkback |
| 144.26000 | | NFM | Nationwide | Raynet |
| 144.30000 | | SSB | Nationwide | SSB calling Frequency |
| 144.50000 | | NFM | Nationwide | SSTV calling |
| 144.50000 | | CW | Non-geostationary | OSCAR 5 Telemetry Bcn |
| 144.60000 | | NFM | Nationwide | RTTY calling |
| 144.67500 | | NFM | Nationwide | Packet |
| 144.70000 | | NFM | Nationwide | FAX calling |
| 144.75000 | | NFM | Nationwide | ATV calling and talkback |
| 144.77500 | | NFM | Nationwide | Raynet |
| 144.80000 | | NFM | Nationwide | Digital modes |
| 144.91500 | | CW | St Austell | Beacon (GB3MCB) |
| 144.92000 | | CW | Portlaw | Beacon (EI2WRB) |
| 144.92500 | | CW | Wrotham | Beacon (GB3VHF) |
| 144.94200 | | CW | Ballymena | Repeater (GB3NGI) |
| 144.96500 | | CW | Lerwick | Beacon (GB3LER) |
| 144.97500 | | CW | Dundee | Beacon (GB3ANG) |
| 144.98300 | | CW | Nongeostationary | OSCAR 1 & 2 Beacon |
| 145.00000 | 145.60000 | NFM | Brighton | Amateur Repeater (GB3SR) |
| 145.00000 | 145.60000 | NFM | Carlisle | Amature Repeater (GB3AS) |
| 145.00000 | 145.60000 | NFM | East London | Amateur Repeater (GB3EL) |
| 145.00000 | 145.60000 | NFM | Elgin | Amateur Repeater (GB3SS) |
| 145.00000 | 145.60000 | NFM | Fife | Amateur Repeater (GB3FF) |
| 145.00000 | 145.60000 | NFM | Leicester | Amature Repeater (GB3CF) |
| 145.00000 | 145.60000 | NFM | Limavaldy | Amateur Repeater (GB3LY) |
| 145.00000 | 145.60000 | NFM | Manchester | Amateur Repeater (GB3MB) |
| 145.00000 | 145.60000 | NFM | Scarborough | Amateur Repeater (GB3YC) |
| 145.00000 | 145.60000 | NFM | Wells | Amateur Repeater (GB3WR) |
| 145.02500 | 145.62500 | NFM | Bournemouth | Amateur Repeater (GB3SC) |
| 145.02500 | 145.62500 | NFM | Douglas | Amateur Repeater (GB3GD) |
| 145.02500 | 145.62500 | NFM | Dover | Amateur Repeater (GB3KS) |
| 145.02500 | 145.62500 | NFM | Fraserburgh | Amateur Repeater (GB3NG) |
| 145.02500 | 145.62500 | NFM | Northallerton | Amateur Repeater (GB3HG) |
| 145.02500 | 145.62500 | NFM | Norwich | Amateur Repeater (GB3NB) |
| 145.02500 | 145.62500 | NFM | Renfrew | Amateur Repeater (GB3PA) |

| Base | Mobile | Mode | Location | User and Notes |
|---|---|---|---|---|
| 145.02500 | 145.62500 | NFM | St. Ives | Amateur Repeater (GB3SI) |
| 145.02500 | 145.62500 | NFM | West London | Amateur Repeater (GB3WL) |
| 145.05000 | 145.65000 | NFM | Ayrshire | Amateur Repeater (GB3AY) |
| 145.05000 | 145.65000 | NFM | Bedford | Amateur Repeater (GB3BF) |
| 145.05000 | 145.65000 | NFM | Birmingham | Amateur Repeater (GB3EC) |
| 145.05000 | 145.65000 | NFM | Hull | Amateur Repeater (GB3HS) |
| 145.05000 | 145.65000 | NFM | Ipswich | Amateur Repeater (GB3PO) |
| 145.05000 | 145.65000 | NFM | King's Lynn | Amateur Repeater (GB3KY) |
| 145.05000 | 145.65000 | NFM | Kirkwall | Amateur Repeater (GB3OC) |
| 145.05000 | 145.65000 | NFM | Selkirk | Amateur Repeater (GB3SB) |
| 145.05000 | 145.65000 | NFM | South London | Amateur Repeater (GB3SL) |
| 145.05000 | 145.65000 | NFM | St. Helier | Amateur Repeater (GB3GJ) |
| 145.05000 | 145.65000 | NFM | Stockport | Amateur Repeater (GB3MN) |
| 145.05000 | 145.65000 | NFM | Swindon | Amateur Repeater (GB3WH) |
| 145.05000 | 145.65000 | NFM | Torquay | Amateur Repeater (GB3TR) |
| 145.07500 | 145.67500 | NFM | Aldermaston | Amateur Repeater GB3RD) |
| 145.07500 | 145.67500 | NFM | Barnsley | Amateur Repeater GB3NA) |
| 145.07500 | 145.67500 | NFM | Barrow-in-Furness | Amateur Repeater GB3LD) |
| 145.07500 | 145.67500 | NFM | Hastings | Amateur Repeater GB3ES) |
| 145.07500 | 145.67500 | NFM | Lerwick | Amateur Repeater GB3LU) |
| 145.07500 | 145.67500 | NFM | Lochgilphead | Amateur Repeater GB3LG) |
| 145.07500 | 145.67500 | NFM | Perth | Amateur Repeater GB3PR) |
| 145.07500 | 145.67500 | NFM | Peterborough | Amateur Repeater GB3PE) |
| 145.07500 | 145.67500 | NFM | Swansea | Amateur Repeater GB3SA) |
| 145.07500 | 145.67500 | NFM | Wolverhampton | Amateur Repeater GB3BX) |
| 145.10000 | 145.70000 | NFM | Aylesbury | Amateur Repeater GB3VA) |
| 145.10000 | 145.70000 | NFM | Berwick | Amateur Repeater GB3BT) |
| 145.10000 | 145.70000 | NFM | Brecon | Amateur Repeater GB3BB) |
| 145.10000 | 145.70000 | NFM | Buxton | Amateur Repeater GB3HH) |
| 145.10000 | 145.70000 | NFM | Caenarfon | Amateur Repeater GB3AR) |
| 145.10000 | 145.70000 | NFM | Cumbria | Amateur Repeater GB3EV) |
| 145.10000 | 145.70000 | NFM | Maidstone | Amateur Repeater GB3KN) |
| 145.10000 | 145.70000 | NFM | Mull | Amateur Repeater GB3HI) |
| 145.10000 | 145.70000 | NFM | Plymouth | Amateur Repeater GB3WD) |
| 145.11250 | 145.71250 | NFM | Cheltenham | Amateur Repeater GB3CG) |
| 145.12500 | 145.72500 | NFM | Alton | Amateur Repeater GB3SN) |
| 145.12500 | 145.72500 | NFM | Belfast | Amateur Repeater GB3NI) |
| 145.12500 | 145.72500 | NFM | Chelmsford | Amateur Repeater GB3DA) |
| 145.12500 | 145.72500 | NFM | Durham | Amateur Repeater GB3TW) |
| 145.12500 | 145.72500 | NFM | Forfar | Amateur Repeater GB3AG) |
| 145.12500 | 145.72500 | NFM | Inverness | Amateur Repeater GB3BI) |
| 145.12500 | 145.72500 | NFM | Keighley | Amateur Repeater GB3TP) |
| 145.12500 | 145.72500 | NFM | Lincoln | Amateur Repeater GB3LM) |
| 145.12500 | 145.72500 | NFM | St. Austell | Amateur Repeater GB3NC) |
| 145.12500 | 145.72500 | NFM | Stoke-on-Trent | Amateur Repeater GB3VT) |
| 145.15000 | 145.75000 | NFM | Crawley | Amateur Repeater GB3WS) |
| 145.15000 | 145.75000 | NFM | Mansfield | Amateur Repeater GB3MX) |
| 145.15000 | 145.75000 | NFM | Moel-y-Parc | Amateur Repeater GB3MP) |
| 145.15000 | 145.75000 | NFM | Newport, Gwent | Amateur Repeater GB3BC) |
| 145.15000 | 145.75000 | NFM | Royston | Amateur Repeater GB3PI) |
| 145.15000 | 145.75000 | NFM | Salburgh | Amateur Repeater GB3CS) |
| 145.17500 | 145.77500 | NFM | Aberdeen | Amateur Repeater GB3GN) |
| 145.17500 | 145.77500 | NFM | Burnley | Amateur Repeater GB3RF) |
| 145.17500 | 145.77500 | NFM | Clacton-on-Sea | Amateur Repeater GB3TE) |
| 145.17500 | 145.77500 | NFM | Cross Hands | Amateur Repeater GB3WW) |
| 145.17500 | 145.77500 | NFM | Enfield | Amateur Repeater GB3NL) |

| Base | Mobile | Mode | Location | User and Notes |
|------|--------|------|----------|----------------|
| 145.17500 | 145.77500 | NFM | Gatehouse of Fleet | Amateur Repeater GB3DG) |
| 145.17500 | 145.77500 | NFM | Leamington | Amateur Repeater GB3WK) |
| 145.17500 | 145.77500 | NFM | Newtown, Powys | Amateur Repeater GB3PW) |
| 145.17500 | 145.77500 | NFM | Omagh | Amateur Repeater GB3WT) |
| 145.17500 | 145.77500 | NFM | Portsmouth | Amateur Repeater GB3PC) |
| 145.17500 | 145.77500 | NFM | Spilsby | Amateur Repeater GB3FR) |
| 145.17500 | 145.77500 | NFM | Stornoway | Amateur Repeater GB3IG) |
| 145.18500 | 145.78500 | NFM | Buxton | Amateur Repeater GB3SF) |
| 145.20000 | | NFM | Nationwide | Raynet S08 |
| 145.22500 | | NFM | Nationwide | Raynet S09 |
| 145.25000 | | NFM | Nationwide | Channel 10 |
| 145.27500 | | NFM | Nationwide | Channel 11 |
| 145.30000 | | NFM | Nationwide | Channel 12 |
| 145.32500 | | NFM | Nationwide | Channel 13 |
| 145.35000 | | NFM | Nationwide | Channel 14 |
| 145.37500 | | NFM | Nationwide | Channel 15 |
| 145.40000 | | NFM | Nationwide | Channel 16 |
| 145.42500 | | NFM | Nationwide | Channel 17 |
| 145.45000 | | NFM | Nationwide | Channel 18 |
| 145.47500 | | NFM | Nationwide | Channel 19 |
| 145.50000 | | NFM | Nationwide | Channel 20 |
| 145.52500 | | NFM | Nationwide | Channel 21 |
| 145.55000 | | NFM | Nationwide | Channel 22 |
| 145.57500 | | NFM | Nationwide | Channel 23 |
| 145.80000 | | NFM | Nationwide | Raynet |
| 145.81000 | | CW | Nongeostationary | OSCAR 10 Beacon |
| 145.81750 | | CW | Nongeostationary | OSCAR 21 Beacon |
| 145.82500 | | CW | Nongeostationary | OSCAR 9 & 11 Telemetry |
| 145.95000 | | CW | Nongeostationary | OSCAR Beacons |
| 145.97500 | | CW | Nongeostationary | OSCAR 7 Telemetry Bcn |
| 145.98700 | | NFM | Nongeostationary | OSCAR 10 Engineering |
| 145.98750 | | NFM | Nongeostationary | OSCAR 21 calling Channel |

## 146.0000 - 148.0000 MHz   GOVERNMENT AND POLICE
### (REPEATERS + 8.0 MHz)

| Base | Mobile | Mode | Location | User and Notes |
|------|--------|------|----------|----------------|
| 146.01250 | | NFM | Newcastle | Police |
| 146.01250 | 154.95000 | NFM | Gwent | Fire Brigade (WR) |
| 146.01250 | 154.95000 | NFM | Thames Valley | Police |
| 146.02500 | | NFM | Darlington | Police |
| 146.02500 | | NFM | North Wales | Police (M2WA) Channel 2 |
| 146.02500 | | AM | Surrey | Fire Brigade (HF) |
| 146.02500 | | NFM | Tyne & Wear | Fire Brigade (LP) |
| 146.02500 | | NFM | West Mercia | Police (YK) |
| 146.02500 | | AM | West Sussex | Police (M2KB) |
| 146.02500 | 146.02500 | NFM | Dyfed & Powys | Police (M2WH) |
| 146.03750 | | NFM | Gerrards Cross | Police |
| 146.03750 | 154.87500 | NFM | Gwent | Fire Brigade (WP) |
| 146.03750 | 154.87500 | NFM | Thames Valley | Police |
| 146.05000 | | NFM | Colchester | Police |
| 146.05000 | | NFM | Derby | Fire Service ND |
| 146.05000 | | NFM | Essex | Police |
| 146.05000 | | NFM | Newport | Police |
| 146.05000 | | NFM | Yorkshire | Fire Brigade |
| 146.06250 | 154.92500 | NFM | Thames Valley | Police (HB) |
| 146.07500 | 154.96250 | NFM | South Wales | Police (WS) |

| Base | Mobile | Mode | Location | User and Notes |
|------|--------|------|----------|----------------|
| 146.07500 | 154.96250 | NFM | Warwickshire | Police (YJ) |
| 146.07500 | 155.15000 | NFM | Manchester | Police (CK) |
| 146.08750 | | NFM | North Wales | Police (M2WA) Channel 4 |
| 146.10000 | | NFM | Gloucester | Police (M2QL) Channel 1 |
| 146.10000 | | AM | Stockport | Police Mobile |
| 146.10000 | 146.90000 | AM | Suffolk | Police (M2VL) Channel 1 |
| 146.10000 | 154.70000 | NFM | Suffolk | Police (VL) Ch.3 |
| 146.10000 | 155.08750 | NFM | Manchester | Police (CK) |
| 146.10000 | 155.87500 | NFM | Dorset | Police (OC) |
| 146.11250 | 155.63750 | NFM | Cumbria | Police (CC) |
| 146.11250 | 155.63750 | NFM | Warwickshire | Police (YJ) |
| 146.12500 | | NFM | Cardiff | Police (M2WY) |
| 146.12500 | 146.12500 | NFM | Wiltshire | Police (M2QM) |
| 146.12500 | 154.01250 | NFM | Lancashire | Police (BB) |
| 146.12500 | 154.01250 | NFM | North M25 | Police (SM0 |
| 146.12500 | 154.88750 | NFM | South Wales | Police (WL) |
| 146.13500 | | NFM | Colwyn Bay | Police |
| 146.13750 | | NFM | North Wales | Police (M2WA) Ch. 1 |
| 146.13750 | 154.05000 | NFM | West Mercia | Police (K) |
| 146.13750 | 154.10000 | NFM | Thames Valley | Police (HB) |
| 146.15000 | | NFM | Dyfed & Powys | Police (M2WH) |
| 146.15000 | | NFM | Hertfordshire | Police Ch.1 |
| 146.15000 | | NFM | Loansdean | Police (M2LB) |
| 146.15000 | 154.88750 | NFM | South Wales | Police (WY) |
| 146.16250 | 154.08750 | NFM | South M25 | Police (SM) |
| 146.17500 | | NFM | West Mercia | Police (M2YK) |
| 146.17500 | 154.07500 | NFM | Berkshire | Police (G) |
| 146.17500 | 154.07500 | NFM | Devon & Cornwall | Police (OA) |
| 146.17500 | 154.07500 | NFM | Lancashire | Police (BD) |
| 146.17500 | 154.07500 | NFM | Thames Valley | Fire Brigade (M2Q) |
| 146.17500 | 154.12500 | NFM | Cambridgeshire | Fire Brigade (M2VP) |
| 146.17500 | 154.12500 | NFM | London | Fire Brigade (M2FN) |
| 146.17500 | 154.12500 | NFM | Staffordshire | Fire Brigade (M2YG) |
| 146.17500 | 154.12500 | NFM | Wiltshire | Fire Brigade (M2GM) |
| 146.17500 | 154.47000 | NFM | Kent | Fire Brigade (M2HQ) |
| 146.17500 | 154.47500 | NFM | Staffordshire | Fire Brigade (M2YG) |
| 146.17500 | 154.93750 | NFM | South Wales | Police (WX) |
| 146.18750 | | AM | West Sussex | Police (M2KB) |
| 146.18750 | 154.90000 | NFM | Dorset | Police (OC) |
| 146.20000 | | NFM | Essex | Police (M2VB) Channel 2 |
| 146.20000 | | NFM | Jersey | Emer Services On-Site Comms |
| 146.20000 | 155.80000 | NFM | Surrey | Police (HJ) |
| 146.20000 | 155.88750 | NFM | Cumbria | Police (BB) |
| 146.21250 | | NFM | Essex | Police |
| 146.21250 | 146.21250 | NFM | West Haverford | Police (M2WL) |
| 146.21250 | 155.01250 | NFM | Manchester | Police (CK) |
| 146.21250 | 155.46250 | NFM | Devon & Cornwall | Police (GB) |
| 146.22500 | | AM | Devon & Cornwall | Police (M2QD) |
| 146.22500 | | NFM | Staffordshire | Fire Service (M2YT) |
| 146.22500 | | NFM | Staffordshire | Police (M2YB) |
| 146.22500 | | AM | Thames Valley | Police (M2HU) |
| 146.22500 | 155.63750 | NFM | Surrey | Police (HJ) |
| 146.23750 | 155.06250 | NFM | Manchester | Police (CK) |
| 146.23750 | 155.32500 | NFM | Devon & Corwall | Police (GB) |
| 146.25000 | 155.58750 | NFM | Cumbria | Police (BB) |
| 146.25000 | 155.86250 | NFM | Surrey | Police (HJ) |

| Base | Mobile | Mode | Location | User and Notes |
|------|--------|------|----------|----------------|
| 146.26250 | | NFM | Hertfordshire | Police (VH) |
| 146.26250 | 155.36250 | NFM | Devon & Cornwall | Police (DB) |
| 146.26250 | 155.65000 | NFM | Derbyshire | Police (NA) |
| 146.27500 | | NFM | Lancashire | Police Helicopter |
| 146.27500 | 154.67500 | NFM | London | Fire Brigade (FE) |
| 146.27500 | 154.67500 | NFM | Nottinghamshire | Fire Brigade (NZ) |
| 146.27500 | 154.83750 | NFM | Thames Valley | Police (HB) |
| 146.27500 | 154.93750 | NFM | Lancashire | Police (BB) |
| 146.28750 | | NFM | Jersey | Ambulance Ch 3 |
| 146.28750 | 155.57500 | NFM | Cheshire | Fire Brigade (CF) |
| 146.28750 | 155.57500 | NFM | Devon & Cornwall | Police |
| 146.28750 | 155.83750 | NFM | Derbyshire | Police (NA) |
| 146.30000 | | NFM | Jersey | Ambulance Ch.3 |
| 146.30000 | | NFM | Jersey | Fire Brigade Ch 3 |
| 146.30000 | 154.77500 | NFM | Thames Valley | Police |
| 146.30000 | 155.46250 | NFM | Lancashire | Police |
| 146.31250 | | NFM | Jersey | Ambulance Ch 4 |
| 146.31250 | | NFM | Sussex | Police |
| 146.31250 | 155.26250 | NFM | Cheshire | Police |
| 146.32500 | | NFM | Bristol | Police (QP) |
| 146.32500 | | NFM | Dyfed & Powys | Police (M2WH) |
| 146.32500 | | NFM | Humberside | Fire Brigade Ch.2 |
| 146.32500 | | AM | West Sussex | Police (M2KB) |
| 146.32500 | 154.62500 | NFM | West Midlands | Police |
| 146.33750 | 155.22500 | NFM | Sussex | Police |
| 146.33750 | 155.48750 | NFM | Cheshire | Police |
| 146.35000 | | NFM | Gwent | Police (WO/WE) |
| 146.35000 | | NFM | Jersey | Ambulance Ch 9 |
| 146.35000 | | NFM | Jersey | Fire Brigade Ch 4 |
| 146.35000 | | NFM | Newport | Police |
| 146.35000 | 154.17500 | NFM | London | Fire Brigade |
| 146.35000 | 154.45000 | NFM | West Midlands | Police |
| 146.36250 | 154.13750 | NFM | Cambridge | Police |
| 146.36250 | 155.05000 | NFM | Sussex | Police |
| 146.36250 | 155.38750 | NFM | Cheshire | Police |
| 146.37500 | 154.70000 | NFM | West Midlands | Police |
| 146.38750 | | AM | West Sussex | Police Mobile |
| 146.38750 | 155.42500 | NFM | Manchester | Police |
| 146.40000 | | NFM | Cleveland | Police |
| 146.40000 | | NFM | Lincoln | Police |
| 146.40000 | | NFM | Northamptonshire | Police (NB) Channel 2 |
| 146.40000 | 155.08750 | NFM | Hampshire | Police |
| 146.41250 | | AM | Kent | Fire Brigade (KF) |
| 146.41250 | | AM | Stockport | Police Mobile |
| 146.41250 | | NFM | Wetherby | Police Repeater (GS) |
| 146.41250 | 155.28750 | NFM | Sussex | Police |
| 146.41250 | 155.61250 | NFM | Manchester | Police |
| 146.42500 | | NFM | Kent | Fire Brigade (KF) |
| 146.42500 | | NFM | North Wales | Police (M2WA) Ch 1 |
| 146.42500 | | NFM | Staffs | Fire Service YM |
| 146.42500 | 154.97500 | NFM | West Midlands | Police |
| 146.43750 | 155.10000 | NFM | North Wales | Police |
| 146.43750 | 155.11250 | NFM | Hampshire | Police |
| 146.45000 | | NFM | Devon | Police (QB) |
| 146.45000 | | NFM | Essex | Fire Brigade (VD) |
| 146.45000 | | NFM | Northamptonshire | Police (NB) |

| Base | Mobile | Mode | Location | User and Notes |
|------|--------|------|----------|----------------|
| 146.45000 | 154.31250 | NFM | West Midlands | Police |
| 146.45000 | 155.63750 | NFM | Cumbria | Police |
| 146.46250 | 154.42550 | NFM | North Wales | Police |
| 146.46250 | 155.16250 | NFM | Hampshire | Police |
| 146.46250 | 155.53750 | NFM | West Midlands | Police |
| 146.47500 | | NFM | Darlington | Police |
| 146.47500 | | NFM | Lewes | Police |
| 146.47500 | | AM | West Sussex | Police (M2KB) |
| 146.47500 | 154.26250 | NFM | West Midlands | Police |
| 146.48750 | 154.10000 | NFM | North Wales | Police |
| 146.48750 | 154.91250 | NFM | Norfolk | Police |
| 146.48750 | 155.26250 | NFM | Hampshire | Police |
| 146.50000 | | NFM | Colchester | Police (VG) Ch.4 |
| 146.50000 | | NFM | Durham | Fire Brigade (M2LF) |
| 146.50000 | 154.50000 | NFM | Jersey | Police |
| 146.51250 | 154.02500 | NFM | West Mercia | Police |
| 146.52500 | | NFM | Hertfordshire | Police |
| 146.52500 | 154.55000 | NFM | Suffolk | Fire Brigade |
| 146.53750 | 154.05000 | NFM | Derbyshire | Fire Brigade |
| 146.53750 | 154.05000 | NFM | West Mercia | Fire Brigade |
| 146.53750 | 154.05000 | NFM | Yorkshire | Fire Brigade (XK) |
| 146.55000 | | NFM | Jersey | Police (M2GS) Ch 5 |
| 146.55000 | | NFM | Loansdean | Fire Brigade (M2LJ) |
| 146.55000 | | AM | South Glamorgan | Police (WY) |
| 146.55000 | | AM | South Wales | Police (WJ) |
| 146.55000 | 146.55000 | AM | Cardiff | Police (WY) |
| 146.55000 | 152.97500 | NFM | Cambridgeshire | Police Ch.2 (VB) |
| 146.56750 | 154.11250 | NFM | Suffolk | Police (VL) Ch.1 |
| 146.56750 | 154.11250 | NFM | West Mercia | Fire Brigade |
| 146.57500 | 146.92500 | AM | Suffolk | Police |
| 146.57500 | 155.15000 | NFM | Avon & Somerset | Police |
| 146.58750 | 154.20000 | NFM | Staffordshire | Police |
| 146.58750 | 155.10000 | NFM | Kent | Police |
| 146.60000 | | AM | Newcastle | Police |
| 146.60000 | 155.20000 | NFM | Hertfordshire | Police |
| 146.60000 | 155.47500 | NFM | Dyfed & Powys | Police |
| 146.60750 | 154.02500 | NFM | Cambridge | Police (VB) |
| 146.61250 | 154.02500 | NFM | East Sussex | Fire Brigade |
| 146.61250 | 154.55000 | NFM | Staffordshire | Police |
| 146.61250 | 154.93750 | NFM | Kent | Police |
| 146.61750 | 154.96250 | NFM | Kent | Police |
| 146.62500 | 154.62500 | NFM | Jersey | Police |
| 146.62500 | 155.12500 | NFM | Hertfordshire | Police |
| 146.62500 | 155.16250 | NFM | Warwickshire | Police |
| 146.62500 | 155.27500 | NFM | Powys | Police |
| 146.62500 | 155.41250 | NFM | Dyfed & Powys | Police |
| 146.63750 | | AM | Newcastle | Police |
| 146.64500 | | NFM | Hutton | Police Link |
| 146.65000 | 155.20000 | NFM | Dyfed | Police (WH) |
| 146.65000 | 155.23750 | NFM | Hertfordshire | Police (VH) |
| 146.66000 | | NFM | West Midlands | Fire Brigade |
| 146.66250 | | NFM | Staffordshire | Fire Service (SE) |
| 146.66250 | 155.05000 | NFM | South Wales | Police (WA) |
| 146.66250 | 155.13750 | NFM | Kent | Police (KA) |
| 146.67500 | 154.15000 | NFM | Gloucester | Police (OL) |
| 146.67500 | 154.98750 | NFM | Norfolk | Police (VK) |

| Base | Mobile | Mode | Location | User and Notes |
|---|---|---|---|---|
| 146.68750 | 154.97500 | NFM | Hampshire | Police (HK) |
| 146.70000 | 154.22500 | NFM | Gloucester | Fire Brigade (GL) |
| 146.70000 | 154.22500 | NFM | Staffordshire | Fire Brigade (YG) |
| 146.70000 | 154.82500 | NFM | Humberside | Fire Brigade (XT) |
| 146.71250 | | NFM | Gwynedd | Fire Brigade (WC) |
| 146.72500 | | NFM | Norfolk | Fire Brigade (VF) |
| 146.72500 | 154.36250 | NFM | Gloucester | Fire Brigade (GL) |
| 146.72500 | 154.80000 | NFM | Lancashire | Police |
| 146.72500 | 154.80000 | NFM | Leicester | Police |
| 146.72500 | 154.80000 | NFM | Sussex | Fire Brigade (KV) |
| 146.73750 | | AM | Hungerford | Police (HU) |
| 146.73750 | 154.33750 | NFM | Haverfordwest | Police (WH) |
| 146.73750 | 154.33750 | NFM | Thames Valley | Police |
| 146.75000 | | NFM | Kent | Police link |
| 146.75000 | | NFM | Leicester | Police |
| 146.76250 | 155.06250 | NFM | Avon & Somerset | Police |
| 146.76250 | 155.06250 | NFM | Newport | Police Helicopter |
| 146.77500 | | NFM | Humberside | Fire Brigade Ch.1 |
| 146.77500 | 154.91250 | NFM | Gwent | Police |
| 146.77500 | 154.91250 | NFM | Kent Motorway | Police (TD) |
| 146.78750 | 154.80000 | NFM | Norfolk | Police Ch.2 (VK) |
| 146.78750 | 155.03750 | NFM | Avon & Somerset | Police |
| 146.80000 | 154.37500 | NFM | Norfolk | Police Ch.1 (VK) |
| 146.80000 | 154.78750 | NFM | Gwent | Police |
| 146.81250 | 155.01250 | NFM | Avon & Somerset | Police |
| 146.82500 | | NFM | Lewes | Fire Brigade |
| 146.82500 | | NFM | West Sussex | Police (M2KB) |
| 146.82500 | 154.06250 | NFM | Merseyside | Police |
| 146.83750 | 154.90000 | NFM | Bedfordshire | Police |
| 146.83750 | 154.90000 | NFM | Merseyside | Police |
| 146.85000 | 154.98750 | NFM | Avon & Somerset | Police |
| 146.85000 | 154.98750 | NFM | Norfolk | Police |
| 146.86250 | | NFM | West Glamorgan | Fire Brigade (WZ) |
| 146.86250 | 154.73750 | NFM | Bedfordshire | Police |
| 146.87500 | | NFM | Lewes | Police |
| 146.87500 | | NFM | Nottinghamshire | Fire Brigade |
| 146.87500 | | AM | West Hoathly | Police link (M2KB) |
| 146.87500 | 154.81250 | NFM | Gwent | Police |
| 146.88750 | 155.93750 | NFM | Thames Valley | Police |
| 146.90000 | | NFM | Loansdean | Police (M2LB) |
| 146.90000 | | NFM | Merseyside | Police |
| 146.90000 | 154.86250 | NFM | Suffolk | Police (VK) |
| 146.90000 | 154.92500 | NFM | Devon & Cornwall | Police |
| 146.90000 | 154.92500 | NFM | Merseyside | Police (CM) |
| 146.91250 | | NFM | West Midlands | Police (MA) |
| 146.91250 | 155.01250 | NFM | Wiltshire | Police |
| 146.92500 | | NFM | Merseyside | Police |
| 146.92500 | 146.57500 | NFM | Suffolk | Police (VL) Ch.1 |
| 146.92500 | 154.88750 | NFM | Suffolk | Police (VL) |
| 146.92500 | 155.17500 | NFM | Merseyside | Police |
| 146.92500 | 155.51250 | NFM | Devon & Cornwall | Police |
| 146.93750 | 155.85000 | NFM | Wiltshire | Police |
| 146.95000 | | NFM | Lewes | Police |
| 146.95000 | | AM | West Sussex | Police (M2KB) |
| 146.95000 | 155.22500 | NFM | Merseyside | Police |
| 146.95000 | 155.38750 | NFM | Devon & Cornwall | Police |

| Base | Mobile | Mode | Location | User and Notes |
|------|--------|------|----------|----------------|
| 146.96250 | 155.90000 | NFM | Wiltshire | Police |
| 146.97500 | | NFM | Hertfordshire | Police Ch.2 (VH) |
| 146.97500 | 155.30000 | NFM | Devon & Cornwall | Police |
| 146.97500 | 155.32500 | NFM | Merseyside | Police |
| 147.00000 | 155.33750 | NFM | Hampshire | Fire Brigade |
| 147.00000 | 155.40000 | NFM | Hereford & Worcester | Fire Brigade |
| 147.00000 | 155.45000 | NFM | West Midlands | Fire Brigade |
| 147.00000 | 155.60000 | NFM | Staffordshire | Fire Brigade |
| 147.01000 | | NFM | Thames Valley | Police |
| 147.01250 | | AM | Wiltshire | Fire Brigade |
| 147.01250 | 154.40000 | NFM | Bedfordshire | Police CH.1 (VA) |
| 147.01250 | 155.92500 | NFM | Dorset | Police |
| 147.02500 | 154.78750 | NFM | Cambridge | Police |
| 147.03750 | | NFM | Newcastle | Police |
| 147.05000 | | AM | Newcastle | Data Link |
| 147.05000 | 146.57500 | NFM | Shropshire | Fire Brigade (YU) |
| 147.06250 | | NFM | Lewes | Police |
| 147.06250 | | NFM | Northampton | Police |
| 147.06250 | | AM | West Sussex | Police (M2KB) |
| 147.07500 | | NFM | Suffolk | Fire Brigade (VN) |
| 147.07500 | 154.61250 | NFM | Wiltshire | Police |
| 147.08750 | 155.21250 | NFM | Avon & Somerset | Police |
| 147.10000 | | NFM | Nuneaton, Warks | Fire Service (YJ) |
| 147.10000 | | AM | West Sussex | Police (M2KB) |
| 147.11250 | | NFM | Armagh | Fire Brigade |
| 147.12500 | | NFM | Banbury, Oxon | Fire Service Ch 2 |
| 147.12500 | | NFM | Leamington Spa, Warks | Fire Service (YK) |
| 147.12500 | | AM | West Sussex | Police (M2KB) |
| 147.12500 | 147.12500 | NFM | London, Heathrow | Police (IH) |
| 147.15000 | | NFM | Barkingside | Police (JB) |
| 147.16250 | | NFM | Warwickshire | Fire Service (YS) |
| 147.18750 | | NFM | Gloucester | Police |
| 147.21250 | 155.31250 | NFM | Brockley | Police (PK) |
| 147.22500 | 155.32500 | NFM | Banstead | Police (ZB) |
| 147.22500 | 155.32500 | NFM | Edinburgh | Police (K) |
| 147.22500 | 155.32500 | NFM | Sutton | Police (ZT) |
| 147.22500 | 155.32500 | NFM | Waltham Abbey | Police (JA) |
| 147.23000 | | NFM | London | Police Loughton |
| 147.23750 | | AM | Stockport | Police mobile |
| 147.23750 | 155.33750 | NFM | Stoke Newington | Police (GN) |
| 147.25000 | 155.35000 | NFM | Bedfordshire | Police Ch 29 |
| 147.25000 | 155.35000 | NFM | Bedfordshire | Police Ch.29 |
| 147.25000 | 155.35000 | NFM | Borehamwood | Police (SD) Ch.29 |
| 147.25000 | 155.35000 | NFM | Bushey, Herts | Police (SU) |
| 147.25000 | 155.35000 | NFM | Nationwide | Police Ch 29 |
| 147.25000 | 155.35000 | NFM | Radlett | Police (SE) |
| 147.25000 | 155.35000 | NFM | Stoneleigh | Police (ZL) |
| 147.26250 | 155.36250 | NFM | Canterbury | Police |
| 147.26250 | 155.36250 | NFM | Waltham Abbey | Police (JA) Ch.30 |
| 147.27500 | 155.37500 | NFM | Borehamwood | Police (SD) |
| 147.27500 | 155.37500 | NFM | Radlett | Police (SE) |
| 147.27500 | 155.37500 | NFM | Shenley | Police (SY) |
| 147.28750 | 155.38750 | NFM | Croydon | Police (ZD) |
| 147.28750 | 155.38750 | NFM | Waltham Abbey | Police (JA) |
| 147.30000 | 155.40000 | NFM | Shepperton | Police (TG) |
| 147.30000 | 155.40000 | NFM | Staines | Police (TG) |

| Base | Mobile | Mode | Location | User and Notes |
|---|---|---|---|---|
| 147.30000 | 155.40000 | NFM | Staines | Police (TW) |
| 147.31250 | 155.41250 | NFM | Norfolk | Police (VK) |
| 147.31250 | 155.41250 | NFM | Shoot Hill | Police (RH) |
| 147.31250 | 155.41250 | NFM | Westcombe Park | Police (QY) |
| 147.32500 | 155.42500 | NFM | Cheshunt, Herts | Police (YC) Ch.35 |
| 147.32500 | 155.42500 | NFM | Earlsfield, Lincs | Police (WF) |
| 147.32500 | 155.42500 | NFM | Edmonton | Police |
| 147.32500 | 155.42500 | NFM | Staines | Police (TS) |
| 147.35000 | 155.45000 | NFM | Biggin Hill | Police (PH) |
| 147.35000 | 155.45000 | NFM | Chislehurst | Police (PC) |
| 147.35000 | 155.45000 | NFM | Farnborough | Police (PF) |
| 147.35000 | 155.45000 | NFM | Harefield | Police (XF) Ch.37 |
| 147.35000 | 155.45000 | NFM | Ruislip | Police (XB) |
| 147.35000 | 155.45000 | NFM | Uxbridge | Police (XU) |
| 147.35000 | 155.47500 | NFM | Northampton | Police Ch 37 |
| 147.36250 | 155.46250 | NFM | Dagenham | Police (KG) |
| 147.36000 | 155.46250 | NFM | Gloucester | Police |
| 147.36250 | 155.46250 | NFM | Gloucester | Police |
| 147.37500 | 155.47500 | NFM | Hayes | Police (XY) |
| 147.37500 | 155.47500 | NFM | Wellington | Police (AW) Ch.39 |
| 147.37500 | 155.47500 | NFM | West Drayton | Police (XW) |
| 147.42500 | 155.52500 | NFM | Epsom | Police (7P) |
| 147.43750 | 155.53750 | NFM | Waltham Abbey | Police (JA) |
| 147.45000 | 155.55000 | NFM | Brentwood | Police (TB) Ch.45 |
| 147.48750 | 155.58750 | NFM | London | Police Channel 48 (GT) |
| 147.50000 | | NFM | Enniskillen | Military data link |
| 147.50000 | 155.60000 | NFM | London | Police Channel 49 (GT) |
| 147.52500 | 155.62500 | NFM | Bonnyrig | Police |
| 147.52500 | 155.62500 | NFM | Lincolnshire | Fire Brigade (NV) |
| 147.52500 | 155.62500 | NFM | London | Police Wembley/Twickenham Stadiums (GT) Ch. 51 |
| 147.53750 | 154.06250 | NFM | Chichester | Fire Brigade |
| 147.56250 | | NFM | Derby | Police |
| 147.57500 | | NFM | Eastleigh | Fire Brigade |
| 147.57500 | | NFM | Northampton | Police data |
| 147.58750 | 155.68750 | NFM | Norfolk | Police (VK1) |
| 147.60000 | | NFM | Hereford & Worcester | Fire Brigade (YB) |
| 147.60000 | 155.70000 | NFM | Nationwide | RCS Ch.57 |
| 147.60000 | 155.70000 | NFM | Sussex | RCS |
| 147.62500 | 155.72500 | NFM | Nationwide | RCS Ch.59 |
| 147.62500 | 155.72500 | NFM | West Midlands | Police (YM) Ch.58 |
| 147.65000 | | NFM | Lewes | Police |
| 147.65000 | | NFM | Lincolnshire | Police (NC) Channel 1 |
| 147.65000 | | NFM | West Mercia | Police (YK) |
| 147.65000 | 155.75000 | NFM | Nationwide | RCS surveillance Ch.61 |
| 147.66250 | | NFM | Bolton | Police Motorcycle Instructors |
| 147.66250 | | AM | Lancashire | Police (Car to Car) |
| 147.66250 | | NFM | Workington | Motorcycle Training |
| 147.67500 | | NFM | Eastleigh | Fire Brigade |
| 147.70000 | 168.70000 | NFM | Manchester | CID (DVP or Voice) |
| 147.70000 | 168.70000 | NFM | Nationwide | RCS Secure Cougar System |
| 147.72500 | 168.80000 | NFM | Manchester | CID (DVP or Voice) |
| 147.72500 | 168.80000 | NFM | Nationwide | RCS Channel 71 |
| 147.72500 | 168.80000 | NFM | Nationwide | RCS Secure Cougar System |
| 147.75000 | | NFM | Manchester | CID (DVP or Voice) |
| 147.77500 | 155.87500 | NFM | Manchester | CID (DVP or Voice) |
| 147.77500 | 155.87500 | NFM | Nationwide | RCS Ch.71 |

| Base | Mobile | Mode | Location | User and Notes |
|------|--------|------|----------|----------------|
| 147.80000 | 155.90000 | NFM | Jersey | Fire Paging |
| 147.80000 | 155.90000 | AM | Nationwide | Fire Alert |
| 147.81250 | 147.81250 | NFM | Strathclyde | Police |
| 147.81250 | 154.51250 | NFM | Bedfordshire | Police Ch.2 (VA) |
| 147.83750 | | NFM | Manchester | Police (VP) |
| 147.85000 | | NFM | Dumfries and Galloway | Police |
| 147.85000 | | NFM | Lincolnshire | Police (NC) Channel 2 |
| 147.85000 | | AM | Newcastle | MoD Police |
| 147.85000 | | NFM | Strathclyde | Fire Brigade (GX) |
| 147.85000 | | AM | Wiltshire | Police |
| 147.86250 | | NFM | London | Armed anti terrorist stop checks (LEGION) |
| 147.86250 | | NFM | London | CID Surveillance/Handhelds |
| 147.87500 | | NFM | England & Wales | Police Mobiles Channel 21 |
| 147.87500 | | NFM | Kent | Police (Tour De France) |
| 147.87500 | | NFM | London | Police CID/TSG Handhelds |
| 147.87500 | | NFM | London | Police Royal and special escorts Ch.16 |
| 147.88750 | | NFM | Kent | Police (KA) |
| 147.88750 | | NFM | Kent Motorways | Police (TD) |
| 147.88750 | | NFM | Nottingham | Police Ch 3 |
| 147.90000 | | NFM | England | Fire Brigade Pagers |
| 147.90000 | | NFM | Gwent | Fire Brigade (WP0 |
| 147.90000 | | NFM | Newport | Fire Brigade |
| 147.90000 | | NFM | Strathclyde | Fire Brigade (GX) |
| 147.91250 | | NFM | England & Wales | Police Mobiles Channel 22 |
| 147.91250 | | NFM | London | Police Ch.22 CID/TSG Handhelds |
| 147.91250 | | NFM | London, Oxford & Regent St. | CID ops on illegal street traders |
| 147.91250 | | NFM | Nationwide | Police Ch.22 CID & special escorts (also AM) |
| 147.91250 | | NFM | Nationwide | RCS Car to Car Channel 82 |
| 147.91250 | | AM | Sheerness | Police |
| 147.92500 | | NFM | London | Police CID/TSG Handhelds |
| 147.92500 | | NFM | Nottingham | Police Ch 1 |
| 147.92500 | | NFM | Strathclyde | Fire Brigade (GX) |
| 147.93750 | | NFM | Nationwide | RCS Channel 84 |
| 147.95000 | | NFM | London | Police CID and support group |
| 147.95000 | | NFM | Nationwide | RCS Channel 00 |
| 147.97500 | | NFM | Nationwide | RCS Channel 00 |
| 147.97500 | | NFM | Nottingham | Police Ch 2 |

## 148.00000 - 148.99875 MHz    NATIONAL POWER COMPANIES

| Base | Mobile | Mode | Location | User and Notes |
|------|--------|------|----------|----------------|
| 148.00000 | 139.56880 | NFM | Nationwide | Electricity Channel J21 |
| 148.01880 | 139.51880 | NFM | Nationwide | Electricity Channel J22 |
| 148.03130 | 139.51130 | NFM | Nationwide | Electricity Channel J23 |
| 148.04330 | 139.54390 | NFM | Nationwide | Electricity Channel J24 |
| 148.05630 | 139.55630 | NFM | Nationwide | Electricity Channel J25 |
| 148.08110 | | NFM | Luton | Electricity |
| 148.08110 | 139.58130 | NFM | Nationwide | Electricity Channel J27 |
| 148.09380 | 139.59380 | NFM | Nationwide | Electricity Channel J28 |
| 148.10630 | 139.60630 | NFM | Nationwide | Electricity Channel J29 |
| 148.11880 | 139.61880 | NFM | Nationwide | Electricity Channel J30 |
| 148.13130 | 139.63130 | NFM | Nationwide | Electricity Channel J31 |
| 148.14380 | | NFM | Cambridge | Electricity |
| 148.14380 | 139.64380 | NFM | Nationwide | Electricity Channel J32 |
| 148.15630 | 139.65630 | NFM | Nationwide | Electricity Channel J33 |
| 148.15630 | 139.65630 | NFM | Norfolk | Electricity |
| 148.16880 | | NFM | Clacton | Electricity |

| Base | Mobile | Mode | Location | User and Notes |
|------|--------|------|----------|----------------|
| 148.16880 | | NFM | Peterborough | Electricity |
| 148.16880 | 139.66880 | NFM | Nationwide | Electricity Channel J34 |
| 148.18130 | | NFM | Suffolk | Electricity |
| 148.18130 | 139.68130 | NFM | Nationwide | Electricity Channel J35 |
| 148.19380 | | NFM | Norwich | Electricity |
| 148.19380 | 139.69380 | NFM | Nationwide | Electricity Channel J36 |
| 148.20630 | | NFM | Chelmsford | Electricity |
| 148.20630 | | NFM | Clacton | Electricity |
| 148.20630 | | NFM | Ipswich | Electricity |
| 148.20630 | 139.70630 | NFM | Nationwide | Electricity Channel J37 |
| 148.21880 | | NFM | Harrow | Electricity |
| 148.21880 | 139.71880 | NFM | Nationwide | Electricity Channel J38 |
| 148.23130 | | NFM | Enfield | Electricity |
| 148.23130 | | NFM | Ipswich | Electricity |
| 148.23130 | | NFM | Kings Lynn | Electricity |
| 148.23130 | 139.73130 | NFM | Nationwide | Electricity Channel J39 |
| 148.24380 | 139.74380 | NFM | Nationwide | Electricity Channel J40 |
| 148.25630 | 139.75630 | NFM | Nationwide | Electricity Channel J41 |
| 148.26880 | 139.76880 | NFM | Nationwide | Electricity Channel J42 |
| 148.28130 | 139.78130 | NFM | Nationwide | Electricity Channel J43 |
| 148.29380 | 139.79380 | NFM | Nationwide | Electricity Channel J44 |
| 148.30630 | 139.80630 | NFM | Nationwide | Electricity Channel J45 |
| 148.31830 | 139.81830 | NFM | Nationwide | Electricity Channel J46 |
| 148.32500 | | NFM | Bolton | Norweb |
| 148.33130 | 139.83130 | NFM | Nationwide | Electricity Channel J47 |
| 148.34380 | 139.84360 | NFM | Nationwide | Electricity Channel J48 |
| 148.35630 | 139.65630 | NFM | Nationwide | Electricity Channel J49 |
| 148.36880 | 139.86880 | NFM | Nationwide | Electricity Channel J50 |
| 148.38130 | 139.88130 | NFM | Nationwide | Electricity Channel J51 |
| 148.39380 | 139.69380 | NFM | Nationwide | Electricity Channel J52 |
| 148.40630 | | NFM | Nationwide | Electricity Channel J53 |
| 148.41880 | 139.91880 | NFM | Nationwide | Electricity Channel J54 |
| 148.43110 | 139.93130 | NFM | Nationwide | Electricity Channel J55 |
| 148.44380 | 139.94380 | NFM | Nationwide | Electricity Channel J56 |
| 148.45630 | 139.95630 | NFM | Nationwide | Electricity Channel J57 |
| 148.46880 | 139.96680 | NFM | Nationwide | Electricity Channel J58 |
| 148.47500 | 147.96870 | NFM | Burnley | British Gas |
| 148.48130 | 139.98130 | NFM | Nationwide | Electricity Channel J59 |
| 148.49380 | 139.99380 | NFM | Nationwide | Electricity Channel J60 |
| 148.50630 | 140.00630 | NFM | Nationwide | Electricity Channel J61 |
| 148.51880 | 140.01880 | NFM | Nationwide | Electricity Channel J62 |
| 148.53130 | 140.03130 | NFM | Nationwide | Electricity Channel J63 |
| 148.54380 | 140.04380 | NFM | Nationwide | Electricity Channel J64 |
| 148.55000 | | NFM | Devon | South West Electricity |
| 148.55630 | 140.05630 | NFM | Nationwide | Electricity Channel J65 |
| 148.56880 | 140.06880 | NFM | Nationwide | Electricity Channel J66 |
| 148.57500 | | NFM | Channel Islands | JFMG Radio Mic |
| 148.58130 | 140.08130 | NFM | Nationwide | Electricity Channel J67 |
| 148.59380 | 140.09380 | NFM | Nationwide | Electricity Channel J68 |
| 148.60500 | | NFM | Normanton, West Yorkshire | British Gas |
| 148.60630 | 140.10630 | NFM | Nationwide | Electricity Channel J69 |
| 148.61630 | 140.11880 | NFM | Nationwide | Electricity Channel J70 |
| 148.63130 | 140.13130 | NFM | Nationwide | Electricity Channel J71 |
| 148.64380 | 140.14380 | NFM | Nationwide | Electricity Channel J72 |
| 148.65630 | 140.15630 | NFM | Nationwide | Electricity Channel J73 |
| 148.66880 | 140.16880 | NFM | Nationwide | Electricity Channel J74 |

| Base | Mobile | Mode | Location | User and Notes |
|---|---|---|---|---|
| 148.68130 | 140.18130 | NFM | Nationwide | Electricity Channel J75 |
| 148.69380 | 140.19380 | NFM | Nationwide | Electricity Channel J76 |
| 148.70630 | 140.20430 | NFM | Nationwide | Electricity Channel J77 |
| 148.71880 | 140.21880 | NFM | Nationwide | Electricity Channel J78 |
| 148.72500 | | NFM | Channel Islands | JFMG Radio Mic |
| 148.73130 | 140.23130 | NFM | Nationwide | Electricity Channel J79 |
| 148.74380 | 140.24380 | NFM | Nationwide | Electricity Channel J80 |
| 148.75630 | 140.25630 | NFM | Nationwide | Electricity Channel J81 |
| 148.76250 | | NFM | Newcastle | Link |
| 148.76880 | 140.26880 | NFM | Nationwide | Electricity Channel J82 |
| 148.78130 | 140.28130 | NFM | Nationwide | Electricity Channel J83 |
| 148.79380 | 140.29380 | NFM | Nationwide | Electricity Channel J84 |
| 148.80630 | 140.30630 | NFM | Nationwide | Electricity Channel J85 |
| 148.81880 | 140.31880 | NFM | Nationwide | Electricity Channel J86 |
| 148.82000 | | NFM | Durham | British Gas |
| 148.83130 | 140.33130 | NFM | Nationwide | Electricity Channel J87 |
| 148.84360 | 140.34380 | NFM | Nationwide | Electricity Channel J88 |
| 148.85630 | 140.35630 | NFM | Nationwide | Electricity Channel J89 |
| 148.86880 | 140.36890 | NFM | Nationwide | Electricity Channel J90 |
| 148.88130 | 140.38130 | NFM | Nationwide | Electricity Channel J91 |
| 148.89380 | 140.39380 | NFM | Nationwide | Electricity Channel J92 |
| 148.90630 | 140.40630 | NFM | Nationwide | Electricity Channel J93 |
| 148.91880 | 140.41880 | NFM | Nationwide | Electricity Channel J94 |
| 148.93130 | 140.43130 | NFM | Nationwide | Electricity Channel J95 |
| 148.94380 | 140.44380 | NFM | Nationwide | Electricity Channel J96 |
| 148.95000 | 148.95000 | AM | Nationwide | USAF General |
| 148.95630 | 140.45630 | NFM | Nationwide | Electricity Channel J97 |
| 148.96880 | 140.46880 | NFM | Nationwide | Electricity Channel J98 |
| 148.98130 | 140.48130 | NFM | Nationwide | Electricity Channel J99 |

### 149.0000 - 149.9000 MHz    GOVERNMENT & MoD MOULD REPEATERS

| Base | Mobile | Mode | Location | User and Notes |
|---|---|---|---|---|
| 149.00000 | | NFM | Nationwide | MoD Repeaters |
| 149.01000 | | NFM | Space | Russian low orbit navigation satellite (RTTY) |
| 149.01250 | | NFM | Leicester | Mould |
| 149.01250 | | NFM | Sennybridge | Army firing range |
| 149.01250 | | NFM | South Wales | Mould |
| 149.03750 | 149.03750 | NFM | Aberfield | MoD Police |
| 149.03750 | 153.83750 | NFM | Aldershot | Army range wardens control (BEAVER) |
| 149.04000 | | NFM | Space | Russian low orbit navigation satellite (RTTY) |
| 149.05000 | | AM | Mildenhall | Ground |
| 149.06250 | | NFM | England, North West | Army voice communications |
| 149.06250 | | NFM | South Wales | Mould |
| 149.06250 | | NFM | Suffolk | Military |
| 149.07000 | | NFM | Space | Russian low orbit navigation satellite (RTTY) |
| 149.07500 | | NFM | Cornwall | Mould |
| 149.07500 | | AM | Nationwide | ATC Channel V5 |
| 149.07500 | | NFM | South Wales | Mould |
| 149.08750 | 142.41250 | NFM | Cornwall | Mould |
| 149.10000 | 149.10000 | AM | Nationwide | USAF Rescue Helicopter to AART |
| 149.11250 | | NFM | Salisbury | Mould |
| 149.12500 | | NFM | RAF Caerwent | Store Security |
| 149.17500 | | NFM | South Wales | Mould |
| 149.23750 | | NFM | Nationwide | MoD Establishments |
| 149.25000 | | NFM | South Wales | Mould |
| 149.26250 | | NFM | Cornwall | Mould |

| Base | Mobile | Mode | Location | User and Notes |
|---|---|---|---|---|
| 149.27500 | | AM | Nationwide | ATC Channel V6 |
| 149.27500 | | NFM | RAF Spadeadam | Forward Air Controller |
| 149.27500 | 149.27500 | NFM | Nationwide | RAF Cadets Channel V6 |
| 149.28750 | | NFM | Suffolk | Military |
| 149.28750 | | NFM | Tayside | Mould |
| 149.32500 | | NFM | MoD Aberporth | Ops |
| 149.33750 | | NFM | Salisbury | Mould |
| 149.36250 | | NFM | Nationwide | MoD Establishments |
| 149.38750 | | NFM | MoD Aberporth | Ops |
| 149.38750 | | NFM | Nationwide | MoD Establishments |
| 149.38750 | 142.06250 | NFM | Shoeburyness | Mould |
| 149.40000 | | AM | Nationwide | ATC Channel V2 |
| 149.40000 | | NFM | Porton Down | MoD Police |
| 149.40000 | 149.40000 | NFM | Nationwide | RAF ATC Channel V2 |
| 149.41250 | | NFM | Boscombe Down | MoD Police |
| 149.41250 | | NFM | Nationwide | MoD Establishments |
| 149.41250 | | NFM | Porton Down | MoD Police |
| 149.41250 | | NFM | USAF Welford | Bomb dump |
| 149.41250 | 142.11250 | NFM | South Wales | Mould |
| 149.41750 | | NFM | South Wales | Mould Ch 4 |
| 149.42500 | | NFM | Nationwide | Sea Cadets |
| 149.42750 | | NFM | South Wales | Mould |
| 149.46250 | | NFM | London | Mould |
| 149.46250 | | NFM | South Wales | Mould |
| 149.50000 | | NFM | South Wales | Mould |
| 149.53750 | | NFM | Detling Hill | Mould |
| 149.53750 | | NFM | Manchester | Mould |
| 149.53750 | | NFM | Midlands | Mould |
| 149.55000 | | AM | Mildenhall | 352 SOG Air/Air (TALON) |
| 149.62500 | | NFM | Cornwall | Mould |
| 149.63750 | | NFM | MoD Porton Down | Range |
| 149.65000 | | NFM | RAF Mildenhall | US Navy |
| 149.65000 | | NFM | USAF Lakenheath | Radar |
| 149.65000 | 149.65000 | NFM | Nationwide | USAF Air-Air |
| 149.68000 | 154.35000 | NFM | Cambridgeshire | Police Ch.1 (VB) |
| 149.68750 | | NFM | MoD Porton Down | Link to Middle Wallop |
| 149.70000 | | NFM | South Wales | Mould |
| 149.70000 | 149.72150 | NFM | Leicester | Mould |
| 149.71250 | | NFM | Berkshire | Mould |
| 149.71250 | | NFM | England, South West | Mould |
| 149.73750 | | NFM | Brecon Beacons | Mould |
| 149.73750 | | NFM | Caerwent | MoD Ops |
| 149.73750 | | NFM | Manchester | Mould |
| 149.73750 | | NFM | Tayside | Mould |
| 149.73750 | | NFM | Wattisham, Suffolk | MoD Army Air Corp. |
| 149.76250 | | NFM | Nationwide | MoD Establishments |
| 149.76250 | | NFM | Salisbury Plain | Army bio warfare firing |
| 149.77500 | | NFM | London | MI5 and police anti terrorist branch |
| 149.77500 | | NFM | Nationwide | MoD Regional Police Channel 1 |
| 149.77500 | | NFM | Nationwide | USAF Air-Air |
| 149.77500 | 149.77500 | NFM | Nationwide | MoD Police Helicopters |
| 149.78750 | | NFM | Aldermaston | Atomic Weapons Establishment fire/rescue (RED) |
| 149.80000 | | NFM | South Wales | Mould |
| 149.81250 | | NFM | Chesterfield | Mould |
| 149.81250 | | NFM | England, South West | Mould |
| 149.81250 | | NFM | Salisbury Plain | Army |

| Base | Mobile | Mode | Location | User and Notes |
|------|--------|------|----------|----------------|
| 149.81250 | 149.83750 | NFM | South Wales | Mould |
| 149.82500 | | NFM | Portsmouth | Whale Island MoD Police (PD) |
| 149.82500 | 149.82500 | NFM | London | MoD Police |
| 149.85000 | | NFM | Colchester | MoD Police |
| 149.85000 | | NFM | DRA Farnborough | MoD Police (FP) |
| 149.85000 | | NFM | Hadleigh | MoD Police |
| 149.85000 | | NFM | Nationwide | MoD Police Channel 3 |
| 149.85000 | | NFM | Portsmouth Naval Docks | Whale Island MoD Police (PD) |
| 149.85000 | 149.85000 | NFM | Aldershot Barracks | MoD Police |
| 149.86250 | | NFM | Berkshire | Mould |
| 149.86750 | | NFM | South Wales | Mould |
| 149.86750 | | NFM | Tayside | Mould |
| 149.88750 | | NFM | England, South West | Mould |
| 149.90000 | | NFM | Caerleon | ATC Ch 2 |
| 149.90000 | | NFM | London | Police CID/TSG Handhelds |
| 149.90000 | 149.90000 | NFM | Nationwide | RAF Air Training Corps Chan2 |
| 149.91250 | | NFM | Salisbury | Army RTTY link |

### 149.9000 - 150.0500 MHz   RADIONAVIGATION AND SOVIET SATELLITE BEACONS

| Base | Mobile | Mode | Location | User and Notes |
|------|--------|------|----------|----------------|
| 149.970 | | NFM | Space | Polar Bear 8688A |
| 149.980 | | NFM | Space | Soviet Cosmos Satellites |
| 150.000 | | NFM | Space | Russian low orbit navigation satellite (RTTY) |

### 150.0500 - 152.0000 MHz   RADIO ASTRONOMY, PAGING AND MoD

| Base | Mobile | Mode | Location | User and Notes |
|------|--------|------|----------|----------------|
| 150.03000 | | NFM | Space | Russian low orbit navigation satellite (RTTY) |
| 150.05000 | | NFM | London | MoD Procurement Executive Ch 1 |
| 150.07500 | | NFM | London | MoD Procurement Executive Ch 2 |
| 150.07500 | | AM | Yorkshire | MoD |
| 150.11000 | | NFM | Nationwide | Oil Slick Markers |
| 150.18500 | | NFM | Nationwide | Oil Slick Markers |
| 150.30000 | | NFM | Non-Geostationary | Russian Cosmos Geodetic |
| 150.50000 | | NFM | Nationwide | Nissan Racing Team |
| 150.50000 | | AM | Yorkshire | MoD |
| 150.56250 | | NFM | Enniskillen | Military Data Link |
| 151.32500 | | NFM | Nationwide | Army Bomb Squad |
| 151.60000 | | NFM | Essex | Colchester Docks |
| 151.60000 | | NFM | London | Tower Bridge Control |
| 151.60000 | 156.60000 | NFM | Gravesend | Pool Control |
| 151.67500 | | NFM | Newmarket | Paging |
| 151.77500 | | NFM | Galway | University Hospital Paging |
| 151.77500 | | NFM | London | Madonna's American bodyguards (American Business Radio Service) |

### 152.0000 - 152.9875 MHz   POLICE & FIRE PMR 12.5 KHz

| Base | Mobile | Mode | Location | User and Notes |
|------|--------|------|----------|----------------|
| 152.00000 | 143.07500 | NFM | Leicester | Police (NL) Channel 1 |
| 152.01250 | 143.16250 | NFM | Dumfries & Galloway | Police (AJ) |
| 152.01250 | 143.16250 | AM | Isle of Man | Police (MX) Channel 1 |
| 152.01250 | 143.16250 | NFM | Strathclyde | Police Data Channel |
| 152.01250 | 143.56250 | AM | West Yorkshire | Police (XW) Channel 3 |
| 152.02000 | | NFM | Glasgow | Police Ch 1 |
| 152.02500 | | NFM | Humberside | Fire Brigade Ch.1 |
| 152.02500 | 143.02500 | NFM | Strathclyde | Police Channel 1 |
| 152.02500 | 143.06250 | NFM | London | Police Area Crime Squad |
| 152.03750 | 143.07500 | NFM | Dumfries & Galloway | Police (AJ) |

| Base | Mobile | Mode | Location | User and Notes |
|------|--------|------|----------|----------------|
| 152.03750 | 143.07500 | AM | Leicester | Police (NL) Channel 1 |
| 152.05000 | 143.05000 | NFM | Glasgow | Police (AS) Ch 2 |
| 152.05000 | 143.11250 | NFM | London | Police car to car Ch.5 |
| 152.05000 | 143.58500 | AM | West Yorkshire | Police (XW) Channel 5 |
| 152.05000 | 143.58750 | NFM | Co. Durham | Police |
| 152.05000 | 143.58750 | NFM | Dumfries & Galloway | Police (AJ) |
| 152.06250 | 143.11250 | NFM | Hawick | Police |
| 152.06250 | 143.31250 | NFM | Mosspaul | Police |
| 152.06250 | 143.31250 | AM | North Yorkshire | Police (XN) Channel 2 |
| 152.06250 | 143.31250 | AM | Scarborough | Police 'D' Division |
| 152.07500 | | NFM | London | Police photo intelligence units at demos |
| 152.07500 | 143.43750 | NFM | Strathclyde | Police Channel 32 |
| 152.07500 | 143.43750 | NFM | Yorkshire | Fire Brigade Control |
| 152.07500 | 152.07500 | NFM | Dumfries and Galloway | Police |
| 152.07500 | 152.07500 | NFM | Langholm | Police |
| 152.07500 | 152.67500 | NFM | Ottercops | Police (M2LB) |
| 152.08750 | 143.07500 | AM | Northumberland | Police (M2LB) Channel 1 |
| 152.08750 | 143.07500 | NFM | Strathclyde | Fire Brigade (GX) Channel 11 |
| 152.08750 | 143.07500 | NFM | Wisham | Fire Brigade |
| 152.08750 | 143.08750 | NFM | Berwick | Police |
| 152.08750 | 143.08750 | NFM | Edinburgh | Police (Fringe Festival) |
| 152.08750 | 152.08750 | NFM | Lincolnshire | Police (NC) |
| 152.10000 | 143.26250 | NFM | London | Police Channel 11 (MP) OSCAR Channel |
| 152.10000 | 143.43750 | NFM | Strathclyde | Police Channel 31 |
| 152.12500 | | NFM | Ayr | Police (R) |
| 152.12500 | 143.02500 | NFM | Strathclyde | Police Channel 4 |
| 152.12500 | 146.95000 | NFM | Beacon Lough | Police (M2LB) |
| 152.12500 | 152.72500 | NFM | Quarry House | Police (M2LB) |
| 152.13750 | | NFM | Staffordshire | Police and Fire brigade trunked network (YF/YG) |
| 152.13750 | 143.31250 | NFM | London | Police (MP) Channel 13 OSCAR |
| 152.13750 | 143.51250 | NFM | Dumfries and Galloway | Police (AJ) |
| 152.15000 | | FM | Glasgow | Traffic Management |
| 152.15000 | | NFM | Staffordshire | Police and Fire brigade trunked network (YF/YG) |
| 152.15000 | 143.20000 | NFM | Strathclyde | Police Channel 11 |
| 152.15000 | 143.36250 | AM | North Yorkshire | Police (XN) Channel 4 |
| 152.16250 | 143.37500 | NFM | Strathclyde | Fire Brigade (GX) Channel 5 |
| 152.16250 | 143.37500 | NFM | Strathclyde | Police Ch 3 |
| 152.16250 | 143.42500 | NFM | South Yorkshire | Police (XS) Channel 5 |
| 152.17500 | | NFM | Teesside | Police |
| 152.17500 | 143.10000 | AM | Leicester | Police (NL) Channel 3 |
| 152.17500 | 143.20000 | NFM | Strathclyde | Police Channel 12 |
| 152.18750 | 143.03750 | NFM | Strathclyde | Fire Brigade (GX) Channel 2 |
| 152.18750 | 143.13750 | NFM | Bovington | Police |
| 152.18750 | 143.13750 | NFM | Brockley | Police |
| 152.18750 | 143.13750 | NFM | Dumfries & Galloway | Fire Brigade Channel 15 |
| 152.18750 | 143.13750 | NFM | Sandwich | Police |
| 152.18800 | 143.10000 | AM | Northumberland | Police (M2LB) Channel 2 |
| 152.20000 | | NFM | Dumfries and Galloway | Police (AJ) |
| 152.20000 | 143.20000 | NFM | Strathclyde | Police Channel 09 |
| 152.20000 | 143.58750 | NFM | Staffordshire | Police (YF) Channel 1 |
| 152.21250 | | NFM | Dumfries and Galloway | Police (AJ) |
| 152.21250 | 143.41250 | NFM | Strathclyde | Police Channel 36 |
| 152.22500 | 143.13750 | NFM | London | Police Ch 6 (MP) |
| 152.22500 | 143.27500 | NFM | Strathclyde | Police Channel 18 |
| 152.22500 | 143.27500 | NFM | Wigton | Police (W) |
| 152.22500 | 146.15000 | NFM | Quarry House | Police (M2LB) |

| Base | Mobile | Mode | Location | User and Notes |
|------|--------|------|----------|----------------|
| 152.22500 | 152.22500 | NFM | Dumfries and Galloway | Police |
| 152.23750 | | NFM | Nottingham | Police |
| 152.23750 | 143.03750 | NFM | Strathclyde | Fire Brigade (GX) Channel 23 |
| 152.23750 | 143.46250 | NFM | Strathclyde | Fire Brigade (GX) Channel 2 |
| 152.23750 | 143.66250 | NFM | Strathclyde | Fire Brigade (GX) Channel 7 |
| 152.23750 | 143.71250 | NFM | Strathclyde | Fire Brigade (GX) Channel 35 |
| 152.25000 | 143.27500 | NFM | Strathclyde | Police Channel 5 |
| 152.25000 | 143.51250 | NFM | Dumfries and Galloway | Police (AJ) |
| 152.26250 | | NFM | Bridge of Orchy | Police |
| 152.26250 | | NFM | Kirkcudbright | Police |
| 152.26250 | | NFM | Staffordshire | Police and Fire brigade trunked network (YF/YG) |
| 152.26250 | 143.18750 | NFM | London | Police diplomatic and royalty protection |
| 152.26250 | 143.18750 | NFM | London | Police special movements (MP) Ch.8 |
| 152.26250 | 143.26250 | NFM | Strathclyde | Police Channel 45 |
| 152.26250 | 143.38750 | AM | North Yorkshire | Police (XN) Channel 5 |
| 152.26250 | 143.41250 | NFM | Strathclyde | Police Channel 37 |
| 152.27500 | 143.40000 | NFM | Dumfries and Galloway | Police (AJ) |
| 152.27500 | 143.45000 | NFM | Strathclyde | Police Channel 26 |
| 152.27500 | 152.66250 | NFM | Ottercops | Police (M2LB) |
| 152.28750 | 143.03750 | NFM | Strathclyde | Fire Brigade (GX) Channel 56 |
| 152.28750 | 143.13750 | NFM | Strathclyde | Fire Brigade (GX) Channel 11 |
| 152.28750 | 143.28750 | NFM | Strathclyde | Fire Brigade (GX) Channel 48 |
| 152.28750 | 143.46250 | NFM | Strathclyde | Fire Brigade (GX) Channel 7 |
| 152.28750 | 143.66250 | NFM | Strathclyde | Fire Brigade (GX) Channel 9 |
| 152.28750 | 143.71250 | NFM | Strathclyde | Fire Brigade (GX) Channel 36 |
| 152.28750 | 143.72500 | NFM | Dumfries and Galloway | Fire Brigade (Control) Ch16 |
| 152.30000 | 143.20000 | NFM | Strathclyde | Police Channel 14 |
| 152.30000 | 143.23750 | NFM | London | Police Area Traffic Channel 10 (GT) |
| 152.30000 | 153.00000 | NFM | Dumfries and Galloway | Police |
| 152.31250 | | NFM | Staffordshire | Police and Fire brigade trunked network (YF/YG) |
| 152.31250 | 143.03750 | NFM | Strathclyde | Fire Brigade Channel 2 |
| 152.31250 | 143.13750 | NFM | Strathclyde | Fire Brigade (GX) Channel 11 |
| 152.31250 | 143.15000 | NFM | Dumfries and Galloway | Fire Brigade (Fire Control) |
| 152.31250 | 143.16250 | AM | Humberside | Police (XH) |
| 152.31250 | 143.28750 | NFM | Strathclyde | Fire Brigade (GX) |
| 152.32500 | 143.16250 | NFM | London | Police Ch 7 (MP) |
| 152.32500 | 143.16250 | NFM | London | Police Crime squad and Anti Terrorist Branch Ch.7 |
| 152.32500 | 143.27500 | NFM | Ayr | Police |
| 152.32500 | 152.85000 | NFM | Quarry House | Police (M2LB) |
| 152.32500 | 152.85000 | NFM | Strathclyde | Police |
| 152.33750 | 143.03750 | AM | West Yorkshire | Police (XW) Channel 1 |
| 152.33750 | 143.06250 | NFM | Strathclyde | Fire Brigade (GX) |
| 152.33750 | 143.33750 | NFM | Strathclyde | Fire Brigade (GX) |
| 152.33750 | 143.37500 | NFM | Strathclyde | Fire Brigade (GX) |
| 152.33750 | 143.46250 | NFM | Strathclyde | Fire Brigade (GX) |
| 152.33750 | 143.46250 | NFM | Strathclyde | Police Channel 26 |
| 152.35000 | 143.12500 | AM | Leicester | Police (NL) Channel 4 |
| 152.35000 | 143.20000 | NFM | Strathclyde | Police Channel 10 |
| 152.35000 | 143.31250 | NFM | Strathclyde | Police Channel 50 |
| 152.35000 | 143.32500 | NFM | Dumfries and Galloway | Police (AJ) |
| 152.35000 | 143.63750 | NFM | Strathclyde | Police Channel 30 |
| 152.36000 | | NFM | London | Police Ch 2 (MP) |
| 152.36250 | 143.03750 | NFM | London | Police Area Crime divisions E,Q,D,C,A,S Ch.1 |
| 152.36250 | 143.36250 | NFM | Strathclyde | Fire Brigade (GX) |
| 152.37500 | 143.38750 | NFM | Strathclyde | Police Channel 19 |
| 152.37500 | 143.38750 | NFM | Strathclyde | Police Channel 27 |

| Base | Mobile | Mode | Location | User and Notes |
|---|---|---|---|---|
| 152.37500 | 143.45000 | NFM | Ayr | Police |
| 152.37500 | 143.45000 | NFM | Dumfries and Galloway | Police (AJ) |
| 152.37500 | 146.90000 | NFM | Round Meadows | Police (M2LB) |
| 152.38500 | | NFM | London | Police Ch 1 (MP) |
| 152.38750 | 143.01250 | NFM | London | Police Area Crime divisions J,N,H,K,Y,G Ch.2 |
| 152.38750 | 143.23750 | AM | Cleveland | Police (LZ) Channel 1 |
| 152.38750 | 143.38750 | NFM | Strathclyde | Fire Brigade (GX) |
| 152.40000 | 143.20000 | AM | Nottinghamshire | Police (NH) Channel 1 |
| 152.40000 | 143.27500 | NFM | Strathclyde | Police Channel 16 |
| 152.40000 | 152.40000 | NFM | Dumfries and Galloway | Police |
| 152.41250 | 143.12500 | NFM | Ballantrae | Police (ROMEO ALPHA) |
| 152.41250 | 143.12500 | NFM | Girvan | Police (ROMEO ALPHA) |
| 152.41250 | 143.12500 | NFM | London | Police City of London |
| 152.41250 | 143.12500 | AM | Northumberland | Police (M2LB) |
| 152.41250 | 143.12500 | NFM | Strathclyde | Police Channel 33 |
| 152.42500 | 143.22500 | AM | Nottinghamshire | Police (NH) Channel 2 |
| 152.42500 | 143.23750 | NFM | Isle of Man | Fire Brigade |
| 152.42500 | 143.23750 | AM | Manchester | Police |
| 152.42500 | 143.26250 | NFM | Strathclyde | Police Channel 48 |
| 152.42500 | 143.65000 | NFM | Strathclyde | Police Channel 20 |
| 152.43750 | | NFM | Staffordshire | Police and Fire brigade trunked network data command ch. (YF & YG) |
| 152.43750 | 143.45000 | NFM | Strathclyde | Police Channel 29 |
| 152.43750 | 143.51250 | NFM | Dumfries and Galloway | Police (AJ) |
| 152.43750 | 143.51250 | NFM | London | Police City of London |
| 152.44000 | | FM | Kilmarnock | Police U Division Control Room |
| 152.45000 | 143.18750 | AM | Humberside | Police (XH) |
| 152.45000 | 143.45000 | NFM | Strathclyde | Police Channel 28 |
| 152.45000 | 143.51250 | NFM | Dumfries and Galloway | Police (AJ) |
| 152.45000 | 143.51250 | NFM | Ferrybridge | Police |
| 152.46000 | | NFM | London | Police Ch 4 (MP) |
| 152.46250 | 143.08750 | NFM | London | Police (MN) |
| 152.46250 | 143.08750 | NFM | London | Police Area Crime divisions T,B,X,V,F,W Ch.4 |
| 152.46250 | 143.28750 | NFM | Strathclyde | Fire Brigade (GX) |
| 152.46250 | 143.37500 | NFM | Strathclyde | Police Channel 40 |
| 152.46250 | 143.52500 | NFM | Strathclyde | Fire Brigade (GX) |
| 152.47500 | 143.06250 | NFM | Strathclyde | Fire Brigade (GX) |
| 152.47500 | 143.33750 | NFM | Strathclyde | Fire Brigade (GX) |
| 152.47500 | 143.77500 | NFM | Coatbridge | Fire Brigade |
| 152.47500 | 143.77500 | NFM | Dumfries & Galloway | Police Channel 17 |
| 152.47500 | 143.77500 | NFM | Paisley | Fire Brigade |
| 152.48750 | 143.26250 | AM | Cleveland | Police (LZ) |
| 152.48750 | 143.31250 | NFM | Strathclyde | Police Channel 51 |
| 152.48750 | 143.65000 | NFM | Strathclyde | Police Channel 19 |
| 152.50000 | 143.25000 | AM | Nottinghamshire | Police air support (NH) Channel 3 |
| 152.50000 | 143.53750 | NFM | Strathclyde | Police Channel 23 |
| 152.51250 | | AM | Manchester | Police |
| 152.51250 | 143.06250 | NFM | Canonbie | Fire Brigade |
| 152.51250 | 143.06250 | NFM | Langholm | Fire Brigade |
| 152.51250 | 143.08750 | AM | West Yorkshire | Police (XW) Channel 4 |
| 152.51250 | 143.66250 | NFM | Strathclyde | Fire Brigade (GX) |
| 152.51250 | 143.71250 | NFM | Strathclyde | Fire Brigade (GX) |
| 152.51250 | 143.71250 | NFM | Strathclyde | Police Ch 25 |
| 152.52500 | | NFM | Humberside | Fire Brigade Ch.2 |
| 152.52500 | | NFM | Lothian and Borders | Police (E) East Lothian |
| 152.52500 | 143.03750 | NFM | Strathclyde | Fire Brigade (GX) |

| Base | Mobile | Mode | Location | User and Notes |
|------|--------|------|----------|----------------|
| 152.52500 | 143.46250 | NFM | Strathclyde | Fire Brigade (GX) |
| 152.53750 | | NFM | Staffordshire | Police and Fire brigade trunked network (YF/YG) |
| 152.53750 | 143.53750 | NFM | Strathclyde | Police Channel 22 |
| 152.55000 | | NFM | Staffordshire | Police and Fire brigade trunked network (YF/YG) |
| 152.55000 | 143.15000 | AM | Northumberland | Police (M2LB) |
| 152.55000 | 143.28750 | NFM | London | Police Channel 12 (MP) OSCAR channel |
| 152.55000 | 143.28750 | NFM | London | Police traffic and info. Room Ch.12 (OSCAR) |
| 152.55000 | 143.66250 | NFM | Strathclyde | Fire Brigade (GX) |
| 152.55000 | 143.71250 | NFM | Strathclyde | Fire Brigade (GX) |
| 152.56000 | | NFM | Glasgow | Police Ch6 (ES) |
| 152.56250 | 143.65000 | NFM | Strathclyde | Police Channel 21 |
| 152.57500 | 143.02500 | AM | Northamptonshire | Police (NG) |
| 152.57500 | 143.02500 | NFM | Strathclyde | Police (AS) Channel 3 |
| 152.58750 | | NFM | London | Police Royal Palaces |
| 152.58750 | 143.11250 | AM | West Yorkshire | Police (XW) Channel 6 |
| 152.58750 | 143.53750 | NFM | Strathclyde | Police Channel 24 |
| 152.60000 | | NFM | Kent | Government agency |
| 152.60000 | 143.06250 | NFM | Strathclyde | Fire Brigade (GX) |
| 152.60000 | 143.17500 | NFM | Dumfries and Galloway | Fire Brigade (Fire Control) |
| 152.60000 | 143.17500 | AM | Northumberland | Police (M2LB) |
| 152.60000 | 143.28750 | NFM | Strathclyde | Police Channel 46 |
| 152.60000 | 143.33750 | NFM | Strathclyde | Fire Brigade (GX) |
| 152.60000 | 143.37500 | NFM | Strathclyde | Fire Brigade (GX) |
| 152.60000 | 143.52500 | NFM | Strathclyde | Fire Brigade (GX) |
| 152.61250 | 143.90000 | AM | Humberside | Police |
| 152.61250 | 143.90000 | NFM | Strathclyde | Police Channel 42 |
| 152.62500 | 143.26250 | NFM | Strathclyde | Police Channel 46 |
| 152.62500 | 143.70000 | NFM | Dumbarton | Police L Div Control Room |
| 152.62500 | 143.70000 | NFM | Strathclyde | Police Channel 38 |
| 152.62500 | 152.62500 | NFM | Dumfries and Galloway | Police |
| 152.63750 | 143.66250 | NFM | Strathclyde | Fire Brigade (GX) |
| 152.63750 | 143.71250 | NFM | Strathclyde | Fire Brigade (GX) |
| 152.63750 | 152.63750 | NFM | Northern Ireland | Fire Brigade Handhelds |
| 152.65000 | 143.90000 | NFM | Strathclyde | Police Channel 41 |
| 152.66250 | 143.90000 | NFM | Strathclyde | Police Channel 44 |
| 152.66250 | 146.55000 | NFM | Quarry House | Fire Brigade (M2LJ) |
| 152.68750 | | NFM | Ferrybridge | Police |
| 152.68750 | | AM | Humberside | Police (XH) Channel 3 |
| 152.68750 | 143.51250 | NFM | Dumfries and Galloway | Police Lowther Hills (AJ) |
| 152.70000 | 143.05000 | NFM | Dumfries and Galloway | Police (AJ) |
| 152.70000 | 143.05000 | AM | Northamptonshire | Police (NG) Channel 2 |
| 152.70000 | 143.70000 | NFM | Strathclyde | Police |
| 152.71250 | | NFM | London | Police trunked trials Hammersmith (FH) |
| 152.71250 | 143.06250 | AM | West Yorkshire | Police (XW) Channel 2 |
| 152.71250 | 143.37500 | NFM | Strathclyde | Fire Brigade (GX) |
| 152.71250 | 143.52500 | NFM | Strathclyde | Fire Brigade (GX) |
| 152.71250 | 143.77500 | NFM | Dumfries and Galloway | Fire Brigade (Fire Control) |
| 152.72500 | 143.37500 | AM | Lincolnshire | Police (NC) Channel 1 |
| 152.73750 | | NFM | Humberside | Fire Brigade Ch.2 |
| 152.74000 | 152.74000 | NFM | Dumfries and Galloway | Police |
| 152.75000 | 143.53750 | NFM | Strathclyde | Police Channel 25 |
| 152.75000 | 152.75000 | NFM | Dumfries and Galloway | Police |
| 152.76250 | | NFM | Arrochar | Police (L) |
| 152.76250 | | NFM | Machrahanish | Police (L) |
| 152.76250 | | NFM | Oban | Police (L) |
| 152.76250 | 143.31250 | NFM | Strathclyde | Police Channel 52 |

| Base | Mobile | Mode | Location | User and Notes |
|------|--------|------|----------|----------------|
| 152.76250 | 143.63750 | NFM | Strathclyde | Police Channel 30 |
| 152.76250 | 146.90000 | NFM | Quarry House | Police (M2LB) |
| 152.77500 | 143.46250 | AM | Lincolnshire | Police (NC) Channel 2 |
| 152.77500 | 146.90000 | NFM | Ottercops | Police (M2LB) |
| 152.77500 | 152.77500 | NFM | Dumfries and Galloway | Police |
| 152.78750 | 143.27500 | AM | South Yorkshire | Police (XS) Channel 1 |
| 152.78750 | 143.66250 | NFM | Strathclyde | Fire Brigade (GX) |
| 152.78750 | 143.71250 | NFM | Strathclyde | Police |
| 152.79000 | 152.79000 | NFM | Dumfries and Galloway | Police |
| 152.80000 | | AM | County Durham | Police (LA) Channel 1 |
| 152.80000 | | NFM | Girvan | Police (R) |
| 152.80000 | | AM | Newcastle | Police |
| 152.80000 | 143.02500 | NFM | Strathclyde | Police Data Channel |
| 152.80500 | 143.45000 | NFM | Ayr | Police control from Glasgow for R&R Divisions Ch 8 |
| 152.81250 | | AM | Manchester | Police |
| 152.81250 | 143.13750 | AM | West Yorkshire | Police (XW) Channel 7 |
| 152.81250 | 143.43750 | NFM | Strathclyde | Police Channel 30 |
| 152.82500 | | NFM | Castlebar | Paging |
| 152.82500 | | NFM | Humberside | Fire Brigade Ch.1 |
| 152.82500 | 143.70000 | NFM | Strathclyde | Police Channel 39 |
| 152.82500 | 152.82500 | NFM | Dumfries and Galloway | Police |
| 152.83750 | | NFM | Staffordshire | Police and Fire brigade trunked network (YF/YG) |
| 152.83750 | 143.05000 | NFM | Ayr | Fire Brigade (D) |
| 152.83750 | 143.05000 | AM | Durham | Police (LA) Channel 2 |
| 152.83750 | 143.66250 | NFM | Strathclyde | Fire Brigade (GX) |
| 152.83750 | 143.71250 | NFM | Strathclyde | Police |
| 152.83750 | 146.57500 | NFM | Ipswich | Police (VL) |
| 152.85000 | 143.32500 | AM | South Yorkshire | Police (XS) Channel 3 |
| 152.86000 | 152.86000 | NFM | Dumfries and Galloway | Police |
| 152.86250 | | NFM | Humberside | Fire Brigade Ch.1 |
| 152.87500 | | NFM | London | Wellington Barracks (sometimes DVP) |
| 152.87500 | 143.13750 | NFM | Strathclyde | Fire Brigade (GX) |
| 152.87500 | 143.28750 | NFM | Strathclyde | Fire Brigade (GX) |
| 152.87500 | 143.77500 | NFM | Dumfries & Galloway | Fire Brigade Channel 17 |
| 152.88500 | | NFM | Dumfries and Galloway | Police |
| 152.88500 | | NFM | Glasgow | Police Hampden Football Club |
| 152.88750 | | NFM | Co. Durham | Police (LA) |
| 152.88750 | 143.18750 | NFM | Isle of Man | Police (MX) Channel 2 |
| 152.90000 | 143.30000 | AM | Doncaster | Police |
| 152.90000 | 143.30000 | NFM | Dumfries and Galloway | Police (K) |
| 152.90000 | 143.30000 | AM | South Yorkshire | Police (XS) Channel 2 |
| 152.90000 | 143.90000 | NFM | Strathclyde | Police Channel 43 |
| 152.91000 | 152.91000 | NFM | Dumfries and Galloway | Police |
| 152.92000 | 143.12500 | NFM | Ayr | Police R Div Control covering RB Div Cumnock Ch 10 |
| 152.92500 | | NFM | Dumfries and Galloway | Police (AJ) |
| 152.92500 | 143.35000 | AM | South Yorkshire | Police (XS) Channel 4 |
| 152.92500 | 146.15000 | NFM | Ottercops | Police (M2LB) |
| 152.93750 | 146.55000 | NFM | Round Meadows | Fire Brigade (M2LJ) |
| 152.95000 | 143.13750 | NFM | Strathclyde | Fire Brigade (GX) |
| 152.95000 | 143.28750 | AM | North Yorkshire | Police (XN) |
| 152.96250 | 143.21250 | AM | Isle of Man | Police (MX) Channel 3 |
| 152.96250 | 143.21250 | NFM | Lincolnshire | Police Channel 2 |
| 152.97500 | | NFM | Cambridge | Police standby ch. (VB) |
| 152.97500 | | NFM | Ferrybridge | Police (WM) |
| 152.97500 | | AM | Ingleton | Police (M2XN) |
| 152.97500 | 143.33750 | AM | North Yorkshire | Police (XN) |

| Base | Mobile | Mode | Location | User and Notes |
|---|---|---|---|---|
| 152.97500 | 152.97500 | NFM | Dumfries and Galloway | Police |
| 152.98000 | 152.98000 | NFM | Dumfries and Galloway | Police |
| 152.98750 | | NFM | Lincolnshire | Police Channel 1 |
| 152.98750 | 146.55000 | NFM | Ottercops | Fire Brigade (M2LJ) |

**153.0125 - 153.4875 MHz     NATIONAL PAGING**

| Base | Mobile | Mode | Location | User and Notes |
|---|---|---|---|---|
| 153.02500 | | NFM | Nationwide | National Paging Ch 1 |
| 153.05000 | | NFM | Nationwide | National Paging Ch 2 |
| 153.05000 | | NFM | Warwickshire | Fire Brigade pagers |
| 153.07500 | | NFM | Nationwide | National Paging Ch 3 |
| 153.12500 | | NFM | Nationwide | BT Paging Ch 5 |
| 153.15000 | | NFM | Manchester | Paging |
| 153.15000 | | NFM | Nationwide | Redifon Paging Ch 6 |
| 153.17500 | | NFM | Nationwide | BT Paging Ch 7 |
| 153.20000 | | NFM | Nationwide | National Paging Ch 8 |
| 153.20000 | | NFM | Nationwide | UK Paging Test & Development |
| 153.22500 | | NFM | Nationwide | Redifon  Paging Ch 9 |
| 153.23750 | | NFM | Nationwide | Paging |
| 153.25000 | | NFM | Nationwide | National Paging Ch 10 |
| 153.27500 | | NFM | Nationwide | Air Call  Paging Ch 11 |
| 153.30000 | | NFM | Galway | University Hospital Paging |
| 153.30000 | | NFM | Nationwide | National Paging Ch 12 |
| 153.32500 | | NFM | Nationwide | Air Call Paging Ch 13 |
| 153.33750 | | NFM | Nationwide | Paging |
| 153.34500 | | NFM | Lincoln | Paging |
| 153.35000 | | NFM | Nationwide | Inter City Pagers Ch 14 |
| 153.36250 | | NFM | Nationwide | Paging |
| 153.37500 | | NFM | Jersey | Paging |
| 153.37500 | | NFM | Nationwide | National Paging Ch 15 |
| 153.40000 | | NFM | Nationwide | UKAEA Paging Ch 16 |
| 153.42500 | | NFM | Guernsey | Paging |
| 153.42500 | | NFM | Nationwide | National Paging Ch 17 |
| 153.42500 | | NFM | Tayside | Voice Paging |
| 153.45000 | | NFM | Guernsey | Life Boat Pagers |
| 153.45000 | | NFM | Nationwide | National Paging Ch 18 |
| 153.45000 | | NFM | Nationwide | Paging |
| 153.47500 | | NFM | Cambridge | City Council Paging |
| 153.47500 | | NFM | Nationwide | National Paging Ch 19 |
| 153.50000 | | NFM | Nationwide | National Paging Ch 20 |

**153.5000 - 154.0000 MHz     MoD TACTICAL COMMUNICATIONS AND RED CROSS  25 kHz NFM SIMPLEX**

| Base | Mobile | Mode | Location | User and Notes |
|---|---|---|---|---|
| 153.53750 | | NFM | South Wales | MoD Paging |
| 153.58750 | | NFM | Bristol | MoD Link |
| 153.60000 | | NFM | Belfast | Army |
| 153.71250 | | NFM | Nationwide | Red Cross |
| 153.71250 | | NFM | Suffolk | Red Cross (RED & RED X) |
| 153.76250 | | NFM | Belfast | Army |
| 153.80000 | | AM | Nationwide | ATC Ch.V (also NFM) |
| 153.82500 | | NFM | Co Mayo | Paging |
| 153.82500 | | NFM | Galway | Garda Paging |
| 153.82500 | | AM | Nationwide | ATC Ch.V4 (also NFM) |
| 153.82500 | 153.82500 | NFM | Nationwide | RAF Cadets Channel V4 |
| 153.83750 | 149.03750 | NFM | Aldershot | Range Wardens (BEAVER CONTROL) |
| 153.85000 | | NFM | Belfast | Army |

| Base | Mobile | Mode | Location | User and Notes |
|---|---|---|---|---|

**154.0000 - 155.9875 MHz**   POLICE BASE REPEATERS 12.5 kHz

| Base | Mobile | Mode | Location | User and Notes |
|---|---|---|---|---|
| 154.00000 | 146.10000 | NFM | Kirkcaldy | Police (Encrypted) |
| 154.00000 | 146.50000 | NFM | Jersey | Police (M2GS) Ch 1 |
| 154.00500 | 154.00500 | NFM | Dumfries and Galloway | Police |
| 154.01250 | 146.12500 | NFM | Fife | Fire Brigade |
| 154.01250 | 146.12500 | NFM | Lancashire | Police (BD) Channel 3 |
| 154.01250 | 146.12500 | NFM | London | Police M25 North (SM) Ch1 |
| 154.01250 | 146.12500 | NFM | Preston | Police |
| 154.01250 | 154.01250 | NFM | London | Police Met Surveillance |
| 154.02500 | 146.02500 | NFM | Glenrothes | Police |
| 154.02500 | 146.05000 | NFM | Fife | Police Traffic Division (ZT) |
| 154.02500 | 146.13750 | NFM | Inverness | Police (UR) |
| 154.02500 | 146.13750 | NFM | Shropshire | Police (YK) |
| 154.02500 | 146.51250 | AM | West Mercia | Police (YK1) |
| 154.02500 | 146.51250 | AM | Worcester | Police (M2YK) |
| 154.02500 | 154.02500 | NFM | Inverness | Fire Brigade |
| 154.03750 | 146.00000 | NFM | Northern Ireland | RUC |
| 154.03750 | 146.90000 | NFM | Beacon Lough | Police (M2LB) |
| 154.03750 | 146.90000 | NFM | Newcastle | Police |
| 154.05000 | 146.05000 | NFM | Fife | Police Traffic Division (ZT) |
| 154.05000 | 146.05000 | AM | Perry Bar | Police Motorway Ch 1 |
| 154.05000 | 146.05000 | NFM | Shropshire | Police (YK) |
| 154.05000 | 146.05000 | NFM | West Mercia | Police (YK2) |
| 154.05000 | 146.53750 | NFM | Derbyshire | Fire Brigade (M2ND) |
| 154.05000 | 146.53750 | NFM | Edinburgh | Police (T) |
| 154.06250 | 146.21250 | NFM | Inverness | Fire Brigade (UF) |
| 154.06250 | 146.90000 | NFM | Dunfermline | Fire Brigade (F) |
| 154.06250 | 146.90000 | NFM | Edinburgh | Fire Brigade (F) |
| 154.06250 | 146.90000 | NFM | High Spen | Police (M2LB) |
| 154.06250 | 147.53750 | NFM | Burton Down | Fire Brigade |
| 154.07500 | | NFM | Staffordshire | Police and Fire brigade trunked network (YF/YG) |
| 154.07500 | 146.13750 | NFM | Inverness | Police (UR) |
| 154.07500 | 146.17500 | NFM | Berkshire | Fire Brigade (M2HD) |
| 154.07500 | 146.17500 | NFM | Devon | Fire Brigade (M2QA) |
| 154.07500 | 146.17500 | NFM | Lancashire | Police (BD) Channel 4 |
| 154.07500 | 146.17500 | NFM | Leven | Police (L) |
| 154.07500 | 146.17500 | AM | M6/M52/M62 | Police |
| 154.07500 | 146.17500 | AM | Manchester | Police traffic |
| 154.07500 | 146.87500 | NFM | Truleigh Hill | Police |
| 154.07500 | 154.97500 | NFM | Inverness | Fire Brigade |
| 154.08500 | | NFM | Fife | Fire Brigade |
| 154.08750 | | NFM | Staffordshire | Police and Fire brigade trunked network (YF & YG) |
| 154.08750 | 146.15000 | NFM | High Spen | Police (M2LB) |
| 154.08750 | 146.16250 | NFM | London | Police M25 South (SM) Ch.2 |
| 154.10000 | | NFM | Kirkcaldy | Police (E) Scrambled |
| 154.10000 | 146.13750 | AM | Thames Valley | Police (HB) Channel 2 |
| 154.10000 | 146.48750 | NFM | North Wales | Police (WA) Channel 4 |
| 154.10000 | 146.48750 | AM | Oxford | Police |
| 154.11250 | | NFM | Aberdeen | Fire Control |
| 154.11250 | | NFM | Dunfermline | Fire Brigade (F) |
| 154.11250 | | NFM | Norfolk | Police Ch 1 |
| 154.11250 | 146.56250 | AM | West Mercia | Police (YK3) |
| 154.11250 | 146.95000 | NFM | Truleigh Hill | Police |
| 154.12500 | | NFM | Humberside | Fire Brigade Ch.2 |
| 154.12500 | 146.05000 | NFM | Fife | Police Traffic Division (ZT) |

| Base | Mobile | Mode | Location | User and Notes |
|------|--------|------|----------|----------------|
| 154.12500 | 146.13750 | NFM | Edinburgh | Police (T) |
| 154.12500 | 146.13750 | NFM | Inverness | Police (UR) |
| 154.12500 | 146.13750 | NFM | London | Fire Brigade (M2FN) |
| 154.12500 | 146.13750 | NFM | Staffordshire | Fire Brigade (M2YG) |
| 154.12500 | 146.13750 | NFM | West Mercia | Police (YK) Channel 2 |
| 154.12500 | 146.17500 | NFM | Cambridge | Fire Brigade (M2VF) |
| 154.12500 | 147.65000 | NFM | Beddingham | Police |
| 154.13750 | 146.05000 | NFM | Fife | Police (ZT) |
| 154.13750 | 146.05000 | NFM | Southampton | Police |
| 154.13750 | 146.36250 | AM | Cambridge | Police (VB) Channel 3 |
| 154.15000 | 146.48750 | NFM | Lothian and Borders | Police |
| 154.15000 | 146.55000 | NFM | High Spen | Fire Brigade (M2LJ) |
| 154.15000 | 146.67500 | NFM | Glasgow | Police Drug Squad |
| 154.15000 | 146.67500 | AM | Gloucester | Police (QL) Channel 1 |
| 154.15000 | 146.67500 | NFM | Stirling | Fire Brigade (F) |
| 154.15000 | 146.67500 | AM | Stroud | Police |
| 154.16250 | 146.16250 | NFM | Fife | Police (B) |
| 154.16500 | 146.52500 | NFM | Beacon Lough | Police (M2LB) |
| 154.17500 | | NFM | Dunfermline | Police (D) |
| 154.17500 | | NFM | Stirling | Fire Brigade (F) |
| 154.17500 | 146.47500 | NFM | West Hoathly | Police |
| 154.17500 | 154.17500 | FM | Cambridge | Police (VB) Car Return |
| 154.18750 | 146.05000 | NFM | Fife | Police (ZT) |
| 154.18750 | 146.10000 | NFM | Newmarket | Police data |
| 154.18750 | 146.10000 | NFM | Rannoch Moor | Police |
| 154.18750 | 146.10000 | NFM | Sussex | Police |
| 154.18750 | 146.15000 | NFM | Beacon Lough | Police (M2LB) |
| 154.18750 | 146.42500 | NFM | Lochaber | Police (UR) |
| 154.18750 | 146.87500 | NFM | Burton Down | Police |
| 154.18750 | 154.18750 | NFM | Inverness | Fire Brigade |
| 154.20000 | | NFM | Bedfordshire | Police |
| 154.20000 | | AM | Cheshire | Police |
| 154.20000 | | NFM | Fife | Police |
| 154.20000 | | NFM | Hertfordshire | Police Ch.2 |
| 154.20000 | | AM | Perry Bar | Police Motorway Ch 2 |
| 154.20000 | 146.52500 | NFM | High Spen | Police (M2LB) |
| 154.20000 | 146.58750 | AM | Staffordshire | Police (YF) Channel 1 |
| 154.20000 | 147.65000 | NFM | Fairlight | Police |
| 154.21250 | | NFM | Fife | Fire Brigade |
| 154.22500 | | AM | Bristol | Police |
| 154.22500 | | AM | East Sussex | Police (KB) |
| 154.22500 | | AM | Gloucester | Police (QL) Channel 2 |
| 154.22500 | | NFM | Lanark | Police (ZS) |
| 154.22500 | | NFM | Norfolk | Police Ch 2 |
| 154.22500 | 146.00000 | NFM | Cheshire | Fire Brigade (CF) |
| 154.22500 | 146.65000 | NFM | Fairlight | Police |
| 154.22500 | 146.70000 | NFM | Staffordshire | Fire Brigade (M2YG) |
| 154.23750 | | NFM | Surrey | Fire Brigade repeater |
| 154.23750 | 147.23750 | NFM | Bathgate | Police |
| 154.23750 | 147.23750 | NFM | Edinburgh | Police |
| 154.23750 | 147.23750 | NFM | Lanark | Police (ZS) |
| 154.23750 | 147.23750 | NFM | Lothian and Borders | Police (F and ZH) |
| 154.23750 | 147.23750 | NFM | West Lothian | Police |
| 154.24000 | | NFM | Edinburgh | Police Ch 1 (ZH) |
| 154.25000 | | NFM | Edinburgh | Police E Div HQ Ch.5 |
| 154.25000 | 146.25000 | NFM | Lothian and Borders | Police (ZHE) East/Mid Lothian |

| Base | Mobile | Mode | Location | User and Notes |
|---|---|---|---|---|
| 154.26000 | | AM | Worcester | Police (M2YK) |
| 154.26250 | | NFM | Edinburgh | Police Traffic Division (T) |
| 154.26250 | 146.47500 | AM | Birmingham | Police (YM) |
| 154.26250 | 147.06250 | NFM | Truleigh Hill | Police |
| 154.27500 | 146.15000 | NFM | Round Meadows | Police (M2LB) |
| 154.27500 | 146.57500 | NFM | Ipswich | Police (VL) Channel 1 |
| 154.28750 | | NFM | Edinburgh | Police (ZH) Ch 1 |
| 154.30000 | 146.30000 | NFM | Edinburgh, Fettes | Police (ZH) Ch 1 |
| 154.31250 | | NFM | Borders | Police (G and ZH) |
| 154.31250 | | NFM | Galashiels | Police |
| 154.31250 | 146.45000 | AM | Birmingham | Police (YM) Channel 5 |
| 154.32500 | 147.82500 | NFM | Peebles | Police |
| 154.33750 | 146.73750 | NFM | Thames Valley | Police (HB) Channel 1 |
| 154.33750 | 146.73750 | NFM | Wales | Police (WH) Channel 3 |
| 154.33750 | 147.17500 | NFM | Greater Manchester | Police |
| 154.33750 | 147.17500 | NFM | Hungerford | Police (HB) Channel 1 |
| 154.35000 | 146.35000 | NFM | Edinburgh, Fettes | Police (ZH) Ch.2 |
| 154.35000 | 146.42500 | NFM | Lochaber | Police (UR) |
| 154.35000 | 146.42500 | NFM | Onich | Police |
| 154.36750 | 146.72500 | AM | Gloucester | Police (QL) Channel 3 |
| 154.37500 | | NFM | Edinburgh | Police Radio Engineers |
| 154.37500 | | NFM | Kent | Police |
| 154.37500 | | NFM | Livingston | Police |
| 154.37500 | | NFM | Norfolk | Police Ch 3 |
| 154.38750 | | NFM | Edinburgh | Police E Div HQ |
| 154.38750 | | NFM | Surrey | Fire Brigade repeater |
| 154.38750 | | NFM | West Mercia | Police (YK) |
| 154.38750 | 146.25000 | NFM | Lothian and Borders | Police (ZHE) |
| 154.40000 | | NFM | Nationwide | M1 Low Volume |
| 154.40000 | 147.82500 | NFM | Meigle Hill | Police |
| 154.41250 | 146.08750 | NFM | Warwickshire | Police (YJ) Channel 1 |
| 154.41250 | 146.08750 | AM | West Mercia | Police (YK) |
| 154.41250 | 147.65000 | NFM | Truleigh Hill | Police |
| 154.41250 | 147.82500 | NFM | Hardens Hill | Police |
| 154.42500 | | NFM | Galashiels | Police (D) |
| 154.42500 | 146.46250 | NFM | North Wales | Police (WA) Channel 3 |
| 154.42500 | 146.46250 | NFM | Peebles | Police |
| 154.43750 | | NFM | Edinburgh | Police (T) Traffic Division |
| 154.45000 | 146.35000 | AM | Birmingham | Police (YM) |
| 154.45000 | 146.35000 | AM | Bristol | Police |
| 154.45000 | 147.18750 | NFM | Perth | Police (W) |
| 154.45000 | 147.18750 | NFM | Pitlochry | Police (WP) |
| 154.46000 | | NFM | Lochaber | Police |
| 154.46250 | | AM | Preston | Police |
| 154.46250 | 143.58750 | AM | Bedfordshire | Police Ch.3 (VA) |
| 154.46250 | 146.25000 | NFM | Lothian and Borders | Police (ZHE) East/Mid Lothian |
| 154.46250 | 146.42500 | NFM | Dalkeith | Police |
| 154.46250 | 146.42500 | NFM | Edinburgh | Police E Div HQ |
| 154.46250 | 146.42500 | NFM | Fort William | Police (UR) |
| 154.46250 | 146.42500 | NFM | Galashiels | Police |
| 154.46250 | 146.42500 | NFM | Lochaber | Police (UR) |
| 154.46250 | 146.48750 | NFM | Lothian and Borders | Police |
| 154.47500 | 146.17500 | NFM | Kent | Fire Brigade (HO5) |
| 154.47500 | 146.60000 | AM | Dyfed | Police (WH) Ch. 1 |
| 154.47500 | 146.62500 | NFM | Edinburgh | Fire Brigade (F) |
| 154.48750 | 146.48750 | NFM | Lothian and Borders | Police |

| Base | Mobile | Mode | Location | User and Notes |
|---|---|---|---|---|
| 154.48750 | 147.06250 | NFM | Beddingham | Police |
| 154.48750 | 147.06250 | NFM | Central Scotland | Police |
| 154.49000 | | NFM | Stirling | Police HQ Ch 1 (AH) |
| 154.50000 | | NFM | Avon | Fire Brigade (M2QC) |
| 154.50000 | | NFM | Eyemouth | Police |
| 154.50000 | 146.50000 | NFM | Jersey | Police (M2GS) Channel 1 |
| 154.50000 | 147.65000 | NFM | West Hoathly | Police |
| 154.51250 | 146.25000 | NFM | Lothian and Borders | Police (ZHE) East/Mid Lothian |
| 154.51250 | 146.42500 | NFM | Ballachulish | Police |
| 154.51250 | 146.87500 | NFM | Beddingham | Police |
| 154.51250 | 146.87500 | NFM | Dalkeith | Police |
| 154.51250 | 146.87500 | NFM | Edinburgh | Police 'E' Div HQ |
| 154.52500 | | AM | East Sussex | Police (KB) |
| 154.52500 | | NFM | Humberside | Fire Brigade |
| 154.52500 | | NFM | West Mercia | Police (YK) |
| 154.52500 | 146.48750 | NFM | Central Scotland | Police Traffic Division (T) |
| 154.52500 | 146.48750 | NFM | Galashiels | Police |
| 154.52500 | 146.48750 | NFM | Lothian and Borders | Police |
| 154.52500 | 146.85000 | NFM | Easter Ross | Police (UR) |
| 154.52500 | 147.87500 | NFM | Fairlight | Police |
| 154.53750 | 143.55000 | AM | Bedfordshire | Police Ch.4 (VA) |
| 154.53750 | 146.53750 | NFM | Edinburgh | Fire Brigade (F) |
| 154.55000 | | NFM | Jersey | Fire Brigade Channel 5 |
| 154.55000 | | NFM | Kent | Fire Brigade (M2MK) |
| 154.55000 | | AM | Merseyside | Police |
| 154.55000 | 146.55000 | NFM | Channel Islands | Police harbour |
| 154.55000 | 146.55000 | NFM | Jersey | Police (M2GS) Channel 5 |
| 154.55000 | 146.61250 | AM | Staffordshire | Police (YF) Channel 2 |
| 154.55000 | 146.71250 | NFM | Kyle of Lochalsh | Police (UR) |
| 154.55000 | 147.82500 | NFM | Ashkirk | Police |
| 154.56250 | 146.48750 | NFM | Lothian and Borders | Police |
| 154.56250 | 146.52500 | NFM | Caithness | Police |
| 154.56250 | 146.86250 | NFM | Dingwall | Police (UR) |
| 154.56250 | 154.56250 | NFM | Inverness | Fire Brigade |
| 154.57500 | | NFM | Belfast | Military Tone Encryption |
| 154.57500 | 146.65000 | NFM | Skye | Fire Brigade (UR) |
| 154.58750 | | NFM | Bedfordshire | Police Ch.2 (VA) |
| 154.58750 | | NFM | Belfast | Military Tone Encryption |
| 154.58750 | | NFM | Galashiels | Police |
| 154.58750 | | NFM | West Mercia | Police (YK) |
| 154.58750 | 146.52500 | NFM | Caithness | Police |
| 154.58750 | 147.82500 | NFM | Hawick | Police (ZH) Ch.4 |
| 154.60000 | | NFM | Belfast | Military Tone Encryption |
| 154.60000 | | NFM | Edinburgh | Police (ZH) Fettes |
| 154.60000 | | NFM | Enniskillen | Royal Ulster Constabulary |
| 154.60000 | | NFM | Essex | Police |
| 154.60000 | | AM | Guernsey Airport | Fire Services |
| 154.60000 | | NFM | London | Police bomb jamming van used with 143.900 |
| 154.60000 | 147.23750 | NFM | Perth | Police (W) |
| 154.61250 | | AM | Bristol | Police |
| 154.61250 | | NFM | Edinburgh | Police |
| 154.61250 | | NFM | Galashiels | Police |
| 154.61250 | 147.07500 | AM | Wiltshire | Police (QJ) Channel 4 |
| 154.61250 | 147.82500 | NFM | Hardens Hill | Police |
| 154.61250 | 147.82500 | NFM | Lanark | Police (S) |
| 154.61250 | 147.82500 | NFM | Manchester | Police |

| Base | Mobile | Mode | Location | User and Notes |
|------|--------|------|----------|----------------|
| 154.61250 | 147.82500 | AM | Melksham | Police |
| 154.61250 | 154.61250 | FM | Norfolk | Police (VK) Ch 4 |
| 154.62500 | 146.32500 | AM | Birmingham | Police (YM) Channel 1 |
| 154.62500 | 146.47500 | NFM | Truleigh Hill | Police |
| 154.62500 | 146.62500 | NFM | Central Scotland | Fire Brigade (AYS) |
| 154.62500 | 146.62500 | NFM | Edinburgh | Fire Brigade (F) |
| 154.62500 | 146.62500 | NFM | Jersey | Police (M2GS) Channel 2 |
| 154.62500 | 146.62500 | NFM | London, Wimbledon | Fire Brigade |
| 154.62500 | 146.62500 | AM | Perry Bar | Police Motorway Ch 3 |
| 154.63750 | | NFM | Aberdeen | Police |
| 154.63750 | | AM | Hertfordshire | Police Ch.4 |
| 154.63750 | | NFM | Poolewe | Police (UR) |
| 154.63750 | 146.28750 | AM | Kent | Police (KA) Channel 5 |
| 154.63750 | 146.52500 | NFM | Caithness | Police |
| 154.63750 | 146.86250 | NFM | Dingwall | Police (UR) |
| 154.63750 | 147.82500 | NFM | Langholm | Police (ZH) Ch.4 |
| 154.63750 | 154.63750 | NFM | Inverness | Fire Brigade |
| 154.65000 | | NFM | Edinburgh | Fire Brigade (F) |
| 154.65000 | | NFM | Jersey | Ambulance Service Ch.1 |
| 154.65000 | 146.11250 | NFM | Warwickshire | Police (YJ) Channel 2 |
| 154.65000 | 146.11250 | AM | West Mercia | Police (YK) |
| 154.65000 | 146.05000 | NFM | Skyo | Fire Brigade |
| 154.65000 | 146.95000 | NFM | West Hoathly | Police |
| 154.66250 | 146.11250 | NFM | Jersey | Ambulance Service |
| 154.66250 | 146.66250 | NFM | Perth | Fire Brigade (Fire Control) |
| 154.66250 | 146.87500 | NFM | West Hoathly | Police |
| 154.67500 | 146.27500 | NFM | Nottinghamshire | Fire Brigade (M2NZ) |
| 154.68750 | 146.65000 | NFM | Skye | Fire Brigade |
| 154.68750 | 146.87500 | NFM | Caithness | Fire Brigade (UF) |
| 154.68750 | 154.68750 | NFM | Northern Ireland | Fire Brigade Handhelds Ch 3 |
| 154.70000 | 146.10000 | NFM | Suffolk | Police (VL) Channel 3 |
| 154.70000 | 146.37500 | AM | Birmingham | Police (YM) |
| 154.70000 | 146.80000 | NFM | Sutherland | Police (UR) |
| 154.70000 | 146.95000 | NFM | Burton Down | Police |
| 154.70000 | 147.82500 | NFM | Dunion Hill | Police |
| 154.71250 | 146.52500 | NFM | Caithness | Police |
| 154.71250 | 146.71250 | NFM | Kyle of Lochalsh | Police (UR) |
| 154.71250 | 146.96250 | NFM | Perth | Police (W) |
| 154.72500 | | NFM | Castlebar, Eire | Garda |
| 154.72500 | | NFM | Staffordshire | Police and Fire brigade trunked network (YF & YG) |
| 154.72500 | 146.71250 | NFM | Kyle of Lochalsh | Police Applecross (UR) |
| 154.72500 | 146.72500 | NFM | Norfolk | Fire Brigade (VF) |
| 154.73750 | 146.86250 | AM | Bedfordshire | Police (M2VA) Channel 2 |
| 154.75000 | | NFM | Suffolk | Police (VL) |
| 154.75000 | 146.13750 | NFM | Inverness | Police (UR) |
| 154.75000 | 146.22500 | NFM | Jersey | Ambulance Service Ch2 |
| 154.75000 | 147.06250 | NFM | West Hoathly | Police |
| 154.76250 | 146.80000 | NFM | Sutherland | Police (UR) |
| 154.76250 | 147.23750 | NFM | Perth | Police (W) |
| 154.77500 | 146.30000 | AM | Berkshire | Police (Motorway Patrols) |
| 154.77500 | 146.30000 | AM | Thames Valley | Police (HB) Channel 8 |
| 154.78750 | | NFM | Aberdeen | Fire Brigade (Fire Control) |
| 154.78750 | | NFM | Lanark | Police (ZS) |
| 154.78750 | 146.02500 | AM | Cambridge | Police (VB) Channel 1 |
| 154.78750 | 146.02500 | AM | Newmarket | Police |
| 154.78750 | 146.80000 | AM | Gwent | Police (WE) Channel 2 |

| Base | Mobile | Mode | Location | User and Notes |
|------|--------|------|----------|----------------|
| 154.78750 | 146.86250 | NFM | Dingwall | Police (UR) |
| 154.78750 | 146.86250 | NFM | Ullapool | Police (UR) |
| 154.78750 | 146.95000 | NFM | Perth | Fire Brigade (Fire Control) |
| 154.78750 | 154.78750 | NFM | Inverness | Fire Brigade |
| 154.80000 | 146.18750 | NFM | Bournemouth | Police |
| 154.80000 | 146.18750 | AM | Dorset | Police (QC) Channel 3 |
| 154.80000 | 146.72500 | AM | Lancashire | Police (BD) Channel 5 |
| 154.80000 | 146.72500 | NFM | Leicestershire | Police (NL) Channel 1 |
| 154.80000 | 146.80000 | NFM | Sutherland | Police (UR) |
| 154.81250 | 146.80000 | NFM | Helmsdale | Police (UR) |
| 154.81250 | 146.80000 | NFM | North Wales | Police Channel 1 |
| 154.81250 | 146.80000 | NFM | Sutherland | Police (UR) |
| 154.81250 | 146.87500 | AM | Gwent | Police (WN) Channel 3 |
| 154.82500 | | NFM | Staffordshire | Police and Fire brigade trunked network (YF & YG) |
| 154.82500 | 146.68750 | AM | Cambridge | Police (VB) Channel 2 |
| 154.82500 | 146.70000 | AM | Cheshire | Police (BA) |
| 154.82500 | 146.70000 | NFM | Hull | Fire Brigade (XT) |
| 154.83750 | | NFM | Bicester | Police (SD) |
| 154.83750 | 146.27500 | AM | Thames Valley | Police (HB) Channel 4 |
| 154.83750 | 146.85000 | NFM | Easter Ross | Police (UR) |
| 154.83750 | 146.96250 | NFM | Perth | Police (W) |
| 154.85000 | | NFM | Chelmsford | Police |
| 154.85000 | | AM | Lakenheath | Police |
| 154.85000 | 146.85000 | NFM | Easter Ross | Police (UR) |
| 154.85000 | 147.06250 | NFM | Burton Down | Police |
| 154.86250 | | NFM | Bridgend | Police (WY) |
| 154.86250 | | AM | Bristol | Police |
| 154.86250 | | AM | Cheshire | Police traffic |
| 154.86250 | | AM | Haverfordwest | Police (WH) |
| 154.86250 | | NFM | Inverness | Fire Brigade |
| 154.86250 | | NFM | Ipswich | Police (VL) |
| 154.86250 | | AM | Newmarket | Police |
| 154.86250 | | AM | Swansea, Severn Bridge | Police (BQ) |
| 154.86250 | 146.12500 | AM | Brecon | Police (WL) |
| 154.86250 | 146.82500 | AM | Merseyside | Police (CH) Channel 1 |
| 154.86250 | 146.86250 | NFM | Dingwall | Police (UR) |
| 154.86250 | 146.90000 | AM | Suffolk | Police (VL) Channel 1 |
| 154.87500 | 146.03750 | AM | Thames Valley | Police (HB) Channel 6 |
| 154.87500 | 146.66250 | NFM | Perth | Fire Brigade (Fire Control) |
| 154.88750 | | NFM | Aberfeldy | Police (W) |
| 154.88750 | | NFM | Ipswich | Police (VL) Channel 2 |
| 154.88750 | | NFM | Isle Of Man | Police |
| 154.88750 | | NFM | South Wales | Police (WY) Channel 2 |
| 154.88750 | | NFM | Staffordshire | Police and Fire brigade trunked network (YF & YG) |
| 154.88750 | | NFM | Sussex | Police |
| 154.88750 | 146.15000 | AM | Brecon | Police (WL) |
| 154.88750 | 146.47500 | NFM | Burton Down | Police |
| 154.88750 | 146.71250 | NFM | Kyle of Lochalsh | Police (UR) |
| 154.88750 | 146.92500 | AM | Newmarket | Police (VL) Channel 2 |
| 154.88750 | 146.92500 | NFM | Suffolk | Police (VL) Channel 2 |
| 154.88750 | 147.23750 | NFM | Perth | Police (W) |
| 154.90000 | | NFM | Merseyside | Police (A) |
| 154.90000 | 146.83750 | AM | Bedfordshire | Police (M2VA) Channel 1 |
| 154.90000 | 146.85000 | AM | Merseyside | Police (CH) Channel 2 |
| 154.91250 | | NFM | Lochaber | Fire Brigade |
| 154.91250 | | NFM | Perth | Police (W) |

| Base | Mobile | Mode | Location | User and Notes |
|---|---|---|---|---|
| 154.91250 | 146.48750 | AM | Norfolk | Police (VK) Channel 1 |
| 154.91250 | 146.77500 | AM | Gwent | Police (WO) Channel 1 |
| 154.91250 | 147.05000 | NFM | Blairgowrie | Police (WB) |
| 154.92500 | | NFM | Grampian | Police |
| 154.92500 | 146.06250 | AM | Thames Valley | Police (HB) Channel 5 |
| 154.92500 | 146.90000 | AM | Merseyside | Police (CH) Channel 3 |
| 154.93750 | | NFM | Lancashire | Police (BD) Channel 2 |
| 154.93750 | | NFM | South Wales | Police (WX) Channel 4 |
| 154.93750 | 146.17500 | AM | Brecon | Police (WL) |
| 154.93750 | 146.27500 | AM | Oxford | Police |
| 154.93750 | 146.61250 | AM | Kent | Police (KA) Channel 2 |
| 154.93750 | 146.93750 | NFM | Perth | Fire Brigade (Fire Control) |
| 154.95000 | | NFM | Aberdeen | Fire Brigade (Fire Control) |
| 154.95000 | | AM | Hampshire | Police (Motorway Patrols) |
| 154.95000 | | AM | Motorways M4/M40/M25 | Police |
| 154.95000 | 146.01250 | AM | Thames Valley | Police (HB) Channel 7 |
| 154.95000 | 146.85000 | AM | Birkenhead | Police (M53) |
| 154.96000 | | AM | Kent | Police (KB) |
| 154.96000 | | NFM | London | Police (MP) |
| 154.96000 | | NFM | Rayleigh | Police Ch.4 |
| 154.96250 | | NFM | Kent Motorways | Police (TD) |
| 154.96250 | 146.07500 | NFM | Brecon | Police (WL) |
| 154.96250 | 146.07500 | NFM | South Wales | Police (WS) Channel 3 |
| 154.96250 | 146.63750 | AM | Kent | Police (KA) |
| 154.96250 | 146.96250 | NFM | Perth | Police (W) |
| 154.97500 | 146.42500 | AM | Birmingham | Police (YM) Channel 4 |
| 154.97500 | 146.68750 | AM | Hampshire | Police (HC) Channel 5 |
| 154.97500 | 146.68750 | NFM | Isle of Wight | Police surveillance and ops. Ch.5 |
| 154.97500 | 147.05000 | NFM | Aberdeen | Fire Brigade (Fire Control) |
| 154.97500 | 147.05000 | NFM | Blairgowrie | Police (WB) |
| 154.97500 | 147.05000 | NFM | Perth | Police (W) |
| 154.98500 | 146.67500 | NFM | Norfolk | Police (VK) Ch.5 |
| 154.98750 | | NFM | Grampian | Police |
| 154.98750 | | AM | Somerset | Police (QP) Channel 3 |
| 154.98750 | 146.67500 | AM | Norfolk | Police (VK) |
| 154.98750 | 146.85000 | AM | Avon | Police (M2QP) Channel 3 |
| 155.00000 | | NFM | Belfast | RUC |
| 155.00000 | | NFM | Jersey | Civil Defence |
| 155.00000 | | NFM | Kirkcaldy | Police (Special Events) |
| 155.00000 | | AM | London, Ealing | Police, Hounslow (TD) |
| 155.00000 | 146.31250 | AM | West Sussex | Police (M2KB1) Ctrl & Traffic |
| 155.00000 | 147.00000 | NFM | Jersey | Police (M2GS) Ch 4 |
| 155.00000 | 154.70000 | AM | Sussex | Police (M2KB) Ch 1 |
| 155.01250 | | AM | Somerset | Police (QP) Channel 7 |
| 155.01250 | 146.21250 | AM | Manchester | Police (CK) Channel 1 |
| 155.01250 | 146.81250 | AM | Avon | Police (M2QP) Channel 7 |
| 155.01250 | 146.81250 | NFM | Chorlton-cum-Hardy | Police |
| 155.01250 | 147.56250 | NFM | Grampian | Police (UBE) |
| 155.02500 | | AM | Chelmsford | Police (VG) Ch.1 |
| 155.02500 | | NFM | Hereford & Worcester | Fire Brigade (YB) |
| 155.02500 | | AM | Newmarket | Police |
| 155.02500 | 146.21250 | AM | Essex | Police (VG) Channel 1 |
| 155.02500 | 147.02500 | NFM | Dundee | Police (ZS) |
| 155.02500 | 147.13750 | AM | Manchester | Police (Traffic) |
| 155.03750 | 146.78750 | AM | Avon | Police (M2QP) Channel 6 |
| 155.03750 | 146.78750 | AM | Somerset | Police (QP) Channel 6 |

| Base | Mobile | Mode | Location | User and Notes |
|------|--------|------|----------|----------------|
| 155.03750 | 147.06250 | NFM | Perth | Fire Brigade (Fire Control) |
| 155.03750 | 147.18750 | NFM | Co. Fermanagh | Fire Brigade |
| 155.05000 | 146.36250 | AM | Llandudno | Police |
| 155.05000 | 146.36250 | AM | West Sussex | Police (M2KB) Channel 3 |
| 155.05000 | 146.66250 | AM | Powys | Police (WA) Channel 1 |
| 155.05000 | 147.05000 | NFM | Blairgowrie | Police (WB) |
| 155.05000 | 147.05000 | NFM | Perth | Police (W) |
| 155.06250 | 146.76250 | AM | Avon | Police (M2QP) Channel 5 |
| 155.06250 | 146.76250 | AM | Bristol | Police |
| 155.06250 | 146.76250 | AM | Salisbury | Police |
| 155.06250 | 146.76250 | AM | Somerset | Police (QP) Channel 5 |
| 155.06250 | 147.06250 | NFM | Perth | Fire Brigade (Fire Control) |
| 155.06250 | 147.23750 | AM | Manchester | Police (CK) Channel 4 |
| 155.06250 | 147.23750 | AM | Merseyside | Police |
| 155.07500 | | NFM | Aberdeen | Fire Brigade (Fire Control) |
| 155.07500 | | AM | Bristol | Police |
| 155.07500 | | AM | Chelmsford | Police (VG) Ch.2 |
| 155.07500 | | NFM | Staffordshire | Police and Fire brigade trunked network (YF & YG) |
| 155.07500 | 147.18750 | AM | Essex | Police (VG) Channel 2 |
| 155.07500 | 147.18750 | AM | Manchester | Police Traffic (CK) Ch5 |
| 155.08750 | 146.40000 | AM | England & Wales | Police. General comms calling ASU Boxer 1-0, dog units, SOCO, firearms and SELCAL units (M2HC) Ch.1 |
| 155.08750 | | NFM | Holyhead | Police |
| 155.08750 | | AM | Manchester | Police Channel 5 (CK) |
| 155.08750 | 146.10000 | AM | Hampshire | Police (HC) Channel 1 |
| 155.10000 | | NFM | Chelmsford | Police |
| 155.10000 | | AM | Lancashire | Police Ch.10 |
| 155.10000 | | NFM | North Wales | Police |
| 155.10000 | 146.43750 | AM | Anglesey | Police (WA) |
| 155.10000 | 146.58750 | AM | Kent | Police (KA) Channel 1 |
| 155.10000 | 147.18750 | AM | Colwyn Bay | Police HQ |
| 155.10000 | 147.18750 | NFM | Perth | Police (W) |
| 155.10000 | 147.18750 | NFM | Pitlochry | Police (WP) |
| 155.10000 | 147.18750 | AM | Powys | Police (WA) Channel 2 |
| 155.10000 | 147.18750 | AM | Southport | Police |
| 155.10000 | 147.18750 | NFM | St Andrews | Police |
| 155.10000 | 147.18750 | NFM | Wrexham | Police (WA) |
| 155.11250 | 146.43750 | NFM | Northern England | Police Motorways (M2M) Ch. 2 |
| 155.11250 | | NFM | Staffordshire | Police and Fire brigade trunked network (YF & YG) |
| 155.11250 | 146.43750 | AM | Hampshire | Police (HC) Channel 2 |
| 155.11250 | 147.06250 | NFM | County Down | Fire Brigade |
| 155.12500 | | AM | Watford | Police Ch.4 |
| 155.12500 | 146.62500 | AM | Hertfordshire | Police (VH) Channel 2 |
| 155.12500 | 147.48750 | NFM | Crumhaugh Hill | Fire Brigade |
| 155.12500 | 147.48750 | NFM | Lothian and Borders | Fire Brigade (ZF) |
| 155.13750 | 146.66250 | AM | Kent | Police (KA) Channel 4 |
| 155.13750 | 147.08750 | NFM | County Armagh | Fire Brigade |
| 155.13750 | 147.13750 | NFM | Perth | Fire Brigade (Fire Control) |
| 155.15000 | | AM | Somerset | Police (QP) Channel 4 |
| 155.15000 | 146.07500 | AM | Manchester | Police (CK) Channel 6 |
| 155.15000 | 146.57500 | AM | Avon | Police (M2QP) Channel 4 |
| 155.15000 | 146.57500 | AM | Bristol | Police |
| 155.15000 | 147.22500 | NFM | Perth | Police (W) |
| 155.16000 | | NFM | Isle of Wight | Police |
| 155.16250 | | NFM | Blairgowrie | Police (WB) |

| Base | Mobile | Mode | Location | User and Notes |
|------|--------|------|----------|----------------|
| 155.16250 | 146.46250 | NFM | Isle of Wight | Police (M2Z1) Ch.4 |
| 155.16250 | | NFM | Newmarket | Police |
| 155.16250 | | NFM | North Wales | Police Repeater Channel 2 |
| 155.16250 | 146.46250 | AM | Hampshire | Police (HC) Channel 4 |
| 155.16250 | 147.11250 | NFM | County Tyrone | Fire Brigade |
| 155.16250 | 147.61250 | AM | Warwickshire | Police (YJ) Channel 3 |
| 155.16500 | | AM | Isle of Wight | Police |
| 155.17500 | | AM | Newmarket | Police |
| 155.17500 | 146.16250 | AM | Chelmsford | Police (VG) Ch.3 |
| 155.17500 | 146.16250 | AM | Essex | Police (VG) Channel 3 |
| 155.17500 | 146.92500 | AM | Merseyside | Police (CH) Channel 4 |
| 155.17500 | 147.48750 | NFM | Lothian and Borders | Fire Brigade (ZF) |
| 155.18750 | | NFM | Kent | Police |
| 155.18750 | 146.38750 | AM | Essex | Police (VG) |
| 155.18750 | 146.38750 | AM | Manchester | Police (Traffic) |
| 155.18750 | 146.38750 | NFM | North Wales | Police |
| 155.18750 | 147.18750 | NFM | Perth | Police (W) |
| 155.18750 | 147.48750 | NFM | Lothian and Borders | Fire Brigade (ZF) |
| 155.18750 | 154.41250 | AM | West Sussex | Police (M2KB) Channel 4 |
| 155.20000 | 146.60000 | AM | Hertfordshire | Police (VH) Channel 1 |
| 155.20000 | 146.60000 | AM | Manchester | Police |
| 155.20000 | 146.65000 | NFM | Dyfed | Police (WH) Channel 2 |
| 155.20000 | 146.65000 | NFM | Skye | Fire Brigade |
| 155.20000 | 147.06250 | NFM | Perth | Fire Brigade (Fire Control) |
| 155.21250 | | NFM | Hertfordshire | Police Ch.1 |
| 155.21250 | | AM | Manchester | Police |
| 155.21250 | | AM | Somerset | Police (QP) Channel 1 |
| 155.21250 | | NFM | Staffordshire | Police and Fire brigade trunked network (YF & YG) |
| 155.21250 | 146.50000 | AM | Avon | Police (M2QP) Channel 1 |
| 155.21250 | 146.50000 | AM | Bristol | Police |
| 155.21250 | 147.22500 | NFM | Perth | Police (W) |
| 155.22500 | 146.33750 | AM | West Sussex | Police (M2KB2) Ctrl & Traffic Ch 2 |
| 155.22500 | 146.95000 | AM | Merseyside | Police (CH) Channel 5 |
| 155.22500 | 147.22500 | NFM | Perth | Police (W) |
| 155.23750 | | AM | Mold | Police |
| 155.23750 | 146.65000 | AM | Hertfordshire | Police (VH) Channel 3 |
| 155.23750 | 147.03750 | NFM | Northern Ireland | Fire Brigade B, C and E districts |
| 155.23750 | 147.23750 | NFM | Perth | Police (W) |
| 155.25000 | | AM | Bristol | Police |
| 155.25000 | | AM | Cheltenham | Police (QL) |
| 155.25000 | | NFM | Glasgow | Fire Brigade (ZF) |
| 155.25000 | | AM | Gloucester | Police (QL) |
| 155.25000 | | NFM | Kent | Police (KA) |
| 155.25000 | | NFM | Newmarket | Police |
| 155.25000 | | AM | Somerset | Police (QP) |
| 155.25000 | 146.27500 | AM | Lancashire | Police (BD) |
| 155.25000 | 146.52500 | AM | Avon | Police (M2QP) Channel 2 |
| 155.25000 | 146.52500 | AM | Manchester | Police |
| 155.25000 | 147.15000 | NFM | London | Police (GT) Channel 51 |
| 155.25000 | 147.48750 | NFM | Hawick | Fire Brigade (ZF) |
| 155.25000 | 147.48750 | NFM | Lothian and Borders | Fire Brigade (ZF) |
| 155.26250 | | NFM | Fife | Police |
| 155.26250 | | AM | Manchester | Police traffic |
| 155.26250 | 146.31250 | AM | Cheshire | Police (BA 03) Channel 2 |
| 155.26250 | 146.48750 | AM | Hampshire | Police (HC) Channel 3 |
| 155.26250 | 146.48750 | NFM | Southern England | Police Motorways (M2M) Ch.3 |

| Base | Mobile | Mode | Location | User and Notes |
|------|--------|------|----------|----------------|
| 155.26500 | 155.26500 | NFM | Leeds | Police traffic |
| 155.27500 | | AM | Devon | Police (QB) Channel 2 |
| 155.27500 | 146.17500 | NFM | Belfast | RUC |
| 155.27500 | 146.62500 | AM | Powys | Police (WH) Channel 4 |
| 155.27500 | 146.90000 | AM | Cornwall | Police (QB) Channel 2 |
| 155.28750 | | NFM | Aberdeen | Police |
| 155.28750 | | NFM | Grampian | Police (UBG) |
| 155.28750 | 146.41250 | AM | West Sussex | Police (M2KB) Channel 5 |
| 155.28750 | 147.22500 | NFM | Perth | Police (W) |
| 155.29000 | 147.22750 | NFM | Perth | Police (W) |
| 155.30000 | | NFM | Banchory | Police (UBK) |
| 155.30000 | | NFM | Braemar | Police (UBH) |
| 155.30000 | | AM | Devon | Police (QB) Channel 7 |
| 155.30000 | | NFM | Staffordshire | Police and Fire brigade trunked network (YF & YG) |
| 155.30000 | 146.97500 | AM | Cornwall | Police (QB) Channel 7 |
| 155.30000 | 147.13750 | NFM | Londonderry | Fire Brigade (North) |
| 155.30000 | 147.20000 | NFM | London | Diplomatic Prot(Ranger) |
| 155.31250 | 147.23750 | NFM | Perth | Police (W) |
| 155.32500 | 146.23750 | AM | Cornwall | Police (QB) Channel 4 |
| 155.32500 | 146.23750 | AM | Devon | Police (QB) Channel 4 |
| 155.32500 | 146.97500 | NFM | Merseyside | Police (CH, D) Channel 6 |
| 155.33750 | | NFM | West Midlands | Fire Brigade (FB) |
| 155.33750 | 147.18750 | NFM | Perth | Police (W) |
| 155.33750 | 147.18750 | NFM | Pitlochry | Police (WP) |
| 155.35000 | | NFM | Belfast | RUC |
| 155.35000 | | NFM | Cannock, Staffs | Fire Service YG |
| 155.35000 | 147.56250 | NFM | Grampian | Police (UBE) |
| 155.36250 | 146.26250 | AM | Cornwall | Police (QB) Channel 5 |
| 155.36250 | 146.26250 | AM | Devon | Police (QB) Channel 5 |
| 155.37500 | | NFM | Grampian | Police (UBG) |
| 155.37500 | 147.16250 | NFM | Londonderry | Fire Brigade (South) |
| 155.38750 | 146.36250 | AM | West Cheshire | Police (BA 01) Channel 1 |
| 155.38750 | 146.95000 | AM | Cornwall | Police (QB) Channel 6 |
| 155.38750 | 146.95000 | AM | Devon | Police (QB) Channel 6 |
| 155.40000 | | NFM | Edinburgh | Fire Brigade (F) |
| 155.40000 | | NFM | Perth | Fire Brigade (Fire Control) |
| 155.40000 | 146.40000 | NFM | Belfast | RUC |
| 155.41250 | | NFM | Ballachulish | Fire |
| 155.41250 | | NFM | Hampshire | Police |
| 155.41250 | | NFM | Lochaber | Fire Brigade (UF) |
| 155.41250 | | NFM | Staffordshire | Police and Fire brigade trunked network (YF & YG) |
| 155.41250 | 146.62500 | AM | Dyfed | Police (WH) Channel 2 |
| 155.41250 | 147.03750 | NFM | Highlands and Islands | Fire Brigade |
| 155.42500 | | NFM | Aberdeen | Police |
| 155.42500 | | AM | Cheshire | Police Ch 3 |
| 155.42500 | 146.38750 | AM | Manchester | Police (CK) Channel 2 |
| 155.42500 | 147.23750 | NFM | Perth | Police (W) |
| 155.42500 | 147.57500 | NFM | Northern Ireland | Royal Ulster Constabulary |
| 155.43750 | | NFM | Perth | Fire Brigade (Fire Control) |
| 155.43750 | | NFM | Staffordshire | Police and Fire brigade trunked network (YF & YG) |
| 155.43750 | 146.60000 | AM | Dyfed | Police (WH) |
| 155.45000 | | NFM | Belfast | RUC |
| 155.45000 | 146.45000 | NFM | Jersey | Airport Fire Service Ch1 |
| 155.45000 | 147.56250 | NFM | Grampian | Police (UBE) |
| 155.46250 | 146.21250 | AM | Cornwall | Police (QB) Channel 1 |
| 155.46250 | 146.21250 | AM | Devon | Police (QB) Channel 1 |

| Base | Mobile | Mode | Location | User and Notes |
|---|---|---|---|---|
| 155.46250 | 146.30000 | NFM | Lancashire | Police (BD) Channel 1 |
| 155.46250 | 147.56250 | NFM | Grampian | Police (UBE) |
| 155.47500 | 146.12500 | NFM | West Mercia | Police (YK) Channel 2 |
| 155.47500 | 146.60000 | NFM | Dyfed & Powys | Police (WH) Channel 1 |
| 155.47500 | 147.45000 | NFM | Northern Ireland | Royal Ulster Constabulary |
| 155.47500 | 147.56250 | NFM | Grampian | Police (UBE) |
| 155.48750 | 146.33750 | AM | Cheshire | Police (BA 02) Channel 3 |
| 155.48750 | 147.48750 | NFM | Denholm | Fire Brigade (ZF) |
| 155.48750 | 147.48750 | NFM | Lothian and Borders | Fire Brigade (ZF) |
| 155.50000 | | NFM | County Tyrone | RUC |
| 155.50000 | | NFM | Shrewsbury | Police |
| 155.50000 | 146.65000 | AM | Dyfed | Police (WH) |
| 155.50000 | 147.56250 | NFM | Grampian | Police (UBE) |
| 155.51250 | | NFM | Belfast | RUC Voice Encryption |
| 155.51250 | 146.92500 | AM | Cornwall | Police (QB) Channel 3 |
| 155.51250 | 146.92500 | AM | Devon | Police (QB) Channel 3 |
| 155.51250 | 147.48750 | NFM | Langholm | Fire Brigade (ZF) |
| 155.51250 | 147.48750 | NFM | Peebles | Fire Brigade |
| 155.52500 | | NFM | Staffordshire | Police and Fire brigade trunked network (YF & YG) |
| 155.52500 | 147.70000 | NFM | Northern Ireland | Royal Ulster Constabulary |
| 155.53750 | | NFM | Colwyn Bay | Police |
| 155.53750 | 146.46250 | AM | Powys | Police (WA) |
| 155.53750 | 146.46250 | NFM | West Midlands | Police (YH) Channel 6 |
| 155.53750 | 147.56250 | NFM | Aberdeen | Police |
| 155.53750 | 147.56250 | NFM | Grampian | Police (UBE) |
| 155.55000 | | NFM | Aberdeen | Police |
| 155.55000 | | NFM | Staffordshire | Police and Fire brigade trunked network (YF & YG) |
| 155.55000 | 147.55000 | NFM | Northern Ireland | Royal Ulster Constabulary |
| 155.56250 | | NFM | Perth | Police (W) |
| 155.56250 | | NFM | Staffordshire | Police and Fire brigade trunked network (YF & YG) |
| 155.56250 | 147.01250 | NFM | Belfast | Royal Ulster Constabulary |
| 155.56250 | 147.01250 | NFM | Northern Ireland | Fire Brigade A and F districts |
| 155.56250 | 147.48750 | NFM | Edinburgh | Police (ZS) |
| 155.56250 | 147.48750 | NFM | Galashiels | Fire Brigade |
| 155.56250 | 147.48750 | NFM | Lothian and Borders | Fire Brigade (ZF) |
| 155.56250 | 148.48750 | NFM | London | Police Tactical Support Group |
| 155.57500 | | NFM | Derbyshire | Police Ch.1 |
| 155.57500 | | AM | Devon | Police (QB) Channel 8 |
| 155.57500 | | NFM | Grampian | Police (UBG) |
| 155.57500 | | NFM | Perth | Police (W) |
| 155.57500 | | NFM | Stafford | Fire Service |
| 155.57500 | 146.28750 | AM | Cornwall | Police (QB) Channel 8 |
| 155.57500 | 147.52500 | NFM | Northern Ireland | Royal Ulster Constabulary |
| 155.58750 | | NFM | Aberdeen | Police |
| 155.58750 | | NFM | Grampian | Police |
| 155.58750 | | NFM | Preston | Police |
| 155.58750 | 146.25000 | AM | Cumbria | Police (BB3) M6 Motorway |
| 155.60000 | | AM | Derbyshire | Police (NA) |
| 155.60000 | 147.75000 | NFM | Northern Ireland | Royal Ulster Constabulary |
| 155.61250 | | NFM | Hartside Hill | Fire Brigade |
| 155.61250 | | NFM | Lochaber | Fire Brigade (UF) |
| 155.61250 | | NFM | Staffordshire | Police and Fire brigade trunked network (YF & YG) |
| 155.61250 | 146.41250 | AM | Manchester | Police (CK) Channel 3 |
| 155.61250 | 147.03750 | NFM | Highlands and Islands | Fire Brigade |
| 155.61250 | 147.48750 | NFM | Lothian and Borders | Fire Brigade (ZF) |
| 155.62500 | | NFM | Aberdeen | Police |

| Base | Mobile | Mode | Location | User and Notes |
|------|--------|------|----------|----------------|
| 155.62500 | | AM | Colwyn Bay | Police (WA) Traffic |
| 155.62500 | | NFM | Derbyshire | Fire Brigade repeater |
| 155.62500 | | NFM | North Wales | Police |
| 155.62500 | 146.48750 | AM | Powys | Police (WA) |
| 155.62500 | 147.62500 | NFM | Grampian | Police (UB) |
| 155.62500 | 147.77500 | NFM | Northern Ireland | Royal Ulster Constabulary |
| 155.63750 | 146.45000 | AM | Cumbria | Police (BB) Channel 2 |
| 155.63750 | 147.93750 | NFM | Jersey | Fire Brigade Ch 1 |
| 155.65000 | | NFM | Penicuik | Police |
| 155.65000 | 146.26250 | AM | Derbyshire | Police (NA) Channel 1 |
| 155.65000 | 147.90000 | NFM | Northern Ireland | Royal Ulster Constabulary |
| 155.66250 | 146.20000 | AM | Cumbria | Police (BB) |
| 155.66250 | 147.88750 | NFM | Northern Ireland | Royal Ulster Constabulary |
| 155.66250 | 147.95000 | AM | Guernsey | Fire Brigade Ch 1 |
| 155.67500 | | NFM | Nationwide | Police Regional Crime Squad (DVP/Voice) |
| 155.67500 | | NFM | Suffolk | Police Regional Crime Squads |
| 155.67500 | 147.87500 | NFM | Northern Ireland | Royal Ulster Constabulary |
| 155.67500 | 147.96250 | NFM | Jersey | Fire Brigade Ch 2 |
| 155.68500 | | AM | Rhyl | Police |
| 155.70000 | | NFM | Jersey | Police CID Encrypted (M2GS) Ch 6 |
| 155.70000 | | NFM | London | Police Regional Crime Squad Handheld (CS) |
| 155.70000 | | AM | Manchester | Police |
| 155.70000 | | NFM | Nationwide | Police Regional Crime Squad Ch 02 |
| 155.70000 | | NFM | Northern Ireland | RUC |
| 155.70000 | | NFM | Suffolk | Police Regional Crime Squads |
| 155.70000 | | NFM | Wiltshire | Police CID |
| 155.72500 | | AM | Manchester | Police Surveillance Squad |
| 155.72500 | | NFM | Nationwide | Police Regional Crime Squad Ch 03 |
| 155.72500 | | NFM | Suffolk | Police Regional Crime Squads |
| 155.72500 | 155.72500 | NFM | London | Police Regional Crime Squad Handheld (CS) |
| 155.73750 | | NFM | Grampian | Fire Brigade (Fire Control) |
| 155.73750 | 147.03750 | NFM | Highlands and Islands | Fire Brigade |
| 155.75000 | | AM | Chester | Police |
| 155.75000 | | NFM | Jersey | Police Drug Squad |
| 155.75000 | | NFM | London | Police Regional Crime Squad Handheld (CS) |
| 155.75000 | | NFM | Nationwide | Police Regional Crime Squad Ch 01 |
| 155.75000 | | NFM | Northern Ireland | RUC |
| 155.75000 | 155.75000 | AM | Manchester | Police |
| 155.77500 | | AM | Colwyn Bay | Police |
| 155.77500 | | NFM | Suffolk | Police Regional Crime Squads |
| 155.77500 | 147.95000 | NFM | Northern Ireland | Royal Ulster Constabulary |
| 155.77500 | 155.77500 | NFM | London | Police Regional Crime Squad Handheld (CS) |
| 155.78750 | | NFM | Grampian | Fire Brigade (Fire Control) |
| 155.78750 | | NFM | Northern Ireland | Security Forces |
| 155.78750 | 147.93750 | NFM | Northern Ireland | Royal Ulster Constabulary |
| 155.80000 | | NFM | Aberdeen | Police |
| 155.80000 | | AM | Durham | Police |
| 155.80000 | | NFM | Grampian | Police (UBG) |
| 155.80000 | | AM | Kent | Police Ch.45 |
| 155.80000 | 146.20000 | AM | Surrey | Police (HJ) Channel 1 |
| 155.80000 | 147.76250 | AM | Guernsey | Police (QY) Ch 1 |
| 155.80000 | 147.92500 | NFM | Bangor | Royal Ulster Constabulary |
| 155.80000 | 147.92500 | NFM | Belfast | Royal Ulster Constabulary (U) |
| 155.80000 | 147.92500 | NFM | Larne | Royal Ulster Constabulary |
| 155.80000 | 147.92500 | NFM | Northern Ireland | Royal Ulster Constabulary |
| 155.81250 | | AM | Gloucester | Police (QL) |

| Base | Mobile | Mode | Location | User and Notes |
|------|--------|------|----------|----------------|
| 155.81250 | | NFM | Grampian | Police |
| 155.81250 | | NFM | Staffordshire | Police and Fire brigade trunked network (YF & YG) |
| 155.81250 | 146.57500 | NFM | Ipswich | Police |
| 155.81250 | 146.57500 | NFM | Suffolk | Police (VL) Channel 3 |
| 155.81250 | 146.91250 | AM | Wiltshire | Police (QJ) Channel 1 |
| 155.82500 | 147.40000 | NFM | Belfast | Royal Ulster Constabulary |
| 155.82500 | 147.40000 | NFM | Larne | Royal Ulster Constabulary |
| 155.82500 | 147.40000 | NFM | Northern Ireland | Royal Ulster Constabulary |
| 155.82500 | 147.97500 | AM | Guernsey | Fire Brigade Ch 2 |
| 155.83750 | 146.22500 | AM | Surrey | Police (HJ) Channel 2 |
| 155.83750 | 146.28750 | AM | Derbyshire | Police (NA) Channel 2 |
| 155.85000 | | AM | Bristol | Police |
| 155.85000 | | AM | Swindon | Police |
| 155.85000 | 146.93750 | AM | Wiltshire | Police (QJ) Channel 2 |
| 155.85000 | 147.42500 | NFM | Northern Ireland | Royal Ulster Constabulary |
| 155.86250 | | NFM | Humberside | Police Helicopter |
| 155.86250 | | NFM | Merseyside | Police |
| 155.86250 | 146.25000 | AM | Surrey | Police (HJ) Channel 3 |
| 155.86250 | 147.75000 | NFM | Jersey | Police (M2GS) Ch 3 |
| 155.87500 | | NFM | Dunfermline | Fire Brigade (F) |
| 155.87500 | | NFM | Staffordshire | Police and Fire brigade trunked network (YF & YG) |
| 155.87500 | | AM | Winforth | Police |
| 155.87500 | 146.10000 | AM | Dorset | Police (QC) Channel 1 |
| 155.87500 | 147.85000 | NFM | Belfast | Royal Ulster Constabulary (Index) |
| 155.87500 | 147.85000 | NFM | Northern Ireland | Royal Ulster Constabulary |
| 155.88750 | 146.20000 | AM | Cumbria | Police (BB1) South Lakes |
| 155.90000 | | NFM | Norfolk | Police Ch 6 |
| 155.90000 | | AM | Swindon | Police |
| 155.90000 | 146.96250 | AM | Wiltshire | Police (QJ) Channel 3 |
| 155.90000 | 147.47500 | NFM | Belfast | Royal Ulster Constabulary |
| 155.90000 | 147.47500 | AM | Bristol | Police |
| 155.90000 | 147.47500 | NFM | Northern Ireland | Royal Ulster Constabulary |
| 155.90000 | 147.85000 | AM | Guernsey | Police (QY) Ch 2 |
| 155.91250 | | NFM | Hertfordshire | Police (VH) |
| 155.91250 | | NFM | Newport | Police |
| 155.92500 | | NFM | Belfast | Royal Ulster Constabulary |
| 155.92500 | | NFM | Norfolk | Police Ch 7 |
| 155.92500 | 147.01250 | AM | Dorset | Police (QC) Channel 2 |
| 155.92500 | 147.62500 | NFM | Northern Ireland | Royal Ulster Constabulary |
| 155.93750 | | NFM | Bournemouth | Police |
| 155.93750 | | AM | Slough | Police |
| 155.93750 | 146.88750 | AM | Thames Valley | Police (HB) Channel 3 |
| 155.93750 | 147.96250 | NFM | Northern Ireland | Royal Ulster Constabulary |
| 155.95000 | 147.97500 | NFM | Belfast | Royal Ulster Constabulary |
| 155.95000 | 147.97500 | NFM | Larne | Royal Ulster Constabulary |
| 155.95000 | 147.97500 | NFM | Northern Ireland | Royal Ulster Constabulary |
| 155.96000 | 146.23750 | AM | Chelmsford | Police (VG) Ch.4 |
| 155.96250 | | NFM | Newmarket | Police |
| 155.96250 | 146.23750 | AM | Essex | Police (VG) Channel 4 |
| 155.96250 | 147.98750 | NFM | Jersey | Ambulances Ch 6 |
| 155.96250 | 147.98750 | NFM | Jersey | Fire Brigade Ch 8 |
| 155.96250 | 147.98750 | NFM | Jersey | Police (M2GS) Ch 6 |
| 155.96250 | 147.98750 | NFM | Jersey | Police Speed Traps |
| 155.96250 | 155.96250 | NFM | Jersey | Police and Fire Services Ch 7 |
| 155.96500 | 154.50000 | NFM | Essex | Police Ch.4 |
| 155.97500 | 147.67500 | AM | Devon | Police (QB) Channel 7 |

| Base | Mobile | Mode | Location | User and Notes |
|------|--------|------|----------|----------------|
| 155.97500 | 147.67500 | NFM | Northern Ireland | Fire Brigade control |
| 155.97500 | 147.67500 | NFM | Northern Ireland | Royal Ulster Constabulary |
| 155.97500 | 147.67500 | NFM | West Midlands | Fire Brigade (FB) |

### 156.0000 - 162.5000 MHz    MARITIME BAND 25 kHz (BUSINESS RADIO)

| Base | Mobile | Mode | Location | User and Notes |
|------|--------|------|----------|----------------|
| 156.02500 | 160.62500 | NFM | Land's End | Trans Atlantic shipping |
| 156.02500 | 160.62500 | NFM | Port of Heysham | British Gas |
| 156.10000 | 160.70000 | NFM | Portsmouth | Harbour Boat Tours |
| 156.12500 | 160.72500 | NFM | Birkenhead | Alfred Docks |
| 156.12500 | 160.72500 | NFM | Bournemouth | Fishing trawlers |
| 156.22500 | 160.82500 | NFM | Dover | Ferry ops. |
| 156.25000 | 160.85000 | NFM | Liverpool | Alfred Dock Ops |
| 156.25000 | 160.85000 | NFM | Liverpool | Gladstone Dock Ops |
| 156.35000 | 160.95000 | NFM | Eastham | Manchester Ship Canal |
| 156.35000 | 160.95000 | NFM | Ilfracombe | Marine Ship to Shore |
| 156.35000 | 160.95000 | NFM | North Foreland | Working Channel |
| 156.55000 | | NFM | Portsmouth | Navy divers and operations |
| 156.57500 | | NFM | Manchester Canal | Weather Navigation |
| 156.57500 | | NFM | Portsmouth | Dockyard Tours |
| 156.57500 | | NFM | RNAS Portland | Royal Navy |
| 156.60000 | | NFM | Avonmouth | Avonmouth Docks (AVONMOUTH RADIO) |
| 156.60000 | | NFM | Humber | Vessel Traffic System |
| 156.60000 | | NFM | Isle of Man | Douglas Harbour Control |
| 156.60000 | | NFM | Langstone Harbour | Port |
| 156.60000 | | NFM | Leith | Harbour |
| 156.60000 | | NFM | Liverpool | Mersey Radio |
| 156.60000 | | NFM | Milford Haven | Milford Haven Docks, Patrol & Pilot Launch |
| 156.60000 | | NFM | Padstow | Working Channel |
| 156.60000 | | NFM | Plymouth | Royal Navy marine traffic |
| 156.60000 | | NFM | Plymouth | Sutton Lock |
| 156.60000 | | NFM | Portsmouth | Royal Navy Marine Traffic |
| 156.60000 | | NFM | Solent | Vessel Traffic System |
| 156.60000 | | NFM | Southampton | VTS |
| 156.60000 | | NFM | St Malo | Port |
| 156.60000 | | NFM | St Peter Port | Working Channel |
| 156.61250 | | NFM | Plymouth | Warships calling ferry |
| 156.62500 | | NFM | Pole | Police Harbour |
| 156.65000 | | NFM | Gravesend | Shipping Channel |
| 156.65000 | | NFM | North West England | County Rescue |
| 156.65000 | | NFM | Plymouth | Tug to tug comms. |
| 156.67500 | | NFM | Nationwide | Intership |
| 156.67500 | | NFM | Plymouth | Tugs |
| 156.70000 | | NFM | Ayr | Harbour Control |
| 156.70000 | | NFM | Bristol Channel | Pilots (CARDIFF PILOTS) |
| 156.70000 | | NFM | Bristol Channel | Pilots (NEWPORT PILOTS) |
| 156.70000 | | NFM | Chichester | Port |
| 156.70000 | | NFM | Eastham | Manchester Ship Canal |
| 156.70000 | | NFM | Glensanda | Super Quarry |
| 156.70000 | | NFM | Grangemouth | Grangemouth Locks |
| 156.70000 | | NFM | Harwich | Port |
| 156.70000 | | NFM | Heysham | Port Ops |
| 156.70000 | | NFM | Humber | Pilot |
| 156.70000 | | NFM | Liverpool | Out Bound Ships |
| 156.70000 | | NFM | Manchester | Ship Canal |
| 156.70000 | | NFM | Manchester Canal | Eastham Control |
| 156.70000 | | NFM | Milford Haven | Elf & Gulf Oil Terminals |

| Base | Mobile | Mode | Location | User and Notes |
|---|---|---|---|---|
| 156.70000 | | NFM | Milford Haven | Milford Haven Docks |
| 156.70000 | | NFM | Milford Haven | Patrol & Pilot Launch |
| 156.70000 | | NFM | Milford Haven | Texaco Oil Terminal |
| 156.70000 | | NFM | Plymouth | Plymouth Pilots |
| 156.70000 | | NM | Poole | Harbour Control |
| 156.70000 | | NFM | Ramsgate | Ramsgate Port Control (Romeo) |
| 156.70000 | | NFM | Shoreham | Port |
| 156.70000 | | NFM | St Helier | Port & Marina |
| 156.70000 | | NFM | Teesside | Tees Harbour Radio |
| 156.70000 | | NFM | Woolwich | Thames Pilot |
| 156.72500 | | NFM | Alderney | Working Channel |
| 156.72500 | | NFM | Cullercoats | Harbour |
| 156.72500 | | NFM | Gloucester | Docks |
| 156.72500 | | NFM | Gorey | Working Channel |
| 156.72500 | | NFM | Kent | Medway Radio |
| 156.72500 | | NFM | Land's End | Transatlantic shipping |
| 156.72500 | | NFM | Lochaber | Caledonian Canal |
| 156.72500 | | NFM | Nationwide | Ports, Lock |
| 156.72500 | | NFM | Plymouth | Liberty Boats |
| 156.75000 | | NFM | Liverpool Bay/ | Offshore gas rig supply vessels |
| 156.75000 | | NFM | Nationwide | On-board Handhelds |
| 150.00000 | | NFM | Crail | HM Coastguard |
| 156.80000 | | NFM | Milford Haven | Elf & Gulf Oil Terminals |
| 156.80000 | | NFM | Milford Haven | Milford Haven Docks |
| 156.80000 | | NFM | Milford Haven | Patrol & Pilot Launch |
| 156.80000 | | NFM | Milford Haven | Texaco Oil Terminal |
| 156.80000 | | NFM | Swansea | Coastguard |
| 156.85000 | | NFM | English Channel | BCIF |
| 156.87500 | | NFM | Swansea Docks | Swansea-Cork Ferry |
| 156.90000 | 161.50000 | NFM | Manchester Canal | Barton and Irlam Docks |
| 156.90000 | 161.50000 | NFM | Milford Haven | Elf & Gulf Oil Terminals |
| 156.90000 | 161.50000 | NFM | Port En Bessin | Marina Chan |
| 156.92500 | 161.52500 | NFM | St Peter Port | Working Channel |
| 156.95000 | 161.55000 | NFM | Tranmere | Shell Oil Terminal |
| 157.00000 | 161.60000 | NFM | Liverpool | Garston Docks |
| 157.00000 | 161.60000 | NFM | Manchester Canal | Stanlow Docks |
| 157.00000 | 161.60000 | NFM | Stanlow | Shell Refinery |
| 157.02500 | | NFM | Dover | Coastguard |
| 157.02500 | | NFM | Hull | Hull Marina |
| 157.02500 | | NFM | Milford Haven | Marine & Yacht Station |
| 157.02500 | 161.62500 | NFM | Brighton | Marina Ops |
| 157.05000 | | NFM | Milford Haven | Texaco Oil Terminal |
| 157.05000 | 161.65000 | NFM | Liverpool | Manchester Canal, Langton Docks |
| 157.07500 | | NFM | Niton | Working Channel |
| 157.07500 | 161.67500 | NFM | Anglesey | Working Channel |
| 157.10000 | 161.70000 | NFM | Kent | Medway Radio |
| 157.11000 | 161.70000 | NFM | Wirral | Community Patrol (Secret Officer Ch ) |
| 157.12500 | | NFM | Morecambe Bay | Working Channel |
| 157.12500 | | NFM | Orfordness | Working Channel |
| 157.12500 | 161.72500 | NFM | Jersey | Working Channel |
| 157.15000 | | NFM | Malin Head | Working Channel |
| 157.15000 | | NFM | Nationwide | Shore TX Also |
| 157.15000 | | NFM | Rosslare | Working Channel |
| 157.15000 | 161.75000 | NFM | Bantry | Working Channel |
| 157.17500 | | NFM | Minehead | Working Channel |
| 157.17500 | | NFM | Thames | Working Channel |

| Base | Mobile | Mode | Location | User and Notes |
|------|--------|------|----------|----------------|
| 157.17500 | 161.77500 | NFM | Dublin | Working Channel |
| 157.20000 | | NFM | Collafirth | Working Channel |
| 157.20000 | | NFM | Forth | Working Channel |
| 157.20000 | | NFM | Glen Head | Working Channel |
| 157.20000 | | NFM | Humber | Working Channel |
| 157.20000 | | NFM | Shannon | Working Channel |
| 157.20000 | | NFM | Skye | Working Channel |
| 157.20000 | | NFM | Valentia | Working Channel |
| 157.20000 | 161.80000 | NFM | Celtic | Working Channel |
| 157.22500 | 161.82500 | NFM | Cromarty | Working Channel |
| 157.25000 | | NFM | Islay | Working Channel |
| 157.25000 | | NFM | Jersey | Working Channel |
| 157.25000 | | NFM | Minehead | Severn Radio |
| 157.25000 | | NFM | Portishead | Severn Radio |
| 157.25000 | | NFM | Whitby | Working Channel |
| 157.25000 | 161.85000 | NFM | Buchan | Working Channel |
| 157.27500 | | NFM | Humber | Working Channel |
| 157.27500 | | NFM | Lands End | Working Channel |
| 157.27500 | | NFM | Malin End | Working Channel |
| 157.27500 | | NFM | Niton | Working Channel |
| 157.27500 | 161.87500 | NFM | Bantry | Working Channel |
| 157.30000 | | NFM | Clyde | Working Channel |
| 157.30000 | | NFM | Cork | Working Channel |
| 157.30000 | | NFM | Cullercoats | Working Channel |
| 157.30000 | | NFM | Hebrides | Working Channel |
| 157.30000 | | NFM | Humber | Working Channel |
| 157.30000 | | NFM | Illfracombe | Severn Radio |
| 157.30000 | | NFM | North Foreland | Working Channel |
| 157.30000 | | NFM | Orkney | Working Channel |
| 157.30000 | | NFM | Start Point | Working Channel |
| 157.30000 | | NFM | Stonehaven | Working Channel |
| 157.30000 | 161.90000 | NFM | Anglesey | Working Channel |
| 157.35000 | | NFM | Grimsby | Working Channel |
| 157.35000 | | NFM | Lands End | Working Channel |
| 157.35000 | | NFM | Portpatrick | Working Channel |
| 157.35000 | | NFM | Shetland | Working Channel |
| 157.37500 | | NFM | Buchan | Working Channel |
| 157.37500 | | NFM | Niton | Working Channel |
| 157.40000 | | NFM | Cromarty | Working Channel |
| 157.40000 | | NFM | Niton | Working Channel |
| 157.40000 | | NFM | Shannon | Working Channel |
| 157.40000 | | NFM | Valentia | Working Channel |
| 157.40000 | | NFM | Whitby | Working Channel |
| 157.40000 | 162.00000 | NFM | Anglesey | Working Channel |
| 157.42500 | | NFM | Lands End | Working Channel |
| 157.42500 | | NFM | North Foreland | Lighthouse |
| 157.42500 | | NFM | Pillar Rock Pt | Lighthouse |
| 157.42500 | 162.02500 | NFM | Anvil Point | Lighthouse |
| 157.45000 | | NFM | Jersey | Local Fishing Boats |
| 157.45000 | | NFM | Nationwide | Channel 29 |
| 157.45000 | | NFM | Plymouth | Torpoint Ferries |
| 157.45000 | | NFM | Torpoint Ferry | Operations |
| 157.45000 | 162.05000 | NFM | Channel Island | BI Ferries Channel 29 |
| 157.47500 | 162.07500 | NFM | Nationwide | Channel 89 |
| 157.50000 | | NFM | English Channel | Herm Seaway Channel 30 |
| 157.50000 | 162.10000 | NFM | Swansea Docks | Trinity Lighthouse Crews |

| Base | Mobile | Mode | Location | User and Notes |
|---|---|---|---|---|
| 157.52500 | 162.12500 | NFM | Nationwide | Patrol Boats Channel 90 |
| 157.55000 | | NFM | Nationwide | RNLI Private Channel |
| 157.55000 | | NFM | Sark | Working Channel 31 |
| 157.55000 | 162.15000 | NFM | Nationwide | Fisheries Protection Channel 31 |
| 157.57500 | 162.17500 | NFM | Nationwide | Channel 91 |
| 157.60000 | 162.20000 | NFM | Nationwide | Channel 32 |
| 157.62500 | 162.22500 | NFM | Nationwide | Channel 92 |
| 157.65000 | | NFM | English Channel | Hovercraft Channel 33 |
| 157.65000 | | NFM | Norfolk | Broadlands River inspectors Ch.33 |
| 157.65000 | 162.25000 | NFM | English Channel | Fishermens Cooperative Ch 33 |
| 157.67500 | | NFM | Nationwide | Channel 93 |
| 157.67500 | 162.27500 | NFM | Greencastle | Fishermens Cooperative Ch 93 |
| 157.70000 | | NFM | Nationwide | RNLI Private Channel |
| 157.70000 | 162.30000 | NFM | English Channel | Herm Channel 34 |
| 157.72500 | | NFM | Nationwide | Channel 94 |
| 157.72500 | 162.32500 | NFM | Jersey | Local Fishing Boats |
| 157.75000 | | NFM | Jersey | Local Fishing Boats |
| 157.75000 | 162.35000 | NFM | Dover | Hovercraft Channel 35 |
| 157.77500 | 162.37500 | NFM | Nationwide | Channel 95 |
| 157.78750 | 162.38750 | NFM | Thames | Pilot to Tug |
| 157.80000 | | NFM | Nationwide | Channel 36 |
| 157.80000 | | NFM | Scilly Isles | St Mary's Boatmans Association |
| 157.80000 | 162.40000 | NFM | Brighton | Marina Security Channel 36 |
| 157.82500 | 162.42500 | NFM | Nationwide | Channel 96 |
| 157.85000 | | NFM | Hartlepool | Yacht Marina |
| 157.85000 | | NFM | Jersey | St Catherines Yacht Club |
| 157.85000 | | NFM | Milford Haven | Marine & Yacht Station |
| 157.85000 | | NFM | Nationwide | Marinas Channel M1 |
| 157.85000 | | NFM | Penarth | Penarth Marina (CAMPER BASE) |
| 157.85000 | | NFM | Plymouth | Queen Anne's Battery |
| 157.85000 | 162.45000 | NFM | Brighton | Mariner |
| 157.87500 | 162.47500 | NFM | Nationwide | Channel 97 |
| 157.90000 | | NFM | Guernsey | Sealink Channel 38 |
| 157.90000 | | NFM | Isle of Man | Steam Packet Ferries |
| 157.90000 | | NFM | London | Police Thames |
| 157.90000 | 162.50000 | NFM | English Channel | British Ferries Channel 38 |
| 157.92500 | 162.52500 | NFM | Nationwide | Channel 98 |
| 157.95000 | 162.55000 | NFM | Nationwide | Channel 39 |
| 157.95000 | 162.55000 | NFM | Runcorn | Shipping Company |
| 157.97500 | 157.97500 | NFM | Montrose Docks | Cam Shipping |
| 157.97500 | 162.57500 | NFM | Nationwide | Channel 99 |
| 158.00000 | 162.60000 | NFM | Nationwide | Channel 40 |
| 158.02500 | 162.62500 | NFM | Nationwide | Channel 100 |
| 158.05000 | | NFM | Harwich | Scandinavian Seaways Private Ch. |
| 158.05000 | | NFM | Jersey | Local Fishing Boats |
| 158.05000 | 162.65000 | NFM | English Channel | Battricks Channel 41 |
| 158.07500 | 162.67500 | NFM | Nationwide | Channel 101 |
| 158.10000 | 162.70000 | NFM | Jersey | Local Fishing Boats |
| 158.10000 | 162.70000 | NFM | Nationwide | Channel 42 |
| 158.12500 | 162.72500 | NFM | Nationwide | Channel 102 |
| 158.15000 | 162.75000 | NFM | Nationwide | Channel 43 |
| 158.15000 | 162.75000 | NFM | Swansea | Shipping Pilots for Docks Pilot HQ |
| 158.17500 | 162.77500 | NFM | Nationwide | Channel 103 |
| 158.20000 | 162.80000 | NFM | Moray Firth | Beatrice Alpha/Bravo Platform Ch 44 |
| 158.21250 | | NFM | Nationwide | Channel 104 |
| 158.21250 | 168.81250 | NFM | Jersey | Marine FAX |

| Base | Mobile | Mode | Location | User and Notes |
|------|--------|------|----------|----------------|
| 158.22500 | 162.82500 | NFM | Nationwide | Marine FAX Channel 104B |
| 158.25000 | 162.85000 | NFM | Jersey | Local Fishing Boats |
| 158.25000 | 162.85000 | NFM | Moray Firth | Beatrice Alpha/Bravo Platform Ch |
| 158.27500 | 162.87500 | NFM | Nationwide | Channel 105 |
| 158.30000 | 162.90000 | NFM | Jersey | Local Fishing Boats |
| 158.30000 | 162.90000 | NFM | Moray Firth | Beatrice Alpha/Bravo Platform Ch 46 |
| 158.31250 | 162.91250 | NFM | Nationwide | Channel 106 |
| 158.35000 | 162.92500 | NFM | Moray Firth | Beatrice Alpha/Bravo Platform Ch 47 |
| 158.37500 | 162.97500 | NFM | Nationwide | Channel 107 |
| 158.40000 | 163.00000 | NFM | Aberdeen | Dockside Ch 48 |
| 158.42500 | | NFM | Nationwide | Channel 108 |
| 158.42500 | | NFM | Nationwide | Coast Guards |
| 158.42500 | 163.02500 | NFM | English Channel | Condor Hydrofoils |
| 158.45000 | | NFM | Isle Of Rhum | Scottish National Heritage |
| 158.45000 | | NFM | Jersey | Channel Islands Yacht Services |
| 158.45000 | | NFM | Lowestoft | Lifeguards |
| 158.45000 | | NFM | Moray Firth | Beatrice Alpha/Bravo Platform Ch 49 |
| 158.45000 | | NFM | Nigg Bay | Oil Tanker Ldg Channel 49 |
| 158.45000 | 163.05000 | NFM | Bowness | Lake Windermere Steamers |
| 158.47500 | | NFM | Jersey | Ag & Fisheries |
| 158.47500 | 163.07500 | NFM | Aberdeen | Shipping Info Channel 109 |
| 158.50000 | | NFM | English Channel | Emeraude Line Channel 50 |
| 158.50000 | | NFM | Gosport & Fareham | Inshore rescue |
| 158.50000 | | NFM | Nationwide | Private Shipping Ch 50 |
| 158.50000 | | NFM | Nigg Bay | Oil Tanker Ldg Channel 50 |
| 158.50000 | | NFM | Solent | Solent Sea Rescue Org. |
| 158.50000 | 163.10000 | NFM | Dorset | Police Marine Division Ch.50 |
| 160.60000 | | NFM | Aberdeen | Aberdeen Coastguard |
| 160.60000 | | NFM | Brixham | Brixham Coastguard |
| 160.60000 | | NFM | Crail | Crail Coastguard |
| 160.60000 | | NFM | Falmouth | Falmouth Coastguard |
| 160.60000 | | NFM | Great Yarmouth | Lifeboat |
| 160.60000 | | NFM | Nationwide | HM Coastguard Ch 99 |
| 160.60000 | | NFM | Redcar | Redcar Coastguard |

## 158.5250 - 160.54375 MHz   PMR AND DATA 12.5 KHZ NFM

| Base | Mobile | Mode | Location | User and Notes |
|------|--------|------|----------|----------------|
| 158.53750 | 163.03750 | NFM | Nationwide | Channel 1 |
| 158.55000 | 163.05000 | NFM | Nationwide | Private Shipping Ch 51 |
| 158.60000 | 163.10000 | NFM | Nationwide | Private Shipping Ch 52 |
| 158.63750 | 163.13750 | NFM | Nationwide | Channel 2 |
| 158.65000 | | NFM | Nationwide | Private Shipping Ch 53 |
| 158.65000 | | NFM | Nationwide | RAF Mountain Rescue |
| 158.65000 | | NFM | Scotland | National Mountain Rescue |
| 158.65000 | 158.65000 | NFM | Fort William | Police Rescue Services |
| 158.70000 | 163.30000 | NFM | Nationwide | Private Shipping Ch 54 |
| 158.73750 | 163.23750 | NFM | Nationwide | Channel 3 |
| 158.75000 | 163.35000 | NFM | Nationwide | Private Shipping Ch 55 |
| 158.78750 | | NFM | Brighton | Columbia Pictures End of the Affair Film |
| 158.83750 | 163.33750 | NFM | Nationwide | Channel 4 |
| 158.85000 | 163.35000 | NFM | Nationwide | British Telecom |
| 158.93750 | 163.43750 | NFM | Nationwide | Channel 5 |
| 159.00000 | 159.00000 | NFM | Nationwide | Shipping Rescue |
| 159.01250 | 159.01250 | NFM | Tamworth | Alfred McAlpine Construction |
| 159.03750 | 163.53750 | NFM | Nationwide | Channel 6 |
| 159.13750 | 163.63750 | NFM | Nationwide | Channel 7 |
| 159.18750 | | NFM | Jersey | Surveyors |

| Base | Mobile | Mode | Location | User and Notes |
|------|--------|------|----------|----------------|
| 159.23750 | 163.73750 | NFM | Nationwide | Channel 8 |
| 159.25000 | | NFM | North Weald Airfield | Security Ch 3 |
| 159.33750 | 163.83750 | NFM | Nationwide | Channel 9 |
| 159.40000 | 163.90000 | NFM | Bar Hill | AR Benstead |
| 159.40000 | 163.90000 | NFM | Belfast | A1 Taxis |
| 159.40000 | 163.90000 | NFM | Bury St Edmunds | A1 & A3 Cars |
| 159.40000 | 163.90000 | NFM | Cambridge | ADAS |
| 159.40000 | 163.90000 | NFM | Douglas, IOM | A1 Radio Cabs |
| 159.40000 | 163.90000 | NFM | Ely | AK Taxis |
| 159.40000 | 163.90000 | NFM | Fulbourn | AM Alarms Maintenance |
| 159.40000 | 163.90000 | NFM | Haverhill | AM Cars |
| 159.40000 | 163.90000 | NFM | Huntingdon | A&D Private Hire |
| 159.40000 | 163.90000 | NFM | Huntington | ATS |
| 159.40000 | 163.90000 | NFM | Kings Lynn | AA Taxis |
| 159.40000 | 163.90000 | NFM | Kings Lynn | AB Cars |
| 159.40000 | 163.90000 | NFM | Nationwide | Short Term Hire |
| 159.40000 | 163.90000 | NFM | Peterborough | 1st Ace Hereward |
| 159.40000 | 163.90000 | NFM | Reading | APC Comms |
| 159.40000 | 163.90000 | NFM | Sandy | AJ Hart and Son Ltd |
| 159.40000 | 163.90000 | NFM | Thetford | 1 Ace Taxis |
| 159.40000 | 163.90000 | NFM | Thetford | A&S Taxis |
| 159.40000 | 163.90000 | NFM | Thetford | A1 Cars |
| 159.42500 | 163.92500 | NFM | Nationwide | Short Term Hire |
| 159.43750 | 163.93750 | NFM | Nationwide | Channel 10 |
| 159.45000 | | NFM | Swansea | Jinks Taxis |
| 159.45000 | 163.95000 | NFM | Stevenage | Academy Bar, Kings Leisure Site |
| 159.48750 | | NFM | Exeter | Imperial Hotel doorman |
| 159.48750 | | NFM | London | Arsenal Football Club Box Office |
| 159.48750 | | NFM | London | Shorrocks Ltd. |
| 159.48750 | | NFM | Mildenhall | Service Provider |
| 159.48750 | | NFM | Nationwide | Short Term Hire |
| 159.48750 | 159.48750 | NFM | London | Plaza Shopping Centre Oxford St |
| 159.48750 | 159.48750 | NFM | Nationwide | RAC Network Q Rally |
| 159.48750 | 163.98750 | NFM | Kent | Tour de France Forward Convoy |
| 159.50000 | 164.00000 | NFM | Carlisle | B+Q |
| 159.50000 | 164.00000 | NFM | Llanelli | Trostre Tinplate Works |
| 159.50000 | 164.00000 | NFM | London | Brent Cross Shopping Centre |
| 159.50000 | 164.00000 | NFM | London, Oxford St | Plaza Shopping Centre security |
| 159.50000 | 164.00000 | NFM | Nationwide | Short Term Hire |
| 159.51250 | | NFM | London | Integrated Security Group |
| 159.52500 | | NFM | Chessington | World Of Adventures |
| 159.52500 | 164.03750 | NFM | Bristol | Balloon Festival |
| 159.52500 | 164.03750 | NFM | London, Heathrow | Pink Elephant Parking |
| 159.52500 | 164.03750 | NFM | Nationwide | Channel 11 |
| 159.58750 | 163.90000 | NFM | Aberdeen | Aberdeen Radio |
| 159.58750 | 163.90000 | NFM | Belfast | Air Phone Communications |
| 159.58750 | 163.90000 | NFM | Bath | Ashley Communications Ltd |
| 159.58750 | 163.90000 | NFM | Bexleyheath | Abercorn Car Hire |
| 159.58750 | 163.90000 | NFM | Blanford | Alyson Comms |
| 159.58750 | 163.90000 | NFM | Bristol | Avon & Cheddar Gorge Rescure |
| 159.58750 | 163.90000 | NFM | Bury St Edmunds | Bonnet Ltd |
| 159.58750 | 163.90000 | NFM | Cambridge | Ace Taxis |
| 159.58750 | 163.90000 | NFM | Cambridge | Bourn Hall Clinic |
| 159.58750 | 163.90000 | NFM | Cambridge | Botany School, Cambridge University |
| 159.58750 | 163.90000 | NFM | Cambridge | G Asbridge |
| 159.58750 | 163.90000 | NFM | Ely | Allen Skip Hire |

| Base | Mobile | Mode | Location | User and Notes |
|------|--------|------|----------|----------------|
| 159.58750 | 163.90000 | NFM | Foxton | Ansells Comms |
| 159.58750 | 163.90000 | NFM | Fulbourn | Abington Farms Ltd. |
| 159.58750 | 163.90000 | NFM | Glasgow | Argyll Communications Ltd |
| 159.58750 | 163.90000 | NFM | Holyhead | Anglesy Comms |
| 159.58750 | 163.90000 | NFM | Hounslow | Midas Security Primark Clothes |
| 159.58750 | 163.90000 | NFM | Hunstanton | Ace Cabs |
| 159.58750 | 163.90000 | NFM | London, Stratford | Shopping Centre security |
| 159.58750 | 163.90000 | NFM | LLandudno | Airlink Comms Dervice |
| 159.58750 | 163.90000 | NFM | LLandudno | Wern Bach Farm |
| 159.58750 | 163.90000 | NFM | Manchester | Aircomm Communications |
| 159.58750 | 163.90000 | NFM | March | Anglia Telecomms Ltd |
| 159.58750 | 163.90000 | NFM | Milton Keynes | Ace Cars |
| 159.58750 | 163.90000 | NFM | Newmarket | Anglia Windscreens |
| 159.58750 | 163.90000 | NFM | Newmarket | CW Bradfield & Son |
| 159.58750 | 163.90000 | NFM | Nationwide | Short Term Hire |
| 159.58750 | 163.90000 | NFM | Redditch | Arca Ltd |
| 159.58750 | 163.90000 | NFM | Rugby | Rugby Cement Ch.8 |
| 159.58750 | 163.90000 | NFM | Southampton | Airsys Select |
| 159.58750 | 163.90000 | NFM | Stanstead | Anglia Cars |
| 159.58750 | 164.03750 | NFM | Stoneleigh | Royal Show |
| 159.58750 | 163.90000 | NFM | Swansea | Airwave Comms Systems |
| 159.58750 | 163.90000 | NFM | Swanton | Academy Cars |
| 159.58750 | 163.90000 | NFM | Thetford | Ace Taxis |
| 159.58750 | 163.90000 | NFM | Thetford | Andys Taxis |
| 159.58750 | 163.90000 | NFM | Totness | RM Arnold Ltd |
| 159.58750 | 164.08750 | NFM | Kent | Tour de France Marshalls & Security |
| 159.62500 | | NFM | London | Queens Club Stella Artois Championships |
| 159.62500 | | NFM | Rugby | Rugby Cement Ch.7 |
| 159.62500 | 159.62500 | NFM | Llanelli | Trostre Tinplate Works |
| 159.62500 | 159.62500 | NFM | Nationwide | Short Term Hire |
| 159.62500 | 164.12500 | NFM | Kent | Tour de France Channel 4 TV |
| 159.63750 | 164.13750 | NFM | Nationwide | Channel 12 |
| 159.68750 | | NFM | London | Town And Country Outside Events Security |
| 159.68750 | | NFM | Rugby | Rugby Cement Ch.6 |
| 159.68750 | 164.13750 | NFM | Nationwide | Short Term Hire |
| 159.68750 | 164.18750 | NFM | Kent | Tour de France Start/Finish |
| 159.73750 | 164.23750 | NFM | Nationwide | Channel 13 |
| 159.83750 | 164.33750 | NFM | Nationwide | Channel 14 |
| 159.91250 | 158.51250 | NFM | Nationwide | British Telecom Radiophone |
| 160.06000 | | NFM | Southampton | Healthcall Services (Doctors) |
| 160.06250 | 164.56250 | NFM | Bolton | Doctors Service |
| 160.11500 | | NFM | Yorkshire | Recovery service |
| 160.12500 | 164.62500 | NFM | Kent | Tour de France (Italian) |
| 160.15000 | 160.15000 | NFM | Blackpool | Doctors Messages |
| 160.25000 | | NFM | London | St. Johns Ambulance |
| 160.30000 | | NFM | Eastbourne | Doctors on call |
| 160.45000 | | NFM | London | St. Johns Ambulance |
| 160.54000 | | NFM | Gateshead | Council Housing |

## 160.54375 - 160.6000 MHz   LOCAL AUTHORITY EMERGENCY ALARMS

| Base | Mobile | Mode | Location | User and Notes |
|------|--------|------|----------|----------------|
| 160.55000 | | NFM | Nationwide | OAP Alarm System |
| 160.56250 | | NFM | Nationwide | OAP Alarm System |
| 160.57500 | | NFM | Nationwide | OAP Alarm System |

| Base | Mobile | Mode | Location | User and Notes |
|------|--------|------|----------|----------------|

**160.6000 - 160.9750 MHz**     INTERNATIONAL MARITIME BAND

| Base | Mobile | Mode | Location | User and Notes |
|------|--------|------|----------|----------------|
| 156.00000 | 156.00000 | NFM | Nationwide | Channel 0 Coastguard/Lifeboat Primary Airborne Rescue Coordination |
| 160.62500 | 156.02500 | NFM | Nationwide | Channel 60 |
| 160.65000 | 156.05000 | NFM | Nationwide | Channel 01 Port Ops |
| 160.67500 | 156.07500 | NFM | Nationwide | Channel 61 |
| 160.70000 | 156.10000 | NFM | Nationwide | Channel 02 |
| 160.72500 | 156.12500 | NFM | Nationwide | Channel 62 |
| 160.75000 | 156.15000 | NFM | Nationwide | Channel 03 |
| 160.77500 | 156.17500 | NFM | Nationwide | Channel 63 |
| 160.80000 | 156.20000 | NFM | Nationwide | Channel 04 |
| 160.82500 | 156.22500 | NFM | Nationwide | Channel 64 |
| 160.85000 | 156.25000 | NFM | Nationwide | Channel 05 |
| 160.87500 | 156.27500 | NFM | Nationwide | Channel 65 |
|  | 156.30000 | NFM | Nationwide | Channel 06 Ship to Ship and Search and Rescure with aircraft |
| 160.92500 | 156.32500 | NFM | Nationwide | Channel 66 |
| 160.95000 | 156.35000 | NFM | Nationwide | Channel 07 |
| 156.37500 | 156.37500 | NFM | Nationwide | Channel 67 |
| 156.40000 | 156.40000 | NFM | Nationwide | Channel 08 |
| 156.42500 | 156.42500 | NFM | Nationwide | Channel 68 Port ops. and ship movement |
| 156.45000 | 156.45000 | NFM | Nationwide | Channel 09 |
| 156.47500 | 156.47500 | NFM | Nationwide | Channel 69 Port ops. and ship movement |
| 156.50000 | 156.50000 | NFM | Nationwide | Channel 10 Pollution |
| 156.52500 | 156.52500 | NFM | Nationwide | Channel 70 Digital Selective calling for distress, safety and calling |
| 156.55000 | 156.55000 | NFM | Nationwide | Channel 11 Port ops. and ship movement |
| 156.57500 | 156.57500 | NFM | Nationwide | Channel 71 Port ops. and ship movement |
| 156.60000 | 156.60000 | NFM | Nationwide | Channel 12 Port ops. and ship movement |
|  | 156.62500 | NFM | Nationwide | Channel 72 Intership Comms |
| 156.65000 | 156.65000 | NFM | Nationwide | Channel 13 Primarily intership navigation safety |
| 156.67500 | 156.67500 | NFM | Nationwide | Channel 73 Coastguard |
| 156.70000 | 156.70000 | NFM | Nationwide | Channel 14 Port ops. and ship movement |
| 156.72500 | 156.72500 | NFM | Nationwide | Channel 74 Port ops. and ship movement |
| 156.75000 | 156.75000 | NFM | Nationwide | Channel 15 On-board Handhelds |
| 156.75000 | 156.75000 | NFM | Nationwide | Channel 15 Port Ops |
| 156.78750 | 156.76250 | NFM | Nationwide | Channel 75 Guard Band |
| 156.80000 | 156.80000 | NFM | Nationwide | Channel 16 Distress & calling |
| 156.83750 | 156.81250 | NFM | Nationwide | Channel 76 Guard Band |
| 156.85000 | 156.85000 | NFM | Nationwide | Channel 17 On-board Handhelds |
|  | 156.87500 | NFM | Nationwide | Channel 77 Intership |
| 161.50000 | 156.90000 | NFM | Nationwide | Channel 18 |
| 161.52500 | 156.92500 | NFM | Nationwide | Channel 78 |
| 161.55000 | 156.95000 | NFM | Nationwide | Channel 19 |
| 161.57500 | 156.97500 | NFM | Nationwide | Channel 79 Port ops. and ship movement |
| 161.60000 | 157.00000 | NFM | Nationwide | Channel 20 |
| 161.62500 | 157.02500 | NFM | Nationwide | Channel 80 Port ops. and ship movement |
| 161.65000 | 157.05000 | NFM | Nationwide | Channel 21 |
| 161.67500 | 157.07500 | NFM | Nationwide | Channel 81 |
| 161.70000 | 157.10000 | NFM | Nationwide | Channel 22 |
| 161.72500 | 157.12500 | NFM | Nationwide | Channel 82 |
| 161.75000 | 157.15000 | NFM | Nationwide | Channel 23 |
| 161.77500 | 157.17500 | NFM | Nationwide | Channel 83 |
| 161.80000 | 157.20000 | NFM | Nationwide | Channel 24 |
| 161.82500 | 157.22500 | NFM | Nationwide | Channel 84 |
| 161.85000 | 157.25000 | NFM | Nationwide | Channel 25 |

| Base | Mobile | Mode | Location | User and Notes |
|------|--------|------|----------|----------------|
| 161.87500 | 157.27500 | NFM | Nationwide | Channel 85 |
| 161.90000 | 157.30000 | NFM | Nationwide | Channel 26 |
| 161.92500 | 157.32500 | NFM | Nationwide | Channel 86 Calling with automatic telephone system |
| 161.95000 | 157.35000 | NFM | Nationwide | Channel 27 |
| 161.97500 | 157.37500 | NFM | Nationwide | Channel 87 |
| 162.00000 | 157.40000 | NFM | Nationwide | Channel 28 |
| 162.02500 | 157.42500 | NFM | Nationwide | Channel 88 |

160.9750 - 161.4750 MHz   PAGING ACKNOWLEDGEMENT CHANNELS &
INTERNATIONAL MARITIME SERVICE BUSINESS
MARINE RADIO AND LOCAL COMMUNITY
SERVICES 25 kHz NFM SIMPLEX

| Base | Mobile | Mode | Location | User and Notes |
|------|--------|------|----------|----------------|
| 161.000 | 31.7250 | NFM | Nationwide | Hospital Paging |
| 161.012 | | NFM | Windsor Castle | PSA |
| 161.025 | 31.7500 | NFM | Nationwide | Hospital Paging |
| 161.037 | 459.375 | NFM | Ipswich | B.H.S Paging |
| 161.050 | 31.7750 | NFM | Eastbourne | Hospital paging |
| 161.050 | 31.7750 | NFM | London | LWTV Park Royal Ch 2 |
| 161.050 | 31.7750 | NFM | Nationwide | Hospital Paging |
| 161.075 | 459.437 | NFM | Swansea City | Royal Mail |
| 161.085 | 164.510 | NFM | Newcastle-under-Lyme | Homebase Paging |
| 161.130 | | NFM | Manchester | Norweb |
| 161.150 | | NFM | Nationwide | Paging Returns |
| 161.150 | | NFM | Port of Heysham | British Gas |
| 161.195 | | NFM | Leicester | Electricity Board |
| 161.200 | 161.200 | NFM | Bacton | Philips Petroleum |
| 161.205 | | NFM | Manchester | Norweb |
| 161.230 | | NFM | Northampton | Electricity Repairs |
| 161.245 | 161.200 | NFM | Manchester | Norweb |
| 161.245 | 161.200 | NFM | Pembroke | Taxi |
| 161.245 | 161.200 | NFM | Preston | Electric Board Meter Changes |
| 161.275 | | NFM | Nationwide | Radio Alarms |
| 161.300 | | NFM | Cardiff | Haulage Firm |
| 161.300 | | NFM | English Channel | British Ch. Island Ferries |
| 161.300 | | NFM | Felixstowe | Alexandra Towing Tugs |
| 161.300 | | NFM | Nationwide | On-Board Handhelds |
| 161.300 | | NFM | Swansea Docks | AB Ports |
| 161.325 | | NFM | Newmarket | Turners of Soham Ltd |
| 161.325 | | NFM | Preston | Granada shops |
| 161.345 | | NFM | Northampton | Company Radio |
| 161.350 | | NFM | English Channel | BCIF 'Pride of Portsmouth' |
| 161.350 | | NFM | Europort | Townsend Torisson Ferry Loading |
| 161.350 | | NFM | Fleetwood | Pandora Loading |
| 161.350 | | NFM | Jersey | BCIF 'Pride of Portsmouth' |
| 161.350 | | NFM | Manchester | Norweb |
| 161.350 | | NFM | Nationwide | On-Board Handhelds |
| 161.387 | | NFM | Croydon | ITV Thames TV Ch 2 |
| 161.425 | | NFM | Jersey | Local Fishing Boats |
| 161.425 | | NFM | Jersey | Marina |
| 161.425 | | NFM | Marina & Yachts | Channel M2 |
| 161.425 | | NFM | Newport, Wales | Race control for yacht racing |
| 161.445 | | NFM | Machynlleth | Marina |
| 161.450 | | NFM | Croydon | ITV Thames TV Ch 3 |
| 161.450 | | NFM | London | LWT Park Royal |
| 161.450 | | NFM | Nationwide | On-Board Handhelds |

| Base | Mobile | Mode | Location | User and Notes |
|---|---|---|---|---|
| 161.450 | | NFM | Northampton | Works Radio |
| 161.470 | | NFM | Manchester | Norweb |
| 161.500 | 156.900 | NFM | Liverpool | Mersey Radio Radar |

**161.4750 - 162.0500 MHz   INTERNATIONAL MARITIME SHORE TRANSMIT**

| Base | Mobile | Mode | Location | User and Notes |
|---|---|---|---|---|
| 161.525 | | NFM | Hartlepool | Security Firm |
| 161.550 | | NFM | Blyth | Harbour |
| 161.550 | 156.950 | NFM | Liverpool | Mersey Radio Radar |
| 161.575 | 161.575 | NFM | Manchester | Canal tugs - outgoing |
| 161.580 | | NFM | Lancashire | Preston Gas Servicers |
| 161.600 | 157.000 | NFM | Garston | Garston Dock Ops |
| 161.600 | 161.500 | NFM | Brixham | Fishing trawlers |
| 161.625 | | NFM | Penarth | Penarth Marina (CAMPER BASE) |
| 161.625 | 161.625 | NFM | Dover | Ferry ops. |
| 161.650 | 157.050 | NFM | Liverpool | Langton Dock Ops |
| 161.675 | | NFM | Nationwide | Marinas and Yacht Clubs Ch M2 |
| 161.675 | | NFM | Port of Heysham | British Gas |
| 161.680 | | NFM | Lancashire | Leyland Gas Servicers |
| 161.700 | 157.100 | NFM | Liverpool | Mersey Radio Radar |
| 161.725 | 161.725 | NFM | Liverpool | Dredgers |
| 161.775 | 161.775 | NFM | Dover | Sally Line Ferries |
| 161.800 | | NFM | Edinburgh | International Marine |

**162.0500 - 163.03125 MHz   PRIVATE MARINE ALLOCATION AND PMR**
**25 KHZ NFM**

| Base | Mobile | Mode | Location | User and Notes |
|---|---|---|---|---|
| 161.82500 | 161.82500 | NFM | Poole | Cross Channel ferries |
| 161.87500 | 161.87500 | NFM | London | Thames Barge traffic |
| 161.90000 | 161.90000 | NFM | Portsmouth | Dockyard cranes |
| 161.92500 | 161.92500 | NFM | Poole | Fishing trawlers |
| 161.95000 | 161.95000 | NFM | Poole | Police harbour |
| 161.97500 | 161.97500 | NFM | Lyme Regis | Dredgers |
| 162.00000 | 162.00000 | NFM | Plymouth | Tugs |
| 162.05000 | 157.45000 | NFM | Jersey | BCIF Ch 29 |
| 162.05000 | 157.45000 | NFM | Tamworth | Keywatch Security |
| 162.07500 | 157.47500 | NFM | London | Contract Dustcarts |
| 162.07500 | 157.47500 | NFM | London | Fortnum and Mason |
| 162.07500 | 157.47500 | NFM | London | Target Couriers |
| 162.07500 | 157.47500 | NFM | Nationwide | Motorola UK Channel 1 |
| 162.07500 | 157.47500 | NFM | Teesside | Harbour Pilot |
| 162.08750 | 157.48750 | NFM | London | Target Couriers |
| 162.08750 | 157.48750 | NFM | Walsall | All-Points Couriers |
| 162.10000 | 157.50000 | NFM | Jersey | Herm Seaway Ch 30 |
| 162.12500 | | NFM | Brent C | Shell PMR |
| 162.13750 | 157.53750 | NFM | Brighton | British Gas |
| 162.13750 | 157.53750 | NFM | Nationwide | RAC Network Q Rally-Subaru |
| 162.15000 | 157.55000 | NFM | Edinburgh Airport | PMR Channel 16 |
| 162.15000 | 157.55000 | NFM | Isle of Sark | Shipping Ch 31 |
| 162.17500 | 157.57500 | NFM | Driffield | J.R. Hood |
| 162.17500 | 157.57500 | NFM | London | Securicor Trunks |
| 162.17500 | 157.57500 | NFM | Nationwide | Motorola UK Channel 2 |
| 162.17500 | 157.57500 | NFM | Nationwide | Subaru Rally Team |
| 162.20000 | 157.60000 | NFM | London | Target Couriers |
| 162.20000 | 157.60000 | NFM | Merry Hill | Drinks Machines Company |
| 162.20000 | 157.60000 | NFM | Nationwide | Motorola UK Channel 3 |
| 162.21250 | | NFM | West Midlands | Coaches |

| Base | Mobile | Mode | Location | User and Notes |
|---|---|---|---|---|
| 162.22500 | 157.62500 | NFM | Bristol | Security Company |
| 162.22500 | 157.62500 | NFM | Cheshire | Delivery Company |
| 162.22500 | 157.62500 | NFM | Lincoln | Taxi Service |
| 162.22500 | 157.62500 | NFM | Nationwide | Motorola UK Channel 4 |
| 162.24500 | | NFM | Machynlleth | British Gas |
| 162.25000 | 157.65000 | NFM | Jersey | Fishermans Co-Op |
| 162.27500 | 157.67500 | NFM | Blackpool | Builders |
| 162.27500 | 157.67500 | NFM | Hull | Container Terminal |
| 162.27500 | 157.67500 | NFM | Manchester | Delivery Company |
| 162.30000 | 157.30000 | NFM | Felixstowe | Shipping Company |
| 162.30000 | 157.70000 | NFM | Jersey | Shipping Company |
| 162.32500 | 157.72500 | NFM | Boston | Fossitt & Thorne Tyres Ltd |
| 162.32500 | 157.72500 | NFM | Felixstowe | Shipping Company |
| 162.32500 | 157.72500 | NFM | London | Contract Buses |
| 162.32500 | 157.72500 | NFM | London | Courier |
| 162.32500 | 157.72500 | NFM | London | Securicor trunked network |
| 162.32500 | 157.72500 | NFM | Nationwide | Motorola UK Channel 5 |
| 162.35000 | 157.75000 | NFM | Bournemouth | Off-Shore Drilling Ch 35 |
| 162.36000 | | NFM | Droitwich | Securicor Base |
| 162.36250 | 157.76250 | NFM | Nationwide | Motorola UK Channel 6 |
| 162.36250 | 157.76250 | NFM | Solihull | Courier |
| 162.37500 | 157.77500 | NFM | London | Securicor Trunks |
| 162.37500 | 157.77500 | NFM | Nationwide | Motorola UK Channel 7 |
| 162.37500 | 157.77500 | NFM | Swindon | Skip Company |
| 162.40000 | 157.80000 | NFM | Hull | Humber Tugs |
| 162.40000 | 157.80000 | NFM | Space | NOAA Satellite |
| 162.40000 | 157.80000 | AM | Wigan | Toyota Emergency Repairs |
| 162.42500 | 157.82500 | NFM | Blackpool | Hospital Cleaners |
| 162.42500 | 157.82500 | NFM | Liverpool | Engineers |
| 162.42500 | 157.82500 | NFM | London, North | Taxis |
| 162.42500 | 157.82500 | NFM | Nationwide | Motorola UK Channel 8 |
| 162.42500 | 157.82500 | NFM | Space | NOAA Satellite |
| 162.45000 | | NFM | Nationwide | Differential GPS |
| 162.47500 | | NFM | Space | NOAA Satellite |
| 162.47500 | 157.87500 | NFM | Bristol | Contractor |
| 162.47500 | 157.87500 | NFM | London | Buses |
| 162.47500 | 157.87500 | NFM | London | Securicor Trunks |
| 162.47500 | 157.87500 | NFM | Manchester | Delivery Company |
| 162.47500 | 157.87500 | NFM | Nationwide | Motorola UK Channel 9 |
| 162.47500 | 157.87500 | NFM | Preston | Meals on Wheels |
| 162.50000 | 157.90000 | NFM | Dieppe | Ferry Co. Ch 38 |
| 162.50000 | 157.90000 | NFM | Guernsey | Sealink |
| 162.50000 | 157.90000 | NFM | Harwich | Pilots |
| 162.50000 | 157.90000 | NFM | Isle of Man | Steam Packet Ferries |
| 162.50000 | 157.90000 | NFM | London | Police Thames boats |
| 162.50000 | 157.90000 | NFM | Newhaven | Sealink Ch 38 |
| 162.52500 | 157.92500 | NFM | Leatherhead | Taxi |
| 162.52500 | 157.92500 | NFM | Staffs | Haulage |
| 162.53750 | 157.93750 | NFM | Nationwide | Network Q Rally - Toyota |
| 162.55000 | | NFM | Space | NOAA Satellite |
| 162.55000 | 157.95000 | NFM | Nationwide | Townsend Thorenson Ch 39 |
| 162.57500 | 157.97500 | NFM | Nationwide | Motorola UK Channel 10 |
| 162.57500 | 157.97500 | NFM | Ninian North Chevron | Back-up to Ninian S |
| 162.65000 | 158.02500 | NFM | Liverpool | Shipping Agents |
| 162.65000 | 158.02500 | NFM | Wallesey | Mersey Ferries |
| 162.68000 | 158.08000 | NFM | Manchester | Piccadilly Radio |

| Base | Mobile | Mode | Location | User and Notes |
|------|--------|------|----------|----------------|
| 162.70000 | 158.10000 | NFM | Bristol | Dock Tugs Ch 42 |
| 162.85000 | 162.85000 | NFM | Liverpool | Ship Ops |
| 162.87500 | | NFM | Manchester | Building Firm |
| 162.87500 | | NFM | Manchester | Delivery Company |
| 162.92500 | 158.32500 | NFM | Boston | Fossitt & Thorne Tyres Ltd |
| 162.92500 | 158.32500 | NFM | London | Securicor Trunks |
| 162.92500 | 158.32500 | NFM | London, Wembley | Bus Hoppas |
| 162.92500 | 158.32500 | NFM | Manchester | Delivery Company |
| 162.93750 | 158.33750 | NFM | Bristol | Coast Guard |
| 162.97500 | 158.37500 | NFM | Boston | Fossitt & Thorne Tyres Ltd |
| 162.97500 | 158.37500 | NFM | Oldham | Service Engineers |
| 163.00000 | 158.40000 | NFM | London | BB Securities Ltd. |
| 163.00000 | 158.40000 | NFM | Southampton | MediCall Ch 1 |
| 163.02500 | | NFM | Isle of Man | Calf of Man Telephone Link |
| 163.02500 | | NFM | Nationwide | Differential GPS |

**163.03125 - 165.0000 MHz     PMR Band**

| Base | Mobile | Mode | Location | User and Notes |
|------|--------|------|----------|----------------|
| 163.05000 | 158.55000 | NFM | Cumnock | Gibson Whyte, heating engineers |
| 163.05000 | 158.55000 | NFM | Hampshire | Bus Company |
| 163.05000 | 158.55000 | NFM | Jersey | Amal-grow |
| 163.05000 | 158.55000 | NFM | Jersey | Besco |
| 163.05000 | 158.55000 | NFM | Jersey | Cable TV |
| 163.05000 | 158.55000 | NFM | Jersey | Dynarod |
| 163.05000 | 158.55000 | NFM | Jersey | Gorey Cabs |
| 163.05000 | 158.55000 | NFM | Jersey | Securicor |
| 163.05000 | 158.55000 | NFM | Peterborough | Hector |
| 163.06000 | | NFM | Irvine | Parcel Force |
| 163.06250 | 158.56250 | NFM | Peterborough | Various Users |
| 163.07500 | 158.57500 | NFM | Brighton | Construction Company |
| 163.07500 | 158.57500 | NFM | Colchester | Pub and club link to police |
| 163.07500 | 158.57500 | NFM | Manchester | Bus Inspectors |
| 163.08750 | 158.58750 | NFM | Nationwide | Road Construction Engineers |
| 163.11250 | 158.61250 | NFM | Dublin | District Police Surveillance |
| 163.13750 | 158.63750 | NFM | Dublin | District Police Surveillance |
| 163.13750 | 158.63750 | NFM | London | Wembley Stadium contract cleaners |
| 163.15000 | 163.15000 | NFM | Chessington | World Of Adventures |
| 163.15000 | 163.15000 | NFM | London | Police Royal Parks Ch 2 (RZ) |
| 163.15000 | 163.15000 | NFM | Swansea | Council Warden Ch 2 |
| 163.16250 | 158.66250 | NFM | Dublin | District Police Surveillance |
| 163.18750 | | NFM | London | Dept. of Environment |
| 163.20000 | 158.70000 | NFM | Bangor | DSS |
| 163.20000 | 158.70000 | NFM | Birmingham | City Hospital medical engineers |
| 163.20000 | 158.70000 | NFM | Jersey | Amal-grow |
| 163.20000 | 158.70000 | NFM | Jersey | Besco |
| 163.20000 | 158.70000 | NFM | Jersey | Cable TV |
| 163.20000 | 158.70000 | NFM | Jersey | Dynarod |
| 163.20000 | 158.70000 | NFM | Jersey | Gorey Cabs |
| 163.20000 | 158.70000 | NFM | Jersey | Securicor |
| 163.20000 | 158.70000 | NFM | Peterborough | CBS Repeater |
| 163.20000 | 158.70000 | NFM | Preston | Lowe's Plant Hire |
| 163.21250 | 158.71250 | NFM | London | Doctors & Medics |
| 163.21250 | 158.71250 | NFM | Perthshire | Electricians |
| 163.21250 | 158.71250 | NFM | Peterborough | CBS Repeater |
| 163.21250 | 158.71250 | NFM | South Woodhan Ferrers | R W Crawford |
| 163.21250 | 158.71250 | NFM | Tayside | Heating Engineers |
| 163.22500 | 158.72500 | NFM | Handcross | Comrep |

| Base | Mobile | Mode | Location | User and Notes |
|------|--------|------|----------|----------------|
| 163.22500 | 158.72500 | NFM | Manchester Gorton | Steves Bakery |
| 163.22500 | 158.72500 | NFM | Oldham | Emergency Doctor |
| 163.22500 | 158.72500 | NFM | Peterborough | Community Repeater |
| 163.28750 | 158.68750 | NFM | Farnborough Airshow | TNT Car Parking Services (T) |
| 163.28750 | 158.68750 | NFM | London | Town And Country Outside Events |
| 163.28750 | 158.68750 | NFM | Somerleyton, Suffolk | Somerleyton Hall Grounds |
| 163.30000 | 158.70000 | NFM | Derby | Civil Engineers |
| 163.30000 | 158.70000 | NFM | Fleetwood | Golf Club |
| 163.30000 | 158.70000 | NFM | Lea Valley | Hoddesdon & Herts Buses |
| 163.30000 | 158.70000 | NFM | London | BB Security |
| 163.30000 | 158.70000 | NFM | London | M11 construction security |
| 163.30000 | 158.70000 | NFM | Nationwide | Contactor |
| 163.30000 | 158.70000 | NFM | West Yorkshire | Haulage Firm |
| 163.32500 | 158.82500 | NFM | London | Islington Refuse |
| 163.35000 | 158.85000 | NFM | Co Durham | Waste Disposal |
| 163.35000 | 158.85000 | NFM | Cornwall | Repeater |
| 163.35000 | 158.85000 | NFM | Devon | Associated Leisure |
| 163.35000 | 158.85000 | NFM | Jersey | Amal-grow |
| 163.35000 | 158.85000 | NFM | Jersey | Besco |
| 163.35000 | 158.85000 | NFM | Jersey | Cable TV |
| 163.35000 | 158.85000 | NFM | Jersey | Dynarod |
| 163.35000 | 158.85000 | NFM | Jersey | Gorey Cabs |
| 163.35000 | 158.85000 | NFM | Jersey | Securicor |
| 163.35000 | 158.85000 | NFM | Newton Abbot | Amtrack |
| 163.35000 | 158.85000 | NFM | Okehampton | Target Express |
| 163.35000 | 158.85000 | NFM | Peterborough | Octane |
| 163.35000 | 158.85000 | NFM | Plymouth | Granada TV |
| 163.36250 | 158.86250 | NFM | Cambridge | Vehicle Towaway |
| 163.36250 | 158.86250 | NFM | Cirencester | By Pass Construction |
| 163.36250 | 158.86250 | NFM | Cleveland | Private Message |
| 163.36250 | 158.86250 | NFM | Manchester Lees | Battery Deliveries |
| 163.36250 | 158.86250 | NFM | Newcastle | Security Firm |
| 163.36250 | 158.86250 | NFM | Peterborough | CBS Repeater |
| 163.37500 | 158.87500 | NFM | Nationwide | Contactor |
| 163.37500 | 158.87500 | NFM | Preston | Taxis |
| 163.38750 | 158.78750 | NFM | Newport | Community Repeater |
| 163.38750 | 158.78750 | NFM | West Perthshire | Data Link |
| 163.42500 | 163.42500 | NFM | Cambridge | ACA Test Frequency |
| 163.43750 | 158.93750 | NFM | Aberdeen | Message Handling |
| 163.51250 | 159.01250 | NFM | Lichfield | Tarmac |
| 163.51250 | 159.01250 | NFM | Stoke on Trent | Civil Engineers |
| 163.51250 | 159.12500 | NFM | Coventry | Mowlem Construction |
| 163.51250 | 159.12500 | NFM | M6 | Motorway Maintenance |
| 163.51250 | 159.12500 | NFM | Nationwide | Contactor |
| 163.51500 | | NFM | Leicester | Emergency Doctor |
| 163.60000 | 159.10000 | NFM | Tyneside | UK Security |
| 163.61250 | 159.11250 | NFM | M25 | Engineers |
| 163.68750 | 159.18750 | NFM | London | Community Repeater |
| 163.90000 | 159.40000 | NFM | Bridlington | Leisure World Entertainments Complex Catering |
| 163.90000 | 159.40000 | NFM | Grimsby | Murphy Construction |
| 163.90000 | 159.40000 | NFM | Haverhill | AM Cars |
| 163.90000 | 159.40000 | NFM | Huntingdon | A&D Private Hire |
| 163.90000 | 159.40000 | NFM | Kent | Tour De France Race Direction |
| 163.90000 | 159.40000 | NFM | Lichfield | Tarmac |
| 163.90000 | 159.40000 | NFM | London | Notting Hill Carnival |
| 163.90000 | 159.40000 | NFM | London | Town And Country Outside Events Catering |

| Base | Mobile | Mode | Location | User and Notes |
|---|---|---|---|---|
| 163.90000 | 159.40000 | NFM | Nationwide | RAC Network Q Rally |
| 163.90000 | 159.40000 | NFM | Nationwide | Short Term Hire |
| 163.90000 | 159.40000 | NFM | Peterborough | Viscount Buses |
| 163.90000 | 159.40000 | NFM | Sandy | AJ Hart and Son Ltd |
| 163.90000 | 159.40000 | NFM | Sheffield | Murphy Hire Ltd Ch 1 |
| 163.90000 | 159.40000 | NFM | Warwickshire | Tarmac |
| 163.90000 | 163.90000 | NFM | Dudley | Construction Company |
| 163.90000 | 163.90000 | NFM | Newport, Gwent | Newport Hospital Security (RGH) |
| 163.91250 | 159.41250 | NFM | Jersey | Island Cabs |
| 163.91250 | 163.91250 | NFM | Cambridge | Data Link |
| 163.92500 | 159.42500 | NFM | Ipswich | Maritime Events |
| 163.92500 | 159.42500 | NFM | Kent | Tour de France Tour & Press |
| 163.92500 | 159.42500 | NFM | London | Oval Cricket Ground Stewards |
| 163.92500 | 159.42500 | NFM | London | Saddlers Wells Theatre Front Of House Staff |
| 163.92500 | 159.42500 | NFM | London | Satellite electronic news gathering |
| 163.92500 | 159.42500 | NFM | Martlesham | Heatfi British Telecom Research Labs Open Day |
| 163.92500 | 159.42500 | NFM | Nationwide | Short Term Hire |
| 163.92500 | 159.42500 | NFM | Sheffield | Gleason Builders |
| 163.92500 | 159.42500 | NFM | Sheffield | Murphy Hire Ltd Ch2 |
| 163.93750 | 159.43750 | NFM | Rickmansworth | Fleet Cars Voice and Data |
| 163.95000 | 159.45000 | NFM | Chesterfield | Royal Hospital Porters |
| 163.95000 | 159.45000 | NFM | Felixstowe | AAA Cars On Hire Ch 13 |
| 163.95000 | 159.45000 | NFM | Langford | D. Jays Taxis |
| 163.96250 | 159.46250 | NFM | Birmingham | School Maintenance |
| 163.96250 | 159.46250 | NFM | Fleetwood | Pharmacy Agency |
| 163.96250 | 159.46250 | NFM | Peterborough | CBS Repeater |
| 163.97500 | 159.47500 | NFM | Lichfield | Taxi |
| 163.97500 | 159.47500 | NFM | M25 | Recovery |
| 163.97500 | 159.47500 | NFM | Peterborough | Various Users |
| 163.98000 | 163.98000 | NFM | Bedford | Repeater |
| 163.98750 | 159.48750 | NFM | Chessington | World Of Adventure Entertainments |
| 163.98750 | 159.48750 | NFM | Ipswich | Docks Security |
| 163.98750 | 159.48750 | NFM | Ipswich | Maritime Events |
| 163.98750 | 159.48750 | NFM | London, Oxford Street | Plaza Shopping Centre security |
| 163.98750 | 159.48750 | NFM | Nationwide | NSR Communications |
| 163.98750 | 159.48750 | NFM | Nationwide | Short Term Hire |
| 163.98750 | 159.48750 | NFM | Rugby | Rugby Cement Ch.5 |
| 164.00000 | 159.50000 | NFM | Bletchley Park | Securicor guards |
| 164.00000 | 159.50000 | NFM | Jersey | Motor Traffic Dept Ch3 |
| 164.00000 | 159.50000 | NFM | London, Oxford St. | Plaza Shopping Centre |
| 164.00000 | 159.50000 | NFM | Nationwide | Short Term Hire |
| 164.00000 | 159.50000 | NFM | Rugby | Rugby Cement Ch.4 |
| 164.01250 | 164.01250 | NFM | Chessington | World Of Adventures |
| 164.01250 | 164.01250 | NFM | Guernsey | Aurigny Airlines |
| 164.01500 | | NFM | England (Southern) | O'Rourke Construction Ch4 |
| 164.02500 | 159.52500 | NFM | Chessington | World Of Adventures Parking/Admin |
| 164.02500 | 159.52500 | NFM | Dublin | District Police (E) |
| 164.02500 | 159.52500 | NFM | Edinburgh | Police (Easter Road Match Control) |
| 164.02500 | 159.52500 | NFM | London | Chelsea Football Club stewards |
| 164.03750 | 159.53750 | NFM | Dublin | District Police (N) |
| 164.03750 | 159.53750 | NFM | Hendon | RAF Museum (BLUE CONTROL) |
| 164.03750 | 159.53750 | NFM | Jersey | Aurigny Airlines Handhelds |
| 164.03750 | 159.53750 | NFM | London, Covent Garden | Jubilee Market security |
| 164.04900 | | NFM | West Midlands | St John's Ambulance Ch 4 |
| 164.05000 | 159.55000 | NFM | City of London | Bus Company |
| 164.05000 | 159.55000 | NFM | Dublin | District Police (R) |

| Base | Mobile | Mode | Location | User and Notes |
|---|---|---|---|---|
| 164.05000 | 159.55000 | NFM | Edinburgh | Sheriff Court Security |
| 164.05000 | 159.55000 | NFM | Humberside | Boy Scouts Ch1 |
| 164.05000 | 159.55000 | NFM | Jersey | European Golf Championships |
| 164.05000 | 159.55000 | NFM | Kent | St. Johns Ambulance Ch.7 |
| 164.05000 | 159.55000 | NFM | London | Warner Bros Cinema Staff/Security at 02 Centre |
| 164.05000 | 159.55000 | NFM | London, Oxford St. | HMV Shop Security |
| 164.05000 | 159.55000 | NFM | Nationwide | National Scout Association |
| 164.05000 | 159.55000 | NFM | Nationwide | Short Term Hire |
| 164.05000 | 159.55000 | NFM | Nationwide | St John's Ambulance Ch 4 |
| 164.05000 | 159.55000 | NFM | Newmarket | Security Company |
| 164.05000 | 159.55000 | NFM | Northampton | Golf Club |
| 164.05000 | 159.55000 | NFM | Northern Ireland | St. Johns Ambulance Ch.6 |
| 164.05000 | 159.55000 | NFM | Suffolk | St. Johns Ambulance Ch.4 (DG) |
| 164.06100 |  | NFM | Birmingham, Aston Villa | St John's Ambulance Ch 3 |
| 164.06250 | 159.56250 | NFM | Carnforth | Tarmac |
| 164.06250 | 159.56250 | NFM | Dublin | District Police (K) |
| 164.06250 | 159.56250 | NFM | Jersey | European Golf Championships |
| 164.06250 | 159.56250 | NFM | Jersey | Tilbury Douglas |
| 164.06250 | 159.56250 | NFM | Kent | St. Johns Ambulance Ch.8 |
| 164.06250 | 159.56250 | NFM | Morecambe | Sea Scout |
| 164.06250 | 159.56250 | NFM | Nationwide | National Scout Association |
| 164.06250 | 159.56250 | NFM | Nationwide | St John's Ambulances Ch 3 |
| 164.06250 | 159.56250 | NFM | Northern Ireland | St. Johns Ambulance Ch.7 |
| 164.06250 | 159.56250 | NFM | Stevenage | British Home Stores network |
| 164.06250 | 159.56250 | NFM | Suffolk | St. Johns Ambulance Ch.3 (DG) |
| 164.07500 | 159.57500 | NFM | Dublin | District Police (C) |
| 164.08750 | 159.58750 | NFM | Dublin | District Police (L) |
| 164.08750 | 159.58750 | NFM | Glasgow | Taxis |
| 164.08750 | 159.58750 | NFM | Heathrow | Train Terminal Building |
| 164.08750 | 159.58750 | NFM | Kent | Tour De France TV Cameras |
| 164.08750 | 159.58750 | NFM | London | Met Police Cadets |
| 164.08750 | 159.58750 | NFM | Nationwide | NSR Communications |
| 164.08750 | 159.58750 | NFM | Nationwide | RAC Network Q Rally |
| 164.08750 | 159.58750 | NFM | Nationwide | Short Term Hire |
| 164.08750 | 159.58750 | NFM | Nationwide | Whitby Davison Production (films) |
| 164.08750 | 159.58750 | NFM | Rugby | Rugby Cement Ch.3 |
| 164.08750 | 159.58750 | NFM | Stevenage | Multiplex Cinema staff net |
| 164.08750 | 159.58750 | NFM | Stockport | Sainsbury's security |
| 164.10000 | 159.60000 | NFM | Dublin | District Police (W) |
| 164.11250 | 159.61250 | NFM | Dublin | District Police (J) |
| 164.12500 | 159.62500 | NFM | Ashford | Council (Tour De France) |
| 164.12500 | 159.62500 | NFM | Dublin | District Police (F) |
| 164.12500 | 159.62500 | NFM | England (Southern) | O'Rourke Construction Ch1 |
| 164.12500 | 159.62500 | NFM | Humberside Airport | Security |
| 164.12500 | 159.62500 | NFM | London | Serco Security Admiralty Government Buildings |
| 164.12500 | 159.62500 | NFM | London, Soho | Village pub doorman |
| 164.12500 | 159.62500 | NFM | Luton | Vauxhall Car Plant |
| 164.12500 | 159.62500 | NFM | Nationwide | Short Term Hire |
| 164.12500 | 159.62500 | NFM | Rugby | Rugby Cement Ch.2 |
| 164.12500 | 159.62500 | NFM | Southampton | Taxis |
| 164.12500 | 164.12500 | NFM | Nationwide | O'Rourke Construction |
| 164.13750 | 159.63750 | NFM | Dublin | District Police (A) |
| 164.13750 | 159.63750 | NFM | Edinburgh | Data Link |
| 164.13750 | 159.63750 | NFM | Jersey | Jersey Telecom Cable Laying |
| 164.13750 | 159.63750 | NFM | Newmarket | Security (OB) |
| 164.14500 |  | NFM | England (Southern) | O'Rourke Construction Ch2 |

| Base | Mobile | Mode | Location | User and Notes |
|---|---|---|---|---|
| 164.16250 | 159.66250 | NFM | Dublin | District Police (H) |
| 164.17500 | 159.67500 | NFM | Dublin | District Police (M) |
| 164.18500 | 164.18500 | NFM | Newmarket | Abbey Security |
| 164.18750 | 159.68750 | NFM | Ipswich | Anglian Water Sewage Works Staff |
| 164.18750 | 159.68750 | NFM | London | Alexandra Palace security |
| 164.18750 | 159.68750 | NFM | London | Queens Club Stella Artois Championships |
| 164.18750 | 159.68750 | NFM | Nationwide | RAC Network Q Rally-Toyota |
| 164.18750 | 159.68750 | NFM | Nationwide | Short Term Hire |
| 164.18750 | 159.68750 | NFM | Rugby | Rugby Cement Ch.1 |
| 164.18750 | 159.68750 | NFM | Woodbridge | Macfarlanes Road Construction Stop/Go Boards |
| 164.19500 | | NFM | England (Southern) | O'Rourke Construction Ch3 |
| 164.20000 | | NFM | Nationwide | Paging Speech Return |
| 164.20000 | 159.70000 | NFM | Dublin | District Police (D) |
| 164.21250 | 159.71250 | NFM | Dublin | District Police (G) |
| 164.22500 | | NFM | Dublin | District Police (P) |
| 164.22500 | | NFM | Galway | Community Repeater |
| 164.22500 | 159.72500 | NFM | Nationwide | Pacnet Data |
| 164.23750 | 159.72500 | NFM | Tayside | Data Link |
| 164.23750 | 159.73750 | NFM | Nationwide | Pacnet Data |
| 164.25000 | 159.75000 | NFM | Glasgow | Data Link |
| 164.25000 | 159.75000 | NFM | Nationwide | Pacnet |
| 164.26260 | 159.76250 | NFM | Newcastle | Data Link |
| 164.26250 | 159.76250 | NFM | Tayside | Data Link |
| 164.27500 | 159.77500 | NFM | Ashton under Lyme | Tyre Co. Deliveries |
| 164.27500 | 159.77500 | NFM | Lancashire | Securicor (LIMA) |
| 164.27500 | 159.77500 | NFM | Nationwide | Pacnet Data |
| 164.28750 | 159.78750 | NFM | Nationwide | Pacnet Data |
| 164.30000 | 159.80000 | NFM | Blackburn | DMC Private Hire |
| 164.30000 | 159.80000 | NFM | Glasgow | Data Link |
| 164.30000 | 159.80000 | NFM | Nationwide | Pacnet |
| 164.30000 | 159.80000 | NFM | Newport | Community Repeater |
| 164.31250 | 159.81250 | NFM | Nationwide | Pacnet Data |
| 164.32500 | 159.82500 | NFM | Nationwide | Pacnet Data |
| 164.32500 | 159.82500 | NFM | Newcastle | Data Link |
| 164.32500 | 159.82500 | NFM | Tayside | Data Link |
| 164.33750 | 159.83750 | NFM | Glasgow | Data Link |
| 164.33750 | 159.83750 | NFM | Nationwide | Pacnet |
| 164.35000 | 159.85000 | NFM | Nationwide | Pacnet |
| 164.35000 | 159.85000 | NFM | Tayside | Data Link |
| 164.36250 | 159.86250 | NFM | Glasgow | Data Link |
| 164.36250 | 159.86250 | NFM | Nationwide | Pacnet Data |
| 164.37500 | 159.87500 | NFM | Blackburn | Chippy's Private Hire |
| 164.37500 | 159.87500 | NFM | Nationwide | Pacnet Data |
| 164.37500 | 159.87500 | NFM | Newmarket | Security |
| 164.38750 | 159.88750 | NFM | Manchester Hyde | Lewis Food Co |
| 164.38750 | 159.88750 | NFM | Nationwide | Airport Duty Officer Ch2 |
| 164.38750 | 159.88750 | NFM | Nationwide | Pacnet |
| 164.40000 | 159.90000 | NFM | Blackburn | C&M Private Hire |
| 164.40000 | 159.90000 | NFM | Manchester | Service Engineers |
| 164.40000 | 159.90000 | NFM | Nationwide | BT Selcal to Mobiles |
| 164.42740 | 160.17350 | NFM | Nottingham | Medics |
| 164.43750 | 159.93750 | NFM | Nationwide | Mobile Phone Link |
| 164.43750 | 159.93750 | NFM | Queensbury | Calderdale Council |
| 164.44500 | 159.94500 | AM | Bedfordshire | Repeater |
| 164.44500 | 159.94500 | NFM | London | Vehicle Recovery |
| 164.45000 | 159.94500 | NFM | Dyfed | Riverlea Tractors |

| Base | Mobile | Mode | Location | User and Notes |
|------|--------|------|----------|----------------|
| 164.45000 | 159.95000 | NFM | Cleveland | Security Firm |
| 164.45000 | 159.95000 | NFM | Haverfordwest | Coin Machines |
| 164.45000 | 159.95000 | NFM | Newmarket | Taxis |
| 164.45000 | 159.95000 | NFM | Pembrokeshire | Riverlea Tractors |
| 164.45000 | 159.95000 | NFM | Peterborough | Beeline |
| 164.45000 | 159.95000 | NFM | Peterborough | Ranger |
| 164.45000 | 159.95000 | NFM | Worcester | A W Taxis |
| 164.45000 | 164.45000 | NFM | Manchester | Security |
| 164.46250 | 159.96250 | NFM | Devon, North | Vet |
| 164.46250 | 159.96250 | NFM | Glasgow | Community Repeater |
| 164.46250 | 159.96250 | NFM | Gloucester | Security Firm |
| 164.46250 | 159.96250 | NFM | Horsham | Comrep |
| 164.46250 | 159.96250 | NFM | Penrith | County Taxis |
| 164.46250 | 159.96250 | NFM | Peterborough | Various Users |
| 164.46250 | 159.96250 | NFM | Southampton | Aircall |
| 164.47500 | 159.97500 | NFM | Brighton | Aircall (Doctors) |
| 164.47500 | 159.97500 | NFM | Cambridge | White Security |
| 164.47500 | 159.97500 | NFM | Nationwide | Aircall Ch 10 |
| 164.47500 | 159.97500 | NFM | Peterborough | Optic |
| 164.47500 | 159.97500 | NFM | Warwick | Council boarding-up service |
| 164.48750 | 159.98750 | NFM | Bishop Stortford | Taxis |
| 164.48750 | 159.98750 | NFM | Crewe | Recovery Vehicles |
| 164.48750 | 159.98750 | NFM | Poole | Repeater |
| 164.48750 | 159.98750 | NFM | Southampton | Taxis |
| 164.50000 | 160.00000 | NFM | Bolton | Transport Service |
| 164.50000 | 160.00000 | NFM | Bournemouth | Medicare |
| 164.50000 | 160.00000 | NFM | Cardiff | Emergency Doctors |
| 164.50000 | 160.00000 | NFM | Glasgow | Strathclyde Medicall |
| 164.50000 | 160.00000 | NFM | London | Parcel Deliveries |
| 164.50000 | 160.00000 | NFM | London | School busses |
| 164.50000 | 160.00000 | NFM | Manchester Hyde | Security Firm |
| 164.50000 | 160.00000 | NFM | Nationwide | Doctors Common |
| 164.50000 | 160.00000 | NFM | Poole | Paramedics |
| 164.50000 | 160.00000 | NFM | Sheffield | Medicare |
| 164.50000 | 160.00000 | NFM | Southampton | Skip Hire Co |
| 164.50000 | 160.00000 | NFM | Wakefield | Doctor's DepService |
| 164.50000 | 160.00000 | NFM | Warrington | Garden Centre |
| 164.50000 | 164.50000 | NFM | Cheshire | Haulage |
| 164.51250 | 160.01250 | NFM | Nationwide | Aircall |
| 164.51250 | 160.01250 | NFM | Newport | Parcel Company |
| 164.51250 | 160.01250 | NFM | Peterborough | Various Users |
| 164.51250 | 160.01250 | NFM | Portsmouth | Nynex |
| 164.52500 | 160.02500 | NFM | Kent | Amtrak |
| 164.52500 | 160.02500 | NFM | Kent | Drainage Engineers (MD) |
| 164.52500 | 160.02500 | NFM | Kent | Gold Taxis |
| 164.52500 | 160.02500 | NFM | Worthing | Taxi |
| 164.53750 | 160.03750 | NFM | East Durham | Doctors On Call |
| 164.53750 | 160.03750 | NFM | Galway | Community Repeater |
| 164.53750 | 160.03750 | NFM | Nottingham | Emergency doctors |
| 164.53750 | 160.03750 | NFM | West Midlands | All Waist |
| 164.55000 | 160.05000 | NFM | Blackburn | CRM Private Hire |
| 164.55000 | 160.05000 | NFM | Cardiff | Emergency Doctors |
| 164.55000 | 160.05000 | NFM | Co Durham | Alarm Engineers |
| 164.55000 | 160.05000 | AM | Grimsby | Aircall |
| 164.55000 | 160.05000 | NFM | Hull | Dynarod Ltd |
| 164.55000 | 160.05000 | NFM | Hull | East Yorkshire Buses |

| Base | Mobile | Mode | Location | User and Notes |
|------|--------|------|----------|----------------|
| 164.55000 | 160.05000 | NFM | Manchester Hyde | Builders Yard |
| 164.55000 | 160.05000 | NFM | Nationwide | Aircall Ch 5 |
| 164.55000 | 160.05000 | NFM | Peterborough | Castor |
| 164.55000 | 160.05000 | NFM | Swansea | BT Security |
| 164.56200 | 160.06250 | NFM | Coventry | Doctors (HEALTHCALL) |
| 164.56250 | 160.06250 | NFM | Bournemouth | Emergency Services |
| 164.56250 | 160.06250 | NFM | Coventry | Medics |
| 164.56250 | 160.06250 | NFM | Nationwide | Aircall |
| 164.56250 | 160.06250 | NFM | Peterborough | Various Users |
| 164.56250 | 160.06250 | NFM | South Yorkshire | Aircall Medical |
| 164.56250 | 160.06250 | NFM | Southampton | MediCall Ch 2 |
| 164.56250 | 160.06250 | NFM | Tyne & Wear | Doctors On Call |
| 164.56250 | 164.56250 | NFM | Manchester | Doctors Dep Service |
| 164.57500 | 160.07500 | NFM | Maidstone | Scan Electronics |
| 164.57500 | 160.07500 | NFM | Nationwide | Aircall |
| 164.57500 | 160.07500 | NFM | Peterborough | Various Users |
| 164.58750 | 160.08750 | NFM | Bury | Emergency Doctor |
| 164.58750 | 160.08750 | NFM | Croydon | Minicab Firm |
| 164.58750 | 160.08750 | NFM | Hull | Emergency Doctors |
| 164.58750 | 160.08750 | NFM | Manchester | Emergency Doctors |
| 164.58750 | 160.08750 | NFM | Peterborough | CBS Repeater |
| 164.59000 | | NFM | Gateshead | Security |
| 164.60000 | 160.10000 | NFM | Nationwide | Aircall |
| 164.60000 | 160.10000 | NFM | Newcastle | UK Waste Skip Hire |
| 164.60000 | 160.10000 | NFM | Poole | Repeater |
| 164.60000 | 160.10000 | NFM | Sheffield | Community Repeater |
| 164.60000 | 160.10000 | NFM | Sheffield | Forge Alert security |
| 164.61250 | 160.11250 | NFM | Bournemouth | Council Road Gangs |
| 164.61250 | 160.11250 | NFM | Nationwide | Aircall Ch 2 |
| 164.61250 | 160.11250 | NFM | Poole | Repeater |
| 164.62500 | 160.12500 | NFM | Bournemouth | St John's |
| 164.62500 | 160.12500 | NFM | Bristol | Hospital Transport |
| 164.62500 | 160.12500 | NFM | Glasgow | Springburn College |
| 164.62500 | 160.12500 | NFM | Hampshire | Aircall |
| 164.62500 | 160.12500 | NFM | Kent | Tunbridge Freight |
| 164.62500 | 160.12500 | NFM | London | Medic Pager |
| 164.62500 | 160.12500 | NFM | Nationwide | Aircall Ch 5 |
| 164.62500 | 160.12500 | NFM | Parkstone | Aristoview |
| 164.62500 | 160.12500 | NFM | Plymouth | Emergency Doctors Service |
| 164.62500 | 160.12500 | NFM | Poole | Repeater |
| 164.62500 | 160.12500 | NFM | Staffordshire | Emergency Doctor |
| 164.63750 | 160.13750 | NFM | Glasgow | Doctors Service |
| 164.63750 | 160.13750 | NFM | Newport | Paramedic Doctors Service |
| 164.63750 | 160.13750 | NFM | Portsmouth | MediCall Ch 1 |
| 164.63750 | 160.13750 | NFM | Southampton | Taxis |
| 164.63750 | 160.13750 | NFM | Swansea City | Doctors on Call |
| 164.63750 | 160.13750 | NFM | Tyne & Wear | Taxis |
| 164.63750 | 160.13750 | NFM | Wolverhampton | Doctors Service |
| 164.65000 | 160.15000 | NFM | Birmingham | Doctors Service |
| 164.65000 | 160.15000 | NFM | Bristol | Healthcare Services Ltd. |
| 164.65000 | 160.15000 | NFM | Cannock | Doctors |
| 164.65000 | 160.15000 | NFM | Newcastle | Doctors on Call |
| 164.65000 | 160.15000 | NFM | Newport, Wales | GP's deputising service (HEALTHCALL CARDIFF) |
| 164.65000 | 160.15000 | NFM | South Glamorgan | Doctor on call |
| 164.66250 | 160.16250 | NFM | Leeds | Vanguard Security |
| 164.66250 | 160.16250 | NFM | Poole | Repeater |

| Base | Mobile | Mode | Location | User and Notes |
|------|--------|------|----------|----------------|
| 164.67500 | 160.17500 | NFM | Preston | Business Post |
| 164.67500 | 160.17500 | NFM | Severn Bridge | Toll Booths |
| 164.68750 | 160.18750 | NFM | County Durham | Doctor's Medicall |
| 164.68750 | 160.18750 | NFM | Gloucester | District Council |
| 164.68750 | 160.18750 | NFM | London | CB Motors Vehicle Recovery |
| 164.68750 | 160.18750 | NFM | London | Seymour Car Services Ltd |
| 164.68750 | 160.18750 | NFM | Newcastle | Security Firm |
| 164.68750 | 160.18750 | NFM | Tyneside | Security |
| 164.70000 | 160.20000 | NFM | Nationwide | Teleacoustic |
| 164.70000 | 160.20000 | NFM | Newcastle | Council |
| 164.70000 | 160.20000 | NFM | Tyneside | Plumbing Repairs |
| 164.70000 | 160.20000 | NFM | West Midlands | Burglar Alarms |
| 164.71250 | 160.21250 | NFM | Gloucester | Repeater |
| 164.71250 | 160.21250 | NFM | London | Medical & Rescue Services |
| 164.71250 | 160.21250 | NFM | Peterborough | Various Users |
| 164.72500 | 160.22500 | NFM | Crewe | Taxis |
| 164.72500 | 160.22500 | NFM | Gravesend | Doctors |
| 164.72500 | 160.22500 | NFM | London | Bermondsey Council |
| 164.72500 | 160.22500 | NFM | London | Security Company |
| 164.72500 | 160.22500 | NFM | Newmarket | Trunked Network |
| 164.72500 | 160.22500 | NFM | Peterborough | Spark |
| 164.72500 | 160.22500 | NFM | Poole | Repeater |
| 164.73750 | 160.23750 | NFM | Cleveland | Doctors On Call |
| 164.73750 | 160.23750 | NFM | Nationwide | Lodge Radio Service |
| 164.75000 | 160.25000 | NFM | Ely | Taxis |
| 164.75000 | 160.25000 | NFM | London | St. Johns Ambulance repeater |
| 164.75000 | 160.25000 | NFM | Oxford | Hospital Services |
| 164.75000 | 160.25000 | NFM | Southern England | Saxon Security |
| 164.75000 | 160.25000 | NFM | Wrexham | Haulage Contractor |
| 164.76250 | 160.26250 | NFM | Kent | Eurotunnel |
| 164.76250 | 160.26250 | NFM | London | Medicall South London |
| 164.76250 | 160.26250 | NFM | Lothian & Borders | Lothian Regional Council |
| 164.76250 | 160.26250 | NFM | Newmarket | Transport Firm |
| 164.76250 | 160.26250 | NFM | Perthshire | Delivery Company |
| 164.76250 | 160.26250 | NFM | Portsmouth | Taxis |
| 164.76250 | 160.26250 | NFM | Shelford, Cambs | Clothing Distributor 1835Hz |
| 164.76250 | 160.27500 | AM | Leeds | Taxis |
| 164.76250 | 164.76256 | FM | Cambridge | John Hendry & Son |
| 164.78750 | 160.28750 | NFM | Blackpool | Haulage Contractors |
| 164.78750 | 160.28750 | NFM | Bournemouth | Council Lighting |
| 164.78750 | 160.28750 | NFM | Nationwide | Teleacoustic |
| 164.80000 | 160.30000 | NFM | Biggleswade | Sandy Skips |
| 164.80000 | 160.30000 | NFM | Biggleswade | Sues Recovery |
| 164.80000 | 160.30000 | NFM | Biggleswade | Travis Perkins |
| 164.80000 | 160.30000 | NFM | Bodmin | Vet Services |
| 164.80000 | 160.30000 | NFM | Bournemouth | Aircall Radio |
| 164.80000 | 160.30000 | NFM | Nationwide | Teleacoustic |
| 164.80000 | 160.30000 | NFM | Newcastle | Council |
| 164.80000 | 160.30000 | NFM | Norfolk | Red Star Parcels |
| 164.80000 | 160.30000 | NFM | Walsall | Refuse Collectors |
| 164.81250 | 160.01250 | NFM | Bath | Strode Sound CBS |
| 164.81250 | 160.01250 | NFM | Bristol | Taxis |
| 164.81250 | 160.01250 | NFM | Leicester | Council office Security |
| 164.81250 | 160.01250 | NFM | Poole | Repeater |
| 164.82500 | 160.32500 | NFM | Central London | Motor Rescue Service |
| 164.82500 | 160.32500 | NFM | London | Auto Breakdown Service |

| Base | Mobile | Mode | Location | User and Notes |
|---|---|---|---|---|
| 164.82500 | 160.32500 | NFM | London | National Rescue |
| 164.82500 | 160.32500 | NFM | London | St Mary's Hospital Ambulances |
| 164.82500 | 160.32500 | NFM | Poole | Repeater |
| 164.82500 | 160.32500 | NFM | Tamworth | Bluebell Taxi |
| 164.82500 | 160.32500 | NFM | West Sussex | Recovery Firm |
| 164.82500 | 160.32500 | NFM | Worcester | Delta Sierra Base |
| 164.83750 | 160.33750 | NFM | Birmingham | Glaziers |
| 164.83750 | 160.33750 | NFM | Bournemouth | Express Carriers |
| 164.83750 | 160.33750 | NFM | Poole | Repeater |
| 164.85000 | 160.35000 | NFM | Colwyn Bay | BR Station |
| 164.85000 | 160.35000 | NFM | Nationwide | Message Handling |
| 164.85000 | 160.35000 | NFM | Wadesbridge | Builder's Merchants |
| 164.86250 | 160.36250 | NFM | Manchester | Bouncy Castle Hire |
| 164.86250 | 160.36250 | NFM | Manchester | Plant Firm |
| 164.86250 | 160.36250 | NFM | South West Wales | DSS Fraud Teams |
| 164.86250 | 160.86250 | NFM | Swansea | Council Warden Ch 1 |
| 164.87500 | 160.37500 | NFM | Nationwide | Mobile Phone Link |
| 164.87500 | 160.37500 | NFM | Newcastle | British Gas |
| 164.87500 | 160.37500 | NFM | Norfolk | Alpha Drains |
| 164.87500 | 160.37500 | NFM | Northern Ireland | NCF Milk Tankers |
| 164.87500 | 160.37500 | NFM | Poole | Repeater |
| 164.87500 | 160.37500 | NFM | Sussex Coast | Coastway Hospital Radio |
| 164.88750 | 160.38750 | AM | Bedfordshire | Vehicle Recovery |
| 164.88750 | 160.38750 | NFM | Burton, Staffs | Skips |
| 164.88750 | 160.38750 | NFM | London | Security Company |
| 164.88750 | 160.38750 | NFM | Nationwide | Mobile Phone Link Ch 2B |
| 164.88750 | 160.38750 | NFM | Newcastle | Data Link |
| 164.90000 | 160.40000 | AM | Bedfordshire | Repeater |
| 164.90000 | 160.40000 | NFM | Cheshire | Tyre Services |
| 164.90000 | 160.40000 | NFM | Lincoln | Gas Suppliers |
| 164.90000 | 160.40000 | NFM | Manchester | Delivery Company |
| 164.90000 | 160.40000 | NFM | Wirral | Data Link |
| 164.91250 | 160.41250 | NFM | Bournemouth | Taxi Hire Co. |
| 164.91250 | 160.41250 | NFM | Ipswich | Garage |
| 164.91250 | 160.41250 | NFM | Newport | Central Heating Company |
| 164.92500 | 160.42500 | NFM | Brighton | RCS Comrep Ch 8 |
| 164.92500 | 160.42500 | NFM | Kent | Tour De France (French) |
| 164.92500 | 160.42500 | NFM | Norfolk | ANC Parcels |
| 164.92500 | 160.42500 | NFM | Peterborough | Anglo |
| 164.92500 | 160.42500 | NFM | Suffolk | Morlings TV Rentals |
| 164.93750 | 160.43750 | NFM | Bristol | Security Co |
| 164.93750 | 160.43750 | NFM | Poole | Repeater |
| 164.95000 | 160.45000 | NFM | Glasgow | Taxi |
| 164.95000 | 160.45000 | NFM | Gloucester | Group 4 Static Guards |
| 164.95000 | 160.45000 | NFM | Grangetown | Private Message |
| 164.95000 | 160.45000 | NFM | London | Ambulance Service |
| 164.95000 | 160.45000 | NFM | London | Dinning In Services Ltd. |
| 164.95000 | 160.45000 | NFM | Nottingham | Taxi |
| 164.96250 | 160.46250 | NFM | Birmingham | Leisure Services Security |
| 164.96250 | 160.46250 | NFM | Birmingham | A. S. Security Co. |
| 164.96250 | 160.46250 | NFM | Jersey | Links CBS 4 |
| 164.96250 | 160.46250 | NFM | London | Winters Skip Hire |
| 164.97500 | 160.47500 | NFM | London | Doctors Scheme |
| 164.97500 | 160.47500 | NFM | Merseyside | Surveyors |
| 164.98750 | 160.48750 | NFM | Kent | Tour de France (French) |

165.0125- 168.2250 MHz    VHF High Band PMR Base/Repeaters
(Mobile Split + 4.8 Mhz) Ambulance
Services (England & Wales)

| Base | Mobile | Mode | Location | User and Notes |
|------|--------|------|----------|----------------|
| 165.00000 | 160.50000 | NFM | Aberdeen | Northern Garage |
| 165.00000 | 160.50000 | NFM | Bath | Bath University Research |
| 165.00000 | 160.50000 | NFM | Blackburn | City Private Hire |
| 165.00000 | 160.50000 | NFM | Cornwall | Repeater |
| 165.00000 | 160.50000 | NFM | Dorking | RCS Comrep Ch 3 |
| 165.00000 | 160.50000 | NFM | Felixstowe | Paging |
| 165.00000 | 160.50000 | NFM | Ipswich | Paging |
| 165.00000 | 160.50000 | NFM | Kent | Doctors On Call |
| 165.00000 | 160.50000 | NFM | London | ODRATS Ch5 |
| 165.00000 | 160.50000 | NFM | Manchester | Plant hire company |
| 165.00000 | 160.50000 | NFM | Manchester | Security |
| 165.00000 | 160.50000 | NFM | Morecambe | Security Vans |
| 165.00000 | 160.50000 | NFM | New Malden | North West Cars |
| 165.00000 | 160.50000 | NFM | Newmarket | Medical |
| 165.00000 | 160.50000 | NFM | Poole | Taxi |
| 165.01250 | 160.51250 | NFM | London/Kent | British Oxygen plc |
| 165.01250 | 160.51250 | NFM | London/Kent | Doctors On Call |
| 165.01250 | 160.51250 | NFM | Tamworth, Staffs | Quarry |
| 165.02500 | 169.82500 | NFM | Avon | Search and Rescue |
| 165.02500 | 169.82500 | NFM | Bath | Bath University Research |
| 165.02500 | 169.82500 | NFM | Blackpool | First Aid Council Post |
| 165.02500 | 169.82500 | NFM | Bristol | City Link Parcel Express |
| 165.02500 | 169.82500 | NFM | Burnley | Delivery Service |
| 165.02500 | 169.82500 | NFM | Cardiff | Commercial Rigging |
| 165.02500 | 169.82500 | NFM | Dover | Castle Comms |
| 165.02500 | 169.82500 | NFM | Guernsey | Links CBS 3 |
| 165.02500 | 169.82500 | NFM | Newcastle | Housing Repairs |
| 165.02500 | 169.82500 | NFM | North Yorkshire | Doctor Service |
| 165.02500 | 169.82500 | NFM | Staffordshire | Forestry Rangers |
| 165.03500 | 169.83500 | NFM | Cardiff Area | Delivery Company |
| 165.03750 | 169.83750 | NFM | Bristol | Bristol Dogs Home |
| 165.03750 | 169.83750 | NFM | Jersey | Eurocar Hire |
| 165.03750 | 169.83750 | NFM | London | City of Westminster Cleansing |
| 165.03750 | 169.83750 | NFM | Newcastle | Site Delivery |
| 165.03750 | 169.83750 | NFM | Newport | Community Repeater |
| 165.03750 | 169.83750 | NFM | Nottingham | Taxis |
| 165.03750 | 169.83750 | NFM | Poole | Repeater |
| 165.03750 | 169.83750 | NFM | Preston | Farm Suppliers |
| 165.03750 | 169.83750 | NFM | Tyne & Wear | British Gas |
| 165.05000 | 169.85000 | NFM | Bathgate | Taxi |
| 165.05000 | 169.85000 | NFM | Birmingham | Ambulance Service |
| 165.05000 | 169.85000 | NFM | Blackburn | B&B Private Hire |
| 165.05000 | 169.85000 | NFM | Bournemouth | Critax Taxis |
| 165.05000 | 169.85000 | NFM | Cambridge | City Council Services |
| 165.05000 | 169.85000 | NFM | Cheetham | Ekko Private Hire |
| 165.05000 | 169.85000 | NFM | Dumfries | Taxis |
| 165.05000 | 169.85000 | NFM | Glasgow | Kwik Save security |
| 165.05000 | 169.85000 | NFM | Guernsey | Circuit Skips |
| 165.05000 | 169.85000 | NFM | Hull | Taxis |
| 165.05000 | 169.85000 | NFM | Jersey | SGB Scaffolding Erectors |
| 165.05000 | 169.85000 | NFM | Lincoln | A2B Taxis |
| 165.05000 | 169.85000 | NFM | Manchester | Taxi |

| Base | Mobile | Mode | Location | User and Notes |
|------|--------|------|----------|----------------|
| 165.05000 | 169.85000 | NFM | Newtown | Newtown Taxis |
| 165.05000 | 169.85000 | NFM | Peterborough | Osbourne Plumbing |
| 165.05000 | 169.85000 | NFM | Plymouth | AA Taxis |
| 165.05000 | 169.85000 | NFM | Swindon | Inta-Car Taxis |
| 165.06250 | 169.86250 | NFM | Aberdeen | ANC |
| 165.06250 | 169.86250 | NFM | Bristol | Auto Glass |
| 165.06250 | 169.86250 | NFM | Carlisle | Biffa |
| 165.06250 | 169.86250 | NFM | Crewe | Garage |
| 165.06250 | 169.86250 | NFM | Cromer | Tylers Waste Management |
| 165.06250 | 169.86250 | NFM | Essex | Warrior Skips |
| 165.06250 | 169.86250 | NFM | Guernsey | Links Community Repeater 1 |
| 165.06250 | 169.86250 | NFM | Indian Queens | Interlink Parcels |
| 165.06250 | 169.86250 | NFM | Ipswich | Keiths Co |
| 165.06250 | 169.86250 | NFM | Perth | King Contractors (King Base) |
| 165.06250 | 169.86250 | NFM | Perth | Perth Council Investigators |
| 165.06250 | 169.86250 | NFM | Pocklington | Town Travel Taxis |
| 165.06250 | 169.86250 | NFM | Poole | Repeater |
| 165.06250 | 169.86250 | NFM | Rillington | H Atkinson Slaughter House |
| 165.06250 | 169.86250 | NFM | Scarborough | TWDB |
| 165.06250 | 169.86250 | NFM | Suffolk | Garage Supplies |
| 165.06500 | 165.06500 | NFM | Haverfordwest | Taxi |
| 165.07500 | 169.87500 | NFM | Coventry | Security |
| 165.07500 | 169.87500 | NFM | Dover Castle | Security / Works Dept |
| 165.07500 | 169.87500 | NFM | Fife | Council |
| 165.07500 | 169.87500 | NFM | London | Amey Roadstone Motorway Maintenance Teams |
| 165.07500 | 169.87500 | NFM | London | Central Government |
| 165.07500 | 169.87500 | NFM | M1 | Associated Asphalt |
| 165.07500 | 169.87500 | NFM | Nationwide | Road Engineers |
| 165.07500 | 169.87500 | NFM | Newport | R.E. |
| 165.07500 | 169.87500 | NFM | Norfolk | May Gurney |
| 165.07500 | 169.87500 | NFM | Perth | Community Repeater |
| 165.07500 | 169.87500 | NFM | Suffolk | May Gurney & Co |
| 165.08750 | 169.88750 | NFM | Biggleswade | Jordans Cereals |
| 165.08750 | 169.88750 | NFM | Blackpool | C Cabs |
| 165.08750 | 169.88750 | NFM | Chestwood | Chestwood Mushrooms |
| 165.08750 | 169.88750 | NFM | Hatfield | Tarmac Construction |
| 165.08750 | 169.88750 | NFM | Ipswich | Motorways Recovery M5 |
| 165.08750 | 169.88750 | NFM | Jersey | Normans Ltd Ch 1 |
| 165.08750 | 169.88750 | NFM | Jersey | Securicor |
| 165.08750 | 169.88750 | NFM | Kemble | MoD private security company |
| 165.08750 | 169.88750 | NFM | Liverpool | Local Authority Security |
| 165.08750 | 169.88750 | NFM | London | Minicab Firm Penge |
| 165.08750 | 169.88750 | NFM | Plymouth | University Security |
| 165.08750 | 169.88750 | NFM | Portsmouth | Bus Service |
| 165.10000 | 169.90000 | NFM | Blackpool | C Cabs |
| 165.10000 | 169.90000 | NFM | Bournemouth | Wade's Taxis |
| 165.10000 | 169.90000 | NFM | Bristol | Durston Plant |
| 165.10000 | 169.90000 | NFM | Carlisle | Abbey Skip Hire |
| 165.10000 | 169.90000 | NFM | Clacton | Clacton Taxis |
| 165.10000 | 169.90000 | NFM | Coventry | Taxi |
| 165.10000 | 169.90000 | NFM | Edinburgh | Taxis |
| 165.10000 | 169.90000 | NFM | Fordham | D Jenkins TV |
| 165.10000 | 169.90000 | NFM | Glasgow | Drumchapel Taxis |
| 165.10000 | 169.90000 | NFM | Gorleston-on-Sea | Ace Day & Night Taxis |
| 165.10000 | 169.90000 | NFM | Guernsey | Transfer Taxis |
| 165.10000 | 169.90000 | NFM | Havant | Taxis |

| Base | Mobile | Mode | Location | User and Notes |
|------|--------|------|----------|----------------|
| 165.10000 | 169.90000 | NFM | Hazelgrove | Lynx Private Hire |
| 165.10000 | 169.90000 | NFM | Kings Lynn | Geoff's Taxis |
| 165.10000 | 169.90000 | NFM | Kirkcaldy | Taxis |
| 165.10000 | 169.90000 | NFM | Korleston | Ace Day and Night |
| 165.10000 | 169.90000 | NFM | Leigh | Swift Next Day |
| 165.10000 | 169.90000 | NFM | Lincoln | City Taxis |
| 165.10000 | 169.90000 | NFM | Little Downham | Mott Farmers |
| 165.10000 | 169.90000 | NFM | London | SEB Scaffold |
| 165.10000 | 169.90000 | NFM | London, Acton | Minicab Firm |
| 165.10000 | 169.90000 | NFM | London, Croydon | Minicab Firm |
| 165.10000 | 169.90000 | NFM | Manchester | Bishop's security Company |
| 165.10000 | 169.90000 | NFM | Manchester, Gorton | Taxi |
| 165.10000 | 169.90000 | NFM | Montrose | Taxis |
| 165.10000 | 169.90000 | NFM | Newcastle | Taxis |
| 165.10000 | 169.90000 | NFM | Newtown | Police |
| 165.10000 | 169.90000 | NFM | Peterborough | Evening Telegraph |
| 165.10000 | 169.90000 | NFM | Poole | Rapid Lads |
| 165.10000 | 169.90000 | NFM | Saxmundham | Fishwick Vets |
| 165.10000 | 169.90000 | NFM | Seaforth | Dale's Taxis |
| 165.10000 | 169.90000 | NFM | St Austell | Davis Automatics |
| 165.10000 | 169.90000 | NFM | Stockport | Taxis |
| 165.10000 | 169.90000 | NFM | Stoke-on-Trent | Taxis |
| 165.10000 | 169.90000 | NFM | Wickford | Taxis |
| 165.10000 | 169.90000 | NFM | Woodbridge | TV Repairs |
| 165.11000 | 169.91000 | NFM | Kilmarnock | Taxis |
| 165.11000 | 169.91000 | NFM | Wakefield | Taxis |
| 165.11250 | 169.91250 | AM | Barrow | Taxis |
| 165.11250 | 169.91250 | NFM | Bournemouth | Brown Motors |
| 165.11250 | 169.91250 | NFM | Cambridge | Inter-City Cabs |
| 165.11250 | 169.91250 | NFM | Carlisle | Borders Cabs |
| 165.11250 | 169.91250 | NFM | Dyfed | J Lawrence Tractors |
| 165.11250 | 169.91250 | NFM | Dymchurch | Dymchurch Light Railway |
| 165.11250 | 169.91250 | NFM | Glasgow | Taxis |
| 165.11250 | 169.91250 | NFM | Guernsey | Fuel Supplies |
| 165.11250 | 169.91250 | NFM | Hull | Madgeleys Scrap |
| 165.11250 | 169.91250 | NFM | Jersey | Beeline Taxis Ch1 |
| 165.11250 | 169.91250 | NFM | London | Minicab Firm North London |
| 165.11250 | 169.91250 | NFM | Pembrokeshire | J Lawrence Tractors |
| 165.11250 | 169.91250 | NFM | Sandy | Ariston Group Service |
| 165.11250 | 169.91250 | NFM | Sheffield | Network Taxis |
| 165.11250 | 169.91250 | NFM | Swansea | Abba Taxis |
| 165.11250 | 169.91250 | NFM | Walton-on-Thames | Vending Machine Company |
| 165.12500 | 169.92500 | AM | Aberdeen | Amtrak |
| 165.12500 | 169.92500 | NFM | Alderton | Mortiers, Cedar Farms |
| 165.12500 | 169.92500 | NFM | Aylesbury | Fosters Taxis |
| 165.12500 | 169.92500 | NFM | Burnley | Taxis |
| 165.12500 | 169.92500 | NFM | Cosham | Taxis |
| 165.12500 | 169.92500 | NFM | Dalkeith | Police |
| 165.12500 | 169.92500 | NFM | Edinburgh | Taxis |
| 165.12500 | 169.92500 | NFM | Failsworth | Embassy Cars |
| 165.12500 | 169.92500 | NFM | Glasgow | Taxis |
| 165.12500 | 169.92500 | NFM | Guernsey | C. Richard Vehicle Recovery |
| 165.12500 | 169.92500 | NFM | Hadleigh | Wilsons Corn & Milling |
| 165.12500 | 169.92500 | NFM | Hawick | Stuarts Taxis |
| 165.12500 | 169.92500 | NFM | Hinkley | Station Taxi |
| 165.12500 | 169.92500 | NFM | Huntingdon | Mercury Bluebird Taxis |

| Base | Mobile | Mode | Location | User and Notes |
|------|--------|------|----------|----------------|
| 165.12500 | 169.92500 | NFM | Immingham | Taxis |
| 165.12500 | 169.92500 | NFM | Jersey | Farm |
| 165.12500 | 169.92500 | NFM | London | Minicab Firm Croydon |
| 165.12500 | 169.92500 | NFM | London | Temple Cars Data |
| 165.12500 | 169.92500 | NFM | Manchester Gorton | Security |
| 165.12500 | 169.92500 | NFM | Oldham | Embassy Cars |
| 165.12500 | 169.92500 | NFM | Perth | Taxis |
| 165.12500 | 169.92500 | NFM | Portsmouth | Taxis |
| 165.12500 | 169.92500 | NFM | Slough | Topcars |
| 165.12500 | 169.92500 | NFM | Sudbury | Wilsons Corn & Milling Co |
| 165.12500 | 169.92500 | NFM | Sudbury | Woods Taxis |
| 165.12500 | 169.92500 | NFM | Waltham | Ariston Group Service |
| 165.12500 | 169.92500 | NFM | Weymouth | Taxi Co |
| 165.13750 | 169.93750 | NFM | Aberystwyth | County Council Highways |
| 165.13750 | 169.93750 | NFM | Coalville | Witherly Coalville |
| 165.13750 | 169.93750 | NFM | Guernsey | Stan Brouard Ltd |
| 165.13750 | 169.93750 | NFM | Hull | Reckitts Security |
| 165.13750 | 169.93750 | NFM | Isle of Man | Manx Electricity |
| 165.13750 | 169.93750 | NFM | London | Lambeth Council |
| 165.13750 | 169.93750 | NFM | London | Police Royal Parks |
| 165.13750 | 169.93750 | NFM | London | Redbridge Council |
| 165.13760 | 169.93750 | NFM | Manchester | Motorway Maintenance |
| 165.13750 | 169.93750 | NFM | Poole | Repeater |
| 165.13750 | 169.93750 | NFM | Portsmouth | MoD guards at naval base |
| 165.13750 | 169.93750 | NFM | RAF Cardington | MoD |
| 165.13750 | 169.93750 | NFM | RAF Cardington | PSA Fire safety centre |
| 165.13750 | 169.93750 | NFM | Swaffham | Reed & Mikik Ltd |
| 165.15000 | 165.16000 | NFM | Brighton | Group 4 |
| 165.15000 | 165.16000 | NFM | Edinburgh | Private Traffic Wardens (APCOA) |
| 165.15000 | 165.16000 | NFM | Glasgow | Taxis |
| 165.15000 | 165.16000 | NFM | Grimsby | Doctors Night Call Service |
| 165.15000 | 165.16000 | NFM | Guernsey | Norman Piette |
| 165.15000 | 165.16000 | NFM | Jersey | R.G. Romeril Plant Hire |
| 165.15000 | 165.16000 | NFM | Merry Hill | Centre Maintenance |
| 165.15000 | 165.16000 | NFM | Nationwide | Group Four Security Ch1 |
| 165.15000 | 165.16000 | NFM | Oxford | Timbmet Ltd |
| 165.15000 | 165.16000 | NFM | Telford | Wrekin District Council |
| 165.15000 | 165.16000 | NFM | Walsgrove on Stowe | Hospital Porters |
| 165.15000 | 169.95000 | NFM | Anglesey | Council Bin men |
| 165.15000 | 169.95000 | NFM | Bury St Edmunds | United Taxis |
| 165.15000 | 169.95000 | NFM | Coventry | Walsgrave Hospital Porters |
| 165.15000 | 169.95000 | NFM | Loudham-Melton | Warburg Hall Farm |
| 165.16000 | 169.96000 | NFM | Bonnybridge | United Distillers Security |
| 165.16250 | 169.96250 | NFM | Bedfordshire | Repeater |
| 165.16250 | 169.96250 | NFM | Bournemouth | Beach Patrol |
| 165.16250 | 169.96250 | NFM | Cambridge | Hotel |
| 165.16250 | 169.96250 | NFM | Doncaster | Transline |
| 165.16250 | 169.96250 | NFM | Elverdon | Centre Parcs, First Aid And Security |
| 165.16250 | 169.96250 | NFM | Guernsey | Vehicle Recovery Service |
| 165.16250 | 169.96250 | NFM | Hull | Reckitts Security |
| 165.16250 | 169.96250 | NFM | Ipswich | Spotcheck Security |
| 165.16250 | 169.96250 | NFM | London | Tottenham Hotspur Football Club |
| 165.16250 | 169.96250 | NFM | Nottingham | Nottingham University |
| 165.16250 | 169.96250 | NFM | Perth | Perth Royal Infirmary security & maintenance |
| 165.16250 | 169.96250 | NFM | Wakefield | The Riding Centre |
| 165.17500 | 169.97500 | NFM | Bristol | Group 4 Security |

| Base | Mobile | Mode | Location | User and Notes |
|------|--------|------|----------|----------------|
| 165.17500 | 169.97500 | NFM | Cleveland | Group 4 Security |
| 165.17500 | 169.97500 | NFM | Nationwide | Group 4 Security Ch 2 |
| 165.18750 | 169.98750 | NFM | Aberdeen | Security |
| 165.18750 | 169.98750 | NFM | Bedford | Abbey Taxis |
| 165.18750 | 169.98750 | NFM | Birmingham | Selly Oak Hospital porters |
| 165.18750 | 169.98750 | NFM | Bournemouth | Securitas Security |
| 165.18750 | 169.98750 | NFM | Bristol | Store Detectives |
| 165.18750 | 169.98750 | NFM | Burnley | CCTV System |
| 165.18750 | 169.98750 | NFM | Cambridge | Abbey Security |
| 165.18750 | 169.98750 | NFM | Elverdon | Centre Parcs. General Leisure Centre and Lifeguards |
| 165.18750 | 169.98750 | NFM | Exeter | Store Watch scheme |
| 165.18750 | 169.98750 | NFM | Hastings | Cable Contractors |
| 165.18750 | 169.98750 | NFM | Hull | Security Firm |
| 165.18750 | 169.98750 | NFM | London | Dept of Environment transport (ERGUM) |
| 165.18750 | 169.98750 | NFM | London | Wembley Stadium Security Control |
| 165.18750 | 169.98750 | NFM | Manchester | Manchester United Football Club stewards |
| 165.18750 | 169.98750 | NFM | Norfolk | Pritchard Security |
| 165.18750 | 169.98750 | NFM | Perth | Taxis |
| 165.18750 | 169.98750 | NFM | Scotland | St. Andrews Ambulance |
| 165.20000 | 170.00000 | NFM | Aberdeen | Aberdeen Vets |
| 165.20000 | 170.00000 | NFM | Bere Regis | Ferndown Skips |
| 165.20000 | 170.00000 | NFM | Butley Capel | St Andrew Farms |
| 165.20000 | 170.00000 | NFM | Cambs/N.Herts | D&C Cablelines |
| 165.20000 | 170.00000 | NFM | Cheshire | Alternative Taxis |
| 165.20000 | 170.00000 | NFM | Edinburgh | Taxis |
| 165.20000 | 170.00000 | NFM | Guernsey | States Works |
| 165.20000 | 170.00000 | NFM | Huntingdon | Cambridge Cable co. |
| 165.20000 | 170.00000 | NFM | Isle of Man | Manx Electricity |
| 165.20000 | 170.00000 | NFM | London | Cabetel Installation Ltd |
| 165.20000 | 170.00000 | NFM | Newmarket | Cambridge Cable |
| 165.20000 | 170.00000 | NFM | Newport, Gwent | Maintenance Repair Company |
| 165.20000 | 170.00000 | NFM | Norwich | Esso Heating |
| 165.20000 | 170.00000 | NFM | Peterborough | CBS Repeater |
| 165.20000 | 170.00000 | NFM | Poole | Repeater |
| 165.20000 | 170.00000 | NFM | Swansea | Group 4 Security |
| 165.21000 | 165.21000 | NFM | Merry Hill | Centre Cleaners |
| 165.21000 | 170.01000 | NFM | Cardiff | Cardiff University security |
| 165.21250 | 170.01250 | NFM | Bolton | College Security |
| 165.21250 | 170.01250 | NFM | Bressingham | Steam Museum Staff |
| 165.21250 | 170.01250 | NFM | Cambridge | Grafton Centre |
| 165.21250 | 170.01250 | NFM | Coventry | GEC Security |
| 165.21250 | 170.01250 | NFM | Edinburgh | Scottish & Newcastle Brewers |
| 165.21250 | 170.01250 | NFM | Elverdon | Centre Parcs, Grounds and Technical Services |
| 165.21250 | 170.01250 | NFM | Exeter | University security and porters |
| 165.21250 | 170.01250 | NFM | Grafton | Grosvenor Estates |
| 165.21250 | 170.01250 | NFM | Hull | Security Firm |
| 165.21250 | 170.01250 | NFM | Ipswich | Dock Security |
| 165.21250 | 170.01250 | NFM | London | US Embassy Secret Service |
| 165.21250 | 170.01250 | NFM | Lowestoft | Shopwatch Security |
| 165.21250 | 170.01250 | NFM | Milton Keynes | Milton Keynes Taxis |
| 165.21250 | 170.01250 | NFM | Sheffield | Group 4 Security |
| 165.21250 | 170.01250 | NFM | Swansea | Quadrant Shopping Centre Security |
| 165.22500 | 170.02500 | NFM | Blackburn | Arcade Private Hire |
| 165.22500 | 170.02500 | NFM | Frome | Blue Taxis |
| 165.22500 | 170.02500 | NFM | Halifax | 4 Ways Taxis |
| 165.22500 | 170.02500 | NFM | Hawick | WE Taxis |

| Base | Mobile | Mode | Location | User and Notes |
|---|---|---|---|---|
| 165.22500 | 170.02500 | NFM | Hitchin | Castle Taxis |
| 165.22500 | 170.02500 | NFM | Jersey | Flying Dragon Cabs |
| 165.22500 | 170.02500 | NFM | Langley | Station Minicabs |
| 165.22500 | 170.02500 | NFM | Leicester | LCL Cable Comms |
| 165.22500 | 170.02500 | NFM | Letchworth | Duggans Taxis |
| 165.22500 | 170.02500 | NFM | London | Minicab Firm Woodford |
| 165.22500 | 170.02500 | NFM | London, Heathrow | Interlink |
| 165.22500 | 170.02500 | NFM | Nottingham | Taxis |
| 165.22500 | 170.02500 | NFM | Portishead | Esso Fuels Docks |
| 165.22500 | 170.02500 | NFM | Slough | Minicab Firm |
| 165.22500 | 170.02500 | NFM | Southampton | Taxis |
| 165.22500 | 170.02500 | NFM | Tamworth | A2B Taxis |
| 165.22500 | 170.02500 | NFM | Weymouth | Dorset Alarms |
| 165.23750 | 170.03750 | NFM | Anglesey | Benji's Taxis |
| 165.23750 | 170.03750 | AM | Barrow | Acacia Taxis |
| 165.23750 | 170.03750 | NFM | Birmingham | Castle Taxi |
| 165.23750 | 170.03750 | NFM | Bristol | Black & White Taxis |
| 165.23750 | 170.03750 | NFM | Cardiff | Amber Taxis Ch 2 |
| 165.23750 | 170.03750 | NFM | Carlisle | Taxis |
| 165.23750 | 170.03750 | NFM | Crewe | Taxis |
| 165.23750 | 170.03750 | NFM | Glasgow | Taxis |
| 165.23750 | 170.03750 | NFM | Glossop | Thameside Council |
| 165.23750 | 170.03750 | NFM | Guernsey | Access Skips |
| 165.23750 | 170.03750 | NFM | Leighton Buzzard | Choake Billington |
| 165.23750 | 170.03750 | NFM | London | Minicab Firm Ealing |
| 165.23750 | 170.03750 | NFM | Orfordness | National Trust |
| 165.23750 | 170.03750 | NFM | Plymouth | Taxis |
| 165.23750 | 170.03750 | NFM | Poole | Repeater |
| 165.23750 | 170.03750 | NFM | Torpoint | Taxis |
| 165.23750 | 170.03750 | NFM | Wales | Black and White Taxis |
| 165.25000 | 170.05000 | AM | Aberdeen | Lucas |
| 165.25000 | 170.05000 | NFM | Airdrie | Monkland Independent Taxis |
| 165.25000 | 170.05000 | NFM | Birmingham Northfield | Taxis |
| 165.25000 | 170.05000 | NFM | Chingford | Bell Cabs |
| 165.25000 | 170.05000 | NFM | Coventry | Taxi |
| 165.25000 | 170.05000 | NFM | Elvington | Warter Estate Farms |
| 165.25000 | 170.05000 | NFM | Glasgow | Taxis |
| 165.25000 | 170.05000 | NFM | Guernsey | Island Taxis |
| 165.25000 | 170.05000 | NFM | Hawick | D&G Taxis |
| 165.25000 | 170.05000 | NFM | Lancing | Taxis |
| 165.25000 | 170.05000 | NFM | London | Am London Bridge Cars NW1O |
| 165.25000 | 170.05000 | NFM | Manchester | Taxis |
| 165.25000 | 170.05000 | NFM | March | Middle Level Commissioner |
| 165.25000 | 170.05000 | NFM | Milton Keynes | Ace Cars |
| 165.25000 | 170.05000 | NFM | Montrose | Radio TV Company |
| 165.25000 | 170.05000 | NFM | Newcastle | Taxis |
| 165.25000 | 170.05000 | NFM | Slough | Compass Cars |
| 165.25000 | 170.05000 | NFM | Southend | Taxis |
| 165.25000 | 170.05000 | NFM | Walthamstow | Ruby Radio Cars |
| 165.25000 | 170.05000 | NFM | Wirral | Taxis |
| 165.26250 | 170.06250 | NFM | Ashington | Heating Repairs |
| 165.26250 | 170.06250 | AM | Bedfordshire | Parcels Service |
| 165.26250 | 170.06250 | AM | Buckinghamshire | Parcels Service |
| 165.26250 | 170.06250 | NFM | Cheltenham | Bus Engineers |
| 165.26250 | 170.06250 | NFM | Dudley | TV Repairs |
| 165.26250 | 170.06250 | NFM | Ipswich | Security |

| Base | Mobile | Mode | Location | User and Notes |
| --- | --- | --- | --- | --- |
| 165.26250 | 170.06250 | NFM | Jersey | CSL Repeater |
| 165.26250 | 170.06250 | NFM | Lancashire | Barkley Council |
| 165.26250 | 170.06250 | NFM | Neath | Port Talbot Council |
| 165.26250 | 170.06250 | NFM | Newcastle | Council Housing |
| 165.26250 | 170.06250 | NFM | Poole | Repeater |
| 165.26250 | 170.06250 | NFM | Preston | Council Dog Warden |
| 165.26250 | 170.06250 | NFM | Reading | Centurian Security |
| 165.26250 | 170.06250 | NFM | Sheffield | Crystal Peaks Security |
| 165.26250 | 170.06250 | NFM | Snaefell, Isle of Man | Repeater |
| 165.26250 | 170.06250 | NFM | Southampton | B & K Security |
| 165.26250 | 170.06250 | NFM | Southampton | Ravenscroft Motors |
| 165.26250 | 170.06250 | NFM | Walsall | GB Engineering |
| 165.27000 | 170.07000 | NFM | London, Barnes | St. Paul's School boat club |
| 165.27000 | 170.07000 | NFM | West Sussex | Berkshire Recovery Services |
| 165.27400 | 170.07400 | NFM | West Sussex | Taxis |
| 165.27500 | 170.07500 | NFM | Ashington | Ashington Taxi |
| 165.27500 | 170.07500 | NFM | Bath | Orange Grove Taxis |
| 165.27500 | 170.07500 | NFM | Benfleet | Wheel's Taxis |
| 165.27500 | 170.07500 | NFM | Brierley Hill | Lady Cabs |
| 165.27500 | 170.07500 | NFM | Dover | A2B Cars |
| 165.27500 | 170.07500 | NFM | Exeter | City Minibus Co. |
| 165.27500 | 170.07500 | NFM | Felling | Taxis |
| 165.27500 | 170.07500 | NFM | Fleetwood | Doctors |
| 165.27500 | 170.07500 | NFM | Glasgow | Taxis |
| 165.27500 | 170.07500 | NFM | Guernsey | H.F. Gaudion |
| 165.27500 | 170.07500 | NFM | Halstead | Gosling Bros |
| 165.27500 | 170.07500 | NFM | Ipswich | Comm Repeater |
| 165.27500 | 170.07500 | NFM | Kingston | Minicab Firm |
| 165.27500 | 170.07500 | NFM | London | Minicab Firm Holloway |
| 165.27500 | 170.07500 | NFM | Manchester | Taxis |
| 165.27500 | 170.07500 | NFM | Mansfield | Ace Taxis |
| 165.27500 | 170.07500 | NFM | Montrose | Taxis |
| 165.27500 | 170.07500 | NFM | Newport | Show Taxis |
| 165.27500 | 170.07500 | NFM | Perth | Data |
| 165.27500 | 170.07500 | NFM | Poole | Repeater |
| 165.27500 | 170.07500 | NFM | Portsmouth | Taxis |
| 165.27500 | 170.07500 | NFM | Shire Oaks | Shire Oaks Colliery Security |
| 165.27500 | 170.07500 | NFM | Swindon | Swindon Taxis |
| 165.28650 | 170.08650 | NFM | London, Barnes | Builders at St. Paul's School |
| 165.28650 | 170.08650 | NFM | Louth | Allied Mills |
| 165.28750 | 170.08750 | NFM | Blaxhall | Greenfields, Lime Tree Farm |
| 165.28750 | 170.08750 | NFM | Chesterford | Park Research |
| 165.28750 | 170.08750 | NFM | Cleveland | Boro Taxis |
| 165.28750 | 170.08750 | NFM | Colchester | Taxis |
| 165.28750 | 170.08750 | NFM | Cumbria | South Lakes District Council |
| 165.28750 | 170.08750 | NFM | Downham Market | Lindsay Smith |
| 165.28750 | 170.08750 | NFM | Falkirk | Taxis |
| 165.28750 | 170.08750 | NFM | Ferndown | Taxis |
| 165.28750 | 170.08750 | NFM | Jersey | Polar Car Hire |
| 165.28750 | 170.08750 | NFM | Lincoln | Imp Taxis |
| 165.28750 | 170.08750 | NFM | London, Beckenham | Minicab Firm |
| 165.28750 | 170.08750 | NFM | London, Bromley | Minicab Firm |
| 165.28750 | 170.08750 | NFM | Macclesfield | Silvertown Taxis |
| 165.28750 | 170.08750 | NFM | Montrose | Taxis |
| 165.28750 | 170.08750 | NFM | New Quay | New Quay Taxis |
| 165.28750 | 170.08750 | NFM | Rochdale | Streamline Taxis |

| Base | Mobile | Mode | Location | User and Notes |
|---|---|---|---|---|
| 165.28750 | 170.08750 | NFM | Rochester | Marconi Avionics security |
| 165.28750 | 170.08750 | NFM | Spalding | Baytree Nurseries |
| 165.28750 | 170.08750 | NFM | Stotford, Beds | Bewes Electrical |
| 165.28750 | 170.08750 | NFM | Warwickshire | Farm |
| 165.28750 | 170.08750 | NFM | Woolwich | Taxis |
| 165.30000 | 170.10000 | NFM | Colwyn Bay | Taxis |
| 165.30000 | 170.10000 | NFM | East Dereham | Dereham Taxis |
| 165.30000 | 170.10000 | NFM | Edinburgh | Taxis |
| 165.30000 | 170.10000 | NFM | Fleet | Crystal Taxis |
| 165.30000 | 170.10000 | NFM | Fleet | Jockey Taxis |
| 165.30000 | 170.10000 | NFM | Guernsey | Links Community Repeater 2 |
| 165.30000 | 170.10000 | NFM | Hook | Crystal Taxis |
| 165.30000 | 170.10000 | NFM | Lichfield | Taxis |
| 165.30000 | 170.10000 | NFM | London, Shannon Corner | Tesco |
| 165.30000 | 170.10000 | NFM | Midlands | Delta Delivery |
| 165.30000 | 170.10000 | NFM | Midlands | Target Delivery |
| 165.30000 | 170.10000 | NFM | Newcastle | Plumbers |
| 165.30000 | 170.10000 | NFM | Oxfordshire | Security Firm |
| 165.30000 | 170.10000 | NFM | Taplow Area | Farm |
| 165.30000 | 170.10000 | NFM | Worcester | Security Company |
| 165.31250 | 170.11250 | NFM | Christchurch | Taxis |
| 165.31250 | 170.11250 | AM | Cleethorpes | Taxis |
| 165.31250 | 170.11250 | NFM | Coventry | M J De Courcey Coaches |
| 165.31250 | 170.11250 | NFM | Croydon | The Croydon Carriage Company |
| 165.31250 | 170.11250 | NFM | Ely | Garrett |
| 165.31250 | 170.11250 | NFM | Glasgow | Taxis |
| 165.31250 | 170.11250 | NFM | Glossop | Padtax Taxis |
| 165.31250 | 170.11250 | NFM | Jersey | Harbour Dept |
| 165.31250 | 170.11250 | NFM | Launceston | Roscar Electronics |
| 165.31250 | 170.11250 | NFM | Leigh | Avacab |
| 165.31250 | 170.11250 | NFM | London | Minicab Firm Putney |
| 165.31250 | 170.11250 | NFM | Luton | Skyline Cars |
| 165.31250 | 170.11250 | NFM | Manchester | Taxis |
| 165.31250 | 170.11250 | NFM | Merseyside | Taxis |
| 165.31250 | 170.11250 | NFM | Morecambe | Taxis |
| 165.31250 | 170.11250 | NFM | Northampton | Taxis |
| 165.31250 | 170.11250 | NFM | Nottingham | Taxis |
| 165.31250 | 170.11250 | NFM | Oxfordshire | Government helicopter |
| 165.31250 | 170.11250 | NFM | Peterborough | Euro Cabs |
| 165.31250 | 170.11250 | NFM | Plymouth | Council Security |
| 165.31250 | 170.11250 | NFM | Southampton | Taxis |
| 165.31250 | 170.11250 | NFM | Stansted | Aircars |
| 165.31250 | 170.11250 | NFM | Swindon | Ace Taxis |
| 165.31250 | 170.11250 | NFM | Tamworth | Acorn Cabs |
| 165.31250 | 170.11250 | NFM | Taunton | Alpha/Apex Taxis |
| 165.31500 | | NFM | Newcastle | Taxis |
| 165.32400 | 165.32500 | NFM | Runcorn | Parcel Delivery |
| 165.32500 | 170.12500 | NFM | Bristol | Paramedics |
| 165.32500 | 170.12500 | NFM | Coventry | Linkline Parcels |
| 165.32500 | 170.12500 | NFM | Edinburgh | Taxis |
| 165.32500 | 170.12500 | NFM | Humberside | Haulage Co |
| 165.32500 | 170.12500 | NFM | Lincoln | Council |
| 165.32500 | 170.12500 | NFM | London | Diplomatic Transport |
| 165.32500 | 170.12500 | NFM | Peterborough | CBS Repeater |
| 165.32500 | 170.12500 | NFM | Plymouth | City Security (Papa Control) |
| 165.32500 | 170.12500 | NFM | Poole | Repeater |

| Base | Mobile | Mode | Location | User and Notes |
|---|---|---|---|---|
| 165.32500 | 170.12500 | NFM | Sheffield | Kay & Hodgkinson plant hire |
| 165.32500 | 170.12500 | NFM | Southampton | Taxis |
| 165.32500 | 170.12500 | NFM | Swansea | A & M Parcel Delivery Service |
| 165.32500 | 170.12500 | NFM | Warwickshire | Farmers |
| 165.33500 | 170.13500 | NFM | Glasgow | Taxis |
| 165.33750 | 170.13750 | NFM | Calne | Taxis |
| 165.33750 | 170.13750 | NFM | Carlisle | Auto Recoveries |
| 165.33750 | 170.13750 | NFM | Clacton-on-Sea | Bernies Taxis |
| 165.33750 | 170.13750 | NFM | Cleethorpes | AA Car Taxis |
| 165.33750 | 170.13750 | NFM | Coventry | Linkline Parcels |
| 165.33750 | 170.13750 | NFM | East London | Traffic Wardens |
| 165.33750 | 170.13750 | NFM | Eccles | Minicars Ltd |
| 165.33750 | 170.13750 | NFM | Glasgow | Clydeside Taxi |
| 165.33750 | 170.13750 | NFM | Kings Lynn | Simons |
| 165.33750 | 170.13750 | NFM | Letchwood | John's Taxis |
| 165.33750 | 170.13750 | NFM | London | Borough Of Brent Parking Wardens |
| 165.33750 | 170.13750 | NFM | London | Minicab Firm Campden |
| 165.33750 | 170.13750 | NFM | London, Wembley | Traffic Wardens |
| 165.33750 | 170.13750 | NFM | Lytham | Lytham Taxis |
| 165.33750 | 170.13750 | NFM | Manchester | Taxis |
| 165.33750 | 170.13750 | NFM | Nationwide | MoD Police |
| 165.33750 | 170.13750 | NFM | Southampton | Taxis |
| 165.33750 | 170.13750 | NFM | Stoke On Trent | Z Cars Taxis |
| 165.33750 | 170.13750 | NFM | Stowmarket | ICI Paint Depot |
| 165.33750 | 170.13750 | NFM | Swindon | Taxis |
| 165.33750 | 170.13750 | NFM | Winchester | Taxis |
| 165.33750 | 170.13750 | NFM | Wrexham | Atax Taxis |
| 165.34000 | 170.14000 | NFM | Newcastle | Taxi |
| 165.34000 | 170.14000 | NFM | Stockport | Nick's Blue Taxis |
| 165.35000 | 170.15000 | NFM | Bath | Twerton Taxis |
| 165.35000 | 170.15000 | NFM | Bury | Star Taxis |
| 165.35000 | 170.15000 | NFM | Cambridge | Cabs |
| 165.35000 | 170.15000 | NFM | Clacton | Ace Taxis |
| 165.35000 | 170.15000 | NFM | Dumfries | Diamond Taxis |
| 165.35000 | 170.15000 | NFM | Felling | Taxis |
| 165.35000 | 170.15000 | NFM | Glasgow | Taxis |
| 165.35000 | 170.15000 | NFM | Great Melton | Downham Farm Services |
| 165.35000 | 170.15000 | NFM | Lichfield | Taxis |
| 165.35000 | 170.15000 | NFM | Lincoln | Security |
| 165.35000 | 170.15000 | NFM | London | Minicab Firm Lewisham |
| 165.35000 | 170.15000 | NFM | Luton | Victor Taxis |
| 165.35000 | 170.15000 | NFM | Manchester | Taxis |
| 165.35000 | 170.15000 | NFM | Newcastle | Northumbria University |
| 165.35000 | 170.15000 | NFM | Nottingham | Doctors Service |
| 165.35000 | 170.15000 | NFM | Peterborough | ABC Taxis |
| 165.36250 | 165.36250 | NFM | Birkenhead | Car Breakdown Recovery |
| 165.36250 | 170.16250 | NFM | Bournemouth | CBS Lynx Carriers |
| 165.36250 | 170.16250 | NFM | Derby | Community Repeater |
| 165.36250 | 170.16250 | NFM | Dundee | Car Hire Service |
| 165.36250 | 170.16250 | NFM | Edinburgh | Community Repeater |
| 165.36250 | 170.16250 | NFM | Gosport | Taxis |
| 165.36250 | 170.16250 | NFM | Greenham | Council |
| 165.36250 | 170.16250 | NFM | Isle of Wight | Plant Hire |
| 165.36250 | 170.16250 | NFM | Kent | Thanet Bus Company |
| 165.36250 | 170.16250 | NFM | Leicester | Taxis |
| 165.36250 | 170.16250 | NFM | Liverpool | Taxis |

| Base | Mobile | Mode | Location | User and Notes |
|------|--------|------|----------|----------------|
| 165.36250 | 170.16250 | NFM | London | Net Cars |
| 165.36250 | 170.16250 | NFM | London | Streetwise Buses |
| 165.36250 | 170.16250 | NFM | London | Tosca Skips |
| 165.36250 | 170.16250 | NFM | London | West London Skips |
| 165.36250 | 170.16250 | NFM | Matlock | Haulage Company |
| 165.36250 | 170.16250 | NFM | Mendlesham | Norcon Sky |
| 165.36250 | 170.16250 | NFM | Milford Haven | Skip Lorries |
| 165.36250 | 170.16250 | NFM | Oxfordshire | Security Firm |
| 165.36250 | 170.16250 | NFM | Perth | Community Repeater |
| 165.36250 | 170.16250 | NFM | Plymouth | Devro Security |
| 165.36250 | 170.16250 | NFM | Poole | Repeater |
| 165.36250 | 170.16250 | NFM | Southampton | Security |
| 165.36250 | 170.16250 | NFM | St. Monans | Bass Rock Oil Co. Ltd |
| 165.36500 | 170.16250 | NFM | Worcester | Double Glazing Company |
| 165.37500 | 170.17500 | NFM | Bath | Rainbow Taxis |
| 165.37500 | 170.17500 | NFM | Cambridge | Able Cars |
| 165.37500 | 170.17500 | NFM | Chelmsford | Taxis |
| 165.37500 | 170.17500 | NFM | Dumfries | Bee Hive Taxis |
| 165.37500 | 170.17500 | NFM | Glasgow | Taxis |
| 165.37500 | 170.17500 | NFM | Harlow | Regency Cars |
| 165.37500 | 170.17500 | NFM | London | Minicab Firm Nine Elms |
| 165.37500 | 170.17500 | NFM | London | US Embassy Secret Service |
| 165.37500 | 170.17500 | NFM | Plymouth | Olympic Taxis |
| 165.37500 | 170.17500 | NFM | Ramsbottom | Snobs Private Hire |
| 165.37500 | 170.17500 | NFM | Reading | Checkers Cars |
| 165.37500 | 170.17500 | NFM | Warrington | Warrington Borough County |
| 165.38750 | 170.18750 | NFM | Cambridge | Alf Bucks |
| 165.38750 | 170.18750 | NFM | Carlisle | Taxis |
| 165.38750 | 170.18750 | NFM | Clacton-on-Sea | Apollo Taxis |
| 165.38750 | 170.18750 | NFM | Cumbria | Community Repeater S. Lakes |
| 165.38750 | 170.18750 | NFM | Fakenham | Race course security |
| 165.38750 | 170.18750 | NFM | Fakenham | Selective Fertilisers |
| 165.38750 | 170.18750 | NFM | Glasgow | Taxis |
| 165.38750 | 170.18750 | NFM | Gloucester | District Council |
| 165.38750 | 170.18750 | NFM | Grampian | Farm Workers |
| 165.38750 | 170.18750 | NFM | Hoylake | Hoylake Radio Station Taxis |
| 165.38750 | 170.18750 | NFM | Jersey | F. Brown Recovery |
| 165.38750 | 170.18750 | NFM | Louth | Community Repeater |
| 165.38750 | 170.18750 | NFM | Luton Airport | Lep Transport |
| 165.38750 | 170.18750 | NFM | Medway | Kingsferry Coaches |
| 165.38750 | 170.18750 | NFM | Morecambe | Joe's Taxis |
| 165.38750 | 170.18750 | NFM | Motherwell | United Taxis |
| 165.38750 | 170.18750 | NFM | Newport | Red Dragon Taxis Ch 1 |
| 165.38750 | 170.18750 | NFM | Peterlee | Yellow Cabs |
| 165.38750 | 170.18750 | NFM | Portsmouth | Taxis |
| 165.38750 | 170.18750 | NFM | Retford | Malcolm's Taxis |
| 165.38750 | 170.18750 | NFM | Sheffield | City Cars |
| 165.38750 | 170.18750 | NFM | Soham | Tompsett |
| 165.38750 | 170.18750 | NFM | Tayside | Farm Workers |
| 165.40000 | 170.20000 | NFM | Aberdeen | Oil Fabricators |
| 165.40000 | 170.20000 | NFM | Bedford | Community Repeater |
| 165.40000 | 170.20000 | NFM | Cambourne | Vending Firm |
| 165.40000 | 170.20000 | NFM | Cornwall | Houpers Haulage |
| 165.40000 | 170.20000 | NFM | Cumbria | Community Repeater South Lakes |
| 165.40000 | 170.20000 | NFM | East Durham | Private Message |
| 165.40000 | 170.20000 | NFM | Haverfordwest | Jewsons |

| Base | Mobile | Mode | Location | User and Notes |
|------|--------|------|----------|----------------|
| 165.40000 | 170.20000 | NFM | Ipswich | Repeater |
| 165.40000 | 170.20000 | NFM | Lancashire | Andersons Pumps |
| 165.40000 | 170.20000 | NFM | London | IBA Maintenance |
| 165.40000 | 170.20000 | NFM | London | London Underground, Baker Street |
| 165.40000 | 170.20000 | NFM | London | London Underground, Balham |
| 165.40000 | 170.20000 | NFM | London | London Underground, Clapham Common |
| 165.40000 | 170.20000 | NFM | London | London Underground, Clapham North |
| 165.40000 | 170.20000 | NFM | London | London Underground, Clapham South |
| 165.40000 | 170.20000 | NFM | London | London Underground, Monument |
| 165.40000 | 170.20000 | NFM | London | London Underground, Neasden |
| 165.40000 | 170.20000 | NFM | London | London Underground, Oxford Circus |
| 165.40000 | 170.20000 | NFM | London | London Underground, Spare Channel |
| 165.40000 | 170.20000 | NFM | London | London Underground, Tooting Bec |
| 165.40000 | 170.20000 | NFM | London | London Underground, Tooting Broadway |
| 165.40000 | 170.20000 | NFM | London | Saunders Heavy Rescue |
| 165.40000 | 170.20000 | NFM | Milton Keynes | Repeater |
| 165.40000 | 170.20000 | NFM | Morecambe | Delivery Service |
| 165.40000 | 170.20000 | NFM | Morpeth | Garden Centre |
| 165.40000 | 170.20000 | NFM | Nottingham | Taxis |
| 165.40000 | 170.20000 | NFM | Peterborough | CBS Repeater |
| 165.40000 | 170.20000 | NFM | Worthing | Transport Co. |
| 165.41250 | 170.21250 | NFM | Brighton | Dyke Golf Club |
| 165.41250 | 170.21250 | NFM | Bristol | Avon Alpha Control |
| 165.41250 | 170.21250 | NFM | Cornwall | Kay Base |
| 165.41250 | 170.21250 | NFM | Ellesmere Port | Ellesmere Port Council |
| 165.41250 | 170.21250 | NFM | Fife | Fife Regional Council |
| 165.41250 | 170.21250 | NFM | Leeds | Motor Factors |
| 165.41250 | 170.21250 | NFM | London | London Underground, Bakerloo line |
| 165.41250 | 170.21250 | NFM | London | London Underground, Circle line |
| 165.41250 | 170.21250 | NFM | London | London Underground, District line |
| 165.41250 | 170.21250 | NFM | Newcastle | Plumbers |
| 165.41250 | 170.21250 | NFM | Perth | King Contractors |
| 165.41250 | 170.21250 | NFM | Plymouth | Ranger Base |
| 165.41250 | 170.21250 | NFM | Shrewsbury | Flower Show Officials |
| 165.42500 | 170.22500 | NFM | Birmingham Sparkhill | Taxis |
| 165.42500 | 170.22500 | NFM | Calne | Taxis |
| 165.42500 | 170.22500 | NFM | Cambridge | Agricultural Equipment Supplier |
| 165.42500 | 170.22500 | NFM | Chatteris | W Barnes |
| 165.42500 | 170.22500 | AM | Cleethorpes | Beavers Cars |
| 165.42500 | 170.22500 | NFM | Falkirk | Bruce Taxis |
| 165.42500 | 170.22500 | NFM | Hitchin | DER Television |
| 165.42500 | 170.22500 | NFM | Hull | Taxis |
| 165.42500 | 170.22500 | NFM | Lichfield | Taxis |
| 165.42500 | 170.22500 | NFM | Milford Haven | Taxis |
| 165.42500 | 170.22500 | NFM | Newcastle | Taxis |
| 165.42500 | 170.22500 | NFM | Plymouth | Night Watch Security |
| 165.42500 | 170.22500 | NFM | Pontypridd | Regal Taxis |
| 165.42500 | 170.22500 | NFM | Sheffield | EMI Homeserve |
| 165.42500 | 170.22500 | NFM | Wakefield | Taxis |
| 165.43750 | 170.23750 | NFM | Barrow in Furness | CAW Skip Hire & Haulage |
| 165.43750 | 170.23750 | NFM | Birmingham | Castle Security |
| 165.43750 | 170.23750 | NFM | Brecon | Mountain Rescue (S) |
| 165.43750 | 170.23750 | NFM | Bristol | Taxis |
| 165.43750 | 170.23750 | NFM | Carlisle | H & E Trotter |
| 165.43750 | 170.23750 | NFM | Carnforth | Council Roads Department |
| 165.43750 | 170.23750 | NFM | Haverfordwest | Taxis |

| Base | Mobile | Mode | Location | User and Notes |
|------|--------|------|----------|----------------|
| 165.43750 | 170.23750 | NFM | Humberside | Cash Register Co |
| 165.43750 | 170.23750 | NFM | London | London Underground, City line |
| 165.43750 | 170.23750 | NFM | London | London Underground, Metropolitan line |
| 165.43750 | 170.23750 | NFM | London | London Underground, Piccadilly Line |
| 165.43750 | 170.23750 | NFM | Manchester | Taxis |
| 165.43750 | 170.23750 | NFM | Mansfield | Doctors Service |
| 165.43750 | 170.23750 | NFM | Peterborough | City Aerials Ltd |
| 165.43750 | 170.23750 | NFM | Staffordshire | Security Co |
| 165.43750 | 170.23750 | NFM | Truro | Pellows Waste |
| 165.43750 | 170.23750 | NFM | West Midlands | Castle Security |
| 165.45000 | 170.25000 | NFM | Edinburgh | Central Taxis |
| 165.45000 | 170.25000 | NFM | Frome | Taxis |
| 165.45000 | 170.25000 | NFM | Hastings | Conquest Hospital Porters |
| 165.45000 | 170.25000 | NFM | London | Minicab Firm Greenford |
| 165.45000 | 170.25000 | NFM | London, Southall | Club Cars |
| 165.45000 | 170.25000 | NFM | Milton Keynes | Municipal Cleaning Services |
| 165.45000 | 170.25000 | NFM | Nationwide | ITC Maintenance |
| 165.45000 | 170.25000 | NFM | Newport | Alfa Taxis |
| 165.45000 | 170.25000 | NFM | Poole | Repeater |
| 165.45000 | 170.25000 | NFM | Southminster | Badnocks Farm |
| 165.45000 | 170.25000 | NFM | West Midlands | Meridian Delivery |
| 165.46250 | 170.26250 | AM | Belfast | Water Board |
| 165.46250 | 170.26250 | NFM | Bristol | Community Repeater |
| 165.46250 | 170.26250 | NFM | Eye, Suffolk | T G Asher, agric haulage |
| 165.46250 | 170.26250 | NFM | Gloucester | Repeater |
| 165.46250 | 170.26250 | NFM | Ipswich | Kengrove Aggregates (K-Base) |
| 165.46250 | 170.26250 | NFM | Ipswich | Nightfreight (East) Ltd (B) |
| 165.46250 | 170.26250 | NFM | Ipswich | Polar Base Freezers |
| 165.46250 | 170.26250 | NFM | London | London Underground, Central line |
| 165.46250 | 170.26250 | NFM | London | London Underground, Jubilee line |
| 165.46250 | 170.26250 | NFM | London | London Underground, Victoria line |
| 165.46250 | 170.26250 | NFM | Poole | Repeater |
| 165.46250 | 170.26250 | NFM | Tayside | Vets |
| 165.46250 | 170.26250 | NFM | Worthing | Nynex Cable Comms |
| 165.46250 | 170.56200 | NFM | Glasgow | Salone Services |
| 165.47500 | 170.27500 | NFM | Fort Regent, Jersey | Honorary Police Ch 1 |
| 165.47500 | 170.27500 | NFM | Newport | Community Repeater |
| 165.47500 | 170.27500 | NFM | Norfolk | Carphones |
| 165.47500 | 170.27500 | NFM | Peterborough | CBS Repeater |
| 165.47500 | 170.27500 | NFM | Plymouth | Red Lightning Dispatch |
| 165.47500 | 170.27500 | NFM | Poole | Repeater |
| 165.47500 | 170.27500 | NFM | Scunthorpe | Courier Service |
| 165.47500 | 170.27500 | NFM | Southampton | MediCall Ch 3 |
| 165.47500 | 170.27500 | NFM | Suffolk | Carphones |
| 165.48570 | 170.28750 | NFM | Millom | Pete's Taxis |
| 165.48750 | 170.28750 | NFM | Ashton-under-Lyne | Stamford Private Hire |
| 165.48750 | 170.28750 | NFM | Barry | Flat Holm Maintenance |
| 165.48750 | 170.28750 | NFM | Birmingham | Taxis |
| 165.48750 | 170.28750 | NFM | Bristol | Several Bridge Maintenance (Jasmine) |
| 165.48750 | 170.28750 | NFM | Carlisle | Taxis |
| 165.48750 | 170.28750 | NFM | Exeter | Maxi Cabs |
| 165.48750 | 170.28750 | NFM | Leicestershire | Farm |
| 165.48750 | 170.28750 | NFM | Little Hulton | Radio Cars Ltd Taxis |
| 165.48750 | 170.28750 | NFM | London | ODRATS |
| 165.48750 | 170.28750 | NFM | Manchester | Taxi |
| 165.48750 | 170.28750 | NFM | Milton Keynes | Quicker Cars |

| Base | Mobile | Mode | Location | User and Notes |
|------|--------|------|----------|----------------|
| 165.48750 | 170.28750 | NFM | Montrose | Taxis |
| 165.48750 | 170.28750 | NFM | Oldham | Delta Cars |
| 165.48750 | 170.28750 | NFM | Runcorn | Taxis |
| 165.48750 | 170.28750 | NFM | West Midlands | Arrow Taxi |
| 165.50000 | 170.30000 | NFM | Bournemouth | Token Amusements Ltd |
| 165.50000 | 170.30000 | NFM | Cambridge | DER Television |
| 165.50000 | 170.30000 | AM | Cleethorpes | Fon-a-Car |
| 165.50000 | 170.30000 | NFM | Dover | P&O Ferries Bus System |
| 165.50000 | 170.30000 | AM | Glasgow | Taxis |
| 165.50000 | 170.30000 | NFM | Gorton | Beue Vue Cars |
| 165.50000 | 170.30000 | NFM | Holyhead | Taxis |
| 165.50000 | 170.30000 | NFM | Letchwood | G Folly Builders |
| 165.50000 | 170.30000 | NFM | London | Fitzpatrick Builders |
| 165.50000 | 170.30000 | NFM | Martlesham | Independent Taxis Ltd Ch 1 |
| 165.50000 | 170.30000 | NFM | Paisley | Taxis |
| 165.50000 | 170.30000 | NFM | Plymouth | Tower Cabs |
| 165.50000 | 170.30000 | NFM | Stoke Newington | Rons Cars |
| 165.50000 | 170.30000 | NFM | Swansea | Ystrad Cabs,Ystradgynlais |
| 165.51250 | 170.31250 | NFM | Aberdeen | Taxis |
| 165.51250 | 170.31250 | NFM | Aberystwyth | Aber Cars |
| 165.51250 | 170.31250 | NFM | Ashton under Lyme | Courier Service |
| 165.51250 | 170.31250 | NFM | Birkenhead | Delta Cars |
| 165.51250 | 170.31250 | NFM | Bishop Stortford | Taxis |
| 165.51250 | 170.31250 | NFM | Bolton | Halliwell Taxis |
| 165.51250 | 170.31250 | NFM | Cambridge | Browns Taxis |
| 165.51250 | 170.31250 | NFM | Gloucester | TV Repairs |
| 165.51250 | 170.31250 | NFM | Jersey | States |
| 165.51250 | 170.31250 | NFM | Liverpool | Taxis |
| 165.51250 | 170.31250 | NFM | London, Gatwick | Airport Parking |
| 165.51250 | 170.31250 | NFM | Manchester | Taxis |
| 165.51250 | 170.31250 | NFM | Nottingham, Hucknall | Apex Taxis |
| 165.51250 | 170.31250 | NFM | Poole | Repeater |
| 165.51250 | 170.31250 | NFM | Sheffield | Bradwell Skips Services |
| 165.51250 | 170.31250 | NFM | Stockport | Taxis |
| 165.51250 | 170.31250 | NFM | Swansea | Lakes Taxis |
| 165.51250 | 170.31250 | NFM | Worthing | Taxis |
| 165.51250 | 170.31250 | NFM | Wrexham | Club Taxis |
| 165.52500 | 170.32500 | NFM | Bristol | Community Repeater |
| 165.52500 | 170.32500 | NFM | Dudley | Merry Hill Security |
| 165.52500 | 170.32500 | NFM | Halifax | ABC Taxis |
| 165.52500 | 170.32500 | NFM | London | Embassy Cars |
| 165.52500 | 170.32500 | NFM | Manchester | Taxis |
| 165.52500 | 170.32500 | NFM | Mid Kent | Farm (B) |
| 165.52500 | 170.32500 | NFM | Peterborough | DER Television |
| 165.52500 | 170.32500 | NFM | Reading | 1st Yellow Cars |
| 165.52500 | 170.32500 | NFM | Urmston | Phoenix Taxis |
| 165.52500 | 170.32500 | NFM | Wiltshire | TV Repairs |
| 165.53750 | 170.33750 | NFM | Abingdon | Eagle Security Co |
| 165.53750 | 170.33750 | NFM | Askam in Furness | Furness Car & Commercial Recovery Service |
| 165.53750 | 170.33750 | NFM | Heathfield | Comrep |
| 165.53750 | 170.33750 | NFM | North Yorkshire | Doctor Service |
| 165.53750 | 170.33750 | NFM | Oxford | Community Repeater |
| 165.53750 | 170.33750 | NFM | Oxfordshire | Car Windscreen Repair Co |
| 165.53750 | 170.33750 | NFM | Oxfordshire | Central Heating Co |
| 165.53750 | 170.33750 | NFM | Oxfordshire | Courier Co |
| 165.53750 | 170.33750 | NFM | Scarborough | Shopwatch |

| Base | Mobile | Mode | Location | User and Notes |
| --- | --- | --- | --- | --- |
| 165.53750 | 170.33750 | NFM | Scunthorpe | British Steel Emergency |
| 165.53750 | 170.33750 | NFM | Wolverhampton | Skip Hire |
| 165.55000 | 170.35000 | NFM | Blackburn | Intack Private Hire |
| 165.55000 | 170.35000 | NFM | Edinburgh | Tarmac Roadstone |
| 165.55000 | 170.35000 | NFM | Eskdale | Ravenglass and Eskdale Railway |
| 165.55000 | 170.35000 | NFM | London | Dry Cleaning Company |
| 165.55000 | 170.35000 | NFM | London | Vehicle wheel clamping |
| 165.55000 | 170.35000 | NFM | London, Camden | Council Traffic Wardens |
| 165.55000 | 170.35000 | NFM | Plymouth | Military Security (RM) |
| 165.55000 | 170.35000 | NFM | Southampton | Taxis |
| 165.55000 | 170.35000 | NFM | Warwickshire South | Farmers |
| 165.56000 | 170.36000 | NFM | Wakefield | Council heating department |
| 165.56250 | 170.36250 | NFM | Brighton | Security Company |
| 165.56250 | 170.36250 | NFM | Bristol | Community Repeater |
| 165.56250 | 170.36250 | NFM | Cheltenham | Bus Inspectors |
| 165.56250 | 170.36250 | NFM | Cheltenham | Gaming Machine Repairs |
| 165.56250 | 170.36250 | NFM | Cheltenham | Monarch Security |
| 165.56250 | 170.36250 | NFM | Cheltenham | Refuse Collectors |
| 165.56250 | 170.36250 | NFM | Edinburgh | Carpet Fitting Co. |
| 165.56250 | 170.36250 | NFM | Edinburgh | Castle Security |
| 165.56250 | 170.36250 | NFM | Edinburgh | Trinity Roofing |
| 165.56250 | 170.36250 | NFM | Glasgow | Taxis |
| 165.56250 | 170.36250 | NFM | Gloucester | Fruit Machine Engineers Ch 1 |
| 165.56250 | 170.36250 | NFM | Gloucester | Monarch Security |
| 165.56250 | 170.36250 | NFM | Lancaster | City Council |
| 165.56250 | 170.36250 | NFM | London | Thames Water engineers |
| 165.56250 | 170.36250 | NFM | Nationwide | Subaru Rally Team |
| 165.56250 | 170.36250 | NFM | Norwich | Blueline Taxis |
| 165.56250 | 170.36250 | NFM | Poole | Fernside Recovery |
| 165.56250 | 170.36250 | NFM | Portsmouth | Bus Co |
| 165.56250 | 170.36250 | NFM | Starford | Tree surgeons |
| 165.56250 | 170.36250 | NFM | Suffolk | East Counties Farmers Ch2 |
| 165.56250 | 170.36250 | NFM | Swindon | Games Machines |
| 165.56250 | 170.36250 | NFM | Tyne & Wear | Healthcall Service |
| 165.56250 | 170.36250 | NFM | Wirral | Brombourgh Cabs |
| 165.56250 | 170.36250 | NFM | Yorkshire | Yorkshire Water |
| 165.56750 | 170.37500 | NFM | Worksop | Trumpet Taxis |
| 165.57500 | 170.37500 | NFM | Accrington | D-Line Cars |
| 165.57500 | 170.37500 | NFM | Cambridge | H Robinson |
| 165.57500 | 170.37500 | NFM | Edinburgh | Eden Aerial Riggers |
| 165.57500 | 170.37500 | NFM | Felixstowe | Taxis |
| 165.57500 | 170.37500 | AM | Grimsby | Taxis |
| 165.57500 | 170.37500 | NFM | Haverhill | Jennings Transport |
| 165.57500 | 170.37500 | NFM | Kings Lynn | DER Television |
| 165.57500 | 170.37500 | AM | Manchester | New United Taxis |
| 165.57500 | 170.37500 | NFM | Montrose | Farm Workers |
| 165.57500 | 170.37500 | NFM | Newport | Star Taxis |
| 165.57500 | 170.37500 | NFM | Sheffield | Star Cars |
| 165.57500 | 170.37500 | NFM | Woodbridge | K Tuckwell Engineers |
| 165.58000 | 170.38750 | NFM | Newhaven | Taxi |
| 165.58750 | 170.38750 | NFM | Blackburn | A&B Private Hire |
| 165.58750 | 170.38750 | NFM | Coventry | Neil Bartlett Haulage |
| 165.58750 | 170.38750 | NFM | Harpenden | DER Television |
| 165.58750 | 170.38750 | NFM | Hewhaven | Taxis |
| 165.58750 | 170.38750 | NFM | Hull | Rediffusion TV Rental |
| 165.58750 | 170.38750 | NFM | Luton | DER Television |

| Base | Mobile | Mode | Location | User and Notes |
|------|--------|------|----------|----------------|
| 165.58750 | 170.38750 | NFM | Macclesfield | Taxis |
| 165.58750 | 170.38750 | NFM | Manchester | Taxis |
| 165.58750 | 170.38750 | NFM | Stockport | Taxis |
| 165.58750 | 170.38750 | NFM | Swinton | Radio Cars Ltd |
| 165.58760 | 170.38750 | NFM | Sheffield | FW Collins Ltd. skips |
| 165.60000 | 170.40000 | NFM | Aldridge | Alpha Taxis |
| 165.60000 | 170.40000 | NFM | Bridlington | Coastline Cabs |
| 165.60000 | 170.40000 | NFM | Bury | Taxis |
| 165.60000 | 170.40000 | NFM | Cornwall | English China Clay |
| 165.60000 | 170.40000 | NFM | Glasgow | Taxis |
| 165.60000 | 170.40000 | NFM | Glossop | Shadow Taxis |
| 165.60000 | 170.40000 | NFM | Ipswich | Elite Taxis and Fleet Cabs |
| 165.60000 | 170.40000 | NFM | London | Carreras Rothmans Displays |
| 165.60000 | 170.40000 | NFM | Manchester | Taxis |
| 165.60000 | 170.40000 | NFM | Paddington | Z Car hire |
| 165.60000 | 170.40000 | NFM | Paisley | Taxis |
| 165.60000 | 170.40000 | NFM | Stockport | Taxis |
| 165.60000 | 170.40000 | NFM | Strathclyde | British Transport Police (D) |
| 165.60000 | 170.40000 | NFM | Swansea Docks | Train Signal Box |
| 165.61000 | 165.61000 | NFM | Bury St Edmunds | Taxis |
| 165.61250 | 170.41250 | NFM | Castleton | Castleton Cars |
| 165.61250 | 170.41250 | NFM | Dunstable | Hunter Taxis |
| 165.61250 | 170.41250 | NFM | Grimsby | Council Maintenance |
| 165.61250 | 170.41250 | NFM | Jersey Airport | Airport Duty Officer Ch1 |
| 165.61250 | 170.41250 | NFM | Kirkham | Taxis |
| 165.61250 | 170.41250 | NFM | Lakenheath | Base Taxis |
| 165.61250 | 170.41250 | NFM | Linlithgow | Taxi |
| 165.61250 | 170.41250 | NFM | Mildenhall | M&L Taxis |
| 165.61250 | 170.41250 | NFM | Neath | Dragon Cabs |
| 165.61250 | 170.41250 | NFM | Newcastle | Buses |
| 165.61250 | 170.41250 | NFM | Perth | Council plumbers |
| 165.61250 | 170.41250 | NFM | Scunthorpe | Steel Works Maintenance |
| 165.61250 | 170.41250 | NFM | Sheffield | Indoor Market Security |
| 165.61250 | 170.41250 | NFM | St Austell | ECC Pits |
| 165.61250 | 170.41250 | NFM | Stanstead | Taxis |
| 165.62500 | 170.42500 | NFM | Bolton | Tonge Moor Private Hire |
| 165.62500 | 170.42500 | NFM | Bridlington | Star Cars |
| 165.62500 | 170.42500 | NFM | Brighton | British Rail Transport Police |
| 165.62500 | 170.42500 | AM | Bristol | Bond Delivery |
| 165.62500 | 170.42500 | NFM | Co. Durham | Haulage Coal Wagons |
| 165.62500 | 170.42500 | NFM | East Dereham | Acab Taxis |
| 165.62500 | 170.42500 | NFM | Edinburgh | Special Events |
| 165.62500 | 170.42500 | NFM | Glasgow | Taxis |
| 165.62500 | 170.42500 | NFM | Leicester | City Buses |
| 165.6250 | 170.42500 | NFM | London | Ambulance Service |
| 165.62500 | 170.42500 | NFM | London | Transport Police |
| 165.62500 | 170.42500 | NFM | Nationwide | Transport Police Channel 3 |
| 165.62500 | 170.42500 | NFM | Newcastle | Taxi |
| 165.62500 | 170.42500 | NFM | Oxford | Royal Taxis |
| 165.62500 | 170.42500 | NFM | Plymouth | Central Taxis |
| 165.62500 | 170.42500 | NFM | Sheffield | Sheffield United Football Club stewards |
| 165.62500 | 170.42500 | NFM | Sittingbourne | Swale Taxis |
| 165.62500 | 170.42500 | NFM | Southampton | Buses |
| 165.62500 | 170.42500 | NFM | Swansea | Swallow Cars |
| 165.62500 | 170.42500 | NFM | Walton,Essex | Dancabs Taxis |
| 165.62500 | 170.42500 | NFM | Worcester | Take-Away Delivery Service |

| Base | Mobile | Mode | Location | User and Notes |
|---|---|---|---|---|
| 165.63750 | 170.42500 | NFM | Birmingham | British Transport Police |
| 165.63750 | 170.42500 | NFM | Bristol | British Transport Police |
| 165.63750 | 170.42500 | NFM | Chester | British Transport Police |
| 165.63750 | 170.42500 | NFM | Crewe | British Transport Police |
| 165.63750 | 170.42500 | NFM | Liverpool | British Transport Police |
| 165.63750 | 170.42500 | NFM | London | British Transport Police (Victoria) |
| 165.63750 | 170.42500 | NFM | London | Police Royal Parks Ch 2 |
| 165.63750 | 170.42500 | NFM | Manchester | British Transport Police |
| 165.63750 | 170.42500 | NFM | Nationwide | British Transport Police Channel 2 |
| 165.63750 | 170.42500 | NFM | Newport | British Transport Police (GOLF CONTROL) |
| 165.63750 | 170.42500 | NFM | Swansea | British Transport Police |
| 165.63750 | 170.47500 | NFM | London | Ambulance Service |
| 165.64000 | 170.42500 | NFM | Newcastle | British Transport Police |
| 165.65000 | 170.42500 | NFM | Glasgow | Railway Workmen |
| 165.65000 | 170.42500 | NFM | London | London Underground Transport Police |
| 165.65000 | 170.42500 | NFM | Lothian & Borders | Transport Police (DA) |
| 165.65000 | 170.42500 | NFM | Nationwide | Transport Police Channel 1 |
| 165.65000 | 170.45000 | NFM | Brighton | British Transport Police |
| 165.65000 | 170.85000 | NFM | London | Ambulance Service |
| 165.66250 | 170.46250 | NFM | Bristol | City Line Buses |
| 165.66250 | 170.46250 | NFM | Consett | Taxis |
| 165.66250 | 170.46250 | NFM | Cornwall | English China Clay (Clay Control) |
| 165.66250 | 170.46250 | NFM | Jersey | Public Services |
| 165.66250 | 170.46250 | NFM | Llandudno | Taxi Service |
| 165.66250 | 170.46250 | NFM | London | Auto Car Repair |
| 165.66250 | 170.46250 | NFM | Lowestoft | Bluebird Taxis |
| 165.66250 | 170.46250 | NFM | Macclesfield | Macc Radio Cars |
| 165.66250 | 170.46250 | NFM | Manchester | Taxis |
| 165.66250 | 170.46250 | NFM | Medway | Hydro Descaling |
| 165.66250 | 170.46250 | NFM | Rochdale | Strand Private Hire |
| 165.66250 | 170.46250 | AM | Scarborough | Laker Taxis |
| 165.66250 | 170.46250 | NFM | Sheffield | Direct & Class Cars |
| 165.67500 | 170.47500 | NFM | Bolton | Taxis |
| 165.67500 | 170.47500 | NFM | Dunstable | E. J Allan |
| 165.67500 | 170.47500 | NFM | Hull | Railtrack |
| 165.67500 | 170.47500 | AM | Ipswich | Crown Taxis |
| 165.67500 | 170.47500 | NFM | Manchester | Taxis |
| 165.67500 | 170.47500 | NFM | Reading | ABC Cars |
| 165.67500 | 170.47500 | AM | Scarborough | Laker Taxis |
| 165.67500 | 170.47500 | NFM | Scunthorpe | British Steel Transport |
| 165.67500 | 170.47500 | NFM | Sheffield | Taxis |
| 165.67500 | 170.47500 | NFM | St Annes | West Star Taxis |
| 165.67500 | 170.47500 | NFM | Stanwell | TNT Carriers |
| 165.67500 | 170.47500 | NFM | Wolds | Tennants Farms |
| 165.67500 | 170.57500 | NFM | London, Southall | Amber Radio Cars |
| 165.68750 | 170.48750 | NFM | Cheshire | Bell Fruit Machines |
| 165.68750 | 170.48750 | NFM | Edinburgh | Bell Fruit Machines |
| 165.68750 | 170.48750 | NFM | Ipswich | Bell Fruit Machines |
| 165.68750 | 170.48750 | NFM | Lincoln | Bell Fruit Machines |
| 165.68750 | 170.48750 | NFM | London | Bell Fruit Machines |
| 165.68750 | 170.48750 | NFM | Peterborough | Bell Fruit Machines |
| 165.68750 | 170.48750 | NFM | Sheffield | Paymaster Ltd. |
| 165.70000 | 170.50000 | NFM | Brighton | Taxis |
| 165.70000 | 170.50000 | NFM | Chatteris | Catwood Potatoes |
| 165.70000 | 170.50000 | AM | Christchurch | Critax Taxis |
| 165.70000 | 170.50000 | NFM | Glasgow | Taxis |

| Base | Mobile | Mode | Location | User and Notes |
|------|--------|------|----------|----------------|
| 165.70000 | 170.50000 | NFM | Guernsey | T & D Services |
| 165.70000 | 170.50000 | NFM | Hamilton | Cadzow Cars |
| 165.70000 | 170.50000 | NFM | Humberside | Transport Co |
| 165.70000 | 170.50000 | NFM | Ipswich | Clarke Demolition |
| 165.70000 | 170.50000 | NFM | Ipswich | Thompson & Morgan |
| 165.70000 | 170.50000 | NFM | Jersey | T & D Services |
| 165.70000 | 170.50000 | NFM | Kings Lynn | Ambassador Taxis |
| 165.70000 | 170.50000 | NFM | Luton | District Cars |
| 165.70000 | 170.50000 | NFM | Portsmouth | Aqua Taxis |
| 165.70000 | 170.50000 | NFM | Saffron Walden | Crusader Cars |
| 165.70000 | 170.50000 | NFM | Southampton | Taxis |
| 165.71250 | 170.21250 | NFM | Carnforth | PR Taxis |
| 165.71250 | 170.51250 | NFM | Aldershot | Taxis |
| 165.71250 | 170.51250 | NFM | Basildon | Taxis |
| 165.71250 | 170.51250 | NFM | Bedford | Keycars |
| 165.71250 | 170.51250 | NFM | Bognor Regis | Taxis |
| 165.71250 | 170.51250 | NFM | Bristol | Blue Iris Coaches |
| 165.71250 | 170.51250 | NFM | Cambridge | Four Four Taxis |
| 165.71250 | 170.51250 | NFM | Crewe | Taxis |
| 165.71250 | 170.51250 | NFM | Edinburgh | Taxis |
| 165.71250 | 170.51250 | NFM | Folkestone | Folkestone City Buses |
| 165.71250 | 170.51250 | NFM | Headham | Gower Ltd |
| 165.71250 | 170.51250 | NFM | Hollesley | W.J. Mills |
| 165.71250 | 170.51250 | NFM | Ipswich | E H Roberts |
| 165.71250 | 170.51250 | NFM | Newcastle | Castle Cars |
| 165.71250 | 170.51250 | NFM | Tamworth | Acorn Taxis |
| 165.71250 | 170.51250 | NFM | Valley, Wales | Teds Taxis |
| 165.72500 | 165.72500 | NFM | Ayr | Railway Workmen |
| 165.72500 | 170.52500 | NFM | Blackburn | Manhattan Private Hire |
| 165.72500 | 170.52500 | NFM | Bolton | MacArthur Private Hire |
| 165.72500 | 170.52500 | NFM | Bournemouth | Southern Dispatch Couriers |
| 165.72500 | 170.52500 | NFM | Hatfield | Tarmac Construction |
| 165.72500 | 170.52500 | NFM | Hockwold Cum Wilton | Bob's Taxis |
| 165.72500 | 170.52500 | NFM | Ipswich | DER |
| 165.72500 | 170.52500 | NFM | Medway | Council Housing Dept. |
| 165.72500 | 170.52500 | NFM | Nationwide | Tarmac Construction Co |
| 165.72500 | 170.52500 | NFM | Scunthorpe | British Steel Trains |
| 165.72500 | 170.52500 | NFM | Truro | Hospital Services |
| 165.73000 | 165.73000 | NFM | Carlisle | Doctors on call |
| 165.73750 | 170.53750 | NFM | Belfast | TNT Carriers |
| 165.73750 | 170.53750 | NFM | Bury | Royal Taxis |
| 165.73750 | 170.53750 | NFM | Coventry | Lion Taxis |
| 165.73750 | 170.53750 | NFM | Runcorn | Taxis |
| 165.73750 | 170.53750 | NFM | Stockton-on-Tees | Taxi Service |
| 165.73750 | 170.53750 | NFM | Sudbury | Amey Roadstones |
| 165.73750 | 170.53750 | NFM | Swindon | Tramps Radio Cars |
| 165.73750 | 170.53750 | NFM | Widnes | Taxis |
| 165.75000 | 170.55000 | NFM | Bournemouth | Dustvans |
| 165.75000 | 170.55000 | NFM | Cambridge | Cambus |
| 165.75000 | 170.55000 | NFM | Carlisle | Council Highways |
| 165.75000 | 170.55000 | NFM | Dundee | Taxis |
| 165.75000 | 170.55000 | NFM | Exeter | Council |
| 165.75000 | 170.55000 | NFM | Fylde | Town Council |
| 165.75000 | 170.55000 | NFM | Halifax | Binmen FOCSA |
| 165.75000 | 170.55000 | NFM | Hove | Council |
| 165.75000 | 170.55000 | NFM | Lancaster | City Council |

| Base | Mobile | Mode | Location | User and Notes |
|---|---|---|---|---|
| 165.75000 | 170.55000 | NFM | Leamington Spa | Council |
| 165.75000 | 170.55000 | NFM | London | Enfield Borough Council |
| 165.75000 | 170.55000 | NFM | Luton | Luton Borough Council |
| 165.75000 | 170.55000 | NFM | Machynlleth | Hendre Quarry |
| 165.75000 | 170.55000 | NFM | Newark | Taxis |
| 165.75000 | 170.55000 | NFM | Norfolk | Bus Company |
| 165.75000 | 170.55000 | NFM | Norwich | ECOC |
| 165.75000 | 170.55000 | NFM | Perth | Taxis |
| 165.75000 | 170.55000 | NFM | Peterborough | Viscount Travel |
| 165.75000 | 170.55000 | NFM | Reading | Council |
| 165.75000 | 170.55000 | NFM | Stoke-on-Trent | Council |
| 165.75000 | 170.55000 | NFM | Swindon | Town Council |
| 165.75000 | 170.55000 | NFM | Wiltshire | Thamesdown Council |
| 165.75000 | 170.55000 | NFM | Wirral, Woodchurch | A-Z Private Hire |
| 165.76000 | 170.56000 | NFM | Ayr | Council Services |
| 165.76000 | 170.56000 | NFM | Stoke on Trent | Town Council |
| 165.76250 | 170.56250 | NFM | Aberdeen | Waste Masters |
| 165.76250 | 170.56250 | NFM | Bedfordshire | District Council |
| 165.76250 | 170.56250 | NFM | Bolton | District Council |
| 165.76250 | 170.56250 | NFM | Bournemouth | Public Transport Ch 1 |
| 165.76250 | 170.56250 | NFM | Bridlington | Borough Council Repairs |
| 165.76250 | 170.56250 | NFM | Brierley Hill | Council |
| 165.76250 | 170.56250 | NFM | Bristol | Buses |
| 165.76250 | 170.56250 | NFM | Cunninghame | SRC Local Council Services |
| 165.76250 | 170.56250 | NFM | Dundee | City Council Dog Catcher |
| 165.76250 | 170.56250 | NFM | East Yorkshire | Borough Council |
| 165.76250 | 170.56250 | NFM | Edinburgh | Lothian Regional Council |
| 165.76250 | 170.56250 | NFM | Ipswich | Housing Department |
| 165.76250 | 170.56250 | NFM | Llanelli | Council |
| 165.76250 | 170.56250 | AM | London | Southall Council |
| 165.76250 | 170.56250 | NFM | Luton | Contractor |
| 165.76250 | 170.56250 | NFM | Norfolk | Norfolk County Council |
| 165.76250 | 170.56250 | NFM | Poole | Repeater |
| 165.76250 | 170.56250 | NFM | Preston | District Council |
| 165.76250 | 170.56250 | NFM | St Saviour Parish, Jersey | Honorary Police Ch 5 |
| 165.76250 | 170.56250 | NFM | Suffolk | County Council |
| 165.76500 | 170.56500 | NFM | Gateshead | Council |
| 165.77000 | 170.57000 | NFM | Carlisle | Doctors |
| 165.77500 | 170.57500 | NFM | Barrow | Dog Wardens |
| 165.77500 | 170.57500 | NFM | Congleton | Taxi |
| 165.77500 | 170.57500 | NFM | Cwmbran | Cwmbran Plumbing Plc |
| 165.77500 | 170.57500 | NFM | Dudley | Council |
| 165.77500 | 170.57500 | NFM | Glasgow | Strathkelvin District Council |
| 165.77500 | 170.57500 | NFM | Havant | Council |
| 165.77500 | 170.57500 | NFM | Hayling Island | Council |
| 165.77500 | 170.57500 | NFM | High Wycombe | Council Parks Dept |
| 165.77500 | 170.57500 | NFM | Huntingdon | Council (PATHFINDER BASE) |
| 165.77500 | 170.57500 | NFM | Ipswich | Brough Transport |
| 165.77500 | 170.57500 | NFM | Jersey | States of Jersey Repeater |
| 165.77500 | 170.57500 | AM | London | Croydon Council |
| 165.77500 | 170.57500 | NFM | North Yorkshire | Doctor Service |
| 165.77500 | 170.57500 | NFM | Norwich | Norwich City Council |
| 165.77500 | 170.57500 | NFM | Portsmouth | City Council |
| 165.77500 | 170.57500 | NFM | Skegness | Council |
| 165.77500 | 170.57500 | NFM | Somerset | County Council |
| 165.77500 | 170.57500 | NFM | Southend on Sea | District Council |

| Base | Mobile | Mode | Location | User and Notes |
| --- | --- | --- | --- | --- |
| 165.77500 | 170.57500 | NFM | Stoke-on-Trent | Council Parks Dept. |
| 165.77500 | 170.57500 | NFM | Taunton | Parking inspectors |
| 165.77500 | 170.57500 | NFM | Tenring | Lifeguards |
| 165.77500 | 170.57500 | NFM | West Cambs | District Council |
| 165.77500 | 170.57500 | NFM | Wiltshire | Wilts County Council |
| 165.78750 | 170.58750 | NFM | Boston | Organic Lincolnshire Growers Association |
| 165.78750 | 170.58750 | NFM | Bournemouth | Council |
| 165.78750 | 170.58750 | NFM | Bromley | Borough Council |
| 165.78750 | 170.58750 | NFM | Carlisle | County Contracting North |
| 165.78750 | 170.58750 | NFM | Coventry | West Midlands Gas |
| 165.78750 | 170.58750 | NFM | Fawley | Power Station |
| 165.78750 | 170.58750 | NFM | Hyndburn | Accrington Bus Control |
| 165.78750 | 170.58750 | NFM | London | US Embassy Secret Service |
| 165.78750 | 170.58750 | NFM | Manchester | Motorway Maintenance |
| 165.78750 | 170.58750 | NFM | Peterborough | Betta Cars Amalgamated |
| 165.78750 | 170.58750 | NFM | Poole | Repeater |
| 165.78750 | 170.58750 | NFM | Stoke-on-Trent | Skip Hire |
| 165.78750 | 170.58750 | NFM | Suffolk | Mid Suffolk District Council |
| 165.78750 | 170.58750 | NFM | Swindon | Thamesdown Council |
| 165.78750 | 170.58750 | NFM | West Midlands | Council Refuse |
| 165.79500 | 170.59500 | NFM | Ayr | North of Scotland Water Authority |
| 165.80000 | 170.60000 | NFM | Brighton | Streamline Taxis |
| 165.80000 | 170.60000 | NFM | Bristol | RSPCA |
| 165.80000 | 170.60000 | NFM | Derby Langley Mill | Taxis |
| 165.80000 | 170.60000 | NFM | Dudley | Five Star Taxis |
| 165.80000 | 170.60000 | NFM | Dundee | Taxis |
| 165.80000 | 170.60000 | NFM | Exeter | Castle Cars |
| 165.80000 | 170.60000 | NFM | Felixstowe | Peewit Caravans |
| 165.80000 | 170.60000 | NFM | Jersey | Normans Channel 2 |
| 165.80000 | 170.60000 | NFM | Kent | Tour De France (French) |
| 165.80000 | 170.60000 | NFM | Kilmarnock | Taxis |
| 165.80000 | 170.60000 | NFM | London | Taxis |
| 165.80000 | 170.60000 | NFM | Luton | C.J. Private Hire |
| 165.80000 | 170.60000 | NFM | Newcastle | RSPCA |
| 165.80000 | 170.60000 | NFM | Norwich | Beeline & Dolphin Taxis |
| 165.80000 | 170.60000 | NFM | Sheffield | Taxis |
| 165.80000 | 170.60000 | NFM | Swansea | Hooper Taxis |
| 165.80000 | 170.60000 | NFM | Wickham Market | Haywards Farms |
| 165.81250 | 170.61250 | NFM | Bath | Abbey Taxis Ch 2 |
| 165.81250 | 170.61250 | NFM | Cambridge | Panther Cars |
| 165.81250 | 170.61250 | NFM | Cleethorpes | Bob's Cars |
| 165.81250 | 170.61250 | NFM | Coventry | Godiva Taxis |
| 165.81250 | 170.61250 | NFM | Coventry | Lewis Taxis |
| 165.81250 | 170.61250 | NFM | London | Odrats |
| 165.81250 | 170.61250 | NFM | Preston | Cabtax Taxis |
| 165.81250 | 170.61250 | NFM | St Austell | Taxis |
| 165.82500 | 170.62500 | NFM | Bath | Abbey Taxis Ch 1 |
| 165.82500 | 170.62500 | NFM | Bolton | ABA Private Hire |
| 165.82500 | 170.62500 | NFM | Dudley | Midland Taxis |
| 165.82500 | 170.62500 | NFM | Glasgow | Taxi Company |
| 165.82500 | 170.62500 | NFM | Ipswich | Wilding & Smith |
| 165.82500 | 170.62500 | NFM | March | Worrall Potatoes |
| 165.82500 | 170.62500 | NFM | Oxford | ABC Taxis |
| 165.83750 | 170.62750 | NFM | Cardiff | Transport Firm |
| 165.83750 | 170.62750 | NFM | Ely | A.E. Lee Farms |
| 165.83750 | 170.62750 | NFM | Glasgow | Taxis |

| Base | Mobile | Mode | Location | User and Notes |
|---|---|---|---|---|
| 165.83750 | 170.62750 | NFM | London | ODRATS |
| 165.83750 | 170.62750 | NFM | Macclesfield | Taxis |
| 165.83750 | 170.62750 | NFM | Oldham | Limeline Private Hire |
| 165.83750 | 170.62750 | NFM | Peterborough | Hereward Ace Taxis |
| 165.83750 | 170.62750 | NFM | Plymouth | Taxis |
| 165.83750 | 170.62750 | NFM | Sheffield | Airport Express (TEX) |
| 165.83750 | 170.62750 | NFM | St. Osyth | Tudor Taxis |
| 165.83750 | 170.63730 | NFM | Halifax | Vinneys Taxis |
| 165.83750 | 170.63750 | NFM | Caistor | Hurdiss Quarries |
| 165.83750 | 170.63750 | NFM | Liverpool, Garston | Allerton Taxis |
| 165.84000 | 170.64000 | NFM | Falkirk | Taxis |
| 165.84000 | 170.64000 | NFM | Newcastle | Taxis |
| 165.85000 | 170.65000 | NFM | Bristol | RSPCA |
| 165.85000 | 170.65000 | NFM | Carlisle | Carlisle Drivers |
| 165.85000 | 170.65000 | NFM | Falkirk | Blue Star Taxis (Star) |
| 165.85000 | 170.65000 | NFM | Gt. Manchester | Avacabs |
| 165.85000 | 170.65000 | NFM | Haddenham | A.F. Buck |
| 165.85000 | 170.65000 | AM | Jersey | Tantivy Coaches |
| 165.85000 | 170.65000 | NFM | Leigh | Avacabs |
| 165.85000 | 170.65000 | NFM | Liverpool | City Cars |
| 165.85000 | 170.65000 | NFM | London | Dial A Cab Data Boxes |
| 165.85000 | 170.65000 | NFM | London | ODRATS |
| 165.85000 | 170.65000 | NFM | Newport, Gwent | Royal Cars |
| 165.85000 | 170.65000 | NFM | Plymouth | Estate Security |
| 165.85000 | 170.65000 | NFM | Three Holes | Hallsworth Framing Co. |
| 165.86000 | 170.66000 | NFM | Ayr | Taxis |
| 165.86250 | 170.66250 | NFM | Cambridge | Securicor |
| 165.86250 | 170.66250 | NFM | Coventry | Security |
| 165.86250 | 170.66250 | NFM | Hythe | Hythe Ferry and Pier |
| 165.86250 | 170.66250 | NFM | Jersey | Pony Express Delivery |
| 165.86250 | 170.66250 | NFM | Leeds | Courier Service |
| 165.86250 | 170.66250 | NFM | Nationwide | Securicor Channel 6 |
| 165.87500 | 170.67500 | NFM | Birmingham | Black Cabs |
| 165.87500 | 170.67500 | NFM | Birmingham | Driving School |
| 165.87500 | 170.67500 | NFM | Coventry | Security |
| 165.87500 | 170.67500 | NFM | Edinburgh | Pony Express Couriers |
| 165.87500 | 170.67500 | NFM | Fleetwood | Nightwatchmen |
| 165.87500 | 170.67500 | NFM | Guernsey | Securicor |
| 165.87500 | 170.67500 | NFM | Nationwide | Securicor Channel 2 |
| 165.87500 | 170.67500 | NFM | Wokington | Council |
| 165.88750 | 170.68750 | NFM | Bournemouth | Council Tarmac Gang |
| 165.88750 | 170.68750 | NFM | Horwich | Duval Security |
| 165.88750 | 170.68750 | NFM | Nationwide | Securicor Channel 3 |
| 165.88750 | 170.68750 | NFM | Preston | Builders |
| 165.90000 | 170.70000 | NFM | Airdrie | Twin Cabs |
| 165.90000 | 170.70000 | NFM | Colchester | Town Cars |
| 165.90000 | 170.70000 | NFM | Dartford | Abba Dart Taxis |
| 165.90000 | 170.70000 | NFM | Dundee | Taxis |
| 165.90000 | 170.70000 | NFM | Hitchin | Duggan's Taxis |
| 165.90000 | 170.70000 | NFM | Ipswich | Taxis |
| 165.90000 | 170.70000 | NFM | London | US Embassy Secret Service |
| 165.90000 | 170.70000 | NFM | Manchester | Atherton Cab Co. |
| 165.90000 | 170.70000 | NFM | Rochdale | Norden Cars |
| 165.90000 | 170.70000 | NFM | Sevenoaks | Beeline Radio Taxis |
| 165.90000 | 170.70000 | NFM | Sheffield | Amusement Machine Servicing |
| 165.90000 | 170.70000 | NFM | Sheffield | Paymaster Ltd. |

| Base | Mobile | Mode | Location | User and Notes |
|------|--------|------|----------|----------------|
| 165.90000 | 170.70000 | NFM | Swansea | Lloyds Taxis |
| 165.90000 | 170.70000 | AM | Swindon | Viking Taxis |
| 165.90000 | 170.70000 | NFM | Tilbury | Tilbury Taxis |
| 165.90000 | 170.70000 | NFM | Wantage | Robert's Taxis |
| 165.90000 | 170.70000 | NFM | West Drayton | LHR Express Cars |
| 165.91250 | 170.71250 | NFM | Devizes | Community Repeater |
| 165.91250 | 170.71250 | NFM | Jersey | A1 Double Glazing |
| 165.91250 | 170.71250 | NFM | Nationwide | Securicor Channel 7 |
| 165.91250 | 170.71250 | NFM | Walsall | MFI Deliveries |
| 165.92500 | 170.72500 | NFM | Aberdeen | Oil Industry |
| 165.92500 | 170.72500 | NFM | Brighton | Car Mechanics Ch 1 |
| 165.92500 | 170.72500 | NFM | Cirencester | Gerry's Cars |
| 165.92500 | 170.72500 | NFM | Cleveland | 6767 Taxis |
| 165.92500 | 170.72500 | NFM | Jersey | Hire Cars |
| 165.92500 | 170.72500 | NFM | Manchester | Taxis |
| 165.92500 | 170.72500 | NFM | Middleton | Middleton Radio Cars |
| 165.92500 | 170.72500 | NFM | Newcastle | Taxis |
| 165.92500 | 170.72500 | NFM | Nottingham, Hucknall | Bells Taxis |
| 165.92500 | 170.72500 | NFM | Poole | Data Repeater |
| 165.92500 | 170.72500 | NFM | Portsmouth | Aqua Cabs |
| 165.92500 | 170.72500 | NFM | Sheffield | Arc Taxis (AZTEC) |
| 165.92500 | 170.72500 | NFM | Sheffield | Valley Taxis |
| 165.92500 | 170.72500 | NFM | Stockton-on-Tees | Taxi Service |
| 165.93750 | 170.73750 | NFM | Liverpool | Gas Fitters |
| 165.93750 | 170.73750 | NFM | Nationwide | Securicor Channel 8 |
| 165.93750 | 170.73750 | NFM | Newcastle | Central Heating Co |
| 165.93750 | 170.73750 | AM | Portsmouth | American News |
| 165.93750 | 170.73750 | NFM | Swansea | Thorn Homeserve |
| 165.95000 | 170.75000 | NFM | Brighton | Car Mechanics Ch 2 |
| 165.95000 | 170.75000 | NFM | Cumbria | South Lakes Refuse Collection |
| 165.95000 | 170.75000 | NFM | Dundee | Taxis |
| 165.95000 | 170.75000 | NFM | Ellesmere Port | Cosy Cars |
| 165.95000 | 170.75000 | AM | Grimsby | Fletchers Taxis |
| 165.95000 | 170.75000 | NFM | Jersey | Collas & Le Sueur |
| 165.95000 | 170.75000 | NFM | Kendal | District Council |
| 165.95000 | 170.75000 | NFM | London | Minicab Firm Southall |
| 165.95000 | 170.75000 | NFM | March | Guy Morton |
| 165.95000 | 170.75000 | NFM | Norfolk | Norfolk Farm Produce |
| 165.95000 | 170.75000 | NFM | Northampton | Taxis |
| 165.95000 | 170.75000 | NFM | Norwich | Taxis |
| 165.96250 | 170.76250 | NFM | Birmingham | Car Repair Co |
| 165.96250 | 170.76250 | NFM | Birmingham | Driving School |
| 165.96250 | 170.76250 | NFM | Birmingham | Gas Contractors |
| 165.96250 | 170.76250 | NFM | Bournemouth | Council Parks Division |
| 165.96250 | 170.76250 | NFM | Isle of Wight | Landscaping Service |
| 165.96250 | 170.76250 | NFM | Liverpool | Taxis |
| 165.96250 | 170.76250 | NFM | Nationwide | Securicor Channel 4 |
| 165.97500 | 170.77500 | NFM | Brighton | Securicor |
| 165.97500 | 170.77500 | NFM | Bristol | Video Company |
| 165.97500 | 170.77500 | NFM | Haverfordwest | Securicor |
| 165.97500 | 170.77500 | NFM | London | Omega Parcels |
| 165.97500 | 170.77500 | NFM | Nationwide | Securicor Chan 1 Emergency |
| 165.97500 | 170.77500 | NFM | St Annes | Night Security |
| 165.98750 | 170.78750 | NFM | Jersey | Securicor |
| 165.98750 | 170.78750 | NFM | Nationwide | Securicor Channel 5 |
| 166.00000 | 170.80000 | NFM | Barrow in Furness | Z-Cars Taxis |

| Base | Mobile | Mode | Location | User and Notes |
|------|--------|------|----------|----------------|
| 166.00000 | 170.80000 | NFM | Cannock, Staffs | Taxis |
| 166.00000 | 170.80000 | NFM | Chelmsford | Farmers Supplies |
| 166.00000 | 170.80000 | NFM | Glasgow | Taxis |
| 166.00000 | 170.80000 | NFM | Guernsey | Vaudins Taxi |
| 166.00000 | 170.80000 | NFM | Hull | Taxis |
| 166.00000 | 170.80000 | NFM | Kenilworth | Taxi Co |
| 166.00000 | 170.80000 | NFM | Linlithgow | Taxis |
| 166.00000 | 170.80000 | NFM | Martham | Fleggmart |
| 166.00000 | 170.80000 | NFM | Perth | Taxis |
| 166.00000 | 170.80000 | NFM | Prestatyn | Robert's Taxis |
| 166.00000 | 170.80000 | NFM | Sheffield | Ace Taxis |
| 166.00000 | 170.80000 | NFM | South Shields | Taxis |
| 166.00000 | 170.80000 | NFM | Stevenage | Parker Cars |
| 166.00000 | 170.80000 | NFM | Swansea | Taxi Shop |
| 166.00000 | 170.80000 | NFM | Tollerton | Gadd's Farm |
| 166.00000 | 170.80000 | NFM | Torpoint | Taxis |
| 166.00000 | 170.80000 | NFM | West Drayton | Station Cars |
| 166.00000 | 170.80000 | NFM | Winton | M&G Electronics |
| 166.01250 | 170.81250 | NFM | Aberdeen | Taxis |
| 166.01250 | 170.81250 | NFM | Bedford | B.C. Cars |
| 166.01250 | 170.81250 | NFM | Birmingham | Taxi Co |
| 166.01250 | 170.81250 | NFM | Cardiff | Roath Taxis |
| 166.01250 | 170.81250 | NFM | Glasgow | Taxis |
| 166.01250 | 170.81250 | NFM | Hamilton | Taxi Owners Association |
| 166.01250 | 170.81250 | NFM | Kings Lynn | Baconpac Co |
| 166.01250 | 170.81250 | NFM | Peterborough | On Site Tyres |
| 166.01250 | 170.81250 | NFM | Sheffield | Swallownest Taxis |
| 166.02500 | 170.82500 | AM | Aberdeen | Oil Industry |
| 166.02500 | 170.82500 | NFM | Birmingham, Sheldon | Taxis |
| 166.02500 | 170.82500 | NFM | Bolton | Taxis |
| 166.02500 | 170.82500 | NFM | Cornwall | English China Clay |
| 166.02500 | 170.82500 | NFM | Doncaster | Mucks Taxis |
| 166.02500 | 170.82500 | NFM | Hillingdon | Civic Centre Security |
| 166.02500 | 170.82500 | NFM | Hitchin | Allpoints Taxis |
| 166.02500 | 170.82500 | NFM | Kennyhill | J.A Butcher |
| 166.02500 | 170.82500 | NFM | Manchester | Taxis |
| 166.02500 | 170.82500 | NFM | Newcastle | Taxis |
| 166.02500 | 170.82500 | NFM | Oldham | Taxis |
| 166.02500 | 170.82500 | NFM | Peterborough | Hotpoint |
| 166.02500 | 170.82500 | NFM | Woodbridge | Council Vans |
| 166.03750 | 170.83750 | AM | Aberdeen | Taxis |
| 166.03750 | 170.83750 | NFM | Cambridge | Cabco Taxis |
| 166.03750 | 170.83750 | NFM | Cromer | Biffa Ltd |
| 166.03750 | 170.83750 | NFM | Croydon | Kendall Cars |
| 166.03750 | 170.83750 | AM | Grimsby | Taxis |
| 166.03750 | 170.83750 | NFM | Jersey | Pentagon Ltd |
| 166.03750 | 170.83750 | NFM | London | Biffa Waste Disposal |
| 166.03750 | 170.83750 | NFM | London, East | Taxis |
| 166.03750 | 170.83750 | NFM | London, NW2 | Alpine Radio Cars (A) |
| 166.03750 | 170.83750 | NFM | Macclesfield | Atax |
| 166.03750 | 170.83750 | NFM | Motherwell | Forgewood Security |
| 166.03750 | 170.83750 | NFM | Newport | A1 Ship Hire |
| 166.03750 | 170.83750 | NFM | Peterborough | A2B Taxis |
| 166.03750 | 170.83750 | NFM | Redruth | Amtrack Deliveries |
| 166.05000 | 170.85000 | AM | Belfast | Water Board |
| 166.05000 | 170.85000 | NFM | Cardiff | Council |

| Base | Mobile | Mode | Location | User and Notes |
| --- | --- | --- | --- | --- |
| 166.05000 | 170.85000 | NFM | Chelmsford | Borough Council |
| 166.05000 | 170.85000 | NFM | Doncaster | Council Manual Workers |
| 166.05000 | 170.85000 | NFM | Dover | District Council |
| 166.05000 | 170.85000 | NFM | East Anglia | Ambulance Service |
| 166.05000 | 170.85000 | NFM | Glasgow | City Council |
| 166.05000 | 170.85000 | NFM | Gloucester | District Council |
| 166.05000 | 170.85000 | NFM | Hawick | Roxburg |
| 166.05000 | 170.85000 | NFM | Lake Windermere | Rangers & Wardens |
| 166.05000 | 170.85000 | NFM | Lancashire | Road Repairs |
| 166.05000 | 170.85000 | NFM | Leicester | Council |
| 166.05000 | 170.85000 | NFM | Liverpool | Bruno Security |
| 166.05000 | 170.85000 | NFM | London | Hillingdon Council |
| 166.05000 | 170.85000 | NFM | Manchester | Security |
| 166.05000 | 170.85000 | NFM | Milton Keynes | Council |
| 166.05000 | 170.85000 | NFM | Motherwell | District Council |
| 166.05000 | 170.85000 | NFM | Oxford | Oxford City Council |
| 166.05000 | 170.85000 | NFM | Powys | Ambulance |
| 166.05000 | 170.85000 | NFM | Preston | Council |
| 166.05000 | 170.85000 | NFM | Southampton | Council Engineering |
| 166.05000 | 170.85000 | NFM | Suffolk | Suffolk Coastal Council |
| 166.05000 | 170.85000 | NFM | Walsall | Environmental Health |
| 166.05000 | 170.85000 | NFM | Wokinghan | Council Berks |
| 166.06000 | 170.86000 | NFM | Crewe | Heating Engineers |
| 166.06250 | 170.86250 | NFM | Barrow in Furness | District Council |
| 166.06250 | 170.86250 | NFM | Barrow in Furness | SITA Cleansing Department |
| 166.06250 | 170.86250 | NFM | Blackburn | Silverline Private Hire |
| 166.06250 | 170.86250 | NFM | Bournemouth | Council engineers |
| 166.06250 | 170.86250 | AM | Brent | Council |
| 166.06250 | 170.86250 | NFM | Cleethorpes | Borough Council |
| 166.06250 | 170.86250 | NFM | Colchester | Borough Council |
| 166.06250 | 170.86250 | NFM | Deeside | Deeside Council |
| 166.06250 | 170.86250 | NFM | Dundee | City Council Workshop |
| 166.06250 | 170.86250 | NFM | Eakring | BP Depot |
| 166.06250 | 170.86250 | NFM | Forest of Dean | Gritters |
| 166.06250 | 170.86250 | NFM | Hertfordshire | County Council |
| 166.06250 | 170.86250 | NFM | Luton | Repeater |
| 166.06250 | 170.86250 | NFM | Manchester | City Council |
| 166.06250 | 170.86250 | NFM | Newbury | Council |
| 166.06250 | 170.86250 | NFM | Newcastle | City Council |
| 166.06250 | 170.86250 | NFM | North Herts | District Council Refuse |
| 166.06250 | 170.86250 | NFM | Sheffield | Council Housing Dept Area 5 |
| 166.06250 | 170.86250 | NFM | Slough | Borough Council |
| 166.06250 | 170.86250 | NFM | Taunton | Taunton Borough Council |
| 166.06250 | 170.86250 | NFM | Tonbridge | Tonbridge & Malling Council |
| 166.07500 | 170.87500 | NFM | Cannock, Staffs | Council |
| 166.07500 | 170.87500 | NFM | Carlisle | County Contracting East |
| 166.07500 | 170.87500 | NFM | Chelmsford | Council Dustcart |
| 166.07500 | 170.87500 | NFM | Cleveland | Gritters |
| 166.07500 | 170.87500 | NFM | Edinburgh | Lothian Regional Council |
| 166.07500 | 170.87500 | NFM | Hertfordshire | District Council |
| 166.07500 | 170.87500 | NFM | Ipswich | Borough Council (Parks) |
| 166.07500 | 170.87500 | NFM | Jersey | Elizabeth Castle |
| 166.07500 | 170.87500 | NFM | London, Harringay | Council Floods Control |
| 166.07500 | 170.87500 | NFM | Luton | Repeater |
| 166.07500 | 170.87500 | NFM | Manchester | Trafford Council |
| 166.07500 | 170.87500 | NFM | Nationwide | Securicor |

| Base | Mobile | Mode | Location | User and Notes |
|------|--------|------|----------|----------------|
| 166.07500 | 170.87500 | NFM | Southampton | MediCall Ch 4 |
| 166.07500 | 170.87500 | NFM | Stroud | Gritters |
| 166.07500 | 170.87500 | NFM | Wirral | Community Patrol Ch 2 |
| 166.07500 | 170.87500 | NFM | Wirral | Council Parks and Gardens |
| 166.08500 | 170.88500 | NFM | Wirral | Community Patrol Ch 1 |
| 166.08750 | 170.88750 | NFM | Berkshire | Council Ch 1 |
| 166.08750 | 170.88750 | NFM | Birmingham | Council |
| 166.08750 | 170.88750 | NFM | Bolton | District Council |
| 166.08750 | 170.88750 | NFM | Bristol | Ambulance Service |
| 166.08750 | 170.88750 | NFM | Burton, Staffs | Council |
| 166.08750 | 170.88750 | NFM | Cleethorpes | G.C. Transport |
| 166.08750 | 170.88750 | NFM | Edinburgh | Lothian Regional Council |
| 166.08750 | 170.88750 | NFM | Essex | Havering Council |
| 166.08750 | 170.88750 | NFM | Fleetwood | Wyre Council |
| 166.08750 | 170.88750 | NFM | Grimsby | Stagecoach Buses |
| 166.08750 | 170.88750 | NFM | Halifax | Council |
| 166.08750 | 170.88750 | NFM | London | Westminster Council |
| 166.08750 | 170.88750 | NFM | Oldham | Council Rubbish Men |
| 166.08750 | 170.88750 | NFM | Perth | Council Leisure & Recreation |
| 166.08750 | 170.88750 | NFM | Poulton | Council |
| 166.08750 | 170.88750 | NFM | Romford | Traffic Wardens |
| 100.08750 | 170.88750 | NFM | Southampton | City Buses |
| 166.08750 | 170.88750 | NFM | Surrey | Surrey Council (callsign zulu) |
| 166.08750 | 170.88750 | NFM | Wirral | Education Security |
| 166.10000 | 170.90000 | NFM | Bristol | Ambulance Service |
| 166.10000 | 170.90000 | NFM | Chester | Ambulance Service |
| 166.10000 | 170.90000 | NFM | Devizes | Council |
| 166.10000 | 170.90000 | NFM | Halifax | A Star Taxis |
| 166.10000 | 170.90000 | NFM | Jersey | Turner/Bluebird Cabs |
| 166.10000 | 170.90000 | NFM | London | Ambulance Service |
| 166.10000 | 170.90000 | NFM | Merseyside | Ambulance Service |
| 166.10000 | 170.90000 | NFM | Norfolk | Ambulance Service |
| 166.10000 | 170.90000 | NFM | North Yorkshire | Ambulance Service |
| 166.10000 | 170.90000 | NFM | Northumberland | Ambulance Service |
| 166.10000 | 170.90000 | NFM | Nottinghamshire | Ambulance Service |
| 166.10000 | 170.90000 | NFM | Oxfordshire | Ambulance Service |
| 166.10000 | 170.90000 | NFM | Sandwell | Medicall |
| 166.10000 | 170.90000 | NFM | Scotland | Scottish Ambulance Service |
| 166.10000 | 170.90000 | NFM | Tyne and Wear | Ambulance Service |
| 166.11250 | 170.91250 | NFM | Ashington | Wansbeck District Council |
| 166.11250 | 170.91250 | NFM | Doncaster | Council Metro Clean |
| 166.11250 | 170.91250 | NFM | Douglas, Isle of Man | Douglas Gas |
| 166.11250 | 170.91250 | NFM | Grimsby | Town Council |
| 166.11250 | 170.91250 | NFM | Isle of Man | Local Government |
| 166.11250 | 170.91250 | NFM | Lincolnshire | Council |
| 166.11250 | 170.91250 | NFM | London | Camden Council |
| 166.11250 | 170.91250 | NFM | London | Tower Hamlets Council |
| 166.11250 | 170.91250 | NFM | Newcastle | Council |
| 166.11250 | 170.91250 | NFM | Newmarket | British Legion Security |
| 166.11250 | 170.91250 | NFM | Poole | Repeater |
| 166.11250 | 170.91250 | NFM | South Glamorgan | Council |
| 166.11250 | 170.91250 | NFM | Wakefield | District Council. |
| 166.12500 | 170.92500 | NFM | Atherstone, Warks | Council |
| 166.12500 | 170.92500 | NFM | Aylesbury | District Council |
| 166.12500 | 170.92500 | NFM | Bexley Heath | Council |
| 166.12500 | 170.92500 | NFM | Buckinghamshire | Council |

| Base | Mobile | Mode | Location | User and Notes |
|------|--------|------|----------|----------------|
| 166.12500 | 170.92500 | NFM | Canterbury | City Council |
| 166.12500 | 170.92500 | NFM | Cardiff | Cardiff International Arena security |
| 166.12500 | 170.92500 | NFM | Carlisle | County Contracting West |
| 166.12500 | 170.92500 | NFM | Doncaster | Council Emergency Callout |
| 166.12500 | 170.92500 | NFM | Hounslow | Traffic Wardens |
| 166.12500 | 170.92500 | NFM | London | Ambulance Service |
| 166.12500 | 170.92500 | NFM | London | Bexley Council |
| 166.12500 | 170.92500 | NFM | Newcastle | Housing Repairs |
| 166.12500 | 170.92500 | NFM | Newport | Neighbourhood Watch |
| 166.12500 | 170.92500 | NFM | Peterborough | Holland Farms |
| 166.12500 | 170.92500 | NFM | Poole | Repeater |
| 166.12500 | 170.92500 | NFM | Salford | Council |
| 166.12500 | 170.92500 | NFM | Scarborough | Council |
| 166.12500 | 170.92500 | NFM | Swansea City | Roads Department |
| 166.13000 | 170.93000 | NFM | South Glamorgan | Doctors on call |
| 166.13750 | 170.93750 | NFM | Basildon | District Council |
| 166.13750 | 170.93750 | NFM | Brent | Council |
| 166.13750 | 170.93750 | NFM | Chippenham | Council |
| 166.13750 | 170.93750 | NFM | Doncaster | Highways Dept |
| 166.13750 | 170.93750 | NFM | Glasgow | Taxis |
| 166.13750 | 170.93750 | NFM | Hertfordshire | District Council |
| 166.13750 | 170.93750 | NFM | London | Harrow Council Maintenance |
| 166.13750 | 170.93750 | NFM | Merseyside | Ambulance Service |
| 166.13750 | 170.93750 | NFM | Newmarket | McCourts Ch 9 |
| 166.13750 | 170.93750 | NFM | Newport | Refuse Skip Control |
| 166.13750 | 170.93750 | NFM | Northern Ireland | Northern Ireland Railways |
| 166.13750 | 170.93750 | NFM | Oxford | Bus Company |
| 166.13750 | 170.93750 | NFM | Scotland | Scottish Ambulance Service |
| 166.13750 | 170.93750 | NFM | Sheffield | Brown Construction |
| 166.13750 | 170.93750 | NFM | South Glamorgan | Council |
| 166.13750 | 170.93750 | NFM | Surrey | Council |
| 166.15000 | 170.95000 | NFM | Aberdeen | Dee Van Hire |
| 166.15000 | 170.95000 | NFM | Berkshire | Council Ch 2 |
| 166.15000 | 170.95000 | NFM | Brighton | Brough Council |
| 166.15000 | 170.95000 | NFM | Bromley | Council |
| 166.15000 | 170.95000 | NFM | Doncaster | City Council |
| 166.15000 | 170.95000 | NFM | Lichfield | Council |
| 166.15000 | 170.95000 | NFM | Liverpool | City Council |
| 166.15000 | 170.95000 | NFM | Llandudno | Flood Planning |
| 166.15000 | 170.95000 | NFM | London | Bromley Council |
| 166.15000 | 170.95000 | NFM | London | Enfield Council |
| 166.15000 | 170.95000 | NFM | London | Epping Forest Council |
| 166.15000 | 170.95000 | NFM | London | Southwark Council |
| 166.15000 | 170.95000 | NFM | Macclesfield | Cheshire County Council cleansing dept. |
| 166.15000 | 170.95000 | NFM | Newport | Council Ch 1 |
| 166.15000 | 170.95000 | NFM | Poole | Repeater |
| 166.15000 | 170.95000 | NFM | South Glamorgan | Council contractors |
| 166.15000 | 170.95000 | NFM | Telford | Council |
| 166.15000 | 170.95000 | NFM | Windsor | Council |
| 166.15000 | 170.95000 | NFM | Wirral | Community Patrol Ch 3 |
| 166.15000 | 170.95000 | NFM | Wirral | Council Housing |
| 166.16000 | 170.96000 | NFM | Kilmarnock | Doctor on Call |
| 166.16250 | 170.96250 | NFM | Bracknell | District Council |
| 166.16250 | 170.96250 | NFM | Forest Heath | Council |
| 166.16250 | 170.96250 | NFM | London | Hammersmith Council |
| 166.16250 | 170.96250 | NFM | Salford | District Council |

| Base | Mobile | Mode | Location | User and Notes |
|------|--------|------|----------|----------------|
| 166.16250 | 170.96250 | NFM | Sheffield | Parks Security |
| 166.16250 | 170.96250 | NFM | Solihull | Council |
| 166.16250 | 170.96250 | NFM | Winboune | Council |
| 166.16250 | 172.96250 | NFM | Eastbourne | Community Transport |
| 166.17500 | 170.97500 | NFM | Abingdon | Council |
| 166.17500 | 170.97500 | NFM | Belfast | Northern Ireland Railways |
| 166.17500 | 170.97500 | NFM | Birmingham Sheldon | Severn Trent Water |
| 166.17500 | 170.97500 | NFM | Bridlington | Borough Council Car Parks |
| 166.17500 | 170.97500 | NFM | Brighton | Local Authority |
| 166.17500 | 170.97500 | NFM | Burnley | Council Inspectors |
| 166.17500 | 170.97500 | NFM | Burton Staffs | Council |
| 166.17500 | 170.97500 | NFM | Cambridge | District Council |
| 166.17500 | 170.97500 | NFM | Cardiff | Cardiff Council |
| 166.17500 | 170.97500 | NFM | Christchurch | Council |
| 166.17500 | 170.97500 | NFM | Cumbria | Lake District National Park |
| 166.17500 | 170.97500 | NFM | Gateshead | Council |
| 166.17500 | 170.97500 | NFM | Grays | District Council |
| 166.17500 | 170.97500 | NFM | Grimsby | Council |
| 166.17500 | 170.97500 | NFM | Harrow | Council |
| 166.17500 | 170.97500 | NFM | Heysham | Power Station |
| 166.17500 | 170.97500 | NFM | Ipswich | Jewsons Builders Merchants |
| 166.17500 | 170.97500 | NFM | Kings Lynn | District Council |
| 166.17500 | 170.97500 | NFM | Lanark | Council Repairs |
| 166.17500 | 170.97500 | NFM | Lancaster | Council |
| 166.17500 | 170.97500 | NFM | Lincolnshire | Council |
| 166.17500 | 170.97500 | NFM | London | Lewisham Council |
| 166.17500 | 170.97500 | NFM | London | Thames Ditton Council |
| 166.17500 | 170.97500 | NFM | Macclesfield | Taxis |
| 166.17500 | 170.97500 | NFM | Manchester | City Council |
| 166.17500 | 170.97500 | NFM | Morecambe | Council |
| 166.17500 | 170.97500 | NFM | Newcastle | Council Housing Repairs |
| 166.17500 | 170.97500 | NFM | Newport | Council Dustbins |
| 166.17500 | 170.97500 | NFM | Norfolk | District Council |
| 166.17500 | 170.97500 | NFM | Nottinghamshire | Ambulance Service |
| 166.17500 | 170.97500 | NFM | St Albans | Council Maintenance |
| 166.17500 | 170.97500 | NFM | Staffordshire | Council |
| 166.17500 | 170.97500 | NFM | Stirling | Stirling Council |
| 166.17500 | 170.97500 | NFM | Thanet | District Council |
| 166.17500 | 170.97500 | NFM | Vale of White Horse | District Council |
| 166.17500 | 170.97500 | NFM | Viewpark | Council Repairs |
| 166.17500 | 170.97500 | NFM | Welwyn Garden City | Welwyn & Hatfield Council |
| 166.17500 | 170.97500 | NFM | West Norfolk | Council |
| 166.18750 | 170.98750 | NFM | Aberdeen | Council Roads Department |
| 166.18750 | 170.98750 | NFM | Carlisle | City Council |
| 166.18750 | 170.98750 | NFM | Dudley | Ambulance Service |
| 166.18750 | 170.98750 | NFM | Folkestone | District Council |
| 166.18750 | 170.98750 | NFM | Hull | City Council |
| 166.18750 | 170.98750 | NFM | Ipswich | Doctor's Call Out |
| 166.18750 | 170.98750 | NFM | Kilwinning | Eglington Park Rangers (RANGERS) |
| 166.18750 | 170.98750 | NFM | Kings Lynn | Council |
| 166.18750 | 170.98750 | NFM | London | Ealing Borough Maintenance |
| 166.18750 | 170.98750 | NFM | Maidstone | Borough Council |
| 166.18750 | 170.98750 | NFM | Manchester | North West Water |
| 166.18750 | 170.98750 | NFM | Nottingham | County Council |
| 166.18750 | 170.98750 | NFM | Poole | Repeater |
| 166.18750 | 170.98750 | NFM | Spelthorth | Council |

| Base | Mobile | Mode | Location | User and Notes |
|------|--------|------|----------|----------------|
| 166.18750 | 170.98750 | NFM | Tandridge | Council |
| 166.18750 | 170.98750 | NFM | Telford | Council |
| 166.18750 | 170.98750 | NFM | Trafford | Council roads dept. |
| 166.18750 | 170.98750 | NFM | West Midlands | Environmental Health |
| 166.20000 | 171.00000 | NFM | Cheshire | Ambulance Service |
| 166.20000 | 171.00000 | NFM | Chichester | St Richards Hospital |
| 166.20000 | 171.00000 | NFM | Cleveland | Ambulance Service |
| 166.20000 | 171.00000 | NFM | Dorset | Ambulance Service |
| 166.20000 | 171.00000 | NFM | Dudley | Ambulance Service |
| 166.20000 | 171.00000 | NFM | Dyfed | Ambulance Service |
| 166.20000 | 171.00000 | NFM | Hampshire | Ambulance Service |
| 166.20000 | 171.00000 | NFM | Lancashire | Ambulance Service |
| 166.20000 | 171.00000 | NFM | Leeds Centre | Security |
| 166.20000 | 171.00000 | NFM | Lincolnshire | Ambulance Service |
| 166.20000 | 171.00000 | NFM | London | Ambulance (GREEN) South East |
| 166.20000 | 171.00000 | NFM | Merseyside | Ambulance Service |
| 166.20000 | 171.00000 | NFM | Mid Glamorgan | Ambulance Service |
| 166.20000 | 171.00000 | NFM | Nationwide | Government various users |
| 166.20000 | 171.00000 | NFM | Nationwide | Manpower Services Commission |
| 166.20000 | 171.00000 | NFM | Perth | Community Data Repeater |
| 166.20000 | 171.00000 | NFM | Scotland | Scottish Ambulance Service |
| 166.20000 | 171.00000 | NFM | Wakefield | Ambulance |
| 166.20000 | 171.00000 | NFM | Wakefield | Hospital Services |
| 166.20000 | 171.00000 | NFM | Warrington | Ambulance Service |
| 166.20000 | 171.00000 | NFM | West Midlands | Ambulance Service |
| 166.20000 | 171.00000 | NFM | West Yorkshire | Ambulance Service |
| 166.20000 | 171.00000 | NFM | Worcester | Gritters and Snowploughs |
| 166.20000 | 171.00000 | NFM | Worthing | Hospital Services |
| 166.21250 | 170.01250 | NFM | Cardiff | Bunnon |
| 166.21250 | 170.12500 | NFM | Castle Point | Borough Council |
| 166.21250 | 171.01250 | NFM | Chiltern | Council Amersham Ducks |
| 166.21250 | 171.01250 | NFM | Crawley | Crawley Council |
| 166.21250 | 171.01250 | NFM | Essex | Council |
| 166.21250 | 171.01250 | NFM | Glasgow | Taxis |
| 166.21250 | 171.01250 | NFM | Gloucester | District Council |
| 166.21250 | 171.01250 | NFM | Greenwich | Council |
| 166.21250 | 171.01250 | NFM | Hampshire | Council |
| 166.21250 | 171.01250 | NFM | Hinchley | Council |
| 166.21250 | 171.01250 | NFM | London | US Embassy Secret Service |
| 166.21250 | 171.01250 | NFM | Manchester | District Council |
| 166.21250 | 171.01250 | NFM | Newport | Gwent Council Decorators |
| 166.21250 | 171.01250 | NFM | Norfolk | ICL |
| 166.21250 | 171.01250 | NFM | Northern Ireland | Northern Ireland Railways |
| 166.21250 | 171.01250 | NFM | Swindon | Cooper's Metals |
| 166.21250 | 171.01250 | NFM | Woking | Council |
| 166.21500 | 171.01500 | NFM | Gateshead | Council |
| 166.21500 | 171.01500 | NFM | Worcester | City Council Depot |
| 166.22500 | 171.02500 | NFM | Aberdeen | Fish Market |
| 166.22500 | 171.02500 | NFM | Ashford | District Council |
| 166.22500 | 171.02500 | FM | Ayr | Sewer Maintenance |
| 166.22500 | 171.02500 | NFM | Birmingham | Park Patrol Central Control |
| 166.22500 | 171.02500 | NFM | Bridgnorth | Bridgnorth District Council |
| 166.22500 | 171.02500 | NFM | Cambridge | Council |
| 166.22500 | 171.02500 | NFM | Coventry | Council Environmental Dept. Abatement Notice |
| 166.22500 | 171.02500 | NFM | Eastleigh | Council |
| 166.22500 | 171.02500 | NFM | Guildford | Council |

| Base | Mobile | Mode | Location | User and Notes |
|------|--------|------|----------|----------------|
| 166.22500 | 171.02500 | NFM | Gwent | Blaena Gwent Council |
| 166.22500 | 171.02500 | NFM | Jersey | British Gas |
| 166.22500 | 171.02500 | NFM | Kilmarnock | Parks Department |
| 166.22500 | 171.02500 | NFM | Lewisham | Council |
| 166.22500 | 171.02500 | NFM | Lincoln | Local Authority |
| 166.22500 | 171.02500 | NFM | Livingston | West Lothian District Council |
| 166.22500 | 171.02500 | NFM | London | Kensington Council |
| 166.22500 | 171.02500 | NFM | London | Newham Council |
| 166.22500 | 171.02500 | NFM | Mid Glamorgan | Council |
| 166.22500 | 171.02500 | NFM | Nationwide | Local Authorities |
| 166.22500 | 171.02500 | NFM | Newham | Council |
| 166.22500 | 171.02500 | NFM | Nottingham | Taxis |
| 166.22500 | 171.02500 | NFM | Plymouth | City Bus Company |
| 166.22500 | 171.02500 | NFM | Preston | Council Maintenance |
| 166.22500 | 171.02500 | NFM | Reigate & Banstead | Council |
| 166.22500 | 171.02500 | NFM | Sunderland | Council |
| 166.23750 | 171.03750 | NFM | Aberdeen | TV Repairs |
| 166.23750 | 171.03750 | NFM | Bathgate | Streamline Taxis (Streamline) |
| 166.23750 | 171.03750 | NFM | Chichester | Council |
| 166.23750 | 171.03750 | NFM | Coventry, Stoneleigh | National Agricultural Centre |
| 166.23750 | 171.03750 | NFM | Cwmbran | Council |
| 166.23750 | 171.03750 | NFM | Manchester | Thameside Council |
| 166.23750 | 171.03750 | NFM | Norfolk | Haller's Skip Hire |
| 166.23750 | 171.03750 | NFM | Oldham | Halroyd Skips |
| 166.25000 | 171.05000 | NFM | Basingstoke | Council |
| 166.25000 | 171.05000 | NFM | Birmingham | Traffic lights maintenance |
| 166.25000 | 171.05000 | NFM | Brighton | Brighton Council |
| 166.25000 | 171.05000 | NFM | Bury St Edmunds | Bury Council |
| 166.25000 | 171.05000 | NFM | Chandlers Ford | Taxis |
| 166.25000 | 171.05000 | NFM | Dundee | Electrical Repairs |
| 166.25000 | 171.05000 | NFM | Elmbridge | Council |
| 166.25000 | 171.05000 | NFM | Harlow | Council |
| 166.25000 | 171.05000 | NFM | Hertfordshire | District Council |
| 166.25000 | 171.05000 | NFM | Hull | Council parks dept. |
| 166.25000 | 171.05000 | NFM | Ipswich | G.I.S. / Goldlink Guards Security |
| 166.25000 | 171.05000 | NFM | Jersey | Tantivy Holiday Coaches |
| 166.25000 | 171.05000 | NFM | Kingston | Council |
| 166.25000 | 171.05000 | NFM | Lambeth | Council |
| 166.25000 | 171.05000 | NFM | Manchester | House Calls |
| 166.25000 | 171.05000 | NFM | Mid Glamorgan | Council |
| 166.25000 | 171.05000 | NFM | Northern Ireland | Northern Ireland Railways |
| 166.25000 | 171.05000 | NFM | Poole | Repeater |
| 166.25000 | 171.05000 | NFM | Trowbridge | Builders |
| 166.25000 | 171.05000 | NFM | Tyneside | Tyne Tunnel |
| 166.26250 | 171.06250 | NFM | Bolton | Dog Warden |
| 166.26250 | 171.06250 | NFM | Braintree | Borough Council |
| 166.26250 | 171.06250 | NFM | Chesterfield | Bus Company |
| 166.26250 | 171.06250 | NFM | Dundee | Data Link |
| 166.26250 | 171.06250 | NFM | Edinburgh | Citadel Couriers (City) |
| 166.26250 | 171.06250 | NFM | Essex | Council Ch 2 |
| 166.26250 | 171.06250 | NFM | Leicester | Dustmen |
| 166.26250 | 171.06250 | NFM | Leven | DCL Security |
| 166.26250 | 171.06250 | NFM | London | Buses |
| 166.26250 | 171.06250 | NFM | London, Raynes Park | Merton Council rubbish collectors |
| 166.26250 | 171.06250 | NFM | Nuneaton & Bedworth | Council |
| 166.26250 | 171.06250 | NFM | Preston | Preston Buses |

| Base | Mobile | Mode | Location | User and Notes |
|------|--------|------|----------|----------------|
| 166.26250 | 171.06250 | NFM | Richmond | Council |
| 166.26250 | 171.06250 | NFM | Rochford | Council |
| 166.26250 | 171.06250 | NFM | Salford | Council cleansing dept. |
| 166.26250 | 171.06250 | NFM | Thetford | Broadland Council |
| 166.26500 | 171.06250 | NFM | Newcastle | Taxi |
| 166.27500 | 171.07500 | NFM | Grangemouth | Central Taxis (Central) |
| 166.27500 | 171.07500 | NFM | Hawick | Ambulance (voice & data) |
| 166.27500 | 171.07500 | NFM | Lancashire | Ambulance Service |
| 166.27500 | 171.07500 | NFM | Lincolnshire | Ambulance Service |
| 166.27500 | 171.07500 | NFM | London | Ambulance (Orange) South West |
| 166.27500 | 171.07500 | NFM | Northern Ireland | Ambulance Ch.09 (spare channel) |
| 166.27500 | 171.07500 | NFM | Scotland | Scottish Ambulance Service |
| 166.27500 | 171.07500 | NFM | Somerset | Ambulance Service |
| 166.27500 | 171.07500 | NFM | South Cumbria | Ambulance Service |
| 166.27500 | 171.07500 | NFM | Sussex | Ambulance Service |
| 166.27500 | 171.07500 | NFM | West Midlands | Ambulance Service Data Ch vehicle location |
| 166.28700 | 171.08700 | NFM | West Midlands | Ambulance Service |
| 166.28750 | 171.08750 | NFM | Ashford | Doctors on call |
| 166.28750 | 171.08750 | NFM | Belfast | Ambulance Service North patient transport Ch.5 |
| 166.28750 | 171.08750 | NFM | Buckinghamshire | Ambulance Service |
| 166.28750 | 171.08750 | NFM | Cornwall | Ambulance Service |
| 166.28750 | 171.08750 | NFM | Derby | Ambulance Service |
| 166.28750 | 171.08750 | NFM | Kent | Ambulance Service |
| 166.28750 | 171.08750 | NFM | Manchester | Ambulance Service |
| 166.28750 | 171.08750 | NFM | Northumberland | Ambulance Service |
| 166.28750 | 171.08750 | NFM | Nottinghamshire | Ambulance Service |
| 166.28750 | 171.08750 | NFM | Oxfordshire | Paramedics |
| 166.28750 | 171.08750 | NFM | Powys | Ambulance Service |
| 166.28750 | 171.08750 | NFM | Surrey | Ambulance Service |
| 166.28750 | 171.08750 | NFM | Tyne and Wear | Ambulance Service |
| 166.28750 | 171.08750 | AM | Withenshaw | Paramedics |
| 166.29000 | 171.09000 | NFM | Gateshead | Ambulance Service |
| 166.30000 | 171.10000 | NFM | Carlisle | Ambulance Service |
| 166.30000 | 171.10000 | NFM | Cumbria | Ambulance Service |
| 166.30000 | 171.10000 | NFM | Dorset | Ambulance Service |
| 166.30000 | 171.10000 | NFM | Humberside | Ambulance Service |
| 166.30000 | 171.10000 | NFM | Leicestershire | Ambulance Service |
| 166.30000 | 171.10000 | NFM | London | Ambulance (Gold) North East |
| 166.30000 | 171.10000 | NFM | Manchester | Ambulance Service |
| 166.30000 | 171.10000 | NFM | Pontypridd | Doctors Service |
| 166.30000 | 171.10000 | NFM | South Glamorgan | Ambulance Service |
| 166.30000 | 171.10000 | NFM | West Yorkshire | Ambulance Service |
| 166.31250 | 171.11250 | NFM | Cambridgeshire | Ambulance Service |
| 166.31250 | 171.11250 | NFM | Derby | Ambulance Service |
| 166.31250 | 171.11250 | NFM | Devon | Ambulance |
| 166.31250 | 171.11250 | NFM | Dyfed | Doctor's Radio |
| 166.31250 | 171.11250 | NFM | Gwynedd | Ambulance Service |
| 166.31250 | 171.11250 | NFM | London | Ambulance (Red) East |
| 166.31250 | 171.11250 | NFM | Northern Ireland | Ambulance Service East patient transport Ch.6 |
| 166.31250 | 171.11250 | NFM | Plymouth | Devon Ambulance Service |
| 166.31250 | 171.11250 | NFM | Powys | Ambulance Service |
| 166.31250 | 171.11250 | NFM | Preston | District Nurses |
| 166.31250 | 171.11250 | NFM | Salop | Ambulance Service Ch 3 |
| 166.32150 | 171.11250 | NFM | Merthyr, Powys | Mountain Rescue Air Ambulance |
| 166.32500 | 171.11250 | NFM | Humberside | Ambulance Service |
| 166.32500 | 171.12500 | NFM | Lincolnshire | Ambulance Service |

| Base | Mobile | Mode | Location | User and Notes |
|------|--------|------|----------|----------------|
| 166.32500 | 171.12500 | NFM | London | Ambulance (ORANGE) S. East |
| 166.32500 | 171.12500 | NFM | Merseyside | Ambulance Service |
| 166.32500 | 171.12500 | NFM | Mid Glamorgan | Ambulance Service |
| 166.32500 | 171.12500 | NFM | Northern Ireland | Ambulance Service North A&E Ch.1 |
| 166.32500 | 171.12500 | NFM | Nuneaton | Private Ambulance |
| 166.32500 | 171.12500 | NFM | Rhymney Valley | Ambulance Service |
| 166.32500 | 171.12500 | NFM | Scotland | Scottish Ambulance Service |
| 166.32500 | 171.12500 | NFM | Warwickshire | Ambulance service |
| 166.33750 | 171.13750 | NFM | Bedfordshire | Ambulance Service |
| 166.33750 | 171.13750 | NFM | Dundee | City Council Data Link |
| 166.33750 | 171.13750 | NFM | Hertfordshire | Ambulance Service |
| 166.33750 | 171.13750 | NFM | Isle of Wight | Ambulance |
| 166.33750 | 171.13750 | NFM | Kent | Ambulance Service |
| 166.33750 | 171.13750 | NFM | Merseyside | Ambulance Service |
| 166.33750 | 171.13750 | NFM | North Yorkshire | Ambulance Service |
| 166.33750 | 171.13750 | NFM | Northern Ireland | Ambulance Service West A&E Ch.4 |
| 166.33750 | 171.13750 | NFM | Portsmouth | Health Service |
| 166.33750 | 171.13750 | NFM | Somerset | Ambulance Service |
| 166.33750 | 171.13750 | NFM | Suffolk | Ambulance Service |
| 166.35000 | 171.15000 | NFM | Cambridgeshire | Ambulance Service |
| 166.35000 | 171.15000 | NFM | Cleveland | Ambulance Service |
| 166.35000 | 171.15000 | NFM | Coventry | Ambulance patient transport service |
| 166.35000 | 171.15000 | NFM | Cumbria | Ambulance Service |
| 166.35000 | 171.15000 | NFM | East Anglia | Ambulance Service |
| 166.35000 | 171.15000 | NFM | London | Ambulance (Red) East |
| 166.35000 | 171.15000 | NFM | Manchester | Satellite Installers |
| 166.35000 | 171.15000 | NFM | Nuneaton | Council |
| 166.35000 | 171.15000 | NFM | Peterborough | MAGPAS |
| 166.35000 | 171.15000 | NFM | Sheffield | Health Centre |
| 166.35000 | 171.15000 | NFM | Suffolk | Ambulance Service |
| 166.35000 | 171.15000 | NFM | Swansea | Ambulance Service |
| 166.35000 | 171.15000 | NFM | West Glamorgan | Ambulance Service |
| 166.35000 | 171.15000 | NFM | West Midlands | Ambulance Service |
| 166.35000 | 171.15000 | NFM | Whittlesey | Luxicabs |
| 166.36000 | 171.16000 | NFM | Merseyside | Ambulance Service |
| 166.36250 | 171.16250 | NFM | Channel Tunnel | Maintenance |
| 166.36250 | 171.16250 | NFM | Cheshire | Ambulance Service |
| 166.36250 | 171.16250 | NFM | Chester | Ambulance Service |
| 166.36250 | 171.16250 | NFM | Crewe | Ambulance Service |
| 166.36250 | 171.16250 | NFM | Dyfed | Ambulance Service |
| 166.36250 | 171.16250 | NFM | East Anglia | Ambulance Service |
| 166.36250 | 171.16250 | NFM | Essex | Ambulance Service |
| 166.36250 | 171.16250 | NFM | Gloucester | Ambulance Service |
| 166.36250 | 171.16250 | NFM | Hampshire | Ambulance Service |
| 166.36250 | 171.16250 | NFM | Lincolnshire | Ambulance Service |
| 166.36250 | 171.16250 | NFM | Liverpool | Ambulance Service |
| 166.36250 | 171.16250 | NFM | Pembroke | Ambulance Service |
| 166.37500 | 171.17500 | NFM | Barrow in Furness | Ambulance Service |
| 166.37500 | 171.17500 | NFM | Cumbria | Ambulance Service |
| 166.37500 | 171.17500 | NFM | Derbyshire | Ambulance Service |
| 166.37500 | 171.17500 | NFM | Dundee | Taxis |
| 166.37500 | 171.17500 | NFM | Fleetwood | Medicall |
| 166.37500 | 171.17500 | NFM | Herefordshire | Ambulance Service |
| 166.37500 | 171.17500 | NFM | Isle of Wight | Ambulance Service |
| 166.37500 | 171.17500 | NFM | London South East | Ambulance (GREEN) |
| 166.37500 | 171.17500 | NFM | Stockport | Ambulance Service |

| Base | Mobile | Mode | Location | User and Notes |
|---|---|---|---|---|
| 166.37500 | 171.17500 | NFM | Sussex | Ambulance Service |
| 166.37500 | 171.17500 | NFM | Whittlesey | Jenner Health Centre |
| 166.37500 | 171.17500 | NFM | Worcestershire | Ambulance Service |
| 166.38250 | 171.18250 | NFM | East Sussex | Ambulance Service |
| 166.38750 | 171.18750 | NFM | Berkshire | Ambulance Service |
| 166.38750 | 171.18750 | NFM | Cambridgeshire | Ambulance Service |
| 166.38750 | 171.18750 | NFM | Kent | Ambulance Service |
| 166.38750 | 171.18750 | NFM | Lancashire | Ambulance Service |
| 166.38750 | 171.18750 | NFM | North Yorkshire | Ambulance Service |
| 166.38750 | 171.18750 | NFM | Peterborough | Ambulance Service |
| 166.38750 | 171.18750 | NFM | Preston | Ambulance Service |
| 166.38750 | 171.18750 | NFM | Scotland | Scottish Ambulance Service |
| 166.38750 | 171.18750 | NFM | Staffordshire | Ambulance Service Ch 3 (TROJAN) |
| 166.38750 | 171.18750 | NFM | Warrington | Ambulance Service |
| 166.38750 | 171.18750 | NFM | West Midlands | St Johns Ambulance |
| 166.38750 | 171.18750 | NFM | West Yorkshire | Ambulance Service |
| 166.40000 | 171.20000 | NFM | Blackburn | Ambulance Service |
| 166.40000 | 171.20000 | NFM | Derbyshire | Ambulance Service |
| 166.40000 | 171.20000 | NFM | East Sussex | Ambulance Service |
| 166.40000 | 171.20000 | NFM | Gwent | Ambulance Service |
| 166.40000 | 171.20000 | NFM | Humberside | Ambulance Service |
| 166.40000 | 171.20000 | NFM | Lincolnshire | Ambulance Service |
| 166.40000 | 171.20000 | NFM | London | US Embassy Secret Service |
| 166.40000 | 171.20000 | NFM | Northern Ireland | Ambulance Service East A&E Ch.2 |
| 166.40000 | 171.20000 | NFM | Northumberland | Ambulance Service |
| 166.40000 | 171.20000 | NFM | Tyne and Wear | Ambulance Service (Red) |
| 166.40000 | 171.20000 | NFM | West & South Yorkshire | Ambulance Service |
| 166.41250 | 171.21250 | NFM | Clwyd | Ambulance Service |
| 166.41250 | 171.21250 | NFM | Dalton in Furness | Taxi |
| 166.41250 | 171.21250 | NFM | Dyfed | Doctor's Radio |
| 166.41250 | 171.21250 | NFM | Dyfed, East | Ambulance    Service |
| 166.41250 | 171.21250 | NFM | Leicestershire | Ambulance Service |
| 166.41250 | 171.21250 | NFM | Lincoln | Ambulance Service |
| 166.41250 | 171.21250 | NFM | London | Ambulance (Red) South Ch 3. |
| 166.41250 | 171.21250 | NFM | Nottinghamshire | Ambulance Service |
| 166.41250 | 171.21250 | NFM | Rhyl | Dee's Taxis |
| 166.41250 | 171.21250 | NFM | Salop | Ambulance |
| 166.41250 | 171.21250 | NFM | Shropshire | Ambulance Service |
| 166.41250 | 171.21250 | NFM | Swindon | Ambulance Service |
| 166.41250 | 171.21250 | NFM | West Yorkshire | Ambulance Service |
| 166.41250 | 171.21250 | NFM | Wiltshire | Ambulance Service |
| 166.42500 | 171.22500 | NFM | Birmingham | Locums Service |
| 166.42500 | 171.22500 | NFM | Bradford | Doctors On Call |
| 166.42500 | 171.22500 | NFM | Cambridge | Dr Lankester |
| 166.42500 | 171.22500 | NFM | Devon | Ambulance |
| 166.42500 | 171.22500 | NFM | Devon, North | Ambulance patients transport service |
| 166.42500 | 171.22500 | NFM | Glasgow | Taxis |
| 166.42500 | 171.22500 | NFM | Kilmarnock | Johnnie Walker Distillery |
| 166.42500 | 171.22500 | NFM | Kings Lynn | Dr Ewlett |
| 166.42500 | 171.22500 | NFM | Liverpool | Emergency Doctors |
| 166.42500 | 171.22500 | NFM | London | Ambulance (Gold) North East |
| 166.42500 | 171.22500 | NFM | Norfolk | Emergency Doctor Service |
| 166.42500 | 171.22500 | NFM | Salop | Midwives Ch 4 |
| 166.42500 | 171.22500 | NFM | Shropshire | Ambulance Service |
| 166.42500 | 171.22500 | AM | Stoke on Trent | Emergency Doctor |
| 166.42500 | 171.22500 | NFM | West Midlands | Doctors on Call |

| Base | Mobile | Mode | Location | User and Notes |
|------|--------|------|----------|----------------|
| 166.42500 | 171.22500 | NFM | West Yorkshire | Deputising Service |
| 166.43500 | 166.43500 | NFM | Chester | Ambulance Service |
| 166.43750 | 171.23750 | NFM | Bedfordshire | Ambulance Emergency Relay |
| 166.43750 | 171.23750 | NFM | Berkshire | Ambulance Emergency Relay |
| 166.43750 | 171.23750 | NFM | Buckinghamshire | Ambulance Emergency Relay |
| 166.43750 | 171.23750 | NFM | Cambridgeshire | Ambulance Emergency Relay |
| 166.43750 | 171.23750 | NFM | Cheshire | Ambulance Emergency Relay |
| 166.43750 | 171.23750 | NFM | Cleveland | Ambulance Emergency Relay |
| 166.43750 | 171.23750 | NFM | Devon | Air Ambulance |
| 166.43750 | 171.23750 | NFM | East Anglia | Ambulance Service |
| 166.43750 | 171.23750 | NFM | East Sussex | Ambulance Emergency Relay |
| 166.43750 | 171.23750 | NFM | Essex | Ambulance Emergency Relay |
| 166.43750 | 171.23750 | NFM | Hampshire | Ambulance Emergency Relay |
| 166.43750 | 171.23750 | NFM | Humberside | Ambulance Emergency Relay |
| 166.43750 | 171.23750 | NFM | Leicestershire | Ambulance Emergency Relay |
| 166.43750 | 171.23750 | NFM | Lincolnshire | Ambulance Emergency Relay |
| 166.43750 | 171.23750 | NFM | London | Ambulance Service (RED) |
| 166.43750 | 171.23750 | NFM | London | St. Johns Ambulance Ch.10 |
| 166.43750 | 171.23750 | NFM | Manchester Airport | Ambulance |
| 166.43750 | 171.23750 | NFM | Merseyside | Ambulance Emergency Relay |
| 166.43750 | 171.23750 | NFM | Nationwide | Emergency Ambulance Channel |
| 166.43750 | 171.23750 | NFM | Norfolk | Ambulance Emergency Relay |
| 166.43750 | 171.23750 | NFM | North Yorkshire | Ambulance Emergency Relay |
| 166.43750 | 171.23750 | NFM | Northamptonshire | Ambulance Emergency Relay |
| 166.43750 | 171.23750 | NFM | Northern Ireland | Ambulance Service reserve channel Ch.10 |
| 166.43750 | 171.23750 | NFM | Staffordshire | Ambulance patient transport (TROJAN) |
| 166.43750 | 171.23750 | NFM | Suffolk | Ambulance Emergency Relay |
| 166.43750 | 171.23750 | NFM | Surrey | Ambulance Emergency Relay |
| 166.43750 | 171.23750 | NFM | Tyne and Wear | Ambulance Emergency Relay |
| 166.43750 | 171.23750 | NFM | Warwickshire | Ambulance service relay |
| 166.43750 | 171.23750 | NFM | West Midlands | Ambulance Emergency Relay |
| 166.43750 | 171.23750 | NFM | West Sussex | Ambulance Emergency Relay |
| 166.43750 | 171.23750 | NFM | West Yorkshire | Ambulance Emergency Relay |
| 166.45000 | 166.45000 | NFM | Newport, Gwent | Breakdown Recovery Company |
| 166.45000 | 171.25000 | NFM | Birmingham | Community Midwives |
| 166.45000 | 171.25000 | NFM | Blackburn | Blackburn Health Authority |
| 166.45000 | 171.25000 | NFM | Bradford | Doctor Dep Service |
| 166.45000 | 171.25000 | NFM | Bristol | Roman Taxis |
| 166.45000 | 171.25000 | NFM | Derby | District Nurses |
| 166.45000 | 171.25000 | NFM | Jersey | Honorary Police St Ouen Ch 2 |
| 166.45000 | 171.25000 | NFM | Kings Lynn | Doctors |
| 166.45000 | 171.25000 | NFM | London | Ambulance (BLUE) North West |
| 166.45000 | 171.25000 | NFM | Manchester | Ambulance Service |
| 166.45000 | 171.25000 | NFM | Normanton, West Yorkshire | Taxi |
| 166.45000 | 171.25000 | NFM | Poole | East Dorset Health Authority |
| 166.45000 | 171.25000 | NFM | W Yorkshire | Lexicon Deputising Service |
| 166.45000 | 171.25000 | NFM | Wantage | Doctors |
| 166.45000 | 171.25000 | NFM | Wisbech | Clarkson Health Centre |
| 166.46250 | 171.26250 | NFM | Bedfordshire | Ambulance Service |
| 166.46250 | 171.26250 | NFM | Cheltenham | Metro Buses |
| 166.46250 | 171.26250 | NFM | Clwyd | Ambulance Service |
| 166.46250 | 171.26250 | NFM | Coventry | Ambulance Service |
| 166.46250 | 171.26250 | NFM | Hertfordshire | Ambulance patients transport service |
| 166.46250 | 171.26250 | NFM | London | US Embassy Secret Service |
| 166.46250 | 171.26250 | NFM | North Yorkshire | Ambulance Service |
| 166.46250 | 171.26250 | NFM | Ravenglass | Steam Railway |

| Base | Mobile | Mode | Location | User and Notes |
|------|--------|------|----------|----------------|
| 166.46250 | 171.26250 | NFM | Rhyl (Clwyd) | Emergency Ambulances |
| 166.46250 | 171.26250 | NFM | Swindon | Metro Buses |
| 166.46250 | 171.26250 | NFM | West Midlands | Ambulance Service B Div Ch 2 |
| 166.46250 | 171.26250 | NFM | West Sussex | Ambulance Service |
| 166.46250 | 171.26250 | NFM | West Yorkshire | Ambulance Service |
| 166.47500 | 171.27500 | NFM | Bristol | Ambulance Service |
| 166.47500 | 171.27500 | NFM | Gloucestershire | Ambulance Service |
| 166.47500 | 171.27500 | NFM | Gwynedd | Ambulance Service |
| 166.47500 | 171.27500 | NFM | Hampshire | Ambulance Service |
| 166.47500 | 171.27500 | NFM | Herefordshire | Ambulance Service |
| 166.47500 | 171.27500 | NFM | Jersey | Honorary Police Channel 4 |
| 166.47500 | 171.27500 | NFM | London | Ambulance (Blue) North West |
| 166.47500 | 171.27500 | NFM | Merseyside | Ambulance Service |
| 166.47500 | 171.27500 | NFM | North Yorkshire | Ambulance Service |
| 166.47500 | 171.27500 | NFM | Scarborough | Ambulance Service |
| 166.47500 | 171.27500 | NFM | Scotland | Scottish Ambulance Service |
| 166.47500 | 171.27500 | NFM | South Glamorgan | Ambulance Service |
| 166.47500 | 171.27500 | NFM | Worcestershire | Ambulance Service |
| 166.48750 | 171.28750 | NFM | Blackburn | Ambulance Service |
| 166.48750 | 171.28750 | NFM | Dorset | Ambulance Service |
| 166.48750 | 171.28750 | NFM | Essex | Ambulance Service |
| 166.48750 | 171.28750 | NFM | Jersey | Honorary Police Ch 3 |
| 166.48750 | 171.28750 | NFM | Liverpool | Ambulance Service |
| 166.48750 | 171.28750 | NFM | London | US Embassy Secret Service |
| 166.48750 | 171.28750 | NFM | Manchester | Ambulance Service |
| 166.48750 | 171.28750 | NFM | Northumberland | Ambulance Service |
| 166.48750 | 171.28750 | NFM | Oxfordshire | Ambulance Service |
| 166.48750 | 171.28750 | NFM | Scotland | Scottish Ambulance Service |
| 166.48750 | 171.28750 | NFM | South Yorkshire | Ambulance Service |
| 166.48750 | 171.28750 | NFM | Staffordshire | Patients Transport Service (TROJAN) |
| 166.48750 | 171.28750 | NFM | Tyne and Wear | Ambulance Service |
| 166.50000 | 171.30000 | NFM | Avon | Ambulance (BLUE BASE) |
| 166.50000 | 171.30000 | NFM | Birmingham | Selly Oaks Hospital transport |
| 166.50000 | 171.30000 | NFM | Blackpool | Ambulance Service |
| 166.50000 | 171.30000 | NFM | Bolton | Ambulance Service |
| 166.50000 | 171.30000 | NFM | Bristol | Ambulance Service |
| 166.50000 | 171.30000 | NFM | Bury | Medical |
| 166.50000 | 171.30000 | NFM | Cambridgeshire | Ambulance Service |
| 166.50000 | 171.30000 | NFM | Cornwall | Ambulance Service |
| 166.50000 | 171.30000 | NFM | London | Ambulance (Gold) North East |
| 166.50000 | 171.30000 | NFM | Manchester | Ambulance Service |
| 166.50000 | 171.30000 | NFM | North Yorkshire | Ambulance Service |
| 166.50000 | 171.30000 | NFM | Northern Ireland | Ambulance Ch.3 South A&E |
| 166.50000 | 171.30000 | NFM | Northumberland | Ambulance Service |
| 166.50000 | 171.30000 | NFM | Northwich | Ambulance Service |
| 166.50000 | 171.30000 | NFM | Scilly Isles | Ambulance Service |
| 166.50000 | 171.30000 | NFM | Scotland | Scottish Ambulance Service |
| 166.50000 | 171.30000 | NFM | South Glamorgan | Ambulance Service |
| 166.50000 | 171.30000 | NFM | Staffordshire | Ambulance Service |
| 166.50000 | 171.30000 | NFM | Wakefield | Medical supplier |
| 166.50000 | 171.30000 | NFM | Warwickshire | Ambulance Service |
| 166.50000 | 171.30000 | NFM | West Midlands | Ambulance Service |
| 166.51250 | 171.31250 | NFM | Cambridge | Ambulance Service |
| 166.51250 | 171.31250 | NFM | County Durham | Ambulance Service (DC) |
| 166.51250 | 171.31250 | NFM | Lancashire | Ambulance Service |
| 166.51250 | 171.31250 | NFM | Leeds | Wymas to Hospital |

| Base | Mobile | Mode | Location | User and Notes |
|---|---|---|---|---|
| 166.51250 | 171.31250 | NFM | London | US Embassy Secret Service |
| 166.51250 | 171.31250 | NFM | Manchester | Ambulance Service |
| 166.51250 | 171.31250 | NFM | Northumberland | Ambulance Service |
| 166.51250 | 171.31250 | NFM | Oldham | Ambulance Service |
| 166.51250 | 171.31250 | NFM | Peterborough | Ambulance Service |
| 166.51250 | 171.31250 | NFM | Salop | Ambulance |
| 166.51250 | 171.31250 | NFM | Shropshire | Ambulance PTS |
| 166.51250 | 171.31250 | NFM | Surrey | Ambulance Service |
| 166.51250 | 171.31250 | NFM | Warwickshire | Ambulance Service |
| 166.52500 | 171.32500 | NFM | Dorset | Ambulance Service |
| 166.52500 | 171.32500 | NFM | East Anglia | Ambulance Service |
| 166.52500 | 171.32500 | NFM | East Ridding | Ambulance Service |
| 166.52500 | 171.32500 | NFM | Hampshire | Ambulance Service |
| 166.52500 | 171.32500 | NFM | Humberside | Ambulance Service |
| 166.52500 | 171.32500 | NFM | Lancashire | Ambulance Service |
| 166.52500 | 171.32500 | NFM | London | Ambulance (Red) South |
| 166.52500 | 171.32500 | NFM | Mid Glamorgan | Ambulance Service |
| 166.52500 | 171.32500 | NFM | North Yorkshire | Ambulance Service |
| 166.52500 | 171.32500 | NFM | Suffolk | Ambulance Service |
| 166.52500 | 171.32500 | NFM | Warwickshire | Ambulance Service |
| 166.52500 | 171.32500 | NFM | West Sussex | Ambulance Service |
| 166.53750 | 171.33750 | NFM | Blackburn | Ambulance Service |
| 166.53750 | 171.33750 | NFM | Halifax | Ambulance Service |
| 166.53750 | 171.33750 | NFM | Leeds | Doctors Service |
| 166.53750 | 171.33750 | NFM | Leicestershire | Ambulance Service |
| 166.53750 | 171.33750 | NFM | North Yorkshire | Ambulance Service |
| 166.53750 | 171.33750 | NFM | Surrey | Ambulance Service |
| 166.53750 | 171.33750 | NFM | West Yorkshire | Ambulance Service |
| 166.55000 | 171.35000 | NFM | Ayrshire | Ambulance Service |
| 166.55000 | 171.35000 | NFM | Cirencester | Hospital Doctors |
| 166.55000 | 171.35000 | NFM | Devon | Patient Ambulance Service |
| 166.55000 | 171.35000 | NFM | Doncaster | Doctors On Call |
| 166.55000 | 171.35000 | NFM | Essex | Ambulance Service |
| 166.55000 | 171.35000 | NFM | Hampshire | Ambulance Service |
| 166.55000 | 171.35000 | NFM | Humberside | Ambulance Service |
| 166.55000 | 171.35000 | NFM | Lancashire | Ambulance Service |
| 166.55000 | 171.35000 | NFM | Northamptonshire | Ambulance Service |
| 166.55000 | 171.35000 | NFM | Portsmouth | Ambulance Service |
| 166.55000 | 171.35000 | NFM | Sheffield | Ambulance Emergency |
| 166.55000 | 171.35000 | NFM | South Yorkshire | Ambulance Service |
| 166.55000 | 171.35000 | NFM | West Midlands | Ambulance Service |
| 166.55000 | 171.35000 | NFM | West Yorkshire | Ambulance Service |
| 166.56250 | 171.36250 | NFM | Barnsley | Hospital services. |
| 166.56250 | 171.36250 | NFM | Bournemouth | Hospital Minibus |
| 166.56250 | 171.36250 | NFM | Bristol | Ambulance |
| 166.56250 | 171.36250 | NFM | Buckinghamshire | Ambulance Service |
| 166.56250 | 171.36250 | NFM | Clwyd | Ambulance Service |
| 166.56250 | 171.36250 | NFM | Devon | Ambulance Service |
| 166.56250 | 171.36250 | NFM | Dundee | National Carriers |
| 166.56250 | 171.36250 | NFM | East Anglian | Ambulance |
| 166.56250 | 171.36250 | NFM | Herefordshire | Ambulance Service |
| 166.56250 | 171.36250 | NFM | Mold (Clwyd) | Ambulance Service |
| 166.56250 | 171.36250 | NFM | Norfolk | Ambulance Service |
| 166.56250 | 171.36250 | NFM | Northern Ireland | Ambulance Ch.8 West patient transport |
| 166.56250 | 171.36250 | NFM | Perth | Ready Mixed Concrete |
| 166.56250 | 171.36250 | NFM | Sheffield | Ambulance Out-Patients |

| Base | Mobile | Mode | Location | User and Notes |
|------|--------|------|----------|----------------|
| 166.56250 | 171.36250 | NFM | South Yorkshire | Ambulance Service |
| 166.56250 | 171.36250 | NFM | West Sussex | Ambulance Service |
| 166.56250 | 171.36250 | NFM | Worcestershire | Ambulance Service |
| 166.57500 | 171.37500 | NFM | Ayrshire | Patient Transport Service |
| 166.57500 | 171.37500 | NFM | Bolton | Doctors On Call |
| 166.57500 | 171.37500 | NFM | Gwent | Ambulance Service |
| 166.57500 | 171.37500 | NFM | Gwynedd | Ambulance Service |
| 166.57500 | 171.37500 | NFM | Hampshire | Ambulance Service |
| 166.57500 | 171.37500 | NFM | Hereford & Worcester | Ambulance Service |
| 166.57500 | 171.37500 | NFM | Humberside | Ambulance Service |
| 166.57500 | 171.37500 | NFM | Leeds | Ambulance Service |
| 166.57500 | 171.37500 | NFM | London | Ambulance (White) Inner London |
| 166.57500 | 171.37500 | NFM | London, south east | Ambulance Service |
| 166.57500 | 171.37500 | NFM | Merseyside | Ambulance Service |
| 166.57500 | 171.37500 | NFM | Norfolk | Ambulance A&E link |
| 166.57500 | 171.37500 | NFM | North Yorkshire | Ambulance Service |
| 166.57500 | 171.37500 | NFM | Northamptonshire | Ambulance Service |
| 166.57500 | 171.37500 | NFM | Northumberland | Ambulance Service |
| 166.57500 | 171.37500 | NFM | West Glamorgan | Ambulance Service |
| 166.57500 | 171.37500 | NFM | West Yorkshire | Ambulance |
| 166.58750 | 171.38750 | NFM | Aberdeen | Surveyors |
| 166.58750 | 171.38750 | NFM | Durham | Ambulance Service |
| 166.58750 | 171.38750 | NFM | Hampshire | Ambulance Service |
| 166.58750 | 171.38750 | NFM | Hertfordshire | Ambulance Service |
| 166.58750 | 171.38750 | NFM | Lincolnshire | Ambulance |
| 166.58750 | 171.38750 | NFM | Merseyside | Ambulance Service |
| 166.58750 | 171.38750 | NFM | Northern Ireland | Ambulance Ch.7 South patient transport |
| 166.58750 | 171.38750 | NFM | South Glamorgan | Ambulance Service |
| 166.58750 | 171.38750 | NFM | South Yorkshire | Ambulance Service |
| 166.58750 | 171.38750 | NFM | Staffordshire | Ambulance Service Ch 4 (major accidents) |
| 166.60000 | 171.40000 | NFM | Colchester | Medical Couriers |
| 166.60000 | 171.40000 | NFM | Doncaster | Midwives |
| 166.60000 | 171.40000 | AM | England & Wales | Doctors Special Services |
| 166.60000 | 171.40000 | NFM | Essex, North East | Doctors |
| 166.60000 | 171.40000 | NFM | Ipswich | Doctor's Surgery |
| 166.60000 | 171.40000 | NFM | Manchester | Ambulance Service |
| 166.60000 | 171.40000 | NFM | Northumberland | Ambulance Service |
| 166.60000 | 171.40000 | NFM | Peterborough | Dr. Gray |
| 166.60000 | 171.40000 | NFM | Preston | Electricians |
| 166.60000 | 171.40000 | AM | Saffron Walden | Accident Group |
| 166.60000 | 171.40000 | AM | Swaffham | Dr. Pilkington |
| 166.60000 | 171.40000 | NFM | Tyne and Wear | Ambulance Service |
| 166.60000 | 171.40000 | NFM | West Midlands | Ambulance Service A Div Ch 3 |
| 166.60000 | 171.40000 | NFM | Worcestershire | Doctors Scheme |
| 166.61250 | 171.41250 | NFM | Barking | Council |
| 166.61250 | 171.41250 | NFM | Berkshire | Ambulance Service |
| 166.61250 | 171.41250 | NFM | Havant | Dixies Taxis |
| 166.61250 | 171.41250 | NFM | Hertfordshire | Ambulance Service |
| 166.61250 | 171.41250 | NFM | Humberside | Ambulance Service |
| 166.61250 | 171.41250 | NFM | North Yorkshire | Ambulance Service |
| 166.61250 | 171.41250 | NFM | Oxfordshire | Ambulance Service |
| 166.61250 | 171.41250 | NFM | Perthshire | Electricians |
| 166.61250 | 171.41250 | NFM | Staffordshire | Ambulance Service Ch 2 |
| 166.61250 | 171.41250 | NFM | Stoke on Trent | Ambulance Service |
| 166.61250 | 171.41250 | NFM | Welwyn | Ambulance Service |
| 166.61250 | 171.41250 | NFM | Wiltshire | Ambulance Service |

| Base | Mobile | Mode | Location | User and Notes |
|---|---|---|---|---|
| 166.62500 | 171.42500 | AM | Aberdeen | Retail Park |
| 166.62500 | 171.42500 | NFM | Bath | Francis Plant Hire |
| 166.62500 | 171.42500 | NFM | Bolton | Cobra Taxis |
| 166.62500 | 171.42500 | NFM | Bournemouth | Breakdown Recovery |
| 166.62500 | 171.42500 | NFM | Bristol | Red Taxis |
| 166.62500 | 171.42500 | NFM | Cambridge | Cambridge Growers |
| 166.62500 | 171.42500 | NFM | Cardiff | City Taxis |
| 166.62500 | 171.42500 | NFM | Dundee | Taxis |
| 166.62500 | 171.42500 | NFM | Eltham | Taxis |
| 166.62500 | 171.42500 | NFM | Hampshire | Streamline Cabs |
| 166.62500 | 171.42500 | NFM | Ipswich | DHSS |
| 166.62500 | 171.42500 | NFM | Lytham | Whitesides Taxis |
| 166.62500 | 171.42500 | NFM | Manchester | Taxi |
| 166.62500 | 171.42500 | AM | Nationwide | Ambulance-to-Hospital Link |
| 166.62500 | 171.42500 | NFM | Poole | Repeater |
| 166.62500 | 171.42500 | NFM | Stirling | Thistle Centre |
| 166.62500 | 171.42500 | NFM | Worcester | Delta Taxis |
| 166.63750 | 171.43750 | NFM | Aberdeen | Radio Specialists |
| 166.63750 | 171.43750 | NFM | Ashington | Toward Taxis |
| 166.63750 | 171.43750 | NFM | Bolton | Taxis |
| 166.63750 | 171.43750 | NFM | Collyhurst | Taxis |
| 166.63750 | 171.43750 | NFM | Coventry | Lewis Taxis |
| 166.63750 | 171.43750 | NFM | Drayton | Draytax Taxis |
| 166.63750 | 171.43750 | NFM | Glasgow, Pitt Street | DSS |
| 166.63750 | 171.43750 | NFM | Isle of Wight | Grange Taxis |
| 166.63750 | 171.43750 | NFM | Lancing | Access Cars |
| 166.63750 | 171.43750 | NFM | London | Taxis |
| 166.63750 | 171.43750 | NFM | Manchester | Crestra Car Hire |
| 166.63750 | 171.43750 | NFM | Nationwide | Rediffussion Comms |
| 166.63750 | 171.43750 | NFM | Oldham | Taxis |
| 166.63750 | 171.43750 | NFM | Peacehaven | Dave's Taxis |
| 166.63750 | 171.43750 | NFM | Royston | Farmers Fertilisers |
| 166.63750 | 171.43750 | NFM | Whittlesey | S & S Tractors |
| 166.63750 | 171.43750 | NFM | Woodbridge | Greenwell Farms |
| 166.65000 | 171.45000 | NFM | Bedfordshire | Bedfordshire Growers |
| 166.65000 | 171.45000 | NFM | Bury | Byford Taxis |
| 166.65000 | 171.45000 | NFM | Cardiff | ICL Computers |
| 166.65000 | 171.45000 | NFM | Central London | Taxis |
| 166.65000 | 171.45000 | NFM | Flixton | Beaumont's Private Hire |
| 166.65000 | 171.45000 | NFM | Glasgow | Taxis |
| 166.65000 | 171.45000 | NFM | Halifax | Crossleys Taxis |
| 166.65000 | 171.45000 | NFM | Hampshire | Wessex Plant Hire |
| 166.65000 | 171.45000 | NFM | Huntingdon | R. O'Connell |
| 166.65000 | 171.45000 | NFM | Ipswich | Taxi Association |
| 166.65000 | 171.45000 | NFM | Leeds | Bell Cable engineers Ch.3 |
| 166.65000 | 171.45000 | NFM | London | ODRATS |
| 166.65000 | 171.45000 | NFM | Maidstone | Streamline Taxis |
| 166.65000 | 171.65000 | NFM | Belfast | Ferguson Flowers |
| 166.65500 | 171.45500 | NFM | Woodingdean | Taxis |
| 166.66250 | 171.46250 | NFM | Baldock | Butts Taxis |
| 166.66250 | 171.46250 | NFM | Barkway | British Sugar |
| 166.66250 | 171.46250 | NFM | Bristol | Aerial Riggers |
| 166.66250 | 171.46250 | NFM | Bury | British Sugar |
| 166.66250 | 171.46250 | NFM | Cantley | British Sugar |
| 166.66250 | 171.46250 | NFM | Cheltenham | Celtax Couriers |
| 166.66250 | 171.46250 | NFM | Dullingham | P.BTaylor |

| Base | Mobile | Mode | Location | User and Notes |
|------|--------|------|----------|----------------|
| 166.66250 | 171.46250 | NFM | Exeter | Al Cars |
| 166.66250 | 171.46250 | NFM | Felixstowe | Wizard Taxis Ch 2 |
| 166.66250 | 171.46250 | NFM | Grimsby | Peter Sheffield Buses |
| 166.66250 | 171.46250 | NFM | London | Scorpio Cars |
| 166.66250 | 171.46250 | NFM | Manchester | Taxis |
| 166.66250 | 171.46250 | NFM | Methil | Taxis |
| 166.66250 | 171.46250 | NFM | Nationwide | ICL Channel 1 |
| 166.66250 | 171.46250 | NFM | Perth | Taylors Taxis |
| 166.66250 | 171.46250 | NFM | Sudbury | A Line Taxis |
| 166.66250 | 171.46250 | NFM | Sussex | Tarmac Contractors |
| 166.66250 | 171.46250 | NFM | Swinton | Skytax |
| 166.67500 | 171.47500 | NFM | Alconbury | Steve's Taxis |
| 166.67500 | 171.47500 | NFM | Alderney | Alderney Taxis |
| 166.67500 | 171.47500 | NFM | Bolton | Best Way Taxis |
| 166.67500 | 171.47500 | NFM | Ealing | Taxis |
| 166.67500 | 171.47500 | NFM | Elvington | Rolawn Turf Suppliers |
| 166.67500 | 171.47500 | NFM | Glasgow | Taxi Company |
| 166.67500 | 171.47500 | NFM | Hampshire | Ace Taxis |
| 166.67500 | 171.47500 | NFM | Hounslow | Minicab Co |
| 166.67500 | 171.47500 | NFM | Hull | Security Co |
| 166.67500 | 171.47500 | NFM | Ipswich | Hawk Express |
| 166.67500 | 171.47500 | NFM | Lancaster | District Nurse |
| 166.67500 | 171.47500 | NFM | London, Wimbledon | Minicab Firm |
| 166.67500 | 171.47500 | NFM | Morecambe | District Nurse |
| 166.67500 | 171.47500 | NFM | Mostyn | Dave's Taxis |
| 166.67500 | 171.47500 | NFM | Nationwide | ICL Channel 2 |
| 166.67500 | 171.47500 | NFM | Northampton | Taxis |
| 166.67500 | 171.47500 | NFM | Radcliffe | Harvey's Taxis |
| 166.67500 | 171.47500 | NFM | Southampton | A2B Taxis |
| 166.67500 | 171.47500 | NFM | Southhall | Taxis |
| 166.67500 | 171.47500 | NFM | West Midlands | Cashmore's Steel |
| 166.67500 | 171.47500 | NFM | Winbourne | Skiphire |
| 166.68750 | 171.48750 | NFM | Berinsfield | Star Cars |
| 166.68750 | 171.48750 | NFM | Bury St Edmonds | British Sugar |
| 166.68750 | 171.48750 | NFM | Buxton | Crane & Son |
| 166.68750 | 171.48750 | NFM | Chatteris | Whitworth Produce |
| 166.68750 | 171.48750 | NFM | East Kilbride | Kelvin Kabs |
| 166.68750 | 171.48750 | NFM | Glasgow | Taxis |
| 166.68750 | 171.48750 | NFM | Guernsey | AC Heating |
| 166.68750 | 171.48750 | NFM | Guernsey | Cobo Building |
| 166.68750 | 171.48750 | NFM | Ipswich | Ransomes |
| 166.68750 | 171.48750 | NFM | Kings Lynn | British Sugar |
| 166.68750 | 171.48750 | NFM | London | Tipper lorry base |
| 166.68750 | 171.48750 | NFM | Newport | Town Taxis |
| 166.68750 | 171.48750 | NFM | Norfolk | Crane & Son |
| 166.68750 | 171.48750 | NFM | Northampton | Taxis |
| 166.68750 | 171.48750 | NFM | Peterborough | Co-Op TV Services |
| 166.68750 | 171.48750 | NFM | Portsmouth | CTE Television |
| 166.68750 | 171.48750 | NFM | Swindon | Starlight Taxis |
| 166.69000 | 171.49000 | NFM | Newport, Gwent | ABC Taxis |
| 166.70000 | 171.50000 | NFM | Bestway | Taxis |
| 166.70000 | 171.50000 | NFM | Birmingham, Shard End | Taxi |
| 166.70000 | 171.50000 | NFM | Cirencester | Radio Cars |
| 166.70000 | 171.50000 | NFM | Guernsey | Central Transfers |
| 166.70000 | 171.50000 | NFM | Hampshire | Haverson Electronics |
| 166.70000 | 171.50000 | NFM | Hull | Parks Department |

| Base | Mobile | Mode | Location | User and Notes |
|------|--------|------|----------|----------------|
| 166.70000 | 171.50000 | NFM | London | US Embassy Secret Service |
| 166.70000 | 171.50000 | NFM | Methwold | Darby Bros Farms |
| 166.70000 | 171.50000 | NFM | Montrose | Taxis |
| 166.70000 | 171.50000 | NFM | Northampton | Taxis |
| 166.70000 | 171.50000 | NFM | Norwich | Bestway Taxis |
| 166.70000 | 171.50000 | NFM | Nottingham, Hucknall | Phoenix Cars |
| 166.70000 | 171.50000 | NFM | Sheffield | Taxis |
| 166.70000 | 171.50000 | NFM | Southampton | RMS Motors |
| 166.71250 | 171.51250 | NFM | Abingdon | JMB Plant Hire |
| 166.71250 | 171.51250 | NFM | Canvey Island | Taxis |
| 166.71250 | 171.51250 | NFM | Coventry | Taxi |
| 166.71250 | 171.51250 | NFM | Edinburgh | Festival Cars |
| 166.71250 | 171.51250 | NFM | Grimsby | Taxis |
| 166.71250 | 171.51250 | NFM | Havant | Jacks Taxis |
| 166.71250 | 171.51250 | NFM | Morecambe | Taxis |
| 166.71250 | 171.51250 | NFM | Norwich | Knight Benjamin |
| 166.71250 | 171.51250 | NFM | Royston | Johnson Mathey Precious Metals Security |
| 166.71250 | 171.51250 | NFM | Sheffield | RD Cars |
| 166.71250 | 171.51250 | NFM | Southampton | Taxis |
| 166.71250 | 171.51250 | NFM | Wispington | British Sugar |
| 166.72500 | 171.52500 | NFM | Alderney | Alderney Emergency Service |
| 166.72500 | 171.52500 | NFM | Gt. Yarmouth | Birds Eye Vans |
| 166.72500 | 171.52500 | NFM | Lowestoft | Birds Eye |
| 166.72500 | 171.52500 | NFM | Sharnbrook | Unilever |
| 166.73750 | 171.53750 | NFM | Bolton | Cross Private Hire |
| 166.73750 | 171.53750 | AM | Colchester | Rainbow Taxis |
| 166.73750 | 171.53750 | NFM | Essex | Taxis |
| 166.73750 | 171.53750 | NFM | Grampian | Transport Company |
| 166.73750 | 171.53750 | NFM | London | National Radio Cars |
| 166.73750 | 171.53750 | NFM | Manchester | Taxis |
| 166.73750 | 171.53750 | NFM | Nationwide | ICL Channel 3 |
| 166.73750 | 171.53750 | NFM | Norwich | Knight Benjamin |
| 166.73750 | 171.53750 | NFM | Pitsea | Taxis |
| 166.73750 | 171.53750 | NFM | Poulton | Poulton Cabs |
| 166.73750 | 171.53750 | NFM | Rochdale | Globe Taxis |
| 166.73750 | 171.53750 | NFM | Widnes | Kay Cabs |
| 166.74000 | 171.54000 | NFM | West Midlands | JRs Taxis |
| 166.75000 | 171.55000 | NFM | Banchory | Taxis |
| 166.75000 | 171.55000 | NFM | Co Durham | Emergency Doctors Service |
| 166.75000 | 171.55000 | NFM | Crewe | Ambulance |
| 166.75000 | 171.55000 | NFM | Eastbourne | Ambulance Service |
| 166.75000 | 171.55000 | NFM | Lancaster | Council |
| 166.75000 | 171.55000 | NFM | Morecambe | Council |
| 166.75000 | 171.55000 | NFM | Nationwide | DSS Dole Fraud Teams |
| 166.75000 | 171.55000 | NFM | Portsmouth | Ambulance Service |
| 166.75000 | 171.55000 | NFM | Staffordshire | Ambulance Service |
| 166.75000 | 171.55000 | NFM | Surrey | Ambulance Service |
| 166.76000 | 171.56000 | NFM | Burnley | Town centre Storewatch |
| 166.76250 | 171.56250 | NFM | Bournemouth | Traffic Wardens |
| 166.76250 | 171.56250 | NFM | Cambridge | Girton College (TOWER) |
| 166.76250 | 171.56250 | NFM | Canterbury | Shopwatch |
| 166.76250 | 171.56250 | NFM | Castle Donington | Race Control |
| 166.76250 | 171.56250 | NFM | Coventry | Coventry University Maintenance |
| 166.76250 | 171.56250 | NFM | Dudley | Delivery Company |
| 166.76250 | 171.56250 | NFM | Dumfries | District Council |
| 166.76250 | 171.56250 | NFM | Finchley | Medics |

| Base | Mobile | Mode | Location | User and Notes |
| --- | --- | --- | --- | --- |
| 166.76250 | 171.56250 | NFM | Harlow | Harvey Centre Security |
| 166.76250 | 171.56250 | NFM | Ipswich | Taxis |
| 166.76250 | 171.56250 | NFM | Irvine | Shopping Centre Security |
| 166.76250 | 171.56250 | NFM | Kirkcaldy | Mercat Shopping Centre Security |
| 166.76250 | 171.56250 | NFM | Nationwide | DSS Dole Fraud Teams |
| 166.76250 | 171.56250 | NFM | Poole | Guardforce Security |
| 166.76250 | 171.56250 | NFM | Rother Valley | Sports Centre |
| 166.76250 | 171.56250 | NFM | Rugby | Shops Radio Link to Police |
| 166.76250 | 171.56250 | NFM | Swindon | Oasis Leisure Centre |
| 166.77500 | 171.57500 | NFM | Abingdon | Abingdon Hospital |
| 166.77500 | 171.57500 | NFM | Bedfordshire | Ambulance |
| 166.77500 | 171.57500 | NFM | Bedfordshire | Midwives |
| 166.77500 | 171.57500 | NFM | Birmingham | Doctors |
| 166.77500 | 171.57500 | NFM | Burnley | Doctors Call Out |
| 166.77500 | 171.57500 | NFM | Cardiff | Health Service |
| 166.77500 | 171.57500 | NFM | Dover | Council |
| 166.77500 | 171.57500 | NFM | East Anglian | Ambulance Ch.8 link to St. Johns Ambulance |
| 166.77500 | 171.57500 | NFM | Glamorgan | Ambulance Service |
| 166.77500 | 171.57500 | NFM | Hampshire | Ambulance Service |
| 166.77500 | 171.57500 | NFM | Hertfordshire | Ambulance Service |
| 166.77500 | 171.57500 | NFM | Ipswich | Midwives |
| 166.77500 | 171.57500 | NFM | Lancaster | District Nurse |
| 166.77500 | 171.57500 | NFM | Manchester | Taxis |
| 166.77500 | 171.57500 | NFM | Morecambe | District Nurse |
| 166.77500 | 171.57500 | NFM | Nationwide | DSS Dole Fraud Teams |
| 166.77500 | 171.57500 | NFM | Scotland | Scottish Ambulance Service |
| 166.77500 | 171.57500 | NFM | Suffolk | District Nurses |
| 166.77500 | 171.57500 | NFM | Warwickshire | Ambulance Service |
| 166.78500 | 166.78500 | NFM | Stoke on Trent | TV Aerials |
| 166.78500 | 171.58750 | NFM | Glasgow | Stobhill Hospital |
| 166.78750 | 171.58750 | AM | Aberdeen | Oil Servicing |
| 166.78750 | 171.58750 | NFM | Bournemouth | Castle Recovery |
| 166.78750 | 171.58750 | NFM | Caterham Hill | RCS Comrep Ch 5 |
| 166.78750 | 171.58750 | NFM | Cornwall | Vetco Base |
| 166.78750 | 171.58750 | NFM | Dorking | Car Recovery (King Babe) |
| 166.78750 | 171.58750 | NFM | Dumfries | District Council |
| 166.78750 | 171.58750 | NFM | Edinburgh | Diamond Security |
| 166.78750 | 171.58750 | NFM | Grimsby | Lincs Vending |
| 166.78750 | 171.58750 | NFM | Grimsby | Mariner Gas |
| 166.78750 | 171.58750 | NFM | Hampshire | Council |
| 166.78750 | 171.58750 | NFM | Ipswich | Taxis |
| 166.78750 | 171.58750 | NFM | Lancaster | District Nurse |
| 166.78750 | 171.58750 | NFM | Lincolnshire | Community Repeater |
| 166.78750 | 171.58750 | NFM | London | Buses |
| 166.78750 | 171.58750 | NFM | Morecambe | District Nurse |
| 166.78750 | 171.58750 | NFM | Newcastle | Auto Breakdowns |
| 166.78750 | 171.58750 | NFM | Plymouth | Co-Op Store Detectives |
| 166.78750 | 171.58750 | NFM | Tyneside/Northumberland | Recovery Service |
| 166.80000 | 171.60000 | NFM | Doncaster | Royal Infirmary |
| 166.80000 | 171.60000 | NFM | Glossop | District Nurses |
| 166.80000 | 171.60000 | NFM | Gloucester | Ambulance Service Ch2 |
| 166.80000 | 171.60000 | NFM | Manchester | Hospital Porters |
| 166.80000 | 171.60000 | NFM | Mansfield | Kings Mill Hospital |
| 166.80000 | 171.60000 | NFM | Poole | General Hospital |
| 166.80000 | 171.60000 | NFM | Winsford | Doctors Base |
| 166.81250 | 171.61250 | NFM | Chapmanslade | Barters Farm |

| 166.81250 | 171.61250 | NFM | Derby | Hospital Flying Squad (ZULU) |
| 166.81250 | 171.61250 | NFM | Doncaster | Health Centre |
| 166.81250 | 171.61250 | NFM | England & Wales | Common Doctors Freq |
| 166.81250 | 171.61250 | NFM | Essex | Havering Council |
| 166.81250 | 171.61250 | NFM | Haverfordwest | E Williams Transport |
| 166.81250 | 171.61250 | NFM | Hertfordshire | Doctors Channel |
| 166.81250 | 171.61250 | NFM | Isle of Man | Ambulance Service |
| 166.81250 | 171.61250 | NFM | Kings Lynn | District Nurses |
| 166.81250 | 171.61250 | NFM | Llanelli | Doctors on Call |
| 166.81250 | 171.61250 | NFM | Nationwide | Doctors Ch 1 |
| 166.81250 | 171.61250 | NFM | Norfolk | Doctors |
| 166.81250 | 171.61250 | NFM | North Lancashire | Doctors On Call |
| 166.81250 | 171.61250 | NFM | Northampton | Emergency Doctors |
| 166.81250 | 171.61250 | NFM | Oxfordshire | Common Doctors Freq. |
| 166.81250 | 171.61250 | NFM | Runcorn | Doctor Channel |
| 166.81250 | 171.61250 | NFM | Stoke-on-Trent | Doctors Service |
| 166.81250 | 171.61250 | NFM | Sussex | Brighton Council |
| 166.81250 | 171.61250 | NFM | Swindon | Ambulance Service |
| 166.81250 | 171.61250 | NFM | Upwell | Health Centre |
| 166.81250 | 171.61250 | NFM | Welwyn & Hatfield | Accident Services |
| 166.81250 | 171.61250 | NFM | Yorkshire | Medic Service |
| 166.82500 | 171.62500 | NFM | Bournemouth | Emergency Services |
| 166.82500 | 171.62500 | NFM | Burnley | Council Security Patrols |
| 166.82500 | 171.62500 | NFM | Clare | Dr Carter |
| 166.82500 | 171.62500 | NFM | Coventry | Chemtek Cleansing Liquids |
| 166.82500 | 171.62500 | NFM | Hastings | Council |
| 166.82500 | 171.62500 | NFM | Herefordshire | Ambulance Service |
| 166.82500 | 171.62500 | NFM | Ipswich | Wilding & Smith |
| 166.82500 | 171.62500 | NFM | Jersey | Yellow Cabs |
| 166.82500 | 171.62500 | NFM | Kent | Ambulance Service |
| 166.82500 | 171.62500 | NFM | London, Islington | Flood Control |
| 166.82500 | 171.62500 | NFM | Nationwide | DSS Dole Fraud Teams |
| 166.82500 | 171.62500 | NFM | Swansea City | Ambulance Service |
| 166.82500 | 171.62500 | AM | Thanet | Ambulance Service |
| 166.82500 | 171.62500 | NFM | West Glamorgan | Ambulance Service |
| 166.82500 | 171.62500 | NFM | Wirral | District Nurses |
| 166.82500 | 171.62500 | NFM | Worcestershire | Ambulance Service |
| 166.83750 | 171.63750 | NFM | Castle Donington | Medic Control |
| 166.83750 | 171.63750 | NFM | Dorset | Ambulance Service |
| 166.83750 | 171.63750 | NFM | Emsworth | John's Cabs |
| 166.83750 | 171.63750 | NFM | Gateshead | Doctor on Call and Interlink |
| 166.83750 | 171.63750 | NFM | Gloucestershire | Ambulance Service |
| 166.83750 | 171.63750 | NFM | Hampshire | District Nurse |
| 166.83750 | 171.63750 | NFM | Hockley | Doctors |
| 166.83750 | 171.63750 | NFM | Kent | Health Service |
| 166.83750 | 171.63750 | NFM | Leeds | Bell Cable engineers Ch.16 |
| 166.83750 | 171.63750 | NFM | Leeds, Seacroft | Ball Cable Media |
| 166.83750 | 171.63750 | NFM | Mid Glamorgan | Doctors on call |
| 166.83750 | 171.63750 | NFM | Peterborough | Doctors Service |
| 166.83750 | 171.63750 | NFM | S Essex | Mobile Doctors Ch 1 |
| 166.85000 | 171.65000 | NFM | Bradford | Yorkshire Cable |
| 166.85000 | 171.65000 | NFM | Bristol | Washing Machine Engineers |
| 166.85000 | 171.65000 | NFM | Cambridgeshire | Community Nurses |
| 166.85000 | 171.65000 | NFM | Co.Antrim | United Hospitals internal transport |
| 166.85000 | 171.65000 | NFM | Dundee | Christian Salvesen |
| 166.85000 | 171.65000 | NFM | East Sussex | Doctors On Call |

| Base | Mobile | Mode | Location | User and Notes |
|------|--------|------|----------|----------------|
| 166.85000 | 171.65000 | NFM | Edinburgh | Taxis |
| 166.85000 | 171.65000 | NFM | Haverfordwest | Gillmans Quarry |
| 166.85000 | 171.65000 | NFM | Kent | Health Service |
| 166.85000 | 171.65000 | NFM | Medway | Doctors on Call |
| 166.85000 | 171.65000 | NFM | North Humberside | Transport |
| 166.85000 | 171.65000 | NFM | Poole | Taxis |
| 166.85000 | 171.65000 | NFM | South Glamorgan | Doctors on call |
| 166.85000 | 171.65000 | NFM | Swansea | Brisco Skip Hire Waste Disposal Service |
| 166.85000 | 171.65000 | NFM | Tower Hill | Doctors |
| 166.86250 | 171.66250 | AM | Aberdeen | Rig Servicing |
| 166.86250 | 171.66250 | NFM | Coventry | Mayfair Security Ch 1 |
| 166.86250 | 171.66250 | NFM | Crewe | City Council |
| 166.86250 | 171.66250 | NFM | Edinburgh | Housing Dept. |
| 166.86250 | 171.66250 | NFM | Hillingdon | Emergency Radio System |
| 166.86250 | 171.66250 | NFM | Jersey | Pioneer Coaches |
| 166.86250 | 171.66250 | NFM | London | Borough Of Lambeth |
| 166.86250 | 171.66250 | NFM | Newcastle | Taxis |
| 166.86250 | 171.66250 | NFM | Sheffield | Night Security Services |
| 166.86250 | 171.66250 | NFM | Swindon | Thamesdown Buses |
| 166.86250 | 171.66250 | NFM | Wigan | Highways Department |
| 166.86250 | 171.66250 | NFM | Yorkshire | Wimpey Homes |
| 166.87350 | 171.63750 | NFM | Portsmouth | MediCall Ch 2 |
| 166.87350 | 171.63750 | NFM | St Helens | Emergency Doctors |
| 166.87500 | 171.67500 | NFM | Aberdeen | Community Repeater |
| 166.87500 | 171.67500 | NFM | Ayr | Carriers |
| 166.87500 | 171.67500 | NFM | Dundee | Doctors |
| 166.87500 | 171.67500 | NFM | Freethorpe | Aitchison Bros |
| 166.87500 | 171.67500 | NFM | Gateshead | Security |
| 166.87500 | 171.67500 | NFM | Grimsby | Stagecoach Buses |
| 166.87500 | 171.67500 | NFM | Herefordshire | Farmers |
| 166.87500 | 171.67500 | NFM | Irvine | Parcel Force |
| 166.87500 | 171.67500 | NFM | Letchworth | Micks Taxis |
| 166.87500 | 171.67500 | NFM | London | Scaffolding company |
| 166.87500 | 171.67500 | NFM | Manchester | Porter's Dairies |
| 166.87500 | 171.67500 | NFM | Morpeth | Council |
| 166.87500 | 171.67500 | NFM | Norfolk | Auto Windscreens |
| 166.87500 | 171.67500 | NFM | Northumberland | Farm Workers |
| 166.87500 | 171.67500 | NFM | Oxford | Rascal |
| 166.87500 | 171.67500 | NFM | Peterborough | CBS Repeater |
| 166.87500 | 171.67500 | NFM | Poole | Taxis |
| 166.87500 | 171.67500 | NFM | Preston | Dynarod |
| 166.87500 | 171.67500 | NFM | Rhymney Valley | Hotpoint Service Engineers |
| 166.87500 | 171.67500 | NFM | Somerset | Council |
| 166.87500 | 171.67500 | NFM | Warwick | Vet |
| 166.87500 | 171.67500 | NFM | Worcester | Gaming Machine Repairs |
| 166.88750 | 171.68750 | NFM | Benson | A Cabs |
| 166.88750 | 171.68750 | NFM | Birmingham | Taxis |
| 166.88750 | 171.68750 | NFM | Blackpool | Council Transport |
| 166.88750 | 171.68750 | NFM | Bolton | Express Taxis |
| 166.88750 | 171.68750 | NFM | Dorset | Nightguard Security |
| 166.88750 | 171.68750 | NFM | Fleetwood | Works Department |
| 166.88750 | 171.68750 | NFM | Flintwick | Airlink |
| 166.88750 | 171.68750 | NFM | Gateshead | Taxis |
| 166.88750 | 171.68750 | NFM | Hal.fax | Whitehill Taxis |
| 166.88750 | 171.68750 | NFM | Hampshire | PDSA |
| 166.88750 | 171.68750 | NFM | Haworth | Leam Taxis |

| Base | Mobile | Mode | Location | User and Notes |
|------|--------|------|----------|----------------|
| 166.88750 | 171.68750 | NFM | Lancaster | Council |
| 166.88750 | 171.68750 | NFM | Leeds | Bell Cable engineers Ch.11 |
| 166.88750 | 171.68750 | NFM | London | Blackheath Car Services |
| 166.88750 | 171.68750 | NFM | Morecambe | Council |
| 166.88750 | 171.68750 | NFM | Nationwide | Community Repeater |
| 166.88750 | 171.68750 | NFM | Poole | Repeater |
| 166.88750 | 171.68750 | NFM | West Suffolk | Cambridge & East Coast Cable |
| 166.90000 | 171.70000 | NFM | Aberdeen | Aberdeen Vets |
| 166.90000 | 171.70000 | NFM | Brighton | Nynex Cablecomms |
| 166.90000 | 171.70000 | NFM | Cannock | Mr Sparks Garage |
| 166.90000 | 171.70000 | NFM | Cardiff | TNT Deliveries Ch 2 |
| 166.90000 | 171.70000 | NFM | Colchester | A.E Arnold |
| 166.90000 | 171.70000 | NFM | Doncaster | Fone-A-Car |
| 166.90000 | 171.70000 | NFM | Ely | Vets |
| 166.90000 | 171.70000 | NFM | Gloucester | Community Repeater |
| 166.90000 | 171.70000 | NFM | Oldham | Council |
| 166.90000 | 171.70000 | NFM | Worthing | Nynex Cable |
| 166.91250 | 171.71250 | NFM | Bolton | Zodiac Taxis |
| 166.91250 | 171.71250 | NFM | Durham | TNT Carriers |
| 166.91250 | 171.71250 | NFM | Edinburgh | Scottish & Newcastle Security |
| 166.91250 | 171.71250 | NFM | Guernsey | States Electricity |
| 166.91250 | 171.71250 | NFM | Ipswich | British Sugar |
| 166.91250 | 171.71250 | NFM | Maidenhead | Taxis |
| 166.91250 | 171.71250 | NFM | Nationwide | TNT Transport |
| 166.91250 | 171.71250 | NFM | Newark | Taxis |
| 166.91250 | 171.71250 | NFM | Nottingham | Taxis |
| 166.91250 | 171.71250 | NFM | Peterborough | British Sugar |
| 166.91250 | 171.71250 | NFD | Sheffield | Tri-Star Security Ltd. (BULLDOG) |
| 166.91250 | 171.71250 | NFM | Streatham | N Rose Builders |
| 166.92500 | 171.72500 | NFM | Bootle | Taxis |
| 166.92500 | 171.72500 | NFM | Central Manchester | Lion Private Hire |
| 166.92500 | 171.72500 | NFM | Edinburgh | Community Repeater |
| 166.92500 | 171.72500 | NFM | Enfield | Taxis |
| 166.92500 | 171.72500 | NFM | Finchley | Taxis |
| 166.92500 | 171.72500 | NFM | Frome | Taxis |
| 166.92500 | 171.72500 | NFM | Great Yarmouth | Birds Eye Vans |
| 166.92500 | 171.72500 | NFM | Guernsey | States Electricity |
| 166.92500 | 171.72500 | NFM | Littleport | J.H. Martin |
| 166.92500 | 171.72500 | NFM | Lowestoft | Birds Eye |
| 166.92500 | 171.72500 | NFM | Newcastle | Taxis |
| 166.92500 | 171.72500 | NFM | Oldham | Roller's Private Hire |
| 166.92500 | 171.72500 | NFM | Peterborough | 3 Star Taxis |
| 166.92500 | 171.72500 | NFM | Slough | Viking Radio Cars |
| 166.93750 | 171.73750 | NFM | Aberdeen | Retail Park Security |
| 166.93750 | 171.73750 | NFM | Edinburgh | Private Traffic Wardens (APOCA) |
| 166.93750 | 171.73750 | NFM | Greenham County | Council |
| 166.93750 | 171.73750 | NFM | Hindley | Anrich Vets |
| 166.93750 | 171.73750 | NFM | Newcastle | Highway Maintenance |
| 166.93750 | 171.73750 | NFM | Portsmouth | Harbour Security |
| 166.93750 | 171.73750 | NFM | South Glamorgan | Doctors on call |
| 166.93750 | 171.73750 | NFM | Trowbridge | Alpha Taxis |
| 166.95000 | 171.75000 | NFM | Accrington | Doctors callout service |
| 166.95000 | 171.75000 | NFM | East Dereham | Taxis |
| 166.95000 | 171.75000 | NFM | Isle of Man | Harris Electricity |
| 166.95000 | 171.75000 | NFM | Leeds | Bell Cable engineers Ch.14 |
| 166.95000 | 171.75000 | NFM | London | Amey Roadstone |

| Base | Mobile | Mode | Location | User and Notes |
|------|--------|------|----------|----------------|
| 166.95000 | 171.75000 | NFM | Nationwide | BBC TV O/B Crews |
| 166.95000 | 171.75000 | NFM | Sheffield | Vending Machine Company |
| 166.95000 | 171.75000 | NFM | Southampton | Doctors (CANDOC) |
| 166.95000 | 171.75000 | NFM | Surrey | Amey Roadstone M3 maintenance (AMEY) |
| 166.96000 | 171.76000 | NFM | Worthing | Taxis |
| 166.96250 | 171.76250 | NFM | Ashford | Invecta Taxis |
| 166.96250 | 171.76250 | NFM | Coventry | Lnterlink Parcels |
| 166.96250 | 171.76250 | NFM | Glasgow | Taxis |
| 166.96250 | 171.76250 | NFM | Hull | Taxis |
| 166.96250 | 171.76250 | NFM | Irvine | Taxis |
| 166.96250 | 171.76250 | NFM | Letchworth | Garys Taxis |
| 166.96250 | 171.76250 | NFM | London | Taxis |
| 166.96250 | 171.76250 | NFM | Prestwich | Taxis |
| 166.96250 | 171.76250 | NFM | Salford | Taxis |
| 166.96250 | 171.76250 | NFM | Whitefield | Blueline Private Hire |
| 166.96250 | 171.76250 | NFM | Winchester | Taxis |
| 166.97500 | 171.77500 | NFM | Barnsley | Taxis |
| 166.97500 | 171.77500 | NFM | Dyfed | Crane Hire |
| 166.97500 | 171.77500 | NFM | Edinburgh | Community Repeater |
| 166.97500 | 171.77500 | NFM | Guernsey | Channel TV Rent-a-Set |
| 166.97500 | 171.77500 | NFM | Harwich | Daves Taxis |
| 166.97500 | 171.77500 | NFM | Haverfordwest | Crane Hire |
| 166.97500 | 171.77500 | NFM | Manchester | Taxis |
| 166.97500 | 171.77500 | NFM | Oxford | 001 Cars |
| 166.97500 | 171.77500 | NFM | Peterborough | Associated Adams Taxis |
| 166.97500 | 171.77500 | NFM | Poole | Knight |
| 166.97500 | 171.77500 | NFM | Portsmouth | Taxis |
| 166.97500 | 171.77500 | NFM | Sheffield | A1 Cars |
| 166.97500 | 171.77500 | NFM | Southampton | Taxis |
| 166.98750 | 171.78750 | NFM | Bedford | A to B Cars |
| 166.98750 | 171.78750 | NFM | Cambridgeshire | Haulage Co |
| 166.98750 | 171.78750 | NFM | Dunstable | Jim & Jocks Taxis |
| 166.98750 | 171.78750 | NFM | Felixstowe | Road Haulage Co |
| 166.98750 | 171.78750 | NFM | Fleetwood | Wyre Borough Council |
| 166.98750 | 171.78750 | NFM | Glasgow | Taxis |
| 166.98750 | 171.78750 | NFM | Littleport | Sallis Bros |
| 166.98750 | 171.78750 | NFM | Luton | Silverline Taxis |
| 166.98750 | 171.78750 | NFM | Newmarket | E.F. Saltmarsh |
| 166.98750 | 171.78750 | NFM | Poole | Council |
| 166.98750 | 171.78750 | NFM | Portsmouth | Channel Satellites |
| 167.00000 | 171.80000 | NFM | Bedfordshire | Vet Service |
| 167.00000 | 171.80000 | NFM | Ellerker | F.S. & E.M. Wood Haulage |
| 167.00000 | 171.80000 | NFM | Hampshire | Dickson Bros. |
| 167.00000 | 171.80000 | NFM | Humberside | RSPCA |
| 167.00000 | 171.80000 | NFM | Leicester | Taxis |
| 167.00000 | 171.80000 | NFM | Newcastle | Delivery Firm |
| 167.00000 | 171.80000 | NFM | Newcastle | Road Maintenance |
| 167.01250 | 171.81250 | NFM | Binbrook | Nickersons Farmers |
| 167.01250 | 171.81250 | NFM | Burnley | General Hospital Security |
| 167.01250 | 171.81250 | NFM | Cardiff | Council |
| 167.01250 | 171.81250 | NFM | Cardiff | Security |
| 167.01250 | 171.81250 | NFM | Coventry | BFI Waste |
| 167.01250 | 171.81250 | NFM | Essex | Telecom Repeater |
| 167.01250 | 171.81250 | NFM | Humberside | Birds-Eye Foods |
| 167.01250 | 171.81250 | NFM | Ipswich | Yellow Taxis |
| 167.01250 | 171.81250 | NFM | Kenilworth | Brookshire Taxis |

| Base | Mobile | Mode | Location | User and Notes |
|------|--------|------|----------|----------------|
| 167.01250 | 171.81250 | NFM | Newmarket | Suffolk Housing |
| 167.01250 | 171.81250 | NFM | Northampton | Taxis |
| 167.01250 | 171.81250 | NFM | Swindon | Swindon Bus Company |
| 167.01250 | 171.81250 | NFM | Wales | Council Contractors |
| 167.02500 | 171.82500 | NFM | Bedford | A.G.S. |
| 167.02500 | 171.82500 | NFM | Benfleet | Vehicle Recovery Co |
| 167.02500 | 171.82500 | NFM | Birmingham Chelmsley Wood | Taxis |
| 167.02500 | 171.82500 | NFM | Bolton | Lyma Taxis |
| 167.02500 | 171.82500 | NFM | Burnley | Whites Taxis |
| 167.02500 | 171.82500 | NFM | East Dereham | Fransham Farm Co. |
| 167.02500 | 171.82500 | NFM | Ely | Stopps Taxis |
| 167.02500 | 171.82500 | NFM | Glasgow | Taxis |
| 167.02500 | 171.82500 | NFM | Hull | Taxis |
| 167.02500 | 171.82500 | NFM | Leicester | Taxis |
| 167.02500 | 171.82500 | NFM | London | Kerri Cars |
| 167.02500 | 171.82500 | NFM | London | US Embassy Secret Service |
| 167.02500 | 171.82500 | NFM | London, Willesden Green | Enter Mini Cabs |
| 167.02500 | 171.82500 | NFM | Merry Hill | Centre Traffic |
| 167.02500 | 171.82500 | NFM | Poulton | Poulton Cabs |
| 167.02500 | 171.82500 | NFM | Whiston | Britannia Taxis |
| 167.02500 | 171.82500 | NFM | Whitley Bay | Taxis |
| 107.03750 | 171.83670 | NFM | Hartfordshire | Hatfield House staff & security |
| 167.03750 | 171.83750 | NFM | Cambridge | Computer Engineers (ANG 1) |
| 167.03750 | 171.83750 | NFM | Coventry | Security Co (NHP BASE) |
| 167.03750 | 171.83750 | NFM | Elverdon | Centre Parcs, Reception and Admin |
| 167.03750 | 171.83750 | NFM | Gaydon, Warks, | Rover test track and circuit control |
| 167.03750 | 171.83750 | NFM | Glasgow | Securiguard |
| 167.03750 | 171.83750 | NFM | Hull | Birds Eye Pea Vining |
| 167.03750 | 171.83750 | NFM | Hull | East Yorkshire Motor Services |
| 167.03750 | 171.83750 | NFM | Isle of Man | Manx Transport Services |
| 167.03750 | 171.83750 | NFM | Leicester | Security |
| 167.03750 | 171.83750 | NFM | London | Burns Security |
| 167.03750 | 171.83750 | NFM | Lowestoft | Birds Eye |
| 167.03750 | 171.83750 | NFM | Newport | Hales TV Repairs |
| 167.03750 | 171.83750 | NFM | Norfolk | Council Car Parks |
| 167.03750 | 171.83750 | NFM | Swanage | Beach patrols |
| 167.03750 | 171.83750 | NFM | West Midlands | Talk Of Landrovers |
| 167.03750 | 171.83750 | NFM | Wiltshire | Longleat House |
| 167.05000 | 171.85000 | NFM | Cambridge | Cable Ch 2 |
| 167.05000 | 171.85000 | NFM | Nottingham | TV Repairs |
| 167.05000 | 171.85000 | AM | Southampton | TVS |
| 167.06000 | 171.86000 | NFM | Halifax | Ziggys Taxis |
| 167.06250 | 171.86250 | NFM | Abbeywood | Taxis |
| 167.06250 | 171.86250 | AM | Bolton | Private Hire |
| 167.06250 | 171.86250 | NFM | Chelmsford | Car Recovery |
| 167.06250 | 171.86250 | AM | Humberside | Haulage Co |
| 167.06250 | 171.86250 | NFM | Kirkcaldy | Ellis Taxis |
| 167.06250 | 171.86250 | NFM | Leicester | University Security |
| 167.06250 | 171.86250 | NFM | London, south east | Taxis |
| 167.06250 | 171.86250 | NFM | Newark | Taxis |
| 167.06250 | 171.86250 | NFM | Retford | You and Me Parcels |
| 167.06250 | 171.86250 | NFM | Salford | Publicans Warning/Security Net. |
| 167.06250 | 171.86250 | NFM | Sharnbrook | Associated Asphalt |
| 167.06250 | 171.86250 | NFM | Sheffield | A1 Cars Ch 2 |
| 167.06250 | 171.86250 | NFM | Sheffield | KC Cars |
| 167.07500 | 171.87500 | NFM | Chorley | Taxis |

| Base | Mobile | Mode | Location | User and Notes |
|---|---|---|---|---|
| 167.07500 | 171.87500 | NFM | Cleveland | Peter Taxis |
| 167.07500 | 171.87500 | NFM | Forrest Hill | Taxis |
| 167.07500 | 171.87500 | NFM | Glasgow | Taxis |
| 167.07500 | 171.87500 | NFM | Guernsey | Bob Froome |
| 167.07500 | 171.87500 | NFM | Humberside | Haulage Co |
| 167.07500 | 171.87500 | NFM | Manchester | Taxi |
| 167.07500 | 171.87500 | NFM | Motherwell | Redline Cabs |
| 167.07500 | 171.87500 | NFM | North Walsham | Norfolk Canneries |
| 167.07500 | 171.87500 | NFM | Peterborough | CBS Repeater |
| 167.08750 | 171.88750 | NFM | Birmingham | Taxi Company |
| 167.08750 | 171.88750 | NFM | Cwmbran | Aerial Riggers |
| 167.08750 | 171.88750 | NFM | Great Yarmouth | Botton Bros |
| 167.08750 | 171.88750 | NFM | Lincolnshire | Ross Foods |
| 167.08750 | 171.88750 | NFM | London, south west | Taxis |
| 167.08750 | 171.88750 | NFM | Perth | Taxis |
| 167.08750 | 171.88750 | NFM | Poole | Repeater |
| 167.08750 | 171.88750 | NFM | Portsmouth | Council |
| 167.08750 | 171.88750 | NFM | Somerset | Council Ops |
| 167.08750 | 171.88750 | NFM | Swansea City | County Hall Ops |
| 167.08750 | 171.88750 | NFM | Torpoint | Taxis |
| 167.08750 | 171.88750 | NFM | Walsall | Metro Taxis |
| 167.10000 | 171.90000 | NFM | Birmingham 4 Oaks | Taxis |
| 167.10000 | 171.90000 | NFM | Brandon | F Hiam Farms |
| 167.10000 | 171.90000 | NFM | Cambridge | Ace Taxis |
| 167.10000 | 171.90000 | NFM | Cardiff | Capital Taxis |
| 167.10000 | 171.90000 | NFM | Carlisle | Cavrays Security |
| 167.10000 | 171.90000 | NFM | Eltham | Taxis |
| 167.10000 | 171.90000 | NFM | Glasgow | Taxis |
| 167.10000 | 171.90000 | NFM | Guernsey | Bluebird Taxis |
| 167.10000 | 171.90000 | NFM | Hampshire | Council |
| 167.10000 | 171.90000 | NFM | Hemel Hempstead | Minicab Co |
| 167.10000 | 171.90000 | NFM | Hempstead | R. D. Haylock |
| 167.10000 | 171.90000 | NFM | Manchester | Taxis |
| 167.10000 | 171.90000 | NFM | Newcastle | Taxis |
| 167.10000 | 171.90000 | NFM | Perth | Taxis |
| 167.10000 | 171.90000 | NFM | Stockton-on-Tees | Taxi Service |
| 167.10000 | 171.90000 | NFM | Thorley | M.S. Smith |
| 167.11250 | 171.91250 | NFM | Bristol | Peters Taxis |
| 167.11250 | 171.91250 | NFM | Coventry | Central Taxis |
| 167.11250 | 171.91250 | NFM | Dover | Invicta Cars |
| 167.11250 | 171.91250 | NFM | Farnham | Minicab Co |
| 167.11250 | 171.91250 | NFM | Glasgow | Taxi Company |
| 167.11250 | 171.91250 | NFM | Great Yarmouth | J & H Bunn |
| 167.11250 | 171.91250 | NFM | Guernsey | Community Repeater |
| 167.11250 | 171.91250 | NFM | Hull | Birds Eye |
| 167.11250 | 171.91250 | NFM | Kempston | AAA Taxis |
| 167.11250 | 171.91250 | NFM | Manchester | Taxis |
| 167.11250 | 171.91250 | NFM | Rotherham | Crown Taxis |
| 167.11250 | 171.91250 | NFM | South London | National Rescue |
| 167.11250 | 171.91250 | NFM | Swansea | Taxis |
| 167.12500 | 171.92500 | NFM | Bristol | CableTel Ch 2 |
| 167.12500 | 171.92500 | NFM | Burnley | Bus Station Taxi Rank |
| 167.12500 | 171.92500 | NFM | Cardiff | Repair Company |
| 167.12500 | 171.92500 | NFM | Castle Donnington | Racing (rescue) |
| 167.12500 | 171.92500 | NFM | Dudley | Skip Hire |
| 167.12500 | 171.92500 | NFM | Edinburgh | Taxis |

| Base | Mobile | Mode | Location | User and Notes |
|------|--------|------|----------|----------------|
| 167.12500 | 171.92500 | NFM | Folkstone | Taxis |
| 167.12500 | 171.92500 | NFM | Gwent | CableTel Ch 2 |
| 167.12500 | 171.92500 | NFM | Hawick | Buccleugh Estates |
| 167.12500 | 171.92500 | NFM | Hemel Hempstead | Minicab Co |
| 167.12500 | 171.92500 | NFM | Kings Lynn | Watlington Plant |
| 167.12500 | 171.92500 | NFM | Langholm | Buccleugh Estates |
| 167.12500 | 171.92500 | NFM | Liverpool | Taxis |
| 167.12500 | 171.92500 | NFM | March | Ross-Produce |
| 167.12500 | 171.92500 | NFM | Milton Keynes | Pursell Taxis |
| 167.12500 | 171.92500 | NFM | Portsmouth | Dog Catcher |
| 167.12500 | 171.92500 | NFM | Scunthorpe | Transport Firm |
| 167.12500 | 171.92500 | NFM | Selkirk | Buccleugh Estates |
| 167.12500 | 171.92500 | NFM | Swansea | Brynamman Taxis |
| 167.13500 | 171.93750 | NFM | Eastbourne | Taxis |
| 167.13750 | 171.93750 | NFM | Blackburn | Golden Line Private Hire |
| 167.13750 | 171.93750 | NFM | Edinburgh | Eagle Couriers |
| 167.13750 | 171.93750 | NFM | Jersey | Skips |
| 167.13750 | 171.93750 | NFM | Kings Lynn | Wheelers TV Services |
| 167.13750 | 171.93750 | NFM | Lancashire | Bulkers Commercial Refuse |
| 167.13750 | 171.93750 | NFM | Leicester | Taxis |
| 167.13750 | 171.93750 | NFM | London W2 | Chepstow OO7 Car Service |
| 167.13750 | 171.93750 | NFM | Oxford | Streamline Taxis |
| 167.13750 | 171.93750 | NFM | Preston | South Ribble School Bus |
| 167.13750 | 171.93750 | NFM | Scunthorpe | Taxis |
| 167.13750 | 171.93750 | NFM | Tynemouth | Taxis |
| 167.15000 | 171.95000 | NFM | Aberdeen | Taxis |
| 167.15000 | 171.95000 | NFM | Aberystwyth | University Security |
| 167.15000 | 171.95000 | NFM | Barrow in Furness | JC Taxis |
| 167.15000 | 171.95000 | NFM | Bury | Bury Taxi Rank Ltd |
| 167.15000 | 171.95000 | NFM | Carlisle | Radio Taxis |
| 167.15000 | 171.95000 | NFM | Crewe | Taxis |
| 167.15000 | 171.95000 | NFM | Downham Market | T Hurlow |
| 167.15000 | 171.95000 | NFM | Guernsey | Ronez |
| 167.15000 | 171.95000 | NFM | Lancashire | South Ribble Refuse |
| 167.15000 | 171.95000 | NFM | Langholm | Buccleugh Estates, Gamekeepers |
| 167.15000 | 171.95000 | NFM | Manchester | Taxis |
| 167.15000 | 171.95000 | NFM | Newport, Gwent | Servu Taxis |
| 167.15000 | 171.95000 | NFM | Norwich | Taxis |
| 167.15000 | 171.95000 | NFM | Nottingham | Taxis |
| 167.15000 | 171.95000 | NFM | Oldham | Startex Cabs |
| 167.15000 | 171.95000 | NFM | Portsmouth | Repeater |
| 167.15000 | 171.95000 | NFM | St. Neots | T & R Taxis |
| 167.15000 | 171.95000 | NFM | West Midlands | ABS Taxis |
| 167.15000 | 171.95000 | NFM | Wolverhampton | Taxis |
| 167.15000 | 171.95000 | NFM | Workington | Tuckwell |
| 167.16250 | 171.96250 | NFM | Central London | Couriers |
| 167.16250 | 171.96250 | NFM | Coventry | Skyline Taxis |
| 167.16250 | 171.96250 | NFM | Dover | Victory Cars |
| 167.16250 | 171.96250 | NFM | Ipswich | Taxis |
| 167.16250 | 171.96250 | NFM | Keswick | Ambulance |
| 167.16250 | 171.96250 | NFM | Newport | Newport Taxis |
| 167.16250 | 171.96250 | NFM | Norfolk | ICL |
| 167.16250 | 171.96250 | NFM | Sheffield | City Taxis |
| 167.16250 | 171.96250 | NFM | Shillington | New Farm |
| 167.16250 | 171.96250 | NFM | Swindon | Starlight Taxis |
| 167.16250 | 171.96250 | NFM | Wigan | Cable TV Engineers |

| Base | Mobile | Mode | Location | User and Notes |
|------|--------|------|----------|----------------|
| 167.16250 | 171.96250 | NFM | Wrexham | Prostigo Taxis |
| 167.16500 | 171.96500 | NFM | Newcastle | Taxis |
| 167.17500 | 171.97500 | NFM | Bexley Heath | Taxis |
| 167.17500 | 171.97500 | FM | Cambridge | Taxis |
| 167.17500 | 171.97500 | NFM | Cheshire | Choice Taxis |
| 167.17500 | 171.97500 | NFM | Glasgow | Taxis |
| 167.17500 | 171.97500 | NFM | Guernsey | R. J. Le Huray |
| 167.17500 | 171.97500 | NFM | London, East | Couriers |
| 167.17500 | 171.97500 | NFM | Manchester | Taxis |
| 167.17500 | 171.97500 | NFM | Norfolk | ICL |
| 167.17500 | 171.97500 | NFM | Norwich | Canary Cars Taxis |
| 167.17500 | 171.97500 | NFM | Rochdale | Tiger Cars |
| 167.17500 | 171.97500 | NFM | Sidcup | Taxis |
| 167.18750 | 171.98750 | NFM | Bolton | North West Cars |
| 167.18750 | 171.98750 | NFM | Brownhills | Bee-Jays Taxis |
| 167.18750 | 171.98750 | NFM | Bury St Edmunds | Goldline Taxis |
| 167.18750 | 171.98750 | NFM | Colchester | A1 Taxis |
| 167.18750 | 171.98750 | NFM | Coventry | Taxis |
| 167.18750 | 171.98750 | NFM | Glasgow | Mac Cars |
| 167.18750 | 171.98750 | NFM | Great Yarmouth | Taxis |
| 167.18750 | 171.98750 | NFM | Immingham | Oaklands Taxis |
| 167.18750 | 171.98750 | NFM | Lancaster | Council Roads Dept |
| 167.18750 | 171.98750 | NFM | Macclesfield | Taxis |
| 167.18750 | 171.98750 | NFM | Manchester | Midway Taxis |
| 167.18750 | 171.98750 | NFM | Middleton | Swan Cars |
| 167.18750 | 171.98750 | NFM | Milton Keynes | Raffles Taxis |
| 167.18750 | 171.98750 | NFM | Scarborough | Taxis |
| 167.18750 | 171.98750 | NFM | Sheffield | A2B Car Hire |
| 167.18750 | 171.98750 | NFM | Swindon | Handy Gas Shop |
| 167.20000 | 172.00000 | NFM | Ashford | United Taxis |
| 167.20000 | 172.00000 | NFM | Barrow | Mobile Community Watch |
| 167.20000 | 172.00000 | NFM | Bristol | Festival of the Sea (Security) |
| 167.20000 | 172.00000 | NFM | Dunstable | Glider Taxis |
| 167.20000 | 172.00000 | NFM | Edinburgh | Burtons Security |
| 167.20000 | 172.00000 | NFM | Fleetwood | Taxis |
| 167.20000 | 172.00000 | NFM | Jersey | Dock cranes |
| 167.20000 | 172.00000 | NFM | Jersey | Hire Cars |
| 167.20000 | 172.00000 | NFM | Lancaster | Security Service |
| 167.20000 | 172.00000 | NFM | Le-Mans | Halya Sport Team |
| 167.20000 | 172.00000 | NFM | Leicester | Taxis |
| 167.20000 | 172.00000 | NFM | Midland | Hutchings |
| 167.20000 | 172.00000 | NFM | Morecambe | Security Service |
| 167.20000 | 172.00000 | NFM | Nationwide | PMR Short Term Hire |
| 167.20000 | 172.00000 | NFM | Nottinghamshire | Ambulance Service |
| 167.20000 | 172.00000 | NFM | Peterborough | Burghley-House Steeplechase |
| 167.20000 | 172.00000 | NFM | Thetford | Abbey Taxis |
| 167.21250 | 172.01250 | NFM | Belfast | CityCabs |
| 167.21250 | 172.01250 | NFM | Chelmsford | A1 Demolition |
| 167.21250 | 172.01250 | NFM | Chelmsford | Crest Dairies |
| 167.21250 | 172.01250 | NFM | Chester | Dee Cars |
| 167.21250 | 172.01250 | NFM | Cumbernauld | Yellow Star Taxis (Yellow) |
| 167.21250 | 172.01250 | NFM | Edinburgh Airport | Stock Control |
| 167.21250 | 172.01250 | NFM | Glasgow | Taxis |
| 167.21250 | 172.01250 | NFM | Hull | Taxis |
| 167.21250 | 172.01250 | NFM | Jersey | Immigration Department |
| 167.21250 | 172.01250 | NFM | Manchester | Taxis |

| Base | Mobile | Mode | Location | User and Notes |
| --- | --- | --- | --- | --- |
| 167.21250 | 172.01250 | NFM | Newcastle | Silver Cars |
| 167.21250 | 172.01250 | NFM | Newmarket | McCourts |
| 167.21250 | 172.01250 | NFM | Norfolk | ICL |
| 167.21250 | 172.01250 | NFM | Oldham | Home James Taxis |
| 167.21250 | 172.01250 | NFM | Rayleigh | Taxis |
| 167.22500 | 172.02500 | NFM | Coventry | Taxis |
| 167.22500 | 172.02500 | NFM | Downham Market | B.W. Mack |
| 167.22500 | 172.02500 | NFM | Holbeach | Plant Hire |
| 167.22500 | 172.02500 | NFM | Hull | Taxis |
| 167.22500 | 172.02500 | NFM | Humberside | Haulage Co |
| 167.22500 | 172.02500 | NFM | Jersey | Waverley Coaches |
| 167.22500 | 172.02500 | NFM | London | Wimbledon Area Mini Cab Co |
| 167.22500 | 172.02500 | NFM | Mendips | Business Post |
| 167.22500 | 172.02500 | NFM | Midlands | Yellow Cabs |
| 167.22500 | 172.02500 | NFM | Royston | Meltax |
| 167.22500 | 172.02500 | NFM | Stockton-on-Tees | Taxi Service |
| 167.22500 | 172.02500 | NFM | Thetford | Chips Taxis |
| 167.22500 | 172.02500 | NFM | Worksop | Bee Line Taxis |
| 167.23750 | 172.03750 | NFM | Aberdeen | Taxis |
| 167.23750 | 172.03750 | NFM | Ashton | Taxis |
| 167.23750 | 172.03750 | NFM | Chadderton | Chadderton Cars |
| 167.23750 | 172.03750 | NFM | Chepstow | Taxi Co |
| 167.23750 | 172.03750 | NFM | Dartford | Black Cabs |
| 167.23750 | 172.03750 | NFM | Felixstowe | BW Mack |
| 167.23750 | 172.03750 | NFM | Glasgow | Taxis |
| 167.23750 | 172.03750 | NFM | Guernsey | Total Oil |
| 167.23750 | 172.03750 | NFM | Halifax | AA Taxis |
| 167.23750 | 172.03750 | NFM | Hampshire | Vets |
| 167.23750 | 172.03750 | NFM | Haverhill | Chequer Cabs |
| 167.23750 | 172.03750 | NFM | Huntingdon | Pete's Taxis |
| 167.23750 | 172.03750 | NFM | Leicester | Asda Security |
| 167.23750 | 172.03750 | NFM | Norfolk | ICL |
| 167.23750 | 172.03750 | NFM | Oxford | Black Cabs |
| 167.23750 | 172.03750 | NFM | Swansea | Diamond Cabs |
| 167.25000 | 172.05000 | NFM | Aberdeen | Taxis |
| 167.25000 | 172.05000 | NFM | Bolton | Pal Cars Taxis |
| 167.25000 | 172.05000 | NFM | Elvington | Garrowby Estate Farms |
| 167.25000 | 172.05000 | NFM | Guernsey | Post Office |
| 167.25000 | 172.05000 | NFM | Hull | Goldstar Taxis |
| 167.25000 | 172.05000 | NFM | London, N17 | Alan Car Service |
| 167.25000 | 172.05000 | NFM | Newtown | Taxis |
| 167.25000 | 172.05000 | NFM | Plymouth | Armada Taxis |
| 167.25000 | 172.05000 | NFM | Powys | Thomas Jones (Vet) |
| 167.25000 | 172.05000 | NFM | Slough | Interpoint Taxis |
| 167.25000 | 172.05000 | NFM | Swansea | Fishwicks Taxis |
| 167.25000 | 172.05000 | NFM | Upton | Road Runner Taxis |
| 167.25000 | 172.05000 | NFM | Whiston | Diamond Taxis Ltd |
| 167.26250 | 172.02500 | NFM | Blackpool | J Cabs |
| 167.26250 | 172.06250 | NFM | Belfast | Belfast City Council |
| 167.26250 | 172.06250 | NFM | Guernsey | Guernsey Bus |
| 167.26250 | 172.06250 | NFM | Haverhill | Havtaxi |
| 167.26250 | 172.06250 | NFM | Milton Keynes | Embassy Cars |
| 167.26250 | 172.06250 | NFM | Portsmouth | Blue Light Cabs |
| 167.26250 | 172.06250 | NFM | Reading | 1st City Cars |
| 167.26250 | 172.06250 | NFM | Sheffield | Paymaster Ltd. |
| 167.26250 | 172.06250 | NFM | Stevenage | Freewheelers |

| Base | Mobile | Mode | Location | User and Notes |
|---|---|---|---|---|
| 167.26250 | 172.06250 | NFM | West Midlands | Fruit Machine Repairs |
| 167.26250 | 172.06250 | NFM | Worcester | Central Taxis |
| 167.27500 | 172.07500 | NFM | Aberdeen | Office Security |
| 167.27500 | 172.07500 | NFM | Alloa | Taxis |
| 167.27500 | 172.07500 | NFM | Birmingham Moseley | Taxis |
| 167.27500 | 172.07500 | NFM | Bolton | Red Rose Taxis |
| 167.27500 | 172.07500 | NFM | Brighton | Southern Taxis |
| 167.27500 | 172.07500 | NFM | Gt. Stokely | H. Raby & Sons |
| 167.27500 | 172.07500 | NFM | Hockwold Cum Wilton | J. Denney Taxis |
| 167.27500 | 172.07500 | NFM | Hull | Taxis |
| 167.27500 | 172.07500 | NFM | Huntingdon | H. Raby & Sons |
| 167.27500 | 172.07500 | NFM | Jersey | States Motor Traffic Department |
| 167.27500 | 172.07500 | NFM | Nationwide | TNT Transport |
| 167.27500 | 172.07500 | NFM | Newport, Wales | Motorway and trunk road contractors |
| 167.27500 | 172.07500 | NFM | Portsmouth | Taxis |
| 167.27500 | 172.07500 | NFM | Sheffield | Foundry maintenance |
| 167.27500 | 172.07500 | NFM | Southend on Sea | Associated Radio Cars |
| 167.27500 | 172.07500 | NFM | Sutton | Darby Plant |
| 167.27500 | 172.07500 | NFM | Weymouth | Taxi Co |
| 167.28750 | 172.08750 | NFM | Abingdon | Autotaxis |
| 167.28750 | 172.08750 | NFM | Burnley | AK Taxis |
| 167.28750 | 172.08750 | NFM | Cardiff | Taxis |
| 167.28750 | 172.08750 | NFM | Chesterfield | Central Taxis |
| 167.28750 | 172.08750 | NFM | Dalton in Furness | Taxis |
| 167.28750 | 172.08750 | NFM | East Dereham | Breckland Taxis |
| 167.28750 | 172.08750 | NFM | Eastleigh | Taxis |
| 167.28750 | 172.08750 | NFM | Falkirk | Police |
| 167.28750 | 172.08750 | NFM | Glasgow | Taxis |
| 167.28750 | 172.08750 | NFM | Hampshire | Taxis |
| 167.28750 | 172.08750 | NFM | Haverfordwest | Rocky's Taxis |
| 167.28750 | 172.08750 | NFM | Hawick | AH Taxis |
| 167.28750 | 172.08750 | NFM | Leicester | Taxis |
| 167.28750 | 172.08750 | NFM | London, south | Taxis |
| 167.28750 | 172.08750 | NFM | London, west | Couriers |
| 167.28750 | 172.08750 | NFM | Montrose | Taxis |
| 167.28750 | 172.08750 | NFM | Norfolk | ICL |
| 167.28750 | 172.08750 | NFM | Peterborough | CBS Repeater |
| 167.28750 | 172.08750 | NFM | Plymouth | Chequers Cabs |
| 167.28750 | 172.08750 | NFM | Thetford | Breakland Taxis |
| 167.28750 | 172.08750 | NFM | Wrexham | Ace Taxis |
| 167.30000 | 172.10000 | NFM | Blackburn | Super Line Private Hire |
| 167.30000 | 172.10000 | NFM | Gateshead | Builders Merchant |
| 167.30000 | 172.10000 | NFM | Glasgow | Glasgow Fruit Centre |
| 167.30000 | 172.10000 | NFM | Kings Lynn | R.D. Carter |
| 167.30000 | 172.10000 | NFM | London | Grove Cars W12 |
| 167.30000 | 172.10000 | NFM | Luton | Black Cabs |
| 167.30000 | 172.10000 | NFM | Norfolk | ICL |
| 167.30000 | 172.10000 | NFM | Oxford | Radiotaxis |
| 167.30000 | 172.10000 | NFM | Sheffield | Toby Taxis |
| 167.30000 | 172.10000 | NFM | Swindon | Taxis |
| 167.31250 | 172.11250 | NFM | Aberdeen | Office Security |
| 167.31250 | 172.11250 | NFM | Brownhills | Taxi |
| 167.31250 | 172.11250 | NFM | Doncaster | Race Course |
| 167.31250 | 172.11250 | NFM | Glasgow | Taxis |
| 167.31250 | 172.11250 | NFM | London | Government (VULTURE/OSPREY/RAVEN) |
| 167.31250 | 172.11250 | NFM | Newark | Taxis |

| Base | Mobile | Mode | Location | User and Notes |
|------|--------|------|----------|----------------|
| 167.31250 | 172.11250 | NFM | Retford | Golf course |
| 167.31250 | 172.11250 | NFM | Southampton | Taxis |
| 167.32500 | 172.12500 | NFM | Astley | Astley Van Hire |
| 167.32500 | 172.12500 | NFM | Barrow in Furness | Coastline Taxis |
| 167.32500 | 172.12500 | NFM | Bedford | Bedfordia Farms |
| 167.32500 | 172.12500 | NFM | Chatteris | Graves & Graves |
| 167.32500 | 172.12500 | NFM | Chester | Radio Cars |
| 167.32500 | 172.12500 | NFM | Dartford | Taxis |
| 167.32500 | 172.12500 | NFM | Forest Hill | Taxis |
| 167.32500 | 172.12500 | NFM | Glasgow | Taxis |
| 167.32500 | 172.12500 | NFM | Ipswich | Robin Hood Taxis |
| 167.32500 | 172.12500 | NFM | London | Taxis/Couriers |
| 167.32500 | 172.12500 | NFM | Manchester | Astley Van Hire |
| 167.32500 | 172.12500 | AM | Shoreham | Shoreham Airport Taxis |
| 167.32500 | 172.12500 | NFM | Southend | Doctors night callout |
| 167.32500 | 172.12500 | NFM | Swansea | A and M Taxis |
| 167.33750 | 172.13750 | NFM | Biggleswade | Whitbread Farms |
| 167.33750 | 172.13750 | FM | Cambridge | Amtrak |
| 167.33750 | 172.13750 | NFM | Cambridgeshire | Motor Vehicle Repairs |
| 167.33750 | 172.13750 | NFM | Cardiff | Taxis |
| 167.33750 | 172.13750 | NFM | Glasgow | Taxis |
| 167.33750 | 172.13750 | NFM | Heywood | Eagle Cars |
| 167.33750 | 172.13750 | NFM | Stowmarket | Taxis |
| 167.33750 | 172.13750 | NFM | Stretford | New Moon Private Hire |
| 167.33750 | 172.13750 | NFM | Warwickshire | Farmers |
| 167.35000 | 170.15000 | AM | Aberdeen | Taxi |
| 167.35000 | 170.15000 | NFM | Blackpool | R. Walker & Co |
| 167.35000 | 170.15000 | NFM | Burnham | Burnham Radio Cabs |
| 167.35000 | 170.15000 | NFM | Cornwall | English China Clay |
| 167.35000 | 170.15000 | NFM | Coventry | Coventry Aerial Services |
| 167.35000 | 170.15000 | NFM | Eccles | Taxis |
| 167.35000 | 170.15000 | NFM | Fareham | Taxis |
| 167.35000 | 170.15000 | NFM | Fordham | Allen Newport |
| 167.35000 | 170.15000 | NFM | Hampshire | Wayne Haverson |
| 167.35000 | 170.15000 | NFM | Hull | Taxis |
| 167.35000 | 170.15000 | NFM | Jersey | Regal Construction |
| 167.35000 | 170.15000 | NFM | Manchester | Taxis |
| 167.35000 | 170.15000 | NFM | Newport, Gwent | Caxton Taxis |
| 167.35000 | 170.15000 | NFM | Preston | Taxis |
| 167.35000 | 170.15000 | NFM | Rochdale | Central Taxis |
| 167.35000 | 170.15000 | NFM | Salford | Taxis |
| 167.35000 | 170.15000 | NFM | Stockport | Taxis |
| 167.35000 | 170.15000 | NFM | Stoke-on-Trent | Taxis |
| 167.35000 | 170.15000 | NFM | Tamworth | Bennetts Taxis |
| 167.35000 | 170.15000 | NFM | Whiston | Diamond Taxis Ltd |
| 167.35000 | 170.15000 | NFM | Whittlesey | Luxicabs |
| 167.35000 | 172.15000 | NFM | Luton | Super Anglia Cars |
| 167.36250 | 172.16250 | NFM | Bolton | Murtax Taxis |
| 167.36250 | 172.16250 | NFM | Bristol | Paramedics |
| 167.36250 | 172.16250 | NFM | Coventry | City centre store detectives |
| 167.36250 | 172.16250 | NFM | Coventry | Security (METRO DTD) |
| 167.36250 | 172.16250 | NFM | Guernsey | Community Repeater 2 |
| 167.36250 | 172.16250 | NFM | Halifax | Beeline Taxis |
| 167.36250 | 172.16250 | NFM | Hull | Taxis |
| 167.36250 | 172.16250 | NFM | London, east | Taxis |
| 167.36250 | 172.16250 | NFM | Plymouth | Taxis |

| Base | Mobile | Mode | Location | User and Notes |
|------|--------|------|----------|----------------|
| 167.36250 | 172.16250 | NFM | Soham | Greens of Soham |
| 167.36250 | 172.16250 | NFM | Worthing | Wortax Taxis |
| 167.36250 | 172.66250 | NFM | Sheerness Docks | Sheppy Taxis |
| 167.37500 | 172.17500 | NFM | Aberdeen | Tyre Service |
| 167.37500 | 172.17500 | NFM | Chippenham | Taxis |
| 167.37500 | 172.17500 | NFM | Eastbourne | Taxi |
| 167.37500 | 172.17500 | NFM | Maidstone | Cavalier Cabs |
| 167.37500 | 172.17500 | AM | Manchester | Taxifone Taxis |
| 167.37500 | 172.17500 | NFM | Nationwide | Comet Television |
| 167.37500 | 172.17500 | NFM | Northumberland | Open Cast Site |
| 167.37500 | 172.17500 | NFM | Poole | Repeater |
| 167.37500 | 172.17500 | NFM | Southampton | Taxis |
| 167.37500 | 172.17500 | NFM | Winchester | Council |
| 167.37500 | 172.17500 | NFM | Wrexham | Regal Taxis |
| 167.38750 | 172.18750 | NFM | Aberdeen | Taxis |
| 167.36750 | 172.18750 | NFM | Calne | Zula Taxis |
| 167.38750 | 172.18750 | NFM | Cardiff | Plumbing Company |
| 167.38750 | 172.18750 | NFM | Derby | Taxi |
| 167.38750 | 172.18750 | NFM | Devizes | Devizes Taxis |
| 167.38750 | 172.18750 | NFM | Glasgow | Taxis |
| 167.38750 | 172.18750 | NFM | Hull | Taxis |
| 167.38750 | 172.18750 | NFM | Kettering | KLM Taxis |
| 167.38750 | 172.18750 | NFM | London | A.D.C. Despatch Couriers |
| 167.38750 | 172.18750 | NFM | London, Hammersmith | Paul's Plumbers |
| 167.38750 | 172.18750 | NFM | Manchester | Taxis |
| 167.38750 | 172.18750 | NFM | Newport | CableTel Ch 1 |
| 167.38750 | 172.18750 | NFM | Newport, Gwent | BT Engineers |
| 167.38750 | 172.18750 | NFM | Norfolk | ICL |
| 167.38750 | 172.18750 | NFM | Pontypool | Red Dragon Taxis |
| 167.38750 | 172.18750 | NFM | Salford | Swan Private Hire |
| 167.38750 | 172.18750 | NFM | Sheffield | TCS Taxis |
| 167.40000 | 172.20000 | NFM | Birmingham Erdington | Taxi |
| 167.40000 | 172.20000 | NFM | Burnley | Burnley Taxis |
| 167.40000 | 172.20000 | NFM | Colchester | Paxmans Diesels |
| 167.40000 | 172.20000 | NFM | Hampshire | Cascade Cars |
| 167.40000 | 172.20000 | NFM | Leicester | Taxis |
| 167.40000 | 172.20000 | NFM | Leigh on Sea | Kelly's Radio |
| 167.40000 | 172.20000 | NFM | Manchester | Taxis |
| 167.40000 | 172.20000 | NFM | Norfolk | Associated Leisure |
| 167.40000 | 172.20000 | NFM | Oldham | Bluebird Private Hire |
| 167.40000 | 172.20000 | NFM | Perth | Taxis |
| 167.41250 | 172.21250 | NFM | Aberdeen | Estate Security |
| 167.41250 | 172.21250 | NFM | Bury | Harvey's Taxis |
| 167.41250 | 172.21250 | NFM | Dalmellington | Open Cast Mining |
| 167.41250 | 172.21250 | NFM | Dalton | Marj's Cars |
| 167.41250 | 172.21250 | NFM | Edinburgh | Doctors Service |
| 167.41250 | 172.21250 | NFM | Glasgow | Taxis |
| 167.41250 | 172.21250 | NFM | Grimsby | M.D. Cars |
| 167.41250 | 172.21250 | NFM | Leicester | Taxis |
| 167.41250 | 172.21250 | NFM | Manchester | Taxis |
| 167.41250 | 172.21250 | NFM | Newark | Taxis |
| 167.41250 | 172.21250 | NFM | Norfolk | ICL |
| 167.41250 | 172.21250 | NFM | Oxford | City Taxis |
| 167.41250 | 172.21250 | NFM | Portsmouth | Taxis |
| 167.41250 | 172.21250 | NFM | Sheffield | Direct Taxis |
| 167.41250 | 172.21250 | NFM | Stoke on Trent | Haulage Company |

| Base | Mobile | Mode | Location | User and Notes |
|------|--------|------|----------|----------------|
| 167.42500 | 172.22500 | NFM | Aberdeen | Taxis |
| 167.42500 | 172.22500 | NFM | Coventry | Trinity Street Taxis |
| 167.42500 | 177.22500 | NFM | Bloxwich | Abba Taxis |
| 167.42500 | 177.22500 | NFM | Downham Market | B.W. Mack |
| 167.42500 | 177.22500 | NFM | Glasgow | Taxi Company |
| 167.42500 | 177.22500 | NFM | Huntingdon | R. Brading |
| 167.42500 | 177.22500 | NFM | Jersey | HM Prison  La Moye |
| 167.42500 | 177.22500 | NFM | Jersey | Jersey States Repeater |
| 167.42500 | 177.22500 | NFM | Jersey | Lucas Bros. Farm Shop |
| 167.42500 | 177.22500 | NFM | Jersey | Ransom Garden Centre |
| 167.42500 | 177.22500 | NFM | Jersey | States Electronics Dept. |
| 167.42500 | 177.22500 | NFM | Larbert | Plough Taxis |
| 167.42500 | 177.22500 | NFM | Norwich | J.B. Green |
| 167.42500 | 177.22500 | NFM | Nottingham | Taxis |
| 167.42500 | 177.22500 | NFM | Plymouth | Cotton's Taxis |
| 167.42500 | 177.22500 | NFM | Sheffield | Tram Works Construction |
| 167.43750 | 172.23750 | NFM | Airdrie | Taxis |
| 167.43750 | 172.23750 | NFM | Cleveland | City Taxis |
| 167.43750 | 172.23750 | NFM | Coventry | BFI Waste |
| 167.43750 | 172.23750 | NFM | Glasgow | Taxis |
| 167.43750 | 172.23750 | NFM | Montrose | Taxis |
| 167.43750 | 172.23750 | NFM | Newport | French's TV Repairs |
| 167.43750 | 172.23750 | NFM | Norwich | C Wace |
| 167.43750 | 172.23750 | NFM | Steeple Bumpstead | Shore Hall Estates |
| 167.43750 | 172.23750 | NFM | Tywyn, North Wales | Taxis |
| 167.45000 | 172.25000 | NFM | Abingdon | Newtop Taxis |
| 167.45000 | 172.25000 | NFM | Edinburgh | Taxis |
| 167.45000 | 172.25000 | NFM | Knebworth | Vendustrial Ltd |
| 167.45000 | 172.25000 | NFM | Manchester | White Line Taxis |
| 167.45000 | 172.25000 | NFM | Musselburgh | Taxis |
| 167.45000 | 172.25000 | NFM | Newmarket | Chilcotts Taxis |
| 167.45000 | 172.25000 | NFM | Norfolk | ICL |
| 167.45000 | 172.25000 | NFM | Retford | A2B Taxis |
| 167.45000 | 172.25000 | NFM | Sheffield | Alpha Taxis |
| 167.45000 | 172.25000 | NFM | Southsea | Pier Security |
| 167.46250 | 172.26250 | NFM | Aberdeen | Crane Hire |
| 167.46250 | 172.26250 | NFM | Bristol | Works Dispatch |
| 167.46250 | 172.26250 | NFM | Eastbourne | TNT |
| 167.46250 | 172.26250 | NFM | Eastbourne | Taxis |
| 167.46250 | 172.26250 | NFM | Gt. Yarmouth | Birds Eye Vans |
| 167.46250 | 172.26250 | NFM | London, East | Taxis/Couriers |
| 167.46250 | 172.26250 | NFM | Lowestoft | Birds Eye |
| 167.46250 | 172.26250 | NFM | Manchester | District Council |
| 167.46250 | 172.26250 | NFM | Nationwide | TNT |
| 167.46250 | 172.26250 | NFM | Nationwide | Tesco Supermarkets |
| 167.46250 | 172.26250 | NFM | Newport | TNT Deliveries Ch 1 |
| 167.46250 | 172.26250 | NFM | Oldham | Security |
| 167.46250 | 172.26250 | NFM | Peterborough | Tesco |
| 167.46250 | 172.26250 | NFM | Sheffield | Alpha Cars Ch 1 |
| 167.46250 | 172.26250 | NFM | Southampton | Taxis |
| 167.46250 | 172.26250 | NFM | Warminster | Taxis |
| 167.47500 | 172.27500 | NFM | Ancoats | Chariots |
| 167.47500 | 172.27500 | NFM | Bristol | Shell Gas Bottle Delivery |
| 167.47500 | 172.27500 | NFM | Burton, Staffs | Taxis |
| 167.47500 | 172.27500 | NFM | Liverpool | Car Breakdown Recovery |
| 167.47500 | 172.27500 | NFM | London | National Radio Cars |

| Base | Mobile | Mode | Location | User and Notes |
| --- | --- | --- | --- | --- |
| 167.47500 | 172.27500 | NFM | Nottingham, Hucknall | TC Taxis |
| 167.47500 | 172.27500 | NFM | Poole | Repeater |
| 167.47500 | 172.27500 | NFM | Sheffield | Mercury Cars Ch 2 |
| 167.48000 | 172.28000 | NFM | Leeds Seacroft | Taxis |
| 167.48750 | 172.28750 | NFM | Aberdeen | Taxis |
| 167.48750 | 172.28750 | NFM | Eastbourne | Borough Council |
| 167.48750 | 172.28750 | NFM | Edinburgh | Taxis |
| 167.48750 | 172.28750 | NFM | Glasgow | Forge Shopping Mall Security |
| 167.48750 | 172.28750 | NFM | Grampian | Transport |
| 167.48750 | 172.28750 | NFM | Leicester | Taxis |
| 167.48750 | 172.28750 | NFM | Newport | Red Base Taxis |
| 167.48750 | 172.28750 | NFM | Portsmouth | Council |
| 167.48750 | 172.28750 | NFM | Ryton | A1 Taxis |
| 167.48750 | 172.28750 | NFM | Snaefell, Isle of Man | Repeater |
| 167.50000 | 172.30000 | NFM | Aberdeen | Farm |
| 167.50000 | 172.30000 | NFM | Barway | Shropshire Produce |
| 167.50000 | 172.30000 | NFM | Blackpool | Streamline Taxis |
| 167.50000 | 172.30000 | NFM | Brighton | John Jug Ltd |
| 167.50000 | 172.30000 | NFM | Charminster | Bee Cabs |
| 167.50000 | 172.30000 | NFM | Hemingbrough | AIS Brown Butlin Chemicals |
| 167.50000 | 172.30000 | NFM | Rochford | Taxis |
| 167.50000 | 172.30000 | NFM | Saltdean | Taxis |
| 167.50000 | 172.30000 | NFM | Shipham | William Moorfoot |
| 167.50000 | 172.30000 | NFM | Swindon | Link Taxis |
| 167.51250 | 172.31250 | NFM | Blackley | Avenue Cars |
| 167.51250 | 172.31250 | NFM | Cwmbran, Gwent | Chauffeur Taxis |
| 167.51250 | 172.31250 | NFM | Jersey | HM Customs & Excise Channel 5 |
| 167.51250 | 172.31250 | NFM | Manchester | Taxis |
| 167.51250 | 172.31250 | NFM | Newcastle | Taxis |
| 167.51250 | 172.31250 | NFM | Norfolk | ICL |
| 167.51250 | 172.31250 | NFM | Worthing | Nynex Cable |
| 167.52500 | 172.32500 | NFM | Birkenhead | Cavalier Taxis |
| 167.52500 | 172.32500 | NFM | Bolsover | Leeds Castle staff |
| 167.52500 | 172.32500 | NFM | Bradford | Taxi Blackcabs |
| 167.52500 | 172.32500 | NFM | Cambridge | Able Taxis |
| 167.52500 | 172.32500 | NFM | Edinburgh | Phone Line Banking |
| 167.52500 | 172.32500 | NFM | Harlow | Anglie Cable (Techs) |
| 167.52500 | 172.32500 | NFM | Huntingdon | A.E. Abraham |
| 167.52500 | 172.32500 | NFM | Irvine | C-Cars |
| 167.52500 | 172.32500 | NFM | Irvine | Drews |
| 167.52500 | 172.32500 | NFM | Irvine | Norries |
| 167.52500 | 172.32500 | NFM | Jersey, Fort Regent | Leisure Complex Ch3 |
| 167.52500 | 172.32500 | NFM | Letchworth | A-B Taxis |
| 167.52500 | 172.32500 | NFM | Letchworth | Mick's Taxis |
| 167.52500 | 172.32500 | NFM | Normanton, West Yorkshire | Taxis |
| 167.52500 | 172.32500 | NFM | Norwich | Five Star Taxis |
| 167.52500 | 172.32500 | NFM | Nottingham | Taxis |
| 167.52500 | 172.32500 | NFM | Salford | Taxis |
| 167.53750 | 172.33750 | NFM | Aberdeen | Farm |
| 167.53750 | 172.33750 | NFM | Bury | Peel Cars |
| 167.53750 | 172.33750 | NFM | Cornwall | English China Clay |
| 167.53750 | 172.33750 | NFM | Walsall Wood | Barons Taxis |
| 167.55000 | 172.35000 | NFM | Biggleswade | AI CARS |
| 167.55000 | 172.35000 | NFM | Bradford-on-Avon | Taxis |
| 167.55000 | 172.35000 | NFM | Cheltenham | Fort Regent Leisure Complex Ch 1 |
| 167.55000 | 172.35000 | NFM | Colchester | Abbeygate Taxis |

| Base | Mobile | Mode | Location | User and Notes |
|------|--------|------|----------|----------------|
| 167.55000 | 172.35000 | NFM | Grimsby | "Evening Telegraph" |
| 167.55000 | 172.35000 | NFM | Jersey | Fort Regent Leisure Centre |
| 167.55000 | 172.35000 | NFM | London | Taxis |
| 167.55000 | 172.35000 | NFM | Portsmouth | City Wide Taxis |
| 167.55000 | 172.35000 | NFM | Salford | Briffin Cars |
| 167.55000 | 172.35000 | NFM | Weymouth | Taxis |
| 167.56250 | 172.36250 | NFM | Aberdeen | Estate |
| 167.56250 | 172.36250 | NFM | Blackburn | Super B Private Hire |
| 167.56250 | 172.36250 | NFM | Bristol | City Council |
| 167.56250 | 172.36250 | NFM | Cheshire | Station Cars |
| 167.56250 | 172.36250 | NFM | Gillingham | Taxis |
| 167.56250 | 172.36250 | NFM | Glasgow | Taxis |
| 167.56250 | 172.36250 | NFM | Grangemouth | Taxi Owners Association |
| 167.56250 | 172.36250 | NFM | Guernsey | Sunshine Cabs |
| 167.56250 | 172.36250 | NFM | Ipswich | Wilmot Dixon Builders |
| 167.56250 | 172.36250 | NFM | Isle of Wight | Taxis |
| 167.56250 | 172.36250 | NFM | March | G.E. Tribe |
| 167.56250 | 172.36250 | NFM | Newmarket | Sound City Cabs and Style Cars |
| 167.56250 | 172.36250 | AM | Nottingham | Taxis |
| 167.56250 | 172.36250 | NFM | Nottingham | Toton Plant Hire |
| 167.56250 | 172.36250 | NFM | Plymouth | Key Cab Taxis |
| 167.56250 | 172.36250 | NFM | Salford | Dolphin Cars |
| 167.56250 | 172.36250 | NFM | Worthing | Taxis |
| 167.57500 | 172.37500 | NFM | Coventry | Sky Blue Radio Taxis |
| 167.57500 | 172.37500 | NFM | Dumfries | Taxis |
| 167.57500 | 172.37500 | NFM | Erith | Taxis |
| 167.57500 | 172.37500 | NFM | Essex | Taxis |
| 167.57500 | 172.37500 | NFM | Faversham | Starlight Taxis |
| 167.57500 | 172.37500 | NFM | Felixstowe | Aero Taxis |
| 167.57500 | 172.37500 | NFM | London | Courier |
| 167.57500 | 172.37500 | NFM | March | David Johnson Farms |
| 167.57500 | 172.37500 | NFM | Newcastle | Taxis |
| 167.57500 | 172.37500 | NFM | Peterborough | CBS Repeater |
| 167.57500 | 172.37500 | NFM | Salford | Taxis |
| 167.57500 | 172.37500 | NFM | Southampton | Taxis |
| 167.57500 | 172.37500 | NFM | Worthing | Taxis |
| 167.58750 | 167.58750 | NFM | Leeds, Seacroft | Bell cable media installers |
| 167.58750 | 172.38750 | NFM | Bedford | Anglia Cars |
| 167.58750 | 172.38750 | NFM | Bedford | Riverside Taxis |
| 167.58750 | 172.38750 | NFM | Bedworh | Autoway Taxis |
| 167.58750 | 172.38750 | NFM | Elvington | Inturf |
| 167.58750 | 172.38750 | NFM | Glasgow | Taxis |
| 167.58750 | 172.38750 | NFM | Leicester | Taxis |
| 167.58750 | 172.38750 | NFM | Sheffield | RSPCA |
| 167.58750 | 172.38750 | NFM | Swinton | Swintax |
| 167.58750 | 172.38750 | NFM | Wakefield | Bell |
| 167.60000 | 172.40000 | NFM | Cumbernauld | Central Cab Co |
| 167.60000 | 172.40000 | NFM | East Dereham | Venture Taxis |
| 167.60000 | 172.40000 | NFM | Glasgow | Taxis |
| 167.60000 | 172.40000 | NFM | Hitchin | Boxhall Taxis |
| 167.60000 | 172.40000 | NFM | Ipswich | Peter Green |
| 167.60000 | 172.40000 | NFM | Manchester | Taxis |
| 167.60000 | 172.40000 | NFM | Salford | Central Private Hire |
| 167.60000 | 172.40000 | NFM | Swansea | Cabletel |
| 167.60000 | 172.40000 | NFM | Telford | Car Repairs |
| 167.61250 | 172.41250 | NFM | Bedford | Windshield Enterprise |

| Base | Mobile | Mode | Location | User and Notes |
|------|--------|------|----------|----------------|
| 167.61250 | 172.41250 | NFM | Blantyre | Mac Cars |
| 167.61250 | 172.41250 | NFM | Glasgow | Taxis |
| 167.61250 | 172.41250 | NFM | Grimsby | Skip Co |
| 167.61250 | 172.41250 | NFM | London | Taxis |
| 167.61250 | 172.41250 | NFM | Portsmouth | University Security |
| 167.61250 | 172.41250 | NFM | Southampton | Millbank Barracks security company |
| 167.61250 | 172.41250 | NFM | Stevenage | Amber Cars |
| 167.61250 | 172.41250 | NFM | Stevenage | Goldstar Taxis |
| 167.61250 | 172.41250 | NFM | Warwickshire | Farmers (ACORN) |
| 167.62500 | 172.42500 | NFM | Aberdeen | Deeside Shop Fitters |
| 167.62500 | 172.42500 | NFM | Barnstaple | K&J Refrigeration |
| 167.62500 | 172.42500 | NFM | Barway | Shropshire Produce |
| 167.62500 | 172.42500 | NFM | Blackburn | Blackburn's Taxi Ranks |
| 167.62500 | 172.42500 | NFM | Burton, Staffs | Taxis |
| 167.62500 | 172.42500 | NFM | Glasgow | Taxis |
| 167.62500 | 172.42500 | NFM | Ipswich | Surveyors |
| 167.62500 | 172.42500 | NFM | Isle of Wight | Newport Council |
| 167.62500 | 172.42500 | NFM | Jersey | Hospital patients transport |
| 167.62500 | 172.42500 | NFM | Kings Lynn | Kens Cars |
| 167.62500 | 172.42500 | NFM | Lothian and Borders | East Lothian District Council |
| 167.62500 | 172.42500 | NFM | Perth | Tayside Shopper Fitters |
| 167.62500 | 172.42500 | NFM | Rochford | Andrews Taxis |
| 167.62500 | 172.42500 | NFM | Shropshire | Barkway Ely |
| 167.62500 | 172.42500 | NFM | Shropshire | Shropshire Produce |
| 167.62500 | 172.42500 | NFM | Walton | Taxis |
| 167.62500 | 172.42500 | NFM | Warwickshire | Farmers (ACORN) |
| 167.63750 | 172.43750 | NFM | Breckland | Council House Repairs |
| 167.63750 | 172.43750 | NFM | Eastham | Cars |
| 167.63750 | 172.43750 | NFM | Glasgow | Taxis |
| 167.63750 | 172.43750 | NFM | Hitchin | Cabstar Taxis |
| 167.63750 | 172.43750 | NFM | Lees | Cartax |
| 167.63750 | 172.43750 | NFM | Manchester | Taxis |
| 167.63750 | 172.43750 | NFM | Nottingham | Taxis |
| 167.63750 | 172.43750 | NFM | Suffolk | Rumbelows Television |
| 167.63750 | 172.43750 | NFM | Trowbridge | Ace's Taxis |
| 167.65000 | 172.45000 | NFM | Aldershot | Taxi Co |
| 167.65000 | 172.45000 | NFM | Bristol | Hemmings Waste |
| 167.65000 | 172.45000 | NFM | Edinburgh | Airport Taxis |
| 167.65000 | 172.45000 | NFM | Glasgow | Taxi Company |
| 167.65000 | 172.45000 | NFM | Humberside | Mechanics |
| 167.65000 | 172.45000 | NFM | London | Compass Curious |
| 167.65000 | 172.45000 | NFM | London, Kensal Town | Comet Cars |
| 167.65000 | 172.45000 | NFM | Preston | VIP Cabs |
| 167.65000 | 172.45000 | NFM | Southampton | Randals Taxis |
| 167.65000 | 172.45000 | NFM | Welwyn | Target Cars |
| 167.65000 | 172.45000 | NFM | Wickford | Carter & Ward |
| 167.65000 | 172.45000 | NFM | Wirral | Eastham Cabs |
| 167.66250 | 172.46250 | NFM | Bristol | Council maintenance |
| 167.66250 | 172.46250 | NFM | Colchester | Smythe Motors |
| 167.66250 | 172.46250 | NFM | Glasgow | Taxis |
| 167.66250 | 172.46250 | NFM | Leicester | Taxis |
| 167.66250 | 172.46250 | NFM | Swilland | Stennett & Sons Farms |
| 167.66250 | 172.46250 | NFM | Widnes | Taxis |
| 167.67500 | 172.47500 | NFM | Aylesbury | Arrowtax Taxis |
| 167.67500 | 172.47500 | NFM | Glasgow | Glasgow Zoo |
| 167.67500 | 172.47500 | NFM | Guernsey | Central Cabs |

| Base | Mobile | Mode | Location | User and Notes |
|---|---|---|---|---|
| 167.67500 | 172.47500 | AM | Ipswich | Avenue Taxis data |
| 167.67500 | 172.47500 | NFM | Larbert | Taxis |
| 167.67500 | 172.47500 | NFM | Perth | Perth & Kinross Council |
| 167.67500 | 172.47500 | NFM | Pontypool | Real Gwent Taxis |
| 167.67500 | 172.47500 | NFM | Portsmouth | Taxis |
| 167.67500 | 172.47500 | NFM | Rochdale | Cozy Cars |
| 167.67500 | 172.47500 | NFM | Scunthorpe | British Steel |
| 167.67500 | 172.47500 | NFM | Stevenage | Rowleys Taxis |
| 167.67500 | 172.47500 | NFM | Warwickshire | Farmers |
| 167.68750 | 172.48750 | NFM | Aberdeen | Slatters |
| 167.68750 | 172.48750 | NFM | Bedford | County Cars |
| 167.68750 | 172.48750 | NFM | Buxton | Taxi |
| 167.68750 | 172.48750 | NFM | Cardiff | Taxis |
| 167.68750 | 172.48750 | NFM | Dovercourt | Station Taxis |
| 167.68750 | 172.48750 | NFM | Dunstable | Threeways Taxis |
| 167.68750 | 172.48750 | NFM | Leeds | Pegasus Private Hire |
| 167.68750 | 172.48750 | NFM | Medway | Taxis |
| 167.68750 | 172.48750 | NFM | Sale | Trafford Private Hire |
| 167.68750 | 172.48750 | NFM | Trowbridge | Taxis |
| 167.70000 | 172.50000 | AM | Aberdeen | Security |
| 167.70000 | 172.50000 | NFM | Ancoats | Town Cars |
| 167.70000 | 172.50000 | NFM | Glasgow | East Kilbride Taxis |
| 167.70000 | 172.50000 | NFM | Hull | Willingham's Vehicle Recovery |
| 167.70000 | 172.50000 | NFM | Littleport | H Thompson |
| 167.70000 | 172.50000 | NFM | London | Olympic Cars |
| 167.70000 | 172.50000 | NFM | London W5 | Red Caps Radio Cars |
| 167.70000 | 172.50000 | NFM | London, Finchley | Tally Ho Cars |
| 167.70000 | 172.50000 | NFM | Manchester | Taxis |
| 167.70000 | 172.50000 | NFM | Peacehaven | Taxi |
| 167.70000 | 172.50000 | NFM | Peterborough | Bell Cable Media |
| 167.70000 | 172.50000 | NFM | Portsmouth | Taxis |
| 167.70000 | 172.50000 | NFM | Ramsgate | Kent Medical Services |
| 167.70000 | 172.50000 | NFM | Sheffield | Regency Cars |
| 167.70000 | 172.50000 | NFM | Southampton | Taxis |
| 167.71200 | 172.51250 | NFM | London | Direct Cars NW6 |
| 167.71250 | 172.51250 | NFM | Attlebridge | Hales Containers |
| 167.71250 | 172.51250 | NFM | Bristol | City Council |
| 167.71250 | 172.51250 | NFM | Bristol | Council maintenance |
| 167.71250 | 172.51250 | NFM | Cambridge | Jakubowski Builders |
| 167.71250 | 172.51250 | NFM | Chester | Doctors |
| 167.71250 | 172.51250 | NFM | Hayes | Roundabout Cars |
| 167.71250 | 172.51250 | NFM | Ipswich | Hawk Express Cabs Voice |
| 167.71250 | 172.51250 | NFM | London, Heathrow | Heathrow Luxury Cars |
| 167.71250 | 172.51250 | NFM | Prestwich | Magnum Private Hire |
| 167.72500 | 172.52500 | NFM | Barton | Booth transport |
| 167.72500 | 172.52500 | NFM | Gt. Yarmouth | Birds Eye |
| 167.72500 | 172.52500 | NFM | Hampshire | Tesco |
| 167.72500 | 172.52500 | NFM | Kilburn | Taxis |
| 167.72500 | 172.52500 | NFM | Kirkcaldy | Taxis |
| 167.72500 | 172.52500 | NFM | Leicester | Taxis |
| 167.72500 | 172.52500 | NFM | Lowestoft | Birds Eye |
| 167.72500 | 172.52500 | NFM | Nottingham | Co-Op TV Service |
| 167.72500 | 172.52500 | NFM | Poole | Repeater |
| 167.72500 | 172.52500 | NFM | Reading | ABC Taxis |
| 167.72500 | 172.52500 | NFM | Stockport | Taxis |
| 167.72500 | 172.52500 | NFM | Stourbridge | Taxis |

| Base | Mobile | Mode | Location | User and Notes |
|---|---|---|---|---|
| 167.72500 | 172.52500 | NFM | Tamworth, Staffs | Taxis |
| 167.72740 | 172.53750 | NFM | Seaford | Taxis |
| 167.73500 | 172.73500 | NFM | Ayr | Taxis |
| 167.73750 | 171.53750 | NFM | Cheshire | Vet |
| 167.73750 | 172.53750 | NFM | Ashford | Binmen (EF) |
| 167.73750 | 172.53750 | NFM | Bournemouth | Council Electricians |
| 167.73750 | 172.53750 | NFM | Crewe | Doctors Network |
| 167.73750 | 172.53750 | NFM | Dover | Skips |
| 167.73750 | 172.53750 | NFM | Essex | Cleanaway C/S |
| 167.73750 | 172.53750 | NFM | Hull | Taxis |
| 167.73750 | 172.53750 | NFM | Manchester | Veterinary Surgeon |
| 167.73750 | 172.53750 | NFM | Sheffield | Leigh Environmental |
| 167.74000 | 172.54000 | NFM | Newcastle | Grosvenor Taxis |
| 167.75000 | 172.55000 | NFM | Dundee | Taxis |
| 167.75000 | 172.55000 | NFM | Hull | Taxis |
| 167.75000 | 172.55000 | NFM | Lowestoft | Oulton Radio Taxis |
| 167.75000 | 172.55000 | NFM | Nottingham | Yellow Cabs |
| 167.75000 | 172.55000 | NFM | West Midlands | Wheelchair Cabs |
| 167.75000 | 172.55000 | NFM | Wirral | New Brighton Cabs |
| 167.76000 | 172.56000 | NFM | Cumbernauld | Taxis |
| 167.76250 | 172.56250 | NFM | Birmingham | Taxis |
| 167.76250 | 172.56250 | NFM | Bolton | Manor Taxis |
| 167.76250 | 172.56250 | NFM | Bromley | Cannon Cars |
| 167.76250 | 172.56250 | NFM | Cumbernauld | Cita Taxis (Cita) |
| 167.76250 | 172.56250 | NFM | Dunstable | Cannon Cars |
| 167.76250 | 172.56250 | NFM | Felixstowe | Wizard Taxis Ch 1 |
| 167.76250 | 172.56250 | NFM | Gateshead | Council |
| 167.76250 | 172.56250 | NFM | Glasgow | Taxis |
| 167.76250 | 172.56250 | NFM | Halifax | Pennine Taxis |
| 167.76250 | 172.56250 | NFM | Southampton | Hospital Transport |
| 167.76250 | 172.56250 | NFM | Walsall | Taxis |
| 167.77500 | 172.57500 | AM | Boston | Star Taxis |
| 167.77500 | 172.57500 | NFM | Exmouth | Discount Cars |
| 167.77500 | 172.57500 | NFM | Hull | Taxis |
| 167.77500 | 172.57500 | NFM | Manchester | Taxis |
| 167.77500 | 172.57500 | NFM | Norwich | Cablevision |
| 167.77500 | 172.57500 | NFM | Shaftesbury | Alfords Taxis |
| 167.77500 | 172.57500 | NFM | Taplow | Burnham Couriers |
| 167.77500 | 172.57500 | NFM | Welwyn Garden City | Industrial Services |
| 167.77500 | 172.57500 | NFM | Woburn | Speedwell Farms |
| 167.77500 | 172.57500 | NFM | York | Taxis |
| 167.78750 | 172.58750 | NFM | Basildon | Ace Taxi Group |
| 167.78750 | 172.58750 | NFM | Birmingham | Taxis |
| 167.78750 | 172.58750 | NFM | Eccles | New Lyle Cars |
| 167.78750 | 172.58750 | NFM | Edinburgh | Falcon Delivery |
| 167.78750 | 172.58750 | NFM | Jersey | Jersey States Housing Dept. |
| 167.78750 | 172.58750 | NFM | Lincoln | Taxis |
| 167.78750 | 172.58750 | NFM | London | Swiss Cottage Radio Cars |
| 167.78750 | 172.58750 | NFM | Manchester | Taxis |
| 167.78750 | 172.58750 | NFM | Peterborough | ABBA Taxis |
| 167.78750 | 172.58750 | NFM | Rochdale | Town Cars |
| 167.78750 | 172.58750 | NFM | Saddleworth | Taxis |
| 167.78750 | 172.58750 | NFM | St Andrews | Jay Taxis |
| 167.80000 | 172.60000 | AM | Aberdeen | Security |
| 167.80000 | 172.60000 | NFM | Blackburn | Lancs Private Hire |
| 167.80000 | 172.60000 | NFM | Burnley | Taxis |

| Base | Mobile | Mode | Location | User and Notes |
|------|--------|------|----------|----------------|
| 167.80000 | 172.60000 | NFM | Cambridge | United Taxis |
| 167.80000 | 172.60000 | NFM | Coventry | T White Skips |
| 167.80000 | 172.60000 | NFM | Cumbernauld | Taxis |
| 167.80000 | 172.60000 | NFM | Dovercourt | Starling Taxis |
| 167.80000 | 172.60000 | NFM | Glasgow | Taxis |
| 167.80000 | 172.60000 | AM | Grimsby | Revels Taxis |
| 167.80000 | 172.60000 | NFM | Leicester | Slot Machines |
| 167.80000 | 172.60000 | NFM | Manchester | Cresta Cars |
| 167.80000 | 172.60000 | NFM | Nottingham | Amusement Machine Servicing |
| 167.80000 | 172.60000 | NFM | Oldham | Britannia Cars |
| 167.80000 | 172.60000 | NFM | Portsmouth | Coop TV Service |
| 167.80000 | 172.60000 | NFM | Sheffield | Eagle Cars |
| 167.80000 | 172.60000 | NFM | Weymouth | Taxi Co |
| 167.80000 | 172.60000 | NFM | Wirral | 50-50 Cabs |
| 167.81250 | 172.61250 | NFM | Alloa | Taxis |
| 167.81250 | 172.61250 | NFM | Bath | Abbey Taxis |
| 167.81250 | 172.61250 | NFM | Bedford | M.W. Ward |
| 167.81250 | 172.61250 | NFM | Bootle | Taxis |
| 167.81250 | 172.61250 | FM | Cambridge | BT Line Repair Team |
| 167.81250 | 172.61250 | NFM | Cwmbran, Gwent | Gwent Taxis |
| 167.81250 | 172.61250 | NFM | Glasgow | Taxis |
| 167.81250 | 172.61250 | NFM | Manchester, Leverhulme | Kings Private Hire |
| 167.81250 | 172.61250 | NFM | Watlington | Watlington Plant Hire |
| 167.81250 | 172.61250 | NFM | Westmount, Jersey | CSL Repeater |
| 167.81250 | 172.61250 | NFM | Westmount, Jersey | De La Haye Plant Ltd |
| 167.81250 | 172.61250 | NFM | Westmount, Jersey | Fuel Supplies Ltd |
| 167.81250 | 172.61250 | NFM | Westmount, Jersey | Keith Prowse Tours |
| 167.81250 | 172.61250 | NFM | Westmount, Jersey | MacLead & Allan |
| 167.81250 | 172.61250 | NFM | Westmount, Jersey | Ronez Ltd |
| 167.82500 | 172.62500 | NFM | Bolton | Tele Taxis |
| 167.82500 | 172.62500 | NFM | Bristol | Downend Taxis |
| 167.82500 | 172.62500 | NFM | Edinburgh | Taxis |
| 167.82500 | 172.62500 | NFM | Grangemouth | Tartan Line Radio Cabs (Tartan) |
| 167.82500 | 172.62500 | NFM | Ipswich | A.B.C Couriers / Parcels |
| 167.82500 | 172.62500 | NFM | Ipswich | Robin Hood Taxis |
| 167.82500 | 172.62500 | NFM | Liverpool | Cavalier Taxis |
| 167.82500 | 172.62500 | NFM | Tamworth | Polesworth Cars |
| 167.83700 | 172.63700 | NFM | Atherstone | AJ's Taxis |
| 167.83750 | 172.63700 | NFM | Coventry | Security Co |
| 167.83750 | 172.63700 | NFM | Polesworth | Polesworth Cabs |
| 167.83750 | 172.63700 | NFM | Rochdale | Milnrow Cars |
| 167.83750 | 172.63750 | NFM | Canterbury | Longport Taxi |
| 167.83750 | 172.63750 | NFM | Kings Lynn | House Plant Growers |
| 167.83750 | 172.63750 | NFM | Manchester | Taxis |
| 167.83750 | 172.68750 | NFM | Tynemouth | Taxis |
| 167.85000 | 172.65000 | NFM | Bexley Heath | Taxis |
| 167.85000 | 172.65000 | AM | Blackpool | Ace Cabs |
| 167.85000 | 172.65000 | NFM | Bridlington | Q Cars |
| 167.85000 | 172.65000 | NFM | Cambridge | Clearaway |
| 167.85000 | 172.65000 | NFM | Cardiff | Amber Taxis |
| 167.85000 | 172.65000 | NFM | Cleveleys | Ace Cabs |
| 167.85000 | 172.65000 | AM | Ipswich | Taxis |
| 167.85000 | 172.65000 | NFM | London NW2 | Alpine Radio Cars (A) |
| 167.85000 | 172.65000 | NFM | Nottinghamshire | Clumber Park |
| 167.86250 | 172.66250 | NFM | Leicester | Taxis |
| 167.86250 | 172.66250 | NFM | London | Challenger Couriers |

| Base | Mobile | Mode | Location | User and Notes |
|------|--------|------|----------|----------------|
| 167.86250 | 172.66250 | NFM | Manchester | Taxis |
| 167.86250 | 172.66250 | NFM | Middleton | Star Taxis |
| 167.86250 | 172.66250 | NFM | Milton Keynes | City Bus Ltd |
| 167.86250 | 172.66250 | NFM | Ormskirk | Taxis |
| 167.86250 | 172.66250 | NFM | Sheffield | Mercury Taxis |
| 167.86250 | 172.66250 | NFM | Swansea | E and G Taxis |
| 167.86250 | 172.66250 | NFM | Wiltshire | * Bus Inspectors & Mechanics |
| 167.86250 | 172.66250 | NFM | Worthing | Taxis |
| 167.87500 | 172.67500 | NFM | Bedworth | MGM Taxis |
| 167.87500 | 172.67500 | NFM | Plymouth | Taxis |
| 167.87500 | 172.67500 | NFM | Scunthorpe | Taxis |
| 167.87500 | 172.67500 | AM | Sheffield | DB Taxis |
| 167.88750 | 172.68750 | NFM | Atherton | J & K Taxis |
| 167.88750 | 172.68750 | NFM | Chelmsford | Trade Comms |
| 167.88750 | 172.68750 | NFM | Cheshire | Whites Taxis |
| 167.88750 | 172.68750 | NFM | Congleton | Taxi |
| 167.88750 | 172.68750 | NFM | Eastleigh | Taxis |
| 167.88750 | 172.68750 | NFM | Glasgow | Taxi Company |
| 167.88750 | 172.68750 | AM | Ipswich | Taxis |
| 167.88750 | 172.68750 | NFM | Liverpool | Dock Taxis |
| 167.88750 | 172.68750 | NFM | Oldham | Radio Cars |
| 167.88750 | 172.68750 | NFM | Sheffield | Airport Express |
| 167.90000 | 172.70000 | NFM | Coventry | Mercia Taxis |
| 167.90000 | 172.70000 | NFM | Heywood | Heywood Cars |
| 167.90000 | 172.70000 | NFM | Jersey | HM Customs & Excise Channel 1 |
| 167.90000 | 172.70000 | NFM | Leicester | Windscreen Repairs |
| 167.90000 | 172.70000 | NFM | Northampton | Taxis |
| 167.90000 | 172.70000 | NFM | Prescot | All Black Cabs Ltd |
| 167.90000 | 172.70000 | NFM | Welwyn Garden City | Garden City Taxis |
| 167.90000 | 172.70000 | NFM | Winton | Taxis |
| 167.91000 | 172.71000 | NFM | Normanton, West Yorkshire | Cable & Wireless |
| 167.91250 | 172.71250 | AM | Cransford | Normans Transport |
| 167.91250 | 172.71250 | NFM | Dalton in Furness | Taxi |
| 167.91250 | 172.71250 | NFM | Faversham | Reeves Taxis |
| 167.91250 | 172.71250 | NFM | Grain | Geoffrey Clark |
| 167.91250 | 172.71250 | NFM | Hitchin | Boxhalls Taxis |
| 167.91250 | 172.71250 | NFM | Hitchin | Tiny Taxis |
| 167.91250 | 172.71250 | AM | Ipswich | Taxis |
| 167.91250 | 172.71250 | NFM | Leeds | Bell Cable engineers |
| 167.91250 | 172.71250 | NFM | London | Skip Hire |
| 167.91250 | 172.71250 | NFM | Medway | Withers Concrete |
| 167.91250 | 172.71250 | NFM | Newport | Dragon Taxis Ch 1 |
| 167.91250 | 172.71250 | NFM | Royston | B & B Taxis |
| 167.91250 | 172.71250 | NFM | Sheffield | Blue Star Security |
| 167.91250 | 172.71250 | NFM | Woodbridge | Normans Transport |
| 167.91250 | 172.71250 | NFM | Wrexham | Cresta Taxis |
| 167.92500 | 172.72500 | NFM | Ashford | Freightline Parcels |
| 167.92500 | 172.72500 | NFM | Cambridge | College Maintenance |
| 167.92500 | 172.72500 | NFM | Chelmsford | Ace Mini Cabs |
| 167.92500 | 172.72500 | NFM | Cheltenham | Taxis |
| 167.92500 | 172.72500 | NFM | Hertsfordshire | Martini Cars |
| 167.92500 | 172.72500 | NFM | Leeds | Taxis |
| 167.92500 | 172.72500 | NFM | London | Bus Company |
| 167.92500 | 172.72500 | NFM | Newmarket | Sound City Cars |
| 167.92500 | 172.72500 | NFM | Northfleet | Scorpio Taxis |
| 167.92500 | 172.72500 | NFM | Radcliffe | United Private Hire |

| Base | Mobile | Mode | Location | User and Notes |
|------|--------|------|----------|----------------|
| 167.92500 | 172.72500 | NFM | Sheffield | Sita (GB) Ltd., plant and skips |
| 167.92500 | 172.72500 | NFM | Stevenage | Sierra Taxis |
| 167.93750 | 172.73750 | NFM | Bracknell | Bracknell Radio Cars |
| 167.93750 | 172.73750 | NFM | Cambridge | Cam-Doctors On Call |
| 167.93750 | 172.73750 | NFM | Coatbridge | Town Taxis |
| 167.93750 | 172.73750 | NFM | Cumbernauld | Taxis |
| 167.93750 | 172.73750 | NFM | Glasgow | Taxis |
| 167.93750 | 172.73750 | NFM | Hemel Hempstead | Minicab Co |
| 167.93750 | 172.73750 | NFM | London | Bow Taxis |
| 167.93750 | 172.73750 | NFM | London | Mile End Radio Cars |
| 167.93750 | 172.73750 | NFM | Luton | Harvey Plant Hire |
| 167.93750 | 172.73750 | NFM | Oldham | Red Cars |
| 167.93750 | 172.73750 | NFM | Oxford | Traffic wardens |
| 167.93750 | 172.73750 | NFM | Tamworth | Taxi Firm |
| 167.93750 | 172.73750 | NFM | Taunton | Ace Taxis |
| 167.95000 | 172.75000 | NFM | Glasgow | Taxis |
| 167.95000 | 172.75000 | NFM | Ipswich | Taxis |
| 167.95000 | 172.75000 | NFM | Jersey | Clarendon Cabs |
| 167.95000 | 172.75000 | NFM | Lichfield | Taxi |
| 167.95000 | 172.75000 | NFM | Nationwide | Search and Rescue |
| 167.95000 | 172.75000 | NFM | Rochdale | Kings Private Hire |
| 167.96250 | 172.76250 | NFM | Birkenhead | Robo's Taxis |
| 167.96250 | 172.76250 | NFM | Bootle | Taxis |
| 167.96250 | 172.76250 | NFM | Brighton | Taxis |
| 167.96250 | 172.76250 | NFM | Cambridge | River Punting Co Operations |
| 167.96250 | 172.76250 | NFM | Coventry | J K Lynch Construction |
| 167.96250 | 172.76250 | NFM | Jersey | Falles Hire Cars |
| 167.96250 | 172.76250 | NFM | Nottingham, Bulwell | Central Cars |
| 167.96250 | 172.76250 | NFM | Peterborough | Clover Cars |
| 167.96250 | 172.76250 | NFM | Peterborough | Horrells Dairies |
| 167.96250 | 172.76250 | NFM | Pocklington | Central Taxis |
| 167.96250 | 172.76250 | NFM | Sheffield | KC Cars |
| 167.96250 | 172.76250 | NFM | Sheffield | Moss Cabs |
| 167.97500 | 172.77500 | NFM | Edinburgh | Taxis |
| 167.97500 | 172.77500 | NFM | Glasgow | Croft Radio Cars |
| 167.97500 | 172.77500 | NFM | Ipswich | Hawk's Taxis |
| 167.97500 | 172.77500 | NFM | Ipswich | Tarmac Roadstones Ltd |
| 167.97500 | 172.77500 | NFM | Lincoln | Taxis |
| 167.97500 | 172.77500 | NFM | Liverpool | Taxis |
| 167.97500 | 172.77500 | NFM | London | Taxis |
| 167.97500 | 172.77500 | NFM | March | Coy & Manchett |
| 167.97500 | 172.77500 | NFM | Neath | Abbey Cabs |
| 167.97500 | 172.77500 | NFM | Peterborough | Crown Taxis |
| 167.97500 | 172.77500 | NFM | Portsmouth | Taxis |
| 167.97500 | 172.77500 | NFM | Royton | Royton Private Hire |
| 167.98750 | 172.78750 | NFM | Airdrie | M. Moffat Cars |
| 167.98750 | 172.78750 | NFM | Cannock | TNT Carriers |
| 167.98750 | 172.78750 | NFM | Exeter | Taxis control |
| 167.98750 | 172.78750 | NFM | Glasgow | Taxis |
| 167.98750 | 172.78750 | NFM | Halifax | Railway Taxis |
| 167.98750 | 172.78750 | NFM | Jersey | HM Customs & Excise Channel 3 |
| 167.98750 | 172.78750 | NFM | Leicester | Taxis |
| 167.98750 | 172.78750 | NFM | London, Whitechapel | Star Cars |
| 167.98750 | 172.78750 | NFM | Manchester | Taxis |
| 167.98750 | 172.78750 | NFM | Salford | Shopping City Security |
| 167.98750 | 172.78750 | NFM | Seaford | Taxi |

| Base | Mobile | Mode | Location | User and Notes |
|---|---|---|---|---|
| 167.98750 | 172.78750 | NFM | Sussex | Brighton Marina Security |
| 167.98750 | 172.78750 | NFM | Swansea Docks | Crane Crews |
| 167.98750 | 172.78750 | NFM | Thanet | B.C. Taxis |
| 167.98750 | 172.78750 | NFM | Walkden | Star Private Hire |
| 167.98750 | 172.78750 | NFM | Wrexham | Gold Star Taxis |
| 168.00000 | 172.80000 | NFM | Bristol | Dial A Cab |
| 168.00000 | 172.80000 | NFM | Burnley | Day Rider Couriers |
| 168.00000 | 172.80000 | NFM | Cambridge | Camtax |
| 168.00000 | 172.80000 | NFM | Falkirk | Express Taxis (Express) |
| 168.00000 | 172.80000 | NFM | Glasgow | Eastwood Taxis |
| 168.00000 | 172.80000 | NFM | Jersey | Pioneer Holiday Coaches |
| 168.00000 | 172.80000 | NFM | Manchester | Taxis |
| 168.00000 | 172.80000 | NFM | Preston | Buses |
| 168.00000 | 172.80000 | NFM | Salford | Taxis |
| 168.00000 | 172.80000 | NFM | Stoke On Trent | Abbey Taxis |
| 168.00000 | 172.80000 | NFM | West Glamorgan | S Wales Bus Co |
| 168.00000 | 172.80000 | NFM | Weymouth | Brewers Quay Exhibition |
| 168.01250 | 168.01250 | NFM | Brighton | Taxis |
| 168.01250 | 172.81250 | NFM | Baldock | KP Taxis |
| 168.01250 | 172.81250 | NFM | Baldock | Martin's Taxis |
| 168.01250 | 172.81250 | NFM | Doncaster | A1 Taxis |
| 168.01250 | 172.81250 | NFM | Edinburgh | Capital Cabs Ch 1 |
| 168.01250 | 172.81250 | NFM | London | Speed Couriers |
| 168.01250 | 172.81250 | NFM | London | Taxis |
| 168.01250 | 172.81250 | NFM | Salford | Mainline Taxis |
| 168.01250 | 172.81250 | NFM | Sheffield | Taxis |
| 168.01250 | 172.81250 | NFM | Stoke on Trent | Fourstar Taxis |
| 168.02500 | 172.82500 | NFM | Glasgow | Taxis |
| 168.02500 | 172.82500 | NFM | Hitchin | Swan Garage |
| 168.02500 | 172.82500 | NFM | Ipswich | Cambridge & East Coast Cable |
| 168.02500 | 172.82500 | NFM | Ipswich | Robin Hood Taxis |
| 168.02500 | 172.82500 | NFM | Leamington | Binmen |
| 168.02500 | 172.82500 | NFM | Swansea | ABC Taxis |
| 168.02500 | 172.82500 | NFM | Warwick | Warwick District Council |
| 168.03750 | 172.83750 | NFM | Barnet | Metrocars |
| 168.03750 | 172.83750 | NFM | Edinburgh | Capital Cabs Ch 2 |
| 168.03750 | 172.83750 | NFM | Glasgow | Taxis |
| 168.03750 | 172.83750 | NFM | Guernsey | D.J. Machan Engineering |
| 168.03750 | 172.83750 | NFM | London | New Barnet Cars |
| 168.03750 | 172.83750 | NFM | March | Rowe |
| 168.05000 | 172.85000 | NFM | Bristol | Z Cars Taxis |
| 168.05000 | 172.85000 | NFM | Cambridge | A1 Taxis |
| 168.05000 | 172.85000 | NFM | Central London | Taxis |
| 168.05000 | 172.85000 | NFM | Colchester | AA Taxis |
| 168.05000 | 172.85000 | NFM | Cowley | Rover Plant Ambulance |
| 168.05000 | 172.85000 | NFM | London, Heathrow | Airport Cars |
| 168.05000 | 172.85000 | NFM | Nationwide | Pretty Things Road Crew |
| 168.05000 | 172.85000 | NFM | Oldham | Delta Taxis |
| 168.05000 | 172.85000 | NFM | St Andrews | Golf City Taxis |
| 168.05000 | 172.85000 | NFM | Tamworth | Alpha Cars |
| 168.05000 | 172.85000 | NFM | Worksop | J.J & J.R. Jacksons |
| 168.05000 | 172.85000 | NFM | Worthing | Taxis |
| 168.06250 | 172.86250 | NFM | Bedford | Eagle Cars |
| 168.06250 | 172.86250 | NFM | Birmingham | Taxi |
| 168.06250 | 172.86250 | NFM | Hull | Hull Daily Mail Paper |
| 168.06250 | 172.86250 | NFM | London, south east | Taxis |

| Base | Mobile | Mode | Location | User and Notes |
|------|--------|------|----------|----------------|
| 168.06250 | 172.86250 | NFM | Manchester, Reddish | Taxis |
| 168.06250 | 172.86250 | NFM | Manchester, Walkden | Taxis |
| 168.06250 | 172.86250 | NFM | Peterborough | ABC Taxis |
| 168.07500 | 172.87500 | NFM | Beverley | Council |
| 168.07500 | 172.87500 | NFM | Cheshunt | Atlas Cars |
| 168.07500 | 172.87500 | NFM | Coventry, Bedworth | Edwards Taxis |
| 168.07500 | 172.87500 | NFM | Heywood | New Embassy Taxis |
| 168.07500 | 172.87500 | NFM | Liverpool | City Centre Taxis |
| 168.07500 | 172.87500 | NFM | London, central | Taxis |
| 168.07500 | 172.87500 | NFM | Newport | Reliance Taxis |
| 168.07500 | 172.87500 | NFM | Potters Bar | Radio Cars |
| 168.07500 | 172.87500 | NFM | West Bergholt | John Willsher |
| 168.08750 | 172.88750 | NFM | Ascot | Cooper 24Hr Taxis |
| 168.08750 | 172.88750 | NFM | Barrow in Furness | Taxis |
| 168.08750 | 172.88750 | NFM | Birmingham | Taxis |
| 168.08750 | 172.88750 | NFM | Cardiff | Taxis |
| 168.08750 | 172.88750 | NFM | Colchester | AA Cars |
| 168.08750 | 172.88750 | NFM | Colchester | Micraline Taxis |
| 168.08750 | 172.88750 | NFM | Glasgow | Taxis |
| 168.08750 | 172.88750 | NFM | Guernsey | Stan Brouard |
| 168.08750 | 172.88750 | NFM | Guernsey | Unigrow |
| 168.08750 | 172.88750 | NFM | Ipswich | Matthew's TV & Electrical |
| 168.08750 | 172.88750 | NFM | Severn Bridge | Contractors |
| 168.08750 | 172.88750 | NFM | Sittingbourne | Channel Taxis |
| 168.08750 | 172.88750 | NFM | Stevenage | W.G. Silverton |
| 168.08750 | 172.88750 | NFM | Walney | Avon Cars |
| 168.10000 | 172.90000 | NFM | Bristol | Streamline Taxis |
| 168.10000 | 172.90000 | NFM | Burnley | Taxis |
| 168.10000 | 172.90000 | NFM | Cardiff | Taxis |
| 168.10000 | 172.90000 | NFM | Co Durham | Taxis |
| 168.10000 | 172.90000 | NFM | Cumbernauld | Taxis |
| 168.10000 | 172.90000 | NFM | Edinburgh | Taxis |
| 168.10000 | 172.90000 | NFM | Edinburgh | United Artist Cable TV |
| 168.10000 | 172.90000 | NFM | Glasgow | Kingsway Taxis |
| 168.10000 | 172.90000 | NFM | Hamilton | Wellman Taxis |
| 168.10000 | 172.90000 | NFM | Newark | Taxis |
| 168.10000 | 172.90000 | NFM | Slough | A-2-B Taxis |
| 168.10000 | 172.90000 | NFM | Southampton | ESSO Fawley Security |
| 168.10000 | 172.90000 | NFM | Sussex | Palace Pier Security |
| 168.10000 | 172.90000 | NFM | Tottington | Tram Cars |
| 168.10000 | 172.90000 | NFM | Welwyn Garden City | 752 Taxis |
| 168.11250 | 172.91250 | NFM | Baldock | Rushbridges Garage |
| 168.11250 | 172.91250 | NFM | Bath | Taxis |
| 168.11250 | 172.91250 | NFM | Bromley | Taxis |
| 168.11250 | 172.91250 | NFM | Caister | Avenue Taxis |
| 168.11250 | 172.91250 | NFM | Cardiff | Capital Taxis |
| 168.11250 | 172.91250 | NFM | Cardiff | Green Cabs |
| 168.11250 | 172.91250 | NFM | Edinburgh | Taxis |
| 168.11250 | 172.91250 | NFM | Glasgow | Head End |
| 168.11250 | 172.91250 | NFM | Harlow | Buzz Bus |
| 168.11250 | 172.91250 | NFM | Heysham | Heysham Radio Taxis |
| 168.11250 | 172.91250 | NFM | London | Minicab Firm Woodford |
| 168.11250 | 172.91250 | NFM | Preston | Evening Gazette |
| 168.11250 | 172.91250 | NFM | Radcliffe | Centre Radio Cars |
| 168.11250 | 172.91250 | NFM | Sunderland | Star Taxis |
| 168.12500 | 172.92500 | NFM | Dundry | Brinks Mat Security |

| Base | Mobile | Mode | Location | User and Notes |
|------|--------|------|----------|----------------|
| 168.12500 | 172.92500 | NFM | Edinburgh | Taxis |
| 168.12500 | 172.92500 | NFM | Ipswich | Ipswich Buses Ltd |
| 168.12500 | 172.92500 | NFM | Sheffield | Balfour Beatty Base |
| 168.12500 | 172.92500 | NFM | West Midlands | Blue Taxi |
| 168.13250 | 172.93750 | NFM | Aberdeen | Plant Hire |
| 168.13250 | 172.93750 | NFM | Arlesey | Station Cars |
| 168.13250 | 172.93750 | NFM | Bolton | Breightmet Taxis |
| 168.13250 | 172.93750 | NFM | Burton-On-Trent | Lift Maintenance |
| 168.13250 | 172.93750 | NFM | Edinburgh | Black Cabs |
| 168.13250 | 172.93750 | NFM | Glasgow | Taxis |
| 168.13250 | 172.93750 | NFM | Gosport | Taxis |
| 168.13250 | 172.93750 | NFM | Manchester Airport | Taxis |
| 168.13250 | 172.93750 | NFM | Mansfield | A Line Taxis |
| 168.13250 | 172.93750 | NFM | Stoke on Trent | Sid's Taxis |
| 168.13750 | 172.93750 | NFM | Langley, Kent | Farmers (Newshelf) |
| 168.13750 | 172.93750 | NFM | London | Leytonstone & Stratford Car Service |
| 168.15000 | 172.95000 | NFM | Bath | Royal Welsh Show Security |
| 168.15000 | 172.95000 | NFM | Benwick | Bank Farms |
| 168.15000 | 172.95000 | NFM | Dover | District Council |
| 168.15000 | 172.95000 | NFM | Dublin | Dublin Cablelink |
| 168.15000 | 172.95000 | NFM | Ely | Evans Taxis |
| 168.15000 | 172.95000 | NFM | Hull | Taxis |
| 168.15000 | 172.95000 | NFM | Manchester | Town Cars |
| 168.15000 | 172.95000 | AM | Scarborough | Beeline |
| 168.15000 | 172.95000 | NFM | Swansea | S and E Taxis |
| 168.16250 | 172.96250 | NFM | Aberdeen | Taxis |
| 168.16250 | 172.96250 | NFM | Bedford | Al Cars |
| 168.16250 | 172.96250 | NFM | Birmingham 4 Oaks | Taxis |
| 168.16250 | 172.96250 | NFM | Bognor | Home James Taxis |
| 168.16250 | 172.96250 | AM | Cleethorpes | Taxis |
| 168.16250 | 172.96250 | NFM | Essex | Minicab Firm |
| 168.16250 | 172.96250 | NFM | Glasgow | Taxis |
| 168.16250 | 172.96250 | NFM | Goodwood Race Course | Goodwood Control |
| 168.16250 | 172.96250 | NFM | Kent | County Council Highways |
| 168.16250 | 172.96250 | NFM | London | Capital Cars |
| 168.16250 | 172.96250 | NFM | Manchester | Taxis |
| 168.16250 | 172.96250 | NFM | Wisbech | Ellis & Everard |
| 168.17500 | 172.97500 | NFM | Bedford | Key Cars |
| 168.17500 | 172.97500 | NFM | Birmingham Shirley | Taxis |
| 168.17500 | 172.97500 | NFM | Bridlington | Bunton Skips and Scrap Metal |
| 168.17500 | 172.97500 | AM | Grimsby | TV Repairs |
| 168.17500 | 172.97500 | NFM | Humberside | A Brunton & Co Skips and Scrap |
| 168.17500 | 172.97500 | NFM | Newmarket | Triax |
| 168.17500 | 172.97500 | NFM | Rochdale | Castle Private Hire |
| 168.18750 | 172.98750 | NFM | Abingdon | K-9 Security |
| 168.18750 | 172.98750 | NFM | Birmingham, Shard End | Taxis |
| 168.18750 | 172.98750 | NFM | Blackpool | Black Tax Taxis |
| 168.18750 | 172.98750 | NFM | Eastbourne | East College |
| 168.18750 | 172.98750 | NFM | Letchworth | Arena Security |
| 168.18750 | 172.98750 | NFM | Long Melford | A Line Taxis |
| 168.18750 | 172.98750 | NFM | Manchester, Leverhulme | White Line Private Hire |
| 168.18750 | 172.98750 | NFM | Peterborough | DJ Taxis |
| 168.18750 | 172.98750 | NFM | Salisbury | Bros Sutton |
| 168.18750 | 172.98750 | NFM | Sutton | Salisbury Bros. |
| 168.20000 | 173.00000 | NFM | Ayr | Taxis |
| 168.20000 | 173.00000 | NFM | Beswick | UK Cars |

| Base | Mobile | Mode | Location | User and Notes |
|------|--------|------|----------|----------------|
| 168.20000 | 173.00000 | NFM | Brentwood | TNT Carriers |
| 168.20000 | 173.00000 | NFM | Glasgow | Taxis |
| 168.20000 | 173.00000 | AM | Grimsby | Taxis |
| 168.20000 | 173.00000 | NFM | London | Junction Cars of Archway |
| 168.20000 | 173.00000 | NFM | Manchester | Taxis |
| 168.20000 | 173.00000 | NFM | Milton | TNT Carriers |
| 168.20000 | 173.00000 | NFM | Peterborough | Rivergate Security |
| 168.20000 | 173.00000 | NFM | Reading | 1A Cars |
| 168.20000 | 173.00000 | NFM | Shaftesbury | Alford Taxis |
| 168.20000 | 173.00000 | NFM | Shaftesbury | Hilltop Taxis |
| 168.20000 | 173.00000 | NFM | Sheffield | School security |
| 168.21250 | 173.01250 | NFM | Cambridge | Bettacars |
| 168.21250 | 173.01250 | NFM | Cambridge | Bettacars |
| 168.21250 | 173.01250 | NFM | Dukinfield | Taxis |
| 168.21250 | 173.01250 | NFM | Glasgow | Taxis |
| 168.21250 | 173.01250 | NFM | London | Roman Cars |
| 168.21250 | 173.01250 | NFM | Manchester | Zip Dispatch |
| 168.21250 | 173.01250 | NFM | Norfolk | ICL |
| 168.21250 | 173.01250 | NFM | Norwich | Royal Taxis |
| 168.21250 | 173.01250 | NFM | Seven Bridge | Toll collectors |
| 168.21250 | 173.01250 | NFM | Sheffield | Eagle Taxis |
| 168.21250 | 173.01250 | NFM | Sheffield | GT Cars |
| 108.21250 | 173.01250 | NFM | Southminster | Denge Crops Ltd. |
| 168.21250 | 173.01250 | NFM | Stirling | D & M Taxis (D) |
| 168.21250 | 173.01250 | NFM | Swinton | Zip Dispatch |
| 168.21250 | 173.01250 | NFM | Trowbridge | Alpha Taxis |
| 168.22500 | 173.02000 | NFM | Eastbourne | School Bus Service |
| 168.22500 | 173.02500 | NFM | Blackpool | Green Star Taxis |
| 168.22500 | 173.02500 | NFM | Felixstowe | Compass Cars |
| 168.22500 | 173.02500 | NFM | Glasgow | Taxis |
| 168.22500 | 173.02500 | NFM | Jersey | Interlink Delivery |
| 168.22500 | 173.02500 | NFM | London | AZ Couriers |
| 168.22500 | 173.02500 | NFM | Manchester | Taxis |
| 168.22500 | 173.02500 | NFM | March | Central Shopping Security |
| 168.22500 | 173.02500 | NFM | Medway | Countdown Cars |
| 168.22500 | 173.02500 | NFM | Nationwide | Radio Investigations Service |
| 168.22500 | 173.02500 | NFM | Oldham | Untied Private Hire |
| 168.22500 | 173.02500 | NFM | Peterborough | Rivergate Security |
| 168.22500 | 173.02500 | NFM | Stockport | Curry's security |
| 168.22500 | 173.02500 | NFM | Swindon | A2B Taxis |
| 168.22500 | 173.02500 | NFM | West Midlands | Public House Repairs |
| 168.23750 | 173.03750 | NFM | Carlisle | City Taxis |
| 168.23750 | 173.03750 | NFM | Corsham | Taxis |
| 168.23750 | 173.03750 | NFM | Doncaster | Midwives and Home Helps |
| 168.23750 | 173.03750 | NFM | Fakenham | Woodys Haulage |
| 168.23750 | 173.03750 | NFM | Felling | Taxis |
| 168.23750 | 173.03750 | NFM | Great Yarmouth | Halcyon Shipping |
| 168.23750 | 173.03750 | NFM | Llandudno | Taxi Service |
| 168.23750 | 173.03750 | NFM | Luton | Amec Maintenance |
| 168.23750 | 173.03750 | NFM | Nottingham | Holme Pier Water Sports |
| 168.23750 | 173.03750 | NFM | Paddock Wood, Kent | County Council repairs |

## 168.2500 - 169.39375 MHz PMR High Band Simplex, Government
### Agencies & Emergency Simplex 12.5 kHz

| Base | Mobile | Mode | Location | User and Notes |
| --- | --- | --- | --- | --- |
| 168.25000 | | NFM | Dudley | Waterfront Security |
| 168.25000 | | NFM | Ferndown | E.G. Hoare |
| 168.25000 | | NFM | Nationwide | BT Linesmen |
| 168.25000 | | NFM | Nationwide | Radio Investigations |
| 168.25000 | | NFM | Swindon | Cooper's Metals |
| 168.25000 | 173.05000 | NFM | Bletchley | Ready Mix Concrete |
| 168.25000 | 173.05000 | NFM | Leiston | Leisure Centre |
| 168.25000 | 173.05000 | NFM | Midlands, Ashton Court | Bass Leisure |
| 168.25000 | 173.05000 | NFM | Suffolk | Coastal D.C Office Security |
| 168.26250 | | NFM | Alderney | Alderney Electricity |
| 168.26250 | | NFM | Nationwide | BT Cable Laying |
| 168.27500 | | NFM | Dorset | Radiocommunications Agency |
| 168.27500 | | NFM | Hampshire | Radiocommunications Agency |
| 168.27500 | | NFM | Lancashire | Radiocommunications Agency |
| 168.27500 | | NFM | Nationwide | Radiocommunications Agency |
| 168.27500 | | NFM | Preston | Crown Prosecution |
| 168.27500 | | NFM | Worcester | Surveillance Unit |
| 168.28750 | | NFM | Burnley | Taxis |
| 168.28750 | | NFM | Edinburgh | Lothian & Borders Fire Brigade |
| 168.28750 | | NFM | Glasgow | Elderly Persons Warden |
| 168.28750 | | NFM | Nationwide | OAP Alarms control |
| 168.28750 | | NFM | Nationwide | OAP Wardens control |
| 168.30000 | | NFM | Nationwide | BT & Post Office Investigators |
| 168.30000 | | NFM | Nationwide | Radio Investigation |
| 168.32000 | | NFM | Boston | Farmworkers |
| 168.34000 | | NFM | St. Lawrence | R Procter Farms |
| 168.36250 | | NFM | Chesterfield | Government Agency (DVP) |
| 168.36250 | | NFM | Staffordshire | Local Authority Emergency Communications Network |
| 168.38750 | | NFM | Melksham | Taxis |
| 168.40000 | | NFM | Formula One Racing | Williams Team Voice Link |
| 168.43750 | | NFM | Aberdeen | Security |
| 168.47500 | | NFM | Dudley | Hospital Security |
| 168.47500 | | NFM | Tamworth | Drayton Manor Park |
| 168.50000 | | NFM | Staffordshire | Local Authority Emergency Communications Network |
| 168.53750 | | NFM | High Wycombe | Council car park wardens |
| 168.59375 | | NFM | Leeds | Flying Eye for Magic 828, Hallam FM & Viking AM |
| 168.60000 | | NFM | London | Diplomatic Protection (Ranger) |
| 168.72600 | | NFM | Doncaster | Royal Mail |
| 168.75000 | | NFM | Guernsey | Civil Defence Network |
| 168.75000 | | NFM | Jersey | Civil Defence Network |
| 168.75000 | | NFM | Nationwide | DSS Ch.1 |
| 168.75000 | | NFM | Swansea | DSS Fraud Teams |
| 168.76250 | | NFM | Bristol | Badgerline Buses |
| 168.77500 | | NFM | Bedfordshire, South | Government agency (DVP) |
| 168.77500 | | NFM | London | Government agency |
| 168.80000 | | NFM | Dorset | Fire Brigade (QD) |
| 168.80000 | 173.60000 | NFM | Chesterfield | Government engineers testing |
| 168.81250 | | NFM | National | Schuppa Lemans Race Team |
| 168.81250 | | NFM | Nationwide | Police Regional Crime Squad (DVP) |
| 168.82500 | | NFM | Dorset | Fire Brigade (QD) |
| 168.85000 | | NFM | Birmingham | Lucas Aerospace Security (L) |
| 168.85000 | | NFM | Ipswich | Royal Mail Sorting Office |
| 168.85000 | | NFM | London | Royal Mail Sorting Office |

| Base | Mobile | Mode | Location | User and Notes |
|------|--------|------|----------|----------------|
| 168.85000 | | NFM | Swansea City | Royal Mail |
| 168.85000 | | NFM | Weymouth | Mount Vernon Post Office |
| 168.86250 | | NFM | Euro Tunnel, Dover | Shakespeare Clift |
| 168.86250 | | NFM | Glasgow | Taxis |
| 168.86250 | | NFM | Jersey Airport | Beauport Aviation Gnd Staff |
| 168.86250 | | NFM | Nationwide | Local Authority Emergency Services |
| 168.86250 | | NFM | Nationwide | National Seismic Studies |
| 168.86250 | | NFM | Suffolk | Police Regional Crime Squads |
| 168.87500 | | NFM | Cardiff | Cardiff Van Hire |
| 168.87500 | | NFM | Doncaster | DSS |
| 168.87500 | | NFM | Doncaster | Royal Mail |
| 168.87500 | | NFM | Ipswich | DSS Ch.2 |
| 168.87500 | | NFM | London | Wembley Stadium Medics and Fire |
| 168.87500 | | NFM | London, Mount Pleasant | Royal Mail (CONCORDE) |
| 168.87500 | | NFM | Nationwide | DSS Ch.2 |
| 168.87500 | | NFM | Nationwide | Royal Mail cash vans |
| 168.87500 | | NFM | Swansea | DSS Fraud Teams |
| 168.88750 | | NFM | Nationwide | BT Video Set Up Link |
| 168.88750 | | NFM | Nationwide | BT microwave set up for outside broadcasts |
| 168.90000 | | NFM | Guernsey | Lesbirel Agricultural Services |
| 168.90000 | | NFM | Nationwide | British Tele Investigation Teams Digital Voice Protection |
| 168.91250 | | NFM | Ipswich | DSS Ch.3 |
| 168.91250 | | NFM | Jersey | Kingslea Hire |
| 168.91250 | | NFM | Newport | DHSS |
| 168.92000 | | NFM | Mossblown | Sheltered Housing Warden |
| 168.92500 | | NFM | Cardiff, Newport | Royal Mail |
| 168.92500 | | NFM | London | Bullion Movement Security |
| 168.92500 | | NFM | Warwick | Race course stewards |
| 168.93750 | | NFM | Nationwide | Local Authority Alarms |
| 168.95000 | | NFM | Jersey | Driving Tests Chase Vehicle |
| 168.95000 | | NFM | Nationwide | British Telecom |
| 168.95000 | | NFM | RAF Cosford | Museum Staff |
| 168.96000 | | NFM | Barrow in Furness | VSEL Shopfloor & Onboard Communications |
| 168.96250 | | NFM | Aberdeen | Docks |
| 168.96250 | | NFM | Brightwell | Mayhew A.G, Sheerdrift Farm . |
| 168.96250 | | NFM | Bury St Edmunds | Rushbrooke Farms |
| 168.96250 | | NFM | Jersey | Industrial (Motors) Ltd |
| 168.96250 | | NFM | Minehead | Butlins security |
| 168.96250 | | NFM | Moss, Midlands | Gawsworth Hall C/S |
| 168.96250 | | NFM | Scarborough | Brurowick Pavilion Cent. Security |
| 168.96250 | | NFM | Sheffield City Centre | Bus Inspectors |
| 168.97500 | | NFM | Barrow in Furness | VSEL |
| 168.97500 | | NFM | Caversham Park | BBC Monitoring Service |
| 168.97500 | | NFM | Jersey | Horse Racing Shows |
| 168.97500 | | NFM | Leighton Buzzard | Joseph Arnold |
| 168.97500 | | NFM | London | Hopton Holiday Village staff |
| 168.97500 | | NFM | London | Wembley Stadium medics and fire |
| 168.97500 | | NFM | Nationwide | Ordinance Survey |
| 168.97500 | | NFM | Newcastle | British Telecom |
| 168.97500 | | NFM | Newport, Wales | BBC aerial riggers |
| 168.97500 | | NFM | Tamworth | Drayton Manor Park and Zoo staff |
| 168.98750 | | NFM | Aberdeen | Docks |
| 168.98750 | | NFM | Cambridge | Fitzwilliam College |
| 168.98750 | | NFM | Croydon | Crystal Palace Shopping Centre |
| 168.98750 | | NFM | Durham | TNT Carriers |
| 168.98750 | | NFM | Felixstowe | Docks Police |

| Base | Mobile | Mode | Location | User and Notes |
|------|--------|------|----------|----------------|
| 168.98750 | | NFM | Guernsey | Condor Shipping |
| 168.98750 | | NFM | Haverfordwest | Farm |
| 168.98750 | | NFM | Jersey | Harbour (Condor) |
| 168.98750 | | NFM | Leek Wootton | Warwickshire Golf Course |
| 168.98750 | | NFM | London | Wembley Stadium Stewards |
| 168.98750 | | NFM | Manchester | Government agency |
| 168.98750 | | NFM | Nationwide | BBC Engineering Channel |
| 168.98750 | | NFM | Nationwide | ITC Riggers |
| 168.98750 | | NFM | Nationwide | Ordnance Survey teams |
| 168.98750 | | NFM | Newport | Steelworks Handhelds |
| 168.98750 | | NFM | Peterborough | Ferry Meadows Rangers |
| 168.98750 | | NFM | Preston | Moathouse Hotel |
| 168.98750 | | NFM | Prestwick Airport | British Aerospace |
| 169.00000 | | NFM | Bolton | Council Car Park Attendants |
| 169.00000 | | NFM | Bournemouth | Synagogue Security |
| 169.00000 | | NFM | Cambridge | Trinity College |
| 169.00000 | | NFM | Cheltenham | FMR Investigations |
| 169.00000 | | NFM | Coventry | Gravel Base |
| 169.00000 | | NFM | Crewe | Oakley Centre |
| 169.00000 | | NFM | Galston | Loudoun Castle Theme Park |
| 169.00000 | | NFM | Guernsey | PSS Security |
| 169.00000 | | NFM | Kilwinning | Water Bailiffs |
| 169.00000 | | NFM | Nationwide | RAC Rally |
| 169.00000 | | NFM | RAF Cosford | Museum |
| 169.00000 | | NFM | Sheffield | Shinecliffe College |
| 169.00000 | | NFM | Sheffield | Transport Interchange Security |
| 169.00000 | | NFM | Southampton | Dock Security |
| 169.00000 | | NFM | Southampton | TNT Carriers |
| 169.00000 | | NFM | Tilbury | Docks Freightliner Terminal |
| 169.01250 | | NFM | Bentwaters | Park Security |
| 169.01250 | | NFM | Burnley | York House Cabaret |
| 169.01250 | | NFM | Cornwall | T S Brent |
| 169.01250 | | NFM | Dundee | Tay Bridge Maintenance |
| 169.01250 | | NFM | Edinburgh | HMV Record Shop Security |
| 169.01250 | | NFM | Farnborough Airshow | Airbus Industries Security |
| 169.01250 | | NFM | Glasgow | Army ops discrete |
| 169.01250 | | NFM | Gt Yarmouth & Gorlestone | Shopwatch No CTCSS |
| 169.01250 | | NFM | Jersey | DHL Courier |
| 169.01250 | | NFM | Leicester | Airport Ops |
| 169.01250 | | NFM | London | Lords Cricket Ground Stewards |
| 169.01250 | | NFM | London | Nuttall Construction |
| 169.01250 | | NFM | London | Taylor Woodrow building cranes |
| 169.01250 | | NFM | London | Wembley Stadium Merchandise |
| 169.01250 | | NFM | Nationwide | Network Q Rally - Subaru |
| 169.01250 | | NFM | Nationwide | RAC Rally |
| 169.01250 | | NFM | Nationwide | Short Term Hire |
| 169.01250 | | NFM | Parkeston Quay | Harwich Transport |
| 169.01250 | | NFM | Sheffield | Sheffield Arena stewards |
| 169.01250 | | NFM | St Austell | Scrap Car Yard |
| 169.01250 | | NFM | Stevenage | Dales Produce |
| 169.01250 | | NFM | Weymouth | Guardforce Security |
| 169.02000 | | NFM | Enfield | Police |
| 169.02500 | | NFM | Brighton | Pier and Front |
| 169.02500 | | NFM | Bury St Edmonds | Council |
| 169.02500 | | NFM | Bury St Edmunds | Leisure Centre |
| 169.02500 | | NFM | Cambridge | Posthouse Forte Hotel |

| Base | Mobile | Mode | Location | User and Notes |
|------|--------|------|----------|----------------|
| 169.02500 | | NFM | Chippenham | Shopping Centre Security |
| 169.02500 | | NFM | Guernsey | Mainland Market Deliveries |
| 169.02500 | | NFM | Hillingdon | Council |
| 169.02500 | | NFM | Humberside Airport | Servisair |
| 169.02500 | | NFM | Jersey | Deliveries |
| 169.02500 | | NFM | Kent | St. Johns Ambulance Ch.2 |
| 169.02500 | | NFM | Liverpool | Marks & Spencer Security |
| 169.02500 | | NFM | London | Cazenove & Co Stockbrokers |
| 169.02500 | | NFM | Nationwide | RAC Rally |
| 169.02500 | | NFM | Nationwide | St Johns Ambulance Channel B |
| 169.02500 | | NFM | Northern Ireland | St. Johns Ambulance Ch.2 |
| 169.02500 | | NFM | Perth | Security |
| 169.02500 | | NFM | Powys | Powys County Council |
| 169.02500 | | NFM | Prestatyn | Pontins Holiday Camp Security |
| 169.02500 | | NFM | Sheffield | Shinecliffe security (APPLE) |
| 169.02500 | | NFM | Suffolk | St. Johns Ambulance Ch.2 |
| 169.02500 | | NFM | West Midlands | St. Johns Ambulance (ME) |
| 169.03750 | | NFM | Bournemouth | International Centre Security |
| 169.03750 | | NFM | Bristol | Fruit Market |
| 169.03750 | | NFM | Cheltenham | FMR Investigations |
| 169.03750 | | NFM | Clacton | Pier Co |
| 169.03750 | | NFM | Eastbourne | Seafront train |
| 169.03750 | | NFM | Fort William | Nevis Range Ski Co. |
| 169.03750 | | NFM | Hitchin | E&S Scrap Metal |
| 169.03750 | | NFM | Hull | Hull Rugby Stewards |
| 169.03750 | | NFM | Humberside Airport | Servisair Ops |
| 169.03750 | | NFM | Ipswich | University College Suffolk |
| 169.03750 | | NFM | Jersey | Jersey Zoo |
| 169.03750 | | NFM | Lochaber | Nevis Rescue Services |
| 169.03750 | | NFM | London | London Zoo staff |
| 169.03750 | | NFM | Luton Airport | Britannia Ground |
| 169.03750 | | NFM | Maidstone | Leeds Castle Security Staff |
| 169.03750 | | NFM | Manchester | Freightliners Yard Staff |
| 169.03750 | | NFM | Penzance | Antenna Riggers |
| 169.03750 | | NFM | Plymouth | City Centre Shop Security |
| 169.03750 | | NFM | Scarborough | Core Security |
| 169.03750 | | NFM | Sellafield | Construction |
| 169.03750 | | NFM | Tendring | Tendring Hundreds Water |
| 169.03750 | | NFM | Wimbledon | Tennis Championship |
| 169.05000 | | NFM | Bacton | British Gas Corp |
| 169.05000 | | NFM | National | Gas & Electricity Board Handhelds |
| 169.05000 | | NFM | National | Jaguar Racing Team |
| 169.05000 | | NFM | Nationwide | RAC Rally |
| 169.05000 | | NFM | Newport | Tarmac Road Repairs |
| 169.06250 | | NFM | Brighton | Palace Pier |
| 169.06250 | | NFM | Carlisle | Portland Centre |
| 169.06250 | | NFM | Jersey | Commodore Shipping |
| 169.06250 | | NFM | London | Trocadero Security, Piccadilly |
| 169.06250 | | NFM | London | Wembley Stadium Pavilion Shopping Centre |
| 169.06250 | | NFM | London, Oxford St | Debenhams security plain clothes |
| 169.06250 | | NFM | Lowestoft | Christian Salvesen |
| 169.06250 | | NFM | Nationwide | ICL Computers |
| 169.06250 | | NFM | Offley Area | Farm |
| 169.07500 | | NFM | Coventry | Park surveyors |
| 169.07500 | | NFM | Glen Coe | White Corries Ski Co. |
| 169.07500 | | NFM | Guernsey | Balfour Beatty Falla |

| Base | Mobile | Mode | Location | User and Notes |
|---|---|---|---|---|
| 169.07500 | | NFM | Ipswich | Eastgate Shopping Centre |
| 169.07500 | | NFM | Liverpool | Albert Dock Security |
| 169.07500 | | NFM | Llanelli | Pembury Country Park Rangers |
| 169.07500 | | NFM | London | Arsenal Football Club stewards |
| 169.07500 | | NFM | London | Queens Park Rangers Football Club stewards |
| 169.07500 | | NFM | London | West Ham Football Club stewards |
| 169.07500 | | NFM | Martlesham | Kingpin Bowling Centre |
| 169.07500 | | NFM | Newquay | Hendra Caravan Park |
| 169.07500 | | NFM | Poole | Valiant Security |
| 169.07500 | | NFM | Sheffield | Shirecliffe College |
| 169.07500 | | NFM | Turbury Derbyshire | Nestles |
| 169.07500 | | NFM | Tyneside | Five Star Security |
| 169.07500 | | NFM | Warwickshire | County Council Highway |
| 169.08500 | | NFM | Ayr | Water Bailiff Handhelds |
| 169.08700 | | NFM | Nationwide | Red Cross |
| 169.08700 | | NFM | West Midlands | St John's Ambulance Ch 5 |
| 169.08750 | | NFM | Abergavenny | Mountain Rescue Team 1 |
| 169.08750 | | NFM | Bedfordshire | DSS |
| 169.08750 | | NFM | Blackpool | Social Security |
| 169.08750 | | NFM | Bolton | Peak Security |
| 169.08750 | | NFM | Brighton | Place Pier |
| 169.08750 | | NFM | Crownhill | DSS Security Office |
| 169.08750 | | NFM | England, Southeast | British Transport Police Discrete |
| 169.08750 | | NFM | Guernsey | Allied Heating |
| 169.08750 | | NFM | Guernsey | Louis Dekker Bulbs |
| 169.08750 | | NFM | Jersey | European Golf Championships |
| 169.08750 | | NFM | Kent | Red Cross |
| 169.08750 | | NFM | London | Arsenal Football Club security |
| 169.08750 | | NFM | London | DD Film Unit |
| 169.08750 | | NFM | Manchester | Trafford Centre Security |
| 169.08750 | | NFM | Medway | In Sewer Surveys |
| 169.08750 | | NFM | Merseyside | Merseyrail |
| 169.08750 | | NFM | Nationwide | DSS (limited use) |
| 169.08750 | | NFM | Nationwide | Red Cross |
| 169.08750 | | NFM | Newmarket | Bookmakers |
| 169.08750 | | NFM | Norfolk | Red Cross |
| 169.08750 | | NFM | Peterborough | East of England Show Ground Medic Ambulances |
| 169.08750 | | NFM | Plymouth | DSS Security Office |
| 169.08750 | | NFM | Plymouth | Plymouth Market Security |
| 169.08750 | | NFM | RAF St Mawgan | PSA Agency |
| 169.08750 | | NFM | Sheffield | Transport Interchange |
| 169.08750 | | NFM | Southampton | Docks |
| 169.08750 | | NFM | Southern England | Mowlem Civil Engineering |
| 169.08750 | | NFM | Sutton Coldfield | Belfry Golf Course |
| 169.08750 | | NFM | Warwick | Warwick Hospital |
| 169.10000 | | NFM | Belfast | Stenaline HSS |
| 169.10000 | | NFM | Belfrey | Golf Course |
| 169.10000 | | NFM | Cambridge | Medical Research Council |
| 169.10000 | | NFM | Fishguard | Stena Sealink |
| 169.10000 | | NFM | Folkestone | Stena Sealink |
| 169.10000 | | NFM | Isle of Arran | National Trust for Scotland Rangers |
| 169.10000 | | NFM | Larne | Stena Sealink |
| 169.10000 | | NFM | London | Next Shop, Oxford Circus Shopnet |
| 169.10000 | | NFM | Norwich | Football Stewards |
| 169.10000 | | NFM | Southampton | Stenaline |
| 169.10000 | | NFM | Stranraer | Stenaline |

| Base | Mobile | Mode | Location | User and Notes |
|------|--------|------|----------|----------------|
| 169.11250 | | NFM | Ayr | Taxis |
| 169.11250 | | NFM | Bournemouth | International Centre Security |
| 169.11250 | | NFM | Canterbury | University Of Kent |
| 169.11250 | | NFM | Doncaster | Steatley Quarry |
| 169.11250 | | NFM | Dymchurch | Romney Hythe and Dymchurch Railway |
| 169.11250 | | NFM | Grimsby | Shopping Centre |
| 169.11250 | | NFM | Halesworth | K.W. Thomas |
| 169.11250 | | NFM | Kent | Camber Sands |
| 169.11250 | | NFM | London | Kensington Palace State Apartments |
| 169.11250 | | NFM | London, north | Power station |
| 169.11250 | | NFM | Ramsgate | Port Ch 2 |
| 169.11250 | | NFM | Rugby | Swift Valley Industrial Estate |
| 169.11250 | | NFM | Sheffield | Sheffield Arena ops |
| 169.11250 | | NFM | Southend | Central Library |
| 169.11250 | | NFM | St Helier | Reclamation Site |
| 169.11250 | | NFM | Stanton | Marshalls Quarries |
| 169.11250 | | NFM | Swansea | AMEC Mining |
| 169.11250 | | NFM | Trowbridge | Garden Centre |
| 169.11250 | | NFM | University of Kent | Canterbury College |
| 169.11250 | | NFM | Warwick | Warwick Hospital |
| 169.11250 | | NFM | Weymouth | Hospital Security |
| 169.11250 | | NFM | Worksop | Fox Covert Scrap Yard |
| 169.12500 | | NFM | Birkenhead | Shopping Centre Security |
| 169.12500 | | NFM | Gaydon, Warks. | Heritage Motor Centre |
| 169.12500 | | NFM | Greenock | Wilson Coaches |
| 169.12500 | | NFM | Oldham | Merryhill Shopping Centre |
| 169.12500 | | NFM | Plymouth | Plymouth Hospital |
| 169.12500 | | NFM | Scarborough | Scarborough Football Club stewards |
| 169.12500 | | NFM | Sheffield | Beacon Radio |
| 169.12500 | | NFM | Sheffield | Sheffield Arena ops |
| 169.12500 | | NFM | Sheffield,Tinsley Park Estate | Constant Security |
| 169.12500 | | NFM | Woolhampton | Merryhill Shopping Centre |
| 169.12500 | | NFM | Worcester | White Arrow Delivery |
| 169.13000 | | NFM | Grand Prix Circuits | Williams Team Voice Link |
| 169.13500 | | NFM | Northern Ireland | St. Johns Ambulance Ch.3 |
| 169.13700 | | NFM | Walsall | St John's Ambulance Ch 7 (local frequency) |
| 169.13750 | | NFM | Aberdeen | Bon Accord Centre Security |
| 169.13750 | | NFM | Durris | National Trust for Scotland Rangers |
| 169.13750 | | NFM | England, North West | Police Regional Crime Squad (MASC encryption) |
| 169.13750 | | NFM | Hampshire | Council |
| 169.13750 | | NFM | Kent | Inwade Banger Racing Marshalls |
| 169.13750 | | NFM | London | Sega Mega World |
| 169.13750 | | NFM | London | Wembley Stadium Security |
| 169.13750 | | NFM | Nationwide | Short Term Lease PMR |
| 169.13750 | | NFM | Nationwide | St John's Ambulances |
| 169.13750 | | NFM | Pontyclun | Stables |
| 169.13750 | | NFM | Scunthorpe | Balfour Beatty Construction |
| 169.13750 | | NFM | Sheffield | Dry ski slope |
| 169.13750 | | NFM | Suffolk | St. Johns Ambulance |
| 169.13750 | | NFM | Weymouth | RSPB |
| 169.15000 | | NFM | Bournemouth | Beach Wardens |
| 169.15000 | | NFM | Corby | Earls Trees Industrial Estate |
| 169.15000 | | NFM | Jersey | Jersey Builders |
| 169.15000 | | NFM | Lancaster | Boots |
| 169.15000 | | NFM | London | Alexandra Palace Leisure Centre |
| 169.15000 | | NFM | Manchester | Civic Centre Leisure Centre |

| Base | Mobile | Mode | Location | User and Notes |
|---|---|---|---|---|
| 169.15000 | | NFM | Manchester | Pump Services |
| 169.15000 | | NFM | Nationwide | National Trust |
| 169.15000 | | NFM | Nuneaton | Lynx Parcels |
| 169.15000 | | NFM | Offley Area | Farm |
| 169.15000 | | NFM | Sheerness | Sheerness Metal |
| 169.15000 | | NFM | Shottisham | Deben Farms |
| 169.15000 | | NFM | Stanton | East Coast Slag |
| 169.15000 | | NFM | Whitland | Dairy Crest |
| 169.15000 | | NFM | Worksop | Bassetlaw Hospital |
| 169.16000 | | NFM | Luton Airport | Aircraft Cleaning |
| 169.16000 | | NFM | Northern Ireland | St. Johns Ambulance Ch.4 |
| 169.16250 | | NFM | Barrow in Furness | Shopping Centre |
| 169.16250 | | NFM | Bedford | Bedfordshire Festival 1994 |
| 169.16250 | | NFM | Bishop Stortford | Mears Construction |
| 169.16250 | | NFM | Canterbury | Taxi Service |
| 169.16250 | | NFM | Cardigan | Cardi Cabs |
| 169.16250 | | NFM | Coventry | Mayfair Security Ch 2 |
| 169.16250 | | NFM | Coventry | Motorcycle thieves with stolen radios |
| 169.16250 | | NFM | Edinburgh | City Surveyors |
| 169.16250 | | NFM | Essex | Top Guard International |
| 169.16250 | | NFM | Haverfordwest | Cardi Cabs |
| 169.16250 | | NFM | Hitchin | Nollys Taxis |
| 169.16250 | | NFM | Ipswich | RSPCA Ch 2 Discrete |
| 169.16250 | | NFM | Ipswich | WLB Jackson Group, Civil Engineers |
| 169.16250 | | NFM | Jersey | Keith Rogers Building Renovation |
| 169.16250 | | NFM | Kent | St Johns Ambulance Ch.4 |
| 169.16250 | | NFM | Kirkcaldy | Boots Security |
| 169.16250 | | NFM | London | BBC Radio O/B Production |
| 169.16250 | | NFM | London | DSS Discreet |
| 169.16250 | | NFM | London | Logica Ltd Security |
| 169.16250 | | NFM | London | Planet Hollywood Security |
| 169.16250 | | NFM | London | Wembley Stadium Security |
| 169.16250 | | NFM | London, Wimbledon | Lawn Tennis Club groundsmen |
| 169.16250 | | NFM | Luton Airport | Baggage Handlers |
| 169.16250 | | NFM | Nationwide | Short Term Lease PMR |
| 169.16250 | | NFM | Nationwide | St John's Ambulances Ch 5 |
| 169.16250 | | NFM | Queensborough | Sea King Group, Car Dealers |
| 169.16250 | | NFM | Sittingbourne | Forum Shopping Centre Security |
| 169.16250 | | NFM | Suffolk | St. Johns Ambulance Ch.6 (DG) |
| 169.16250 | | NFM | Surrey | Council County Engineer |
| 169.16250 | | NFM | Swansea | Sommervilles Scrap/Car Parts |
| 169.16250 | | NFM | Taplow | Cliveden House Hotel Security |
| 169.16250 | | NFM | Twickenham | Rugby Stewards |
| 169.16250 | | NFM | Windsor & Maidenhead | Council |
| 169.16900 | | NFM | Birmingham | St John's Ambulance Ch 8 (local frequency) |
| 169.16900 | | NFM | Sutton Coldfield | St John's Ambulance Ch 8 (local frequency) |
| 169.16900 | | NFM | Wolverhampton | St John's Ambulance Ch 8 (local frequency) |
| 169.17000 | | NFM | Northern Ireland | St. Johns Ambulance Ch.5 |
| 169.17500 | | NFM | Ballachulish | Glencoe MR Team |
| 169.17500 | | NFM | Barrow in Furness | Tipper Trucks |
| 169.17500 | | NFM | Barrow in Furness | VSEL DDH Shopfloor Services |
| 169.17500 | | NFM | Boston | Organic Lincolnshire Growers Association |
| 169.17500 | | NFM | Cardiff | St Fagans Folk Museum |
| 169.17500 | | NFM | Guernsey | Ronez (Monmains) |
| 169.17500 | | NFM | Martlesham Heath | Department of Energy |
| 169.17500 | | NFM | Nationwide | Mountain Rescue Scotland |

| Base | Mobile | Mode | Location | User and Notes |
|------|--------|------|----------|----------------|
| 169.17500 | | NFM | Perth | Landscape Gardens Ltd |
| 169.17500 | | NFM | Peterborough | East of England Show Ground |
| 169.17500 | | NFM | Snowdon | Mountain Railway |
| 169.17500 | | NFM | Three Holes | Frank Hartley |
| 169.18700 | | NFM | Solihull | St John's Ambulance Ch 9 (local frequency) |
| 169.18750 | | NFM | Ayr | Race Course Sunday market stewards |
| 169.18750 | | NFM | Biggleswade Airfield | Ops |
| 169.18750 | | NFM | Brighton | Marina Asda Supermarket |
| 169.18750 | | NFM | Burnley | Marks & Spencer Security |
| 169.18750 | | NFM | Canterbury | Workmen |
| 169.18750 | | NFM | Garston | Freightliner terminal |
| 169.18750 | | NFM | Grand Prix Circuits | Lotus Team Ch 3 |
| 169.18750 | | NFM | Inglestone | Market Stewards |
| 169.18750 | | NFM | Jersey | Jersey Lift Engineers |
| 169.18750 | | NFM | Kent | St. John's Ambulance Ch.5 |
| 169.18750 | | NFM | Killingholme | National Power Security |
| 169.18750 | | NFM | London | Public Health Labs |
| 169.18750 | | NFM | London | Sega Mega World |
| 169.18750 | | NFM | London | Wembley Stadium Catering |
| 169.18750 | | NFM | London, Oxford Street | Tiger McKenzie Security First Sport |
| 169.18750 | | NFM | Morecambe | Trino's Taxis |
| 169.18750 | | NFM | Nationwide | NCB Emergencies |
| 169.18750 | | NFM | Nationwide | Short Term Lease PMR |
| 169.18750 | | NFM | Nationwide | St John's Ambulances Ch 6 |
| 169.18750 | | NFM | Penrith | Market Security |
| 169.18750 | | NFM | Perth | Security |
| 169.18750 | | NFM | Peterlee | Five Star Taxis |
| 169.18750 | | NFM | Plymouth | Cascade Security |
| 169.18750 | | NFM | Redruth | Land Rover Racing |
| 169.18750 | | NFM | Rugby | Swift Valley Industrial Estate |
| 169.18750 | | NFM | Suffolk | St. John's Ambulance (DG) |
| 169.18750 | | NFM | Wigan | Statesman Security |
| 169.20000 | | NFM | Aberdeen | Aberdeen Ice Rink |
| 169.20000 | | NFM | Ashford | Stour Leisure Centre |
| 169.20000 | | NFM | Belfast Airport | Ground Services |
| 169.20000 | | NFM | Bolton | Peak Security |
| 169.20000 | | NFM | Burnley | Potterton ProdLines Ch 1 |
| 169.20000 | | NFM | Edinburgh | Chamber St. Museum |
| 169.20000 | | NFM | Fort William | BSW Sawmill |
| 169.20000 | | NFM | Gateshead | Fewster Square Leisure Centre |
| 169.20000 | | NFM | Huyton | Ferraris Nightclub Security |
| 169.20000 | | NFM | Ipswich | Sites Total Car Park Management |
| 169.20000 | | NFM | Jersey | Wilson Vets & Animal Shelter |
| 169.20000 | | NFM | London | University College, London University |
| 169.20000 | | NFM | London | Westminster City Hall |
| 169.20000 | | NFM | London, Knightsbridge | Harvey Nichols security |
| 169.20000 | | NFM | Perth | Security |
| 169.20000 | | NFM | Peterborough | Peterborough Regional College |
| 169.20000 | | NFM | Sheffield | British Steel |
| 169.20000 | | NFM | Swansea | Construction |
| 169.20000 | | NFM | Swansea | F.R.F Motors |
| 169.20000 | | NFM | Thanet | Thanet Technical College |
| 169.20000 | | NFM | Ware | Glaxo Operations |
| 169.21250 | | NFM | Bournemouth | Malibu Club Doormen |
| 169.21250 | | NFM | Coventry | Airport |
| 169.21250 | | NFM | Croydon | Water Palace |

| Base | Mobile | Mode | Location | User and Notes |
|------|--------|------|----------|----------------|
| 169.21250 | | NFM | Dover | District Council |
| 169.21250 | | NFM | East Midlands Airport | Airport Security |
| 169.21250 | | NFM | Harwell | UK Atomic Energy Authority |
| 169.21250 | | NFM | Ipswich | Port |
| 169.21250 | | NFM | Jersey | Beachguards |
| 169.21250 | | NFM | Kent | East Gate Centre Security |
| 169.21250 | | NFM | Stoke on Trent | Stoke City Football Club security |
| 169.21250 | | NFM | Wigan | Car Park Security |
| 169.22500 | | NFM | Biggleswade | Middle Farm |
| 169.22500 | | NFM | Carlisle | Thomas Graham & Sons |
| 169.22500 | | NFM | Coventry | Apex Trust |
| 169.22500 | | NFM | Epping | North Weald Airfield Security & Fire |
| 169.22500 | | NFM | Gillingham, Dorset | School caretakers |
| 169.22500 | | NFM | Glasgow University | Security |
| 169.22500 | | NFM | Jersey | Hurricane Despatch |
| 169.22500 | | NFM | Liverpool | Taxi-Taxi Channel |
| 169.22500 | | NFM | London | Embassy Transport and bodyguards |
| 169.22500 | | NFM | Nationwide | RAC Rallies |
| 169.22500 | | NFM | North Weald | Security & Crash Ops |
| 169.22500 | | NFM | Orton | Longueville School |
| 169.22500 | | NFM | Southport | Leisure Lakes |
| 169.22500 | | NFM | Wigan | Rugby Ground Stewards |
| 169.23750 | | NFM | Barnet | Spires Shopping Centre security |
| 169.23750 | | NFM | Chatham | Pentagon Centre security |
| 169.23750 | | NFM | East Anglia | Anglia Water |
| 169.23750 | | NFM | England | Water Bailiffs |
| 169.23750 | | NFM | Lancaster | WH Smiths |
| 169.23750 | | NFM | Liverpool | Dolcis Shop Co Ordering Dept |
| 169.23750 | | NFM | Liverpool | G.H. Lee Security |
| 169.23750 | | NFM | London, Bond Street | Asprey and Garrards Crown Jewellers |
| 169.23750 | | NFM | Stevenage | Westgate Shopping Centre |
| 169.23750 | | NFM | Swansea | Water Bailiffs |
| 169.23750 | | NFM | Worcester Area | Marquee hire company |
| 169.25000 | | NFM | Birmingham | Selly Oaks Hospital contractors |
| 169.25000 | | NFM | Brecon | Mountain Railway |
| 169.25000 | | NFM | Leeds | P&O container distribution |
| 169.25000 | | NFM | Southampton | University Security |
| 169.25000 | | NFM | Trafford | Haulage Company |
| 169.26000 | | FM | Eastbourne | Arndale Centre Security |
| 169.26000 | | NFM | Preston | St. Georges Shopping Centre security |
| 169.26250 | | NFM | Felixstowe | Repcon |
| 169.26250 | | NFM | Great Yarmouth | St.Nicholas Hospital |
| 169.26250 | | NFM | Guernsey | Harlequin Hire Cars |
| 169.26250 | | NFM | Hull | Prospect Shopping Cent. Security |
| 169.26250 | | NFM | Jersey | Builders |
| 169.26250 | | NFM | London | Hopton Holiday Village security |
| 169.26250 | | NFM | London, Brent Cross | John Lewis |
| 169.26250 | | NFM | RAF Chicksands | British Military Intelligence Base |
| 169.26250 | | NFM | Taunton | Musgrove Park Hospital |
| 169.26250 | | NFM | Thetford | A to Z Courier Warehouse Staff |
| 169.27500 | | NFM | Butley | Kendal & Sons Farms |
| 169.27500 | | NFM | Elverdon, Suffolk | Centre Parcs Holiday Village Maintenance |
| 169.27500 | | NFM | Isle of Man | Doctors On Call |
| 169.27500 | | NFM | Leeds | Batleys C&C security and reception |
| 169.27500 | | NFM | London, Edmonton | Pickets Lock Centre |
| 169.27500 | | NFM | Shoreham Airport | Ground Vehicles |

| Base | Mobile | Mode | Location | User and Notes |
|------|--------|------|----------|----------------|
| 169.27500 | | NFM | Southend-on-Sea | Technical College |
| 169.27500 | | NFM | Stansted | Maintenance |
| 169.27500 | | NFM | Woodbridge | Kemball |
| 169.28750 | | NFM | Arlesley | Waste Site Ops |
| 169.28750 | | NFM | Croydon | Croydon Health |
| 169.28750 | | NFM | Felixstowe | Docks |
| 169.28750 | | NFM | Kent | John Jones Contractors |
| 169.28750 | | NFM | Kettering | Metalforce Ltd |
| 169.28750 | | NFM | Southampton | Dock Stevedores |
| 169.28750 | | NFM | Woburn Sands | Plysu Plc |
| 169.30000 | | NFM | Birmingham | West Bromwich Albion Football Club stewards |
| 169.30000 | | NFM | Carlisle | H & H Auction Mart |
| 169.30000 | | NFM | Guernsey | Sarnia Hire Cars |
| 169.30000 | | NFM | Heathrow Airport | Passenger Services |
| 169.30000 | | NFM | London, Heathrow | Airline Passenger Service |
| 169.30000 | | NFM | London, Piccadilly | Tower Records |
| 169.30000 | | NFM | Morecambe | Pleasure Beach Security |
| 169.30000 | | NFM | Newport | Town Centre Security |
| 169.30000 | | NFM | Wirral | Community Patrol Ch 4 (Back to back) |
| 169.31250 | | NFM | Channel Tunnel | Group 4 Security |
| 169.31250 | | NFM | Doncaster | Motorcycle Tests |
| 169.31250 | | NFM | Epping | North Weald Airfield Car Park Stewards |
| 169.31250 | | NFM | Fairburn, West Yorkshire | RSPB wardens |
| 169.31250 | | NFM | Jersey | Commodore Shipping |
| 169.31250 | | NFM | Jersey | Otis Lifts |
| 169.31250 | | NFM | Kidderminster | Safari Park |
| 169.31250 | | NFM | Letchworth | Amec Building Maintenance |
| 169.31250 | | NFM | London | Amec / Bell Four Building |
| 169.31250 | | NFM | London | Wembley Stadium Car Parks |
| 169.31250 | | NFM | London, Embankment | Jubilee Line extension works |
| 169.31250 | | NFM | Nationwide | Network Q Rally - Nissan |
| 169.31250 | | NFM | Nationwide | Titan Fire Services |
| 169.31250 | | NFM | North Weald | Market Organisers and Sabre Ambulance service |
| 169.31250 | | NFM | Warwick | BT engineers |
| 169.31250 | | NFM | Wellesbourne | Market Organisers |
| 169.31250 | | NFM | Wigan | British Waterways |
| 169.32500 | | NFM | Barton-on-Humber | Peter Birse Construction |
| 169.32500 | | NFM | Bath | Theatre Royal |
| 169.32500 | | NFM | Cannock | TNT Carriers |
| 169.32500 | | NFM | Clevedon | Passenger Traffic Control |
| 169.32500 | | NFM | Exeter | Exeter Cathedral |
| 169.32500 | | NFM | Hull | Hull Football Club stewards |
| 169.32500 | | NFM | Luton Airport | Baggage Handlers |
| 169.32500 | | NFM | Newquay | Car Park Attendants |
| 169.32500 | | NFM | Nottingham | American Adventure Theme Park |
| 169.32500 | | NFM | Pwllheli | Butlins Camp Security |
| 169.32600 | | NFM | Norwich | Football Stewards |
| 169.33500 | | NFM | Nationwide | Grand Prix standard RAC race control frequency |
| 169.33750 | | NFM | Brands Hatch | Racing (rescue) |
| 169.33750 | | NFM | Cambridge | Kings College |
| 169.33750 | | NFM | Canvey Island | Knightswick Security |
| 169.33750 | | NFM | Cornwall | Tarmac |
| 169.33750 | | NFM | County Durham | Doctor's Medicall |
| 169.33750 | | NFM | Devon | Tamar Bridge Security |
| 169.33750 | | NFM | Halifax | St. Johns Ambulance |
| 169.33750 | | NFM | Halifax | Websters Brewery Security |

| Base | Mobile | Mode | Location | User and Notes |
|---|---|---|---|---|
| 169.33750 | | NFM | Jersey | Island Sports Officials |
| 169.33750 | | NFM | Knockhill, Fife | Knockhill Racing (marshalls and rescue) |
| 169.33750 | | NFM | Leamington Spa | South Warwickshire College |
| 169.33750 | | NFM | London | Cazenove & Co Stockbrokers |
| 169.33750 | | NFM | Merry Hill | Centre Waterfront Security |
| 169.33750 | | NFM | Oulton Park | Racing (marshalls and rescue) |
| 169.33750 | | NFM | Perth | St John's Centre Security |
| 169.33750 | | NFM | Sellafield | Construction |
| 169.33750 | | NFM | Silverstone | Racing (Marshalls and rescue) |
| 169.33750 | | NFM | Snetterton | Racing (Marshalls and rescue) |
| 169.33750 | | NFM | Thruxton | Racing (marshalls and rescue) |
| 169.35000 | | NFM | Bournemouth | Weymouth House Security |
| 169.35000 | | NFM | Cambridge | City Council |
| 169.35000 | | NFM | Doncaster | Dome Centre |
| 169.35000 | | NFM | Hull | Humber Bridge Control |
| 169.35000 | | NFM | Luton Airport | Monarch Airlines |
| 169.35000 | | NFM | Lynmouth | Security |
| 169.35000 | | NFM | Powys | South Wales Electricity |
| 169.35000 | | NFM | Sussex | St John's Ambulance |
| 169.35000 | | AM | Swansea Airport | Runway & Ground Crews |
| 169.35000 | | NFM | West Midlands | St John's Ambulance |
| 169.35000 | | NFM | Woodbridge | Company Of Four Acting Ground |
| 169.36200 | | NFM | West Midlands | St John's Ambulance Ch 1 |
| 169.36250 | | NFM | Bolton | Bolton Football Club stewards |
| 169.36250 | | NFM | Burnley | Shopping Centre |
| 169.36250 | | NFM | Deptford | Dispatch Company |
| 169.36250 | | NFM | Doncaster | Tesco Distribution Depot |
| 169.36250 | | NFM | Dorset | DADPC Blandford Camp |
| 169.36250 | | NFM | Glasgow | Woyka Timber Mill |
| 169.36250 | | NFM | Kent | St. John's Ambulance Ch.1 |
| 169.36250 | | NFM | Leighton Buzzard | George Garside Sand |
| 169.36250 | | NFM | London | Russian Embassy Transport |
| 169.36250 | | NFM | Nationwide | Dept. of Trade & Industry |
| 169.36250 | | NFM | Nationwide | St John's Ambulance Ch 1 |
| 169.36250 | | NFM | Nationwide | St Johns Ambulance Channel A/1 |
| 169.36250 | | NFM | Northern Ireland | St. Johns Ambulance Ch.1 (priority) |
| 169.36250 | | NFM | Plymouth | Police Plymouth Argyle Football Club |
| 169.36250 | | NFM | Preston | Harris Museum |
| 169.36250 | | NFM | Sheffield | Owlerton Security |
| 169.36250 | | NFM | Suffolk | St. John's Ambulance Ch.1 (DG) |
| 169.36250 | | NFM | Swansea | DSS Fraud Teams |
| 169.36250 | | NFM | West Glamorgan | DSS Pontradulats HQ |
| 169.36250 | | NFM | Whiston | Hexagon (HISS) Security Ltd |
| 169.37500 | | NFM | Bell College | Saffron Walden |
| 169.37500 | | NFM | Coventry | Tyre Fitters |
| 169.37500 | | NFM | Elverdon, Suffolk | Centre Parcs Holiday Village Security |
| 169.37500 | | NFM | Langholm | Eskside Engineering |
| 169.37500 | | NFM | London, Oxford St | Forbidden Planet Ltd |
| 169.37500 | | NFM | London, Southbank | National Theatre |
| 169.37500 | | NFM | Norfolk | HM Prison Wayland |
| 169.37500 | | NFM | Sheffield | Council Housing Department |
| 169.37500 | | NFM | South Walden | Bell College |
| 169.37500 | | NFM | Warwickshire, North | Arable Farm |
| 169.38500 | | NFM | Preston | Bus station |
| 169.38700 | | NFM | West Midlands | St John's Ambulance Ch 2 |
| 169.38750 | | NFM | Blackpool | Car Park Attendants |

| Base | Mobile | Mode | Location | User and Notes |
|------|--------|------|----------|----------------|
| 169.38750 | | NFM | Humberside Airport | Tower-Ground |
| 169.38750 | | NFM | Kent | Prismo Road Surfacing |
| 169.38750 | | NFM | Lowestoft | Holiday Camp |
| 169.38750 | | NFM | National | Prismo Road Surfacing |
| 169.38750 | | NFM | Nationwide | St Johns Ambulance Channel 2 |
| 169.38750 | | NFM | Norwich | School Custodians |
| 169.38750 | | NFM | Nottingham | Technical Services |
| 169.38750 | | NFM | Preston | Council Car Parks |
| 169.38750 | | NFM | Sheffield | Makro car park control |
| 169.38750 | | NFM | Silverstone Airfield | Security & Crash Ops |
| 169.38750 | | NFM | Southwark | Crown Court Security |
| 169.38750 | | NFM | Stevenage | Roye Security Hollywood Bowl |

### 169.39375 - 169.84375 MHz    NEW EUROPEAN MESSAGING SERVICE (ERMES) PMR SIMPLEX 12.5 KHZ NFM

| Base | Mobile | Mode | Location | User and Notes |
|------|--------|------|----------|----------------|
| 169.40000 | | NFM | Gt Yarmouth | Palgrave Brown |
| 169.40000 | | NFM | Newmarket | Harry Wrass Ltd |
| 169.42500 | | NFM | Gt Yarmouth | Shipping Co |
| 169.43750 | | NFM | Eastleigh | Taxis |
| 169.43750 | | NFM | Grimsby | West Marsh Brick Pit Ch 5 |
| 169.43750 | | NFM | Jersey | Hotel de France Conferences |
| 169.43750 | | NFM | Norwich | TV |
| 169.43750 | | NFM | South Midlands | Comms Ltd Demo Ch |
| 169.43750 | | NFM | Southampton | Event Control |
| 169.45000 | | NFM | Coryton | Port Control |
| 169.45000 | | NFM | Wisbech | J.D. Walker Ltd |
| 169.46250 | | NFM | London | Security |
| 169.46250 | | NFM | Tamworth | Road Works |
| 169.47500 | | NFM | Abergavenny | TV Antenna Riggers |
| 169.47500 | | NFM | Caister | Holiday Camp |
| 169.47500 | | NFM | Cambridge | Christ's College |
| 169.47500 | | NFM | Stowmarket | Helmingham Est Farms |
| 169.48750 | | NFM | Bournemouth | Centurian Security |
| 169.48750 | | NFM | Grand Prix Circuits | Benetton Voice |
| 169.48750 | | NFM | Grimsby | Burns Security |
| 169.48750 | | NFM | Grimsby | West Marsh Brick Pit Ch 6 |
| 169.48750 | | NFM | Nationwide | Red Cross Ambulance |
| 169.50000 | | NFM | Lochore | Lochore Meadows Park |
| 169.50000 | | NFM | Nationwide | Carlink Ferries |
| 169.51250 | | NFM | Brandon | F.Hiam Farms |
| 169.52500 | | NFM | Birmingham | Ambicare Private Ambulance |
| 169.52500 | | NFM | Jersey | South Pier Shipyard |
| 169.52500 | | NFM | Luton | Vauxhall Motors |
| 169.52500 | | NFM | Woodbridge | Tubbs Building Supplies |
| 169.53750 | | NFM | Blackpool | R Smith Leisure Services |
| 169.53750 | | NFM | Burnley | Guardhall Security |
| 169.53750 | | NFM | Cambridge | Council |
| 169.53750 | | NFM | Epsom | Race Course |
| 169.53750 | | NFM | Jersey | Rob Thompson Electronics |
| 169.53750 | | NFM | Nationwide | Honda Williams Racing Team |
| 169.53750 | | NFM | Nationwide | Whitbread World Race Security |
| 169.55000 | | NFM | West Bergholt | Wicken Farm Co |
| 169.57500 | | NFM | Canterbury | Cathedral security |
| 169.57500 | | NFM | Chatteris | Nongell Ltd |
| 169.57500 | | NFM | Dorset | Clearway Transport |
| 169.57500 | | NFM | Folkestone | SIS |

| Base | Mobile | Mode | Location | User and Notes |
|------|--------|------|----------|----------------|
| 169.57500 | | NFM | Swansea | Private Detectives |
| 169.57500 | | NFM | Wisbech | J.D. Walker |
| 169.60000 | | NFM | Luton Airport | Britannia Airways |
| 169.61250 | | NFM | Wanton | Morley Farms |
| 169.62500 | | NFM | Dereham | Crane Fruehauf |
| 169.62500 | | NFM | Hythe | Nicholls Quarry |
| 169.62500 | | NFM | Thetford | H. Fledger |
| 169.63750 | | NFM | Bournemouth | Farm Security |
| 169.63750 | | NFM | Cumbria | Community Repeater South Lakes |
| 169.63750 | | NFM | Newhaven Port | Shorrock Security |
| 169.66250 | | NFM | Nottingham | Sheriff Plant Hire |
| 169.66250 | | NFM | Woolverstone | A.W Mayhew Farms |
| 169.67500 | | NFM | Nationwide | DSS Snoopers Ch 01 |
| 169.67500 | | NFM | Nottingham | Claredon College |
| 169.70000 | | NFM | Glenshee | Glenshee Rescue Team |
| 169.70000 | | NFM | Nationwide | DSS Snoopers Ch 02 |
| 169.72500 | | NFM | Bournemouth | Southern Despatch Bikes |
| 169.72500 | | NFM | Jersey | Radio Interference Officer |
| 169.72500 | | NFM | Jersey | States Telecoms |
| 169.72500 | | NFM | Plymouth | St John's Ambulance |
| 169.73750 | | NFM | Birmingham | Bull Ring Security |
| 169.73750 | | NFM | London | Chelsea Football Club stewards |
| 169.75000 | | NFM | Cardiff | Ritzy's Night Club |
| 169.75000 | | NFM | Jersey | Esso Co |
| 169.76250 | | NFM | Bedlinton | Taxis |
| 169.76250 | | NFM | Buckinghamshire | Bucks Council Ch 1 |
| 169.76250 | | NFM | Leicestershire | Gartree Prison works department |
| 169.76250 | | NFM | London Piccadilly | Tower Records Security |
| 169.76250 | | NFM | London, Piccadilly | The Rock Gardens Security |
| 169.76250 | | NFM | Sandwich | Royal St George Golf Club |
| 169.76250 | | NFM | South Midlands | South Midlands Comms Demo |
| 169.76250 | | NFM | Wolverhampton | Tower Records |
| 169.77500 | | NFM | Bedford | Smith & Co |
| 169.77500 | | NFM | Bishop Stortford | College |
| 169.78750 | | NFM | Cambridge | Roy Pett |
| 169.78750 | | NFM | Reading | Council |
| 169.80000 | | NFM | Bath | Bath University Research |
| 169.80000 | | NFM | Bristol | D.O.T. |
| 169.80000 | | NFM | Guernsey | Airport Services |
| 169.81250 | | NFM | Birmingham | Aston Villa Football Club stewards |
| 169.81250 | | NFM | Glenshee | Glenshee Rescue Team |
| 169.81250 | | NFM | Guernsey | Aurigny Ground Services |
| 169.81250 | | NFM | Sheffield | Northern Gen. Hospital Security |
| 169.82500 | | NFM | Bridlington | Forum Leisure Centre |
| 169.82500 | | NFM | Canterbury | Debenham & Marks & Spencer Security |
| 169.82500 | | NFM | Chesterfield | Arnold Lavers Timberyard |
| 169.82500 | | NFM | Folkestone | Burstin Hotel |
| 169.82500 | | NFM | Jersey | Honorary Police Ch 6 |
| 169.82500 | | NFM | Leamington Spa, Warks | The Watch Security |
| 169.82500 | | NFM | Nationwide | DSS Snoopers Ch 03 |
| 169.82500 | | NFM | Nationwide | Inland Revenue Ch 03 |
| 169.82500 | | NFM | Perth | Maintenance |
| 169.83750 | | NFM | Burnley | Potterton ProdLines Ch 2 |
| 169.83750 | | NFM | Hull | Princes Quay Carpark Security |
| 169.83750 | | NFM | London | Wembley Stadium Stewards |
| 169.83750 | | NFM | Oxford | Oxford Football Club stewards |

| Base | Mobile | Mode | Location | User and Notes |
| --- | --- | --- | --- | --- |
| 169.83750 | | NFM | Sheffield | Orchard Square Shopping Centre |
| 169.83750 | | NFM | Southall, Middlesex | Secure Parking |
| 169.83750 | | NFM | St Austell | ECC Pits |
| 169.83750 | | NFM | Warwick | Outdoor wargames centre |
| 169.83750 | | NFM | Wisbech | Corbill Ltd |

**169.84375 - 173.04375 MHz**     PMR HIGH BAND MOBILES
(BASE SPLIT - 4.8 MHz)

| Base | Mobile | Mode | Location | User and Notes |
| --- | --- | --- | --- | --- |
| 169.85000 | | NFM | Lincoln | A2B Taxis |
| 169.88750 | | NFM | Portsmouth | Buses |
| 169.90000 | | NFM | National | Lotus Racing Team |
| 169.91250 | | NFM | Jersey | Beeline Taxis Channel 2 |
| 169.92500 | | NFM | Ulverston | McKenna's Taxis |
| 169.93750 | | NFM | Glasgow | High Court security |
| 169.93750 | | NFM | Jersey | Land Surveyors & Architects |
| 169.94500 | | NFM | Bristol | South West Electric Company |
| 169.96250 | | NFM | East Durham | Private Message |
| 169.96250 | | NFM | Folkestone | Rotunda Park |
| 169.96250 | | NFM | London | Cazenove & Co Stockbrokers |
| 160.06250 | | NFM | Trowbridge | Driving Instructors |
| 169.97500 | | NFM | Felixstowe | Docks |
| 169.98750 | | NFM | Kilmarnock | Rugby Park ground staff (KILLIE) |
| 170.00000 | | NFM | Barrow | BNFL Security |
| 170.03750 | | NFM | Manchester | Thameside Council |
| 170.07500 | | NFM | Fleetwood | Doctors Paging |
| 170.08750 | | NFM | Wrexham | Apollo Taxis |
| 170.12500 | | NFM | Preston | Council wardens |
| 170.18700 | | NFM | West Midlands | St John's Ambulance Ch 6 (local frequency) |
| 170.20000 | | NFM | Bedford | Building Co |
| 170.22500 | | NFM | Milford Haven | A2B Taxis |
| 170.26250 | | NFM | Worthing | Nynex Cable |
| 170.28750 | | NFM | Manchester | Taxis |
| 170.35000 | | NFM | Eskdale | Ravenglass and Eskdale Railway |
| 170.40000 | | NFM | Manchester | Taxis |
| 170.50000 | | NFM | Portsmouth | Taxis |
| 170.51750 | | NFM | Newmarket | La Hoge Farm |
| 170.61250 | | NFM | Perrenporth | Taxis |
| 170.76500 | | NFM | Newcastle | Security |
| 170.97500 | | NFM | Burnley | Corporation Base |
| 171.00000 | | NFM | London | Ambulance Service |
| 171.06000 | | NFM | Nuneaton | Council |
| 171.10000 | | NFM | Manchester | Ambulance Service |
| 171.25000 | | NFM | Carlisle | Doctors on call |
| 171.42500 | | NFM | Ipswich | DSS Ch.4 |
| 171.46250 | | NFM | Barrow | Council Highways & Cleansing |
| 171.47500 | | NFM | Southampton | A2B Taxis |
| 171.56000 | | NFM | Preston | University security |
| 171.56250 | | NFM | Liverpool | Panda Security |
| 171.61250 | | NFM | Isle of Man | Nobles Hospital |
| 171.68500 | | NFM | Haworth | Leam Taxis |
| 171.70000 | | NFM | Manchester | Refuse Collection |
| 171.70000 | | NFM | Nationwide | BBC O/B Link (OL-94) |
| 171.85000 | | NFM | Newport | Steelworks Paging |
| 171.96250 | | NFM | Newbiggin | Taxis |

| Base | Mobile | Mode | Location | User and Notes |
|------|--------|------|----------|----------------|
| 172.00000 | | NFM | Brechin | Builders |
| 172.00000 | | NFM | Jersey | Dock Crane Operators |
| 172.00000 | | NFM | Nationwide | PMR Park and Demo Chan |
| 172.00000 | | NFM | Scotland | Scottish Sports Council |
| 172.00000 | | NFM | Slough | Mars Factory |
| 172.00000 | | NFM | West Midlands | Short term hire Mobiles |
| 172.12500 | | NFM | Grundon | Waste Disposal |
| 172.15000 | | NFM | Haywards Heath | Census Taxis |
| 172.21250 | | NFM | Manchester | Taxis |
| 172.32500 | | NFM | Jersey | Fort Regent Channel 4 |
| 172.35000 | | NFM | Jersey | Fort Regent Channel 2 |
| 172.37500 | | NFM | Cramlinton | Taxis |
| 172.45000 | | NFM | Walsall | Taxi |
| 172.52500 | | NFM | Carno | Laura Ashley Security |
| 172.60000 | | NFM | Nationwide | BBC O/B Link (OL-94) |
| 172.66250 | | NFM | Worthing | Taxis |
| 172.70000 | | NFM | Jersey | HM Customs & Excise Channel 2 |
| 172.75000 | | NFM | Ashington | Collier Taxi |
| 172.78750 | | NFM | Jersey | HM Customs & Excise Channel 4 |
| 172.78750 | | NFM | Swansea | Docks |
| 172.86250 | | NFM | Jersey | Beachguards |
| 172.95000 | | NFM | Farnborough Airshow | Stagecoach Buses |
| 173.00000 | | NFM | Nationwide | Low Power Guitar Systems |
| 173.02500 | | NFM | Nationwide | DTI Ch 1 |

## 173.04375 - 173.09375 MHz   PMR SIMPLEX 12.5 kHz NFM

| Base | Mobile | Mode | Location | User and Notes |
|------|--------|------|----------|----------------|
| 173.05000 | | NFM | Nationwide | DTI Ch 2 |
| 173.06250 | | NFM | Bristol | DHSS |
| 173.06250 | | NFM | Canvey Island | Mobile Surveillance Teams |
| 173.06250 | | NFM | Canvey Island | Poss Abbey Investigations |
| 173.06250 | | NFM | Nationwide | Gerry Cottles Circus |
| 173.06250 | | NFM | Nationwide | RAC Network Q Rally |
| 173.07500 | | NFM | Jersey | Stolen Car Detector Systems |
| 173.07500 | | NFM | Nationwide | DTI Ch 3 |
| 173.08750 | | NFM | East Suffolk | Farming |
| 173.08750 | | NFM | Jersey | Surveyors |
| 173.08750 | | NFM | Torridon | National Trust for Scotland Rangers |

## 173.09375 - 173.9875 MHz   LOW POWER DEVICES, RADIO DEAF AIDS, BIOLOGICAL TELEMETRY & GARAGE DOOR OPENERS

| Base | Mobile | Mode | Location | User and Notes |
|------|--------|------|----------|----------------|
| 173.18750 | | NFM | Nationwide | Mobile Alarm Paging |
| 173.18750 | | NFM | Nationwide | Police Tracker |
| 173.22500 | | NFM | Nationwide | Building Site Alarms |
| 173.22500 | | NFM | Nationwide | Radio Controlled Garage Doors |
| 173.22500 | | NFM | Nationwide | Short Range Security Alarms |
| 173.35000 | | NFM | Jersey | School Deaf Aids |
| 173.40000 | | NFM | Jersey | School Deaf Aids |
| 173.40000 | | NFM | Nationwide | Deaf Aids |
| 173.46250 | | NFM | Jersey | School Deaf Aids |
| 173.46500 | | NFM | Nationwide | Deaf Aids |
| 173.54500 | | NFM | Nationwide | Deaf Aids |

173.2000 - 177.0000 MHz     PMR AND INDOOR RADIO MICROPHONES

| Base | Mobile | Mode | Location | User and Notes |
| --- | --- | --- | --- | --- |
| 173.21250 | | NFM | Llanelli | BSC Trostre Works |
| 173.22000 | | NFM | Scotland | Singing Kettle Entertainment Grp |
| 173.22500 | | NFM | Nationwide | Suma Designs Bugging Devices |
| 173.35000 | | NFM | Llanelli | BSC Trostre Works |
| 173.60000 | | NFM | Worthing | Radio Mic Social Club |
| 173.61000 | | NFM | Wakefield | Police (GP) |
| 173.64000 | | NFM | Jersey | School Deaf Aids |
| 173.64000 | | NFM | Nationwide | Deaf Aids |
| 173.77500 | | NFM | London | French Presidential Guard |
| 173.80000 | | NFM | Canvey Island | JFMG Radio Mic Lead Vocalists |
| 173.80000 | | NFM | Nationwide | Theatre Radio Microphone |
| 173.80000 | | NFM | Nationwide | Yellow Channel |
| 173.80000 | | NFM | Newmarket | Aerobics |
| 173.80000 | | NFM | Perth | Church Radio Microphone |
| 173.80000 | | NFM | Preston | Carey Baptist Church |
| 173.80000 | | NFM | Swansea | Elim Pentecostal Church |
| 173.80000 | | NFM | Worcester | Swan Theatre Radio Mic |
| 173.80000 | | NFM | Worthing | Radio Mic Community Hall |
| 173.80500 | | NFM | Preston | Radio Mic. Jehovahs Witness meeting |
| 173.82500 | | NFM | Newport | Panic-Phone Alarms |
| 173.95000 | | NFM | Jersey | School Deaf Aids |
| 174.00000 | | NFM | London | Transport Co. |
| 174.01250 | | NFM | Nationwide | RAC Network Q Rally |
| 174.02500 | | NFM | Nationwide | RAC Network Q Rally |
| 174.03750 | | NFM | Nationwide | RAC Network Q Rally |
| 174.07500 | | NFM | Bristol | BBC radio mics. |
| 174.10000 | | NFM | Guernsey | Channel TV Radio Mics |
| 174.10000 | | NFM | Nationwide | Phil Collins Radio Mic (2) |
| 174.10000 | | NFM | Nationwide | Red Channel |
| 174.10000 | | NFM | Nationwide | Theatre Radio Microphone |
| 174.11000 | | NFM | Scotland | Singing Kettle Entertainment Grp |
| 174.11800 | | NFM | Scotland | Singing Kettle Entertainment Grp |
| 174.15000 | | NFM | Kirkby | Gala Bingo radio mic |
| 174.20000 | | NFM | Kirkby | Gala Bingo radio mic |
| 174.28750 | | NFM | Edinburgh | Edinburgh Castle Security |
| 174.30000 | | NFM | Nationwide | Church Radio Mics |
| 174.40000 | | NFM | Kirkby | Gala Bingo radio mic |
| 174.41500 | | NFM | Kirkby | Gala Bingo radio mic |
| 174.42500 | | NFM | London | Transport Co. |
| 174.50000 | | NFM | Glasgow | Baptist Church Mic |
| 174.50000 | | NFM | Leicester | Church Radio Mix |
| 174.50000 | | NFM | Nationwide | Blue Channel |
| 174.50000 | | NFM | Nationwide | Phil Collins Radio Mic (1) |
| 174.50000 | | NFM | Worcester | Worcester Cathedral Radio Mic |
| 174.52500 | | NFM | Nationwide | Low Power Guitar Systems |
| 174.60000 | | NFM | Nationwide | Channel Radio Mics |
| 174.66250 | | NFM | Aberdeen | Asda |
| 174.66250 | | NFM | Scarborough | Theatre Mic |
| 174.67500 | | NFM | Nationwide | Channel Radio Mics Green |
| 174.70000 | | WFM | Jersey | BBC Jersey Radio Mics |
| 174.77000 | | NFM | Nationwide | Channel Radio Mics |
| 174.80000 | | NFM | Blackpool | St Thomas Church Radio Mic |
| 174.80000 | | NFM | Nationwide | Green Channel |
| 174.80000 | | NFM | Nationwide | Theatre Radio Microphone |
| 174.80000 | | NFM | Prescot | Leisure Centre Mics |

| Base | Mobile | Mode | Location | User and Notes |
|------|--------|------|----------|----------------|
| 174.80000 | | NFM | Southampton | Mecca Bingo Radio Mic |
| 174.97500 | | NFM | Dorset | 2CR VHF Radio Microphones |
| 175.00000 | | NFM | Ambleside | Methodist Church Radio Mic |
| 175.00000 | | WFM | Jersey | BBC Jersey Radio Mics |
| 175.00000 | | NFM | Nationwide | Theatre Radio Microphone |
| 175.00000 | | NFM | Nationwide | White Channel |
| 175.00000 | | NFM | Scotland | Singing Kettle Entertainment Grp |
| 175.00000 | | NFM | St. Helier | Church Radio Microphone |
| 175.08750 | | NFM | Canvey Island | Trio Radio Cars |
| 175.20000 | | NFM | Kirkby | Gala Bingo radio mic |
| 175.25000 | | NFM | Nationwide | JFMG Radio Mic Common Ch.7E |
| 175.52000 | | NFM | Nationwide | ITV Radio Microphone |
| 175.52500 | | NFM | Nationwide | JFMG Radio Mic ITV Ch.8A |
| 176.16250 | | NFM | Sheffield | City Cars |
| 176.18750 | | NFM | Basildon | Taxis |
| 176.40000 | | NFM | Nationwide | JFMG Radio Mic fixed site Ch.TA |
| 176.40000 | | NFM | Nationwide | Theatre Radio Microphone |
| 176.60000 | | NFM | Nationwide | BBC Radio Microphone |
| 176.60000 | | NFM | Nationwide | JFMG Radio Mic BBC Ch.8B |
| 176.80000 | | NFM | Nationwide | BBC News Radio Mics |
| 177.00000 | | NFM | Nationwide | JFMG Radio Mic fixed site Ch.TB |
| 177.00000 | | NFM | Nationwide | Theatre Radio Microphone |

### 177.2000 - 181.7000 MHz   TRUNKED PMR BASE REPEATERS 12.5 KHZ
### (SPLIT + 8.0 KHZ)

| Base | Mobile | Mode | Location | User and Notes |
|------|--------|------|----------|----------------|
| 177.12500 | 185.12500 | NFM | London | Multi-Business Shared Repeater |
| 177.26250 | 185.26250 | NFM | London, Crystal Palace | Fleetcomm trunked control channel |
| 177.28750 | 185.28750 | NFM | London | Camden Service Team Refuse |
| 177.31250 | 185.3125 | NFM | Croydon | Fleetcomm Trunked control channel |
| 177.31250 | 185.31250 | NFM | London | Ice delivery service. |
| 177.46250 | 185.46250 | NFM | London | Multi-Business Shared Repeater |
| 177.61250 | 185.61250 | NFM | London | Courier Service |
| 177.61250 | 185.61250 | NFM | London, Heathrow | Ground Staff |
| 177.63750 | 185.63750 | NFM | Lincolnshire | Council roads dept. |
| 177.63750 | 185.63750 | NFM | Lincolnshire, north | Council trunked voice channel |
| 177.76250 | 185.76250 | NFM | London | RSPCA |
| 177.78750 | 185.78750 | NFM | Lincolnshire | Council roads dept. |
| 177.78750 | 185.78750 | NFM | Lincolshire, north | Council trunked control channel |
| 177.91250 | 185.91250 | NFM | London | London Bus Co |
| 177.93750 | 185.93750 | NFM | Lincolnshie, north | Council trunked voice channel |
| 178.00000 | 186.00000 | NFM | Hull | North Sea Ferries |
| 178.06250 | 186.06250 | NFM | London | RSPCA |
| 178.11250 | 186.11250 | NFM | Lincolnshire | Council roads dept. |
| 178.23750 | 186.23450 | NFM | Stirling | Data Link |
| 178.26250 | 186.26250 | NFM | London | Courier Service |
| 178.28750 | 186.28750 | NFM | London | Citibank cash in transit vans |
| 178.28750 | 186.28750 | NFM | London | Private ambulance service |
| 178.32500 | 186.32500 | NFM | London | Hammersmith Council |
| 178.36250 | 186.36250 | NFM | London | Courier Service |
| 178.40000 | 186.40000 | NFM | Hull | North Sea Ferries |
| 178.47500 | 186.47500 | NFM | London | Thames Water |
| 178.48750 | 186.48750 | NFM | London | Citibank cash in transit vans |
| 178.51250 | 186.51250 | NFM | London | Multi-Business Shared Repeater |
| 178.58750 | 186.58750 | NFM | London | Citibank cash in transit vans |
| 178.63750 | 186.63750 | NFM | London | Citibank cash in transit vans |
| 178.66250 | 186.66250 | NFM | London | Multi-Business Shared Repeater |

| Base | Mobile | Mode | Location | User and Notes |
|------|--------|------|----------|----------------|
| 178.72500 | 186.72500 | NFM | Tayside | Data Repeater |
| 178.73750 | 186.73750 | NFM | London | Citibank cash in transit vans |
| 178.78750 | 186.78750 | NFM | London | Citibank cash in transit vans |
| 178.80000 | 186.80000 | NFM | Nationwide | JFMG Radio Mic BBC News Ch.8C |
| 178.81250 | 186.81250 | NFM | London | Citibank cash in transit vans |
| 179.03750 | 187.03750 | NFM | London | Hilton Hotel Fleetcomm control channel |
| 178.81250 | 186.81250 | NFM | London | Multi-Business Shared Repeater |
| 178.96250 | 186.96250 | NFM | London | Multi-Business Shared Repeater |
| 179.02500 | 187.02500 | NFM | Tayside | Data Repeater |
| 179.03750 | 187.03750 | NFM | London | Citibank cash in transit vans |
| 179.11250 | 187.11250 | NFM | London | Multi-Business Shared Repeater |
| 179.18750 | 187.18750 | NFM | Glasgow | Data Link |
| 179.28750 | 187.28750 | NFM | London | The Big Bus Company |
| 179.33750 | 187.33750 | NFM | London | Citibank cash in transit vans |
| 179.48750 | 187.48750 | NFM | London | Citibank cash in transit vans |
| 179.50000 | 187.50000 | NFM | London | Citibank cash in transit vans |
| 179.50000 | 187.50000 | NFM | London | The Big Bus Co |
| 179.65000 | 187.65000 | NFM | National | Formula 1 Racing Team |
| 179.71250 | 187.71250 | NFM | London | The Big Bus Co. |
| 179.88750 | 187.88750 | NFM | London | The Big Bus Company |
| 179.90000 | 187.90000 | NFM | London, Alexander Palace | Fleetcomm trunked control channel |
| 179.93750 | 187.93750 | NFM | London | Citibank CIT Vans |
| 180.00000 | 188.00000 | NFM | Nationwide | Illegal Bugging Devices |
| 180.00000 | 188.00000 | NFM | Space | Cosmos 1870 Satellite |
| 180.01250 | 188.01250 | NFM | London | Securiplan Security |
| 180.03750 | 188.03750 | NFM | London | Evening Standard Newstand Delivery |
| 180.12500 | 188.12500 | NFM | Space | Cosmos Satellite |
| 180.15000 | 188.15000 | NFM | Bedford | City Link |
| 180.16250 | 188.16250 | NFM | London | Big Bus tours |
| 180.16250 | 188.16250 | NFM | London | Citibank cash in transit vans |
| 180.30000 | 188.30000 | NFM | Bedfordshire | City Lynks Parcels trunked |
| 180.30000 | 188.30000 | NFM | Hertfordshire | City Lynks Parcels trunked |
| 180.32500 | 187.32500 | NFM | London | The Original Tour Bus (Arriva Buses) |
| 180.41250 | 188.41250 | NFM | Warwickshire | Warwickshire Parcels Ltd |
| 180.42500 | 188.42500 | NFM | London | Multi-Business Shared Repeater |
| 180.53750 | 188.53750 | NFM | Manchester | HGV Haulage |
| 180.57500 | 188.57500 | NFM | London | Locksmith Ambulances |
| 180.72500 | 188.72500 | NFM | London | Multi-Business Shared Repeater |
| 180.82500 | 188.25000 | NFM | Bedfordshire | More Skips |
| 180.82500 | 188.82500 | NFM | Bedfordshire | Buckdale Recovery |
| 180.93750 | 189.93750 | NFM | Bournemouth | Drainbusters Bournemouth |
| 180.93750 | 189.93750 | NFM | Ferndown | Locators |
| 180.93750 | 189.93750 | NFM | Portsmouth | Devro Security |
| 180.93750 | 189.93750 | NFM | Portsmouth | Radio Rentals |
| 180.93750 | 189.93750 | NFM | Southampton | Biffa Bins |
| 180.93750 | 189.93750 | NFM | Southampton | Boarhunt Garage |
| 180.93750 | 189.93750 | NFM | Southampton | Lux Traffic Controls |
| 180.93750 | 189.93750 | NFM | Southampton | Mercury Communications |
| 180.93750 | 189.93750 | NFM | Southampton | Swanwick Construction Ltd |
| 180.93750 | 189.93750 | NFM | Southampton | Tonrin Contractors Ltd. |
| 180.95000 | 188.95000 | NFM | Tayside | Data Repeater |
| 181.00000 | 189.00000 | NFM | Birmingham | Hippodrome Theatre |
| 181.12500 | 189.12500 | NFM | Bedford | City Link |
| 181.12500 | 189.12500 | NFM | Bedford | Council |
| 181.13750 | 189.13750 | NFM | Manchester | Transport Company |
| 181.20000 | 189.20000 | NFM | Pocklington | Orchard Taxis |

| Base | Mobile | Mode | Location | User and Notes |
|------|--------|------|----------|----------------|
| 181.50000 | | NFM | London | BBC Lime Grove Feed to TS2 O/B Mobile |

### 181.7000 - 181.8000 MHz    BROADCASTING LINKS
This band coincides with French TV so is unsuitable for PMR.

### 181.8000 - 183.5000 MHz    PMR 12.5 kHz NFM Duplex

| Base | Mobile | Mode | Location | User and Notes |
|------|--------|------|----------|----------------|
| 182.05000 | | NFM | Hyde | Florist |
| 182.12500 | | NFM | Oldham | Skip hire |
| 182.28750 | | NFM | Oldham | Alarm repairers |
| 182.28750 | | NFM | Oldham | Browns Car Factors |

### 183.5000 - 184.5000 MHz    METER READING
This band also coincides with French TV so is unsuitable for PMR. It is allocated to future remote reading applications.

### 184.5000 - 185.2000 MHz    RADIO MICROPHONES NFM

| Base | Mobile | Mode | Location | User and Notes |
|------|--------|------|----------|----------------|
| 181.69375 | | NFM | Nationwide | JFMG Wide Area TB/Camera CTRl Data |
| 181.80625 | | NFM | Nationwide | JFMG Wide Area TB/Camera CTRl Data |
| 184.60000 | | NFM | Nationwide | BBC News Radio Mics |
| 184.60000 | | NFM | Nationwide | JFMG Radio Mic BBC News Ch.9C |
| 184.80000 | | NFM | Jersey | Channel TV Radio Mics |
| 184.80000 | | NFM | Nationwide | ITV Radio Microphone |
| 184.80000 | | NFM | Nationwide | JFMG Radio Mic ITV Ch. 9A |
| 185.00000 | | NFM | Nationwide | ITV Radio Microphone |
| 185.00000 | | NFM | Nationwide | JFMG Radio Mic ILR Ch. 11D |
| 185.00000 | | NFM | Tayside | Radio Tay OB Mics |

### 185.2000 - 189.7000 MHz    PMR MOBILES COVERING M1 12.5 kHz
### (SPLIT 8.0 kHz)

| Base | Mobile | Mode | Location | User and Notes |
|------|--------|------|----------|----------------|
| 184.00000 | | NFM | London | Transport Co. |
| 184.42500 | | NFM | London | Delivery service |
| 187.01000 | | WFM | London | Community Radio Feeder to 100.6 MHz |
| 187.75000 | 179.75000 | NFM | London | Evening Standard Newstand Delivery |
| 188.00000 | | NFM | London | Police discrete PMG |
| 188.16250 | | NFM | London | Big Bus tours |

### 189.7000 - 189.8000 MHz    BROADCASTING LINKS

| Base | Mobile | Mode | Location | User and Notes |
|------|--------|------|----------|----------------|
| 189.69375 | | NFM | Nationwide | JFMG Wide Area TB/Camera CTRl Data |
| 189.70250 | | NFM | Twickenham | BBC ITV Links Thames TV |
| 189.77500 | | NFM | London | ITN News camera engineering to comms van |
| 189.78130 | | NFM | Twickenham | Thames TV |
| 189.79380 | | NFM | Twickenham | BBC ITV Links Thames TV |
| 189.80625 | | NFM | Nationwide | JFMG Wide Area TB/Camera CTRl Data |

### 189.8000 - 191.5000 MHz    PMR 12.5 kHz NFM Duplex

| Base | Mobile | Mode | Location | User and Notes |
|------|--------|------|----------|----------------|
| 190.150 | 206.15000 | NFM | Penygrain | Railway cab radio link |

### 191.5000 - 193.2000 MHz    RADIO MICROPHONES AND LIMITRD PMR

| Base | Mobile | Mode | Location | User and Notes |
|------|--------|------|----------|----------------|
| 191.700 | | NFM | Nationwide | JFMG Radio Mic |
| 191.900 | | NFM | Nationwide | JFMG Radio Mic mobile Ch.ML1 |
| 191.900 | 191.900 | NFM | Scarborough | Theatre Microphone |
| 192.100 | | NFM | Nationwide | JFMG Radio Mic ILR Ch.14D |
| 192.300 | | NFM | Nationwide | JFMG Radio Mic |
| 192.600 | | NFM | Nationwide | JFMG Radio Mic BBC News Ch. Local |
| 192.600 | 192.600 | NFM | Nationwide | BBC News Radio Mics |

| Base | Mobile | Mode | Location | User and Notes |
|------|--------|------|----------|----------------|
| 192.800 | | NFM | Nationwide | JFMG Radio Mic ITV Ch.10A |
| 192.800 | | WFM | Nationwide | BBC Antiques Roadshow Mics |
| 192.800 | 192.800 | NFM | Nationwide | ITV Radio Microphone |
| 193.000 | | NFM | Nationwide | JFMG Radio Mic BBC Ch.9B |
| 193.000 | 193.000 | NFM | Nationwide | BBC Radio Microphone |

### 199.5000 - 200.5000MHz    BROADCASTING LINKS

| Base | Mobile | Mode | Location | User and Notes |
|------|--------|------|----------|----------------|
| 199.700 | | WFM | NFM | JFMG Radio Mic mobile Ch.ML28 |
| 199.700 | | WFM | NFM | JFMG Stereo sound link |
| 199.700 | | WFM | Nationwide | JFMG Radio Mic |
| 199.700 | | WFM | Nationwide | JFMG Radio Mic |
| 199.900 | | WFM | NFM | JFMG Stereo O/B sound link |
| 200.100 | | WFM | NFM | JFMG Radio Mic |
| 200.300 | | WFM | NFM | JFMG Radio Mic |
| 200.300 | | NFM | Scarborough | Theatre Microphone |

### 200.5000 - 201.2000 MHz    RADIO MICROPHONES NFM

| Base | Mobile | Mode | Location | User and Notes |
|------|--------|------|----------|----------------|
| 200.500 | | NFM | Nationwide | Radio Mics |
| 200.600 | | WFM | NFM | JFMG Radio Mic mobile Ch.ML8 |
| 200.600 | | NFM | Nationwide | BBC Radio Microphone |
| 200.600 | | WFM | Nationwide | BBC Antiques Roadshow Mics |
| 200.800 | | WFM | London | 94.0 Capital Radio Mic. |
| 200.800 | | WFM | NFM | JFMG Radio Mic ITN Ch.12D |
| 200.800 | | NFM | Nationwide | ITV News Radio Mics |
| 201.000 | | NFM | Jersey | Channel TV Radio Mics |
| 201.000 | | WFM | NFM | JFMG Radio Mic ITV Ch.11A |
| 201.000 | | NFM | Nationwide | ITV Radio Microphone |

### 200.5000 - 207.5000 MHz    TRUNKED BASE PMR 12.5 kHz
### (MOBILES - 8.0 MHz)

| Base | Mobile | Mode | Location | User and Notes |
|------|--------|------|----------|----------------|
| 201.00000 | 193.00000 | NFM | Nationwide | Trunked PMR |
| 201.11250 | 193.11250 | NFM | Nationwide | Trunked PMR |
| 201.12500 | 193.12500 | NFM | Nationwide | Trunked PMR |
| 201.13750 | 193.13750 | NFM | Nationwide | Trunked PMR |
| 201.15000 | 193.15000 | NFM | Nationwide | Trunked PMR |
| 201.15250 | 193.15250 | NFM | Glasgow | Strathclyde Buses |
| 201.16250 | 193.16250 | NFM | Nationwide | Trunked PMR |
| 201.17500 | 193.17500 | NFM | Nationwide | Trunked PMR |
| 201.18750 | 193.18750 | NFM | Nationwide | Trunked PMR |
| 201.20000 | 193.20000 | NFM | Nationwide | Trunked PMR |
| 201.21250 | 193.21250 | NFM | Nationwide | Trunked PMR |
| 201.22500 | 193.22500 | NFM | Nationwide | Trunked PMR |
| 201.23750 | 193.23750 | NFM | Nationwide | Trunked PMR |
| 201.25000 | 193.25000 | NFM | Perth | Trunked PMR |
| 201.25000 | 193.25000 | NFM | Rugby | Electricians |
| 201.26250 | 193.26250 | NFM | Nationwide | Trunked PMR |
| 201.27500 | 193.27500 | NFM | Nationwide | Trunked PMR |
| 201.28750 | 193.28750 | NFM | Nationwide | Trunked PMR |
| 201.30000 | 193.30000 | NFM | Nationwide | Trunked PMR |
| 201.31250 | 193.31250 | NFM | Central Scotland | Bus Company |
| 201.31250 | 193.31250 | NFM | Sheffield | S Yorkshire Transport (Lead Mill) |
| 201.31250 | 193.31250 | NFM | South Yorkshire | Bus Company |
| 201.32500 | 193.32500 | NFM | Nationwide | Trunked PMR |
| 201.33750 | 193.33750 | NFM | Nationwide | Trunked PMR |
| 201.35000 | 193.35000 | NFM | Nationwide | Trunked PMR |

| Base | Mobile | Mode | Location | User and Notes |
|---|---|---|---|---|
| 201.35000 | 193.85000 | NFM | Perth | Stagecoach Buses |
| 201.36250 | 193.36250 | NFM | Central Scottish | Bus Company |
| 201.36250 | 193.36250 | NFM | London | Bus Company |
| 201.36250 | 193.36250 | NFM | Newport | Bus Company |
| 201.36250 | 193.36250 | NFM | South Yorkshire | Bus Company |
| 201.37500 | 193.37500 | NFM | Nationwide | Trunked PMR |
| 201.38750 | 193.38750 | NFM | Nationwide | Trunked PMR |
| 201.40000 | 193.40000 | NFM | Perth | Stagecoach Buses |
| 201.40000 | 193.40000 | NFM | Tayside | Trunked PMR |
| 201.41250 | 193.41250 | NFM | Alder Valley | Bus Company |
| 201.41250 | 193.41250 | NFM | Manchester | Bus Company |
| 201.41250 | 193.41250 | NFM | Nationwide | Trunked PMR |
| 201.41250 | 193.41250 | NFM | Strathclyde | Bus Company |
| 201.41750 | 193.43750 | NFM | Nationwide | Trunked PMR |
| 201.42500 | 193.42500 | NFM | Nationwide | Trunked PMR |
| 201.45000 | 193.45000 | NFM | Nationwide | Trunked PMR |
| 201.46250 | 193.46250 | NFM | Glasgow | Bus Company |
| 201.46250 | 193.46250 | NFM | London | London Transport |
| 201.47500 | 193.47500 | NFM | Nationwide | Trunked PMR |
| 201.48750 | 193.48750 | NFM | Nationwide | Trunked PMR |
| 201.50000 | 193.50000 | NFM | London | Securiplan Plc Security |
| 201.51250 | 193.51250 | NFM | Cardiff | Bus Company |
| 201.51250 | 193.51250 | NFM | London | London Transport |
| 201.51250 | 193.51250 | NFM | West Midlands | Bus Company |
| 201.51250 | 193.51250 | NFM | West Yorkshire | Bus Company |
| 201.52500 | 193.52500 | NFM | Hull | Council Housing Repairs |
| 201.52500 | 193.52500 | NFM | Hull | Mobile Doctors Service |
| 201.52500 | 193.52500 | NFM | South Yorkshire | Trunked PMR |
| 201.53750 | 193.53750 | NFM | Nationwide | Trunked PMR |
| 201.55000 | 193.55000 | NFM | Perth | Stagecoach Busses |
| 201.56250 | 193.56250 | NFM | London | Bus Company |
| 201.56250 | 193.56250 | NFM | Manchester | Metrolink Control |
| 201.56250 | 193.56250 | NFM | Northampton | Bus Company |
| 201.56250 | 193.56250 | NFM | Scotland (West) | Bus Company |
| 201.56250 | 193.56250 | NFM | Yorkshire | Bus Company |
| 201.57500 | 193.57500 | NFM | Nationwide | Trunked PMR |
| 201.58750 | 193.50750 | NFM | Nationwide | Trunked PMR |
| 201.60000 | 193.60000 | NFM | Nationwide | Trunked PMR |
| 201.61250 | 193.61250 | NFM | Glasgow | Strathclyde Buses |
| 201.61250 | 193.61250 | NFM | London | London Transport |
| 201.61250 | 193.61250 | NFM | Manchester | Bus Company |
| 201.61250 | 193.61250 | NFM | Strathclyde | Bus Company |
| 201.62500 | 193.62500 | NFM | Nationwide | Trunked PMR |
| 201.63750 | 193.63750 | NFM | Coventry | McNicolas Cable laying contractors |
| 201.65000 | 193.65000 | NFM | Birmingham | Lucas Aerospace Security PA System |
| 201.65000 | 193.65000 | NFM | London | Doctors call out |
| 201.65000 | 193.65000 | NFM | Nationwide | Trunked PMR |
| 201.66250 | 193.66250 | NFM | Birmingham | West Midlands Bus Travel |
| 201.66250 | 193.66250 | NFM | Cardiff | Bus Company |
| 201.66250 | 193.66250 | NFM | Chester | Bus Company |
| 201.66250 | 193.66250 | NFM | Darlington | Bus Company |
| 201.66250 | 193.66250 | NFM | Lancashire | Squires Transport |
| 201.66250 | 193.66250 | NFM | London | Bus Company |
| 201.66250 | 193.66250 | NFM | London | London Transport |
| 201.66250 | 193.66250 | NFM | Manchester | Bus Company |
| 201.66250 | 193.66250 | NFM | Strathclyde | Bus Company |

| Base | Mobile | Mode | Location | User and Notes |
|------|--------|------|----------|----------------|
| 201.67500 | 193.67500 | NFM | Nationwide | Trunked PMR |
| 201.68750 | 193.68750 | NFM | Manchester | Transport |
| 201.68750 | 193.68750 | NFM | Nationwide | Trunked PMR |
| 201.70000 | 193.70000 | NFM | Nationwide | Trunked PMR |
| 201.70000 | 193.70000 | NFM | Perth | Stagecoach Busses |
| 201.71250 | 193.71250 | NFM | Cardiff | Bus Company |
| 201.71250 | 193.71250 | NFM | London | London Transport |
| 201.71250 | 193.71250 | NFM | Nationwide | Trunked PMR |
| 201.71250 | 193.71250 | NFM | Tyne & Wear | Bus Company |
| 201.72500 | 193.72500 | NFM | Nationwide | Trunked PMR |
| 201.73750 | 193.73750 | NFM | Nationwide | Trunked PMR |
| 201.75000 | 193.75000 | NFM | Nationwide | Trunked PMR |
| 201.76000 | 193.76000 | NFM | Falkirk | Midland Bluebird Buses |
| 201.76250 | 193.76250 | NFM | London | London Transport |
| 201.76250 | 193.76250 | NFM | Nationwide | Trunked PMR |
| 201.76250 | 193.76250 | NFM | Rotherham | South Yorkshire Transport |
| 201.76250 | 193.76250 | NFM | Scotland | Midland Scottish |
| 201.76250 | 193.76250 | NFM | South Yorkshire | Bus Company |
| 201.77500 | 193.77500 | NFM | Nationwide | Trunked PMR |
| 201.78500 | 193.78750 | NFM | Hyde | Jacksons Deliveries |
| 201.78750 | 193.78750 | NFM | Nationwide | Trunked PMR |
| 201.80000 | 193.80000 | NFM | London | Security Company |
| 201.80000 | 193.80000 | NFM | Nationwide | Trunked PMR |
| 201.81250 | 193.81250 | NFM | London | United |
| 201.81250 | 193.81250 | NFM | Manchester | United |
| 201.81250 | 193.81250 | NFM | Nationwide | PMR Band III Ch 42 |
| 201.81250 | 193.81250 | NFM | West Midlands | United |
| 201.82500 | 193.82500 | NFM | Nationwide | PMR Band III Channel |
| 201.83750 | 193.83750 | NFM | Nationwide | Trunked PMR |
| 201.85000 | 193.85000 | NFM | Croydon | National Band 3 Ltd. trunked control channel |
| 201.85000 | 193.85000 | NFM | Nationwide | PMR Band III Channel |
| 201.85000 | 193.85000 | NFM | Tayside | Trunked PMR/Data |
| 201.86250 | 193.86250 | NFM | Glasgow | Strathclyde Buses |
| 201.86250 | 193.86250 | NFM | London | Buses |
| 201.86250 | 193.86250 | NFM | London | London Transport |
| 201.86250 | 193.86250 | NFM | Nationwide | PMR Band III Channel 40 |
| 201.86250 | 193.86250 | NFM | Strathclyde | Buses |
| 201.87500 | 193.87500 | NFM | Nationwide | Band III Channel |
| 201.88750 | 193.88750 | NFM | Manchester | Transport |
| 201.88750 | 193.88750 | NFM | Nationwide | Trunked PMR |
| 201.90000 | 193.90000 | NFM | Nationwide | Trunked PMR |
| 201.91250 | 193.91250 | NFM | London | Buses |
| 201.91250 | 193.91250 | NFM | London | London Transport |
| 201.91250 | 193.91250 | NFM | Nationwide | Band III Channel 30 |
| 201.91250 | 193.91250 | NFM | Warrington | Buses |
| 201.91250 | 193.91250 | NFM | West Yorkshire | Buses |
| 201.92500 | 193.92500 | NFM | Nationwide | Trunked PMR |
| 201.92500 | 193.92500 | NFM | Walsall | Council |
| 201.93750 | 193.93750 | NFM | Nationwide | Trunked PMR |
| 201.93750 | 193.93750 | NFM | W Yorkshire | Trunked Radio System |
| 201.95000 | 193.95000 | NFM | Nationwide | Trunked PMR |
| 201.96250 | 193.96250 | NFM | Bristol | Buses |
| 201.96250 | 193.96250 | NFM | London | Transport Co. |
| 201.96250 | 193.96250 | NFM | London | London Transport |
| 201.96250 | 193.96250 | NFM | Manchester | GM Buses |
| 201.96250 | 193.96250 | NFM | Yorkshire | Buses |

| Base | Mobile | Mode | Location | User and Notes |
|---|---|---|---|---|
| 201.97500 | 193.97500 | NFM | Nationwide | Trunked PMR |
| 201.98750 | 193.98750 | NFM | Ipswich | Radio Anglia |
| 201.98750 | 193.98750 | NFM | Nationwide | Trunked PMR |
| 202.00000 | 194.00000 | NFM | Nationwide | Trunked PMR |
| 202.00000 | 194.00000 | NFM | Perth | Stagecoach Buses |
| 202.01250 | 194.01250 | NFM | Bristol | Buses |
| 202.01250 | 194.01250 | NFM | Derby | Buses |
| 202.01250 | 194.01250 | NFM | London | London Transport |
| 202.01250 | 194.01250 | NFM | Manchester | GM Buses |
| 202.01250 | 194.01250 | NFM | Nationwide | PMR Band III Channel |
| 202.01250 | 194.01250 | NFM | Tyne & Wear | Buses |
| 202.02500 | 194.02500 | NFM | Nationwide | PMR Band III Channel |
| 202.03750 | 194.03750 | NFM | Nationwide | PMR Band III Channel |
| 202.05000 | 194.05000 | NFM | Nationwide | PMR Band III Channel |
| 202.06250 | 194.06250 | NFM | England (North West) | PMR |
| 202.06250 | 194.06250 | NFM | London | London Transport |
| 202.06250 | 194.06250 | NFM | Manchester | Metro Link |
| 202.06250 | 194.06250 | NFM | Manchester | Metrolink Control |
| 202.06250 | 194.06250 | NFM | Nationwide | PMR Band III Channel 59 |
| 202.06250 | 194.06250 | NFM | Sheffield | S. Yorkshire Transport (Herris) |
| 202.06250 | 194.06250 | NFM | Sheffield, Olive Grove | Mainline Bases Ch 58 |
| 202.07500 | 194.07500 | NFM | Nationwide | PMR Band III Channel |
| 202.08750 | 194.08750 | NFM | Nationwide | Trunked PMR |
| 202.10000 | 194.10000 | NFM | Nationwide | Trunked PMR |
| 202.11250 | 194.11250 | NFM | Nationwide | National Express Buses |
| 202.11250 | 194.11250 | NFM | Nationwide | Trunked PMR |
| 202.12500 | 194.12500 | NFM | Nationwide | Trunked PMR |
| 202.13750 | 194.13750 | NFM | Nationwide | Trunked PMR |
| 202.15000 | 194.15000 | NFM | Nationwide | PMR Band III Channel |
| 202.15000 | 194.15000 | NFM | Perth | Stagecoach Buses |
| 202.16250 | 194.16250 | NFM | Birmingham | West Midlands Bus Travel |
| 202.16250 | 194.16250 | NFM | Manchester | GM Buses |
| 202.16250 | 194.16250 | NFM | Nationwide | National Express Buses |
| 202.16250 | 194.16250 | NFM | Nationwide | PMR Band III Channel 38 |
| 202.17500 | 194.17500 | NFM | Nationwide | PMR Band III Channel |
| 202.18750 | 194.18750 | NFM | Nationwide | Trunked PMR |
| 202.20000 | 194.20000 | NFM | Nationwide | Trunked PMR |
| 202.21250 | 194.21250 | NFM | Birmingham | West Midlands Bus Travel |
| 202.21250 | 194.21250 | NFM | Hull | Buses |
| 202.21250 | 194.21250 | NFM | London | London Transport |
| 202.21250 | 194.21250 | NFM | Nationwide | Trunked PMR |
| 202.21250 | 194.21250 | NFM | Scotland | East Scottish Buses |
| 202.21250 | 194.21250 | NFM | Sheffield | Supertram |
| 202.21250 | 194.21250 | NFM | West Yorkshire | Buses |
| 202.22500 | 194.22500 | NFM | Nationwide | Trunked PMR |
| 202.23750 | 194.23750 | NFM | Nationwide | PMR Band III Channel |
| 202.25000 | 194.25000 | NFM | Nationwide | Trunked PMR |
| 202.26250 | 194.26250 | NFM | Ely | Buses |
| 202.26250 | 194.26250 | NFM | Maidstone | Buses |
| 202.26250 | 194.26250 | NFM | Manchester | GM Buses |
| 202.26250 | 194.26250 | NFM | Nationwide | Trunked PMR |
| 202.26250 | 194.26250 | NFM | Oxfordshire | Cityline buses |
| 202.26250 | 194.26250 | NFM | West Yorkshire | Northern General |
| 202.27500 | 194.27500 | NFM | Nationwide | Trunked PMR |
| 202.28750 | 194.28750 | NFM | London | London Transport |
| 202.28750 | 194.28750 | NFM | Nationwide | Trunked PMR |

| Base | Mobile | Mode | Location | User and Notes |
|------|--------|------|----------|----------------|
| 202.30000 | 194.30000 | NFM | Nationwide | Trunked PMR |
| 202.30000 | 194.30000 | NFM | Portsmouth | Taxis |
| 202.31250 | 194.31250 | NFM | London | London Transport |
| 202.31250 | 194.31250 | NFM | Manchester | GM Buses |
| 202.31250 | 194.31250 | NFM | Nationwide | Trunked PMR |
| 202.31250 | 194.31250 | NFM | Tyne & Wear | Buses |
| 202.31250 | 194.32150 | NFM | Swindon | Bass |
| 202.31750 | 194.31750 | NFM | London | London Transport |
| 202.31750 | 194.31750 | NFM | London | Revenue Protection Inspectors Ch 2 |
| 202.32500 | 194.32500 | NFM | Nationwide | Trunked PMR |
| 202.33750 | 194.33750 | NFM | Nationwide | Trunked PMR |
| 202.33750 | 194.33750 | NFM | Oldham | Gradwell TV |
| 202.35000 | 194.35000 | NFM | Nationwide | Trunked PMR |
| 202.36250 | 194.36250 | NFM | London | London Transport |
| 202.36250 | 194.36250 | NFM | Manchester | GM Buses |
| 202.36250 | 194.36250 | NFM | Nationwide | PMR Band III Channel 32 |
| 202.36250 | 194.36250 | NFM | Sheffield | S. Yorkshire Transport (East Dark) |
| 202.36250 | 194.36250 | NFM | Tyne & Wear | Buses |
| 202.37500 | 194.37500 | NFM | Nationwide | Trunked PMR |
| 202.38750 | 194.38750 | NFM | Nationwide | Trunked PMR |
| 202.40000 | 194.40000 | NFM | Nationwide | Trunked PMR |
| 202.41250 | 194.41250 | NFM | Nationwide | PMR Band III Channel |
| 202.42500 | 194.42500 | NFM | Nationwide | PMR Band III Channel |
| 202.42500 | 194.42500 | NFM | W Yorkshire | Trunked Radio System |
| 202.43750 | 194.43750 | NFM | Nationwide | Trunked PMR |
| 202.45000 | 194.45000 | NFM | Nationwide | Trunked PMR |
| 202.46250 | 194.46250 | NFM | London | London Transport |
| 202.46250 | 194.46250 | NFM | Manchester | GM Buses |
| 202.46250 | 194.46250 | NFM | Midlands | Buses |
| 202.46250 | 194.46250 | NFM | Nationwide | PMR Band III Channel 31 |
| 202.47500 | 194.47500 | NFM | Nationwide | Trunked PMR |
| 202.50000 | 194.50000 | NFM | Nationwide | Trunked PMR |
| 202.51250 | 194.51250 | NFM | East Kent | Buses |
| 202.51250 | 194.51250 | NFM | Merseyside | Buses |
| 202.51250 | 194.51250 | NFM | Nationwide | PMR Band III Channel |
| 202.51250 | 194.51250 | NFM | South Wales | Buses |
| 202.51250 | 194.51250 | NFM | Tayside | Buses |
| 202.52500 | 194.52500 | NFM | Nationwide | Trunked PMR |
| 202.53750 | 194.53750 | NFM | Nationwide | Trunked PMR |
| 202.55000 | 194.55000 | NFM | Nationwide | Trunked PMR |
| 202.55000 | 194.55000 | NFM | Perth | Stagecoach Buses |
| 202.56250 | 194.56250 | NFM | Nationwide | Trunked PMR |
| 202.57500 | 194.57500 | NFM | Nationwide | Trunked PMR |
| 202.58750 | 194.58750 | NFM | Nationwide | Trunked PMR |
| 202.60000 | 194.60000 | NFM | Nationwide | Trunked PMR |
| 202.61250 | 194.61250 | NFM | Nationwide | Trunked PMR |
| 202.61750 | 194.60750 | NFM | Nationwide | Trunked PMR |
| 202.62500 | 194.62500 | NFM | Nationwide | Trunked PMR |
| 202.65000 | 154.65000 | NFM | Nationwide | Trunked PMR |
| 202.66250 | 194.66250 | NFM | Nationwide | Trunked PMR |
| 202.67500 | 194.67500 | NFM | Nationwide | Trunked PMR |
| 202.68750 | 194.68750 | NFM | East Anglia | Anglia Motor Parts |
| 202.68750 | 194.68750 | NFM | East Anglia | City Link Parcels |
| 202.68750 | 194.68750 | NFM | East Anglia | Hales Skips & Waste. |
| 202.68750 | 194.68750 | NFM | East Anglia | TRi-Mec Skips |
| 202.68750 | 194.68750 | NFM | Essex | Patient Transport Service |

| Base | Mobile | Mode | Location | User and Notes |
|------|--------|------|----------|----------------|
| 202.68750 | 194.68750 | NFM | Nationwide | Trunked PMR |
| 202.70000 | 194.70000 | NFM | Nationwide | Trunked PMR |
| 202.71250 | 194.71250 | NFM | Nationwide | Trunked PMR |
| 202.72500 | 194.68750 | NFM | Coventry | MCN Civil Engineers |
| 202.72500 | 194.68750 | NFM | Nationwide | Trunked PMR |
| 202.73750 | 194.73750 | NFM | Nationwide | Trunked PMR |
| 202.75000 | 194.75000 | NFM | Nationwide | Trunked PMR |
| 202.75000 | 194.75000 | NFM | Stockport | Breakdown Recovery |
| 202.76250 | 194.76250 | NFM | Nationwide | Trunked PMR |
| 202.77500 | 194.77500 | NFM | Nationwide | Trunked PMR |
| 202.78750 | 194.78750 | NFM | Nationwide | Trunked PMR |
| 202.80000 | 194.80000 | NFM | Nationwide | Trunked PMR |
| 202.81250 | 194.81250 | NFM | Nationwide | Trunked PMR |
| 202.82500 | 194.82500 | NFM | Nationwide | Trunked PMR |
| 202.83750 | 194.83750 | NFM | Nationwide | Trunked PMR |
| 202.85000 | 194.85000 | NFM | Nationwide | Trunked PMR |
| 202.86250 | 194.86250 | NFM | Nationwide | Trunked PMR |
| 202.86250 | 194.86250 | NFM | West Midlands | Vehicle Recovery |
| 202.87500 | 194.87500 | NFM | Nationwide | Trunked PMR |
| 202.88750 | 194.88750 | NFM | Nationwide | Trunked PMR |
| 202.90000 | 194.90000 | NFM | Nationwide | Trunked PMR |
| 202.90000 | 194.90000 | NFM | London | Guys Hospital National Band 3 trunked control channel |
| 202.91250 | 194.91250 | NFM | East Anglia | Anglia Motor Parts |
| 202.91250 | 194.91250 | NFM | East Anglia | City Link Parcels |
| 202.91250 | 194.91250 | NFM | East Anglia | Hales Skips & Waste. |
| 202.91250 | 194.91250 | NFM | East Anglia | Tri-Mec Skips |
| 202.91250 | 194.91250 | NFM | Essex | Patient Transport Service |
| 202.91250 | 194.91250 | NFM | Nationwide | Trunked PMR |
| 202.92500 | 194.92500 | NFM | Nationwide | Trunked PMR |
| 202.93750 | 194.93750 | NFM | Nationwide | Trunked PMR |
| 202.95000 | 194.95000 | NFM | Nationwide | Trunked PMR |
| 202.96250 | 194.96250 | NFM | Devon | Buses |
| 202.96250 | 194.96250 | NFM | Fife | Buses |
| 202.96250 | 194.96250 | NFM | London | Buses |
| 202.96250 | 194.96250 | NFM | Nationwide | Trunked PMR |
| 202.96250 | 194.96250 | NFM | West Midlands | Buses |
| 202.96250 | 194.96250 | NFM | West Yorkshire | Buses |
| 202.97560 | 194.97500 | NFM | Nationwide | Trunked PMR |
| 202.98750 | 194.98750 | NFM | Nationwide | Trunked PMR |
| 203.00000 | 195.00000 | NFM | London | R & I Blue Buses |
| 203.00000 | 195.00000 | NFM | Nationwide | Trunked PMR |
| 203.01250 | 195.01250 | NFM | Hampshire | Buses |
| 203.01250 | 195.01250 | NFM | London | London Transport |
| 203.01250 | 195.01250 | NFM | Nationwide | Trunked PMR |
| 203.01250 | 195.01250 | NFM | Scotland | East Scottish Buses |
| 203.01250 | 195.01250 | NFM | Sheffield | Supertrams |
| 203.01250 | 195.01250 | NFM | West Yorkshire | Buses |
| 203.02500 | 195.02500 | NFM | Nationwide | Trunked PMR |
| 203.03750 | 195.03750 | NFM | Manchester | Rescue & Recovery |
| 203.03750 | 195.03750 | NFM | Nationwide | Trunked PMR |
| 203.05000 | 195.05000 | NFM | Nationwide | Trunked PMR |
| 203.06250 | 195.06250 | NFM | Devon | Buses |
| 203.06250 | 195.06250 | NFM | London | Buses |
| 203.06250 | 195.06250 | NFM | Nationwide | Trunked PMR |
| 203.06250 | 195.06250 | NFM | Sheffield | Supertrams |
| 203.06250 | 195.06250 | NFM | Tyne & Wear | Buses |

| Base | Mobile | Mode | Location | User and Notes |
|------|--------|------|----------|----------------|
| 203.06250 | 195.06250 | NFM | West Yorkshire | Buses |
| 203.07500 | 195.07500 | NFM | Nationwide | PMR Band III Channel |
| 203.08750 | 195.08750 | NFM | Nationwide | PMR Band III Channel |
| 203.10000 | 195.10000 | NFM | Coventry | Area Security Co |
| 203.10000 | 195.10000 | NFM | Nationwide | PMR Band III Channel |
| 203.11250 | 195.11250 | NFM | Devon | Buses |
| 203.11250 | 195.11250 | NFM | Gt. Manchester | Buses |
| 203.11250 | 195.11250 | NFM | Maidstone | Buses |
| 203.11250 | 195.11250 | NFM | Nationwide | Trunked PMR |
| 203.11250 | 195.11250 | NFM | Strathclyde | Buses |
| 203.12500 | 195.12500 | NFM | Coventry | Mcn Civil Engineers |
| 203.12500 | 195.12500 | NFM | Nationwide | Trunked PMR |
| 203.13750 | 195.13750 | NFM | Nationwide | Trunked PMR |
| 203.15000 | 195.15000 | NFM | Nationwide | Trunked PMR |
| 203.16250 | 195.16250 | NFM | London | Buses |
| 203.16250 | 195.16250 | NFM | Nationwide | PMR Band III Channel |
| 203.16250 | 195.16250 | NFM | Plymouth | Western National Buses |
| 203.16250 | 195.16250 | NFM | Yorkshire | Yorkshire Traction |
| 203.17500 | 195.17500 | NFM | Nationwide | Trunked PMR |
| 203.18750 | 195.18750 | NFM | Nationwide | PMR Band III Channel |
| 203.20000 | 195.20000 | NFM | London | Brophy Utilities For Thames Water |
| 203.20000 | 195.20000 | NFM | Nationwide | PMR Band III Channel |
| 203.21250 | 195.21250 | NFM | Nationwide | PMR Band III Channel |
| 203.21250 | 195.21250 | NFM | Sheffield | S. Yorkshire Transport (Greenland) |
| 203.22500 | 195.22500 | NFM | Nationwide | PMR Band III Channel |
| 203.23750 | 195.23750 | NFM | Coventry | McNicolas Cable Laying Contractors |
| 203.23750 | 195.23750 | NFM | Manchester | Bus Company |
| 203.23750 | 195.23750 | NFM | North West | PMR |
| 203.23750 | 195.23750 | NFM | Oldham | Traffic lights engineers |
| 203.25000 | 195.25000 | NFM | Nationwide | PMR Band III Channel |
| 203.25750 | 195.21750 | NFM | Nationwide | Band III Channel |
| 203.26250 | 195.26250 | NFM | Chesterfield | Buses |
| 203.26250 | 195.26250 | NFM | Hartlepool | Buses |
| 203.26250 | 195.26250 | NFM | London | London Transport Emergency Ch |
| 203.26250 | 195.26250 | NFM | Nationwide | Band III Channel |
| 203.27500 | 195.27500 | NFM | Nationwide | PMR Band III Channel |
| 203.28750 | 195.28750 | NFM | Nationwide | PMR Band III Channel |
| 203.30000 | 195.30000 | NFM | Nationwide | PMR Band III Channel |
| 203.31250 | 195.31250 | NFM | Lancaster | Buses |
| 203.31250 | 195.31250 | NFM | London | London Transport |
| 203.31250 | 195.31250 | NFM | Nationwide | PMR Band III Channel 37 |
| 203.32500 | 195.32500 | NFM | Nationwide | PMR Band III Channel |
| 203.33750 | 195.33750 | NFM | Nationwide | PMR Band III Channel |
| 203.35000 | 195.35000 | NFM | Nationwide | PMR Band III Channel |
| 203.36250 | 195.36250 | NFM | Burnley | Buses |
| 203.36250 | 195.36250 | NFM | London | London Transport |
| 203.36250 | 195.36250 | NFM | Nationwide | PMR Band III Channel 36 |
| 203.36750 | 195.38750 | NFM | Nationwide | Trunked PMR |
| 203.37500 | 195.37500 | NFM | Nationwide | PMR Band III Channel |
| 203.37500 | 195.37500 | NFM | Nationwide | Railtrack |
| 203.40000 | 195.40000 | NFM | Nationwide | Trunked PMR |
| 203.41250 | 195.41250 | NFM | Nationwide | Trunked PMR |
| 203.42500 | 195.42500 | NFM | London | Hammersmith & Fulham parking enforcement |
| 203.42500 | 195.42500 | NFM | Nationwide | Trunked PMR |
| 203.43750 | 195.43750 | NFM | Nationwide | Trunked PMR |
| 203.45000 | 195.45000 | NFM | Nationwide | Trunked PMR |

| Base | Mobile | Mode | Location | User and Notes |
| --- | --- | --- | --- | --- |
| 203.46250 | 195.46250 | NFM | Nationwide | Trunked PMR |
| 203.46250 | 195.46250 | NFM | W Yorkshire | Trunked Radio System |
| 203.47500 | 195.47500 | NFM | Coventry | MCN Civil Engineers |
| 203.47500 | 195.47500 | NFM | Nationwide | Trunked PMR |
| 203.48750 | 195.00000 | NFM | Dover | Night Page Security |
| 203.48750 | 195.00000 | NFM | Nationwide | PMR Band III Channel |
| 203.50000 | 195.50000 | NFM | Nationwide | Trunked PMR |
| 203.51250 | 195.51250 | NFM | Nationwide | Trunked PMR |
| 203.52500 | 193.52500 | NFM | Nationwide | Trunked PMR |
| 203.53750 | 195.53750 | NFM | Nationwide | Trunked PMR |
| 203.55000 | 195.55000 | NFM | Nationwide | Trunked PMR |
| 203.56250 | 195.56250 | NFM | Nationwide | Trunked PMR |
| 203.56250 | 195.56250 | NFM | Guildford | National Band 3 Ltd. trunked control channel |
| 203.56250 | 195.56250 | NFM | Pocklington | Peter Winn Tyres |
| 203.57500 | 195.57500 | NFM | Nationwide | Trunked PMR |
| 203.58750 | 195.58750 | NFM | Nationwide | Trunked PMR |
| 203.60000 | 195.60000 | NFM | Nationwide | Trunked PMR |
| 203.61250 | 195.61250 | NFM | Nationwide | Trunked PMR |
| 203.62500 | 195.62500 | NFM | Nationwide | Trunked PMR |
| 203.63750 | 195.63750 | NFM | Dover | Night Page Security |
| 203.63750 | 195.63750 | NFM | Nationwide | Trunked PMR |
| 203.65000 | 195.65000 | NFM | Nationwide | Trunked PMR |
| 203.66250 | 195.66250 | NFM | Central Scotland | Buses |
| 203.66250 | 195.66250 | NFM | Cynon Valley | Buses |
| 203.66250 | 195.66250 | NFM | London | London Transport |
| 203.66250 | 195.66250 | NFM | Nationwide | PMR Band III Channel 60 |
| 203.66250 | 195.66250 | NFM | Sheffield | South Yorkshire Transport (Halfway) |
| 203.66250 | 195.66250 | NFM | South Yorkshire | Buses |
| 203.67500 | 195.67500 | NFM | Croydon | Buses |
| 203.67500 | 195.67500 | NFM | Nationwide | Trunked PMR |
| 203.68750 | 195.68750 | NFM | Nationwide | Trunked PMR |
| 203.70000 | 195.70000 | NFM | Nationwide | Trunked PMR |
| 203.71250 | 195.71250 | NFM | London | London Transport |
| 203.71250 | 195.71250 | NFM | Manchester | Buses |
| 203.71250 | 195.71250 | NFM | Nationwide | Trunked PMR |
| 203.71250 | 195.71250 | NFM | Tyne & Wear | Buses |
| 203.72500 | 195.72500 | NFM | Nationwide | Trunked PMR |
| 203.73700 | 195.73750 | NFM | Coventry | Security Co |
| 203.73750 | 195.73750 | NFM | Nationwide | PMR Band III Channel |
| 203.75000 | 195.75000 | NFM | Nationwide | Trunked PMR |
| 203.76250 | 195.76250 | NFM | Midlands | Tec & Development |
| 203.76250 | 195.76250 | NFM | Nationwide | PMR Band III Channel |
| 203.77500 | 195.77500 | NFM | Nationwide | PMR Band III Channel |
| 203.77500 | 195.77500 | NFM | North West | PMR |
| 203.78750 | 195.78750 | NFM | Nationwide | Trunked PMR |
| 203.80000 | 195.80000 | NFM | Nationwide | Trunked PMR |
| 203.80000 | 195.80000 | NFM | Oxford | Stagecoach Witney Bus Depot |
| 203.81250 | 195.81250 | NFM | Cardiff | Buses |
| 203.81250 | 195.81250 | NFM | Nationwide | Trunked PMR |
| 203.81250 | 195.81250 | NFM | Ribble | Buses |
| 203.81250 | 195.81250 | NFM | Sheffield | Main line buses data Ch 49 |
| 203.81250 | 195.81250 | NFM | West Midlands | Buses |
| 203.82500 | 195.82500 | NFM | Manchester | Transport |
| 203.82500 | 195.82500 | NFM | Nationwide | PMR Band III Channel |
| 203.83750 | 195.63750 | NFM | Nationwide | PMR Band III Channel |
| 203.85000 | 195.85000 | NFM | Nationwide | Trunked PMR |

| Base | Mobile | Mode | Location | User and Notes |
|---|---|---|---|---|
| 203.85000 | 195.85000 | NFM | North West | PMR |
| 203.86250 | 195.86250 | NFM | Halton | Buses |
| 203.86250 | 195.86250 | NFM | Nationwide | PMR Band III Channel |
| 203.86250 | 195.86250 | NFM | Oxford | Buses |
| 203.86250 | 195.86250 | NFM | West Yorkshire | Buses |
| 203.86750 | 195.88750 | NFM | Nationwide | PMR Band III Channel |
| 203.87500 | 195.87500 | NFM | Bedfordshire | TNT Parcels trunked |
| 203.87500 | 195.87500 | NFM | Hertfordshire | TNT Parcels trunked |
| 203.87500 | 195.87500 | NFM | Nationwide | PMR Band III Channel |
| 203.87500 | 195.87500 | NFM | North West | PMR |
| 203.90000 | 195.90000 | NFM | Nationwide | Trunked PMR |
| 203.91250 | 195.91250 | NFM | Nationwide | Trunked PMR |
| 203.91250 | 195.91250 | NFM | Reading | Buses |
| 203.91250 | 195.91250 | NFM | Scotland | Highland Scottish Buses |
| 203.91250 | 195.91250 | NFM | West Midlands | Buses |
| 203.91250 | 195.91250 | NFM | West Yorkshire | Buses |
| 203.92500 | 195.92500 | NFM | Nationwide | Trunked PMR |
| 203.93750 | 195.93750 | NFM | Hythe | Nightforce Security |
| 203.93750 | 195.93750 | NFM | Nationwide | PMR Band III Channel |
| 203.95000 | 195.95000 | NFM | Nationwide | Trunked PMR |
| 203.96250 | 195.96250 | NFM | Nationwide | PMR Band III Channel |
| 203.97500 | 195.97500 | NFM | London | Security Company |
| 203.97500 | 195.97500 | NFM | Nationwide | Trunked PMR |
| 203.98750 | 195.98750 | NFM | Nationwide | Trunked PMR |
| 204.00000 | 196.00000 | NFM | Nationwide | Trunked PMR |
| 204.01250 | 196.01250 | NFM | Nationwide | Trunked PMR |
| 204.02500 | 196.02500 | NFM | Nationwide | Trunked PMR |
| 204.03750 | 196.03750 | NFM | Nationwide | PMR Band III Channel |
| 204.05000 | 196.05000 | NFM | Nationwide | Trunked PMR |
| 204.06250 | 196.06250 | NFM | Nationwide | Trunked PMR |
| 204.07500 | 196.07500 | NFM | Nationwide | PMR Band III Channel |
| 204.08750 | 196.08750 | NFM | Nationwide | Trunked PMR |
| 204.10000 | 196.10000 | NFM | Nationwide | Trunked PMR |
| 204.11250 | 196.11250 | NFM | Coventry | MCN Civil Engineers |
| 204.11250 | 196.11250 | NFM | Mid Wales | Railway Repeaters |
| 204.11250 | 196.11250 | NFM | Nationwide | Trunked PMR |
| 204.12500 | 196.12500 | NFM | Nationwide | Trunked PMR |
| 204.13750 | 196.13750 | NFM | Nationwide | Trunked PMR |
| 204.15000 | 196.15000 | NFM | Nationwide | Trunked PMR |
| 204.16250 | 196.16250 | NFM | Nationwide | Trunked PMR |
| 204.17500 | 196.17500 | NFM | Bedfordshire | TNT Parcels trunked |
| 204.17500 | 196.17500 | NFM | Hertfordshire | TNT Parcels trunked |
| 204.17500 | 196.17500 | NFM | Nationwide | PMR Band III Channel |
| 204.18750 | 196.18750 | NFM | Hythe | Nightforce Security |
| 204.18750 | 196.18750 | NFM | Nationwide | Trunked PMR |
| 204.20000 | 196.20000 | NFM | Nationwide | Trunked PMR |
| 204.21250 | 196.21250 | NFM | Nationwide | Trunked PMR |
| 204.22500 | 196.22500 | NFM | Hull | Council Repairs |
| 204.22500 | 196.22500 | NFM | Hull | Doctors On Call |
| 204.22500 | 196.22500 | NFM | Nationwide | PMR Band III Channel |
| 204.23750 | 196.23750 | NFM | Nationwide | Trunked PMR |
| 204.25000 | 196.25000 | NFM | Nationwide | PMR Band III Channel |
| 204.26250 | 196.26250 | NFM | Nationwide | PMR Band III Channel |
| 204.27500 | 196.27500 | NFM | Nationwide | Trunked PMR |
| 204.28750 | 196.28750 | NFM | Nationwide | Trunked PMR |
| 204.28750 | 196.28750 | NFM | South Wales | Rail cab and railway repeater |

| Base | Mobile | Mode | Location | User and Notes |
|------|--------|------|----------|----------------|
| 204.30000 | 196.30000 | NFM | Nationwide | Trunked PMR |
| 204.31250 | 196.31250 | NFM | Nationwide | PMR Band III Channel |
| 204.32500 | 196.32500 | NFM | Nationwide | Trunked PMR |
| 204.33750 | 196.33750 | NFM | Nationwide | Trunked PMR |
| 204.35000 | 196.35000 | NFM | Nationwide | Trunked PMR |
| 204.36250 | 196.36250 | NFM | Nationwide | Trunked PMR |
| 204.37500 | 196.37500 | NFM | Nationwide | Trunked PMR |
| 204.38750 | 196.38750 | NFM | Nationwide | Trunked PMR |
| 204.40000 | 196.40000 | NFM | Liverpool | Electrical engineers |
| 204.40000 | 196.40000 | NFM | Nationwide | Trunked PMR |
| 204.41250 | 196.41250 | NFM | Nationwide | Trunked PMR |
| 204.42500 | 196.42500 | NFM | Nationwide | Trunked PMR |
| 204.43750 | 196.43750 | NFM | Nationwide | Trunked PMR |
| 204.43750 | 196.43750 | NFM | South Wales | Railway cab radio link |
| 204.45000 | 196.45000 | NFM | Nationwide | Trunked PMR |
| 204.46250 | 196.46250 | NFM | London | Paramedico Private Ambulances |
| 204.46250 | 196.46250 | NFM | Nationwide | Trunked PMR |
| 204.47500 | 196.47500 | NFM | Nationwide | Trunked PMR |
| 204.48750 | 196.48750 | NFM | Nationwide | Trunked PMR |
| 204.50000 | 196.50000 | NFM | Nationwide | Trunked PMR |
| 204.51250 | 196.51250 | NFM | Nationwide | Trunked PMR |
| 204.52500 | 196.52500 | NFM | Nationwide | Trunked PMR |
| 204.53750 | 196.53750 | NFM | Nationwide | Trunked PMR |
| 204.55000 | 196.55000 | NFM | Croydon | National Band 3 Ltd. trunked control channel |
| 204.55000 | 196.55000 | NFM | Nationwide | Trunked PMR |
| 204.56250 | 196.56250 | NFM | Nationwide | Trunked PMR |
| 204.57500 | 196.57500 | NFM | Nationwide | Trunked PMR |
| 204.58750 | 196.58750 | NFM | London | Pods ACI Cargo Courier |
| 204.58750 | 196.58750 | NFM | Nationwide | Trunked PMR |
| 204.58750 | 196.58750 | NFM | Tayside | Data Link |
| 204.60000 | 196.60000 | NFM | Nationwide | Trunked PMR |
| 204.61250 | 196.61250 | NFM | Nationwide | Trunked PMR |
| 204.62500 | 196.62500 | NFM | Nationwide | Trunked PMR |
| 204.63750 | 196.63750 | NFM | Nationwide | Trunked PMR |
| 204.65000 | 196.65000 | NFM | Nationwide | Trunked PMR |
| 204.66250 | 196.66250 | NFM | Nationwide | Trunked PMR |
| 204.67500 | 196.67500 | NFM | Nationwide | Trunked PMR |
| 204.68750 | 196.68750 | NFM | Nationwide | Trunked PMR |
| 204.70000 | 196.70000 | NFM | Nationwide | Trunked PMR |
| 204.71250 | 196.71250 | NFM | Birmingham | West Midlands Bus Travel |
| 204.71250 | 196.71250 | NFM | Nationwide | PMR Band III Channel 55 |
| 204.71250 | 196.71250 | NFM | Oxfordshire | Thames Transit |
| 204.71250 | 196.71250 | NFM | Scotland | Tec & Development |
| 204.72500 | 196.72500 | NFM | Nationwide | Trunked PMR |
| 204.73500 | 196.73750 | NFM | South Wales | Railway cab radio link |
| 204.73750 | 196.73750 | NFM | Coventry | Area Security Co |
| 204.73750 | 196.73750 | NFM | Nationwide | Trunked PMR |
| 204.73750 | 196.73750 | NFM | Tayside | Data Link |
| 204.75000 | 196.75000 | NFM | Nationwide | Trunked PMR |
| 204.76250 | 196.76250 | NFM | Birmingham | West Midlands Bus Travel |
| 204.76250 | 196.76250 | NFM | Bristol | Buses |
| 204.76250 | 196.76250 | NFM | London | Buses |
| 204.76250 | 196.76250 | NFM | Manchester | Buses |
| 204.76250 | 196.76250 | NFM | Nationwide | PMR Band III Channel 26 |
| 204.76250 | 196.76250 | NFM | Tyne & Wear | Buses |
| 204.77500 | 196.77500 | NFM | Nationwide | Trunked PMR |

| Base | Mobile | Mode | Location | User and Notes |
|------|--------|------|----------|----------------|
| 204.78750 | 196.78750 | NFM | Nationwide | Trunked PMR |
| 204.80000 | 196.80000 | NFM | Nationwide | Trunked PMR |
| 204.81250 | 196.81250 | NFM | Cleveland | Buses |
| 204.81250 | 196.81250 | NFM | London | London Transport |
| 204.81250 | 196.81250 | NFM | Manchester | GM Buses |
| 204.81250 | 196.81250 | NFM | Midlands | Buses |
| 204.81250 | 196.81250 | NFM | Nationwide | PMR Band III Channel 53 |
| 204.81250 | 196.81250 | NFM | Ribble | Buses |
| 204.82500 | 196.82500 | NFM | Nationwide | Trunked PMR |
| 204.83750 | 196.83750 | NFM | Blackpool | Vehicle Recovery |
| 204.83750 | 196.83750 | NFM | Nationwide | Trunked PMR |
| 204.85000 | 196.85000 | NFM | Garelochead | Railway cab radio link |
| 204.85000 | 196.85000 | NFM | Helensburgh Upper | Railway cab radio link |
| 204.85000 | 196.85000 | NFM | Lochailort | Railway cab radio link |
| 204.85000 | 196.85000 | NFM | Merseyside | Merseyside Electric |
| 204.85000 | 196.85000 | NFM | Nationwide | Railtrack Ch 349 (RETB) |
| 204.85000 | 196.85000 | NFM | Nationwide | Trunked PMR |
| 204.86250 | 196.86250 | NFM | London | London Transport |
| 204.86250 | 196.86250 | NFM | Nationwide | PMR Band III Channel |
| 204.87500 | 196.87500 | NFM | Nationwide | Trunked PMR |
| 204.88750 | 196.88750 | NFM | Nationwide | Trunked PMR |
| 204.88750 | 196.88750 | NFM | South Wales | Railway cab radio link |
| 204.90000 | 196.90000 | NFM | Caersws | Mid Wales Railway Line (RETB) |
| 204.90000 | 196.90000 | NFM | Nationwide | Railtrack Channel 353 (RETB) |
| 204.90000 | 196.90000 | NFM | Nationwide | Trunked PMR |
| 204.90000 | 196.90000 | NFM | Newcastle | Metro Rail System |
| 204.91250 | 196.91250 | NFM | London | London Transport |
| 204.91250 | 196.91250 | NFM | Manchester | GM Buses |
| 204.91250 | 196.91250 | NFM | Nationwide | PMR Band III Channel 29 |
| 204.91250 | 196.91250 | NFM | Tyne & Wear | Buses |
| 204.92500 | 196.92500 | NFM | Nationwide | Trunked PMR |
| 204.92500 | 196.92500 | NFM | South Wales | Rail cab |
| 204.93750 | 196.93750 | NFM | Nationwide | Trunked PMR |
| 204.95000 | 196.95000 | NFM | Ayr | Traincare Depot SPT and ScotRail trains |
| 204.95000 | 196.95000 | NFM | Irvine | Caledonian Paper Mill trains |
| 204.95000 | 196.95000 | NFM | Mauchline | Coal trains |
| 204.95000 | 196.95000 | NFM | Nationwide | Railtrack Channel 357 |
| 204.95000 | 196.95000 | NFM | Paisley | SPT and Ayrline trains |
| 204.95000 | 196.95000 | NFM | Strathclyde | SPT and ScotRail trains |
| 204.95000 | 196.95000 | NFM | Tayside | Data Link |
| 204.96250 | 196.96250 | NFM | Birmingham | West Midlands Bus Travel |
| 204.96250 | 196.96250 | NFM | London | London Transport |
| 204.96250 | 196.96250 | NFM | Manchester | GM Buses |
| 204.96250 | 196.96250 | NFM | Nationwide | PMR Band III Channel 62 |
| 204.96250 | 196.96250 | NFM | Scotland | West Scottish Buses |
| 204.96250 | 196.96250 | NFM | West Riding | Buses |
| 204.97500 | 196.97500 | NFM | Nationwide | Trunked PMR |
| 204.98750 | 196.98750 | NFM | Blackpool | RAC |
| 204.98750 | 196.98750 | NFM | Nationwide | Trunked PMR |
| 205.00000 | 197.00000 | NFM | Nationwide | Railtrack Channel 361 |
| 205.00000 | 197.00000 | NFM | Newport | Railtrack |
| 205.01250 | 197.01250 | NFM | Birmingham | West Midlands Bus Travel |
| 205.01250 | 197.01250 | NFM | Coventry | Buses |
| 205.01250 | 197.01250 | NFM | Coventry | West Tavel |
| 205.01250 | 197.01250 | NFM | Garve | Railway cab radio link |
| 205.01250 | 197.01250 | NFM | London | Capitol Bus |

| Base | Mobile | Mode | Location | User and Notes |
|------|--------|------|----------|----------------|
| 205.01250 | 197.01250 | NFM | London | Buses |
| 205.01250 | 197.01250 | NFM | Nationwide | PMR Band III Channel 10 |
| 205.01250 | 197.01250 | NFM | Portsmouth | Blue Ankiral Buses |
| 205.01250 | 197.01250 | NFM | Sheffield | Don Valley Buses |
| 205.01250 | 197.01250 | NFM | Sheffield | S. Yorkshire Transport (Greenland) |
| 205.02500 | 197.02500 | NFM | Nationwide | Trunked PMR |
| 205.03750 | 197.03750 | NFM | Nationwide | Trunked PMR |
| 205.03750 | 197.03750 | NFM | Tayside | Data Link |
| 205.05000 | 197.05000 | NFM | Achasheen | Railway cab radio link |
| 205.05000 | 197.05000 | NFM | Achnashellach | Railway cab radio link |
| 205.05000 | 197.05000 | NFM | Arrochar | Railway cab radio link |
| 205.05000 | 197.05000 | NFM | Attadale | Railway cab radio link |
| 205.05000 | 197.05000 | NFM | Duirinish | Railway cab radio link |
| 205.05000 | 197.05000 | NFM | Duncraig | Railway cab radio link |
| 205.05000 | 197.05000 | NFM | Fort William | Railtrack |
| 205.05000 | 197.05000 | NFM | Glen Douglas (Loop) | Railway cab radio link |
| 205.05000 | 197.05000 | NFM | Glenfinnan | Railway cab radio link |
| 205.05000 | 197.05000 | NFM | Kyle of Lochalsh | Railway cab radio link |
| 205.05000 | 197.05000 | NFM | Locheilside | Railway cab radio link |
| 205.05000 | 197.05000 | NFM | London | Buses |
| 205.05000 | 197.05000 | NFM | Mallaig | Railway cab radio link |
| 205.05000 | 197.05000 | NFM | Nationwide | Railtrack Channel 365 (RETB) |
| 205.05000 | 197.05000 | NFM | Nationwide | Trunked PMR |
| 205.05000 | 197.05000 | NFM | Plockton | Railway cab radio link |
| 205.05000 | 197.05000 | NFM | Strathcarron | Railway cab radio link |
| 205.05000 | 197.05000 | NFM | Stromferry | Railway cab radio link |
| 205.06250 | 197.06250 | NFM | London | Busses |
| 205.06250 | 197.06250 | NFM | Manchester | City Bus Inspectors |
| 205.06250 | 197.06250 | NFM | Nationwide | PMR Band III Channel 57 |
| 205.06250 | 197.06250 | NFM | Plymouth | City Buses |
| 205.06250 | 197.06250 | NFM | South | Tec & Development. |
| 205.07500 | 197.07500 | NFM | Nationwide | Trunked PMR |
| 205.08750 | 197.08750 | NFM | Nationwide | Trunked PMR |
| 205.10000 | 197.10000 | NFM | Arisaig | Railway cab radio link |
| 205.10000 | 197.10000 | NFM | Beasdale | Railway cab radio link |
| 205.10000 | 197.10000 | NFM | Corrour | Railway cab radio link |
| 205.10000 | 197.10000 | NFM | Dingwall | Railway cab radio link |
| 205.10000 | 197.10000 | NFM | Inverness | Railway cab radio link |
| 205.10000 | 197.10000 | NFM | Morar | Railway cab radio link |
| 205.10000 | 197.10000 | NFM | Muir of Ord | Railway cab radio link |
| 205.10000 | 197.10000 | NFM | Nationwide | Railtrack Channel 369 (RETB) |
| 205.10000 | 197.10000 | NFM | Nationwide | Trunked PMR |
| 205.10000 | 197.10000 | NFM | Roy Bridge | Railway cab radio link |
| 205.10000 | 197.10000 | NFM | South Wales | Railway cab radio link |
| 205.10000 | 197.10000 | NFM | Tulloch | Railway cab radio link |
| 205.11250 | 197.01250 | NFM | Nationwide | Bus National Emergency Channel |
| 205.11250 | 197.01250 | NFM | Nationwide | Trunked PMR |
| 205.12500 | 197.12500 | NFM | Nationwide | Trunked PMR |
| 205.13750 | 197.13750 | NFM | Nationwide | Trunked PMR |
| 205.15000 | 197.15000 | NFM | Bridge of Orchy | Railway cab radio link |
| 205.15000 | 197.15000 | NFM | Nationwide | Railtrack Cab Channel 373 (RETB) |
| 205.15000 | 197.15000 | NFM | Newtown | Mid Wales Railway Line (RETB) |
| 205.15000 | 197.15000 | NFM | Rannoch | Railway cab radio link |
| 205.15000 | 197.15000 | NFM | Shrewsbury | Mid Wales Railway Line (RETB) |
| 205.15000 | 197.15000 | NFM | Sutton Bridge Junction | MWL (RETB) |
| 205.15000 | 197.15000 | NFM | Welshpool | Mid Wales Railway Line (RETB) |

| Base | Mobile | Mode | Location | User and Notes |
|---|---|---|---|---|
| 205.15000 | 197.15000 | NFM | Westbury | Mid Wales Railway Line (RETB) |
| 205.16250 | 197.16250 | NFM | Nationwide | Trunked PMR |
| 205.17500 | 197.17500 | NFM | Nationwide | Trunked PMR |
| 205.18750 | 197.18750 | NFM | Nationwide | Trunked PMR |
| 205.18750 | 197.18750 | NFM | Tayside | Data Link |
| 205.20000 | 197.20000 | NFM | Nationwide | Railtrack Channel 377(early warning) |
| 205.20000 | 197.20000 | NFM | Newport | Railtrack |
| 205.21250 | 197.21250 | NFM | Nationwide | Trunked PMR |
| 205.22500 | 197.22500 | NFM | Nationwide | Trunked PMR |
| 205.23150 | 197.23750 | NFM | Nationwide | Trunked PMR |
| 205.25000 | 197.25000 | NFM | Nationwide | Railtrack Channel 381 (early warning) |
| 205.26250 | 197.26250 | NFM | Nationwide | Trunked PMR |
| 205.27500 | 197.27500 | NFM | Nationwide | Trunked PMR |
| 205.28750 | 197.28750 | NFM | Nationwide | Trunked PMR |
| 205.30000 | 197.30000 | NFM | Nationwide | Railtrack Channel 385 (early warning) |
| 205.31250 | 197.31250 | NFM | Nationwide | PMR Band III Channel |
| 205.32500 | 197.32500 | NFM | Nationwide | PMR Band III Channel |
| 205.33750 | 197.33750 | NFM | Nationwide | Trunked PMR |
| 205.35000 | 197.35000 | NFM | Aberystwyth | Mid Wales Railway Line (RETB) |
| 205.35000 | 197.35000 | NFM | Borth | Mid Wales Railway Line (RETB) |
| 205.35000 | 197.35000 | NFM | Dovey Junction | MWL (RETB) |
| 205.35000 | 197.35000 | NFM | Nationwide | Railtrack Cab Channel 389 (RFTB) |
| 205.35000 | 198.35000 | NFM | Aberystwyth | Railway cab radio link |
| 205.36250 | 197.36250 | NFM | Manchester | Transport |
| 205.36250 | 197.36250 | NFM | Nationwide | Trunked PMR |
| 205.37500 | 197.37500 | NFM | Nationwide | Trunked PMR |
| 205.38750 | 197.38750 | NFM | Nationwide | Trunked PMR |
| 205.40000 | 197.40000 | NFM | Ardlui | Railway cab radio link |
| 205.40000 | 197.40000 | NFM | Caersws | Railway cab radio link |
| 205.40000 | 197.40000 | NFM | Machynlleth | Mid Wales Railway Line (RETB) |
| 205.40000 | 197.40000 | NFM | Nationwide | Railtrack Channel 393 (RETB) |
| 205.40000 | 197.40000 | NFM | Nationwide | Trunked PMR |
| 205.40000 | 197.40000 | NFM | Newtown | Mid Wales Railway Line (RETB) |
| 205.40000 | 197.40000 | NFM | Shrewsbury | Mid Wales Railway Line (RETB) |
| 205.40000 | 197.40000 | NFM | Sutton Bridge Junction | Mid Wales Railway Line (RETB) |
| 205.40000 | 197.40000 | NFM | Welshpool | Mid Wales Railway Line (RETB) |
| 205.40000 | 197.40000 | NFM | Westbury | Mid Wales Railway Line (RETB) |
| 205.41250 | 197.41250 | NFM | Nationwide | Trunked PMR |
| 205.42500 | 197.42500 | NFM | Nationwide | Trunked PMR |
| 205.42500 | 197.42500 | NFM | Weymouth | Heavy Breakdown Recovery |
| 205.43750 | 197.43750 | NFM | Nationwide | Trunked PMR |
| 205.45000 | 197.45000 | NFM | Nationwide | Railtrack Channel 397 |
| 205.45000 | 197.45000 | NFM | Nationwide | Trunked PMR |
| 205.46250 | 197.46250 | NFM | Brighton | Buses |
| 205.46250 | 197.46250 | NFM | Crosville | Buses |
| 205.46250 | 197.46250 | NFM | Nationwide | Trunked PMR |
| 205.46250 | 197.46250 | NFM | Preston | Buses |
| 205.46250 | 197.46250 | NFM | Scotland | Midland Scottish Buses |
| 205.46250 | 197.46250 | NFM | Southdown | Buses |
| 205.46250 | 205.46250 | NFM | Retford | Police Pub Link |
| 205.47500 | 197.47500 | NFM | Nationwide | Trunked PMR |
| 205.48750 | 197.48750 | NFM | Nationwide | Trunked PMR |
| 205.50000 | 197.50000 | NFM | Nationwide | Railtrack Channel 401 |
| 205.50000 | 197.50000 | NFM | Nationwide | Trunked PMR |
| 205.51250 | 197.51250 | NFM | Central Scotland | Buses |
| 205.51250 | 197.51250 | NFM | Fareham | Buses |

| Base | Mobile | Mode | Location | User and Notes |
|------|--------|------|----------|----------------|
| 205.51250 | 197.51250 | NFM | Gosport | Buses |
| 205.51250 | 197.51250 | NFM | Merseyside | Buses |
| 205.51250 | 197.51250 | NFM | Nationwide | Trunked PMR |
| 205.52500 | 197.52500 | NFM | Nationwide | Trunked PMR |
| 205.53750 | 197.53750 | NFM | Nationwide | Trunked PMR |
| 205.55000 | 197.55000 | NFM | Nationwide | Railtrack Channel 405 |
| 205.55000 | 197.55000 | NFM | Nationwide | Trunked PMR |
| 205.56250 | 197.56250 | NFM | Colchester | Buses |
| 205.56250 | 197.56250 | NFM | Crosville | Buses |
| 205.56250 | 197.56250 | NFM | Lothian | Buses |
| 205.56250 | 197.56250 | NFM | Manchester | GM Buses |
| 205.56250 | 197.56250 | NFM | Nationwide | PMR Band III Channel |
| 205.56250 | 197.56250 | NFM | North West | PMR |
| 205.57500 | 197.57500 | NFM | Nationwide | Trunked PMR |
| 205.58750 | 197.58750 | NFM | Nationwide | Railtrack Channel |
| 205.60000 | 197.60000 | NFM | Nationwide | Railtrack Channel 409 |
| 205.60000 | 197.60000 | NFM | Nationwide | Trunked PMR |
| 205.61250 | 197.61250 | NFM | Crosville | Buses |
| 205.61250 | 197.61250 | NFM | Eastbourne | Buses |
| 205.61250 | 197.61250 | NFM | Ipswich | Buses |
| 205.61250 | 197.61250 | NFM | Manchester | GM Buses |
| 205.61250 | 197.61250 | NFM | Nationwide | PMR Band III Channel 9 |
| 205.61250 | 197.61250 | NFM | Ribble | Buses |
| 205.62500 | 197.62500 | NFM | Nationwide | Trunked PMR |
| 205.63750 | 197.63750 | NFM | Nationwide | Trunked PMR |
| 205.65000 | 197.65000 | NFM | Darsham | Railway cab radio link |
| 205.65000 | 197.65000 | NFM | Nationwide | Railtrack Channel 413 |
| 205.65000 | 197.65000 | NFM | Saxmundham | Railway cab radio link |
| 205.66250 | 197.66250 | NFM | Bournemouth | Buses |
| 205.66250 | 197.66250 | NFM | London | Buses |
| 205.66250 | 197.66250 | NFM | Merseyside | Buses |
| 205.66250 | 197.66250 | NFM | Nationwide | Trunked PMR |
| 205.66250 | 197.66250 | NFM | Scotland | East Scottish Buses |
| 205.67500 | 197.67500 | NFM | Nationwide | Railtrack Channel 415 (emergency broadcasts) |
| 205.67500 | 197.67500 | NFM | Nationwide | Trunked PMR |
| 205.68750 | 197.68750 | NFM | Nationwide | Trunked PMR |
| 205.70000 | 197.70000 | NFM | Nationwide | Railtrack Channel 417 |
| 205.71250 | 197.71200 | NFM | Oldham | Supertune Factors |
| 205.71250 | 197.71250 | NFM | Crosville | Buses |
| 205.71250 | 197.71250 | NFM | Lothian | Buses |
| 205.71250 | 197.71250 | NFM | Manchester | GM Buses |
| 205.71250 | 197.71250 | NFM | Nationwide | PMR Band III Channel 17 |
| 205.71250 | 197.71250 | NFM | Portmouth | Buses |
| 205.72500 | 197.72500 | NFM | Nationwide | Railtrack Channel 419 (control) |
| 205.72500 | 197.72500 | NFM | Nationwlde | Trunked PMR |
| 205.73750 | 197.73750 | NFM | Hythe | Nightforce Security |
| 205.73750 | 197.73750 | NFM | Nationwide | PMR Band III Channel |
| 205.75000 | 197.75000 | NFM | Nationwide | Railtrack Channel 421 |
| 205.75000 | 197.75000 | NFM | South Wales | Railway cab radio link |
| 205.76250 | 197.76250 | NFM | East Yorkshire | Buses |
| 205.76250 | 197.76250 | NFM | Isle of Wight | Buses |
| 205.76250 | 197.76250 | NFM | Manchester | Buses |
| 205.76250 | 197.76250 | NFM | Nationwide | PMR Band III Channel |
| 205.77500 | 197.77500 | NFM | Nationwide | Trunked PMR |
| 205.78750 | 197.78750 | NFM | Nationwide | Trunked PMR |
| 205.80000 | 197.80000 | NFM | Brampton | Railway cab radio link |

| Base | Mobile | Mode | Location | User and Notes |
|------|--------|------|----------|----------------|
| 205.80000 | 197.80000 | NFM | Eccles | Railway cab radio link |
| 205.80000 | 197.80000 | NFM | Nationwide | Railtrack Channel 425 (speaking clock) |
| 205.81250 | 197.81250 | NFM | Birmingham | West Midlands Bus Travel |
| 205.81250 | 197.81250 | NFM | Nationwide | National Express |
| 205.81250 | 197.81250 | NFM | Nationwide | PMR Band III Channel 14 |
| 205.82500 | 197.82500 | NFM | London | TNT Couriers |
| 205.82500 | 197.82500 | NFM | London | Thamesway Buses |
| 205.82500 | 197.82500 | NFM | Nationwide | Trunked PMR |
| 205.83750 | 197.83750 | NFM | Nationwide | Railtrack Channel 428 (control) |
| 205.83750 | 197.83750 | NFM | Nationwide | Trunked PMR |
| 205.83750 | 197.83750 | NFM | Tayside | Data Link |
| 205.85000 | 197.85000 | NFM | Nationwide | Railtrack |
| 205.85000 | 197.85000 | NFM | West Yorkshire | Trunked Radio System |
| 205.86250 | 197.86250 | NFM | Nationwide | National Express |
| 205.86250 | 197.86250 | NFM | Nationwide | PMR Band III Channel |
| 205.87500 | 197.87500 | NFM | Nationwide | Trunked PMR |
| 205.88750 | 197.88750 | NFM | Nationwide | Trunked PMR |
| 205.88750 | 197.88750 | NFM | Taunton | Data |
| 205.90000 | 197.90000 | NFM | London | Thamesway Buses |
| 205.90000 | 197.90000 | NFM | Nationwide | Railtrack Channel 433 |
| 205.90000 | 197.90000 | NFM | Westerfield | Railway cab radio link |
| 205.90000 | 197.90000 | NFM | Woodbridge | Railway oab radio link |
| 205.91250 | 197.91250 | NFM | Gt. Yarmouth | Buses |
| 205.91250 | 197.91250 | NFM | London | Thamesway Buses |
| 205.91250 | 197.91250 | NFM | Merseyside | Buses |
| 205.91250 | 197.91250 | NFM | Nationwide | Trunked PMR |
| 205.91250 | 197.91250 | NFM | Southampton | Buses |
| 205.92500 | 197.92500 | NFM | Nationwide | Trunked PMR |
| 205.93750 | 197.93750 | NFM | Nationwide | Trunked PMR |
| 205.93750 | 197.93750 | NFM | Tayside | Data Link |
| 205.95000 | 197.75000 | NFM | Dovey Junction | Railway cab radio link |
| 205.95000 | 197.95000 | NFM | Banavie | Railway cab radio link |
| 205.95000 | 197.95000 | NFM | Barmouth | Railway cab radio link |
| 205.95000 | 197.95000 | NFM | Fort William | Railway cab radio link |
| 205.95000 | 197.95000 | NFM | Llanaber | Railway cab radio link |
| 205.95000 | 197.95000 | NFM | Loch Eil O/B | Railway cab radio link |
| 205.95000 | 197.95000 | NFM | Nationwide | Railtrack Channel 437 (speaking clock) (RETB) |
| 205.95000 | 197.95000 | NFM | Tywtn | Railway cab radio link |
| 205.96250 | 197.96250 | NFM | Manchester | GM Buses |
| 205.96250 | 197.96250 | NFM | Nationwide | PMR Band III Channel |
| 205.97500 | 197.97500 | NFM | Nationwide | Trunked PMR |
| 205.98750 | 197.98750 | NFM | Nationwide | Trunked PMR |
| 206.00000 | 198.00000 | NFM | Barmouth | Railway cab radio link |
| 206.00000 | 198.00000 | NFM | Braemar | Railway cab radio link |
| 206.00000 | 198.00000 | NFM | Nationwide | Railtrack Channel 441 |
| 206.00000 | 198.00000 | NFM | Nationwide | Trunked PMR |
| 206.00000 | 198.00000 | NFM | Oulton Broad South | Railway cab radio link |
| 206.01250 | 198.01250 | NFM | Birmingham | West Midlands Bus Travel |
| 206.01250 | 198.01250 | NFM | Edinburgh | SMT Buses |
| 206.01250 | 198.01250 | NFM | Kent, east | Buses |
| 206.01250 | 198.01250 | NFM | Merseyside | Buses |
| 206.01250 | 198.01250 | NFM | Nationwide | Trunked PMR |
| 206.01250 | 198.01250 | NFM | South Wales | Buses |
| 206.02500 | 198.02500 | NFM | Nationwide | Trunked PMR |
| 206.03750 | 198.03750 | NFM | Nationwide | Trunked PMR |
| 206.06250 | 198.06250 | NFM | Birmingham | West Midlands Bus Travel |

| Base | Mobile | Mode | Location | User and Notes |
|------|--------|------|----------|----------------|
| 206.06250 | 198.06250 | NFM | Blackpool | Buses |
| 206.06250 | 198.06250 | NFM | Glasgow | Bus Company |
| 206.06250 | 198.06250 | NFM | Nationwide | Trunked PMR |
| 206.06250 | 198.06250 | NFM | Southdown | Buses |
| 206.06250 | 198.06250 | NFM | Strathclyde | Buses |
| 206.06250 | 198.06250 | NFM | Wales | Buses |
| 206.07500 | 198.07500 | NFM | Nationwide | Trunked PMR |
| 206.08750 | 198.08750 | NFM | Nationwide | Trunked PMR |
| 206.08750 | 198.08750 | NFM | South Wales | Railway cab radio link |
| 206.10000 | 198.10000 | NFM | Brecon | Data |
| 206.10000 | 198.10000 | NFM | London | Data |
| 206.10000 | 198.10000 | NFM | Manchester | Data |
| 206.10000 | 198.10000 | NFM | Nationwide | Railtrack Channel 449 (speaking clock) (RETB) |
| 206.10000 | 198.10000 | NFM | Nationwide | Trunked PMR |
| 206.11250 | 198.11250 | NFM | Merseyside | Buses |
| 206.11250 | 198.11250 | NFM | Nationwide | Trunked PMR |
| 206.11250 | 198.11250 | NFM | Southdown | Buses |
| 206.11250 | 198.11250 | NFM | Strathclyde | Buses |
| 206.12500 | 198.12500 | NFM | Nationwide | Trunked PMR |
| 206.13750 | 198.13750 | NFM | Nationwide | Trunked PMR |
| 206.15000 | 198.15000 | NFM | Ayr | Traincare and EWS |
| 206.15000 | 198.15000 | NFM | Glasgow | Train divers |
| 206.15000 | 198.15000 | NFM | Harlech | Railway cab radio link |
| 206.15000 | 198.15000 | NFM | Largs | Train drivers |
| 206.15000 | 198.15000 | NFM | Nationwide | Railtrack Channel 453 |
| 206.15000 | 198.15000 | NFM | Penychain | Railway cab radio link |
| 206.15000 | 198.15000 | NFM | Portmadoc | Railway cab radio link |
| 206.15000 | 198.15000 | NFM | Pwllheli | Railway cab radio link |
| 206.15000 | 198.15000 | NFM | Stranraer | Train drivers |
| 206.15000 | 198.15000 | NFM | Strathclyde | EWS Hunterstone Terminal |
| 206.15000 | 198.15000 | NFM | Tayside | Data Link |
| 206.16250 | 198.16250 | NFM | Birmingham | West Midlands Bus Travel |
| 206.16250 | 198.16250 | NFM | Bristol | Lawrence Hill Buses Control |
| 206.16250 | 198.16250 | NFM | Bristol | City Line Buses (Minibuses) |
| 206.16250 | 198.16250 | NFM | London | Busses |
| 206.16250 | 198.16250 | NFM | London | London Transport Talking Clock |
| 206.16250 | 198.16250 | NFM | Manchester | GM Bus Inspectors |
| 206.16250 | 198.16250 | NFM | Manchester | Northern General. |
| 206.16250 | 198.16250 | NFM | Nationwide | PMR Band III Channel |
| 206.17500 | 198.17500 | NFM | Nationwide | Trunked PMR Ch 455 |
| 206.18750 | 198.18750 | NFM | Nationwide | Trunked PMR Ch 456 |
| 206.20000 | 198.18750 | NFM | Glasgow | First Glasgow Buses |
| 206.20000 | 198.20000 | NFM | Nationwide | Railtrack Ch 28 |
| 206.21250 | 198.21250 | NFM | Birmingham | West Midlands Bus Travel |
| 206.21250 | 198.21250 | NFM | London | London Transport Stanford Hill |
| 206.21250 | 198.21250 | NFM | Manchester | GM Buses |
| 206.25000 | 198.25000 | NFM | London, Waterloo Station | Eurostar data |
| 206.25000 | 198.25000 | NFM | Nationwide | Railtrack Channel 461(control) |
| 206.26250 | 198.26250 | NFM | Birmingham | West Midlands Bus Travel |
| 206.26250 | 198.26250 | NFM | London | London Transport Stockwell |
| 206.27500 | 198.27500 | NFM | Bedfordshire | TNT Parcels trunked |
| 206.27500 | 198.27500 | NFM | Hertfordshire | TNT Parcels trunked |
| 206.28750 | 198.28750 | NFM | Ayr | South Ayrshire Council Bin Lorries |
| 206.30000 | 198.30000 | NFM | Nationwide | Railtrack Channel 465 |
| 206.33750 | 195.33700 | NFM | North West England | PMR |
| 206.35000 | 198.35000 | NFM | Dovey Junction | Railway cab radio link |

| Base | Mobile | Mode | Location | User and Notes |
|------|--------|------|----------|----------------|
| 206.40000 | 195.40000 | NFM | Kent | BFI Waste Services |
| 206.42500 | 198.42500 | NFM | Bedfordshire | TNT Parcels trunked |
| 206.42500 | 198.42500 | NFM | Hertfordshire | TNT Parcels trunked |
| 206.45000 | 198.45000 | NFM | Isle Of Sheppey | Railtrack |
| 206.51250 | 198.51250 | NFM | Manchester | Lorries |
| 206.52500 | 198.52500 | NFM | Stockport | Engineers |
| 206.57500 | 198.57500 | NFM | Bedfordshire | TNT Parcels trunked |
| 206.57500 | 198.57500 | NFM | Hertfordshire | TNT Parcels trunked |
| 206.57500 | 206.57500 | FM | Cambridge | Skip Hire Company |
| 206.58750 | 198.58750 | NFM | North West England | PMR |
| 206.63750 | 198.63750 | NFM | Eastbourne | Hobbs Recovery |
| 206.66250 | 198.66250 | NFM | North West England | PMR |
| 206.67500 | 198.67500 | NFM | North West England | PMR |
| 206.72500 | 198.72500 | NFM | Bedfordshire | TNT Parcels trunked |
| 206.72500 | 198.72500 | NFM | Hertfordshire | TNT Parcels trunked |
| 206.76250 | 198.76250 | NFM | London | Medicall |
| 206.76250 | 198.76250 | NFM | Stockport | PMR |
| 206.87500 | 198.87500 | NFM | Bedfordshire | TNT Parcels trunked |
| 206.87500 | 198.87500 | NFM | Hertfordshire | TNT Parcels trunked |
| 206.88750 | 198.88750 | NFM | North West England | PMR |
| 206.91250 | 198.91250 | NFM | London, Wimbledon | DHL Couriers |
| 206.91250 | 198.91250 | NFM | Macclesfield | Delivery |
| 207.02500 | 199.02500 | NFM | Bedfordshire | TNT Parcels trunked |
| 207.02500 | 199.02500 | NFM | Hertfordshire | TNT Parcels trunked |
| 207.05000 | | NFM | London | Securiplan Security |
| 207.43750 | | NFM | London | Christian Salveson Haulage |

## 207.5000 - 208.5000 MHz    BROADCASTING LINKS

| Base | Mobile | Mode | Location | User and Notes |
|------|--------|------|----------|----------------|
| 207.700 | | WFM | Nationwide | JFMG Radio Mic |
| 207.900 | | WFM | Nationwide | JFMG News Gathering Radio Mic |
| 207.900 | | WFM | Nationwide | JFMG Radio Mic |
| 208.100 | | WFM | Nationwide | JFMG Radio Mic |
| 208.300 | | NFM | Jersey | BBC Radio Jersey |
| 208.300 | | NFM | Liverpool | Mecca Bingo radio mic |
| 208.300 | | WFM | Nationwide | JFMG Radio Mic mobile Ch. ML2 |
| 208.400 | | NFM | Liverpool | Mecca Bingo radio mic |

## 208.500 - 224.500 MHz    OUTSIDE BROADCASTS

| Base | Mobile | Mode | Location | User and Notes |
|------|--------|------|----------|----------------|
| 208.50000 | | NFM | Liverpool | Mecca Bingo radio mic |
| 208.60000 | | NFM | Nationwide | BBC Radio 1 Roadshow Mics |
| 208.60000 | | WFM | Nationwide | BBC Antiques Roadshow Mics |
| 208.60000 | | WFM | Nationwide | JFMG Radio Mic BBC Ch.11B |
| 208.70000 | | NFM | Liverpool | Mecca Bingo radio mic |
| 208.80000 | | WFM | Nationwide | JFMG Radio Mic GMTV Ch.13D |
| 208.80000 | | NFM | Nationwide | ITV Radio Microphone |
| 209.00000 | | WFM | Nationwide | JFMG Radio Mic BBC Ch.12B |
| 209.00000 | | NFM | Nationwide | BBC Radio Microphone |
| 209.15000 | | NFM | Jersey | PC Gartmore Speech |
| 211.91875 | | WFM | Nationwide | JFMG area talkback mobile |
| 212.15000 | | WFM | London | BBC O/B |
| 212.19375 | | WFM | Nationwide | JFMG area talkback mobile |
| 212.20000 | | NFM | Wolverhampton | Beacon Radio O/B |
| 213.30000 | | WFM | London | Towndown Radio Feeder |
| 213.87500 | | NFM | Silverstone | BBV Outside Broadcasts |
| 213.95000 | | WFM | London | BBC Radio Car O/B |

| Base | Mobile | Mode | Location | User and Notes |
|------|--------|------|----------|----------------|
| 214.02500 | | NFM | Castle Donington | Grand Prix Radio O/B Link |
| 214.10000 | | WFM | London | BBC Radio Car O/B |
| 215.26875 | | WFM | Nationwide | JFMG temp audio point to point portable |
| 215.49375 | | WFM | Nationwide | JFMG temp audio point to point portable |
| 216.10000 | | NFM | Liverpool | Mecca Bingo radio mic |
| 216.10000 | | WFM | Nationwide | JFMG Radio Mic mobile Ch.ML3 |
| 216.20000 | | NFM | Liverpool | Mecca Bingo radio mic |
| 216.30000 | | NFM | Liverpool | Mecca Bingo radio mic |
| 216.30000 | | WFM | Nationwide | JFMG Radio Mic |
| 216.40000 | | NFM | Liverpool | Mecca Bingo radio mic |
| 216.60000 | | WFM | Nationwide | JFMG Radio Mic ITV Ch.12A |
| 216.80000 | | WFM | Nationwide | BBC Antiques Roadshow Mics |
| 216.80000 | | WFM | Nationwide | JFMG Radio Mic BBC Ch.13B |
| 217.00000 | | WFM | Nationwide | JFMG Radio Mic ITV Ch.13A |
| 224.00625 | | WFM | Nationwide | JFMG portable audio links |
| 224.10000 | | NFM | Sheffield | BBC Radio Sheffield Outside B'casts |
| 224.21810 | | USB | Scotland | BBC Studio Feed |
| 224.23125 | | NFM | Bristol | BBC O/B Talkback |
| 224.23200 | | NFM | Scotland | BBC Clean Feed from Glasgow |
| 224.49375 | | WFM | Nationwide | JFMG portable audio links |

## 225.000 - 400.000 MHz    NATO COMMUNICATIONS  25 KHZ

| Base | Mobile | Mode | Location | User and Notes |
|------|--------|------|----------|----------------|
| 225.200 | | AM | Nationwide | RAF Discrete |
| 225.750 | | AM | Nationwide | Turkish Star 5 Air Display Team |
| 226.600 | | AM | English Channel | Royal Navy |
| 230.050 | | AM | RAF Buchan | Air Defence Region Ops |
| 230.050 | | AM | RAF West Drayton | London Military (Dover/Lydd) |
| 230.150 | | AM | RAF Boulmer | Air Defence Region Ops |
| 230.600 | | AM | Nationwide | Air Defence Region |
| 230.650 | | AM | Nationwide | RAF AWACS Ops |
| 231.075 | | AM | Nationwide | Air Defence Region |
| 231.250 | | AM | Nationwide | Air Defence Region |
| 231.350 | | AM | Nationwide | USAF Ops |
| 231.375 | | AM | RAF Valley | 4FTS Air-to-Air |
| 231.550 | | AM | RAF Buchan | Air Defence Region Ops |
| 231.600 | | AM | Nationwide | NATO Air-Air |
| 231.625 | | AM | RAF West Drayton | London Military (Pole Hill/Irish Sea) |
| 231.975 | | AM | RAF West Drayton | London Military (Seaford/Hurn) |
| 232.075 | | AM | Donna Nook | Range Secondary |
| 232.300 | | AM | Nationwide | AWACS Ops |
| 232.350 | | AM | RAF Neatishead | Air Defence Region Ops |
| 232.550 | | AM | RAF Neatishead | Air Defence Region Ops |
| 232.700 | | AM | RAF Neatishead | Air Defence Region Ops |
| 233.000 | | AM | Royal Navy | Ship-Air |
| 233.150 | | AM | RAF Portreath | Air Defence Region Ops |
| 233.200 | | AM | Royal Navy | Ship-Air |
| 233.700 | | AM | RAF Mildenhall | USAF Air-Air |
| 233.800 | | AM | RAF West Drayton | London Military (London Upper) |
| 233.925 | | AM | English Channel | Royal Navy |
| 234.650 | | AM | Cumbria | RAF Low Flying Air-Air |
| 234.650 | | AM | Nationwide | RAF AWACS Ops |
| 234.900 | | AM | Nationwide | RAF Volmet |
| 235.050 | | AM | RAF West Drayton | London Military (London Upper) |
| 235.250 | | AM | Nationwide | USAF Displays |
| 237.500 | | NFM | Nationwide | Dynamic Sciences Surv. |
| 237.850 | | AM | HMS Invincible | Air-Deck |

# Tuning in the Military
## by William K. Armstrong

The recent war in the Balkans gave us all an insight into the mechanics of war, but for some, it was an insight that few are rewarded with. Military radio enthusiasts in Europe, particularly those in Italy and Greece, were given the rare opportunity of tuning in a war on UHF. Several of these listeners recorded air-to-air conversations between fighters and AWACS aircraft and made them available to the world through the Internet. For those who have heard them, there is one fact that stands out over all others: what you could hear was exactly the same type of traffic that is heard during peacetime exercises, only this time the targets were real and the weapons were hot.

## What Can I Hear?

Military aviation communications on the UHF can roughly be divided into two distinct groups: air traffic control and tactical communications. It may be surprising, but even though the majority of military flights operate autonomously, they still require a degree of air traffic control, for example, when joining or crossing airways. However, by far the largest use of the UHF radio spectrum is for tactical communications. Such communications can be heard almost daily as fighters, such as Tornado F3s from RAF Coningsby, Leeming and Leuchars engage in Air Combat Training exercises up and down the country. Most of these missions are co-ordinated from ground by Ground Control Intercept sites, such as those at RAF Buchan and Neatishead, or by an E3D AWACS from RAF Waddington orbiting high over the exercise area. Communications are brief, precise and filled with nail biting tension. You will actually hear fighters being vectored onto targets, and ultimately the code word "Splash" will be passed as the interception results in a kill. Tuning in an AWACS is the ambition of many listeners for it is the AWACS that often co-ordinates the entire exercise, arranging frequency changes, controlling the Link-11 tactical digital information link and vectoring missions to their tasked patrol areas.

Probably the most visible form of military aviation is Low Level Flying. Because of their low altitude, these missions rarely talk to anyone simply because no one can hear them. Instead they talk to each other on discreet air-to-air frequencies where they discuss bombing runs and scores, tactics and the maintenance states of each aircraft. Many of these missions focus on the half dozen or so bombing ranges around the country and their frequencies can be found on pages 312 to 337. Once the mission pulls up from its Low Level run, it generally checks in on the only air traffic control frequency for a radar service back to base.

Not all military communications are as tense as this! You might as easily pick up a flight of USAF F16s looking for a tanker to carry out an air-to-air refuelling exercise or a lone Netherlands Royal Navy P3 Orion on a navigation exercise around the UK. Of course, that might all be straight forward during the day, but the military can just as easily as active at night!

Over the past year, several Internet resources are been developed for British military enthusiasts. The first of these was the British Military Communications Homepage at www.link11.freeserve.co.uk. This is one site that is worth watching as it has in the past posted up-to-the-minute information on NATO exercises, frequency and call sign changes and a variety of data modes. It has also run a Question and Answer column that allows you to post questions that other readers can then contribute to. Finally, British military communications enthusiasts have a newsgroup at militarycomms@onelist.com. The group focuses on tactical British communications (Army, Royal Navy and Royal Air Force) and regularly swaps information about exercises and frequencies. If you are starting out in the military communications hobby, this might just be the place to begin. Questions from novices are welcomed as is input from anyone with something to say.

## Air Displays

Finally, let's take a quick look at Air Displays.  It is often seen as the most overt example of scanning since so many enthusiasts go to airshows armed with their scanners to tune in the air-to-air commands of the display leader.

### Display Team Frequencies

| | |
|---|---|
| AAC Blue Eagles Display Team | 131.950 (S), 135.975, 136.975(Ch1), 380.2 MHz |
| Aero Stars Aerobatic Team | 122.475 MHz (Manual 2) |
| Air Display Team Frecce Tricolori | 123.475 MHz |
| Air-Air Display Co-ordination | 118.0 MHz |
| Aquilla Spanish Air Display Team | 130.3, 130.5, 252.5 MHz |
| Battle of Britain Flight | 120.8 MHz |
| Chilean Air Force Display Team | 136.175 MHz |
| Crunchie Flight Team | 118.0 MHz |
| Dutch F-16 Display Team | 122.275, 130.9, 316.9 MHz |
| Green March Moroccan Display Team | 135.925, 135.975 MHz |
| Marlboro Aerobatic Display | 118.0 MHz |
| Navy Gazelle Duo | 136.975 MHz |
| Patroulle Swisse Air Display Team | 370.1 MHz |
| Patroulle de Francais Air Display Team | 242.6, 242.650, 242.850 MHz |
| RAF Falcons Parachutists | 255.1 MHz |
| Red Arrows Air Display Team | 242.0, 242.050, 242.2, 243.450, 377.6 MHz |
| Red Star Racing Yaks Team | 123.350 MHz |
| Sharks Helicopter Air Display Team | 136.975, 248.8, 250.475, 388.0 MHz |
| Silver Eagles Display Team | 135.975, 252.9 MHz |
| Swedick Tower Air Display Team | 370.1 MHz |
| Turkish Star 5 Air Display Team | 225.750, 243.0, 279.6 MHz |
| USAF Air Display Team | 235.250, 251.5, 322.950 MHz |

A final note. Be sensible and be careful. Don't be blatantly about our hobby and wave your scanner in the face of authority. You will hear a lot more if your scanner is not confiscated. But above all, enjoy yourself. Scanning is a hobby that might not be is the top-ten but is it harmless and rewarding and ultimately well worth the effort.

Editor's Note:
William K. Armstrong runs the millitary section of the Aeradio Aviation Listeners Group and can be contacted at military@aeradio.fsnet.co.uk.

**225.5000 -227.0000 MHz**    BBC DAB Text Transmissions
(South East England Only)

| Base | Mobile | Mode | Location | User and Notes |
| --- | --- | --- | --- | --- |
| 225.648 | | DAB | London | BBC Radio Ch12B |

**232.000 - 236.000 MHz**    Radio Astronomy

Darnhall, Defford, Jodrell Bank, Knockin, Pickmere and Wardle

**227.0000 - 243.9450 MHz**    Tactical Military Exercise
Communications 25 kHz

| Base | Mobile | Mode | Location | User and Notes |
| --- | --- | --- | --- | --- |
| 240.300 | | AM | Nationwide | Air-Air Refuelling |
| 240.300 | | AM | RAF Neatishead | Radar |
| 240.400 | | AM | AARA 1 (NW Scotland) | Refuelling Primary |
| 240.400 | | AM | AARA 10 (NW Scotland) | Refuelling Primary |
| 240.400 | | AM | AARA 7 (SW England) | Refuelling Primary |
| 240.700 | | AM | Nationwide | Air to air refuelling |
| 241.000 | | AM | Nationwide | Forward Air Controllers |
| 241.000 | | AM | RAF Coningsby | Air-Air |
| 241.175 | | AM | Cowden | Range Primary |
| 241.600 | | AM | Castlemartin | Range Air-Ground |
| 241.625 | | AM | RAF Benson | DATIS |
| 241.650 | | AM | RAF Linton-On-Ouse | ATIS |
| 241.775 | | AM | RAF Cowden | Range |
| 241.825 | | AM | RAF Aldergrove | RAF Ops |
| 241.825 | | AM | RAF St Mawgan | Tower |
| 241.850 | | AM | RAF Neatishead | Radar Ops |
| 241.950 | | AM | RNAS Culdrose | Approach/Radar |
| 241.975 | | AM | RAF Honington | Ground/Ops |
| 242.000 | | AM | Nationwide | Red Arrows air display team |
| 242.050 | | AM | Nationwide | Red Arrows Display |
| 242.057 | | AM | RAF Wittering | Air-Air |
| 242.075 | | AM | RAF Lakenheath | Dep Con |
| 242.150 | | AM | RAF Lakenheath | Defence Exercises |
| 242.200 | | AM | Nationwide | Red Arrows Display |
| 242.275 | | AM | Nationwide | Air Defence Region |
| 242.325 | | AM | RAF Cottesmore | DATIS |
| 242.400 | | AM | RAF Leuchars | 111 Sqn Air-Air |
| 242.450 | | AM | RAF Wittering | 1 Sqn Ops (Willard Ops) |
| 242.475 | | AM | Nationwide | RAF air to air |
| 242.550 | | AM | RAF Coningsby | 5 Sqn Ops |
| 242.600 | | AM | Nationwide | Patroulle De France Display Team |
| 242.600 | | AM | Warton | Test Flights |
| 242.650 | | AM | Nationwide | Patroulle de Francais air display team |
| 242.850 | | AM | Nationwide | Patroulle de Francais air display team |
| 243.000 | | AM | International | Air Distress |
| 243.000 | | AM | International | Maritime Emergency Position Indicating Beacons |
| 243.000 | | AM | Nationwide | Turkish Star 5 Air Display Team |
| 243.325 | | AM | RAF Leeming | 11 Sqn Air-Air |
| 243.450 | | AM | Nationwide | Red Arrows Display |
| 243.475 | | AM | Nationwide | USAF Ops |
| 243.800 | | AM | RAF Aerodrome | Radio Failure Frequency |

## 243.9450 - 244.2500 MHz   US AFSATCOM DOWN LINKS

| Base | Mobile | Mode | Location | User and Notes |
|------|--------|------|----------|----------------|
| 243.945 | | NFM | AFSATCOM F2 | NB Channel 11 |
| 243.955 | | NFM | AFSATCOM F2 | NB Channel 12 |
| 243.960 | | NFM | AFSATCOM F2 | NB Channel 13 |
| 243.965 | | NFM | AFSATCOM F2 | NB Channel 14 |
| 243.970 | | NFM | AFSATCOM F2 | NB Channel 15 |
| 243.975 | | NFM | AFSATCOM F2 | NB Channel 16 |
| 243.980 | | NFM | AFSATCOM F2 | NB Channel 17 |
| 243.985 | | NFM | AFSATCOM F2 | NB Channel 18 |
| 243.990 | | NFM | AFSATCOM F2 | NB Channel 19 |
| 243.995 | | NFM | AFSATCOM F2 | NB Channel 20 |
| 244.000 | | NFM | AFSATCOM F2 | NB Channel 21 |
| 244.010 | | NFM | AFSATCOM F2 | NB Channel 22 |
| 244.045 | | NFM | AFSATCOM F3 | NB Channel 11 |
| 244.055 | | NFM | AFSATCOM F3 | NB Channel 12 |
| 244.060 | | NFM | AFSATCOM F3 | NB Channel 13 |
| 244.065 | | NFM | AFSATCOM F3 | NB Channel 14 |
| 244.070 | | NFM | AFSATCOM F3 | NB Channel 15 |
| 244.075 | | NFM | AFSATCOM F3 | NB Channel 16 |
| 244.080 | | NFM | AFSATCOM F3 | NB Channel 17 |
| 244.085 | | NFM | AFSATCOM F3 | NB Channel 18 |
| 244.090 | | NFM | AFSATCOM F3 | NB Channel 19 |
| 244.095 | | NFM | AFSATCOM F3 | NB Channel 20 |
| 244.100 | | NFM | AFSATCOM F3 | NB Channel 21 |
| 244.110 | | NFM | AFSATCOM F3 | NB Channel 22 |
| 244.145 | | NFM | AFSATCOM F1 | NB Channel 11 |
| 244.155 | | NFM | AFSATCOM F1 | NB Channel 12 |
| 244.160 | | NFM | AFSATCOM F1 | NB Channel 13 |
| 244.165 | | NFM | AFSATCOM F1 | NB Channel 14 |
| 244.170 | | NFM | AFSATCOM F1 | NB Channel 15 |
| 244.175 | | NFM | AFSATCOM F1 | NB Channel 16 |
| 244.180 | | NFM | AFSATCOM F1 | NB Channel 17 |
| 244.185 | | NFM | AFSATCOM F1 | NB Channel 18 |
| 244.190 | | NFM | AFSATCOM F1 | NB Channel 19 |
| 244.195 | | NFM | AFSATCOM F1 | NB Channel 20 |
| 244.200 | | NFM | AFSATCOM F1 | NB Channel 21 |
| 244.210 | | NFM | AFSATCOM F1 | NB Channel 22 |

## 244.21000 - 248.8000 MHz  TACTICAL MILITARY EXERCISE COMMUNICATIONS 25 KHZ

| Base | Mobile | Mode | Location | User and Notes |
|------|--------|------|----------|----------------|
| 244.275 | | AM | RAF Waddington | AWACS Wing Ops |
| 244.300 | | AM | RAF Valley | 4FTS Air-to-Air |
| 244.375 | | AM | Nationwide | Air Defence Region |
| 244.425 | | AM | RAF Northolt | Ops |
| 244.600 | | AM | Nationwide | UK Distress |
| 244.600 | | AM | Plymouth | Plymouth Rescue |
| 244.650 | | AM | AARA 6 (S North Sea) | Refuelling |
| 244.650 | | AM | RAF Buchan | Air Defence Region Ops |
| 244.650 | | AM | RAF Neatishead | Air Defence Region Ops |
| 244.675 | | AM | Nationwide | 4 Sqn Air-Air |
| 244.700 | | AM | RAF Neatishead | Air Defence Region Ops |
| 244.825 | | AM | Nationwide | Air defence ops. |
| 244.875 | | AM | RAF Leconfield | Leconfield Rescue |
| 244.900 | | AM | RAF Leeming | 11 Sqn Air-Air |
| 245.050 | | AM | RAF Boulmer | Air Defence Region Ops |

| Base | Mobile | Mode | Location | User and Notes |
|------|--------|------|----------|----------------|
| 245.100 | | AM | Nationwide | RAF Personal Locator Beacons |
| 245.100 | | AM | RAF Cranwell | RAF Air-Air |
| 245.250 | | AM | RAF Leeming | Air to air ops. |
| 246.050 | | AM | Nationwide | Air-Air Refuelling |
| 246.450 | | AM | Nationwide | Displays |
| 246.700 | | AM | Nationwide | Forward Air Controllers |
| 247.000 | | AM | RAF Boulmer | Air Defence Region |
| 247.175 | | AM | RAF Cranwell | DATIS |
| 247.275 | | AM | Nationwide | Air Defence Region |
| 247.700 | | AM | Nationwide | Forward Air Controllers |
| 248.100 | | AM | RAF Neatishead | Air Defence Region Ops |
| 248.150 | | AM | RAF Lakenheath | 493FS Discreet |
| 248.275 | | AM | RAF Lakenheath | 48FW Air-to-Air |
| 248.300 | | AM | Nationwide | Airborne Intercept Cmd |
| 248.300 | | AM | Nationwide | RAF AWACS Ops |
| 248.400 | | AM | RAF Buchan | Air Defence Region Ops |
| 248.800 | | AM | Nationwide | Sharks Helicopter Display |

## 248.8500 - 249.3500 MHz    US AFSATCOM Down Links

| Base | Mobile | Mode | Location | User and Notes |
|------|--------|------|----------|----------------|
| 248.850 | 302.450 | NFM | MARISAT | Channel 1 |
| 248.875 | 302.475 | NFM | MARISAT | Channel 2 |
| 248.900 | 302.500 | NFM | MARISAT | Channel 3 |
| 248.925 | 302.525 | NFM | MARISAT | Channel 4 |
| 248.950 | 302.550 | NFM | MARISAT | Channel 5 |
| 248.975 | 302.575 | NFM | MARISAT | Channel 6 |
| 249.000 | | NFM | Nationwide | Dynamic Sciences Surv. |
| 249.000 | 302.700 | NFM | MARISAT | Channel 7 |
| 249.025 | 302.725 | NFM | MARISAT | Channel 8 |
| 249.050 | 302.750 | NFM | MARISAT | Channel 9 |
| 249.075 | 302.775 | NFM | MARISAT | Channel 10 |
| 249.100 | 302.800 | NFM | MARISAT | Channel 11 |
| 249.125 | 302.825 | NFM | MARISAT | Channel 12 |
| 249.150 | 302.850 | NFM | MARISAT | Channel 13 |
| 249.175 | 302.875 | NFM | MARISAT | Channel 14 |
| 249.200 | 302.900 | NFM | MARISAT | Channel 15 |
| 249.225 | 302.925 | NFM | MARISAT | Channel 16 |
| 249.250 | 302.950 | NFM | MARISAT | Channel 17 |
| 249.275 | 302.975 | NFM | MARISAT | Channel 18 |
| 249.300 | 303.000 | NFM | MARISAT | Channel 19 |
| 249.325 | 303.025 | NFM | MARISAT | Channel 20 |
| 249.350 | 303.050 | NFM | MARISAT | Channel 21 |

## 249.350 - 269.950 MHz        US FLTSATCOM Fleet
##         Broadcast Down Links and Tactical
##         Military Communcations (25 kHz)

| Base | Mobile | Mode | Location | User and Notes |
|------|--------|------|----------|----------------|
| 249.475 | | AM | Prestwick | Scottish Military |
| 249.525 | | AM | RAF Leeming | AFIS |
| 249.575 | | AM | RAF Leuchars | DATIS |
| 249.600 | | AM | RAF Marham | 617 Sqn Ops (Nigger Ops) |
| 249.625 | | AM | RAF West Drayton | London Military |
| 249.675 | | AM | RAF West Drayton | London Military |
| 249.700 | | NFM | Nationwide | Dynamic Sciences Surv. |
| 249.700 | | AM | RAF Lakenheath | ATIS |
| 249.725 | | AM | RNAS Yeovilton | D School |
| 249.750 | | AM | RAF Mildenhall | Command Post Backup |

| Base | Mobile | Mode | Location | User and Notes |
|---|---|---|---|---|
| 249.800 | | NFM | Nationwide | Dynamic Sciences Surv. |
| 249.800 | | AM | RAF Chivenor | 7FTS Air-Air |
| 249.850 | | AM | RAF Waddington | Departures |
| 250.050 | | AM | RAF Cranwell | Zone |
| 250.050 | | AM | RAF Lossiemouth | Talkdown |
| 250.125 | | AM | RAF Leeming | 23 Sqn. Ops (Red Ops) |
| 250.150 | | AM | Nationwide | Forward Air Controllers (Fortune) |
| 250.275 | | AM | RAF West Drayton | London Military |
| 250.350 | 291.350 | NFM | FLTSATCOM | Channel W1 |
| 250.450 | 291.450 | NFM | FLTSATCOM F1 | Channel X1 |
| 250.475 | 250.475 | AM | Nationwide | Sharks Helicopter Display Team |
| 250.550 | 291.550 | NFM | FLTSATCOM F3 | Channel Y1 |
| 250.650 | 291.650 | NFM | FLTSATCOM F2 | Channel Z1 |
| 250.675 | 250.675 | AM | RAF Lakenheath | 48FW Air-to-Air |
| 250.700 | 250.700 | AM | Nationwide | Air Defence Region |
| 250.900 | | NFM | Nationwide | Dynamic Sciences Surv |
| 251.200 | 251.200 | AM | RNAS Culdrose | Kilderkin Ops |
| 251.375 | 251.375 | AM | RAF Wittering | 20 Sqn Ops (Bronze Ops) |
| 251.500 | 251.500 | AM | Nationwide | USAF Displays |
| 251.600 | | NFM | Nationwide | Dynamic Sciences Surv |
| 251.625 | 251.625 | AM | RAF West Drayton | London Military |
| 251.650 | 251.650 | AM | Nationwide | Air Defence Region |
| 251.725 | 251.725 | AM | RAF Newton | Approach |
| 251.750 | 251.750 | AM | Nationwide | Air Defence Region |
| 251.800 | | NFM | Nationwide | Dynamic Sciences Surv |
| 251.850 | 292.850 | NFM | FLTSATCOM | Channel W 2 |
| 251.900 | | NFM | Nationwide | Dynamic Sciences Surv |
| 251.950 | 292.950 | NFM | FLTSATCOM F1 | Channel X 2 |
| 252.050 | 293.050 | NFM | FLTSATCOM F3 | Channel Y 2 |
| 252.100 | | AM | North Sea | ACMI Range Show Ground 1 |
| 252.150 | 293.150 | NFM | FLTSATCOM F2 | Channel Z 2 |
| 252.400 | 252.400 | AM | Nationwide | Air Defence Region |
| 252.450 | 225.450 | AM | RAF Valley | 4FTS Air-to-Air |
| 252.462 | | AM | Prestwick | Scottish Military |
| 252.475 | | AM | Nationwide | Air defence region |
| 252.500 | | AM | RAF Fairford | IAT Spanish Display Team |
| 252.525 | | AM | RAF St Mawgan | DATIS |
| 252.800 | 252.800 | AM | Nationwide | Search and Rescue Training |
| 252.800 | 252.800 | AM | RAF Chivenor | Chivenor Rescue |
| 252.900 | | AM | Colchester Garrison | Tower |
| 252.900 | | AM | RAF Dishforth | AAC Ops |
| 252.900 | 252.900 | AM | Nationwide | British Army |
| 252.900 | 252.900 | AM | Nationwide | Silver Eagles Helicopter Team |
| 253.000 | | NFM | Nationwide | Dynamic Sciences Surv |
| 253.300 | 253.300 | AM | Nationwide | Forward Air Controllers |
| 253.500 | | AM | Netheravon (Army) | Salisbury Plain |
| 253.550 | 294.550 | NFM | FLTSATCOM | Channel W 3 |
| 253.650 | 294.650 | NFM | FLTSATCOM F1 | Channel X 3 |
| 253.750 | 294.750 | NFM | FLTSATCOM F3 | Channel Y 3 |
| 253.800 | 253.800 | AM | Nationwide | NATO SAR Training |
| 253.850 | 294.850 | NFM | FLTSATCOM F2 | Channel Z 3 |
| 253.900 | | NFM | Nationwide | Dynamic Sciences Surv |
| 254.075 | 254.075 | AM | RAF Marham | 2 Sqn Air-to-Air |
| 254.200 | 254.200 | AM | RAF Lossiemouth | Splash |
| 254.200 | 254.200 | AM | RAF Shawbury | Director |
| 254.225 | 254.225 | AM | RAF West Drayton | London Military |

| Base | Mobile | Mode | Location | User and Notes |
|------|--------|------|----------|----------------|
| 254.250 | | AM | RAF Coltishall | Talkdown |
| 254.350 | 254.350 | AM | Nationwide | NATO Air-Air |
| 254.400 | 254.000 | AM | RAF Lossiemouth | 15 Sqn Ops |
| 254.400 | 254.000 | AM | RAF Marham | 27 Sqn Ops (Nellie Ops) |
| 254.425 | 254.425 | AM | Nationwide | Air Defence Region |
| 254.475 | | AM | RAF Brize Norton | ATIS |
| 254.500 | | AM | Aberporth | Range Tertiary |
| 254.525 | | AM | RAF Church Fenton | Approach |
| 254.650 | 254.650 | AM | RAF Lyneham | Ops |
| 254.675 | | AM | RAF Coningsby | 5 Sqn Ops (Maple Ops) |
| 254.725 | | AM | RAF Coningsby | DATIS |
| 254.775 | | AM | Nationwide | Air to air refuelling |
| 254.825 | 254.825 | AM | RAF West Drayton | London Military |
| 254.875 | | AM | RAF Honington | Approach |
| 254.900 | 254.900 | AM | RAF West Drayton | London Military |
| 255.100 | 255.100 | AM | Nationwide | Forward Air Controllers |
| 255.100 | 255.100 | AM | Nationwide | RAF Falcons Parachutists |
| 255.100 | 255.100 | AM | Weston on the Green | Weston Radio |
| 255.250 | 296.250 | NFM | FLTSATCOM | Channel W 4 |
| 255.275 | 255.275 | AM | RAF Lakenheath | 48FW Aux |
| 255.350 | 296.350 | NFM | FLTSATCOM F1 | Channel X 4 |
| 255.400 | 255.400 | AM | RAF Leuchars | Approach |
| 255.400 | 255.400 | AM | RAF West Drayton | London Military |
| 255.450 | 296.450 | NFM | FLTSATCOM F3 | Channel Y 4 |
| 255.550 | 296.550 | NFM | FLTSATCOM F2 | Channel Z 4 |
| 255.700 | 255.700 | AM | RAF West Drayton | London Military |
| 255.850 | | AM | RAF Cottesmore | Air-to-Air |
| 256.000 | 256.000 | AM | Royal Navy | Ship-Air |
| 256.100 | 256.100 | AM | Royal Navy | Ship-Air |
| 256.125 | | AM | Filton (BAe), Bristol | Approach/Radar |
| 256.600 | | NFM | Nationwide | Dynamic Sciences Surv |
| 256.850 | 297.850 | NFM | FLTSATCOM | Channel W 5 |
| 256.900 | 256.900 | AM | Nationwide | Forward Air Controllers |
| 256.950 | 297.950 | NFM | FLTSATCOM F1 | Channel X 5 |
| 257.050 | 298.050 | NFM | FLTSATCOM F3 | Channel Y 5 |
| 257.100 | | AM | RAF Brize Norton | Brize Radar |
| 257.150 | 298.150 | NFM | FLTSATCOM F2 | Channel Z 5 |
| 257.200 | | AM | Otterburn | Range Primary |
| 257.200 | 257.200 | AM | Nationwide | Forward Air Controllers |
| 257.225 | 257.225 | AM | RAF West Drayton | London Military |
| 257.750 | | AM | RAF Fairford | Fairford Metro |
| 257.750 | 257.750 | AM | RAF Mildenhall | Mildenhall Metro |
| 257.800 | | AM | Nationwide | Forward Air Controllers |
| 257.800 | | AM | RAF Brize Norton | Tower |
| 257.800 | | AM | RAF Church Fenton | Tower |
| 257.800 | | AM | RAF Cottesmore | Tower |
| 257.800 | | AM | RAF Cranwell | Tower |
| 257.800 | | AM | RAF Kinloss | Tower |
| 257.800 | | AM | RAF Lakenheath | Tower |
| 257.800 | | AM | RAF Leeming | Tower |
| 257.800 | | AM | RAF Linton-On-Ouse | Tower |
| 257.800 | | AM | RAF Marham | Tower |
| 257.800 | | AM | RAF Northolt | Tower |
| 257.800 | | AM | RAF Odiham | Tower |
| 257.800 | | AM | RAF St Athan | Tower |
| 257.800 | | AM | RAF Topcliffe | Tower |

| Base | Mobile | Mode | Location | User and Notes |
|------|--------|------|----------|----------------|
| 257.800 | | AM | RAF Valley | Tower |
| 257.800 | | AM | RAF Waddington | Tower |
| 257.800 | | AM | RAF Wittering | Tower |
| 258.050 | | AM | Nationwide | Air-Air Tanker Ops |
| 258.300 | | AM | Nationwide | Forward Air Controllers |
| 258.350 | 299.350 | NFM | FLTSATCOM | Channel W 6 |
| 258.400 | | AM | AARA 10 (NW Scotland) | Refuelling |
| 258.450 | 299.450 | NFM | FLTSATCOM F1 | Channel X 6 |
| 258.500 | | AM | Nationwide | AWACS |
| 258.550 | 299.550 | NFM | FLTSATCOM F3 | Channel Y 6 |
| 258.650 | 299.650 | NFM | FLTSATCOM F2 | Channel Z 6 |
| 258.775 | | AM | RAF Chivenor | 7FTS Air-Air |
| 258.800 | | AM | Nationwide | British Army Air-Air |
| 258.800 | | AM | RAF Benson | 60 Sqn Air-Air |
| 258.825 | | AM | RAF Valley | Radar |
| 258.850 | | AM | RAF Lossiemouth | Lossie Departures |
| 258.975 | | AM | RAF Colerne | Tower |
| 258.975 | | AM | RAF Newton | Ground |
| 259.000 | | AM | Aberporth | Information |
| 259.000 | | AM | DRA Farnborough | Talkdown |
| 259.000 | | AM | MoD West Freugh | Radar |
| 259.075 | | AM | RAF Marham | 2 Sqn Ops (Melbourne Ops) |
| 259.100 | | AM | RAF Neatishead | Air Defence Region Ops |
| 259.125 | | AM | RAF Leuchars | Tower |
| 259.175 | | AM | Prestwick | Scottish Military |
| 259.525 | | AM | Nationwide | RAF Discreet |
| 259.600 | | AM | RAF Neatishead | Air Defence Region Ops |
| 259.700 | | NFM | International | Space Shuttle Down Link |
| 259.725 | | AM | Prestwick | Scottish Military |
| 259.750 | | AM | RNAS Culdrose | Talkdown |
| 259.775 | | AM | Prestwick | Scottish Military |
| 259.800 | | AM | RNAS Yeovilton | D School |
| 259.825 | | AM | RAF Dishforth | Tower |
| 259.875 | | AM | RAF Benson | Talkdown |
| 259.875 | | AM | RAF Linton-On-Ouse | Talkdown |
| 259.925 | | AM | RAF Leuchars | Talkdown |
| 259.950 | | AM | RAF Woodvale | Tower |
| 259.975 | | AM | RAF Fairford | Ground |
| 259.975 | | AM | RAF Kinloss | Director |
| 259.975 | | AM | RAF Lossiemouth | Director |
| 260.000 | | AM | Cowden | Range |
| 260.000 | | AM | RAF St Mawgan | Ops |
| 260.025 | | AM | MoD West Freugh | Approach |
| 260.025 | | AM | RAF West Drayton | London Military |
| 260.150 | | AM | Nationwide | Air Defence Region |
| 260.350 | 293.950 | NFM | FLTSATCOM F1 | WB Channel A/X 1 |
| 260.375 | 293.975 | NFM | FLTSATCOM F1 | WB Channel A/X 2 |
| 260.400 | 294.000 | NFM | FLTSATCOM F1 | WB Channel A/X 3 |
| 260.425 | 294.025 | NFM | FLTSATCOM F1 | WB Channel A/X 4 |
| 260.450 | 294.050 | NFM | FLTSATCOM F1 | WB Channel A/X 5 |
| 260.475 | 294.075 | NFM | FLTSATCOM F1 | WB Channel A/X 6 |
| 260.500 | 294.100 | NFM | FLTSATCOM F1 | WB Channel A/X 7 |
| 260.525 | 294.125 | NFM | FLTSATCOM F1 | WB Channel A/X 8 |
| 260.550 | 294.150 | NFM | FLTSATCOM F1 | WB Channel A/X 9 |
| 260.575 | 294.175 | NFM | FLTSATCOM F1 | WB Channel A/X 10 |
| 260.600 | 294.200 | NFM | FLTSATCOM F1 | WB Channel A/X 11 |

| Base | Mobile | Mode | Location | User and Notes |
|------|--------|------|----------|----------------|
| 260.625 | 294.225 | NFM | FLTSATCOM F1 | WB Channel A/X 12 |
| 260.650 | 294.250 | NFM | FLTSATCOM F1 | WB Channel A/X 13 |
| 260.675 | 294.275 | NFM | FLTSATCOM F1 | WB Channel A/X 14 |
| 260.700 | 294.300 | NFM | FLTSATCOM F1 | WB Channel A/X 15 |
| 260.725 | 294.325 | NFM | FLTSATCOM F1 | WB Channel A/X 16 |
| 260.750 | 294.350 | NFM | FLTSATCOM F1 | WB Channel A/X 17 |
| 260.775 | 294.375 | NFM | FLTSATCOM F1 | WB Channel A/X 18 |
| 260.800 | 294.400 | NFM | FLTSATCOM F1 | WB Channel A/X 19 |
| 260.825 | 294.425 | NFM | FLTSATCOM F1 | WB Channel A/X 20 |
| 260.850 | 294.450 | NFM | FLTSATCOM F1 | WB Channel A/X 21 |
| 260.950 | | AM | RAF Coningsby | Air-to-Air |
| 261.000 | | AM | RAF West Drayton | London Military |
| 261.025 | | AM | RAF West Drayton | London Military |
| 261.050 | | AM | RAF Barkston Heath | Director |
| 261.075 | | AM | RAF Leeming | 23 Sqn Ops (Red Ops) |
| 261.200 | | AM | RAF Marham | ATIS |
| 261.450 | 295.050 | NFM | FLTSATCOM F3 | WB Channel B/Y 1 |
| 261.475 | 295.075 | NFM | FLTSATCOM F3 | WB Channel B/Y 2 |
| 261.500 | 295.100 | NFM | FLTSATCOM F3 | WB Channel B/Y 3 |
| 261.525 | 295.125 | NFM | FLTSATCOM F3 | WB Channel B/Y 4 |
| 261.550 | 295.150 | NFM | FLTSATCOM F3 | WB Channel B/Y 5 |
| 261.575 | 295.175 | NFM | FLTSATCOM F3 | WB Channel B/Y 6 |
| 261.600 | 295.200 | NFM | FLTSATCOM F3 | WB Channel B/Y 7 |
| 261.625 | 295.225 | NFM | FLTSATCOM F3 | WB Channel B/Y 8 |
| 261.650 | 295.250 | NFM | FLTSATCOM F3 | WB Channel B/Y 9 |
| 261.675 | 295.275 | NFM | FLTSATCOM F3 | WB Channel B/Y 10 |
| 261.700 | 295.300 | NFM | FLTSATCOM F3 | WB Channel B/Y 11 |
| 261.725 | 295.325 | NFM | FLTSATCOM F3 | WB Channel B/Y 12 |
| 261.750 | 295.350 | NFM | FLTSATCOM F3 | WB Channel B/Y 13 |
| 261.775 | 295.375 | NFM | FLTSATCOM F3 | WB Channel B/Y 14 |
| 261.800 | 295.400 | NFM | FLTSATCOM F3 | WB Channel B/Y 15 |
| 261.825 | 295.425 | NFM | FLTSATCOM F3 | WB Channel B/Y 16 |
| 261.850 | 295.450 | NFM | FLTSATCOM F3 | WB Channel B/Y 17 |
| 261.875 | 295.475 | NFM | FLTSATCOM F3 | WB Channel B/Y 18 |
| 261.900 | 295.500 | NFM | FLTSATCOM F3 | WB Channel B/Y 19 |
| 261.925 | 295.525 | NFM | FLTSATCOM F3 | WB Channel B/Y 20 |
| 261.950 | 295.550 | NFM | FLTSATCOM F3 | WB Channel B/Y 21 |
| 262.050 | 295.650 | NFM | FLTSATCOM F2 | WB Channel C/Z 1 |
| 262.075 | 295.675 | NFM | FLTSATCOM F2 | WB Channel C/Z 2 |
| 262.100 | 295.700 | NFM | FLTSATCOM F2 | WB Channel C/Z 3 |
| 262.125 | 295.725 | NFM | FLTSATCOM F2 | WB Channel C/Z 4 |
| 262.150 | 295.750 | NFM | FLTSATCOM F2 | WB Channel C/Z 5 |
| 262.175 | 295.775 | NFM | FLTSATCOM F2 | WB Channel C/Z 6 |
| 262.200 | 295.800 | NFM | FLTSATCOM F2 | WB Channel C/Z 7 |
| 262.225 | 295.825 | NFM | FLTSATCOM F2 | WB Channel C/Z 8 |
| 262.250 | 295.850 | NFM | FLTSATCOM F2 | WB Channel C/Z 9 |
| 262.275 | 295.875 | NFM | FLTSATCOM F2 | WB Channel C/Z 10 |
| 262.300 | 295.900 | NFM | FLTSATCOM F2 | WB Channel C/Z 11 |
| 262.325 | 295.925 | NFM | FLTSATCOM F2 | WB Channel C/Z 12 |
| 262.350 | 295.950 | NFM | FLTSATCOM F2 | WB Channel C/Z 13 |
| 262.375 | 295.975 | NFM | FLTSATCOM F2 | WB Channel C/Z 14 |
| 262.400 | 296.000 | NFM | FLTSATCOM F2 | WB Channel C/Z 15 |
| 262.425 | 296.025 | NFM | FLTSATCOM F2 | WB Channel C/Z 16 |
| 262.450 | 296.050 | NFM | FLTSATCOM F2 | WB Channel C/Z 17 |
| 262.475 | 296.075 | NFM | FLTSATCOM F2 | WB Channel C/Z 18 |
| 262.500 | 296.100 | NFM | FLTSATCOM F2 | WB Channel C/Z 19 |

| Base | Mobile | Mode | Location | User and Notes |
|------|--------|------|----------|----------------|
| 262.525 | 296.125 | NFM | FLTSATCOM F2 | WB Channel C/Z 20 |
| 262.550 | 296.150 | NFM | FLTSATCOM F2 | WB Channel C/Z 21 |
| 262.650 | | AM | RAF Valley | 4FTS Air-to-Air |
| 262.700 | | AM | RAF Church Fenton | Tower |
| 262.725 | | AM | RAF Lossiemouth | TWCU Air-to-Air |
| 262.900 | | AM | RAF Cottesmore | Talkdown |
| 262.925 | | AM | RNAS Yeovilton | Royal Navy Ops |
| 262.950 | | AM | RAF Coningsby | Director |
| 262.975 | | AM | RAF West Drayton | London Military |
| 263.075 | | AM | RAF West Drayton | London Military |
| 263.150 | | AM | Nationwide | Air Defence Region |
| 263.500 | | AM | Boscombe Down (MoD) | DATIS |
| 263.550 | 297.150 | NFM | FLTSATCOM | WB Channel W 1 |
| 263.575 | 297.175 | NFM | FLTSATCOM | WB Channel W 2 |
| 263.600 | 297.200 | NFM | FLTSATCOM | WB Channel W 3 |
| 263.625 | 297.225 | NFM | FLTSATCOM | WB Channel W 4 |
| 263.650 | 297.250 | NFM | FLTSATCOM | WB Channel W 5 |
| 263.675 | 297.275 | NFM | FLTSATCOM | WB Channel W 6 |
| 263.700 | 297.300 | NFM | FLTSATCOM | WB Channel W 7 |
| 263.725 | 297.325 | NFM | FLTSATCOM | WB Channel W 8 |
| 263.750 | 297.350 | NFM | FLTSATCOM | WB Channel W 9 |
| 263.775 | 297.375 | NFM | FLTSATCOM | WB Channel W 10 |
| 263.800 | 297.400 | NFM | FLTSATCOM | WB Channel W 11 |
| 263.825 | 297.425 | NFM | FLTSATCOM | WB Channel W 12 |
| 263.850 | 297.450 | NFM | FLTSATCOM | WB Channel W 13 |
| 263.875 | 297.475 | NFM | FLTSATCOM | WB Channel W 14 |
| 263.900 | 297.500 | NFM | FLTSATCOM | WB Channel W 15 |
| 263.925 | 297.525 | NFM | FLTSATCOM | WB Channel W 16 |
| 263.950 | 297.550 | NFM | FLTSATCOM | WB Channel W 17 |
| 263.975 | 297.575 | NFM | FLTSATCOM | WB Channel W 18 |
| 264.000 | 297.600 | NFM | FLTSATCOM | WB Channel W 19 |
| 264.025 | 297.625 | NFM | FLTSATCOM | WB Channel W 20 |
| 264.050 | 297.650 | NFM | FLTSATCOM | WB Channel W 21 |
| 264.100 | | AM | RAF Lakenheath | Radar |
| 264.200 | | AM | Nationwide | Forward Air Controllers |
| 264.400 | | AM | Nationwide | RAF AWACS Ops |
| 264.475 | | AM | RAF West Drayton | London Military (Clacton) |
| 264.675 | | AM | RAF Lakenheath | MATZ Crossing |
| 264.800 | | AM | Faslane | Royal Navy (FOSSANI) |
| 265.250 | 306.250 | NFM | FLTSATCOM | Channel W 7 |
| 265.350 | 306.350 | NFM | FLTSATCOM F1 | Channel X 7 |
| 265.450 | 306.450 | NFM | FLTSATCOM F3 | Channel Y 7 |
| 265.550 | 306.550 | NFM | FLTSATCOM F2 | Channel Z 7 |
| 265.850 | | AM | Nationwide | Air-Air Refuelling |
| 265.900 | | AM | Nationwide | Air Defence Region |
| 266.275 | | AM | RAF Lakenheath | 494FS Discrete |
| 266.450 | | AM | RAF Neatishead | Air Defence Region Ops |
| 266.500 | | AM | Nationwide | USAF Air-Air Refuelling |
| 266.550 | | AM | RAF Neatishead | Air Defence Region Ops |
| 266.750 | 307.750 | NFM | FLTSATCOM | Channel W 8 |
| 266.800 | | NFM | Nationwide | Dynamic Sciences Surv |
| 266.850 | 307.850 | NFM | FLTSATCOM F1 | Channel X 8 |
| 266.950 | 307.950 | NFM | FLTSATCOM F3 | Channel Y 8 |
| 267.050 | 308.050 | NFM | FLTSATCOM F2 | Channel Z 8 |
| 267.400 | | NFM | Nationwide | Dynamic Sciences Surv |
| 267.550 | | AM | RAF Boulmer | Air Defence Region Ops |

| Base | Mobile | Mode | Location | User and Notes |
|------|--------|------|----------|----------------|
| 267.550 | | AM | RAF Neatishead | Air Defence Region Ops |
| 267.900 | | AM | Nationwide | NATO Air-to-Air |
| 268.150 | 309.150 | NFM | FLTSATCOM | Channel W 9 |
| 268.250 | 309.250 | NFM | FLTSATCOM F1 | Channel X 9 |
| 268.350 | 309.350 | NFM | FLTSATCOM F3 | Channel Y 9 |
| 268.400 | | NFM | Nationwide | Dynamic Sciences Surv |
| 268.450 | 309.450 | NFM | FLTSATCOM F2 | Channel Z 9 |
| 268.575 | | AM | Prestwick | Scottish Military |
| 268.600 | | AM | RAF Coltishall | 6 Sqn Ops |
| 268.650 | | AM | RAF Valley | 4FTS Air-to-Air |
| 268.675 | | AM | RAF Chivenor | 7FTS Air-Air |
| 268.700 | | AM | RAF Coningsby | Wing Ops |
| 268.800 | | NFM | Nationwide | Dynamic Sciences Surv |
| 268.825 | | AM | RAF Benson | Approach |
| 268.875 | | AM | RAF Marham | Approach |
| 268.925 | | AM | RAF Chivenor | Ops |
| 269.000 | | AM | Nationwide | Rakie Radar |
| 269.000 | | NFM | Nationwide | Dynamic Sciences Surv |
| 269.025 | | AM | RAF Lossiemouth | DATIS |
| 269.075 | | AM | RAF Lakenheath | Command Post |
| 269.075 | | AM | RAF Lakenheath | Command Post |
| 269.125 | | AM | Woodford | Tower/Radar |
| 269.650 | 310.650 | NFM | FLTSATCOM | Channel W 10 |
| 269.750 | | AM | Nationwide | RAF Discrete |
| 269.750 | 310.750 | NFM | FLTSATCOM F1 | Channel X 10 |
| 269.850 | 310.850 | NFM | FLTSATCOM F3 | Channel Y 10 |
| 269.900 | | NFM | Nationwide | Dynamic Sciences Surv |
| 269.950 | 310.950 | NFM | FLTSATCOM F2 | Channel Z 10 |

## 270.000 - 326.900 MHz — TACTICAL MILITARY EXERCISE COMMUNICATIONS 25 kHz

| Base | Mobile | Mode | Location | User and Notes |
|------|--------|------|----------|----------------|
| 270.000 | | AM | RAF West Drayton | London Military |
| 270.000 | | NFM | Space | NASA Space Shuttle |
| 270.025 | | AM | RAF Odiham | 7 Sqn Air-Air |
| 270.900 | | NFM | Nationwide | Dynamic Sciences Surv |
| 271.500 | | AM | Nationwide | ATC Channel U4 |
| 271.800 | | NFM | Nationwide | Dynamic Sciences Surv |
| 272.075 | | AM | English Channel | Royal Navy Exercises |
| 272.225 | | AM | Nationwide | Air Defence Region |
| 273.000 | | AM | Nationwide | ATC Channel U3 |
| 273.525 | | AM | English Channel | Royal Navy |
| 273.900 | | AM | Nationwide | NATO Low-Level Flying |
| 273.900 | | NFM | Nationwide | Dynamic Sciences Surv |
| 274.400 | | NFM | Nationwide | Dynamic Sciences Surv |
| 274.850 | | AM | Nationwide | Forward Air Controller |
| 275.350 | | AM | Nationwide | USAF Displays |
| 275.350 | | AM | RAF West Drayton | London Military (Central) |
| 275.450 | | AM | RAF Cottesmore | Air-to-Air |
| 275.475 | | AM | RAF West Drayton | London Military |
| 275.550 | | AM | RAF Cranwell | 3FTS Air-to-Air |
| 275.625 | | AM | Prestwick | Scottish Military |
| 275.750 | | AM | Nationwide | Air Defence Region |
| 275.800 | | NFM | Nationwide | Dynamic Sciences Surv |
| 275.800 | | AM | Upavon (Army) | Tower |
| 275.875 | | AM | RAF Coningsby | Tower |
| 275.900 | | AM | RAF Leuchars | 111 Sqn Ops (Sabre Ops) |

| Base | Mobile | Mode | Location | User and Notes |
|------|--------|------|----------|----------------|
| 275.975 | | AM | RAF Coltishall | Talkdown |
| 276.125 | | AM | RAF Cosford | Approach |
| 276.175 | | AM | RAF Odiham | ATIS |
| 276.200 | | AM | RAF Ty Croes | ADR Air-Ground |
| 276.200 | | AM | RAF Valley | 4FTS Air-to-Air |
| 276.225 | | AM | RAF Lakenheath | 48FW Ops |
| 276.250 | | AM | RNAS Yeovilton | 801 Sqn Air-Air |
| 276.600 | | NFM | Nationwide | Dynamic Sciences Surv |
| 276.650 | | AM | RAF Neatishead | Air Defence Region Ops |
| 276.850 | | AM | Boscombe Down (MoD) | Approach/PAR |
| 277.000 | | AM | Nationwide | NATO Magic Surveillance |
| 277.000 | | AM | Royal Navy | Ship-Air |
| 277.075 | | AM | RAF Mildenhall | ATIS |
| 277.125 | | AM | RAF West Drayton | London Military |
| 277.225 | | AM | Cardiff | Approach/Radar |
| 277.225 | | AM | RAF St Athan | Approach |
| 277.275 | | AM | RAF Colerne | Approach |
| 277.300 | | AM | RAF Leuchars | 43 Sqn Ops (Golf Ops) |
| 277.400 | | AM | Nationwide | Air Defence Region |
| 277.450 | | AM | RAF Cottesmore | Air-to-Air |
| 277.500 | | AM | Aberporth | Range Tertiary |
| 277.625 | | AM | RAF Linton-On-Ouse | Departure2 |
| 277.750 | | AM | Nationwide | Air Defence Region |
| 277.775 | | AM | RAF West Drayton | London Military |
| 277.900 | | AM | RAF Chivenor | 7FTS Air-Air |
| 277.925 | | AM | RAF Lynham | ATIS |
| 277.950 | | AM | RAF West Drayton | London Military (Dover/Lydd) |
| 278.025 | | AM | RAF West Drayton | London Military |
| 278.150 | | AM | RAF Mildenhall | Ground |
| 278.150 | | AM | RAF West Drayton | London Military |
| 278.850 | | AM | Nationwide | RAF AWACS Ops |
| 278.900 | | NFM | Nationwide | Dynamic Sciences Surv |
| 279.000 | | NFM | Space | Space Shuttle Down Link |
| 279.175 | | AM | RAF West Drayton | London Military |
| 279.225 | | AM | RAF West Drayton | London Military |
| 279.250 | | AM | RAF Lakenheath | Radar |
| 279.300 | | AM | RAF West Drayton | London Military |
| 279.350 | | AM | RAF Benson | Tower |
| 279.475 | | AM | RAF West Drayton | London Military |
| 279.525 | | AM | Nationwide | Air Defence Region |
| 279.600 | | AM | Nationwide | Turkish Star 5 Air Display Team |
| 279.725 | | AM | Nationwide | Air Defence Region |
| 279.800 | | AM | Nationwide | USAF Air-Air |
| 280.075 | | AM | Nationwide | Tactical |
| 280.400 | | AM | Nationwide | Forward Air Controllers |
| 280.400 | | AM | Otterburn | Range Secondary |
| 280.600 | | NFM | Nationwide | Dynamic Sciences Surv |
| 280.725 | | AM | RAF Lakenheath | Aux-08 "Bite" |
| 281.100 | | AM | Nationwide | Air Defence Region |
| 281.150 | | AM | Lyme Bay | Range Primary |
| 281.200 | | AM | Royal Navy | Ship-Air |
| 281.550 | | AM | Nationwide | Air-Air |
| 281.725 | | AM | English Channel | Naval Exercises |
| 281.800 | | AM | Nationwide | Displays |
| 282.000 | | AM | RAF Cranwell | Director |
| 282.100 | | AM | RNAS Culdrose | ATIS |

| Base | Mobile | Mode | Location | User and Notes |
|------|--------|------|----------|----------------|
| 282.125 | | AM | RAF West Drayton | London Military |
| 282.200 | | AM | RAF West Drayton | London Military |
| 282.250 | | AM | Netheravon (Army) | Salisbury Plain |
| 282.250 | | AM | Salisbury Plain (Army) | Ops |
| 282.275 | | AM | RAF Honington | Tower |
| 282.800 | | AM | Nationwide | NATO SAR |
| 282.800 | | AM | RAF Boulmer | Boulmer Rescue |
| 282.800 | | AM | RAF Leconfield | Leconfield Rescue |
| 282.800 | | AM | RAF Valley | SAR Approach |
| 283.450 | | AM | Nationwide | 9 Sqn Air-Air |
| 283.475 | | AM | Anglia | Anglian Radar |
| 283.525 | | AM | RAF West Drayton | London Military |
| 283.575 | | AM | Wattisham (Army Airfield) | Director |
| 283.600 | | AM | Nationwide | 17 Sqn Air-Air |
| 283.650 | | AM | Nationwide | Air Defence Region |
| 283.675 | | AM | RAF West Drayton | London Military |
| 283.900 | | AM | RAF Lossiemouth | Safety |
| 284.300 | | AM | RAF West Drayton | London Military |
| 284.600 | | AM | Newcastle | Approach/Radar |
| 284.875 | | AM | RAF West Drayton | London Military |
| 284.900 | | AM | RAF Lakenheath | Maintenance |
| 284.925 | | AM | RAF Fairford | B52 Ops (HAVOC) |
| 284.950 | | AM | RAF Lyneham | LI W Air-Air |
| 284.975 | | AM | Nationwide | Air Defence Region |
| 285.025 | | AM | RAF Leuchars | Ops |
| 285.075 | | AM | Prestwick | Scottish Military |
| 285.100 | | AM | Nationwide | FRADU Discreet |
| 285.150 | | AM | RAF Cranwell | Talkdown |
| 285.175 | | AM | RAF West Drayton | London Military |
| 285.650 | | AM | RAF Neatishead | Air Defence Region Ops |
| 285.750 | | AM | RAF Buchan | Air Defence Region Ops |
| 286.650 | | AM | RAF Lossiemouth | 12 Sqn Air-Air |
| 286.900 | | AM | RAF Buchan | Air Defence Region Ops |
| 287.250 | | AM | Nationwide | RAF Air-Air Tanker Ops |
| 287.650 | | AM | RAF Neatishead | Air Defence Region Ops |
| 287.650 | | AM | Royal Navy | Ship-Air |
| 287.700 | | AM | Nationwide | Air Defence Region |
| 288.400 | | AM | RAF Boulmer | Air Defence Region Ops |
| 288.400 | | AM | RAF Neatishead | Air Defence Region Ops |
| 288.400 | | AM | Scotland (South East) | Combat Air Patrol Area |
| 288.600 | | AM | Nationwide | USAF Air-Air |
| 288.600 | | AM | Nationwide | USAF AWACS Ops |
| 289.050 | | AM | RAF Boulmer | Air Defence Region Ops |
| 289.250 | | AM | RAF Lossiemouth | 16 Sqn Air-Air |
| 289.350 | | AM | RAF Neatishead | Air Defence Region Ops |
| 290.050 | | AM | RAF Neatishead | Air Defence Region Ops |
| 290.375 | | AM | Nationwide | Air Defence Region |
| 290.575 | | AM | RAF West Drayton | London Military |
| 290.700 | | AM | RAF West Drayton | London Military |
| 290.800 | | AM | RAF Coningsby | Air-Air |
| 290.825 | | AM | RAF Lakenheath | Radar |
| 290.850 | | AM | RAF Coningsby | 29 Sqn Ops (Triplex Ops) |
| 290.925 | | AM | RAF West Drayton | London Military |
| 290.950 | | AM | Netheravon (Army) | Information |
| 290.950 | | AM | North Sea | ACMI Range Show Ground 4 |
| 291.075 | | AM | Nationwide | Air Defence Region |

| Base | Mobile | Mode | Location | User and Notes |
|------|--------|------|----------|----------------|
| 291.125 | | AM | Wattisham (Army Airfield) | Approach |
| 291.225 | | AM | RAF Lossiemouth | 15 Sqn Air-to-Air |
| 291.650 | | AM | Boscombe Down (MoD) | Director |
| 291.675 | | AM | RAF Waddington | DATIS |
| 291.700 | | AM | RAF Barkston Heath | Departures |
| 291.800 | | AM | RAF West Drayton | London Military (LJAO) |
| 292.450 | | AM | RAF Boulmer | Air Defence Region Ops |
| 292.475 | | AM | RAF Leuchars | Director |
| 292.500 | | AM | Salisbury Plain | Air/Ground |
| 292.525 | | AM | RAF West Drayton | London Military |
| 292.575 | | AM | RAF Shawbury | DATIS |
| 292.600 | | AM | RAF West Drayton | London Military |
| 292.675 | | AM | Prestwick | Scottish Military |
| 292.700 | | AM | RAF Leeming | Zone Radar |
| 292.800 | | AM | RAF Linton-On-Ouse | Departures/Radar |
| 292.800 | | AM | RAF Linton-On-Ouse | Radar |
| 293.425 | | AM | RAF Coltishall | Zone |
| 293.475 | | AM | RAF West Drayton | London Military |
| 293.525 | | AM | RAF West Drayton | London Military |
| 293.575 | | AM | RAF West Drayton | London Military |
| 293.725 | | AM | RAF Lakenheath | Aux-07 493FS |
| 293.775 | | AM | RAF Marham | Director |
| 293.975 | | AM | RAF West Drayton | London Military |
| 294.800 | | AM | Nationwide | Air to Air Refuelling |
| 294.900 | | AM | RAF West Drayton | London Military |
| 295.850 | | AM | Prestwick | Scottish Military |
| 296.400 | | AM | Nationwide | Air Defence Region |
| 296.550 | | AM | Nationwide | Air Defence Region |
| 296.575 | | AM | Nationwide | RAF/USAF Discreet |
| 296.725 | | AM | RAF Kinloss | Information |
| 296.725 | | AM | RNAS Culdrose | 705 Sqn Air-Air |
| 296.725 | | AM | Teesside Airport | Approach/Radar |
| 296.750 | | AM | RAF Waddington | Zone |
| 296.800 | | NFM | International | Space Shuttle Down Link |
| 296.900 | | AM | RAF Neatishead | Air Defence Region Ops |
| 297.800 | | AM | Nationwide | Rescue |
| 297.900 | | AM | RAF Cranwell | Ground |
| 297.900 | | AM | RAF Leuchars | Ground |
| 298.650 | | AM | Nationwide | Air Defence Region |
| 299.100 | | AM | RAF Boulmer | Boulmer Rescue |
| 299.400 | | AM | Boscombe Down (MoD) | Ground |
| 299.400 | | AM | RAF Lossiemouth | Ground |
| 299.400 | | AM | RNAS Culdrose | Ground |
| 299.500 | | AM | Northern North Sea, AARA 3 | Air-Air Refuelling |
| 299.700 | | AM | Nationwide | Air Defence Region |
| 299.975 | | AM | RAF West Drayton | London Military |
| 299.975 | | AM | RAF West Drayton | London Military |
| 300.000 | | AM | RAF Lakenheath | Air-Air |
| 300.050 | | AM | Portland Exercise Area | Ops |
| 300.075 | | AM | RAF Lakenheath | 492FS Bowler Ops |
| 300.100 | | AM | RAF Lyneham | LTW Air-Air |
| 300.150 | | AM | RAF Benbecula | Air Defence Region Ops |
| 300.175 | | AM | Plymouth | Plymouth Rescue |
| 300.200 | | AM | RAF Lakenheath | 492FS Air-to-Air |
| 300.250 | | AM | Boscombe Down (MoD) | ETPS Tester Ops |
| 300.350 | | AM | RAF Northolt | ATIS |

| Base | Mobile | Mode | Location | User and Notes |
|------|--------|------|----------|----------------|
| 300.425 | | AM | RAF Linton-On-Ouse | Tower |
| 300.450 | | AM | RAF Odiham | Talkdown |
| 300.475 | | AM | RAF Lyneham | Director |
| 300.575 | | AM | RAF Waddington | Director |
| 300.600 | | AM | Warton | Ops |
| 300.625 | | AM | RAF Cranwell | 3FTS Air-to-Air |
| 300.650 | | AM | RAF Neatishead | Air Defence Region Ops |
| 300.675 | | AM | Yeovil (Westland) | Radar (Judwin) |
| 300.800 | | AM | Nationwide | NATO Low Level |
| 300.825 | | AM | Lilstock Range (D119) | Range Control |
| 300.825 | | AM | RAF Lakenheath | Dispatcher |
| 300.875 | | AM | RAF Leeming | 11 Sqn Ops (Black Ops) |
| 300.925 | | AM | RAF Coningsby | Talkdown |
| 300.950 | | AM | Nationwide | Air Defence Region |
| 301.325 | | AM | RAF Lakenheath | Air-Air |
| 303.000 | | AM | Nationwide | Air to Air Refuelling |
| 304.000 | | NFM | Worldwide | USAF Satcom Downlink |
| 304.800 | | AM | Nationwide | Air to Air Refuelling |
| 305.900 | | AM | RNAS Culdrose | 750 Sqn Ops |
| 306.400 | | AM | RAF Lakenheath | Operations |
| 306.500 | | AM | Southern North Sea, AARA 6 | Air-Air Refuelling |
| 306.650 | | AM | SW Scotland | Combat Air Patrol Area |
| 307.000 | | AM | RAF Neatishead | Air Defence Region Ops |
| 307.400 | | AM | RAF Cottesmore | TTTE Ops |
| 307.600 | | AM | RAF Neatishead | Air Defence Region Ops |
| 307.800 | | AM | RAF Fairford | Command Post |
| 307.800 | | AM | Stanford | Stanford Ops |
| 308.000 | | AM | Northern North Sea, AARA 3 | Air-Air Refuelling |
| 308.700 | | AM | RAF Fairford | B52 Ops (HAVOC) |
| 308.750 | | AM | RAF Chinevor | Ops |
| 309.075 | | AM | RAF Lakenheath | Radar |
| 309.550 | | AM | RAF Chetwynd | Ternhill Tower |
| 309.625 | | AM | RAF Odiham | Tower |
| 309.650 | | AM | Nationwide | AWACS |
| 309.650 | | AM | RAF Valley | 4FTS Air-to-Air |
| 309.675 | | AM | RAF Waddington | Talkdown |
| 309.725 | | AM | RAF Topcliffe | Tower |
| 309.875 | | AM | RAF Leeming | Talkdown |
| 309.950 | | AM | RAF Honington | Approach |
| 310.000 | | AM | Northern North Sea, AARA 2 | Air-Air Refuelling |
| 310.000 | | AM | RAF Aldergrove | Approach/Tower/Radar |
| 310.900 | | AM | Nationwide | 17 Sqn Air-Air |
| 311.100 | | AM | RAF Ternhill | Talkdown |
| 311.200 | | AM | RAF Valley | 4FTS Air-to-Air |
| 311.300 | | AM | RAF Lossiemouth | 12 Sqn Air-Air |
| 311.300 | | AM | Warton | Approach/Tower |
| 311.325 | | AM | RAF Lossiemouth | Lossie Director |
| 311.325 | | AM | RNAS Yeovilton | Yeovil Ground |
| 311.475 | | AM | Nationwide | USAF Air-Air |
| 311.825 | | AM | RAF Lossiemouth | 15 Sqn Air-to-Air |
| 311.950 | | AM | RAF Wittering | Ground |
| 311.975 | | AM | Nationwide | USAF General Air-Air |
| 312.000 | | AM | Middle Wallop (Army) | Wallop Approach |
| 312.075 | | AM | RAF Cottesmore | Approach/Director |
| 312.225 | | AM | RAF Coningsby | Approach |
| 312.225 | | AM | RAF Coningsby | Stud 13 |

| Base | Mobile | Mode | Location | User and Notes |
|------|--------|------|----------|----------------|
| 312.350 | | AM | RAF Northolt | Tower |
| 312.400 | | AM | RAF Lossiemouth | Talkdown |
| 312.450 | | AM | RAF Mildenhall | Command Post |
| 312.500 | | AM | RAF Waddington | Approach |
| 312.550 | | AM | RAF Marham | Ops |
| 312.625 | | AM | Dunsfold | Approach |
| 312.675 | | AM | Middle Wallop (Army) | Director |
| 312.700 | | AM | RNAS Merryfield | Tower |
| 312.800 | | AM | RAF Woodvale | Approach |
| 313.000 | | AM | Nationwide | USAF Air-Air |
| 313.100 | | AM | RAF Valley | 4FTS Air-to-Air |
| 314.475 | | AM | Nationwide | Air Defence Region |
| 315.000 | | AM | RAF Neatishead | NATO AWACS Coord |
| 315.325 | | AM | RAF Coltishall | Approach |
| 315.525 | | AM | DRA Farnborough | Radar |
| 315.550 | | AM | Edinburgh | UAS Air-Air |
| 315.575 | | AM | RAF Honington | Departure |
| 315.750 | | AM | RAF Benson | SRE |
| 315.850 | | AM | RAF Neatishead | Air Defence Region Ops |
| 315.975 | | AM | RAF Odiham | Odiham Information |
| 316.350 | | AM | Northern North Sea, AARA 8 | Air-Air Refuelling |
| 316.600 | | AM | Northern North Sea, AARA 4 | Air-Air Refuelling |
| 316.700 | | AM | RAF Lakenheath | 493FS Air-to-Air |
| 316.750 | | AM | Nationwide | USAF Air-Air |
| 316.800 | | AM | RAF Lossiemouth | Orange Alert |
| 316.900 | | AM | RAF Fairford | IAT Dutch F-16 Display Team |
| 317.200 | | AM | Northern North Sea, AARA 4 | Air-Air Refuelling |
| 317.375 | | AM | Nationwide | Air Cadets |
| 317.375 | | AM | RAF Lakenheath | 48FW Air-to-Air |
| 317.500 | | AM | Nationwide | Air Defence Region |
| 317.850 | | AM | Nationwide | Air Defence Region |
| 317.850 | | AM | Nationwide | RAF AWACS Ops |
| 318.100 | | AM | Nationwide | Air Defence Region |
| 318.550 | | AM | Nationwide | Air-Air Refuelling |
| 318.550 | | AM | RAF Boulmer | Air Defence Region Ops |
| 318.750 | | AM | RAF Neatishead | Air Defence Region Ops |
| 319.400 | | AM | RAF Neatishead | Air Defence Region Ops |
| 319.600 | | AM | Royal Navy | Ship-Air |
| 322.200 | | AM | Nationwide | USAF Air-Air |
| 322.400 | | NFM | Nationwide | TADIL-A Data Link |
| 322.950 | | AM | Cranfield | Runway 22 |
| 322.950 | | AM | East Anglia | USAF Talk-through |
| 322.950 | | AM | Edinburgh | Runway 07/25 |
| 322.950 | | AM | Kerry | Runway 07/25 |
| 322.950 | | AM | Nationwide | AWACS |
| 322.950 | | AM | Nationwide | USAF Displays |
| 323.200 | | AM | Nationwide | USAF Air-Air |
| 325.200 | | AM | Nationwide | RAF Discrete |
| 326.900 | | AM | North Sea, AARA 5 | Air-Air Refuelling |

326.500 - 328.500 MHz    RADIO ASTRONOMY, JODRELL BANK

## 328.600 - 335.400 MHz   AERONAUTICAL ILS (GLIDESLOPE COMPONENT)

| Base | Mode | Location | User and Notes |
| --- | --- | --- | --- |
| 329.150 | AM | Nationwide | Glideslope (Localiser 108.95 MHz) |
| 329.150 | AM | Woodford | Runway 25 |
| 329.300 | AM | Nationwide | Glideslope (Localiser 108.90 MHz) |
| 329.450 | AM | Filton (BAe), Bristol | Runway 10/28 |
| 329.450 | AM | Nationwide | Glideslope (Localiser 110.55 MHz) |
| 329.600 | AM | Bournemouth | Runway 08/26 |
| 329.600 | AM | London/Stansted | Runway 05/23 |
| 329.600 | AM | Nationwide | Glideslope (Localiser 110.50 MHz) |
| 329.750 | AM | Nationwide | Glideslope (Localiser 108.55 MHz) |
| 329.900 | AM | Nationwide | Glideslope (Localiser 108.50 MHz) |
| 329.900 | AM | RAF Benson | Runway 19 |
| 330.050 | AM | Nationwide | Glideslope (Localiser 110.75 MHz) |
| 330.200 | AM | Cardiff | Runway 12/30 |
| 330.200 | AM | Connaught | Runway 27 |
| 330.200 | AM | London/Heathrow | Runway 23 |
| 330.200 | AM | Nationwide | Glideslope (Localiser 110.70 MHz) |
| 330.200 | AM | RAF Coningsby | Runway 26 |
| 330.350 | AM | Humberside | Runway 21 |
| 330.350 | AM | Nationwide | Glideslope (Localiser 108.75 MHz) |
| 330.500 | AM | Nationwide | Glideslope (Localiser 108.70 MHz) |
| 330.500 | AM | RAF Leuchars | Runway 27 |
| 330.500 | AM | RAF Shawbury | Runway 19 |
| 330.500 | AM | RAF St Mawgan | Runway 31 |
| 330.650 | AM | Nationwide | Glideslope (Localiser 110.95 MHz) |
| 330.800 | AM | Belfast (Aldergrove) | Runway 17 |
| 330.800 | AM | Jersey | Runway 09 |
| 330.800 | AM | Leeds & Bradford | Runway 32/14 |
| 330.800 | AM | London/Gatwick | Runway 08R/26L |
| 330.800 | AM | Nationwide | Glideslope (Localiser 110.90 MHz) |
| 330.800 | AM | Norwich | Runway 27 |
| 330.800 | AM | Ronaldsway, Isle of Man | Runway 27 |
| 330.950 | AM | Nationwide | Glideslope (Localiser 111.95 MHz) |
| 331.250 | AM | Luton | Runway 08/28 |
| 331.250 | AM | Nationwide | Glideslope (Localiser 109.15 MHz) |
| 331.300 | AM | Nationwide | Glideslope (Localiser 111.90 MHz) |
| 331.300 | AM | RAF Brize Norton | Runway 08/26 |
| 331.400 | AM | Nationwide | Glideslope (Localiser 109.10 MHz) |
| 331.550 | AM | Nationwide | Glideslope (Localiser 111.15 MHz) |
| 331.700 | AM | Nationwide | Glideslope (Localiser 111.10 MHz) |
| 331.700 | AM | RAF Fairford | Runway 09/27 |
| 331.700 | AM | RAF Lossiemouth | Runway 23 |
| 331.700 | AM | RAF Waddington | Runway 21 |
| 331.700 | AM | Wattisham (Army Airfield) | Runway 23 |
| 331.850 | AM | Nationwide | Glideslope (Localiser 109.35 MHz) |
| 332.000 | AM | Glasgow Airport | Runway 23 |
| 332.000 | AM | Nationwide | Glideslope (Localiser 109.30 MHz) |
| 332.000 | AM | RAF Church Fenton | Runway 24 |
| 332.150 | AM | Nationwide | Glideslope (Localiser 111.35 MHz) |
| 332.300 | AM | Hatfield | Runway 24 |
| 332.300 | AM | Nationwide | Glideslope (Localiser 111.30 MHz) |
| 332.300 | AM | Teesside | Runway 23 |
| 332.450 | AM | Nationwide | Glideslope (Localiser 109.55 MHz) |
| 332.600 | AM | London/Heathrow | Runway 09R/27L |
| 332.600 | AM | Manchester | Runway 06/24 |

| Base | Mobile | Mode | Location | User and Notes |
|------|--------|------|----------|----------------|
| 332.600 | | AM | Nationwide | Glideslope (Localiser 109.50 MHz) |
| 332.600 | | AM | Plymouth | Runway 31 |
| 332.600 | | AM | Shannon | Runway 24 |
| 332.750 | | AM | Nationwide | Glideslope (Localiser 111.55 MHz) |
| 332.750 | | AM | Newcastle | Runway 07/25 |
| 332.900 | | AM | Nationwide | Glideslope (Localiser 111.50 MHz) |
| 332.900 | | AM | RAF Coltishall | Runway 22 |
| 333.050 | | AM | Coventry | Runway 23 |
| 333.050 | | AM | Nationwide | Glideslope (Localiser 109.75 MHz) |
| 333.200 | | AM | Beauvais | Runway 31 |
| 333.200 | | AM | Belfast (Aldergrove) | Runway 25 |
| 333.200 | | AM | Dinard | Runway 36 |
| 333.200 | | AM | Nationwide | Glideslope (Localiser 109.70 MHz) |
| 333.200 | | AM | RAF Cranwell | Runway 27 |
| 333.200 | | AM | RAF Kinloss | Runway 26 |
| 333.200 | | AM | RAF Lyneham | Runway 25 |
| 333.200 | | AM | RAF Valley | Runway 14 |
| 333.350 | | AM | Liverpool | Runway 09/27 |
| 333.350 | | AM | Nationwide | Glideslope (Localiser 111.75 MHz) |
| 333.500 | | AM | Nationwide | Glideslope (Localiser 111.70 MHz) |
| 333.500 | | AM | RAE Boscombe Down | Runway 24 |
| 333.650 | | AM | Nationwide | Glideslope (Localiser 109.95 MHz) |
| 333.800 | | AM | Aberdeen/Dyce | Runway 16/34 |
| 333.800 | | AM | Cherbourg | Runway 29 |
| 333.800 | | AM | Cork | Runway 17/35 |
| 333.800 | | AM | East Midlands | Runway 09/27 |
| 333.800 | | AM | Exeter | Runway 26 |
| 333.800 | | AM | Nationwide | Glideslope (Localiser 109.90 MHz) |
| 333.800 | | AM | Stornoway | Runway 18 |
| 333.800 | | AM | Warton | Runway 26 |
| 333.950 | | AM | Nationwide | Glideslope (Localiser 108.35 MHz) |
| 334.100 | | AM | Bedford | Runway 27 |
| 334.100 | | AM | Nationwide | Glideslope (Localiser 108.30 MHz) |
| 334.100 | | AM | RAF Lakenheath | Runway 24 |
| 334.250 | | AM | Bristol | Runway 09/27 |
| 334.250 | | AM | Nationwide | Glideslope (Localiser 110.15 MHz) |
| 334.400 | | AM | Birmingham | Runway 15/33 |
| 334.400 | | AM | Glasgow Airport | Runway 05 |
| 334.400 | | AM | Nationwide | Glideslope (Localiser 110.10 MHz) |
| 334.400 | | AM | RAF Marham | ILS Runway 24 |
| 334.550 | | AM | Blackpool | Runway 28 |
| 334.550 | | AM | Lydd | Runway 22 |
| 334.550 | | AM | Nationwide | Glideslope (Localiser 108.15 MHz) |
| 334.700 | | AM | Guernsey | Runway 09/27 |
| 334.700 | | AM | Nationwide | Glideslope (Localiser 108.10 MHz) |
| 334.700 | | AM | RAF Chivenor | Runway 28 |
| 334.700 | | AM | RAF Mildenhall | Runway 11/29 |
| 334.750 | | AM | RAF Neatishead | MRSA |
| 334.850 | | AM | Nationwide | Glideslope (Localiser 110.35 MHz) |
| 335.000 | | AM | Jersey | Runway 27 |
| 335.000 | | AM | London/Heathrow | Runway 09L/27R |
| 335.000 | | AM | Nationwide | Glideslope (Localiser 110.30 MHz) |
| 335.000 | | AM | Prestwick | Runway 13/31 |
| 335.000 | | AM | RAF Cottesmore | Runway 23 |
| 335.000 | | AM | RAF Leeming | Runway 16 |

| Base | Mobile | Mode | Location | User and Notes |
|------|--------|------|----------|----------------|

**335.400 - 338.000 MHz — UHF MILITARY AVIATION 25 kHz**

| Base | Mobile | Mode | Location | User and Notes |
|------|--------|------|----------|----------------|
| 336.150 | | AM | Boscombe Down (MoD) | Radar |
| 336.225 | | AM | Manorbier | Range |
| 336.325 | | AM | Hawarden | Tower |
| 336.350 | | AM | RAF Kinloss | Tower |
| 336.350 | | AM | RAF Leeming | Talkdown |
| 336.350 | | AM | RAF Marham | Ground |
| 336.375 | | AM | RAF Cottesmore | Ground |
| 336.475 | | AM | Filton (BAe), Bristol | Director |
| 336.475 | | AM | Warton | Radar |
| 336.525 | | AM | RAF St Athan | Tower |
| 337.575 | | AM | RAF Fairford | Tower |
| 337.600 | | AM | Jurby | Range Primary |
| 337.600 | | AM | RAF Lakenheath | Rapcon |
| 337.725 | | AM | RAF Valley | Director |
| 337.750 | | AM | Prestwick Airport | Navy Prestwick |
| 337.750 | | AM | RAF Lossiemouth | Tower |
| 337.750 | | AM | RNAS Prestwick | Navy Prestwick Ops |
| 337.825 | | AM | RAF Leeming | Approach |
| 337.850 | | AM | East Scotland | Combat Air Patrol Area A |
| 337.875 | | AM | RAF Cottesmore | Talkdown |
| 337.900 | | AM | RAF Marham | Tower |
| 337.900 | | AM | RAF Shawbury | Ground |
| 337.925 | | AM | MoD West Freugh | Tower |
| 337.950 | | AM | RAF Wittering | Talkdown |
| 337.975 | | AM | RAF Coningsby | Talkdown |

**338.000 - 399.900 MHz — TACTICAL MILITARY COMMUNICATIONS 25 kHz**

| Base | Mobile | Mode | Location | User and Notes |
|------|--------|------|----------|----------------|
| 338.200 | | NFM | Nationwide | TADIL-A Data Link |
| 338.650 | | AM | RAF Brize Norton | Brize Talkdown |
| 338.675 | | AM | RAF Lakenheath | Radar |
| 338.825 | | AM | RAF Ternhill | Tower |
| 338.850 | | AM | RAF Leeming | 11 Sqn Ops |
| 338.875 | | AM | RNAS Yeovilton | Yeovil Director |
| 338.975 | | AM | RNAS Predannack | Tower |
| 339.950 | | AM | RAF Coltishall | Tower |
| 339.950 | | AM | RNAS Culdrose | Radar |
| 339.975 | | AM | RNAS Yeovilton | Talkdown |
| 340.025 | | AM | RAF Linton-On-Ouse | Ground |
| 340.100 | | AM | RAF St Athan | Talkdown |
| 340.175 | | AM | RAF Lyneham | Ground |
| 340.175 | | AM | RAF Valley | Tower |
| 340.200 | | AM | RAF Church Fenton | Ground |
| 340.250 | | AM | Warton | Special Tasks-Test Flying |
| 340.300 | | AM | Central Wales | Combat Air Patrol Area |
| 340.325 | | AM | RAF Benson | Ground |
| 340.350 | | AM | RAF Shawbury | Tower |
| 340.425 | | AM | RAF Lakenheath | 493FS Aux-08 (Iceman) |
| 340.450 | | AM | RAF Neatishead | MRSA |
| 340.475 | | AM | RAF Cranwell | Approach |
| 340.525 | | AM | RAF Barkston Heath | Ground |
| 340.550 | | AM | North Sea | ACMI Range Show Ground 3 |
| 340.575 | | AM | RAF Cottesmore | Approach |
| 341.675 | | AM | Nationwide | Air Defence Region |
| 342.075 | | AM | RAF Barkston Heath | Tower |
| 342.100 | | AM | RAF Valley | 4FTS Air-to-Air |

| Base | Mobile | Mode | Location | User and Notes |
|------|--------|------|----------|----------------|
| 342.125 | | AM | RAF Waddington | Ground |
| 342.150 | | AM | RAF Chivenor | 7FTS Ops |
| 342.175 | | AM | Donna Nook | Range Primary |
| 342.250 | | AM | RAF Coltishall | Director |
| 342.450 | | AM | RAF Brize Norton | Brize Approach |
| 342.650 | | AM | Nationwide | RAF AWACS Ops |
| 342.650 | | AM | RAF Neatishead | Air Defence Region Ops |
| 343.200 | | AM | RAF Ty Croes | ADR Air-Ground |
| 343.300 | | AM | RAF Lakenheath | 493FS Aux-08 (Crusty) |
| 343.300 | | AM | RAF Neatishead | Air Defence Region Ops |
| 343.425 | | AM | RAF Lakenheath | Air-Air |
| 343.475 | | AM | RAF Lakenheath | 48FW Aux |
| 343.600 | | AM | RAF Croughton | Croughton Radio |
| 343.600 | | AM | RAF Lakenheath | 493FS |
| 343.675 | | AM | RAF Lakenheath | 494FS Panther Ops |
| 343.675 | | AM | RAF Leeming | 11 Sqn Air-Air |
| 343.700 | | AM | Warton | Radar |
| 344.000 | | AM | RAF Benson | Director |
| 344.000 | | AM | RAF Brize Norton | Brize Director |
| 344.000 | | AM | RAF Church Fenton | Director |
| 344.000 | | AM | RAF Coningsby | Director |
| 344.000 | | AM | RAF Cranwell | Director |
| 344.000 | | AM | RAF Honington | NATO Director |
| 344.000 | | AM | RAF Leeming | Director |
| 344.000 | | AM | RAF Linton-On-Ouse | Director |
| 344.000 | | AM | RAF Lyneham | Director |
| 344.000 | | AM | RAF Marham | Director |
| 344.000 | | AM | RAF St Mawgan | Director |
| 344.000 | | AM | RAF Valley | Director |
| 344.000 | | AM | RAF Waddington | Director |
| 344.000 | | AM | RAF Wittering | Dep Control |
| 344.100 | | AM | Nationwide | Air to Air Refuelling |
| 344.200 | | AM | RAF Lossiemouth | 16 Sqn Air-Air |
| 344.350 | | AM | RAF Topcliffe | Talkdown |
| 344.350 | | AM | RNAS Yeovilton | Talkdown |
| 344.425 | | AM | RAF Chivenor | 7FTS Air-Air |
| 344.475 | | AM | RAF Linton-On-Ouse | Director |
| 344.500 | | AM | Warton | Operations (Boffin Ops) |
| 344.575 | | AM | RAF Leeming | Tower |
| 344.625 | | AM | RAF Coningsby | Approach |
| 344.700 | | AM | RAF Marham | 13 Sqn Air-to-Air |
| 344.750 | | AM | RAF Cottesmore | Air-to-Air |
| 344.975 | | AM | RAF Northolt | Approach |
| 345.000 | | AM | RAF Neatishead | Air Defence Region Ops |
| 345.025 | | AM | Filton (BAe), Bristol | Tower |
| 345.025 | | AM | RAF Lyneham | Zone |
| 345.100 | | AM | RAF Wittering | 20 Sqn Ops |
| 345.200 | | AM | Larkhill | Range Primary |
| 349.175 | | AM | Prestwick | Scottish Military |
| 352.475 | | AM | Nationwide | AWACS |
| 353.000 | | AM | RAF Boulmer | Air Defence Region Ops |
| 353.050 | | AM | RAF Buchan | Air Defence Region Ops |
| 353.550 | | AM | Aberdeen | Approach/Radar |
| 353.550 | | AM | Boscombe Down (MoD) | Gauntlet Ops |
| 354.450 | | AM | English Channel | Naval Exercises |
| 355.025 | | AM | Nationwide | Forward Air Controllers |

| Base | Mobile | Mode | Location | User and Notes |
|------|--------|------|----------|----------------|
| 355.975 | | AM | Nationwide | 31 Sqn Air-Air |
| 356.175 | | AM | Wattisham (Army Airfield) | Talkdown |
| 356.200 | | AM | Aberporth | Range Primary |
| 356.275 | | AM | RAF Halton | Halton Aero Club |
| 356.325 | | AM | RAF Chetwynd | Shawbury Approach |
| 356.325 | | AM | RAF Shawbury | Approach |
| 356.400 | | AM | RAF Valley | 4FTS Air-to-Air |
| 356.700 | | AM | Stafford | RAF Stafford |
| 356.725 | | AM | RAF Leeming | Seagull Ops |
| 356.750 | | AM | RAF Valley | Ground |
| 356.850 | | AM | Nationwide | RAF AWACS Ops |
| 356.875 | | AM | RAF Brize Norton | Director |
| 356.925 | | AM | RAF Cranwell | Talkdown |
| 356.975 | | AM | RAF Shawbury | Talkdown |
| 357.125 | | AM | RAF Cosford | Tower |
| 357.150 | | AM | RAF Wittering | Tower |
| 357.175 | | AM | RAF St Athan | Approach |
| 357.200 | | AM | RAF St Mawgan | Approach |
| 357.375 | | AM | RAF Dishforth | Approach |
| 357.375 | | AM | RAF Topcliffe | Approach |
| 357.400 | | AM | DRA Farnborough | Tower |
| 357.475 | | AM | RAF Brize Norton | Brize Ops |
| 357.600 | | AM | Nationwide | AWACS |
| 358.400 | | AM | RAF Honington | Radar/NATO T/D |
| 358.475 | | AM | Northern England | Combat Air Patrol Area D West |
| 358.475 | | AM | RAF Kinloss | Ops |
| 358.525 | | AM | RAF Linton-On-Ouse | Talkdown |
| 358.550 | | AM | RAF Coningsby | Ground |
| 358.552 | | AM | Castlemartin | Range Air-Ground |
| 358.575 | | AM | Woodford | Tower/Radar |
| 358.600 | | AM | Wattisham (Army Airfield) | Tower |
| 358.650 | | AM | RAF Leeming | Director |
| 358.675 | | AM | RAF Lakenheath | Tower |
| 358.675 | | AM | RAF Valley | Talkdown |
| 358.725 | | AM | RAF Cottesmore | Director |
| 358.750 | | AM | RAF Honington | Radar |
| 358.750 | | AM | RAF Mona | Tower |
| 358.925 | | AM | Prestwick | Scottish Military |
| 359.400 | | AM | North Sea | ACMI Range Show Ground 2 |
| 359.425 | | AM | English Channel | Naval Exercises |
| 359.500 | | AM | RAF Lyneham | Approach |
| 359.775 | | AM | Boscombe Down (MoD) | Approach |
| 359.825 | | AM | Wattisham (Army Airfield) | Talkdown |
| 360.550 | | AM | RAF St Mawgan | Director |
| 360.725 | | AM | RAF Barkston Heath | Talkdown |
| 360.750 | | AM | RAF Colerne | Ground |
| 360.775 | | AM | Manorbier | Range |
| 361.100 | | AM | RAF Leeming | 11 Sqn Air-Air |
| 361.975 | | AM | North Sea | ACMI Range Show Ground 5 |
| 362.050 | | AM | Salisbury Plain | Salisbury Ops |
| 362.125 | | AM | RAF Lakenheath | Ram Rod |
| 362.175 | | AM | RAF Lossiemouth | 15 Sqn Air-to-Air |
| 362.300 | | AM | Glasgow Airport | Approach/Radar |
| 362.300 | | AM | RAF Benson | Approach/Zone |
| 362.300 | | AM | RAF Brize Norton | Brize Approach |
| 362.300 | | AM | RAF Church Fenton | Fenton Approach/Radar |

| Base | Mobile | Mode | Location | User and Notes |
|------|--------|------|----------|----------------|
| 362.300 | | AM | RAF Colerne | Approach |
| 362.300 | | AM | RAF Coningsby | Approach |
| 362.300 | | AM | RAF Cranwell | Approach |
| 362.300 | | AM | RAF Dishforth | Approach |
| 362.300 | | AM | RAF Kinloss | Approach |
| 362.300 | | AM | RAF Leeming | Approach |
| 362.300 | | AM | RAF Leuchars | Approach |
| 362.300 | | AM | RAF Linton-On-Ouse | Approach |
| 362.300 | | AM | RAF Lossiemouth | Approach |
| 362.300 | | AM | RAF Lyneham | Approach |
| 362.300 | | AM | RAF Marham | Approach |
| 362.300 | | AM | RAF Northolt | Approach |
| 362.300 | | AM | RAF St Athan | Approach |
| 362.300 | | AM | RAF Topcliffe | Approach |
| 362.300 | | AM | RAF Valley | Approach |
| 362.300 | | AM | RAF Waddington | Approach |
| 362.300 | | AM | RAF Wittering | Approach/Radar |
| 362.300 | | AM | RNAS Yeovilton | Approach/Director |
| 362.475 | | AM | RAF Shawbury | Radar |
| 362.525 | | AM | RAF Valley | 4FTS Air-to-Air |
| 362.650 | | AM | Boscombe Down (MoD) | Approach |
| 362.675 | | AM | RAF Linton-On-Ouse | Approach |
| 362.750 | | AM | RAF Marham | Approach |
| 362.825 | | AM | Nationwide | Air Defence Region |
| 362.900 | | AM | RAF Wittering | 1/20 Sqn Air-to-Air |
| 362.975 | | AM | RAF Coningsby | Ransack Ops |
| 364.200 | | AM | Faroe Islands | Pole Star |
| 364.200 | | AM | Nationwide | NATO Magic Surveillance |
| 364.200 | | AM | Nationwide | RAF AWACS Ops |
| 364.200 | | AM | RAF Neatishead | Air Defence Region Ops |
| 364.650 | | AM | RAF Leeming | 25 Sqn Ops (Silver Ops) |
| 364.650 | | AM | RNAS Yeovilton | D School |
| 364.800 | | AM | RAF Coltishall | Ops |
| 364.825 | | AM | Middle Wallop (Army) | Talkdown |
| 364.850 | | AM | RAF Valley | 4FTS Air-to-Air |
| 364.975 | | AM | North Sea | Combat Air Patrol Area E |
| 364.975 | | AM | RAF Coningsby | 56 Sqn Ops (Ransack Ops) |
| 365.025 | | AM | RAF Valley | 4FTS Air-to-Air |
| 365.050 | | AM | RAF Coningsby | Air-to-Air |
| 365.100 | | AM | RAF Mildenhall | Dispatcher |
| 365.675 | | AM | RAF West Drayton | London Military |
| 366.225 | | AM | Manorbier | Range Primary |
| 366.600 | | AM | RNAS Culdrose | 750 Sqn Ops |
| 367.125 | | AM | Nationwide | Air Defence Region |
| 367.200 | | AM | Nationwide | Air Defence Region |
| 367.200 | | AM | Nationwide | USAF Air-Air |
| 367.375 | | AM | Dunsfold | Approach |
| 367.375 | | AM | Dunsfold | Radar |
| 368.300 | | AM | RAF Wittering | 1 Sqn Air-Air |
| 369.000 | | AM | RAF Marham | 13 Sqn Ops (Dagger Ops) |
| 369.050 | | AM | Northern England | Combat Air Patrol Area D East |
| 369.100 | | AM | Faslane | Royal Navy (FOSSANI) |
| 369.125 | | AM | Nationwide | Air Defence Region |
| 369.150 | | AM | RAF Spadeadam | Ops |
| 369.175 | | AM | Nationwide | Air Defence Region |
| 369.375 | | AM | RAF Lakenheath | 493FS Discreet |

| Base | Mobile | Mode | Location | User and Notes |
|------|--------|------|----------|----------------|
| 369.650 | | AM | East Anglia | USAF Talk-through |
| 369.875 | | AM | RNAS Yeovilton | Radar |
| 369.900 | | AM | RAF Coningsby | 56 Sqn Ops (Lion Ops) |
| 369.975 | | AM | Yeovil (Westland) | Approach (Judwin) |
| 370.000 | | AM | RNAS Predannack | Tower |
| 370.050 | | AM | RAF Cottesmore | Tower |
| 370.050 | | AM | RAF Kinloss | Talkdown |
| 370.075 | | AM | RAF Leuchars | Talkdown |
| 370.100 | | AM | Nationwide | Patrolle Swisse air display team (Tower) |
| 370.100 | | AM | Nationwide | Swedick Tower air display team |
| 370.250 | | AM | RAF Mildenhall | Tower |
| 370.300 | | AM | MoD Llanbedr | PAR |
| 370.300 | | AM | RAF Brize Norton | Ground |
| 370.950 | | AM | RAF Mildenhall | AMC Ops |
| 371.200 | | AM | Nationwide | Air Defence Region |
| 371.200 | | AM | RAF Fairford | Command Post |
| 372.050 | | AM | RAF Neatishead | Air Defence Region Ops |
| 372.250 | | AM | RAF Chivenor | 7FTS Air-Air |
| 372.325 | | AM | RAF Valley | Approach |
| 372.350 | | AM | RAF Coltishall | 54 Sqn Ops (Lion Ops) |
| 372.375 | | AM | RAF St Athan | Talkdown |
| 372.425 | | AM | Cambridge | Tower/Radar |
| 372.425 | | AM | HMS Cambridge | Royal Navy |
| 372.425 | | AM | Yeovil (Westland) | Tower (Judwin) |
| 372.575 | | AM | RAF Ternhill | Talkdown |
| 372.625 | | AM | Middle Wallop (Army) | Wallop Tower |
| 372.650 | | AM | RAF Lossiemouth | 617 Sqn Air-Air |
| 372.650 | | AM | RNAS Yeovilton | Tower |
| 373.100 | | AM | Nationwide | Air Defence Region |
| 374.300 | | AM | RAF West Drayton | London Military |
| 374.425 | | AM | RAF Lakenheath | 493FS Discrete |
| 375.200 | | AM | RAF Lyneham | Talkdown |
| 375.325 | | AM | RAF Church Fenton | Director |
| 375.400 | | AM | Dunsfold | Tower |
| 375.425 | | AM | RAF Newton | Tower |
| 375.500 | | AM | RAF Northolt | Director |
| 375.500 | | AM | RAF Northolt | Talkdown |
| 376.525 | | AM | RAF Kinloss | Talkdown |
| 376.575 | | AM | RAF Cottesmore | Departure Control |
| 376.575 | | AM | RAF Wittering | Dep Control |
| 376.600 | | AM | Jurby | Range Secondary |
| 376.625 | | AM | RAF St Mawgan | Ground |
| 376.650 | | AM | RAF Kinloss | Approach |
| 376.650 | | AM | RAF Lossiemouth | Approach |
| 376.675 | | AM | RAF Shawbury | Talkdown |
| 376.900 | | AM | DRA Farnborough | Approach |
| 377.600 | | AM | Nationwide | Red Arrows Display |
| 378.100 | | AM | Nationwide | RAF AWACS Ops |
| 378.150 | | AM | RAF Wittering | 1 Sqn Air-Air |
| 378.200 | | AM | RAF Neatishead | MRSA |
| 379.125 | | AM | Nationwide | RAF AWACS Ops |
| 379.200 | | AM | Aberporth | Range Secondary |
| 379.375 | | AM | RAF Coningsby | Air-to-Air |
| 379.400 | | AM | Aberporth | Range Secondary |
| 379.425 | | AM | RAF Northolt | Director |
| 379.475 | | AM | RAF Fairford | Dispatcher |

| Base | Mobile | Mode | Location | User and Notes |
|------|--------|------|----------|----------------|
| 379.525 | | AM | RAF Cranwell | Tower |
| 379.650 | | AM | RAF Marham | Talkdown |
| 379.675 | | AM | RAF Dishforth | Ground |
| 379.700 | | AM | RAF Mona | Approach |
| 379.750 | | AM | Nationwide | RAF AWACS Ops |
| 379.750 | | AM | RNAS Yeovilton | ATIS |
| 379.800 | | AM | Teesside | Tower |
| 379.850 | | AM | Plymouth | Plymouth Military |
| 379.875 | | AM | Pembury | Range Primary |
| 379.900 | | AM | Nationwide | RAF AWACS Ops |
| 380.200 | | AM | Nationwide | AAC Eagles Air to Air |
| 380.800 | | AM | Nationwide | Air-Air Refuelling |
| 380.875 | | AM | Nationwide | Air Defence Region |
| 381.100 | | AM | RAF Waddington | Raven |
| 381.150 | | AM | RAF Coltishall | 41 Sqn Ops |
| 381.300 | | AM | Nationwide | USAF AWACS Ops |
| 381.575 | | AM | Nationwide | USAF AWACS Ops |
| 382.675 | | AM | Prestwick | Scottish Military |
| 382.900 | | AM | HMS Drake (Plymouth) | Royal Navy |
| 383.150 | | NFM | Nationwide | TADIL-A Data Link |
| 383.375 | | AM | Nationwide | RAF Discrete |
| 383.475 | | AM | RAF West Drayton | London Military |
| 383.600 | | AM | RAF Valley | 4FTS Air-to-Air |
| 385.400 | | AM | RAF Brize Norton | Talkdown |
| 385.400 | | AM | RAF Church Fenton | Talkdown |
| 385.400 | | AM | RAF Leeming | Talkdown |
| 385.400 | | AM | RAF Lyneham | Talkdown |
| 385.400 | | AM | RAF Marham | Talkdown |
| 385.400 | | AM | RAF Northolt | Talkdown |
| 385.400 | | AM | RAF Odiham | Talkdown |
| 385.400 | | AM | RAF St Mawgan | Talkdown |
| 385.400 | | AM | RAF Topcliffe | Talkdown |
| 385.400 | | AM | RAF Valley | Talkdown |
| 385.400 | | AM | RAF Waddington | Talkdown |
| 386.500 | | AM | RAF St Athan | Ground |
| 386.525 | | AM | RAF Leeming | Ground |
| 386.525 | | AM | RNAS Culdrose | Tower |
| 386.650 | | AM | RAF Leuchars | 43 Sqn Air-Air |
| 386.675 | | AM | MoD Llanbedr | Approach |
| 386.700 | | AM | Boscombe Down(MoD) | Tower |
| 386.725 | | AM | Dartmouth | Military Helipad |
| 386.725 | | AM | RAF Church Fenton | Talkdown |
| 386.775 | | AM | RAF Odiham | Approach |
| 386.825 | | AM | RAF Lyneham | Tower |
| 387.450 | | AM | RAF St Mawgan | Talkdown |
| 387.450 | | AM | RAF Topcliffe | Ground |
| 387.550 | | AM | RAF Lossiemouth | 16 Sqn Air-Air |
| 387.750 | | AM | MoD Llanbedr | Tower |
| 387.775 | | AM | RAF Coltishall | Ground |
| 388.000 | | AM | Nationwide | Sharks Helicopter Displays |
| 388.000 | | AM | RNAS Culdrose | Talkdown |
| 388.225 | | AM | RAF Waddington | Tower |
| 388.525 | | AM | RAF Wittering | Approach/Radar |
| 393.200 | | AM | RAF West Drayton | London Military |
| 393.475 | | AM | RAF Coningsby | Air-to-Air |
| 396.700 | | AM | RAF Brize Norton | Tower |

| Base | Mobile | Mode | Location | User and Notes |
|------|--------|------|----------|----------------|
| 396.850 | | AM | RAF Wittering | Talkdown |
| 397.850 | | AM | Nationwide | RAF AWACS Ops |
| 397.975 | | AM | RAF Lakenheath | Ground |
| 398.250 | | AM | Nationwide | NATO Air-Air |
| 398.605 | | NFM | Nationwide | Illegal Bugging Devices |
| 398.875 | | AM | Nationwide | Air Defence Region |
| 399.455 | | NFM | Nationwide | Illegal Bugging Devices |

### 399.9000 - 400.0500 MHz   RADIO NAVIGATION SATELLITE DOWN LINKS

### 400.050 - 401.100 MHz   SATELLITE DOWN LINKS & TELEMETRY

| Base | Mobile | Mode | Location | User and Notes |
|------|--------|------|----------|----------------|
| 400.100 | | NFM | Nationwide | Satellite Standard Frequency |
| 401.000 | | NFM | Nationwide | RAF Target Telemetry |

### 401.0000 - 406.1000 MHz   SATELLITE UPLINKS NFM, MOBILE SATELLITE TERMINAL UP LINK AND METEOROLOGICAL

| Base | Mobile | Mode | Location | User and Notes |
|------|--------|------|----------|----------------|
| 402.11350 | | NFM | Forties B | BP Weather Station |

### 406.000 - 406.100 MHz   LOW POWER MOBILE SATELLITES FOR EMERGENCY POSITION-INDICATIONG RADIO BEACONS AND NORTH SEA RADIO POSITIONS BEACONS

| Base | Mobile | Mode | Location | User and Notes |
|------|--------|------|----------|----------------|
| 406.00000 | | AM | International | Distress Frequency |
| 406.00000 | | NFM | Nationwide | Ship's EPIRB |
| 406.02500 | | AM | Nationwide | RAF Locator Beacons |
| 406.10000 | | AM | International | Distress Frequency Monitored by UK USA & Japan |

### 406.100 - 410.000 MHz   RADIO ASTRONOMY
Cambridge, Chilbolton, Darnhall, Defford, Jodell Bank, Knoockin, Pickmere and Wardle

### 402.450 - 425.000 MHz   MOD, USAF, US EMBASSY CLOSE PROTECTION TEAMS & MOULD USE 25 kHz, FORMULA ONE RACING TEAM LINKS AND NORTH SEA PLATFORMS

| Base | Mobile | Mode | Location | User and Notes |
|------|--------|------|----------|----------------|
| 402.45000 | | NFM | Nationwide | Formula I Racing Team Telemetry |
| 406.01250 | | NFM | Nationwide | Formula I Racing Team Telemetry |
| 406.15000 | | NFM | Nationwide | US Navy On-Board Comms |
| 406.42500 | | NFM | USAF Lakenheath | Ops |
| 406.42500 | | NFM | USAF Mildenhall | Medics |
| 406.55000 | | NFM | Nationwide | US Navy On-Board Comms |
| 406.62500 | | NFM | USAF Fairford | Tower-Ground |
| 406.62500 | | NFM | USAF Lakenheath | Ops |
| 406.62500 | | NFM | USAF Mildenhall | Ops |
| 406.87500 | | NFM | USAF Mildenhall | Fire Channel |
| 406.95000 | | NFM | Nationwide | US Navy On-Board Comms |
| 407.27500 | | NFM | USAF Fairford | Ops |
| 407.27500 | | NFM | USAF Mildenhall | Ops |
| 407.35000 | | NFM | Nationwide | US Navy On-Board Comms |
| 407.42500 | | NFM | London | US Embassy |
| 407.47500 | | NFM | RAF Chicksands | Security Ch 1 |
| 407.72500 | | NFM | London | US Embassy |

| Base | Mobile | Mode | Location | User and Notes |
| --- | --- | --- | --- | --- |
| 407.75000 | | NFM | USAF Mildenhall | Channel 1 |
| 408.00000 | | NFM | Statfjord A & B | Mobil To Hotel |
| 408.12500 | | NFM | Nationwide | US Presidential Advance Team |
| 408.27500 | | NFM | London | US Embassy |
| 408.30000 | | NFM | Jersey | Data Link |
| 408.55000 | | NFM | Nationwide | US Presidential Guard |
| 408.62500 | | NFM | London | US Embassy Marines |
| 408.67500 | | NFM | London | US Embassy Marines |
| 408.72500 | | NFM | USAF Lakenheath | Ops |
| 408.82500 | | NFM | USAF Mildenhall | Ops |
| 409.02500 | 416.55000 | NFM | London | US Embassy (N Control) |
| 409.02500 | 416.55000 | NFM | USAF Lakenheath | Trunked Voice |
| 409.12500 | 408.12500 | NFM | Nationwide | Police Ch 2 |
| 409.42500 | | NFM | Menwith Hill | US NSA spy station |
| 409.75000 | 407.45000 | NFM | Nationwide | US Military Ch 1 |
| 410.00000 | | NFM | Nationwide | USAF Base Common |
| 410.12500 | | NFM | RAF Lynham | Ops |
| 410.25000 | | FM | Lakenheath | RAF Ground Maintenance |
| 410.25000 | | NFM | Lakenheath | USAFE |
| 410.27000 | | NFM | USAF Fairford | Ground Maintenance |
| 410.27000 | | NFM | USAF Mildenhall | Base Ops |
| 410.27500 | 416.90000 | NFM | USAF Lakenheath | Trunked Voice |
| 410.27500 | 416.90000 | NFM | USAF Mildenhall | Trunked Voice |
| 410.28750 | 410.28750 | NFM | USAF Lakenheath | Ground Maintenance |
| 410.32500 | 410.28750 | NFM | USAF Mildenhall | Ops |
| 410.47500 | | NFM | USAF Fairford | Ground Support |
| 410.47500 | | NFM | USAF Fairford | Ops |
| 410.50000 | 410.47500 | NFM | USAF Lakenheath | Ops/Goldnet command |
| 410.50000 | 410.47500 | NFM | USAF Mildenhall | Phone Patches |
| 410.52500 | | NFM | Portsmouth | Navy Provosts |
| 410.60000 | | NFM | USAF Fairford | Base Security |
| 410.60000 | | NFM | USAF Mildenhall | Ops |
| 410.67500 | | NFM | RAF Chicksands | Fire Ch 4 |
| 410.67500 | | NFM | USAF Fairford | Base Security |
| 410.75000 | 410.67500 | NFM | USAF Fairford | Ground Support |
| 410.77000 | | NFM | USAF Mildenhall | Ops |
| 410.77500 | 417.55000 | NFM | USAF Lakenheath | Trunked Voice |
| 410.77500 | 417.55000 | NFM | USAF Mildenhall | Trunked Voice |
| 410.78000 | | NFM | USAF Mildenhall | Ops |
| 410.78750 | | NFM | USAF Lakenheath | Ops |
| 410.80000 | | NFM | RAF Chicksands | Base Ops |
| 410.80000 | | NFM | USAF Fairford | Base Security |
| 410.80000 | | NFM | USAF Lakenheath | Ops |
| 410.80000 | | NFM | USAF Mildenhall | Fuel Tankers Ch 5 |
| 410.85000 | | NFM | Manchester | Piccadilly Radio Studio Link |
| 410.85000 | 410.80000 | NFM | USAF Mildenhall | Ops |
| 410.87500 | | NFM | Nationwide | RAF Bases Air Defence |
| 410.87500 | | NFM | RAF Leuchars | Air Defence |
| 410.87500 | | NFM | RAF Waddington | Air Defence |
| 410.90000 | | NFM | Nationwide | MoD Transport |
| 410.90000 | | NFM | USAF Lakenheath | Ops |
| 410.90000 | | NFM | USAF Mildenhall | Command Network |
| 411.00000 | | NFM | USAF Fairford | Tanker Ops Ch 5 |
| 411.12500 | | NFM | USAF Lakenheath | Red Net |
| 411.15000 | | NFM | USAF Mildenhall | USAF Police |
| 411.18750 | 411.17500 | NFM | USAF Lakenheath | Ops |

| Base | Mobile | Mode | Location | User and Notes |
|---|---|---|---|---|
| 411.25000 | | NFM | Northwood | NATO Command Centre |
| 411.25000 | | NFM | USAF Lakenheath | MTD |
| 411.25000 | | NFM | USAF Mildenhall | Security |
| 411.27500 | | NFM | USAF Lakenheath | Yellow Net |
| 411.30000 | | NFM | USAF Lakenheath | Base Ops |
| 411.40000 | 411.30000 | NFM | USAF Mildenhall | Ops |
| 411.42500 | 417.75000 | NFM | USAF Lakenheath | Trunked Voice (night) |
| 411.42500 | 417.75000 | NFM | USAF Mildenhall | Trunked Voice (night) |
| 411.47500 | 417.75000 | NFM | USAF Mildenhall | Ops |
| 411.50000 | | NFM | USAF Mildenhall | Strategic Command |
| 411.50000 | 426.00000 | NFM | Statfjord A & C | Mobil to Hotel |
| 411.57500 | | NFM | USAF Lakenheath | Ground Maintenance |
| 411.57500 | | NFM | USAF Mildenhall | Maintenance |
| 411.58750 | | NFM | Northwood | NATO Command Centre |
| 411.60000 | | NFM | USAF Lakenheath | Base Ops |
| 411.62500 | | NFM | USAF Mildenhall | Fire Paging |
| 411.67500 | 418.35000 | NFM | RAF Chicksands | Security Ch 2 |
| 411.67500 | 418.35000 | NFM | USAF Lakenheath | Trunked Voice (night) |
| 411.67500 | 418.35000 | NFM | USAF Mildenhall | Trunked Voice (night) |
| 411.70000 | | NFM | USAF Lakenheath | Base Ops |
| 411.72500 | 418.40000 | NFM | USAF Lakenheath | Trunked Voice |
| 411.72500 | 418.40000 | NFM | USAF Mildenhall | Trunked Voice (Bandit) |
| 411.77500 | | NFM | USAF Lakenheath | Ops |
| 411.77500 | | NFM | USAF Mildenhall | Security |
| 411.80000 | | NFM | USAF Lakenheath | Ops |
| 411.80000 | | NFM | USAF Mildenhall | Security |
| 411.90000 | | NFM | USAF Mildenhall | Security |
| 412.17500 | | NFM | USAF Lakenheath | Ops |
| 412.17500 | | NFM | USAF Mildenhall | Maintenance |
| 412.27500 | | NFM | USAF Fairford | USAF Ground |
| 412.27500 | 418.50000 | NFM | USAF Lakenheath | Trunked Voice (Dispatch) |
| 412.27500 | 418.50000 | NFM | USAF Mildenhall | Trunked voice and data (night) |
| 412.37500 | 418.50000 | NFM | USAF Mildenhall | Services Squadron |
| 412.47500 | 418.50000 | NFM | USAF Fairford | Ops |
| 412.52500 | 418.50000 | NFM | Brecon | MoD Mould Repeater |
| 412.55000 | | NFM | USAF Lakenheath | Command Network |
| 412.55000 | | NFM | USAF Mildenhall | Base Ops |
| 412.58750 | 412.55000 | NFM | USAF Lakenheath | Ops |
| 412.77500 | | NFM | USAF Mildenhall | Ops |
| 412.80000 | | NFM | USAF Mildenhall | Ops |
| 412.83750 | 412.80000 | NFM | Brecon | MoD Mould Repeater |
| 412.90000 | | NFM | USAF Mildenhall | Ops |
| 412.92500 | | FM | Mildenhall | RAF Maintenance |
| 412.92500 | 418.75000 | NFM | Lakenheath | USAFE |
| 412.92500 | 418.75000 | NFM | Mildenhall | USAFE |
| 413.00000 | | NFM | USAF Mildenhall | Ops |
| 413.00000 | | NFM | USAF Mildenhall | USAF Police |
| 413.07500 | | NFM | USAF Lakenheath | Scrambled |
| 413.07500 | | NFM | USAF Mildenhall | Transit Alert |
| 413.08000 | | NFM | USAF Lakenheath | Base Ops |
| 413.10000 | | NFM | Nationwide | USAF Displays |
| 413.12000 | | NFM | USAF Lakenheath | Base Ops |
| 413.12500 | | NFM | USAF Mildenhall | Ops |
| 413.15000 | | NFM | Nationwide | USAF Base Common |
| 413.17500 | | NFM | USAF Lakenheath | Ops |
| 413.17500 | | NFM | USAF Mildenhall | Dispatch |

| Base | Mobile | Mode | Location | User and Notes |
|------|--------|------|----------|----------------|
| 413.20000 | | NFM | RAF Chicksands | Command & Control Ch 8 |
| 413.27500 | | NFM | USAF Fairford | Ground Support F1 control |
| 413.30000 | | NFM | USAF Mildenhall | Ground |
| 413.37000 | | NFM | USAF Mildenhall | Base Ops |
| 413.37500 | | NFM | USAF Mildenhall | Trunked Data Signalling |
| 413.37500 | 418.65000 | NFM | USAF Lakenheath | Trunked Data Signalling |
| 413.42500 | | NFM | Malvern (MoD) | Security |
| 413.45000 | | NFM | Nationwide | MoD Transport |
| 413.50000 | 428.05000 | NFM | Statfjord B & C | Mobil To Hotel |
| 413.70000 | | NFM | USAF Mildenhall | Ground |
| 413.75000 | | NFM | USAF Mildenhall | Maintenance |
| 413.77500 | | NFM | USAF Lakenheath | Base Ops |
| 413.80000 | | NFM | Nationwide | Nuclear Security |
| 413.80000 | | NFM | USAF Mildenhall | Ops |
| 413.85000 | | NFM | USAF Mildenhall | Ground |
| 413.90000 | | NFM | USAF Mildenhall | Maintenance |
| 414.15000 | | NFM | USAF Lakenheath | Base Ops |
| 414.15000 | | NFM | USAF Mildenhall | Command Network |
| 414.25000 | | NFM | USAF Mildenhall | Ground |
| 414.30000 | | NFM | USAF Fairford | USAF Base Security |
| 414.30000 | | NFM | USAF Lakenheath | Base Ops |
| 414.30000 | | NFM | USAF Mildenhall | Aircraft maintenance Ops |
| 414.30000 | 414.90000 | NFM | London | US Embassy |
| 414.30000 | 414.90000 | NFM | USAF Fairford | Ops |
| 414.30000 | 414.90000 | NFM | USAF Mildenhall | Base Ops |
| 414.40000 | | NFM | USAF Mildenhall | Ground |
| 414.48750 | | NFM | Grand Prix Circuits | McLaren Team Voice Link |
| 414.70000 | | NFM | USAF Lakenheath | Security |
| 414.98000 | | NFM | USAF Lakenheath | Ops |
| 415.35000 | | NFM | USAF Fairford | Ops |
| 415.40000 | | NFM | USAF Mildenhall | Ground |
| 415.56250 | | NFM | Belfast | British Military Data Link |
| 415.70000 | 407.85000 | NFM | Nationwide | Air Force One Air-Ground |
| 415.75000 | | NFM | USAF Mildenhall | Ground |
| 415.98750 | | NFM | Grand Prix Circuits | McLaren Team Voice Link |
| 416.00000 | | NFM | Newport | Moss Car Alarms Remote |
| 416.17500 | | NFM | Northwood | NATO Command Centre |
| 416.21750 | | NFM | Newmarket | RAF Security |
| 416.47500 | | NFM | Mildenhall | RAF SP Control/ Main gate police |
| 416.47500 | 413.00000 | NFM | RAF Chicksands | Enlisted Spouses Assoc. |
| 416.47500 | 413.00000 | NFM | USAF Lakenheath | Ops |
| 416.47500 | 413.00000 | NFM | USAF Mildenhall | Ops |
| 416.55000 | | NFM | Ashford | Royal Marines Intelligence Unit |
| 416.55000 | | NFM | USAF Lakenheath | Base Ops |
| 416.55000 | | NFM | USAF Mildenhall | Ops |
| 416.58750 | | NFM | USAF Mildenhall | Crash Ops |
| 416.70000 | | NFM | USAF Mildenhall | Ground |
| 416.90000 | | NFM | USAF Lakenheath | Security (Dispatch) |
| 417.10000 | | NFM | Colchester | Pulse Signal Constant. |
| 417.20000 | | NFM | USAF Mildenhall | Base Ops |
| 417.30000 | | NFM | USAF Lakenheath | Security |
| 417.52500 | | NFM | USAF Lakenheath | Ops |
| 417.52500 | | NFM | USAF Mildenhall | Aircrew Reception |
| 417.53000 | | NFM | USAF Lakenheath | Base Ops |
| 417.57500 | | NFM | USAF Fairford | Military Police |
| 417.93750 | | NFM | Manchester | Mould |

| Base | Mobile | Mode | Location | User and Notes |
|------|--------|------|----------|----------------|
| 418.00000 | | NFM | Newport | Moss House Alarms |
| 418.05000 | | FM | Mildenhall | RAF Ground Crew Ops |
| 418.20000 | | NFM | Normandy | French Marine Ch 16 Link |
| 418.22500 | | NFM | USAF Mildenhall | Ops |
| 418.23000 | | NFM | USAF Lakenheath | Base Ops |
| 418.30000 | | NFM | Jersey | Data Link |
| 418.32500 | | NFM | Nationwide | US Presidential Guard |
| 418.35000 | | NFM | USAF Lakenheath | Operations |
| 418.50000 | | NFM | USAF Lakenheath | Engineering (Spectre 1) |
| 419.20000 | | FM | Lakenheath | RAF Channel 4 Ops |
| 419.27500 | | NFM | USAF Lakenheath | Scrambled |
| 419.27500 | | NFM | USAF Mildenhall | Scrambled |
| 419.62500 | | NFM | Newmarket | RAF Security |
| 419.98750 | | NFM | Grand Prix Circuits | McLaren Team Voice Link |
| 420.01250 | | NFM | Manchester | Mould |
| 420.11250 | | NFM | Nationwide | Formula I Racing Team Telemetry |
| 420.40000 | | NFM | London | Wellington Barracks |
| 420.47500 | | NFM | Nationwide | Grand Prix  Minarde Team |
| 421.56250 | | NFM | Manchester | Mould |
| 421.78750 | | NFM | Manchester | Mould |
| 421.91250 | | NFM | Lyenham, Wiltshire | Mould |
| 421.01260 | | NFM | Strathclyde | Mould |
| 421.98175 | | NFM | Hertfordshire | Mould |
| 421.98750 | | NFM | Strathclyde | Mould |
| 422.01250 | | NFM | Nationwide | Tyrell Formula I Racing Team |
| 422.12500 | | NFM | RAF Waddington | Ops |
| 422.13750 | | NFM | London | Trooping the Colour 1994. |
| 422.13750 | | NFM | Nationwide | MoD Police |
| 422.15000 | 427.65000 | NFM | London | Ircheck |
| 422.21250 | | NFM | Hertfordshire | Mould |
| 422.23750 | | NFM | Henlow | Mould |
| 422.25000 | | NFM | Nationwide | RAF Bases Bomb Disposal |
| 422.25000 | | NFM | RAF Waddington | Bomb Disposal |
| 422.27500 | 465.17500 | NFM | Grays, Essex | Police (FD) relay Ch.57 |
| 422.36250 | | NFM | Strathclyde | Mould |
| 422.37500 | | NFM | London Houseguard Parade | Trooping the Colour |
| 422.38750 | | NFM | Colchester | Garrison Constant Carrier. |
| 422.41250 | | NFM | Hertfordshire | Mould |
| 422.95000 | 411.95000 | FM | Lakenheath | RAF Motor Pool Ops |
| 423.00000 | 408.50000 | NFM | Flotel | Mobil To Statfjord A & B |
| 424.25000 | | NFM | Belfast | Police Mobile Data Link |
| 424.75000 | | NFM | Northern Ireland | Special Branch |

## 420.000 - 425.000 MHz    TETRA PMR Civilian and Grovernment
## (Transmit -10 MHz)

| Base | Mobile | Mode | Location | User and Notes |
|------|--------|------|----------|----------------|
| 420.32500 | | NFM | North Herts | Civil TETRA |
| 420.33750 | | NFM | Reading | Civil TETRA |
| 420.37500 | | NFM | London | Tetra Data Carrier |
| 420.41250 | | NFM | London | TETRA data carrier |
| 420.42500 | | NFM | London | TETRA data carrier |
| 420.43750 | | NFM | London | Civil TETRA Foxton. |
| 420.50000 | | NFM | North Herts | Civil TETRA |
| 420.58750 | | NFM | Didcot. | Civil TETRA |
| 420.58750 | | NFM | London | TETRA data carrier |
| 420.60000 | | NFM | London | TETRA data carrier |

| Base | Mobile | Mode | Location | User and Notes |
|------|--------|------|----------|----------------|
| 420.61250 | | NFM | London | TETRA data carrier |
| 420.62500 | | NFM | North Herts | Civil TETRA |
| 420.66250 | | NFM | Moreton-In-Marsh. | Civil TETRA |
| 420.66250 | | NFM | Reading. | Civil TETRA |
| 420.67500 | | NFM | London | TETRA data carrier |
| 420.68750 | | NFM | Reading. | Civil TETRA |
| 420.72500 | | NFM | North Herts | Civil TETRA |
| 420.78750 | | NFM | London | Civil TETRA Foxton |
| 421.00000 | | NFM | Maidstone | Civil TETRA |
| 421.53750 | | NFM | Eversham. | Civil TETRA |
| 421.56250 | | NFM | Eversham. | Civil TETRA |
| 421.58750 | | NFM | Evesham | Civil TETRA |
| 421.80000 | | NFM | London, Wood Green | Civil TETRA |
| 421.82500 | | NFM | London | Civil TETRA |
| 421.82500 | | NFM | London, Heathrow | Civil TETRA |
| 421.83750 | | NFM | London, Heathrow | Civil TETRA |
| 421.93750 | | NFM | London, Heathrow | Civil TETRA |
| 421.98750 | | NFM | Moreton-In-Marsh. | Civil TETRA |
| 422.00000 | | NFM | Maidstone | Civil TETRA |
| 422.01250 | | NFM | Moreton-In-March | Civil TETRA |
| 422.03750 | | NFM | Oxford | Civil TETRA |
| 422.21250 | | NFM | Pershore | Civil TETRA |
| 422.23750 | | NFM | Pershore | Civil TETRA |
| 422.28750 | | NFM | London | TETRA data carrier |
| 422.28750 | | NFM | Oxford | Civil TETRA |
| 422.30000 | | NFM | London | TETRA data carrier |
| 422.30000 | | NFM | Maidstone | Civil TETRA |
| 422.31250 | | NFM | Oxford | Civil TETRA |
| 422.40000 | | NFM | Maidstone | Civil TETRA |
| 422.41250 | | NFM | London | Civil Tetra London Custom House. |
| 422.42500 | | NFM | Maidstone | Civil TETRA |
| 422.43750 | | NFM | London, Customs House | Civil TETRA |
| 422.62500 | | NFM | London | TETRA data carrier |
| 422.65000 | | NFM | Maidstone | Civil TETRA |
| 423.31250 | | NFM | Moreton-In-Marsh | Civil TETRA |
| 423.33750 | | NFM | Moreton-In-Marsh | Civil TETRA |
| 423.43750 | | NFM | London | Civil Tetra London Custom House |
| 423.43750 | | NFM | London, Heathrow | Civil TETRA |
| 424.08750 | | NFM | London | TETRA data carrier |
| 424.10000 | | NFM | London | TETRA data carrier |
| 424.11250 | | NFM | London | TETRA data carrier |
| 424.13750 | | NFM | London | TETRA data carrier |
| 424.15000 | | NFM | London | TETRA data carrier |
| 424.20000 | | NFM | London, London Bridge | Civil TETRA |
| 424.21250 | | NFM | London, Heathrow | Civil TETRA |
| 424.23750 | | NFM | London, Heathrow | Civil TETRA |
| 424.25000 | | NFM | London, Waterloo | Civil TETRA |
| 424.40000 | | NFM | Maidstone | Civil TETRA |
| 424.47500 | | NFM | Maidstone | Civil TETRA |

| Base | Mobile | Mode | Location | User and Notes |
|------|--------|------|----------|----------------|

### 425.3125 - 428.0125 MHz    BROADCASTING LINKS

| Base | Mobile | Mode | Location | User and Notes |
|------|--------|------|----------|----------------|
| 425.31250 | | NFM | Nationwide | JFMG Temp Point-Point Audio Links Sth/Sth West UK |
| 425.48750 | | NFM | Dorset | 2CR UHF Radio Microphones |
| 425.56250 | | NFM | Nationwide | JFMG Temp Point-Point Audio Links Sth/Sth West UK |
| 427.76250 | | NFM | Nationwide | JFMG Wide Area Talkback |
| 427.81250 | | NFM | Manchester | ITN O/B Studio Link |
| 428.00000 | | NFM | Birmingham | Xtra Am Radio 0/B Link |
| 428.01250 | | NFM | Nationwide | JFMG Wide Area Talkback |

### 428.325 - 432.475 MHz    MoD ALLOCATION

| Base | Mobile | Mode | Location | User and Notes |
|------|--------|------|----------|----------------|
| 428.32500 | | NFM | RAF Chicksands | Disaster Repeater Ch 7 |
| 429.06250 | | NFM | Didcot | Mould |
| 429.08750 | | NFM | Strathclyde | Mould |
| 429.11250 | | NFM | Strathclyde | Mould |
| 430.90000 | | NFM | RAF Newton | Base Security |
| 432.47500 | | NFM | London | Ruislip Mod Police Mobile Patrols |
| 433.18750 | | NFM | Colchester | Ptarmigan Link. |
| 433.18750 | | NFM | Strathclyde | Mould |
| 433.21250 | | NFM | London, North West | Mould |
| 433.26250 | | NFM | Strathclyde | Mould |
| 433.28750 | | NFM | Birmingham | Mould |
| 433.38750 | | NFM | Strathclyde | Mould |
| 433.43750 | 435.00000 | NFM | Strathclyde | Mould |

### 430.0000 - 440.0000 MHz    70CM AMATEUR RADIO BAND

| Base | Mobile | Mode | Location | User and Notes |
|------|--------|------|----------|----------------|
| 430.00000 | | SSB | Nationwide | Digital communications |
| 430.99000 | | SSB | Nationwide | Digital communications |
| 432.00000 | | SSB | Space | Moonbounce |
| 432.35000 | | SSB | Nationwide | Microwave talkback calling |
| 432.60000 | | SSB | Nationwide | RTTY (fsk) centre |
| 432.62500 | | NFM | Nationwide | Packet radio |
| 432.65000 | | NFM | Nationwide | Packet radio |
| 432.67500 | | NFM | Nationwide | Packet radio |
| 432.70000 | | NFM | Nationwide | Fax |
| 432.89000 | | CW | Sutton Coldfield | Beacon (GB3SUT) |
| 432.91000 | | CW | Emley Moor | Beacon (GB3MLY) |
| 432.93400 | | CW | Bristol | Beacon (GB3BSL) |
| 432.96500 | | CW | Lerwick | Beacon (GB3LER) |
| 432.97000 | | CW | St Austell | Beacon (GB3MCB) |
| 432.98000 | | CW | Dundee | Beacon (GB3ANG) |
| 433.40000 | | NFM | Nationwide | Channel 16 |
| 433.42500 | | NFM | Nationwide | Channel 17 |
| 433.45000 | | NFM | Nationwide | Channel 18 |
| 433.47500 | | NFM | Nationwide | Channel 19 |
| 433.50000 | | NFM | Nationwide | Channel 20 calling |
| 433.52500 | | NFM | Nationwide | Channel 21 |
| 433.55000 | | NFM | Nationwide | Channel 22 |
| 433.57500 | | NFM | Nationwide | Channel 23 |
| 433.60000 | | NFM | Nationwide | Channel 24 RTTY (afsk) |
| 433.70000 | | NFM | Leicester | Raynet |
| 433.72500 | | NFM | Leicester | Raynet |
| 433.77500 | | NFM | Mildenhall | Raynet |
| 434.60000 | 433.00000 | NFM | Ashford | Repeater (GB3CK) |
| 434.60000 | 433.00000 | NFM | Bishop Stortford | Repeater (GB3SV) |
| 434.60000 | 433.00000 | NFM | Blackburn | Repeater (GB3PF) |

| Base | Mobile | Mode | Location | User and Notes |
|---|---|---|---|---|
| 434.60000 | 433.00000 | NFM | Blandford Forum | Repeater (GB3DT) |
| 434.60000 | 433.00000 | NFM | Boston | Repeater (GB3SO) |
| 434.60000 | 433.00000 | NFM | Bracknell | Repeater (GB3BN) |
| 434.60000 | 433.00000 | NFM | Exeter | Repeater (GB3EX) |
| 434.60000 | 433.00000 | NFM | Llandudno | Repeater (GB3LL) |
| 434.60000 | 433.00000 | NFM | London Central | Repeater (GB3EL) |
| 434.60000 | 433.00000 | NFM | Milton Keynes | Repeater (GB3MK) |
| 434.60000 | 433.00000 | NFM | Newcastle | Repeater (GB3NT) |
| 434.60000 | 433.00000 | NFM | Norwich | Repeater (GB3NR) |
| 434.60000 | 433.00000 | NFM | Perth | Repeater (GB3PU) |
| 434.60000 | 433.00000 | NFM | Scarborough | Repeater (GB3NY) |
| 434.60000 | 433.00000 | NFM | Sheffield | Repeater (GB3US) |
| 434.60000 | 433.00000 | NFM | Wolverhampton | Repeater (GB3WN) |
| 434.62500 | 433.02500 | NFM | Bury | Repeater (GB3MA) |
| 434.62500 | 433.02500 | NFM | Doncaster | Repeater (GB3DV) |
| 434.62500 | 433.02500 | NFM | Harrogate | Repeater (GB3HJ) |
| 434.62500 | 433.02500 | NFM | Hemel Hempstead | Repeater (GB3BV) |
| 434.62500 | 433.02500 | NFM | Horsham | Repeater (GB3HO) |
| 434.62500 | 433.02500 | NFM | Melton Mowbray | Repeater (GB3EM) |
| 434.62560 | 433.02500 | NFM | Stonehaven | Repeater (GB3BA) |
| 434.62560 | 433.02500 | NFM | Wincanton | Repeater (GB3TC) |
| 434.65000 | 433.05000 | NFM | Aylesbury | Repeater (GB3AV) |
| 434.65000 | 433.05000 | NFM | Belfast | Repeater (GB3UL) |
| 434.65000 | 433.05000 | NFM | Blackpool | Repeater (GB3FC) |
| 434.65000 | 433.05000 | NFM | Corby | Repeater (GB3CI) |
| 434.65000 | 433.05000 | NFM | Crawley | Repeater (GB3NX) |
| 434.65000 | 433.05000 | NFM | Enfield Town Ctre | Repeater (GB3LV) |
| 434.65000 | 433.05000 | NFM | Hawick | Repeater (GB3HK) |
| 434.65000 | 433.05000 | NFM | Lincoln | Repeater (GB3LS) |
| 434.65000 | 433.05000 | NFM | Liskeard | Repeater (GB3CH) |
| 434.65000 | 433.05000 | NFM | Margate | Repeater (GB3EK) |
| 434.65000 | 433.05000 | NFM | Portsmouth | Repeater (GB3PH) |
| 434.65000 | 433.05000 | NFM | Stoke on Trent | Repeater (GB3ST) |
| 434.65000 | 433.05000 | NFM | Stourbridge | Repeater (GB3OS) |
| 434.65000 | 433.05000 | NFM | Wells | Repeater (GB3NN) |
| 434.65000 | 433.05000 | NFM | Yeovil | Repeater (GB3YS) |
| 434.67500 | 433.07500 | NFM | Chelmsford | Repeater (GB3ER) |
| 434.67500 | 433.07500 | NFM | Chichester | Repeater (GB3CC) |
| 434.67500 | 433.07500 | NFM | Hull | Repeater (GB3HU) |
| 434.67500 | 433.07500 | NFM | Kidderminster | Repeater (GB3KR) |
| 434.67500 | 433.07500 | NFM | Kilmarnock | Repeater (GB3KA) |
| 434.67500 | 433.07500 | NFM | Mansfield | Repeater (GB3MD) |
| 434.67500 | 433.07500 | NFM | Northampton | Repeater (GB3NH) |
| 434.67500 | 433.07500 | NFM | Swindon | Repeater (GB3TD) |
| 434.67500 | 433.07500 | NFM | Taunton | Repeater (GB3VS) |
| 434.67500 | 433.07500 | NFM | Uxbridge | Repeater (GB3HL) |
| 434.67500 | 433.27500 | NFM | Newhaven | Repeater (GB3LR) |
| 434.70000 | 433.10000 | NFM | Appleby, Cumbria | Repeater (GB3VE) |
| 434.70000 | 433.10000 | NFM | Bath | Repeater (GB3UB) |
| 434.70000 | 433.10000 | NFM | Bo'ness | Repeater (GB3OH) |
| 434.70000 | 433.10000 | NFM | Goole | Repeater (GB3GC) |
| 434.70000 | 433.10000 | NFM | Ipswich | Repeater (GB3IH) |
| 434.70000 | 433.10000 | NFM | Kings Lynn | Repeater (GB3KL) |
| 434.70000 | 433.10000 | NFM | Leicester | Repeater (GB3LE) |
| 434.70000 | 433.10000 | NFM | Pembroke | Repeater (GB3SP) |
| 434.70000 | 433.10000 | NFM | Wrotham | Repeater (GB3NK) |

| Base | Mobile | Mode | Location | User and Notes |
|---|---|---|---|---|
| 434.72500 | 433.12500 | NFM | Brentwood | Repeater (GB3EB) |
| 434.72500 | 433.12500 | NFM | Cheltenham | Repeater (GB3GH) |
| 434.72500 | 433.12500 | NFM | Douglas | Repeater (GB3IM) |
| 434.72500 | 433.12500 | NFM | Haywards Heath | Repeater (GB3HY) |
| 434.72500 | 433.12500 | NFM | Huntingdon | Repeater (GB3OV) |
| 434.72500 | 433.12500 | NFM | Scunthorpe | Repeater (GB3WJ) |
| 434.72500 | 433.12500 | NFM | Weston Super Mere | Repeater (GB3WB) |
| 434.72500 | 433.15000 | NFM | Ampthill | Repeater (GB3BD) |
| 434.72500 | 433.15000 | NFM | Canterbury | Repeater (GB3SK) |
| 434.72500 | 433.15000 | NFM | London, central | Repeater (GB3LW) |
| 434.72500 | 433.15000 | NFM | Mold, Clywd | Repeater (GB3CR) |
| 434.72500 | 433.15000 | NFM | Newtown, Powys | Repeater (GB3CW) |
| 434.72500 | 433.15000 | NFM | Rugby | Repeater (GB3ME) |
| 434.75000 | 433.15000 | NFM | Barnsley | Repeater (GB3SY) |
| 434.75000 | 433.15000 | NFM | Brighton | Repeater (GB3BR) |
| 434.75000 | 433.15000 | NFM | Didcot | Repeater (GB3DI) |
| 434.75000 | 433.15000 | NFM | Hereford | Repeater (GB3HC) |
| 434.75000 | 433.15000 | NFM | Hornsea | Repeater (GB3HA) |
| 434.75000 | 433.15000 | NFM | Port Talbot | Repeater (GB3WG) |
| 434.75000 | 433.15000 | NFM | Wolverhampton | Repeater (GB3MM) |
| 434.77500 | 433.17500 | NFM | Bedford | Repeater (GB3BL) |
| 434.77500 | 433.17500 | NFM | Dridgend | Repeater (GB3MG) |
| 434.77500 | 433.17500 | NFM | Halifax | Repeater (GB3WY) |
| 434.77500 | 433.17500 | NFM | Macclesfield | Repeater (GB3MF) |
| 434.77500 | 433.17500 | NFM | Nottingham | Repeater (GB3NM) |
| 434.77500 | 433.20000 | NFM | Amlwick | Repeater (GB3AN) |
| 434.80000 | 433.20000 | NFM | Banbury | Repeater (GB3EH) |
| 434.80000 | 433.20000 | NFM | Cambridge | Repeater (GB3PY) |
| 434.80000 | 433.20000 | NFM | Carmarthen | Repeater (GB3CM) |
| 434.80000 | 433.20000 | NFM | Leeds | Repeater (GB3LA) |
| 434.80000 | 433.20000 | NFM | Southampton | Repeater (GB3EA) |
| 434.80000 | 433.20000 | NFM | Telford | Repeater (GB3TF) |
| 434.82500 | 433.22500 | NFM | Bury St Edmunds | Repeater (GB3BE) |
| 434.82500 | 433.22500 | NFM | Clacton | Repeater (GB3CL) |
| 434.82500 | 433.25000 | NFM | Wirksworth | Repeater (GB3DY) |
| 434.85000 | 433.25000 | NFM | Airdrie | Repeater (GB3ML) |
| 434.85000 | 433.25000 | NFM | Banstead | Repeater (GB3NS) |
| 434.85000 | 433.25000 | NFM | Bristol | Repeater (GB3BS) |
| 434.85000 | 433.25000 | NFM | Derby | Repeater (GB3DY) |
| 434.85000 | 433.25000 | NFM | Dundee | Repeater (GB3DD) |
| 434.85000 | 433.25000 | NFM | Leamington Spa | Repeater (GB3MW) |
| 434.85000 | 433.25000 | NFM | Liverpool | Repeater (GB3LI) |
| 434.85000 | 433.25000 | NFM | Luton | Repeater (GB3LT) |
| 434.85000 | 433.25000 | NFM | Newbury | Repeater (GB3AW) |
| 434.85000 | 433.25000 | NFM | Peterborough | Repeater (GB3PB) |
| 434.87500 | 433.27500 | NFM | Aldermaston | Repeater (GB3BK) |
| 434.87500 | 433.27500 | NFM | Grantham | Repeater (GB3GR) |
| 434.87500 | 433.27500 | NFM | Grimsby | Repeater (GB3GY) |
| 434.87500 | 433.27500 | NFM | Hinckley | Repeater (GB3HT) |
| 434.87500 | 433.27500 | NFM | Honiton | Repeater (GB3SH) |
| 434.87500 | 433.27500 | NFM | Hyde | Repeater (GB3WP) |
| 434.87500 | 433.27500 | NFM | Maidstone | Repeater (GB3RE) |
| 434.87500 | 433.27500 | NFM | Newhaven | Repeater (GB3LR) |
| 434.87500 | 433.27500 | NFM | Stafford | Repeater (GB3ZI) |
| 434.87500 | 433.27500 | NFM | Sunderland | Repeater (GB3DC) |
| 434.87500 | 433.27500 | NFM | Swaffham | Repeater (GB3AH) |

| Base | Mobile | Mode | Location | User and Notes |
|------|--------|------|----------|----------------|
| 434.90000 | 433.30000 | NFM | Bolton | Repeater (GB3MT) |
| 434.90000 | 433.30000 | NFM | Boroughbridge | Repeater (GB3HM) |
| 434.90000 | 433.30000 | NFM | Chesterfield | Repeater (GB3EE) |
| 434.90000 | 433.30000 | NFM | Guildford | Repeater (GB3GF) |
| 434.90000 | 433.30000 | NFM | Oxford | Repeater (GB3OX) |
| 434.90000 | 433.30000 | NFM | Royston | Repeater (GB3PT) |
| 434.92500 | 433.32500 | NFM | Carlisle | Repeater (GB3CA) |
| 434.92500 | 433.32500 | NFM | Daventry | Repeater (GB3XX) |
| 434.92500 | 433.32500 | NFM | Leek | Repeater (GB3SM) |
| 434.92500 | 433.32500 | NFM | Louth | Repeater (GB3LC) |
| 434.92500 | 433.32500 | NFM | Romford | Repeater (GB3HW) |
| 434.92500 | 433.32500 | NFM | St Peter Port | Repeater (GB3GU) |
| 434.92500 | 433.32500 | NFM | Welwyn Garden City | Repeater (GB3VH) |
| 434.92500 | 433.32500 | NFM | Worksop | Repeater (GB3DS) |
| 434.92500 | 433.32500 | NFM | York | Repeater (GB3CY) |
| 434.95000 | 433.35000 | NFM | Aberdeen | Repeater (GB3AB) |
| 434.95000 | 433.35000 | NFM | Bideford | Repeater (GB3ND) |
| 434.95000 | 433.35000 | NFM | Birmingham | Repeater (GB3CB) |
| 434.95000 | 433.35000 | NFM | Colchester | Repeater (GB3CE) |
| 434.95000 | 433.35000 | NFM | Edinburgh | Repeater (GB3ED) |
| 434.95000 | 433.35000 | NFM | Glasgow | Repeater (GB3GL) |
| 434.95000 | 433.35000 | NFM | Harrow | Repeater (GB3HR) |
| 434.95000 | 433.35000 | NFM | Hastings | Repeater (GB3HE) |
| 434.95000 | 433.35000 | NFM | Lancaster | Repeater (GB3LF) |
| 434.95000 | 433.35000 | NFM | Leeds | Repeater (GB3WF) |
| 434.95000 | 433.35000 | NFM | Lowestoft | Repeater (GB3YL) |
| 434.95000 | 433.35000 | NFM | Spalding | Repeater (GB3TL) |
| 434.95000 | 433.35000 | NFM | Stockport | Repeater (GB3MR) |
| 434.95000 | 433.35000 | NFM | Weymouth | Repeater (GB3SD) |
| 434.97500 | 433.37500 | NFM | Bournemouth | Repeater (GB3SZ) |
| 434.97500 | 433.37500 | NFM | Cardiff | Repeater (GB3SG) |
| 434.97500 | 433.37500 | NFM | Farnham | Repeater (GB3FN) |
| 434.97500 | 433.37500 | NFM | Omagh | Repeater (GB3OM) |
| 434.97500 | 433.37500 | NFM | Preston | Repeater (GB3PP) |
| 434.97500 | 433.37500 | NFM | Shrewsbury | Repeater (GB3LH) |
| 434.97500 | 433.37500 | NFM | St Austell | Repeater (GB3HB) |
| 434.97500 | 433.37500 | NFM | Sudbury | Repeater (GB3SU) |
| 434.97500 | 433.37500 | NFM | Tamworth | Repeater (GB3TH) |
| 434.97500 | 433.37500 | NFM | Wakefield | Repeater (GB3WU) |
| 434.97500 | 433.37500 | NFM | Wisbech | Repeater (GB3WI) |
| 435.07500 | | NFM | Space | Oscar 14 |
| 435.15000 | | NFM | Space | Oscar 19 Data |
| 435.25000 | | NFM | Space | Oscar 14 |
| 435.91000 | | NFM | Space | Oscar 20 Beacon |
| 438.02500 | | NFM | Nationwide | Fast scan TV |
| 438.20000 | | NFM | Nationwide | Fast scan TV |
| 438.57500 | | NFM | Nationwide | Fast scan TV |

433.720 - 434.120 MHz     VEHICLE RADIO KEYS

433.6250 - 439.4500 MHz     MOD, BROADCASTING LINKS,

## Radiocommunications Agency UHF Band I and Band II Channel Allocations

Each radio frequency has a channel number. Some of the channel numbers have been worked out and these are the tie-ups found so far. Transitory means that the radios can be used anywhere in the UK, similar to SRBR but in theory the licence holder is supposed to notify the local RCA office of the time and place of intended use. People in the London area who wish to try and work out more channel numbers, write to the RCA library or phone on 0171 211 0211 and ask for a copy of RA343/RA336. Both of these publications are free of charge and list UHF band users location and power and even how many mobiles/handhelds the user has.

RCA UHF 1

| MHz | MHz | Radio Users |
|-----|-----|-------------|
| 440.350 | 425.850 | On site 8 dual |
| 440.375 | 425.875 | On site 9 dual |
| 440.900 | 426.400 | On site 16 dual |
| 440.950 | 426.450 | On site 18 dual |
| 441.1125 | 426.6125 | On site 20 dual |
| 442.525 | 428.025 | On site 26 dual |
| 442.625 | 428.125 | On site 30 dual |
| 442.650 | 428.150 | On site 31 dual |
| 442.750 | 428.250 | On site 34 dual |
| 442.775 | 428.275 | On site 39 dual |
| 442.875 | 428.375 | Wide area shared 43 dual |
| 442.900 | 428.400 | Wide area shared 45 dual |
| 443.025 | 428.525 | On site 41 dual |
| 443.050 | 428.550 | On site 43 dual |
| 443.450 | 428.950 | On site 61 dual |
| 443.475 | 428.975 | On site 53 dual |
| 445.725 | 425.225 | On site 57 dual |
| 445.750 | 425.250 | On site 58 dual |
| 445.775 | 425.275 | On site 59 dual |
| 445.800 | 425.300 | On site 60 dual |
| 445.975 | 425.475 | Wide area shared 62 dual |
| 446.000 | | On site 1 single |
| 446.00625 | | Ch.1 PMR446 |
| 446.0125 | | On site 2 single |
| 446.01875 | | Ch.2 PMR446 |
| 446.025 | | On site 3 single |
| 446.03125 | | Ch.3 PMR446 |
| 446.0375 | | On site 4 single |
| 446.04375 | | Ch.4 PMR446 |
| 446.050 | | On site 5 single |
| 446.05625 | | Ch.5 PMR446 |

| Base | Mobile | Mode | Location | User and Notes |
|------|--------|------|----------|----------------|

| MHz | Radio Users |
|-----|-------------|
| 446.0625 | On site 6 single |
| 446.06875 | Ch.6 PMR446 |
| 446.075 | On site 7 single |
| 446.08125 | Ch.7 PMR446 |
| 446.0875 | On site 8 single |
| 446.09375 | Ch.8 PMR446 |
| 446.100 | On site 9 single |
| 446.1125 | On site 10 single |
| 446.125 | On site 11 single |
| 446.1375 | On site 12 single |
| 446.150 | On site 13 single |
| 446.1625 | On site 14 single |
| 446.175 | On site 15 single |
| 446.1875 | On site 16 single |
| 446.200 | On site 17 single |
| 446.2125 | On site 18 single |
| 446.225 | On site 19 single |
| 446.2375 | On site 20 single |
| 446.250 | On site 21 single |
| 446.2625 | On site 22 single |
| 446.275 | On site 23 single |
| 446.2875 | On site 24 single |
| 446.2875 | On site 24 single |
| 446.300 | On site 25 single |
| 446.3125 | On site 26 single |
| 446.325 | On site 27 single |
| 446.3375 | On site 28 single |
| 446.350 | On site 29 single |
| 446.3625 | On site 30 single |
| 446.375 | On site 31 single |
| 446.3875 | On site 32 single |
| 446.400 | On site 33 single |
| 447.650 | On site 34 single |
| 447.6625 | On site 35 single |
| 447.6875 | On site 37 single |
| 447.7125 | On site 38 single |
| 447.725 | On site 39 single |
| 447.7875 | On site 41 single |
| 447.8125 | On site 42 single |
| 447.825 | On site 43 single |

RCA UHF 2

| MHz | MHz | Radio Users |
| --- | --- | --- |
| 453.025 | 459.525 | On site 1 dual |
| 453.0625 | 459.5625 | On site 2 dual |
| 453.075 | | On site 31 single |
| 453.075 | 459.575 | On site 1 dual |
| 453.0875 | 459.5875 | On site 3 dual |
| 453.100 | 459.600 | On site 4 dual |
| 453.1125 | 459.6125 | On site 5 dual |
| 453.125 | | On site 32 single |
| 453.125 | 459.625 | Split dual 2 |
| 453.175 | 459.675 | On site 6 dual |
| 453.250 | 459.750 | Wide area shared 4 dual |
| 453.350 | | On site 35 single |
| 453.350 | 459.850 | Split dual 5 |
| 453.450 | | On site 38 single |
| 453.450 | 459.950 | Split dual 8 |
| 453.475 | 459.975 | On site 7 dual |
| 453.500 | 460.000 | On site 8 dual |
| 453.525 | | On site 39 single |
| 453.550 | 460.050 | National 4 dual |
| 453.550 | | UK general use |
| 453.575 | | On site 40 single |
| 453.600 | 460.100 | On site 9 dual |
| 453.625 | | On site 41 single |
| 453.650 | 460.150 | Split dual 12 |
| 453.650 | | On site 42 single |
| 453.675 | 460.175 | Split dual 13 |
| 453.675 | | On site 43 single |
| 453.750 | 460.250 | On site 11 dual |
| 453.775 | 460.275 | On site 12 dual |
| 453.875 | 460.375 | Split dual 15 |
| 453.875 | | On site 45 single |
| 453.900 | 460.400 | National 5 dual |
| 453.900 | | UK general use |
| 453.925 | 460.425 | On site 14 dual |
| 453.975 | 460.475 | Wide area shared 7 dual |
| 456.000 | 461.500 | National 18 dual security ch |
| 456.025 | 461.525 | On site 15 dual |
| 456.050 | 461.550 | Wide area shared 8 dual |
| 456.2625 | 461.7625 | National 35 dual |
| 456.350 | 461.850 | On site 16 dual |
| 456.375 | 461.875 | National 38 dual |
| 456.400 | 461.900 | National 39 dual |
| 456.4125 | 461.9125 | National 40 dual |

| Base | Mobile | Mode | Location | User and Notes |
|------|--------|------|----------|----------------|

<u>RCA UHF 2 (cont.)</u>

| MHz | MHz | | | Radio Users |
|------|------|---|---|-------------|
| 456.425 | 461.925 | | | National 41 dual |
| 456.450 | 461.950 | | | National 42 dual |
| 456.475 | 461.975 | | | Wide area shared 9 dual |
| 456.600 | 462.100 | | | On site 18 dual |
| 456.625 | | | | On site 48 single |
| 456.625 | 462.125 | | | Split dual 18 |
| 456.650 | 462.150 | | | On site 19 dual |
| 456.675 | 462.175 | | | On site 20 dual |
| 456.725 | 462.225 | | | Split dual 19 |
| 456.725 | | | | On site 49 dual |
| 456.825 | 462.325 | | | On site 23 dual |
| 456.875 | 462.375 | | | On site 24 dual |
| 456.900 | | | | On site 52 single |
| 456.900 | 462.400 | | | Split dual 22 |
| 456.975 | 462.475 | | | Split dual 23 |
| 456.975 | | | | National coach emergency channel |
| 459.575 | | | | On site 1 single |
| 459.625 | | | | On site 2 single |
| 459.850 | | | | On site 5 single |
| 459.950 | | | | On site 8 single |
| 460.025 | | | | On site 9 single |
| 460.150 | | | | On site 12 single |
| 460.175 | | | | On site 13 single |
| 460.375 | | | | On site 15 single |
| 461.2875 | | | | UK general 1 [transitory] |
| 461.3125 | | | | On site 17 single |
| 461.325 | | | | On site 18 single |
| 461.3375 | | | | On site 19 single |
| 461.350 | | | | On site 20 single |
| 461.3625 | | | | On site 21 single |
| 461.375 | | | | UK general 2 [transitory] |
| 461.3875 | | | | On site 22 single |
| 461.400 | | | | On site 23 single |
| 461.450 | | | | UK general 3 [transitory] |
| 461.4625 | | | | On site 24 single |
| 462.100 | | | | UK general |
| 462.125 | | | | On site 26 single |
| 462.225 | | | | On site 27 single |
| 462.400 | | | | On site 30 single |
| 462.475 | | | | Short term hire 1 single |

By looking at the above allocations one can find particular users much easier. Say for instance you are looking for the frequencies in use by a large car factory, the first place to look would be *On Site Dual Allocations*. UHF I Allocations are only in certain large cities, so for most parts of UK UHF II is used.

So lets say the end user is in Luton, concentrate On UHF 2 Allocation as the radio searches for signals it stops on 456.025 and 453.0625 *On site 15 dual* and *On site 2 dual* respectively. Knowing these are On site Allocations paying attention to both of these frequencies find if they are talking about a car production line. During searching the scanner stopped on other frequency but they were not normal On Site Alocations, but take a note of them and check them later. You can't rely on this method 100 % but it is quite effective. At any one site there might be a variety of channels available, so don't just find one frequency and think that is the site finished with, check *On site single Allocations* as well because they are bound to have at least one available to them, then think of the users on the site. A car factory would have frequencies used by production, maybe one for management or administration, another for security, maintenance, catering etc. At some sites it has been found if a large amount of on site duplex channels are in use on site or in the area. Other allocations will be given to the user such as a Wlde Area Shared.

There are also VHF on site duplex allocations.

| MHz | MHz |
| --- | --- |
| 165.0250 | 169.8250 |
| 165.0750 | 169.8750 |
| 165.0875 | 169.8875 |
| 165.1625 | 169.9625 |
| 165.1875 | 169.9875 |
| 165.2125 | 170.0125 |
| 165.2375 | 170.0375 |
| 165.2875 | 170.0875 |
| 166.7125 | 171.5125 |
| 166.7625 | 171.5625 |
| 166.8375 | 171.6375 |
| 167.0375 | 171.8375 |

UHF Wide Area Shared channels will tend to be used by taxis, couriers and council services. Community repeaters are not listed because these are easily identified by the amount of different users on one frequency. Small shops, restaurants, clubs, factories etc. will use on site single allocations short term hire, parking & demo SRBR PMR446 etc.

## NORTH SEA RIGS AND SPACE

| Base | Mobile | Mode | Location | User and Notes |
| --- | --- | --- | --- | --- |
| 433.62500 | | NFM | Nationwide | CH4 The Big Breakfast O/B |
| 433.76250 | | AM | Mildenhall | Air Display Co-ordination |
| 433.87500 | | NFM | USAF Mildenhall | Ops |
| 435.62500 | | NFM | Nationwide | RAF Cadets Channel U2 |
| 435.72500 | | NFM | Nationwide | RAF Cadets Channel U5 Data |
| 435.75000 | | AM | Nationwide | ATC Channel U1 |
| 435.75000 | | NFM | Nationwide | RAF Cadets NATO Channel U1 |
| 435.97500 | | NFM | Space | Polar Bear 8688A |
| 436.20000 | | NFM | Oldham | Satellite equipment installer |
| 437.47500 | | NFM | London, North West | Constant Carrier Signal. |
| 437.73500 | | NFM | Nationwide | Grand Prix Benetton pits to cars |
| 437.88750 | | NFM | London | Capital Radio Relay |
| 438.07500 | | NFM | USAF Mildenhall | Ops |
| 438.35000 | | NFM | North Sea | Ekofisk Senter Phillips |
| 438.40000 | | NFM | North Sea | Ekofisk Senter Phillips |
| 438.45000 | | NFM | North Sea | Ekofisk Senter Phillips |
| 438.50000 | | NFM | North Sea | Ekofisk Senter Phillips |
| 438.55000 | | NFM | Edinburgh | Sky TV Sound Relay |
| 438.60000 | | NFM | North Sea | Ekofisk Senter Phillips |
| 439.00000 | 446.00000 | NFM | North Sea | Ekofisk Senter Phillips |
| 439.20000 | 446.20000 | NFM | North Sea | Amoco Valhalla Field |
| 439.22500 | 446.22500 | NFM | North Sea | Ekofisk Senter Phillips |
| 439.27500 | 446.27500 | NFM | North Sea | Amoco Valhalla Field |
| 439.30000 | | NFM | Farnborough Airshow | U.S. Dept of Defence |
| 439.45000 | 446.45000 | NFM | North Sea | Amoco Valhalla Field |

## 440.00625 - 442.25625 MHz    PMR BASE REPEATERS 12.5 kHz
## (SPLIT - 14.5 MHz)

| Base | Mobile | Mode | Location | User and Notes |
| --- | --- | --- | --- | --- |
| 411.50000 | 426.00000 | NFM | North Sea | Mobil To Statfjord A & C |
| 440.02500 | 425.52500 | NFM | London | Port of London (S) |
| 440.02500 | 425.52500 | NFM | London, Gatwick | Trunked network |
| 440.02500 | 425.52500 | NFM | London, Heathrow | Ground Staff |
| 440.03750 | 425.53750 | NFM | London | RAM Mobile Data Network |
| 440.05000 | 425.55000 | NFM | Billericay | Council Social Services |
| 440.05000 | 425.55000 | NFM | Coventry | Council Roads Dept |
| 440.05000 | 425.55000 | NFM | Lanarkshire | Monklands Direct Works |
| 440.05000 | 425.55000 | NFM | Leicester | City Council Depots |
| 440.07500 | 425.57500 | NFM | Harlow | Council in Chief Emergency |
| 440.07500 | 425.57500 | NFM | Liverpool | Liverpool Ranger Service |
| 440.07500 | 425.57500 | NFM | London | Parking enforcement |
| 440.07500 | 425.57500 | NFM | London | Wandsworth Council Parks |
| 440.07500 | 425.57500 | NFM | London, Islington | Traffic Wardens |
| 440.07500 | 425.57500 | NFM | Newcastle | Highways |
| 440.07500 | 425.57500 | NFM | Solihull | Binmen |
| 440.07500 | 440.07500 | NFM | Dover | HM Customs & Excise |
| 440.10000 | 425.60000 | NFM | Barrow | VSEL Submarine Guards |
| 440.10000 | 425.60000 | NFM | Glasgow | Parcel Firm |
| 440.10000 | 425.60000 | NFM | Leicester | City Council 24hr Repairs |
| 440.10000 | 425.60000 | NFM | Liverpool | Police Mersey Tunnel Ch 1 |
| 440.10000 | 425.60000 | NFM | London | Borough of Wandsworth Council |
| 440.10000 | 425.60000 | NFM | London | Hackney Parking Enforcement |
| 440.10000 | 425.60000 | NFM | London | Wimbledon Borough Council |
| 440.10000 | 425.60000 | NFM | London, Hackney | Traffic Wardens |
| 440.11250 | 425.61250 | NFM | Blackpool | Doctors on Call |

| Base | Mobile | Mode | Location | User and Notes |
|---|---|---|---|---|
| 440.11250 | 425.61250 | NFM | London | Mobile Data Network |
| 440.12500 | 425.62500 | NFM | Birmingham | Fort Retail Park Security |
| 440.12500 | 425.62500 | NFM | Glasgow | Waste Collection |
| 440.12500 | 425.62500 | NFM | London | Parkwest Cars |
| 440.12500 | 425.62500 | NFM | Nationwide | TNT Offices |
| 440.12500 | 425.62500 | NFM | Watford | Watford Borough Council |
| 440.12500 | 425.62500 | NFM | Wigan | Emergency Repairs |
| 440.15000 | 425.67500 | NFM | Birmingham | Park Wardens |
| 440.17500 | 425.67500 | NFM | Liverpool | Police Mersey Tunnel Ch 1 |
| 440.17500 | 425.67500 | NFM | London, East Finchley | Private Mansion Security in Eastern European Language |
| 440.17500 | 425.67500 | NFM | London | London Transport Buses |
| 440.18750 | 425.68750 | NFM | London | RAM Mobile Data Network |
| 440.20000 | 425.70000 | NFM | Greenford | Glaxo Fire and Security |
| 440.20000 | 425.70000 | NFM | London, Gatwick | Delta Airlines |
| 440.20000 | 425.70000 | NFM | Wilton | ICI |
| 440.22500 | 425.72500 | NFM | Bexley | L.B. Bexley |
| 440.22500 | 425.72500 | NFM | Birmingham | NEC Security & Maintenance |
| 440.22500 | 425.72500 | NFM | Glasgow | Regional Council |
| 440.22500 | 425.72500 | NFM | Hull | Hull Telephone Repairs |
| 440.22500 | 425.72500 | NFM | London | London Transport Buses |
| 440.22500 | 425.72500 | NFM | London, Heathrow | Airport trunked |
| 440.22500 | 425.72500 | NFM | Manchester | Data Relay |
| 440.22500 | 425.72500 | NFM | Manchester | International Airport |
| 440.22500 | 425.72500 | NFM | Newcastle | Highways |
| 440.25000 | 425.72500 | NFM | Sinnington | Council |
| 440.25000 | 425.75000 | NFM | Dartford | Elderly Care Service |
| 440.25500 | 425.75500 | NFM | Birmingham, city centre | Traffic Wardens |
| 440.26250 | 425.76250 | NFM | London | RAM Mobile Data Network |
| 440.27500 | 425.77500 | NFM | Dartford | Bluewater Shopping Centre Car Parks Ch 3 |
| 440.27500 | 425.77500 | NFM | Liverpool | Mersey Port Police |
| 440.27500 | 425.77500 | NFM | London, Heathrow | Trunked Network |
| 440.27500 | 425.77500 | NFM | London, Inns of Court | Lord Chancellor's Department of Security |
| 440.27500 | 425.77500 | NFM | Manchester | International Airport |
| 440.28750 | 425.78750 | NFM | London | RAM Mobile Data Network |
| 440.30000 | 425.80000 | NFM | Glasgow | Data Link |
| 440.30000 | 425.80000 | NFM | London | Kenwood Car Service |
| 440.30000 | 425.80000 | NFM | London, Gatwick | Trunked |
| 440.30000 | 425.80000 | NFM | London, Heathrow | Trunked Network |
| 440.30000 | 425.80000 | NFM | Manchester | International Airport |
| 440.30000 | 425.80000 | NFM | Wilton | ICI |
| 440.31250 | 425.81250 | NFM | London | RAM Mobile Data Network |
| 440.32500 | 425.82500 | NFM | Dartford | Bluewater Shopping Centre Maintenance Ch 4 |
| 440.32500 | 425.82500 | NFM | London | Hays Galleria Shops Security |
| 440.32500 | 425.82500 | NFM | London | London Transport Buses |
| 440.33750 | 425.83750 | NFM | Glasgow | Data Link |
| 440.33750 | 425.83750 | NFM | London | RAM Mobile Data Network |
| 440.33750 | 425.83750 | NFM | Newcastle | The Metro Centre Data Link |
| 440.35000 | 425.85000 | NFM | Leeds | Royal Armouries Museum security |
| 440.35000 | 425.85000 | NFM | London | Middlesex Hospital |
| 440.35000 | 425.85000 | NFM | London, Gatwick | Trunked Network |
| 440.35000 | 425.85000 | NFM | London, Heathrow | Trunked Network |
| 440.35000 | 425.85000 | NFM | Redbridge | Council |
| 440.36250 | 425.86250 | NFM | London | Capital Express Couriers |
| 440.37500 | 425.87500 | NFM | London | Canary Wharf security officers |
| 440.37500 | 425.87500 | NFM | Manchester | International Airport |

| Base | Mobile | Mode | Location | User and Notes |
|------|--------|------|----------|----------------|
| 440.37500 | 425.87500 | NFM | Redbridge | Council (UNITY BASE) |
| 440.37500 | 428.57500 | NFM | London | City of Westminster Council |
| 440.40000 | 425.90000 | NFM | Co. Durham | Taxis |
| 440.40000 | 425.90000 | NFM | London | RAM Mobile Data Network |
| 440.40000 | 425.90000 | NFM | Surrey | Ambulance Incident Control |
| 440.42500 | 425.92500 | NFM | London, Heathrow | Ground Staff |
| 440.45000 | 425.95000 | NFM | London | Barts Hospital |
| 440.45000 | 425.95000 | NFM | Nationwide | Frecce Tricolori Groundcrew |
| 440.46250 | 425.96250 | NFM | London | RAM Mobile Data Network |
| 440.47500 | 425.97500 | NFM | London | London Transport Buses |
| 440.47500 | 425.97500 | NFM | M6 | Motorway Maintenance |
| 440.47500 | 425.97500 | NFM | Wilton | ICI |
| 440.48750 | 425.98750 | NFM | London | RAM Mobile Data Network |
| 440.48750 | 425.98750 | NFM | Perthshire, west | Data Link |
| 440.50000 | 426.00000 | NFM | London | London Transport Buses |
| 440.50000 | 426.00000 | NFM | Slough | Reading Numbers |
| 440.52500 | 426.02500 | NFM | Dartford | Bluewater Shopping Centre Command Centre |
| 440.52500 | 426.02500 | NFM | London | London Transport Buses |
| 440.52500 | 426.02500 | | London, Mount Pleasant | Royal Mail Depot |
| 440.52500 | 426.02500 | NFM | Preston | RAC |
| 440.52500 | 426.02500 | NFM | Stonebridge | Royal Mail Depot |
| 440.53750 | 426.03750 | NFM | Coventry | North School/ College |
| 440.53750 | 426.03750 | NFM | London | JJB Sports Security Plaza Shopping Centre. |
| 440.53750 | 426.03750 | NFM | London | Outback Inn |
| 440.53750 | 426.03750 | NFM | London | PMR Parking/Demo |
| 440.53750 | 426.03750 | NFM | Portsmouth | Argos Store |
| 440.53750 | 426.03750 | NFM | Stevenage | British Aerospace Ch 3 |
| 440.53750 | 426.03750 | NFM | Stevenage | Knebworth House Lytton Catering |
| 440.55000 | 426.05000 | NFM | London | London Transport Buses |
| 440.55000 | 426.05000 | NFM | London | Strand Palace Hotel |
| 440.57500 | 426.07500 | NFM | Gateshead | Metro Centre Security |
| 440.57500 | 426.07500 | NFM | Glasgow | TOA Taxis Ch 1 (Data) |
| 440.57500 | 426.07500 | NFM | London | London Taxis North/Central |
| 440.57500 | 426.07500 | NFM | Manchester | Construction Company |
| 440.57500 | 426.07500 | NFM | Wigan | Park Wardens |
| 440.58750 | 426.08750 | NFM | London | London Taxis N1/N7 |
| 440.60000 | 426.10000 | NFM | Glasgow | TOA Taxis Ch 2 (Data) |
| 440.60000 | 426.10000 | NFM | Knowsley | Council Security |
| 440.60000 | 426.10000 | NFM | Leicestershire | Courier Co (LINK) |
| 440.60000 | 426.10000 | NFM | London | London Taxis WC/SW1 |
| 440.62500 | 426.12500 | NFM | Birmingham | NEC Catering |
| 440.62500 | 426.12500 | NFM | Glasgow | TOA Taxis Ch 3 (Voice) |
| 440.62500 | 426.12500 | NFM | London | London Taxis Gt London |
| 440.65000 | 426.15000 | NFM | Birmingham | NEC Catering |
| 440.65000 | 426.15000 | NFM | Edinburgh | Radio Cabs |
| 440.65000 | 426.15000 | NFM | London | London Taxis Gt London |
| 440.66250 | 426.16250 | NFM | Edinburgh | Taxis |
| 440.67500 | 426.17500 | NFM | Birmingham | NEC Traffic |
| 440.67500 | 426.17500 | NFM | Edinburgh | Radio Cabs |
| 440.67500 | 426.17500 | NFM | Glasgow | MoD HQ Security |
| 440.67500 | 426.17500 | NFM | London | Taxis |
| 440.70000 | 426.20000 | NFM | London | Centracom Ltd |
| 440.70000 | 426.20000 | NFM | Stoke on Trent | Plant Hire (Star Base) |
| 440.70000 | 426.20000 | NFM | Sutton | Taxis |
| 440.72500 | 426.22500 | NFM | Birmingham | NEC Maintenance |
| 440.72500 | 426.22500 | NFM | Edinburgh | Acolade Cars |

| Base | Mobile | Mode | Location | User and Notes |
|------|--------|------|----------|----------------|
| 440.72500 | 426.22500 | NFM | London | Central London Messenger |
| 440.75000 | 426.25000 | NFM | London | Taxis |
| 440.75000 | 426.25000 | NFM | London, Gatwick | HM Customs & Excise |
| 440.75000 | 426.25000 | NFM | London, Gatwick | Parking Express courtesy bus |
| 440.75000 | 426.25000 | NFM | London, Heathrow | Airport Passenger Service |
| 440.75000 | 426.25000 | NFM | London, Heathrow | Parking Express courtesy bus |
| 440.75000 | 426.25000 | NFM | Manchester Airport | HM Customs & Immigration |
| 440.75000 | 426.25000 | NFM | Nationwide | Customs & Excise |
| 440.75000 | 426.25000 | NFM | Solihull | Refuse Collectors |
| 440.76250 | 426.26250 | NFM | Coventry | City Centre trunked System. |
| 440.76250 | 426.26250 | NFM | London, Heathrow | Airport Secure Parking |
| 440.76250 | 426.26250 | NFM | London, Heathrow | NMRL CBS Tristar House |
| 440.76250 | 426.26250 | NFM | London, Heathrow | Airport Secure Parking Ltd. |
| 440.77500 | 426.27500 | NFM | Felixstowe | HM Customs & Excise (Port) |
| 440.77500 | 426.27500 | NFM | London, Heathrow | Main Customs Net |
| 440.77500 | 426.27500 | NFM | Luton Airport | HM Customs & Immigration |
| 440.77500 | 426.27500 | NFM | Manchester Airport | HM Customs & Immigration |
| 440.77500 | 426.27500 | NFM | Nationwide | HM Customs & Excise Ch. 4 |
| 440.77500 | 426.27500 | NFM | Ramsgate | HM Customs & Excise (Port) |
| 440.77500 | 426.27500 | NFM | Stanstead Airport | HM Customs & Excise |
| 440.77500 | 440.77500 | NFM | Nationwide | HM Customs & Excise Ch. 1 |
| 440.78750 | 426.28750 | NFM | London | Links Courier Service |
| 440.80000 | 426.30000 | NFM | Central London | Taxis |
| 440.80000 | 426.30000 | NFM | London | Security Company |
| 440.80000 | 426.30000 | NFM | Swansea | HM Customs & Excise |
| 440.80000 | 426.30000 | NFM | Wakefield | Builders |
| 440.82500 | 426.32500 | NFM | London, Heathrow | HM Customs Surveillance |
| 440.82500 | 426.32500 | NFM | London, Heathrow | HM Customs Surveillance |
| 440.82500 | 426.32500 | NFM | Nationwide | HM Customs & Excise Ch 2 |
| 440.82500 | 426.32500 | NFM | Nationwide | HM Customs & Excise Ch 5 |
| 440.82500 | 426.32500 | NFM | North-West | Covert Customs Surveillance |
| 440.82500 | 426.32500 | NFM | Shoreham | HM Customs & Excise |
| 440.85000 | 426.35000 | NFM | Felixstowe | HM Customs & Excise |
| 440.85000 | 426.35000 | NFM | Harwich | HM Customs & Excise |
| 440.85000 | 426.35000 | NFM | London, Heathrow | HM Customs & Excise |
| 440.85000 | 426.35000 | NFM | Nationwide | HM Customs & Excise Ch 6 |
| 440.85000 | 426.35000 | NFM | Newhaven | HM Customs & Excise |
| 440.85000 | 426.35000 | NFM | Southampton Docks | HM Customs & Excise (Aztec) |
| 440.85000 | 426.35000 | NFM | Stanstead Airport | HM Customs & Excise |
| 440.85000 | 440.85000 | NFM | Nationwide | HM Customs & Excise Ch 3 |
| 440.87500 | 426.37500 | NFM | London, North | Taxis |
| 440.87500 | 426.37500 | NFM | Nationwide | HM Customs & Excise Ch 7 |
| 440.90000 | 426.40000 | NFM | Birmingham | Rackhams Security |
| 440.90000 | 426.40000 | NFM | Gillingham | Savacentre Security |
| 440.90000 | 426.40000 | NFM | London | Canary Wharf security Ch.2 |
| 440.90000 | 426.40000 | NFM | London | Goldsmiths College Security |
| 440.90000 | 426.40000 | NFM | London, Gower St | University College London security |
| 440.90000 | 426.40000 | NFM | London, Heathrow | Trunked Network |
| 440.90000 | 426.40000 | NFM | Manchester | Construction/Repairs |
| 440.90000 | 426.40000 | NFM | Wilton | ICI |
| 440.92500 | 426.42500 | NFM | Beds | Council |
| 440.92500 | 426.42500 | NFM | Harlow | Council in Chief Emergency |
| 440.92500 | 426.42500 | NFM | Liverpool | Council Security |
| 440.92500 | 426.42500 | NFM | London | Baking Council |
| 440.92500 | 426.42500 | NFM | London | Barking Council |
| 440.92500 | 426.42500 | NFM | London | Barts Hospital |

| Base | Mobile | Mode | Location | User and Notes |
|------|--------|------|----------|----------------|
| 440.92500 | 426.42500 | NFM | London | Road repairs |
| 440.92500 | 426.42500 | NFM | Manchester | North West Water |
| 440.92500 | 426.42500 | NFM | Rotherham | Council |
| 440.92500 | 426.42500 | NFM | Stockport | Local Authority |
| 440.93750 | 426.43750 | NFM | London | Taxis |
| 440.95000 | 426.45000 | NFM | Liverpool | Arndale Shopping Centre Security |
| 440.95000 | 426.45000 | NFM | London | Canary Wharf security Ch.1 |
| 440.95000 | 426.45000 | NFM | London, Heathrow | Trunked Network |
| 440.95000 | 426.45000 | NFM | London, Marble Arch | C&A shop |
| 440.95000 | 426.45000 | NFM | Wilton | ICI |
| 440.97500 | 426.47500 | NFM | Viewpark | Denton Security |
| 440.98750 | 426.48750 | NFM | Hendon | Couriers |
| 440.98750 | 426.48750 | NFM | London | Green Cars |
| 441.00000 | 426.50000 | NFM | Birmingham | NEC Maintenance |
| 441.00000 | 426.50000 | NFM | City of Westminster | Traffic Wardens |
| 441.00000 | 426.50000 | NFM | Co. Durham | Radio Engineers |
| 441.00000 | 426.50000 | NFM | London, Kings Cross | Premiere Cars |
| 441.00000 | 426.50000 | NFM | Nationwide | Xerox Copiers |
| 441.00000 | 426.50000 | NFM | Plumstead | Taxis |
| 441.01250 | 426.51250 | NFM | London, Heathrow | Trunked |
| 441.02500 | 426.52500 | NFM | Leicester | Leicester Buses |
| 441.02500 | 426.52500 | NFM | London, Heathrow | Airline ops. |
| 441.03750 | 426.53750 | NFM | London, Heathrow | Trunked Network |
| 441.05000 | 426.55000 | NFM | London | Builders |
| 441.05000 | 426.55000 | NFM | London, Heathrow | Trunked Network |
| 441.05000 | 426.55000 | NFM | Retford | Horwich Builders |
| 441.06250 | 426.57500 | NFM | Coventry | Builders Suppliers |
| 441.06250 | 426.57500 | NFM | Coventry | Council |
| 441.07500 | 426.57500 | NFM | Birmingham Hockley | Blocked Drains |
| 441.07500 | 426.57500 | NFM | Birmingham International | Ground Staff |
| 441.07500 | 426.57500 | NFM | Glasgow | Council |
| 441.07500 | 426.57500 | NFM | London, Gatwick | Trunked Network |
| 441.07500 | 426.57500 | NFM | London, Heathrow | Ground Staff |
| 441.07500 | 426.57500 | NFM | London, south east | Couriers |
| 441.08750 | 426.58750 | NFM | Preston | On Call Doctor Service |
| 441.10000 | 426.60000 | NFM | London | Medicall |
| 441.10000 | 426.60000 | NFM | Nationwide | MediCall |
| 441.10000 | 426.60000 | NFM | West Midlands | Bus Co |
| 441.11250 | 426.61250 | NFM | Dagenham | Rhone Poulenc Chemicals |
| 441.11250 | 426.61250 | NFM | London | St Thomas Hospital |
| 441.11250 | 426.61250 | NFM | London | Wellington Hospital |
| 441.11250 | 426.61250 | NFM | London, Heathrow | Trunked Network |
| 441.11250 | 426.61250 | NFM | Nationwide | Formula L Ferrari Team Schumacher |
| 441.12500 | 426.62500 | NFM | Birmingham | Skip Hire Co |
| 441.12500 | 426.62500 | NFM | London, Gatwick | Trunked Network |
| 441.12500 | 426.62500 | NFM | London, Heathrow | Trunked |
| 441.12500 | 426.62500 | NFM | Walsall | Myseal |
| 441.12500 | 426.62500 | NFM | West Midlands | Security Firm |
| 441.13750 | 426.63750 | NFM | London, Heathrow | Aircraft cleaning |
| 441.15000 | 426.65000 | NFM | Birmingham International | AirCall |
| 441.15000 | 426.65000 | NFM | Edinburgh | Taxis |
| 441.15000 | 426.65000 | NFM | London | Alex Brand Couriers |
| 441.15000 | 426.65000 | NFM | London | Courier Company |
| 441.15000 | 426.65000 | NFM | London | GLH Bike & Van Couriers C/S |
| 441.15000 | 426.65000 | NFM | Saddleworth | Haulage Firm |
| 441.15000 | 426.65000 | NFM | Warwickshire | Skip Hire Co |

| Base | Mobile | Mode | Location | User and Notes |
|------|--------|------|----------|----------------|
| 441.15000 | 426.65000 | NFM | Warwickshire | Taxi Co |
| 441.16250 | 426.66250 | NFM | Dartford | Bluewater Shopping Centre Staff |
| 441.16250 | 426.66250 | NFM | London | North Pole Eurostar Depot |
| 441.16250 | 426.66250 | NFM | London, Heathrow | Transport service |
| 441.16250 | 426.66250 | NFM | London, Waterloo Station | Eurostar passenger service |
| 441.16250 | 426.66250 | NFM | London, Woolwich | Thames Barrier control |
| 441.17500 | 426.67500 | NFM | Birmingham | Wheel Clamping. |
| 441.17500 | 426.67500 | NFM | Birmingham, city centre | Eagle Car Clampers |
| 441.17500 | 426.67500 | NFM | Co. Durham | TV Engineers |
| 441.17500 | 426.67500 | NFM | Coatbridge | Shanks McEwan Skip Hire |
| 441.17500 | 426.67500 | NFM | Coventry | Satellite Installation |
| 441.17500 | 426.67500 | NFM | Denton | FMR Investigations |
| 441.17500 | 426.67500 | NFM | Glasgow | Vehicle Removal Unit |
| 441.17500 | 426.67500 | NFM | Luton | Bus Co. |
| 441.17500 | 426.67500 | NFM | Luton | Communications Repeater |
| 441.17500 | 426.67500 | NFM | Manchester | Pub Machine Suppliers |
| 441.17500 | 426.67500 | NFM | Middlesborough | Pritchard Security |
| 441.17500 | 426.67500 | NFM | Perthshire | Builders |
| 441.17500 | 441.17500 | NFM | Manchester | Security |
| 441.18750 | 426.68750 | NFM | Dartford | Bluewater Shopping Centre Staff |
| 441.20000 | 426.70000 | NFM | Birmingham | Police CID Scrambled |
| 441.20000 | 426.70000 | NFM | Cambridge | Community Repeater |
| 441.20000 | 426.70000 | NFM | Dorking | Apollo Cars |
| 441.20000 | 426.70000 | NFM | Dorking | Keynet CBS |
| 441.20000 | 426.70000 | NFM | Dorking | Silver Cars |
| 441.20000 | 426.70000 | NFM | Manchester | Couriers |
| 441.20000 | 426.70000 | NFM | Manchester | TV Repairs |
| 441.21200 | 426.72500 | NFM | Coventry | Parcel Delivery |
| 441.21250 | 426.72500 | NFM | Leicestershire | Car Valeters |
| 441.21250 | 426.72500 | NFM | Leicestershire | Courier Co |
| 441.21250 | 426.72500 | NFM | Leicestershire | Security Co Encrypted |
| 441.21250 | 426.72500 | NFM | Leicestershire | Taxi Co |
| 441.21250 | 426.72500 | NFM | London | Heathrow Airport trunked |
| 441.22500 | 426.72500 | NFM | Coventry | Shopwatch and Security Car Parks. |
| 441.22500 | 426.72500 | NFM | Dorking | Apollo Taxis |
| 441.22500 | 426.72500 | NFM | London | CBS Car Telephones |
| 441.22500 | 426.72500 | NFM | London, Heathrow | Trunked Network |
| 441.22500 | 426.72500 | NFM | London, Plumstead | Parking wardens (P) |
| 441.25000 | 426.75000 | NFM | Aberdeen | Nat Radiofone CBS |
| 441.25000 | 426.75000 | NFM | Bradford | Nat Radiofone CBS |
| 441.25000 | 426.75000 | NFM | Coventry | Shopwatch Security Car Parks. |
| 441.25000 | 426.75000 | NFM | Glasgow Warlaw Hill | Nat Radiofone CBS |
| 441.25000 | 426.75000 | NFM | Leicester | Nat Radiofone CBS |
| 441.25000 | 426.75000 | NFM | London | Churchill Express Couriers |
| 441.25000 | 426.75000 | NFM | London | Onyx UK Ltd cleansing contractors |
| 441.25000 | 426.75000 | NFM | London, Gatwick | Trunked Network |
| 441.25000 | 426.75000 | NFM | London, Heathrow | Ground Staff |
| 441.25000 | 426.75000 | NFM | Manchester | Nat Radiofone CBS |
| 441.25000 | 426.75000 | NFM | Newcastle | Highways |
| 441.25000 | 426.75000 | NFM | Pontop Pike | Nat Radiofone CBS |
| 441.25000 | 426.75000 | NFM | Preston | B.D. Electronics |
| 441.25000 | 426.75000 | NFM | Tyneside | Couriers |
| 441.25000 | 426.75000 | NFM | Waltham-on-Wolds | Nat Radiofone CBS |
| 441.27500 | 426.77500 | NFM | London, Gatwick | Trunked Network |
| 441.27500 | 426.77500 | NFM | London, Heathrow | Airport trunked |
| 441.27500 | 426.77500 | NFM | Stoke on Trent | Medics |

| Base | Mobile | Mode | Location | User and Notes |
|------|--------|------|----------|----------------|
| 441.27500 | 426.77500 | NFM | Stoke-On-Trent | Skip Hire |
| 441.30000 | 426.80000 | NFM | London | Security Company |
| 441.30000 | 426.80000 | NFM | London Hilton | Nat Radiofone CBS |
| 441.30000 | 426.80000 | NFM | Newcastle | Security Firm |
| 441.32500 | 426.82500 | NFM | Co. Durham | Private Security |
| 441.32500 | 426.82500 | NFM | London, Gatwick | Trunked Network |
| 441.35000 | 426.85000 | NFM | Crewe | Taxis |
| 441.35000 | 426.85000 | NFM | Glasgow | Security |
| 441.35000 | 426.85000 | NFM | Home Moss Pennine | Nat Radiofone CBS |
| 441.35000 | 426.85000 | NFM | London, Gatwick | Trunked Network |
| 441.35000 | 426.85000 | NFM | London, Heathrow | Trunked Network |
| 441.35000 | 426.85000 | NFM | Newcastle | Security Firm |
| 441.35000 | 426.85000 | NFM | Wakefield | RJB Mining |
| 441.37500 | 426.87500 | NFM | London | Couriers |
| 441.37500 | 426.87500 | NFM | Manchester | Plant Company |
| 441.37500 | 426.87500 | NFM | Newcastle | Security Firm |
| 441.37500 | 426.87500 | NFM | Tyne & Wear | Security Firm |
| 441.38750 | 426.88750 | NFM | London | Streetwise Couriers |
| 441.40000 | 426.90000 | NFM | Glasgow, Drumchapel | B&Q |
| 441.40000 | 426.90000 | NFM | London | Couriers |
| 441.40000 | 426.90000 | NFM | Manchester | Springfield Hospital Porters |
| 441.40000 | 426.90000 | NFM | Sheffield | A1 Security |
| 441.40000 | 426.90000 | NFM | St Annes | Taxis |
| 441.41250 | 426.92500 | NFM | Coventry | Council Engineers |
| 441.42500 | 426.92500 | NFM | Birmingham | Courier Co |
| 441.42500 | 426.92500 | NFM | London | Motorola engineers |
| 441.43750 | 426.93750 | NFM | London | Courier Company |
| 441.43750 | 426.93750 | NFM | Nottinghamshire | Steetley Haulage Ltd |
| 441.45000 | 426.95000 | NFM | Glasgow | Paramedics |
| 441.45000 | 426.95000 | NFM | London | Apcoa Parking Enforcement Vehicle Removals |
| 441.45000 | 426.95000 | NFM | Manchester Airport | TNT Carriers |
| 441.47400 | 427.07500 | NFM | Tamworth | Delivery Firm |
| 441.47500 | 426.97500 | NFM | Blackburn | Garage Recovery |
| 441.47500 | 426.97500 | NFM | Burnley | Breakdown Recovery |
| 441.47500 | 426.97500 | NFM | Coventry | City engineers |
| 441.50000 | 427.00000 | NFM | London | Select Bike Couriers |
| 441.50000 | 427.00000 | NFM | London | Taxis |
| 441.50000 | 427.00000 | NFM | Turners Hill | Nat Radiofone CBS |
| 441.52500 | 427.02500 | NFM | Coventry | Shopwatch |
| 441.52500 | 427.02500 | NFM | Glasgow | Games Machines Firm |
| 441.52500 | 427.02500 | NFM | Glasgow | Security |
| 441.52500 | 427.02500 | NFM | Highgate | Nat Radiofone CBS |
| 441.52500 | 427.02500 | NFM | Lanark | Security Firm |
| 441.52500 | 427.02500 | NFM | Manchester | Motoring Organisation |
| 441.52500 | 427.02500 | NFM | Newcastle | Security Firm |
| 441.52500 | 427.02500 | NFM | Preston | Drinks Machine Suppliers |
| 441.52500 | 427.02500 | NFM | Tyneside | Safe-Guard Security |
| 441.52500 | 427.05000 | NFM | London | Refrigeration Engineers |
| 441.55000 | 427.05000 | NFM | Frodsham | Nat Radiofone CBS |
| 441.55000 | 427.05000 | NFM | London, Heathrow | Trunked Network |
| 441.55000 | 427.05000 | NFM | Sheffield | Nat Radiofone CBS |
| 441.57500 | 427.07500 | NFM | Cannock | Taxi |
| 441.57500 | 427.07500 | NFM | London | Hospital patient transport |
| 441.57500 | 427.07500 | NFM | London | Vehicle recovery |
| 441.57500 | 427.07500 | NFM | Manchester | Harcross Building Supplies |
| 441.57500 | 427.07500 | NFM | Manchester | NSPCC Investigation Branch |

| Base | Mobile | Mode | Location | User and Notes |
|---|---|---|---|---|
| 441.60000 | 427.10000 | NFM | London | Chase Couriers (CHASE) |
| 441.62500 | 427.12500 | NFM | Doncaster | Constant Security |
| 441.62500 | 427.12500 | NFM | London | Council |
| 441.62500 | 427.12500 | NFM | London | Courier |
| 441.62500 | 427.12500 | NFM | Newham | Parking enforcement |
| 441.65000 | 427.15000 | NFM | Central London | Taxis |
| 441.65000 | 427.15000 | NFM | Chalfont St Peter | OAP transport service |
| 441.65000 | 427.15000 | NFM | London | Borough of Ealing Transport Services (S) |
| 441.65000 | 427.15000 | NFM | London | OAP transport service |
| 441.65000 | 441.65000 | NFM | Alba | FSU Chevron Shuttle DGP Data |
| 441.66200 | 427.17500 | NFM | Preston | Medicall |
| 441.66250 | 427.17500 | NFM | Blackpool | Delivery Firm |
| 441.66250 | 427.17500 | NFM | Skelmersdale | Couriers |
| 441.67500 | 427.17500 | NFM | London | Premier Motorbike Couriers |
| 441.67500 | 427.17500 | NFM | London | Taxis |
| 441.67500 | 427.17500 | NFM | Manchester | Security |
| 441.67500 | 427.17500 | NFM | Walsall | Mygoal |
| 441.70000 | 427.20000 | NFM | London, Gatwick | Airline ops. |
| 441.70000 | 427.20000 | NFM | London, Heathrow | Trunked Network |
| 441.70000 | 427.20000 | NFM | Stoke | Nat Radiofone CBS |
| 441.70000 | 427.20000 | NFM | Waltham-on-Wolds | Nat Radiofone CBS |
| 441.70000 | 441.70000 | NFM | Manchester | Breakdown Recovery |
| 441.71250 | 427.21250 | NFM | London | Apollo Bike Couriers |
| 441.72500 | 427.22500 | NFM | Doncaster | Browns Farm |
| 441.72500 | 427.22500 | NFM | Doncaster | Roy Bolland Skips |
| 441.72500 | 427.22500 | NFM | Glasgow | Medicall |
| 441.72500 | 427.22500 | NFM | London | Surveillance ops used from time to time |
| 441.72500 | 427.22500 | NFM | South London | NMRL CBS |
| 441.72500 | 427.72500 | NFM | Nottingham | Medicall Couriers |
| 441.73750 | 427.23750 | NFM | London | Courier firm |
| 441.75000 | 427.25000 | NFM | London | Medicall |
| 441.75000 | 427.25000 | NFM | London | VIP outside caterers |
| 441.77500 | 427.27500 | NFM | Coventry | Niall Bailley |
| 441.77500 | 427.27500 | NFM | Coventry | Phoenix Couriers |
| 441.78750 | 427.28750 | NFM | Coventry | City Engineers |
| 441.80000 | 427.30000 | NFM | London, Heathrow | Trunked Network |
| 441.80000 | 427.30000 | NFM | Manchester | Security |
| 441.81250 | 427.31250 | NFM | Basildon | Amtrak |
| 441.81250 | 427.31250 | NFM | London | Haulage |
| 441.81500 | 427.81250 | NFM | London, south east | Builders |
| 441.82500 | 427.32500 | NFM | London, Victoria | Minicabs |
| 441.82500 | 427.32500 | NFM | West Midlands | Delivery Service |
| 441.83750 | 427.33750 | NFM | London | Heathrow Airport. |
| 441.85000 | 427.35000 | NFM | Cannock | Taxi |
| 441.85000 | 427.35000 | NFM | Liverpool | Expo Boarding-Up Service |
| 441.85000 | 427.35000 | NFM | London | Delivery Service |
| 441.86250 | 427.36250 | NFM | London, Heathrow | Airport trunked |
| 441.87500 | 427.37500 | NFM | London | Globe & City Bikes Couriers |
| 441.87500 | 427.37500 | NFM | London | Police SAV Repeater |
| 441.87500 | 427.37500 | NFM | London, south east | Taxis |
| 441.87500 | 427.37500 | NFM | Pontop | Nat Radiofone CBS |
| 441.87500 | 441.87500 | NFM | London | Police Repeater |
| 441.88750 | 427.38750 | NFM | London | Police Holland Park |
| 441.88750 | 427.38750 | NFM | London | Vehicle Recovery services |
| 441.90000 | 427.40000 | NFM | Leicester | Security Co |
| 441.90000 | 427.40000 | NFM | London, Hilton | NMRL CBS 2 |

| Base | Mobile | Mode | Location | User and Notes |
|---|---|---|---|---|
| 441.92500 | 427.42500 | NFM | Chalfont St Peters | Frobel Institute |
| 441.92500 | 427.42500 | NFM | London | Frobel Institute and Colleges Security |
| 441.92500 | 427.42500 | NFM | Turners Hill | Nat Radiofone CBS |
| 441.92500 | 441.92500 | NFM | Cheshire | Security |
| 441.95000 | 427.45000 | NFM | London, Gatwick | Trunked network |
| 441.95000 | 427.45000 | NFM | London, Heathrow | Trunked Network |
| 441.95000 | 427.45000 | NFM | London, south east | Taxis |
| 441.95000 | 427.45000 | NFM | Sandiways, Cheshire | Four Ways Granite Quarry |
| 441.97500 | 427.47500 | NFM | Glasgow | Doctors oncall |
| 441.97500 | 427.47500 | NFM | London | Bus Tour Company |
| 441.97500 | 427.47500 | NFM | London | Crime Prevention Guards |
| 441.97500 | 427.47500 | NFM | West Midlands | Delivery Service |
| 442.00000 | 427.70000 | NFM | Gatley | Breakdown Service |
| 442.00000 | 427.70000 | NFM | London Hilton | NMRL CBS 2 |
| 442.00000 | 427.70000 | NFM | London, Heathrow | Trunked Network |
| 442.02500 | 427.52500 | NFM | Coventry | Building Merchant |
| 442.02500 | 427.52500 | NFM | Coventry | D.C.E. |
| 442.02500 | 427.52500 | NFM | Coventry | Nyanza Car Spares |
| 442.02500 | 427.52500 | NFM | Hounslow | Rapid Document Handling Services |
| 442.05000 | 427.75000 | NFM | London, west | Couriers |
| 442.07500 | 427.77500 | NFM | Turners Hill | Nat Radiofone CBS |
| 442.10000 | 427.60000 | NFM | Dartford | Bluewater Shopping Centre Staff |
| 442.10000 | 427.60000 | NFM | Ilford | TW Communications |
| 442.10000 | 427.60000 | NFM | London | Apollo Dispatch |
| 442.10000 | 427.60000 | NFM | London | Circle Security |
| 442.10000 | 427.60000 | NFM | Walsall | Mercia Lifting Gear |
| 442.10000 | 427.60000 | NFM | West Midlands | Security Co |
| 442.10000 | 427.80000 | NFM | London, Highgate | Grovefair Security Services |
| 442.10000 | 442.10000 | NFM | Birmingham | Security |
| 442.12500 | 427.62500 | NFM | London | Lynx Express Deliveries |
| 442.12500 | 427.82500 | NFM | Bournemouth | Lynx Couriers |
| 442.12500 | 427.82500 | NFM | London | Incheck Security Services |
| 442.12500 | 427.82500 | NFM | Waltham-on-Wolds | Nat Radiofone CBS |
| 442.15000 | 427.65000 | NFM | Chelmsford | Boreham Tyre Services |
| 442.15000 | 427.65000 | NFM | London | Security Company |
| 442.17500 | 427.67500 | NFM | London | London Wheel Clamping |
| 442.17500 | 427.67500 | NFM | London | Pronto Bikes |
| 442.17500 | 427.67500 | NFM | Stoke | Doctors on Call |
| 442.20000 | 427.70000 | NFM | Hertsmere | Council Refuse Collectors |
| 442.20000 | 427.70000 | NFM | London | Blackheath Cleansing Dept |
| 442.20000 | 427.70000 | NFM | London | Machine Engineers Ref Newsagent Machine |
| 442.20000 | 427.70000 | NFM | London, Greenwich | Council |
| 442.20000 | 427.70000 | NFM | Manchester | Construction Company |
| 442.22500 | 427.72500 | NFM | Worcestershire | Ambulance repeater |
| 442.25000 | 427.75000 | NFM | London, Westminster | Onyx Council Cleaners |
| 442.25000 | 427.75000 | NFM | Manchester | Centre Builders Merchant |

## 4422625 - 442.5125 MHZ    BROADCASTING LINKS

| Base | Mobile | Mode | Location | User and Notes |
|---|---|---|---|---|
| 442.26250 | 427.76250 | NFM | Nationwide | JFMG Wide Area Talkback |
| 442.27500 | 427.77500 | NFM | London | BBC TV Talkback |
| 442.28750 | 427.78750 | NFM | London | BBC Radio 5 Talkback |
| 442.32500 | 427.82500 | NFM | London | BBC TV Talkback |
| 442.33750 | 427.83750 | NFM | London | BBC TV Talkback |
| 442.36250 | 427.86250 | NFM | London | BBC TV Talkback |
| 442.38650 | 427.88650 | NFM | London | BBC TV Talkback |
| 442.42500 | 427.82500 | NFM | London | ITN Reverse Prog Circuit |

| Base | Mobile | Mode | Location | User and Notes |
|---|---|---|---|---|
| 442.43125 | 427.93125 | NFM | Birmingham | ITN Talkback |
| 442.43750 | 427.93750 | NFM | London | ITV Talkback |
| 442.45000 | 427.95000 | NFM | London | ITV Talkback |
| 442.46250 | 427.96250 | NFM | London | ITN Reverse Prog Circuit |
| 442.47500 | 427.97500 | NFM | Grays | ITN MCR |
| 442.48750 | 427.98750 | NFM | London | ITN Talkback |
| 442.50000 | 428.00000 | NFM | London | ITN News Talkback |
| 442.51250 | 428.01250 | NFM | Nationwide | JFMG Wide Area Talkback |

### 442.51875 - 443.49375     PMR MOBILE 12.5 KHZ NFM
### (SPLIT - 14.5 MHZ)

| Base | Mobile | Mode | Location | User and Notes |
|---|---|---|---|---|
| 433.17500 | 428.67500 | NFM | London | British Gas Engineers |
| 442.52500 | 428.02500 | NFM | Borehamwood | BBC Elstree Studio security |
| 442.52500 | 428.02500 | NFM | Enfield | Council |
| 442.52500 | 428.02500 | NFM | London | Hackney Council |
| 442.52500 | 428.02500 | NFM | London | Lambeth Council |
| 442.52500 | 428.02500 | NFM | London, Acton | BBC security |
| 442.52500 | 428.02500 | NFM | London, Ealing | BBC security |
| 442.52500 | 428.02500 | NFM | London, Park Royal | BBC Security |
| 442.52500 | 428.02500 | NFM | Tilbury | Container Port |
| 442.52500 | 428.02500 | NFM | Wilton | ICI |
| 442.53750 | 428.03750 | NFM | Surrey | Kingswood Cars |
| 442.55000 | 428.05000 | NFM | Leyton | Council |
| 442.55000 | 428.05000 | NFM | London | Canary Wharf security (CW) |
| 442.55000 | 428.05000 | NFM | London | Police Billingsgate Market |
| 442.55000 | 428.05000 | NFM | London | Police Leadenhall Market |
| 442.55000 | 428.05000 | NFM | London | Police Smithfield Market |
| 442.55000 | 428.05000 | NFM | London | Police Spittalfield Market |
| 442.55000 | 428.05000 | NFM | London, Heathrow | Airport Engineers |
| 442.56250 | 428.06250 | NFM | London | BBC TV Talkback |
| 442.57500 | 428.07500 | NFM | London, Heathrow | Airline Ops |
| 442.57500 | 428.07500 | NFM | Tilbury | Container Port |
| 442.58750 | 428.08750 | NFM | Basildon | Integrated Security Group |
| 442.58750 | 428.08750 | NFM | London | PTR Couriers |
| 442.58750 | 428.08750 | NFM | London | Pilkenton Security |
| 442.58750 | 428.08750 | NFM | Manchester | Skip Co |
| 442.60000 | 428.10000 | NFM | Coventry | Jaguar Cars |
| 442.60000 | 428.10000 | NFM | Tilbury | Container Port |
| 442.61250 | 428.11250 | NFM | Hounslow | Hounslow Car Spares |
| 442.61250 | 428.11250 | NFM | Wembley | Actonian School of Motoring |
| 442.62500 | 428.12500 | NFM | City of London | Baltic Exchange |
| 442.62500 | 428.12500 | NFM | Greenwich | National Maritime Museum |
| 442.62500 | 428.12500 | NFM | London | British Museum |
| 442.62500 | 428.12500 | NFM | London | Royal London Hospital |
| 442.62500 | 428.12500 | NFM | London, Heathrow | Ground Staff |
| 442.62500 | 428.12500 | NFM | Maidstone | Chequers Shopping Centre |
| 442.62500 | 428.17500 | NFM | Glasgow | Maryhill Shopping Centre |
| 442.63750 | 428.13750 | NFM | London | Borough of Hackney Cleansing Dept |
| 442.63750 | 428.13750 | NFM | London | Doctors Scheme |
| 442.65000 | 428.15000 | NFM | Liverpool | Merseyside Maritime Museum |
| 442.65000 | 428.15000 | NFM | London | Neptune Museum |
| 442.65000 | 428.15000 | NFM | London, Greenwich | National Maritime Museum |
| 442.67500 | 428.17500 | NFM | Clydebank | Clyde Shopping Centre Security |
| 442.67500 | 428.17500 | NFM | Glenrothes | Kingdom Shopping Centre Security |
| 442.67500 | 428.17500 | NFM | Liverpool | Inshore Lifeboats |

| Base | Mobile | Mode | Location | User and Notes |
|------|--------|------|----------|----------------|
| 442.67500 | 428.17500 | NFM | London | Jubilee Line Extension engineers |
| 442.67500 | 428.17500 | NFM | London, Heathrow | Ground Repeater |
| 442.67500 | 428.17500 | NFM | Wilton | ICI |
| 442.68750 | 428.18750 | NFM | London | City Bikes |
| 442.70000 | 428.20000 | NFM | London | Artwork Despatch |
| 442.71250 | 428.21250 | NFM | London | Johns Delivery Ltd |
| 442.72500 | 428.22500 | NFM | London, Gatwick | American Airlines |
| 442.72500 | 428.22500 | NFM | Tilbury | Container Port |
| 442.72500 | 428.22500 | NFM | Wilton | ICI |
| 442.75000 | 428.25000 | NFM | Birmingham | Police Markets |
| 442.75000 | 428.25000 | NFM | Coventry | Jaguar Cars |
| 442.75000 | 428.25000 | NFM | London, Heathrow | Quantas |
| 442.76250 | 428.26250 | NFM | London | Medicall |
| 442.76250 | 428.26250 | NFM | London | Rushospeed Bike Couriers |
| 442.77500 | 428.27500 | NFM | City of London | Lloyds of London Security. |
| 442.77500 | 428.27500 | NFM | Croydon | Whitgift Security |
| 442.77500 | 428.27500 | NFM | Glasgow | Collins Books |
| 442.77500 | 428.27500 | NFM | Lewisham | Riverdale Shopping Centre Security. |
| 442.77500 | 428.27500 | NFM | London | Cannon Security |
| 442.77500 | 428.27500 | NFM | London | West Middlesex Hospital |
| 442.77500 | 428.27500 | NFM | London, Heathrow | Trunked Network |
| 442.77500 | 428.27500 | NFM | Wimbledon | Centre Court Shopping Centre |
| 442.80000 | 428.30000 | NFM | Glasgow | Council Environmental Dept. |
| 442.80000 | 428.30000 | NFM | Glasgow | Electricians |
| 442.80000 | 428.30000 | NFM | London | Prestige Courier Bike Service |
| 442.80000 | 428.30000 | NFM | London, Heathrow | Trunked Network |
| 442.82500 | 428.32500 | NFM | London | Arrow Express Courier |
| 442.82500 | 428.32500 | NFM | London | Borough of Hackney Housing |
| 442.83750 | 428.33750 | NFM | London | Belsize Bike Couriers |
| 442.85000 | 428.35000 | NFM | Glasgow | Trojan Security |
| 442.85000 | 428.35000 | NFM | London | Addison Lee Bike Couriers |
| 442.85000 | 428.35000 | NFM | London, Gatwick | Virgin Ops |
| 442.85000 | 428.35000 | NFM | London, Gatwick | Handling |
| 442.87500 | 428.37500 | NFM | London, Heathrow | Trunked Network |
| 442.88750 | 428.38750 | NFM | London | Pegasus Couriers |
| 442.90000 | 428.40000 | NFM | Glasgow | Glasgow Transport |
| 442.90000 | 428.40000 | NFM | London | Guys Hospital Porters and Security |
| 442.90000 | 428.40000 | NFM | London Hilton | NMRL CBS 2 |
| 442.91250 | 428.41250 | NFM | Glasgow | Glasgow Transport |
| 442.91250 | 428.41250 | NFM | London | Marathon Couriers |
| 442.91250 | 428.41250 | NFM | London | On Yer Bike Couriers |
| 442.92500 | 428.42500 | NFM | Glasgow | TOA Taxis |
| 442.92500 | 428.42500 | NFM | Nottinghamshire | Target Express Parcels |
| 442.95000 | 428.45000 | NFM | Glasgow | Taxis |
| 442.96250 | 428.46250 | NFM | London | West One Couriers |
| 442.97500 | 428.47500 | NFM | London | Checker Cabs |
| 442.97500 | 428.47500 | NFM | London | Supreme Cabs |
| 442.98750 | 428.48750 | NFM | London | Hornet Bike Couriers |
| 443.00000 | 428.50000 | NFM | London | Chelsea & Westminster Hospital |
| 443.00000 | 428.50000 | NFM | London | National Portrait Gallery security |
| 443.00000 | 428.50000 | NFM | London | Tate Gallery Security |
| 443.00000 | 428.50000 | NFM | Wilton | ICI |
| 443.00000 | 443.02000 | NFM | Retford | Emma's Taxis |
| 443.01250 | 428.51250 | NFM | Biringham Airport | British Airways trunked |
| 443.01250 | 428.51250 | NFM | London | Olympic Couriers |
| 443.01250 | 428.51250 | NFM | London | Security Despatch Ltd |

| Base | Mobile | Mode | Location | User and Notes |
|------|--------|------|----------|----------------|
| 443.02500 | 428.25000 | NFM | Tilbury | Container Port |
| 443.02500 | 428.52500 | NFM | London | Canary Wharf security Ch.3 |
| 443.03750 | 428.53750 | NFM | London | Apollo Despatch Riders |
| 443.05000 | 428.55000 | NFM | London | Videotron Cable TV |
| 443.05000 | 428.55000 | NFM | London , Wapping | London International Financial & Options Exchange |
| 443.05000 | 428.55000 | NFM | London, Gatwick | Continental Ops |
| 443.05000 | 428.55000 | NFM | London, Shoreditch | Hostel, Shipton Street |
| 443.05000 | 428.55000 | NFM | London, Wapping | The LIFFE Exchange |
| 443.05000 | 428.55000 | NFM | Sunbury | RCA Records |
| 443.07500 | 428.57500 | NFM | London | West 1 Cars |
| 443.08750 | 428.58750 | NFM | London | Coach Company |
| 443.10000 | 428.60000 | NFM | London | Superspeed Couriers |
| 443.10000 | 428.60000 | NFM | Merseyside | Guardrite Security |
| 443.11250 | 428.61250 | NFM | Worksop | KB Pizza delivery |
| 443.12500 | 428.62500 | NFM | London | Courier Systems Ltd |
| 443.15000 | 428.65000 | NFM | London | Builders |
| 443.15000 | 428.65000 | NFM | Surrey | Radiofone |
| 443.17500 | 428.67500 | NFM | London | Haulage |
| 443.18750 | 428.68750 | NFM | London | Minicabs |
| 443.18750 | 428.68750 | NFM | Sutton | Home James Cars |
| 443.20000 | 428.70000 | NFM | London, West Drayton | British Gas Engineers |
| 443.21250 | 428.71250 | NFM | London | British Gas Engineers |
| 443.26250 | 428.66250 | NFM | Manchester | Washing Machine Repairs |
| 443.26250 | 428.66250 | NFM | Manchester Shaw | Radio Cars |
| 443.26250 | 428.66250 | NFM | Surrey | Radiofone |
| 443.26250 | 428.76250 | NFM | Gerrards Cross | British Gas Engineers |
| 443.27500 | 428.77500 | NFM | Warrington | Security Company |
| 443.37500 | 428.97500 | NFM | London, SE | Plumbers |
| 443.38700 | 428.88700 | NFM | Coventry | Motor Factors |
| 443.41250 | 428.91250 | NFM | London | Minicabs |
| 443.43700 | 428.93750 | NFM | Birmingham | Cleaning Company |
| 443.43750 | 428.93750 | NFM | London | Pizza Delivery Company |
| 443.45000 | 428.95000 | NFM | Lewisham | Riverdale Shopping Centre security |
| 443.45000 | 428.95000 | NFM | London, Gatwick | Gatwick Handling |
| 443.45000 | 428.95000 | NFM | London, Heathrow | Ground Repeater |
| 443.46250 | 428.96250 | NFM | London | Pizza Delivery Company |
| 443.47500 | 428.97500 | NFM | Lewisham | Council |
| 443.47500 | 428.97500 | NFM | London | Police Kenwood House and Hamstead Heath |
| 443.47500 | 428.97500 | NFM | London | Police Wandsworth Park |
| 443.47500 | 428.97500 | NFM | London, Heathrow | Airport Secure Parking Ltd. |
| 443.47500 | 428.97500 | NFM | Watford | Borough Council |
| 443.48650 | 428.98650 | NFM | Glasgow | Parcel Force |
| 443.48750 | 428.98750 | NFM | London | International Couriers |

### 443.5000 - 445.3000 MHz    MoD Radiolocation & Base Comms 25 kHz

| Base | | Mode | Location | User and Notes |
|------|--|------|----------|----------------|
| 443.57500 | | NFM | Whitehall | Military Police |
| 443.58750 | | NFM | London | Mod Police. |
| 443.67500 | | NFM | Whitehall | Military Police |
| 443.74500 | | NFM | London, Hampstead | Kenwood House |
| 443.75000 | | NFM | Colchester | 36 DWS REME |
| 443.88750 | | NFM | Boscombe Down | Military Police (BD) |
| 443.90000 | | NFM | London | Foreign & Commonwealth Office |
| 443.93750 | | NFM | Boscombe Down | Army transport and escorts |
| 444.02500 | | NFM | Colchester | 36 DWS REME |
| 444.05000 | | NFM | USAF Fairford | International Air Tattoo Tanker Ops |

| Base | Mobile | Mode | Location | User and Notes |
|------|--------|------|----------|----------------|
| 444.07500 | | NFM | Nationwide | Radiocommunications Agency |
| 444.27500 | 449.57500 | NFM | USAF Fairford | International Air Tattoo Campsite |
| 444.30000 | 449.60000 | NFM | USAF Fairford | International Air Tattoo Chalets |
| 444.32500 | | NFM | Colchester | 36 DWS REME |
| 444.33750 | | NFM | Farnborough Airshow | Input 449.725 Airfield ops linked to ground 122.500 |
| 444.37500 | 449.67500 | NFM | USAF Fairford | International Air Tattoo Communications |
| 444.45000 | | NFM | Farnborough | MoD Police |
| 444.45000 | | NFM | Nationwide | Benetton Formula 1 Team Alesi |
| 444.45000 | | NFM | West London | MoD Police Uxbridge Based (RI) |
| 444.47500 | | NFM | London, central | Poss Army Astro DVP |
| 444.50000 | 449.80000 | NFM | USAF Fairford | International Air Tattoo Exhibition Control |
| 444.55000 | 449.85000 | NFM | USAF Fairford | International Air Tattoo Admissions |
| 444.60000 | | NFM | Farnborough Airshow | French Aerospace |
| 444.65000 | | NFM | Colchester | 36 DWS REME |

## 445.5000 - 445.9750 MHz    PMR Base 12.5 kHz NFM
### (Split - 20.5 MHz )

| Base | Mobile | Mode | Location | User and Notes |
|------|--------|------|----------|----------------|
| 445.00000 | | NFM | Manchester | GMS Bases |
| 445.03750 | 445.03750 | NFM | Nationwide | Security Express |
| 445.13750 | | NFM | Newcastle Airport | Stores |
| 445.15000 | | NFM | Birmingham | British Rail Post Office |
| 445.15000 | | NFM | Farnborough Airshow | Courtsey cars for VIPs |
| 445.18750 | | NFM | Portsmouth | Marine Re-fuelling |
| 445.20000 | | NFM | Farnborough Airshow | Courtsey cars for VIPs |
| 445.25000 | | NFM | Aberdeen | BBC Film Crews |
| 445.30000 | | NFM | Farnborough Airshow | Medics/Fire |
| 445.35000 | | NFM | Farnborough Airshow | Courtsey cars for VIPs |
| 445.35000 | 438.35000 | NFM | North Sea | Ekofisk Senter Phillips |
| 445.40000 | 438.40000 | NFM | North Sea | Ekofisk Senter Phillips |
| 445.45000 | 438.45000 | NFM | North Sea | Ekofisk Senter Phillips |
| 445.50000 | 438.50000 | NFM | North Sea | Ekofisk Senter Phillips |
| 445.51250 | 425.01250 | NFM | Crayford | Interlink Couriers |
| 445.51250 | 425.01250 | NFM | London | Post Office |
| 445.52500 | 425.02500 | NFM | London | Taxis |
| 445.55000 | 425.05000 | NFM | Glasgow | Taxis |
| 445.55000 | 425.05000 | NFM | Plymouth | Post Office Security |
| 445.56250 | 425.06250 | NFM | London | Room Service Deliveries |
| 445.56250 | 425.06250 | NFM | Manchester | Mobile mechanic |
| 445.57500 | 425.07500 | NFM | Glasgow | Courier Service |
| 445.57500 | 425.07500 | NFM | London | West Hendon Mini Cabs |
| 445.58750 | 425.08750 | NFM | Bootle | Security Firm |
| 445.60000 | 425.10000 | NFM | Birmingham | City Waste Ltd |
| 445.60000 | 425.10000 | NFM | London, Kensington | Council Traffic Wardens |
| 445.60000 | 425.10000 | NFM | London, south east | Borough Traffic Wardens |
| 445.60000 | 438.60000 | NFM | North Sea | Ekofisk Senter Phillips |
| 445.65000 | 425.15000 | NFM | Coventry | University Security |
| 445.65000 | 425.15000 | NFM | London, Heathrow | British Airways Engineering |
| 445.67500 | 425.17500 | NFM | London | High Court Security |
| 445.67500 | 425.17500 | NFM | London, Gatwick | Virgin ops. Control centre |
| 445.67500 | 425.27500 | NFM | Birmingham | Midwives |
| 445.70000 | 425.20000 | NFM | London, Gatwick | Airline ops. |
| 445.70000 | 425.20000 | NFM | Nationwide | MediCall |
| 445.70000 | 425.20000 | NFM | Newcastle | Trunked Network |
| 445.72500 | 425.22500 | NFM | London | DER Repeater (Crystal Palace) |
| 445.72500 | 425.22500 | NFM | London | Underground Aldgate East |
| 445.72500 | 425.22500 | NFM | London | Underground Bayswater |

| Base | Mobile | Mode | Location | User and Notes |
|------|--------|------|----------|----------------|
| 445.72500 | 425.22500 | NFM | London | Underground Cannon Street |
| 445.72500 | 425.22500 | NFM | London | Underground Chancery Lane |
| 445.72500 | 425.22500 | NFM | London | Underground Earls' Court |
| 445.72500 | 425.22500 | NFM | London | Underground Embankment |
| 445.72500 | 425.22500 | NFM | London | Underground Euston |
| 445.72500 | 425.22500 | NFM | London | Underground Gloucester Road |
| 445.72500 | 425.22500 | NFM | London | Underground Hammersmith |
| 445.72500 | 425.22500 | NFM | London | Underground Holborn |
| 445.72500 | 425.22500 | NFM | London | Underground Kings Cross |
| 445.72500 | 425.22500 | NFM | London | Underground Leicester Square |
| 445.72500 | 425.22500 | NFM | London | Underground Liverpool Street |
| 445.72500 | 425.22500 | NFM | London | Underground Mile End |
| 445.72500 | 425.22500 | NFM | London | Underground Moorgate |
| 445.72500 | 425.22500 | NFM | London | Underground Sloane Square |
| 445.72500 | 425.22500 | NFM | London | Underground South Kensington |
| 445.72500 | 425.22500 | NFM | London | Underground St James's Park |
| 445.72500 | 425.22500 | NFM | London | Underground Stations Channel 1 |
| 445.72500 | 425.22500 | NFM | London | Underground Temple |
| 445.72500 | 425.22500 | NFM | London | Underground Tottenham Crt Rd |
| 445.72500 | 425.22500 | NFM | London | Underground Tower Hill |
| 445.72500 | 425.22500 | NFM | London | Underground Victoria |
| 445.72500 | 425.22500 | NFM | London | Underground Whitechapel |
| 445.72500 | 425.22500 | NFM | London, Heathrow | Underground (Heathrow Control) |
| 445.72500 | 425.32500 | NFM | London | Westinghouse Cubic Ch 1 |
| 445.75000 | 425.25000 | NFM | London | Medicall |
| 445.75000 | 425.25000 | NFM | London | Underground Liverpool Street |
| 445.75000 | 425.25000 | NFM | London | University of East London |
| 445.75000 | 425.25000 | NFM | London, Gower Street | University College |
| 445.75000 | 425.25000 | NFM | London, Heathrow | Catering |
| 445.75000 | 425.25000 | NFM | London, Tooting | St Georges Hospital (MEDNET) |
| 445.75000 | 425.25000 | NFM | London, Wood Lane | BBC TV Centre security |
| 445.75000 | 425.35000 | NFM | London | Westinghouse Cubic Ch 2 |
| 445.76250 | 425.26250 | NFM | London | Medicall |
| 445.77500 | 425.27500 | NFM | London | Underground Blackfriars |
| 445.77500 | 425.27500 | NFM | London | Underground Edgeware Road |
| 445.77500 | 425.27500 | NFM | London | Underground Embankment |
| 445.77500 | 425.27500 | NFM | London | Underground Gloucester Road |
| 445.77500 | 425.27500 | NFM | London | Underground Goldhawk Road |
| 445.77500 | 425.27500 | NFM | London | Underground Hammersmith |
| 445.77500 | 425.27500 | NFM | London | Underground Ladbroke Grove |
| 445.77500 | 425.27500 | NFM | London | Underground Latimer Grove |
| 445.77500 | 425.27500 | NFM | London | Underground Paddington |
| 445.77500 | 425.27500 | NFM | London | Underground Royal Oak |
| 445.77500 | 425.27500 | NFM | London | Underground Shepherds Bush |
| 445.77500 | 425.27500 | NFM | London | Underground Stations Channel 2 |
| 445.77500 | 425.27500 | NFM | London | Underground Wembley Park |
| 445.77500 | 425.27500 | NFM | London | Underground Westbourne Park |
| 445.77500 | 425.27500 | NFM | London | Underground Westminster |
| 445.77500 | 425.37500 | NFM | London | Westinghouse Cubic Ch 3 |
| 445.77500 | 445.77500 | NFM | Nationwide | HM Customs & Excise |
| 445.78750 | 425.28750 | NFM | London | Medicall |
| 445.78750 | 425.28750 | NFM | Manchester | Haulage Company |
| 445.80000 | 425.30000 | NFM | Liverpool | North West Water |
| 445.80000 | 425.30000 | NFM | London | Underground Bow Road |
| 445.80000 | 425.30000 | NFM | London | Underground Farringdon |
| 445.80000 | 425.30000 | NFM | London | Underground High St Kensington |

| Base | Mobile | Mode | Location | User and Notes |
|------|--------|------|----------|----------------|
| 445.80000 | 425.30000 | NFM | London | Underground Ladbroke Grove |
| 445.80000 | 425.30000 | NFM | London | Underground Mansion House |
| 445.80000 | 425.30000 | NFM | London | Underground Stations Channel 3 |
| 445.80000 | 425.30000 | NFM | London, Heathrow | Ground Repeater |
| 445.80000 | 425.40000 | NFM | London | Borough of Hackney Cleansing |
| 445.80000 | 425.40000 | NFM | London | Westinghouse Cubic Ch 4 |
| 445.82500 | 425.32500 | NFM | Central London | Couriers |
| 445.82500 | 425.32500 | NFM | Glasgow | Skypack |
| 445.82500 | 425.32500 | AM | Nationwide | DoT Motorway Spot Checks |
| 445.82500 | 425.32500 | NFM | Nationwide | HM Customs & Excise |
| 445.82500 | 425.42500 | NFM | Kent | Doctors Scheme |
| 445.82500 | 425.42500 | NFM | London | Borough of Hackney Housing |
| 445.83750 | 445.83750 | NFM | Nationwide | BBC |
| 445.85000 | 445.85000 | NFM | Nationwide | HM Customs & Excise |
| 445.90000 | 445.90000 | NFM | Nationwide | BBC |
| 445.90000 | 445.90000 | NFM | Nationwide | BBC O/B Link (OL-94) |
| 445.91250 | 425.41250 | NFM | Manchester | Debt Collectors |
| 445.92500 | 425.52500 | NFM | London | Wings Couriers Ltd |
| 445.96250 | 425.46250 | NFM | Bootle | Site Deliveries |
| 445.96250 | 425.46250 | NFM | Preston | Haulage |
| 445.97500 | 425.47500 | NFM | London | Mobile Wheel Clampers |
| 445.97500 | 425.47500 | NFM | Newcastle | Trunked Network |
| 445.97500 | 425.47500 | NFM | Tyneside | Fencing Contractors |

## 446.00625 - 446.09375 MHz PMR 446 Simplex 12.5 Hz

| Base | Mobile | Mode | Location | User and Notes |
|------|--------|------|----------|----------------|
| 446.00625 | | NFM | Nationwide | Channel 1 |
| 446.01875 | | NFM | Nationwide | Channel 2 |
| 446.03125 | | NFM | Nationwide | Channel 3 |
| 446.04375 | | NFM | Nationwide | Channel 4 |
| 446.05625 | | NFM | Nationwide | Channel 5 |
| 446.06875 | | NFM | Nationwide | Channel 6 |
| 446.08125 | | NFM | Nationwide | Channel 7 |
| 446.09375 | | NFM | Nationwide | Channel 8 |

## 446.000 - 446.475 MHz PMR Simplex 12.5 kHz

| Base | Mobile | Mode | Location | User and Notes |
|------|--------|------|----------|----------------|
| 446.00000 | | NFM | Bromley | Banking |
| 446.00000 | | NFM | London | Alexandra Palace security |
| 446.00000 | | NFM | London | City of London Girls School |
| 446.00000 | | NFM | London | Harbour Exchange Security |
| 446.00000 | | NFM | London | Royal Albert Hall security |
| 446.00000 | | NFM | London | Showsec Security |
| 446.00000 | | NFM | London | Tate Gallery security |
| 446.00000 | | NFM | London | Wembley Stadium security |
| 446.00000 | | NFM | London, Covent Gdns | Roadhouse Restaurant |
| 446.00000 | | NFM | London, EC4 | Security |
| 446.00000 | | NFM | London, Oxford Street | Selfridges |
| 446.00000 | | NFM | London, St James Square | Retailer |
| 446.00000 | | NFM | London, SW14 | School |
| 446.00000 | | NFM | London, Woolwich | Waterfront Leisure Centre |
| 446.00000 | | NFM | North Sea | Ekofisk Senter Phillips |
| 446.00000 | | WFM | Sheffield | BBC Radio Sheffield O/B |
| 446.00000 | | NFM | Solihull | Business Park Security |
| 446.01250 | | NFM | Buckhurst Hill | Nature Reserve |
| 446.01250 | | NFM | London | Elephant & Castle Shopping Centre security |
| 446.01250 | | NFM | London | Buckingham Palace security |
| 446.01250 | | NFM | London | Soho Leisure |

| Base | Mobile | Mode | Location | User and Notes |
|---|---|---|---|---|
| 446.01250 | | NFM | London | Wimbledon Common security |
| 446.01250 | | NFM | London, Chelsea | Royal Hospital |
| 446.01250 | | NFM | London, EC3 | Banking |
| 446.01250 | | NFM | London, Kensington | Security |
| 446.01250 | | NFM | London, Kew Bridge | Security |
| 446.01250 | | NFM | London, SE13 | School |
| 446.01250 | | NFM | London, Thames House | MoD security |
| 446.01250 | | NFM | London, Wapping | News International Newspapers |
| 446.01250 | | NFM | Manchester | Hospital (ALFA) |
| 446.01250 | | NFM | Sunbury | Food Manufacturer |
| 446.02500 | | NFM | Bexley Heath | School |
| 446.02500 | | NFM | Harlow | Security SmithKline Beecham |
| 446.02500 | | NFM | London | Putney Hospital |
| 446.02500 | | NFM | London | Royal Albert Hall |
| 446.02500 | | NFM | London, Covent Gardens | Long Island Ice Tea Bar |
| 446.02500 | | NFM | London, Docklands | Underground Ch 1-3 |
| 446.02500 | | NFM | London, Heathrow | Airport Taxi Service |
| 446.02500 | | NFM | London, Mayfair | Intercontinental Hotel |
| 446.02500 | | NFM | London, Neasden | Ikea. |
| 446.02500 | | NFM | London, SW8 | Covent Garden Market |
| 446.02500 | | NFM | London, WCI | British Medical Association |
| 446.02500 | | NFM | Tadworth, Surrey | Experimental Farm security |
| 446.03125 | | NFM | London, Oxford Circus | JJB Sport |
| 446.03750 | | NFM | Blackpool | Pleasure Beach Staff |
| 446.03750 | | NFM | Chatham | PC World Security |
| 446.03750 | | NFM | Coventry | Alarm Engineers |
| 446.03750 | | NFM | Coventry | PC World Security |
| 446.03750 | | NFM | London | Beckenham Place Park |
| 446.03750 | | NFM | London | Royal Albert Hall |
| 446.03750 | | NFM | Stockport | PC World staff & security |
| 446.05000 | | NFM | Edinburgh | Stevenson College Janitors |
| 446.05000 | | NFM | London | American Airlines |
| 446.05000 | | NFM | London | Hammersmith School |
| 446.05000 | | NFM | London | Lords Cricket Ground staff |
| 446.05000 | | NFM | London | Wembley Hotel |
| 446.05000 | | NFM | London, Knightsbridge | Harrods store security |
| 446.05000 | | NFM | London, Mortlake | Watneys Brewery |
| 446.05000 | | NFM | London, Oxford Street | Berners Park Plaza Hotel |
| 446.05000 | | NFM | London, Piccadilly | Imax Cinema Staff |
| 446.05000 | | NFM | London, Selhurst | Adult Training Centre |
| 446.05000 | | NFM | Manchester | Trafford Centre P055 Rain Forest Cafe |
| 446.06000 | | NFM | London, Trocadero | Emaginator |
| 446.06250 | | NFM | Isleworth, Middlesex | University Hospital |
| 446.06250 | | NFM | London | Redbridge School |
| 446.06250 | | NFM | London, Canary Wharf | Britannia Hotel |
| 446.06250 | | NFM | London, Heathrow | Airport Taxi Service |
| 446.06250 | | NFM | London, SW19 | Southfield School |
| 446.06250 | | NFM | London, SW19 | Southfield Mosque |
| 446.06250 | | NFM | Tadworth, Surrey | Government Offices |
| 446.06875 | | NFM | London, Oxford Circus | JJB Sport |
| 446.07500 | | NFM | Epsom | RAC Golf and Country Club |
| 446.07500 | | NFM | London | Masterpark Car Parking Attendants |
| 446.07500 | | NFM | London, Wapping | News International security |
| 446.07500 | | NFM | Mortlake | Watneys Brewery. |
| 446.07500 | | NFM | National | Baldwin Crane Hire |
| 446.07500 | | NFM | Redbridge | Technical College |

| Base | Mobile | Mode | Location | User and Notes |
|------|--------|------|----------|----------------|
| 446.08750 | | NFM | Croydon | Woodside School |
| 446.08750 | | NFM | Heston, Middlesex | School |
| 446.08750 | | NFM | London | St Mark's Hospital |
| 446.08750 | | NFM | London | Tate Gallery security |
| 446.08750 | | NFM | London | University College Hospital |
| 446.08750 | | NFM | London, Marble Arch | Marks and Spencers |
| 446.08750 | | NFM | London, St. James | Lancaster House |
| 446.08750 | | NFM | Manchester | Praha Gay Club |
| 446.08750 | | NFM | Richmond | Park School |
| 446.09375 | | NFM | London, Oxford Circus | JJB Sport |
| 446.10000 | | NFM | Cheam, Surrey | St. Anthony's Hospital |
| 446.10000 | | NFM | Chessington | Gascoigne Ltd., computer services |
| 446.10000 | | NFM | Downe, Kent | West Kent Golf Course |
| 446.10000 | | NFM | London | Erith Food Mill |
| 446.10000 | | NFM | London | Go Kart Racing |
| 446.10000 | | NFM | London | Wembley Executive Catering |
| 446.10000 | | NFM | London, Piccadilly | "Planet Hollywood" staff |
| 446.10000 | | NFM | London, Woolwich | Thames Flood Barrier |
| 446.10000 | | NFM | Manchester | Hospital Maintenance |
| 446.10000 | | NFM | Thorpe | Fun Park Ch 1 |
| 446.11250 | | NFM | Biggin Hill | Airport Ops. |
| 446.11250 | | NFM | Bromley | School |
| 446.11250 | | NFM | London | Euston Station |
| 446.11250 | | NFM | London | Tate Gallery |
| 446.11250 | | NFM | London | Underground Stations Ch.5 |
| 446.11250 | | NFM | London | Wembley National Leisure Catering |
| 446.11250 | | NFM | London, Bush House | BBC Radio security |
| 446.11250 | | NFM | London, Langham Place | BBC Radio security |
| 446.11250 | | NFM | Morden, Surrey | Merton Technical College security |
| 446.12500 | | NFM | Croydon | Debenhams Security |
| 446.12500 | | NFM | Guildford | Debenhams Security |
| 446.12500 | | NFM | London Kensington | Victoria and Albert Museum security |
| 446.12500 | | NFM | London, Docklands | London Arena admin & security |
| 446.12500 | | NFM | London, Ealing | Thames Valley University |
| 446.12500 | | NFM | London, Soho | Rupert Street Gay Club, NCS Security |
| 446.12500 | | NFM | London, SW14 | Rosslyn Park Rugby Club |
| 446.12500 | | NFM | Manchester | Debenhams Store |
| 446.12500 | | NFM | Mitcham, Surrey | Aquatreat Chemical Services Ltd. |
| 446.12500 | | NFM | North Weald | Airfield Tower To Vehicle Crossing. |
| 446.12500 | | NFM | Nottingham | Debenhams Security |
| 446.12500 | | NFM | Romford | Shopping Centre security |
| 446.12500 | | NFM | Romford | Debenhams Security |
| 446.12500 | | NFM | Stapeley | Stapeley Water Gardens |
| 446.12500 | | NFM | Stirling | Debenhams |
| 446.13750 | | NFM | Birmingham | Digbeth Coach Station |
| 446.13750 | | NFM | London | Hither Green Crematorium |
| 446.13750 | | NFM | London | Securiplan Security |
| 446.13750 | | NFM | London, Aldgate | Education |
| 446.13750 | | NFM | London, Heathrow | Airline Ops |
| 446.13750 | | NFM | London, Hornsey | Ecco Cold Store Ltd. |
| 446.13750 | | NFM | London, Mill Hill | Institute for Medical Research |
| 446.13750 | | NFM | London, Paddington | St. Mary's Hospital |
| 446.13750 | | NFM | London, Piccadilly | Trocadero Sega Megaworld security Ch.3 |
| 446.13750 | | NFM | London, Victoria | PA Consulting |
| 446.13750 | | NFM | Norbiton | Coombe Hill Golf Course |
| 446.15000 | | NFM | City of London | Northern Trust Ltd. Security and Staff |

| --- | --- | --- | --- | --- |
| 446.15000 | | NFM | London | Best Construction Ltd. |
| 446.15000 | | NFM | London, Bethnal Green | Sports Ground |
| 446.15000 | | NFM | London, NW8 | Wellington Hospital |
| 446.15000 | | NFM | London, WC1 | British Medical Association security |
| 446.15000 | | NFM | Newham | The Terrace Macmillan Stadium |
| 446.15000 | | NFM | Romford | Old Church Hospital |
| 446.16250 | | NFM | Dagenham | Becontree Heath School |
| 446.16250 | | NFM | London | Chelsea Football Club |
| 446.16250 | | NFM | London | Clarence House |
| 446.16250 | | NFM | London | Emerson Crane Hire |
| 446.16250 | | NFM | London | Pentonville Road Security |
| 446.16250 | | NFM | London | Wembley Stadium catering |
| 446.17500 | | NFM | Denham | Broad Water Park Industrial Estate |
| 446.17500 | | NFM | Hayes | Factory security |
| 446.17500 | | NFM | London | Lewisham Hospital |
| 446.17500 | | NFM | London, Aldgate | Security |
| 446.17500 | | NFM | London, Aldwych | Inland Revenue |
| 446.17500 | | NFM | London, Kensington | Security |
| 446.17500 | | NFM | London, SE16 | Bacons College |
| 446.17500 | | NFM | London, SW1 | Marlborough House |
| 446.17500 | | NFM | London, Waterloo | St. Thomas Hospital |
| 446.17500 | | NFM | Surbiton | Golf Club |
| 446.17500 | | NFM | Uxbridge | Brunel University |
| 446.18750 | | NFM | Bromley | Church House Gardens |
| 446.18750 | | NFM | Dagenham | Becontree School |
| 446.18750 | | NFM | Denham | Horticulture |
| 446.18750 | | NFM | London | Barnet College security |
| 446.18750 | | NFM | London | Canary Wharf security |
| 446.18750 | | NFM | London | Securiplan Security |
| 446.18750 | | NFM | London, Catford | Halfords Superstore |
| 446.18750 | | NFM | London, E2 | Victoria Park |
| 446.18750 | | NFM | London, Ealing | Thames Valley University |
| 446.18750 | | NFM | London, Greenhithe | Sports Ground |
| 446.18750 | | NFM | London, Kensington | Commonwealth Institute |
| 446.18750 | | NFM | London, Regent St | British Airways Shop security |
| 446.18750 | | NFM | London, Russell Lane | Barnet College |
| 446.18750 | | NFM | London, Victoria | PA Consulting |
| 446.18750 | | NFM | Southall | Retail |
| 446.20000 | | NFM | Croydon | Bethlehem Royal Hospital |
| 446.20000 | | NFM | Croydon | Bethlehem Hospital |
| 446.20000 | | NFM | Dartford | Joyce Green Hospital |
| 446.20000 | | NFM | Edinburgh | Virgin Record Shop Security |
| 446.20000 | | NFM | London | Hyde Park |
| 446.20000 | | NFM | London, Battersea | Rail depot security |
| 446.20000 | | NFM | London, Docklands | London Arena admin & security |
| 446.20000 | | NFM | London, Ealing | BBC Ealing Studios security |
| 446.20000 | | NFM | London, Oxford Circus | Marks & Spencers |
| 446.20000 | | NFM | London, SE5 | Maudsley Hospital security |
| 446.20000 | | NFM | London, WCl | Coram Fields Health Centre |
| 446.20000 | | NFM | North Sea | Valhalla Field Amoco |
| 446.21250 | | NFM | Carshalton | Sutton Hospital |
| 446.21250 | | NFM | Dagenham | Old Park School |
| 446.21250 | | NFM | London | Canary Wharf security |
| 446.21250 | | NFM | London | Charlton Athletic Football Ground |
| 446.21250 | | NFM | London, SW13 | St. Paul's School |
| 446.21250 | | NFM | London, Wapping | St. Katherines Dock Services |

| Base | Mobile | Mode | Location | User and Notes |
|------|--------|------|----------|----------------|
| 446.21250 | | NFM | London, Wimbledon | Centre Court Shopping Centre |
| 446.21500 | | NFM | Worksop | Council parks |
| 446.22500 | | NFM | Croydon | Woodcote Green School |
| 446.22500 | | NFM | Hendon | Hendon Town Hall |
| 446.22500 | | NFM | Kingston | Kingston University School |
| 446.22500 | | NFM | Lewisham | Lewisham Shopping Centre |
| 446.22500 | | NFM | London | National Science Museum |
| 446.22500 | | NFM | London | National History Museum |
| 446.22500 | | NFM | London | Rayners Lane Sports Ground |
| 446.22500 | | NFM | London | Thames Water Board Emergency handhelds |
| 446.22500 | | NFM | London, Old Street | Moorfield Eye Hospital |
| 446.22500 | | NFM | London, Vauxhall | Hostel |
| 446.22500 | | NFM | Manchester | Airport |
| 446.22500 | | NFM | North Sea | Ekofisk Senter Phillips |
| 446.22500 | | NFM | Reading | Thames Water |
| 446.23750 | | NFM | Brentford | T Holloway & Sons |
| 446.23750 | | NFM | Coventry | City Sports Centre |
| 446.23750 | | NFM | London | Apollo Theatre Front of House |
| 446.23750 | | NFM | London | Burlington Arcade security |
| 446.23750 | | NFM | London | Marble Arch Hotel |
| 446.23750 | | NFM | London | Royal Academy of Dramatic Art security |
| 446.23750 | | NFM | London, Hyde Park | Sterling Food Vendors |
| 446.25000 | | NFM | Croydon | School |
| 446.25000 | | NFM | Dagenham | Becontree Heath Park |
| 446.25000 | | NFM | Enfield | Palace Garden Shopping Centre |
| 446.25000 | | NFM | London | Clapham Trinity Hospice |
| 446.25000 | | NFM | London | Erith College of Technology |
| 446.25000 | | NFM | London | Greenwich District Hospital |
| 446.25000 | | NFM | London | Middlesex Hospital |
| 446.25000 | | NFM | London | Royal Albert Hall Catering |
| 446.25000 | | NFM | London | Wandsworth School |
| 446.25000 | | NFM | London | Wapping Property Management |
| 446.25000 | | NFM | London, Gatwick | Thomas Cook |
| 446.25000 | | NFM | London, Heathrow | Holiday Inn Hotel |
| 446.25000 | | NFM | London, Marble Arch | Marks & Spencers |
| 446.25000 | | NFM | London, Oxford St | Virgin Megastore |
| 446.25000 | | NFM | London, Walthamstow | Whipps Cross Hospital |
| 446.25000 | | NFM | Watford | Medical |
| 446.26250 | | NFM | Dartford | River Crossing |
| 446.26250 | | NFM | Edinburgh | The Gyle Centre Security |
| 446.26250 | | NFM | London | Bermondsey Mail Order |
| 446.26250 | | NFM | London | London University College Hospital |
| 446.26250 | | NFM | London | Royal Albert Hall front of house |
| 446.26250 | | NFM | London, Hither Green | Hither Green Saw Mill |
| 446.26250 | | NFM | London, Park Lane | Hilton Hotel |
| 446.26250 | | NFM | London, SW15 | Gloucester Hotel security |
| 446.26250 | | NFM | Rickmansworth | Mount Vernon Hospital |
| 446.27500 | | NFM | Barking | School |
| 446.27500 | | NFM | Carlshalton | Biological Research Labs. |
| 446.27500 | | NFM | Croydon | Shirley Oaks Hospital |
| 446.27500 | | NFM | London | Buckingham Palace Gardeners |
| 446.27500 | | NFM | London | Kentish Town School |
| 446.27500 | | NFM | London | Soho Estate Management |
| 446.27500 | | NFM | London | Tate Gallery security |
| 446.27500 | | NFM | London | Wapping Property Management |
| 446.27500 | | NFM | London, Acton | Security |

| Base | Mobile | Mode | Location | User and Notes |
|------|--------|------|----------|----------------|
| 446.27500 | | NFM | London, Heathrow | Airport retailer |
| 446.27500 | | NFM | London, Piccadilly | Teikoku Oil Co. Ltd. |
| 446.27500 | | NFM | London, SW15 | Gloucester Hotel |
| 446.27500 | | NFM | London, Woolwich | Charlton Athletic Football Ground |
| 446.27500 | | NFM | Luton Airport | TNT Carriers |
| 446.27500 | | NFM | Manchester | Airport |
| 446.27500 | | NFM | Norbiton | Kingston Hospital Engineering |
| 446.27500 | | NFM | North Sea | Amoco Valhalla Field |
| 446.28750 | | NFM | Croydon | Home Office Immigration |
| 446.28750 | | NFM | Isleworth | West Middlesex University Hospital |
| 446.28750 | | NFM | Lea Valley | Leisure Centre Catering |
| 446.28750 | | NFM | London | Bow Church |
| 446.28750 | | NFM | London | Home Office security. |
| 446.28750 | | NFM | London | The Mall Galleries |
| 446.28750 | | NFM | London | Tower Bridge security |
| 446.28750 | | NFM | London | Tower Pageant Exhibition |
| 446.28750 | | NFM | London NW7 | Capital Sports |
| 446.28750 | | NFM | London, Enfield | Council |
| 446.28750 | | NFM | London, Piccadilly | Rainforest Cafe Ch.2 |
| 446.28750 | | NFM | Staines | Shopping Centre Security (ES) |
| 446.30000 | | NFM | Brentford | T Holloway and Sons (Metals) Ltd. |
| 446.30000 | | NFM | Carshalton | College |
| 446.30000 | | NFM | Edinburgh | Lorry Loaders |
| 446.30000 | | NFM | Epson, Surrey | Mounthill Gardens |
| 446.30000 | | NFM | London | Capital Radio Flying Eye |
| 446.30000 | | NFM | London, EC3 | Old Bailey |
| 446.30000 | | NFM | London, Gower Street | University College |
| 446.30000 | | NFM | London, Theobalds Road | University College |
| 446.30000 | | NFM | London, W12 | Wormholt Park Swimming Pool Security |
| 446.30000 | | NFM | Norwood | Harris City Technology Course |
| 446.31250 | | NFM | London, Acton | Skin care manufacturer |
| 446.31250 | | NFM | London, SW8 | Government Transport Depot |
| 446.31250 | | NFM | London, Wandsworth | Arndale Shopping Centre security. |
| 446.31250 | | NFM | Walthamstow | Walton Forest College |
| 446.32500 | | NFM | London | London Underground Stations Ch 6 |
| 446.32500 | | NFM | London | Marble Arch Leisure |
| 446.32500 | | NFM | London | Tate Gallery security |
| 446.32500 | | NFM | London, Erith | Europa Trading Estate Security |
| 446.32500 | | NFM | London, SW13 | Southfields School |
| 446.32500 | | NFM | London, WCI | Bloomsbury Crest Hotel |
| 446.33700 | | NFM | Barnet | Ravenscroft School |
| 446.33750 | | NFM | City of London | 25 Cannon Bridge Securiplan Security/Staff |
| 446.33750 | | NFM | Hounslow | Brinks Mat Cash in transit Base. |
| 446.33750 | | NFM | London | Buckingham Palace Tours |
| 446.33750 | | NFM | London | Holloway Nagshead Shopping Centre Security. |
| 446.33750 | | NFM | London | Old Bailey |
| 446.33750 | | NFM | London | Royal College of Physicians |
| 446.33750 | | NFM | London, Canonbridge | Rothschilds Bank |
| 446.33750 | | NFM | London, Canonbridge | Standard Bank security |
| 446.33750 | | NFM | London, Piccadilly | Rainforest Cafe Ch 1 |
| 446.33750 | | NFM | London, Sevenoaks | Highlands Farm |
| 446.33750 | | NFM | London, White City | BBC TV Centre |
| 446.33750 | | NFM | Retford | Thomas Cook travel |
| 446.35000 | | NFM | Byfleet | Brooklands Museum of Transport |
| 446.35000 | | NFM | Carshalton | Westcroft Leisure |
| 446.35000 | | NFM | Chelmsley Wood | Security |

| Base | Mobile | Mode | Location | User and Notes |
|---|---|---|---|---|
| 446.35000 | | NFM | City of London | Caterers |
| 446.35000 | | NFM | Esher, Surrey | Private school |
| 446.35000 | | NFM | Greenford | Engineering factory |
| 446.35000 | | NFM | London | Avery Hill University of Greenwich |
| 446.35000 | | NFM | London | Northern Telecom Security |
| 446.35000 | | NFM | London, SEl9 | Norwood School |
| 446.35000 | | NFM | North Cheam | Sports Centre |
| 446.35000 | | NFM | Redbridge | Sports Centre |
| 446.35000 | | NFM | West Drayton | Car parking |
| 446.36250 | | NFM | Colingdale | Public Health Labs (DEFENDER) |
| 446.36250 | | NFM | London | Globe Theatre staff and security |
| 446.36250 | | NFM | London, Enfield | Capel Manor Gardens |
| 446.36250 | | NFM | London, Leicester Square | Equinox Discotheque |
| 446.37500 | | NFM | Addington | Addington Court Golf Club |
| 446.37500 | | NFM | City of London | Liverpool Street Property Management |
| 446.37500 | | NFM | London | Aldgate Education |
| 446.37500 | | NFM | London, Mill Hill | National Institute for Medical Research |
| 446.37500 | | NFM | London | Museum of London security |
| 446.37500 | | NFM | London | Victoria Embankment Gardens |
| 446.37500 | | NFM | London | Woolwich Arsenal Education |
| 446.37500 | | NFM | London, Acton | Banking |
| 446.37500 | | NFM | London, Acton | Cash in transit (base) |
| 446.37500 | | NFM | London, Erith | Food miller |
| 446.37500 | | NFM | London, Gt. Russell Street | Bern Shopping Centre |
| 446.37500 | | NFM | London, Hounslow | Shopwatch Security |
| 446.37500 | | NFM | London, Langham Place | BBC security |
| 446.37500 | | NFM | London, Pimlico | Estate agent |
| 446.37500 | | NFM | London, Streatham | St. Michael Convent School |
| 446.37500 | | NFM | London, Victoria | Estate agent |
| 446.37500 | | NFM | London, Walthamstow | Parking Enforcement |
| 446.37500 | | NFM | Sutton | Civic Centre |
| 446.37500 | | NFM | Uxbridge | Civic Centre |
| 446.37500 | | NFM | West Thurrock | Warehouse |
| 446.37500 | | NFM | Weybridge | Warren Pond Engineering |
| 446.38750 | | NFM | Derbyshire, NE | Council Ranger Service (RANGER) |
| 446.38750 | | NFM | London | Old Bailey |
| 446.38750 | | NFM | London, WC1 | Gt. Ormond Street Hospital for Sick Children |
| 446.40000 | | NFM | Coventry | West Orchard Shopping Centre Security |
| 446.40000 | | NFM | Fairlop, Essex | Barnardos Village security |
| 446.40000 | | NFM | London | Islington Conference Centre |
| 446.40000 | | NFM | London | Lords Cricket Ground |
| 446.40000 | | NFM | London | The Queens Club Tennis Security |
| 446.40000 | | NFM | London | Underground Stations Ch.7 |
| 446.40000 | | NFM | London, Woolwich | Thames Flood Barrier |
| 446.40000 | | NFM | Nationwide | Radio Investigations Service |
| 446.40000 | | NFM | Oxted, Surrey | Convent of the Sacred Heart School |
| 446.40000 | | NFM | Walshall | Ikea Furniture Security and Car Parking |
| 446.42500 | | NFM | London | Crown Estates Staff |
| 446.45000 | | NFM | London | Royal Parks (Z) |
| 446.45000 | | NFM | Nationwide | British Pipeline Agency |
| 446.45000 | | NFM | Nationwide | Radio Investigations Service |
| 446.45000 | | NFM | Thetford | British Pipeline Agency |
| 446.45000 | 439.45000 | NFM | North Sea | Valhalla Field Amoco |

**446.4250 - 447.5500 MHz**   BROADCASTING LINKS

| Base | Mobile | Mode | Location | User and Notes |
|------|--------|------|----------|----------------|
| 446.42500 | | NFM | Nationwide | JFMG OB Links within M25 Area |
| 446.51250 | | NFM | Nationwide | JFMG OB Links Within M25 Area |
| 446.51250 | | NFM | Nationwide | JFMG Temp Point-Point/Simplex/Talkback |
| 446.56250 | | NFM | Essex | BBC Radio Essex Links |
| 446.56250 | | WFM | London | BBC-TV London Marathon |
| 446.56250 | | NFM | National | Stewart Formula 1 Racing Team Telemetry |
| 446.57500 | | NFM | Thorpe | Fun Park |
| 446.63750 | | NFM | Nationwide | BBC Local Radio Talkback |
| 446.63750 | | NFM | Nottinghamshire | Radio Nottingham O/B |
| 446.63750 | | NFM | Stoke on Trent | Radio Stoke O/B |
| 446.68750 | 446.62750 | NFM | Nationwide | BBC Talkback |
| 446.70000 | | NFM | London | Medicall |
| 446.73750 | | NFM | London | Greater London Radio Talkback |
| 446.73750 | | NFM | Manchester | BBC GMR O/B |
| 446.73750 | | NFM | Nationwide | BBC Local Radio Talkback |
| 446.78750 | | NFM | Belfry (Ryder Cup) | BBC Radio 5 |
| 446.78750 | | NFM | Kent | BBC Radio O/B |
| 446.78750 | | NFM | London | BBC Radio 5 Talkback |
| 446.83750 | | NFM | Derbyshire | Radio Derby Outside Broadcast |
| 446.83750 | | NFM | Nationwide | BBC Local Radio Talkback |
| 446.83750 | | NFM | Preston | Ladies Lancashire Talk back |
| 446.85000 | | NFM | Kent | BBC Radio O/B |
| 446.90000 | | NFM | London | Post Office (Euston) |
| 446.93750 | | NFM | Nationwide | BBC |
| 446.93750 | | NFM | Nationwide | BBC Local Radio Talkback |
| 446.93750 | 141.30000 | NFM | Leicester | BBC Radio Leicester O/B |
| 446.95000 | | NFM | London | London Underground (Holborn Station) |
| 446.95000 | | NFM | London | Underground, London Bridge Station |
| 447.00000 | | NFM | Silverstone | Japanese TV Talkback |
| 447.08750 | | NFM | Birmingham | 96.4 FM BRMB/Xtra O/B |
| 447.08750 | | NFM | Birmingham | ILR X-tra AM |
| 447.08750 | | NFM | Hull | Viking Radio O/B |
| 447.08750 | | NFM | Peterborough | Hereward Radio car |
| 447.08750 | | NFM | Stoke on Trent | Signal Radio O/B |
| 447.08920 | | NFM | London | Independent Radio Talkback |
| 447.13120 | | NFM | Manchester | Piccadilly Gold |
| 447.18750 | | NFM | Blackpool | Radio Wave O/B |
| 447.18750 | | NFM | Hull | Viking Radio O/B |
| 447.18750 | | NFM | London | Independent Radio Talkback |
| 447.18750 | | NFM | Manchester | Piccadilly Radio Talk back |
| 447.18750 | | NFM | Stockport | Signal Cheshire |
| 447.23750 | | NFM | Manchester | Piccadilly Radio Studio Link |
| 447.23750 | | NFM | Salisbury | Spire FM |
| 447.23750 | | NFM | Warwick | Mercia Radio (Coventry) radio mic. linking radio car |
| 447.28750 | | NFM | London | Independent Radio Talkback |
| 447.28750 | | NFM | Preston | Red Rose Ladies Talkback |
| 447.33750 | | NFM | Birmingham | Buzz FM Outside Broadcasts |
| 447.33750 | | NFM | Liverpool | Radio City Talkback |
| 447.40000 | | NFM | Silverstone | US TV Talkback |
| 447.42500 | | NFM | Ferrybridge | Engineering Talkback |
| 447.42500 | | NFM | Liverpool | Brookside Studio |
| 447.42500 | | NFM | London | ITV camera link |
| 447.42500 | | NFM | Yorkshire | Yorkshire Television |
| 447.43000 | | WFM | Sheffield | Yorkshire TV O/B |
| 447.43750 | | NFM | Leeds | Yorkshire TV O/B |

| Base | Mobile | Mode | Location | User and Notes |
|---|---|---|---|---|
| 447.47500 | | NFM | London | Independent Radio Talkback |
| 447.48750 | | NFM | Liverpool | Brookside TV Director |
| 447.50000 | | NFM | London | ITV camera link |
| 447.50000 | | NFM | London | Independent Radio Talkback |
| 447.50000 | | NFM | Silverstone | US TV Talkback |
| 447.51250 | | NFM | Nationwide | JFMG Temp Point-Point/Simplex/Tback |
| 447.55000 | | NFM | Aberystwyth | Radio 1 Roadshow OB Talkback |

### 447.600 - 447.925 MHz    PMR SIMPLEX

| Base | Mobile | Mode | Location | User and Notes |
|---|---|---|---|---|
| 447.60000 | | NFM | London | Trocadero Centre Funland Centre C112 |
| 447.66250 | | NFM | Dagenham | Ford Motor Plant |
| 447.66250 | | NFM | Glasgow | Buchanan Bus Station |
| 447.66250 | | NFM | London, WC1 | Habitat and Heals security |
| 447.68750 | | NFM | Croydon, Lunar House | Home Office Immigration |
| 447.68750 | | NFM | London | Catford School |
| 447.68750 | | NFM | London | Chelsea Banking and Finance |
| 447.68750 | | NFM | London | Hackney School |
| 447.68750 | | NFM | London | Holloway School |
| 447.68750 | | NFM | London | Kensington Palace |
| 447.68750 | | NFM | London | Woolwich Council offices |
| 447.68750 | | NFM | London, Covent Garden | Doc Martens Shoe Shop |
| 447.68750 | | NFM | London, Covent Garden | Royal Opera House security |
| 447.68750 | | NFM | London, E16 | Keyline Building Merchants |
| 447.68750 | | NFM | London, EI | School |
| 447.68750 | | NFM | London, N13 | Keyline Building Merchants |
| 447.68750 | | NFM | Manchester | New Look Shop security |
| 447.68750 | | NFM | Southall | B &B Building Merchants |
| 447.68750 | | NFM | Woodford, Essex | Woodford Trading Estate Engineering |
| 447.71250 | | NFM | Carshalton | College |
| 447.71250 | | NFM | Leytonstone | Whipps Cross Hospital |
| 447.71250 | | NFM | London | Ealing School. |
| 447.71250 | | NFM | London | Eltham Palace |
| 447.71250 | | NFM | London | Kings College Security |
| 447.71250 | | NFM | London, E2 | Chest Hospital |
| 447.71250 | | NFM | London, N5 | Arsenal Football Club |
| 447.71250 | | NFM | London, NW2 | Communications company |
| 447.71250 | | NFM | London, W2 | Hyde Park. |
| 447.71250 | | NFM | London, Wapping | Banking |
| 447.72500 | | NFM | Croydon | Engineering factory |
| 447.72500 | | NFM | London | Brent Cross Shopping Centre. |
| 447.72500 | | NFM | London | Camberwell Town Hall |
| 447.72500 | | NFM | London | Royal Academy of Arts Exhibition staff |
| 447.72500 | | NFM | London | Silvertown Atlantis Oil and Chemical Ltd. |
| 447.72500 | | NFM | London | Victoria Embankment Gardens |
| 447.72500 | | NFM | London | Whitechapel Hospital |
| 447.72500 | | NFM | London | Wood Green School |
| 447.72500 | | NFM | London, NW8 | Hilton International Hotel |
| 447.72500 | | NFM | London, Oxford Circus | JJD Sports security |
| 447.72500 | | NFM | London, St. James Park | Alfresco Catering |
| 447.72500 | | NFM | London, SW18 | Wandsworth Waste Disposal |
| 447.72500 | | NFM | London, SW6 | Chelsea Football Club |
| 447.72500 | | NFM | London, SW8 | Waste disposal |
| 447.72500 | | NFM | Richmond-Upon-Thames | Athletic Grounds |
| 447.73750 | | NFM | London, Oxford Circus | JJD Sports security |
| 447.78750 | | NFM | Hounslow | Cranford Community School |
| 447.78750 | | NFM | London | Alexandra Palace |

| Base | Mobile | Mode | Location | User and Notes |
|------|--------|------|----------|----------------|
| 447.78750 | | NFM | London | Dartford School |
| 447.78750 | | NFM | London | London Underground Engineering |
| 447.78750 | | NFM. | London | Palace Garden Estate Management |
| 447.78750 | | NFM | London | Royal Academy of Arts |
| 447.78750 | | NFM | London, Canary Wharf | London Underground Ch.4 |
| 447.78750 | | NFM | London, E17 | Higgins Park School |
| 447.78750 | | NFM | London, Kew Bridge | Victoria and Albert Museum security |
| 447.78750 | | NFM | London, NW8 | Hilton International Hotel |
| 447.78750 | | NFM | London, Oxford Circus | New Look security |
| 447.78750 | | NFM | London, Piccadilly | Troccadero Centre |
| 447.78750 | | NFM | London, SW15 | Roehampton Golf Club |
| 447.78750 | | NFM | North Weald | Tower to Emergency Service Vehicle Crossing. |
| 447.78750 | | NFM | Sheffield | Dry ski slope |
| 447.81250 | | NFM | London, E3 | Baltic Exchange security |
| 447.81250 | | NFM | London, N1 | Islington School |
| 447.81250 | | NFM | Norwood | School |
| 447.82500 | | NFM | London | Namco Amusements |
| 447.82500 | | NFM | London | Swiss Cottage School |
| 447.82500 | | NFM | London, | Bow Common School |
| 447.82500 | | NFM | Thurrock | Leisure Lakeside Shopping Centre |
| 447.87500 | | NFM | London | Namco Amusements |
| 447.92500 | | NFM | Farnborough Airshow | Support |

### 448.0625 - 449.0000 MHz    PMR London Area (Mobiles -17 MHz)

| Base | Mobile | Mode | Location | User and Notes |
|------|--------|------|----------|----------------|
| 448.02500 | 431.02500 | NFM | London | Taxis |
| 448.07500 | 431.07500 | NFM | London, east | Taxis |
| 448.12500 | 431.12500 | NFM | Kent | PJM Vehicle Recovery |
| 448.12500 | 431.12500 | NFM | London | Motorbike Couriers |
| 448.19375 | 431.19375 | NFM | London | Courier (PD) |
| 448.22500 | 451.22500 | NFM | Birmingham | French Diplomatic Service |
| 448.22500 | 451.22500 | NFM | Glasgow | DHL Couriers |
| 448.25625 | 431.25625 | NFM | London | London Hilton Trunking System |
| 448.50000 | 431.50000 | NFM | Central London | Contract Wheel Clampers (W) |
| 448.51250 | 431.51250 | NFM | London | Cab data |
| 448.51250 | 431.51250 | NFM | London | Victoria Apcoa Parking Wardens |
| 448.57500 | 431.57500 | NFM | London | Rotherhithe Couriers |
| 448.60000 | 431.60000 | NFM | City of Westminster | Traffic Wardens (PS) |
| 448.60625 | 431.60625 | NFM | London, W2 | Vehicle wheel clampers |
| 448.68750 | 431.68750 | NFM | London | Churchill Cars |
| 448.71250 | 431.71250 | NFM | London Ealing | Oxo Station Taxis |
| 448.82500 | 431.82500 | NFM | London | Absolute Despatch Ltd. |
| 448.87500 | 431.87500 | NFM | Tunbridge Wells | The Wells |
| 448.88125 | 441.88125 | NFM | Maidstone | Addington Vehicle Recovery |
| 448.88750 | 431.88750 | NFM | Dartford | Vehicle recovery garage |
| 448.93750 | 431.93750 | NFM | Aldermaston | AWE support services Ch1 (ESF) |
| 449.23750 | 432.23750 | NFM | London | Borough of Westminster refuse control centre |
| 449.41250 | 432.41250 | NFM | Manchester | ITN O/B Studio Link |
| 449.60000 | 432.60000 | NFM | Farnborough Airshow | Medics Ch.3 |
| 449.65000 | 432.65000 | NFM | Aldermaston | AWE site bus |
| 449.66250 | 432.66250 | NFM | London | Carlton TV Talkback |
| 449.75000 | 432.75000 | NFM | Aldermaston | AWE support services |
| 449.77500 | 432.77500 | NFM | Aldermaston | AWE security Ch 4 |

# London Metropolitan Police Districts

Area 1

Area 2

Area 3

Enfield

Barnet

Harrow

Haringay

Waltham Forest

Redbridge

Havering

Hillingdon

Brent

Camden

Islington

Hackney

Dagenham

Newham

Ealing

Westminster

Kensington

Hammersmith

Tower Hamlets

Southwark

Greenwich

Bexley

Hounslow

Lambeth

Lewisham

Richmond -upon-Thames

Wandsworth

Kingston- upon-Thames

Merton

Sutton

Croydon

Bromley

Area 5

Area 4

# London Metropolitan Police Divisions

### Area 1 – Central
#### Divisions
AB – Belgravia
BH – Nottinghill
BS – Brompton
CD – West End Central
CX – Charing Cross
DM – Marylebone
DP – Paddington
FF – Fulham
FH – Hammersmith

### Area 2 –North West
#### Divisions
EH – Hampstead
EK – Kentish Town
EO – Holburn
NH – Holloway
NI – Islington
OK – Kilburn
QA – Harrow
QD – Wembley
SA – Barnet & Hertsmere
SG – Golders Green
SV – West Hendon
XD – Ealing
XS – Southall
YR – Hornsey
YT – Tottenham

### Area 3 – North East
#### Divisions
GD – Shoreditch & Hackney
GN – Stoke Newington
HH – Limehouse
HT – Whitechapel
JB  - Barkingside
JC – Chingford
JI – Redbridge
JL – Ilford
KD - Havering
KF – Forest Gate
KG – Dagenham
KO – Plaistow
YE - Edmonton
YF – Enfield
YP – Ponders End

### Area 4 – South East
#### Divisions
MD – Southwark
MM – Peckham
M3 – Walworth
PD – Catford
PL – Lewisham
PY – Bromley
RA – Plumstead
RG – Grenwich
RY – Bexleyheath
ZD – Croydon
ZN – South Norwood
ZP – Epsom

### Area 5 – South West
#### Divisions
CO52 – Thames
LD – Brixton
LS – Streatham
LX – Vauxhall
TC – Chiswick
TD – Hounslow
TG – Spelthorne
TW – Twickenham
VK – Kingston
VW – Wimbledon
WA – Battersea
WW - Wandsworth
XH – Hillingdon

## London Metropolitan Police Trunking System

The force uses a Motorola Smartzone Trunking System and the following shows how such a system is made up. For more information on trunking systems see *Scanner Busters 2* (page 596).

### Cell 01 East London (Inner)
Shoreditch, Stoke Newington, Limehouse, Whitechapel, Leyton, Barkingside, Chingford, Forest Gate, Plaistow

| | | | | |
|---|---|---|---|---|
| 450.6500 | 450.2375 | 450.2750 | 450.5125 | 450.5875 |
| 451.7375 | 451.3625 | 451.8375 | 451.9375 | 452.8625 |

### Cell 02 South East London (Inner)
Walworth, South Norwood, Plumstead, Bromley, Catford, Peckham, Bexleyheath, Greenwich, Southwark, Lewisham

| | | | | |
|---|---|---|---|---|
| 450.1000 | 450.3000 | 450.4500 | 450.9875 | 450.3625 |
| 450.8625 | 451.8875 | 451.5875 | 451.8625 | 451.9625 |
| 452.6625 | 452.7125 | 452.8875 | | |

### Cell 03 South West London (Inner)
Streatham, Battersea, Kingston, Vauxhall, Wandsworth, Chiswick, Wimbleton, Hounslow, Peckham, Twickenham, Brixton

| | | | | |
|---|---|---|---|---|
| 450.7500 | 450.8375 | 450.5750 | 451.7875 | 452.2875 |
| 452.7625 | 450.5375 | 450.6375 | 451.7625 | 450.2625 |
| 450.1875 | 452.5375 | | | |

## Cell 04 Central London
Belgravia, Brompton, Paddington, West End Central, Hammersmith, Marylebone, Fulham, Charing Cross, Notting Hill

| | | | | |
|---|---|---|---|---|
| 450.0250 | 450.3250 | 450.9250 | 450.0625 | 450.1625 |
| 451.2375 | 451.4375 | 451.4625 | 451.7125 | 452.2375 |
| 452.9125 | 452.9625 | | | |

## Cell 05 North West London (Inner)
West Hendon, Kentish Town, Tottenham, Hornsey, Hampstead, Ealing, Wembley, Holborn, Islington, Southall, Holloway, Kiburn

| | | | | |
|---|---|---|---|---|
| 450.9750 | 450.7000 | 450.8000 | 450.0875 | 450.1375 |
| 450.2125 | 451.0375 | 451.6125 | 451.9125 | 452.2625 |
| 452.4625 | 452.6875 | 452.9375 | | |

## Cell 06 North East London (Outer)
Edmonton, Enfield

| | | | | |
|---|---|---|---|---|
| 450.4875 | 450.2375 | 450.3750 | 450.8500 | 450.8750 |
| 451.1500 | | | | |

## Cell 7 East London (Middle)
Dagenham, Barking, Ilford, Barkingside, Walthamstow

| | | | | |
|---|---|---|---|---|
| 450.9000 | 451.0000 | 451.0750 | 450.3375 | 450.7750 |
| 452.3500 | 451.3875 | 452.3125 | | |

## Cell 08 East London (Outer)
Havering

| | | | | |
|---|---|---|---|---|
| 451.0500 | 451.0250 | 450.7250 | 450.9375 | 450.4125 |

## Cell 09 South East London (Outer)
Bromley, Lewisham, Bexleyheath, Greenwich

| | | | | |
|---|---|---|---|---|
| 450.5500 | 450.6000 | 451.1250 | 452.6375 | 452.7375 |
| 452.4375 | | | | |

## Cell 10 South London (Outer)
Croydon, Epsom, South Norwood

| | | | | |
|---|---|---|---|---|
| 450.4250 | 450.3875 | 450.7875 | 451.4500 | 452.6125 |
| 452.7875 | | | | |

## Cell 11 South West London (Outer)
Kingston

| | | | | |
|---|---|---|---|---|
| 450.7250 | 451.0250 | 451.0500 | 450.2875 | 450.9375 |

## Cell 12 West London (Outer)
Harrow, Hillingdon, Southall, Spelthrone, Twickenham, Chiswick, Hounslow, Heathrow

| | | | | |
|---|---|---|---|---|
| 451.0750 | 451.0000 | 450.9000 | 450.7750 | 450.3375 |
| 452.3500 | 452.3125 | 451.1625 | | |

## Cell 13 North West London (Outer)
West Hendon, Harrow

| | | | | |
|---|---|---|---|---|
| 451.1250 | 450.5500 | 450.6000 | 450.8250 | 451.0250 |
| 452.4375 | 452.6375 | | | |

| Base | Mobile | Mode | Location | User and Notes |
|------|--------|------|----------|----------------|

**450.0000 - 452.9750 MHz**  POLICE MOBILE PMR SYSTEM
(ENGLAND & WALES)

| Base | Mobile | Mode | Location | User and Notes |
|------|--------|------|----------|----------------|
| 450.02500 | 464.02500 | NFM | Dorset | Police (QC) Ch.4 link to 155.925 |
| 450.02500 | 464.02500 | NFM | Herefordshire | Police Ch.4 |
| 450.02500 | 464.02500 | NFM | London | Police data control |
| 450.02500 | 464.02500 | NFM | Mansfield | Police Channel 1 |
| 450.02500 | 464.02500 | NFM | West Midlands | Police Ch.4 |
| 450.02500 | 464.02500 | NFM | Wilmslow | Police |
| 450.03750 | 464.03750 | NFM | Grays, Essex | Police |
| 450.05000 | 464.05000 | NFM | Ashford | Police (Tour de France) Control |
| 450.05000 | 464.05000 | NFM | Birmingham | Police |
| 450.05000 | 464.05000 | NFM | Blackpool | Police Football Control |
| 450.05000 | 464.05000 | NFM | Blackpool | Police Special Events |
| 450.05000 | 464.05000 | NFM | Bournemouth | Police Coventry City Football Club |
| 450.05000 | 464.05000 | AM | Bradford | Police Bradford City Football Club |
| 450.05000 | 464.05000 | NFM | Carlisle | Police (Football Security) |
| 450.05000 | 464.05000 | NFM | Cheltenham | Police (BRAVO) Ch.60 |
| 450.05000 | 464.05000 | NFM | Chichester | Police |
| 450.05000 | 464.05000 | NFM | Coventry | Police Coventry City Football Club Ch 60 |
| 450.05000 | 464.05000 | NFM | England & Wales | Police CID, special & major events Ch 60 |
| 450.05000 | | NFM | England & Wales | Police CID, special & major events Ch 77 |
| 450.05000 | 464.05000 | NFM | Leicester | Police (Coventry Football Club) |
| 450.05000 | 464.05000 | NFM | London | Police Arsenal Football Club Ch 9 |
| 450.05000 | 464.05000 | NFM | London | Police Chelsea Football Club |
| 450.05000 | 464.05000 | NFM | London | Police City of London Divisional Support Units |
| 450.05000 | 464.05000 | NFM | London | Police Wembley Stadium Ch.9 |
| 450.05000 | 464.05000 | NFM | Luton | Police Luton Town Football Club |
| 450.05000 | 464.05000 | NFM | Milton Keynes | Police MK Bowl Security |
| 450.05000 | 464.05000 | NFM | Oldham | Police Oldham Football Club |
| 450.05000 | 464.05000 | NFM | Sheffield | Police Sheffield Wednesday Security |
| 450.05000 | 464.05000 | NFM | Tranmere | Police Tranmere Rover Football Club |
| 450.05000 | 464.05000 | NFM | West Midlands | Police Dog Handlers |
| 450.05000 | 464.05000 | NFM | Wirral | Police (Tranmere Rov) Ch 1 |
| 450.05000 | 464.05000 | NFM | Wolverhampton | Police Wolverhampton Football Club |
| 450.06250 | 464.06250 | NFM | London | Police central security network |
| 450.07500 | 464.07500 | NFM | Birmingham | Police Aston Villa Football Club |
| 450.07500 | 464.07500 | NFM | Birmingham | Police Birmingham City Football Club |
| 450.07500 | 464.07500 | NFM | Blackpool | Police Blackpool Football Club |
| 450.07500 | 464.07500 | NFM | Blackpool | Police Special Events |
| 450.07500 | 464.07500 | NFM | Bolton | Police Bolton Wanders Football Club |
| 450.07500 | 464.07500 | NFM | Brighton | Police Brighton & Hove Albion Football Club |
| 450.07500 | 464.07500 | NFM | Canvey Island | Police Event Channel |
| 450.07500 | 464.07500 | NFM | Colchester | Police United Football Club Ch.62 |
| 450.07500 | 464.07500 | NFM | Elmarch | HM Prison (M2MB) Ch.61 |
| 450.07500 | 464.07500 | NFM | England & Wales | Police (some forces use this as Ch.61 others as Ch.62) |
| 450.07500 | | NFM | Englang & Wales | Police |
| 450.07500 | 464.07500 | NFM | Folkestone | Police CID, special & major events Ch.78 |
| 450.07500 | 464.07500 | NFM | Goodwood | Police Race Course Security (M2KB) |
| 450.07500 | 464.07500 | NFM | Halifax | Police Football Club Ch 62 |
| 450.07500 | 464.07500 | NFM | Hove | Police |
| 450.07500 | 464.07500 | NFM | London | Police Aston Villa Football Club Ch.61 |
| 450.07500 | 464.07500 | NFM | London | Police Millwall Football Club |
| 450.07500 | 464.07500 | NFM | London | Police Tottenham Football Club |
| 450.07500 | 464.07500 | NFM | London | Police, Charlton Football Club crown control Ch62 |
| 450.07500 | 464.07500 | NFM | Luton Airport | Police Ch.61 |
| 450.07500 | 464.07500 | NFM | Milford Haven | Police |

| Base | Mobile | Mode | Location | User and Notes |
|---|---|---|---|---|
| 450.07500 | 464.07500 | NFM | Northampton | Police Ch 61 |
| 450.07500 | 464.07500 | NFM | Port Vale | Police Port Vale Football Club |
| 450.07500 | 464.07500 | NFM | Scarborough | Police Scarborough Football Club |
| 450.07500 | 464.07500 | NFM | Sheffield | Police Sheffield United Security |
| 450.07500 | 464.07500 | NFM | Shoreham | Police |
| 450.07500 | 464.07500 | NFM | Stoke on Trent | Police Stoke City Football Club |
| 450.07500 | 464.07500 | NFM | Tamworth | Police (Encrypted) |
| 450.07500 | 464.07500 | NFM | Twickenham | Police Rugby Club Ch.10 |
| 450.07500 | 464.07500 | NFM | West Midlands | Police Motorway Accidents |
| 450.07500 | 464.07500 | NFM | Whitby | Police (FW) Ch.62 |
| 450.08750 | 464.08750 | NFM | London | Police trunked division 5 (X) |
| 450.10000 | 464.10000 | NFM | England & Wales | Police CID, special & major events Ch.62 |
| 450.10000 | | NFM | England & Wales | Police CID, special & major events Ch.79 |
| 450.12500 | 464.12500 | NFM | Ashford | Police (Tour de France) Control |
| 450.12500 | 464.12500 | NFM | Blackpool | Police Special Events and TUC Conference |
| 450.12500 | 464.12500 | NFM | England & Wales | Police Channel 63 |
| 450.12500 | | NFM | England & Wales | Police Channel 80 |
| 450.12500 | 464.12500 | NFM | Lancing | Police (WN) Ch.63 |
| 450.12500 | 464.12500 | NFM | Leeds | Police Leeds United Football Club |
| 450.12500 | 464.12500 | NFM | Leicester | Police Leicester City Football Club |
| 450.12500 | 464.12500 | NFM | London | Police Barnett Football Club Ch.63 |
| 450.12500 | 464.12500 | NFM | London | Police Charlton Football Club |
| 450.12500 | 464.12500 | NFM | London | Police Notting Hill Carnival 3 |
| 450.12500 | 464.12500 | NFM | London | Police Queens Park Rangers Football Club |
| 450.12500 | 464.12500 | NFM | London | Police Special Escort Bikes |
| 450.12500 | 464.12500 | NFM | London | Police West Ham Football Club |
| 450.12500 | 464.12500 | NFM | London | Police special use (hotel raids, Kensington) Ch.11 |
| 450.12500 | 464.12500 | NFM | Maidstone | Crown Court  Ch 60 |
| 450.12500 | 464.12500 | NFM | Northampton | Police Ch 63 (SILVER CONTROL) |
| 450.12500 | 464.12500 | NFM | Plymouth | Police Operational Support |
| 450.12500 | 464.12500 | NFM | Portsmouth | Police (Fratton Park) |
| 450.12500 | 464.12500 | NFM | Southend on Sea | Police Southend United Football Club |
| 450.12500 | 464.12500 | NFM | Thames Valley | Police Scrambled |
| 450.12500 | 464.12500 | NFM | West Bromwich | Police West Bromwich Albion Football Club |
| 450.13750 | 464.13750 | NFM | London | Police trunked division 5 (X) |
| 450.15000 | 464.15000 | NFM | Beeston | Police Encrypted |
| 450.15000 | 464.15000 | NFM | Blackpool | Police CID |
| 450.15000 | 464.15000 | NFM | Bradford | Police Bradford City Football Club |
| 450.15000 | 464.15000 | NFM | Brentford | Police Brentford Football Club |
| 450.15000 | 464.15000 | NFM | Burnley | Police Football Security |
| 450.15000 | 464.15000 | NFM | England & Wales | Police Channel 64 |
| 450.15000 | | NFM | England & Wales | Police Channel 81 |
| 450.15000 | 464.15000 | NFM | Essex | Police Ch.64 |
| 450.15000 | 464.15000 | NFM | Gloucester | Police Ch.64 |
| 450.15000 | 464.15000 | NFM | Halifax | Police Rugby Club Ch 64 |
| 450.15000 | 464.15000 | NFM | Liverpool | Police Everton Football Club Ch.1 |
| 450.15000 | 464.15000 | NFM | Liverpool | Police Everton Football Club Ch.1 |
| 450.15000 | 464.15000 | NFM | London | Police Charlton Football Club |
| 450.15000 | 464.15000 | NFM | London | Police Crystal Palace Football Club |
| 450.15000 | 464.15000 | NFM | London | Police Testing (MP2MT) |
| 450.15000 | 464.15000 | NFM | Manchester | Police (Part Time Use) |
| 450.15000 | 464.15000 | NFM | Merseyside | Police Anfield Football Club crowd control |
| 450.15000 | 464.15000 | NFM | Northhamptonshire | Police Ch 64 (NG) |
| 450.15000 | 464.15000 | NFM | Plymouth | Police Special Ops |
| 450.15000 | 464.15000 | NFM | Stockport | Police Stockport Football Club |
| 450.15000 | 464.15000 | NFM | Suffolk | Police Events |

| Base | Mobile | Mode | Location | User and Notes |
|---|---|---|---|---|
| 450.15000 | 464.15000 | NFM | Sunderland | Police Sunderland Football Club |
| 450.15000 | 464.15000 | NFM | Thames Valley | Police |
| 450.15000 | 464.15000 | NFM | Tunbridge Wells | Police (Tour de France) Control |
| 450.15000 | 464.15000 | NFM | Walsall | Police Walsall Football Club |
| 450.16250 | 464.16250 | NFM | London | Police trunked security network |
| 450.17500 | 464.17500 | NFM | Cambridge | Police Cambridge City Football Club |
| 450.17500 | 464.17500 | NFM | England & Wales | Police Channel 65 |
| 450.17500 | | NFM | England & Wales | Police Channel 82 |
| 450.17500 | 464.17500 | NFM | Folkestone | Police (Tour de France) Control |
| 450.17500 | 464.17500 | NFM | Leicester | Police Football Matches |
| 450.17500 | 464.17500 | NFM | London | Police Arsenal Football Club |
| 450.17500 | 464.17500 | NFM | London | Police Barnett Football Club Ch.65 |
| 450.17500 | 464.17500 | NFM | London | Police Ch.13 |
| 450.17500 | 464.17500 | NFM | London | Police Chelsea Football Club |
| 450.17500 | 464.17500 | NFM | London | Police Fulham Football Club |
| 450.17500 | 464.17500 | NFM | London | Police Mounted Police Ch.13 |
| 450.17500 | 464.17500 | NFM | London | Police Notting Hill Carnival 2 |
| 450.17500 | 464.17500 | NFM | Manchester | Police special events and demos |
| 450.17500 | 464.17500 | NFM | Merseyside | Police, St. Helens Rugby League Club |
| 450.17500 | 464.17500 | NFM | Port Vale | Police Port Vale Football Club |
| 450.17500 | 464.17500 | NFM | South Wales | British Transport Police |
| 450.17500 | 464.17500 | NFM | Southend | Police Southend United Football Club |
| 450.17500 | 464.17500 | NFM | Stoke on Trent | Police Stoke City Football Club |
| 450.17500 | 464.17500 | NFM | West Midlands | Police firearms Ch.65 |
| 450.17500 | 464.17500 | NFM | Wirral | Police (Tranmere Rovers) Ch 1 |
| 450.17500 | 464.17500 | NFM | Worthing | Police Special /Events Ch 65 (WO) |
| 450.18750 | 464.18750 | NFM | London Ealing | Police (LD, LS) |
| 450.20000 | 464.20000 | NFM | Blackpool | Police Special Events |
| 450.20000 | 464.20000 | NFM | Cardiff | Police and CID (sometimes encrypted) |
| 450.20000 | 464.20000 | NFM | Chelmsford | Police CID |
| 450.20000 | 464.20000 | NFM | Dover | Police (used on Animal Rights Protest) |
| 450.20000 | 464.20000 | NFM | England & Wales | Police Channel 66 |
| 450.20000 | 464.20000 | NFM | England & Wales | Police Channel 82 |
| 450.20000 | 464.20000 | NFM | Essex | Police Ch.66 Canewoon-Rochford Area J Division |
| 450.20000 | 464.20000 | NFM | Gillingham | Police Gillingham Football Club |
| 450.20000 | 464.20000 | NFM | Gloucester | Police |
| 450.20000 | 464.20000 | NFM | Leeds | Police |
| 450.20000 | 464.20000 | NFM | Liverpool | Football Club |
| 450.20000 | 464.20000 | NFM | Liverpool | Police Everton Football Club Ch.2 |
| 450.20000 | 464.20000 | NFM | London | Police Millwall Football Club |
| 450.20000 | 464.20000 | NFM | London | Police Tottenham Hotspur Football Club |
| 450.20000 | 464.20000 | NFM | Maidstone | Police |
| 450.20000 | 464.20000 | NFM | Manchester | Police Manchester United Football Club |
| 450.20000 | 464.20000 | NFM | MoD Boscombe Down | Police Airfield control Ch 66 |
| 450.20000 | 464.20000 | NFM | Newcastle | Police football control Ch.66 |
| 450.20000 | 464.20000 | NFM | Portsmouth | Police Portsmouth Football Club |
| 450.20000 | 464.20000 | NFM | Tunbridge Wells | Police (Tour de France) Control |
| 450.20000 | 464.20000 | NFM | Windsor | Police Castle daily parades Ch 66 |
| 450.20000 | 464.22000 | NFM | Ipswich | Police Ipswich Football Club |
| 450.21250 | 464.21250 | NFM | London | Police Division 2 (X) Ch. |
| 450.22500 | 464.22500 | NFM | Blackpool | Police Special Events |
| 450.22500 | 464.22500 | NFM | Bolton | Police Bolton Wanderers Football Club |
| 450.22500 | 464.22500 | NFM | Bradford | Police Bradford Bull Rugby League Club |
| 450.22500 | 464.22500 | NFM | Brands Hatch | Police Security |
| 450.22500 | 464.22500 | NFM | Brighton | Police Area Incident Channel |
| 450.22500 | 464.22500 | NFM | Brighton | Police CID Special Ops |

| Base | Mobile | Mode | Location | User and Notes |
|------|--------|------|----------|----------------|
| 450.22500 | 464.22500 | NFM | England & Wales | Police Channel 67 |
| 450.22500 | | NFM | England & Wales | Police Channel 83 |
| 450.22500 | 464.22500 | NFM | Hull | Police Hull Kingston Rovers |
| 450.22500 | 464.22500 | NFM | London | Police Aston Villa Football Club Ch.67 |
| 450.22500 | 464.22500 | NFM | London | Police Crystal Palace Football Club |
| 450.22500 | 464.22500 | NFM | London | Police West Ham Football Club |
| 450.22500 | 464.22500 | NFM | Manchester, Moss Side | Police Drugs Squad |
| 450.22500 | 464.22500 | NFM | Milton Keynes | Police MK Bowl Security |
| 450.22500 | 464.22500 | NFM | Nottingham | Police Nottingham Forest Football Club |
| 450.22500 | 464.22500 | NFM | Southampton | Police Southampton Football Club |
| 450.22500 | 464.22500 | NFM | Worthing | Police Encypted Pro-active Unit |
| 450.25000 | 464.25000 | NFM | Birmingham International | Police MASC (ELMPOL) Ch.68 |
| 450.25000 | 464.25000 | NFM | Blackpool | TUC Conference |
| 450.25000 | 464.25000 | NFM | Blackpool Conference | Army Bomb Squad |
| 450.25000 | 464.25000 | NFM | Bognor Regis | Police |
| 450.25000 | 464.25000 | NFM | Brighton | Police Area Incident Channel |
| 450.25000 | 464.25000 | NFM | Brockenhurst | Police |
| 450.25000 | 464.25000 | NFM | Colchester | Police (Foxtrot) |
| 450.25000 | 464.25000 | NFM | Doncaster | Football Club |
| 450.25000 | 464.25000 | NFM | England & Wales | Police Channel 68 |
| 450.25000 | | NFM | England & Wales | Police Channel 84 |
| 450.25000 | 464.25000 | NFM | Gainsborough | Police (E) |
| 450.25000 | 464.25000 | NFM | Halifax | Police (FA) Ch.68 |
| 450.25000 | 464.25000 | NFM | Langholm | Police |
| 450.25000 | 464.25000 | NFM | London | Police special use Ch.16 |
| 450.25000 | 464.25000 | NFM | Manchester | Police Manchester United crowd control |
| 450.25000 | 464.25000 | NFM | Norwich | Police Norwich City Football Club Ch.68 |
| 450.25000 | 464.25000 | NFM | Plymouth | Police Football Control |
| 450.25000 | 464.25000 | NFM | Tunbridge Wells | Police (Tour de France) Control |
| 450.25000 | 464.25000 | NFM | USAF Fairford | International Air Tattoo Fire Control |
| 450.26250 | 464.26250 | NFM | London | Police trunked division 5 (L/B) |
| 450.27500 | | NFM | England & Wales | Police Channel 69 |
| 450.27500 | | NFM | England & Wales | Police CID, special & major events Ch.85 |
| 450.27500 | 464.27500 | NFM | Gwynedd | Fire Brigade |
| 450.28750 | 464.28750 | NFM | Wallasey | Police (ALPHA) |
| 450.30000 | | NFM | England & Wales | Fire Command Channel 70 |
| 450.31250 | 464.31250 | NFM | Crosby | Police (B3) Ch.96 |
| 450.32500 | 464.32500 | NFM | London | Police trunked data control |
| 450.33750 | 464.33750 | NFM | London | Police trunked overload channel (GT) |
| 450.35000 | 464.35000 | NFM | Liverpool | Ashworth Mental Hospital |
| 450.36250 | 464.36250 | NFM | London | Police divisions P/R/M and part of Z trunked |
| 450.37500 | 464.37500 | NFM | London | Police trunked overload channel (GT) |
| 450.38750 | 464.38750 | NFM | Coventry | Police divisional operations Ch.5 |
| 450.38750 | 464.38750 | NFM | London | Police divisions P/R/M and part of Z trunked |
| 450.40000 | 464.44000 | NFM | London | Police divisions G/H/J/K |
| 450.40000 | 464.44000 | NFM | Thames Valley | Police |
| 450.45000 | 464.55000 | NFM | London | Police trunked overload channel (GT) |
| 450.47500 | 464.47500 | NFM | Dorset | Police (QC) linked to 155.925 |
| 450.52500 | 464.47500 | NFM | Gloucester | Police |
| 450.52500 | 464.52500 | NFM | Hereford | Police Ch.1 |
| 450.52500 | 464.52500 | NFM | Liverpool | Police Ch.1 |
| 450.52500 | 464.52500 | NFM | Manchester, Irlam | Police |
| 450.52500 | 464.52500 | NFM | Murton | Police |
| 450.52500 | 464.52500 | NFM | Poole | Police Ch.1 |
| 450.52500 | 464.52500 | NFM | Stratford-upon-Avon | Police Ch.1 relays 155.1625 AM |
| 450.52500 | 464.52500 | NFM | York | Police |

| Base | Mobile | Mode | Location | User and Notes |
|------|--------|------|----------|----------------|
| 450.53750 | 464.53750 | NFM | London | Police divisions L/V trunked |
| 450.55000 | 464.55000 | NFM | Birmingham | Police |
| 450.55000 | 464.55000 | NFM | Crewe | Police |
| 450.55000 | 464.55000 | NFM | Herefordshire | Police Ch.2 |
| 450.55000 | 464.55000 | NFM | Solihull | Police (LX) Ch 2 |
| 450.57500 | 464.57500 | NFM | Birmingham | Police |
| 450.57500 | 464.57500 | NFM | Colwyn Bay | Police (WA) Ch.3 |
| 450.57500 | 464.57500 | NFM | Coventry | Police (MX/M2) Ch 3 |
| 450.57500 | 464.57500 | NFM | Crewe | Police MASC Ch.3 |
| 450.57500 | 464.57500 | NFM | Ellesmere Port | Police |
| 450.57500 | 464.57500 | NFM | Herefordshire | Police Ch.3 |
| 450.57500 | 464.57500 | NFM | Llandudno | Police (WA) |
| 450.57500 | 464.57500 | NFM | London | Police divisions L/V trunked |
| 450.57500 | 464.57500 | NFM | St Helens | Police |
| 450.57500 | 464.57500 | NFM | Warrington | Police |
| 450.57500 | 464.57500 | NFM | Wimslow | Police |
| 450.58750 | 464.58750 | NFM | London | Police divisions G/H/J/K trunked |
| 450.60000 | 464.60000 | NFM | Elmarch | HM Prison (M2MB) Ch.4 |
| 450.60000 | 464.60000 | NFM | London | Police P/R/M and part of Z trunked |
| 450.60000 | 464.60000 | NFM | Portsmouth | Police |
| 450.62500 | | NFM | Hampshire | Police Helicopter Optica (Boxer 10) |
| 450.62500 | | NFM | Herefordshire | Police Helicopter |
| 450.62500 | | NFM | Lancashire | Police Helicopter |
| 450.62500 | | NFM | Leicester | Police Helicopters Ch80 |
| 450.62500 | | NFM | Luton Airport | Police Air Support Unit (XA99) |
| 450.62500 | | NFM | Merseyside | Police Helicopter (M1) |
| 450.62500 | | NFM | Northants | Police Helicopters Air/Ground Ch 88 |
| 450.62500 | | NFM | Shropshire | Police Helicopter |
| 450.62500 | | NFM | Skelmersdale | Police Helicopter |
| 450.62500 | | NFM | South Wales | Police Helicopter (WO99) |
| 450.62500 | | NFM | West Midlands | Police Helicopter (AO1) |
| 450.62500 | | NFM | West Sussex | Police Helicopter (Hotel 900) |
| 450.62500 | | NFM | Worcester | Air Ambulance Delta 03 |
| 450.62500 | | NFM | Worcester | Police Helicopter Air 1 |
| 450.62500 | 464.62500 | NFM | Birmingham | Police |
| 450.62500 | 464.62500 | NFM | England & Wales | Police Channel 88 Air-to-Ground |
| 450.62500 | 464.62500 | NFM | Rhyl | Police |
| 450.63750 | 464.63750 | NFM | London | Police division X trunked |
| 450.67500 | 450.67500 | NFM | Birmingham | Police |
| 450.67500 | 450.67500 | NFM | England & Wales | Police Channel 89 Air-to-Ground |
| 450.67500 | 450.67500 | NFM | Herefordshire | Fire Brigade Ch.89 |
| 450.67500 | 450.67500 | NFM | Lancashire | Police Helicopter |
| 450.67500 | 450.67500 | NFM | Leicester | Police Helicopter |
| 450.67500 | 450.67500 | NFM | Northampton Sywel | Police Chopper Ch 89 |
| 450.67500 | 450.67500 | NFM | Warwickshire | Police Helicopter |
| 450.75000 | 464.75000 | NFM | London | Police division X trunked |
| 450.77500 | 464.77500 | NFM | Birmingham | Police |
| 450.77500 | 464.77500 | NFM | Gloucester | Police |
| 450.77500 | 464.77500 | NFM | London | Police divisions T/X trunked |
| 450.78750 | 464.78750 | NFM | Colwyn Bay | Police |
| 450.78750 | 464.78750 | NFM | London | Police divisions P/R/M and part of Z |
| 450.80000 | 464.80000 | NFM | Birmingham | Police |
| 450.80000 | 464.80000 | NFM | Gatley | Police |
| 450.80000 | 464.80000 | NFM | Herefordshire | Police Ch.50 |
| 450.80000 | 464.80000 | NFM | Liverpool, Toxteth | Police Ch.50 |
| 450.80000 | 464.80000 | NFM | Manchester | Police (Encrypted) |

| Base | Mobile | Mode | Location | User and Notes |
|------|--------|------|----------|----------------|
| 450.80000 | 464.80000 | NFM | Merseyside | Police Drug Squad (Encrypted) |
| 450.80000 | 464.80000 | NFM | Rhyl | Police |
| 450.80000 | 464.80000 | NFM | West Midlands | Police Motorway Incident Unit Ch.50 |
| 450.82500 | 464.82500 | NFM | Herefordshire | Police Ch.72 |
| 450.82500 | 464.82500 | NFM | Leamington | Police Ch.72 |
| 450.82500 | 464.82500 | NFM | North Wales | Police (D) |
| 450.82500 | 464.82500 | NFM | Rhyl | Police (WA) Ch.72 |
| 450.82500 | 464.82500 | NFM | Salwick | Police AEA |
| 450.82500 | 464.82500 | NFM | Sandwell | Police (MK) Ch.72 |
| 450.82500 | 464.82500 | NFM | Southam | Police Ch.72 |
| 450.82500 | 464.82500 | NFM | Warwickshire | Police Ch 72 |
| 450.82500 | 464.82500 | NFM | Wiltshire | Fire Brigade repeater (M2QS) |
| 450.82500 | 464.82500 | NFM | Wrexham | Police Ch.72 |
| 450.85000 | 450.85000 | NFM | Barton Airfield | Police Helicopter |
| 450.85000 | 464.85000 | NFM | Birmingham | Police |
| 450.85000 | 464.85000 | NFM | Chelmsley Wood | Police (LX L1) |
| 450.85000 | 464.85000 | NFM | Herefordshire | Police Ch.38 |
| 450.85000 | 464.85000 | NFM | Manchester Airport | Police |
| 450.85000 | 464.85000 | NFM | Manchester Ringway | Police |
| 450.86250 | 464.86250 | NFM | London | Police divisions P/R/M and part of Z |
| 450.88750 | 464.88750 | NFM | London | Police divisions P/R/M and part of Z |
| 450.92500 | 464.92500 | NFM | London | Police data control |
| 450.96250 | 464.96250 | NFM | London | Police divisions P/R/M and part of Z |
| 450.98750 | 464.98750 | NFM | London | Police divisions P/R/M and part of Z |
| 451.00000 | 464.00000 | NFM | Nationwide | Local Authorities Emergency Network |
| 451.02500 | 464.02500 | NFM | England & Wales | Police Channel |
| 451.03750 | 464.03750 | NFM | London | Police division X trunked |
| 451.03750 | 464.03750 | NFM | West Midlands | Police (YM) |
| 451.05000 | 464.95000 | NFM | London | Police trunked X division |
| 451.05000 | 464.95000 | NFM | Sunderland AFC | Police Security |
| 451.07500 | 464.97500 | NFM | Hendon | Police Training College |
| 451.07500 | 464.97500 | NFM | London | Police divisions X/T data command trunked |
| 451.10000 | 465.10000 | NFM | England & Wales | Police Channel |
| 451.10000 | 465.10000 | NFM | Preston | Police |
| 451.12500 | 465.02500 | NFM | England & Wales | Bomb Disposal Unit (BRAVO) |
| 451.12500 | 465.02500 | NFM | London | Police divisions P/R/M and part of Z |
| 451.13750 | 465.13750 | NFM | Colwyn Bay | Police |
| 451.15000 | 465.05000 | NFM | Chelmsford | Police Ch.47 |
| 451.15000 | 465.05000 | NFM | England & Wales | Police Air Support air/ground Ch.92 |
| 451.15000 | 465.05000 | NFM | Wigan | Motor bike Training |
| 451.16250 | 465.06250 | NFM | London | Police divisions T/X trunked |
| 451.17500 | 465.07500 | NFM | Birmingham | Police |
| 451.17500 | 465.07500 | NFM | Colwyn Bay | Police (WA) Ch.87 |
| 451.17500 | 465.07500 | NFM | Cosham | Police |
| 451.17500 | 465.07500 | NFM | England & Wales | Police Channel 87 |
| 451.17500 | 465.07500 | NFM | Kidsgrove | Police |
| 451.17500 | 465.07500 | NFM | Leicester, south | Police Ch.87 |
| 451.17500 | 465.07500 | NFM | Llandudno | Police |
| 451.17500 | 465.07500 | NFM | Market Harbour | Police Ch.87 |
| 451.17500 | 465.07500 | NFM | North Wales | Police (A) |
| 451.17500 | 465.07500 | NFM | Portsmouth | Police |
| 451.17500 | 465.07500 | NFM | Preston | Police Ch.87 |
| 451.17500 | 465.07500 | NFM | Southend | Police |
| 451.17500 | 465.07500 | NFM | Wigston | Police (SIERRA) |
| 451.20000 | 465.10000 | NFM | Ashford | Police (JZ/JL) Ch.86 |
| 451.20000 | 465.10000 | NFM | England & Wales | Police Channel 86 |

| Base | Mobile | Mode | Location | User and Notes |
|------|--------|------|----------|----------------|
| 451.20000 | 465.10000 | NFM | Liverpool | Police |
| 451.20000 | 465.10000 | NFM | Manchester, Gorton | Police |
| 451.20000 | 465.10000 | NFM | Manchester, Greenheys | Police |
| 451.20000 | 465.10000 | NFM | Manchester, Leverhulme | Police |
| 451.20000 | 465.10000 | NFM | Manchester, Longsight | Police |
| 451.20000 | 465.10000 | NFM | Manchester, Moss Side | Police |
| 451.20000 | 465.10000 | NFM | Manchester, Whalley Range | Police |
| 451.20000 | 465.10000 | NFM | New Brighton | Police |
| 451.20000 | 465.10000 | NFM | Pow-t-Ffordd | Police |
| 451.20000 | 465.10000 | NFM | Wallasey | Police (A1) |
| 451.20000 | 465.10000 | NFM | Walsall | Traffic Wardens |
| 451.20000 | 465.10000 | NFM | Warrington | Police (V) Ch.3 |
| 451.20000 | 465.10000 | NFM | Wirral | Police |
| 451.21250 | 465.11250 | NFM | Kent | Police Ch.10 |
| 451.22500 | 465.12500 | NFM | Ashford | Police (JZ) Ch.85 |
| 451.22500 | 465.12500 | NFM | Cleveland | Police |
| 451.22500 | 465.12500 | NFM | England & Wales | Police Channel 85 |
| 451.22500 | 465.12500 | NFM | Kenilworth | Police (JK) Ch.3 |
| 451.22500 | 465.12500 | NFM | Lydd | Police (JZ) Ch.85 |
| 451.22500 | 465.12500 | NFM | Manchester | Police (Gorton) |
| 451.22500 | 465.12500 | NFM | Redford | HM Prison Ranby (M2OY) |
| 451.22500 | 465.12500 | NFM | Tenterten | Police (JZ) Ch.85 |
| 451.22500 | 465.12500 | NFM | Warrington | Police (B2) Ch.3 |
| 451.22500 | 465.12500 | NFM | Windsor | Police castle security Ch 85 |
| 451.23750 | 465.13750 | NFM | London | Police central security network trunked |
| 451.25000 | 465.15000 | NFM | England & Wales | Police Channel 84 |
| 451.25000 | 465.15000 | NFM | London | Police Diplomatic Protection |
| 451.27500 | 465.17500 | NFM | Birmingham International | Police (M2YMEA) |
| 451.27500 | 465.17500 | NFM | Broadstairs | Police (E/E) Ch 5 |
| 451.27500 | 465.17500 | NFM | Cambridge | Police VB Ch 1 Repeater |
| 451.27500 | 465.17500 | NFM | Cheadle | Police |
| 451.27500 | 465.17500 | NFM | Dartford | Police (AZ) Ch.58 |
| 451.27500 | 465.17500 | NFM | England & Wales | Police Reserve Channel 05 |
| 451.27500 | 465.17500 | NFM | Gravesend | Police (CA) |
| 451.27500 | 465.17500 | NFM | Humberside | Police Channel 02 |
| 451.27500 | 465.17500 | NFM | London | Police |
| 451.27500 | 465.17500 | NFM | Manchester, Bredbury | Police |
| 451.27500 | 465.17500 | NFM | Manchester, Brinnington | Police |
| 451.27500 | 465.17500 | NFM | Manchester, Cheadle | Police |
| 451.27500 | 465.17500 | NFM | Manchester, Hazel Grove | Police |
| 451.27500 | 465.17500 | NFM | Manchester, Marple | Police |
| 451.27500 | 465.17500 | NFM | Manchester, Reddish | Police |
| 451.27500 | 465.17500 | NFM | Margate | Police (E/D) Ch 5 |
| 451.27500 | 465.17500 | NFM | Stockport | Police |
| 451.27500 | 465.17500 | NFM | Thames Valley | Police Ch 5 |
| 451.27500 | 465.17500 | NFM | West Midlands | Police (encrypted) Ch.2 |
| 451.30000 | 465.20000 | NFM | Cwmbran | Police Training College |
| 451.30000 | 465.20000 | NFM | England & Wales | Police Motorcycle Training Ch.71 |
| 451.30000 | 465.20000 | NFM | England & Wales | Police Traffic Helicopters Air/Ground Ch.71 some use as Ch.88 & 89 |
| 451.30000 | 465.20000 | NFM | England & Wales | Police Airborne |
| 451.30000 | 465.20000 | NFM | Herefordshire | Police motorcycle training Ch.71 |
| 451.30000 | 465.20000 | NFM | London, Gatwick | Immigration Ch 71 |
| 451.30000 | 465.20000 | NFM | Martlesham Heath | Police |
| 451.30000 | 465.20000 | NFM | South Yorkshire | Police training Ch.6 |
| 451.30000 | 465.20000 | NFM | Thames Valley | Police |

| Base | Mobile | Mode | Location | User and Notes |
|------|--------|------|----------|----------------|
| 451.30000 | 465.20000 | NFM | Trowbridge | Police Speed Traps |
| 451.31250 | 465.21250 | NFM | Birmingham | Police |
| 451.31250 | 465.21250 | NFM | Hastings | Police (H) |
| 451.31250 | 465.21250 | NFM | Newport | Police Newport Football Club |
| 451.32500 | 465.22500 | NFM | Burnley | Police Ch7 |
| 451.32500 | 465.22500 | NFM | Dover | Police Football Security |
| 451.32500 | 465.22500 | NFM | England & Wales | Police CID/VASCAR Speed Traps/Special Branch close support Ch.7 |
| 451.32500 | 465.22500 | NFM | Essex | Police Helicopter (H900) |
| 451.32500 | 465.22500 | NFM | Herefordshire | Police underwater search teams Ch.90 |
| 451.32500 | 465.22500 | NFM | Heysham (Port) | Police Special Branch |
| 451.32500 | 465.22500 | NFM | Ingoldmells | Police |
| 451.32500 | 465.22500 | NFM | Kent | Police (Tour de France) |
| 451.32500 | 465.22500 | NFM | London | HM Customs/Police Link |
| 451.32500 | 465.22500 | NFM | London | Police link to Customs & Excise |
| 451.32500 | 465.22500 | NFM | London, Gatwick | Police Armed Tactical Liaison |
| 451.32500 | 465.22500 | NFM | London, Heathrow | Police Armed Tactical Liaison |
| 451.32500 | 465.22500 | NFM | Manchester | Police surveillance |
| 451.32500 | 465.22500 | NFM | Neath | Police |
| 451.32500 | 465.22500 | NFM | Oxford | Fire Brigade handsets |
| 451.32500 | 465.22500 | NFM | Plymouth Airport | Fire Appliance |
| 451.32500 | 465.22500 | NFM | Scarborough | Specials and CID covert |
| 451.32500 | 465.22500 | NFM | Thames Valley | Police Traffic |
| 451.32500 | 465.22500 | NFM | Wales, north | Police Helicopter (W1) |
| 451.32500 | 465.22500 | NFM | Wellingborough | Police CID Ch 7 |
| 451.32500 | 465.22500 | NFM | Worthing | Police Back to Back Ch 7 (WO) |
| 451.35000 | 465.25000 | NFM | Birmingham | Police |
| 451.35000 | 465.25000 | NFM | Birmingham International | Immigration |
| 451.35000 | 465.25000 | NFM | Dover | Immigration Control |
| 451.35000 | 465.25000 | NFM | England & Wales | Airport Immigration Ch.8 |
| 451.35000 | 465.25000 | NFM | Liverpool, Port | HM Immigration Ch.8 |
| 451.35000 | 465.25000 | NFM | London | Police London Port Authority |
| 451.35000 | 465.25000 | NFM | London, Gatwick | HM Immigration Ch.8 (AO) |
| 451.35000 | 465.25000 | NFM | London, Heathrow | HM Immigration Ch.8 |
| 451.35000 | 465.25000 | NFM | Newhaven | HM Immigration |
| 451.35000 | 465.25000 | NFM | Stansted | HM Immigration |
| 451.36250 | 465.26250 | NFM | London | Police divisions G/H/J/K trunked |
| 451.37500 | 465.27500 | NFM | Abergele | Police |
| 451.37500 | 465.27500 | NFM | Acklington | HM Prison Acklington (M2MU) |
| 451.37500 | 465.27500 | NFM | Andover | Police |
| 451.37500 | 465.27500 | NFM | Bangor | Police |
| 451.37500 | 465.27500 | NFM | Basildon | Police |
| 451.37500 | 465.27500 | NFM | Birmingham | HM Prison Winston Green |
| 451.37500 | 465.27500 | NFM | Birmingham | Police |
| 451.37500 | 465.27500 | NFM | Brighton | Police (CB) Ch.9 |
| 451.37500 | 465.27500 | NFM | Burnley | Police Traffic Ch9 |
| 451.37500 | 465.27500 | NFM | Canvey Island | Police (JC) Ch.9 |
| 451.37500 | 465.27500 | NFM | Cardiff | Police |
| 451.37500 | 465.27500 | NFM | Cleveland | HM Prison Homehouse |
| 451.37500 | 465.27500 | NFM | Droitwich | Police |
| 451.37500 | 465.27500 | NFM | England & Wales | Police Channel 09 |
| 451.37500 | 465.27500 | NFM | Farnborough | Police |
| 451.37500 | 465.27500 | NFM | Feltham | HM Prison Feltham Ch.9 |
| 451.37500 | 465.27500 | NFM | Frankley | Police (RA) |
| 451.37500 | 465.27500 | NFM | Gloucester | Police |
| 451.37500 | 465.27500 | NFM | High Wycombe | Police (AE) Ch.9 |

| Base | Mobile | Mode | Location | User and Notes |
|------|--------|------|----------|----------------|
| 451.37500 | 465.27500 | NFM | Horley | Police |
| 451.37500 | 465.27500 | NFM | Huntingdon | HM Prison Liddle Hay (KL) |
| 451.37500 | 465.27500 | NFM | Kirkby Lonsdale | Police |
| 451.37500 | 465.27500 | NFM | Leeds, Holbeck | Police (CA) Ch.9 |
| 451.37500 | 465.27500 | NFM | Littlehey | HM Prison |
| 451.37500 | 465.27500 | NFM | Liverpool | Police |
| 451.37500 | 465.27500 | NFM | London | HM Prison Pentonville |
| 451.37500 | 465.27500 | NFM | London | HM Prison Holloway (JH) Ch.9 |
| 451.37500 | 465.27500 | NFM | Manchester City Centre | Police |
| 451.37500 | 465.27500 | NFM | Manchester, Arndale Centre | Police |
| 451.37500 | 465.27500 | NFM | Manchester, Bootle Street | Police |
| 451.37500 | 465.27500 | NFM | Manchester, Newton Street | Police |
| 451.37500 | 465.27500 | NFM | Marlow | Police |
| 451.37500 | 465.27500 | NFM | Milford Haven | Police |
| 451.37500 | 465.27500 | NFM | MoD Boscombe Down | Police Control link Ch 9 |
| 451.37500 | 465.27500 | NFM | North Wales | Police Mobile Repeater |
| 451.37500 | 465.27500 | NFM | Northampton | Police Ch 9 |
| 451.37500 | 465.27500 | NFM | Nottingham | Police City Centre |
| 451.37500 | 465.27500 | NFM | Pembroke | Police |
| 451.37500 | 465.27500 | NFM | Preston | HM Prison Garth |
| 451.37500 | 465.27500 | NFM | Preston | HM Prison Kirkham |
| 451.37500 | 465.27500 | NFM | Renishaw | Police |
| 451.37500 | 465.27500 | NFM | Rye | Police (M2KBEO+EH) Ch.9 |
| 451.37500 | 465.27500 | NFM | Spalling | Police |
| 451.37500 | 465.27500 | NFM | St Asaph | Police |
| 451.37500 | 465.27500 | NFM | Stockton-on-Tees | HM Prison Stockton |
| 451.37500 | 465.27500 | NFM | Tetford | HM Prison Wayland Ch.9 |
| 451.37500 | 465.27500 | NFM | Thames Valley | Police (SA) |
| 451.37500 | 465.27500 | NFM | Wayland, Norfolk | HM Prison Wayland |
| 451.37500 | 456.27500 | NFM | West Midlands | Newbolt Ribel Prison Training College (M2XQ) Ch.9 |
| 451.37500 | 465.27500 | NFM | Wisbech | Police |
| 451.37500 | 465.27500 | NFM | York | HM Prison Full Sutton Ch.9 |
| 451.38750 | 465.28750 | NFM | London | Police divisions G/H/J/K trunked |
| 451.38750 | 465.28750 | NFM | Southend | Police |
| 451.40000 | 465.30000 | NFM | Edinburgh | Fire Brigade |
| 451.40000 | | NFM | England & Wales | Voluntary and industrial fire brigades |
| 451.40000 | | NFM | England & Wales | Fire Services Channel 01 |
| 451.40000 | 465.30000 | NFM | England & Wales | Police/Fire Link Channel 97 |
| 451.40000 | 465.30000 | NFM | England & Wales | Police Channel 10 |
| 451.40000 | 465.30000 | NFM | Falmouth | Police |
| 451.40000 | 465.30000 | NFM | Guernsey | Fire Brigade |
| 451.40000 | 465.30000 | NFM | London | Fire Brigade |
| 451.40000 | 465.30000 | NFM | Nationwide | Special Air Services (encrypted) |
| 451.40000 | 465.30000 | NFM | Newport | Radio Auth. Surveillance |
| 451.40000 | 465.30000 | NFM | Newquay | Police |
| 451.40000 | 465.30000 | NFM | Northampton | Police Ch 64 |
| 451.42500 | 465.32500 | NFM | Aylesbury | Police (AA) |
| 451.42500 | 465.32500 | NFM | Birmingham, Acocks Green | Police |
| 451.42500 | 465.32500 | NFM | Birmingham, Dunstall Rd | Police |
| 451.42500 | 465.32500 | NFM | Bristol | Police |
| 451.42500 | 465.32500 | NFM | Catherton | Police |
| 451.42500 | 465.32500 | NFM | Clayton | Police (ALPHA 2) |
| 451.42500 | 465.32500 | NFM | Connah's Quay | Police |
| 451.42500 | 465.32500 | NFM | Ecclesfied, S. Yorkshire | Police (F2) Ch.11 |
| 451.42500 | 465.32500 | NFM | England & Wales | Police Channel 11 |

| Base | Mobile | Mode | Location | User and Notes |
|------|--------|------|----------|----------------|
| 451.42500 | 465.32500 | NFM | Essex | Police |
| 451.42500 | 465.32500 | NFM | Faringdon | Police |
| 451.42500 | 465.32500 | NFM | Garston | Police (D2) |
| 451.42500 | 465.32500 | NFM | Gloucestershire | Police |
| 451.42500 | 465.32500 | NFM | Grays | Police |
| 451.42500 | 465.32500 | NFM | Herefordshire | Police Ch.11 linked to 155.200 Ch.1 |
| 451.42500 | 465.32500 | NFM | Kingswood | Police (FOXTROT) Ch.11 |
| 451.42500 | 465.32500 | NFM | Leeds, Pudsey | Police |
| 451.42500 | 465.32500 | NFM | Liverpool, St Helens | Police |
| 451.42500 | 465.32500 | NFM | Long Eaton | Police |
| 451.42500 | 465.32500 | NFM | Malton | Police |
| 451.42500 | 465.32500 | NFM | Manchester, Ancoats | Police |
| 451.42500 | 465.32500 | NFM | Manchester, Blackley | Police |
| 451.42500 | 465.32500 | NFM | Manchester, Bradford | Police |
| 451.42500 | 465.32500 | NFM | Manchester, Cheetham Hill | Police |
| 451.42500 | 465.32500 | NFM | Manchester, Collyhurst | Police |
| 451.42500 | 465.32500 | NFM | Manchester, Harpurhey | Police |
| 451.42500 | 465.32500 | NFM | Manchester, Newton Heath | Police |
| 451.42500 | 465.32500 | NFM | Millom, Cumbria | HM Prison Haverigg |
| 451.42500 | 465.32500 | NFM | Newbury | Police (M2FA) |
| 451.42500 | 465.32500 | NFM | Nottingham | Police Eastwood |
| 451.42500 | 465.32500 | NFM | Portsmouth, Ferry Point | Immigration |
| 451.42500 | 465.32500 | NFM | Pudsey | Police |
| 451.42500 | 465.32500 | NFM | Rayleigh | Police |
| 451.42500 | 465.32500 | NFM | Reading, east | Police (EX) Ch.11 |
| 451.42500 | 465.32500 | NFM | Reading, west | Police (EA) Ch.11 |
| 451.42500 | 465.32500 | NFM | Rossington | Police |
| 451.42500 | 465.32500 | NFM | Shaftesbury | Young Offenders Institution Guys Marsh (BB) |
| 451.42500 | 465.32500 | NFM | Southwold | Police (J8S) Ch.11 |
| 451.42500 | 465.32500 | NFM | Speke | Police (D1) |
| 451.42500 | 465.32500 | NFM | Stansted Airport | Police (KF) |
| 451.42500 | 465.32500 | NFM | Stokesley | Police (CA) Ch.11 |
| 451.42500 | 465.32500 | NFM | Thames Valley | Police (AB) |
| 451.42500 | 465.32500 | NFM | Wantage | Police |
| 451.42500 | 465.32500 | NFM | Wendover | Police |
| 451.42500 | 465.32500 | NFM | Whitley Bay | Police (M2LBC2)/(H1) |
| 451.42500 | 465.32500 | NFM | Wickford | Police |
| 451.42500 | 465.32500 | NFM | Windsor | Police Special Branch Ch 11 |
| 451.42500 | 465.32500 | NFM | Witney | Police |
| 451.42500 | 465.32500 | NFM | Wolverhampton | Police North (M2YMG) |
| 451.42500 | 465.32500 | NFM | Woodbridge | HM Prison Hollesley Bay Colony Ch.11 linked to 131.800 |
| 451.43750 | 465.33750 | NFM | London | Police central security network trunked |
| 451.45000 | 465.35000 | NFM | Atherstone | Police (TA) |
| 451.45000 | 465.35000 | NFM | Bedworth | Police Ch.11 |
| 451.45000 | 465.35000 | NFM | Dudley | Police |
| 451.45000 | | NFM | England | Fire Service Channel 02 |
| 451.45000 | | NFM | England & Wales | Fire Services Channel 12 |
| 451.45000 | 465.35000 | NFM | England & Wales | Police Channel 12 |
| 451.45000 | 465.35000 | NFM | Merseyside | Police (Encrypted) |
| 451.45000 | 465.35000 | NFM | Pudsey | Police (CD) Ch.12 |
| 451.45000 | 465.35000 | NFM | St. Helens | Police (ECHO) |
| 451.46250 | 465.36250 | NFM | London | Police central security network trunked |
| 451.47500 | 465.37500 | NFM | Aldridge | Police (M2YMHX) |
| 451.47500 | 465.37500 | NFM | Alton | Police Ch.13 |
| 451.47500 | 465.37500 | NFM | Basildon | Police relay (BD) Ch.13 |

| Base | Mobile | Mode | Location | User and Notes |
|------|--------|------|----------|----------------|
| 451.47500 | 465.37500 | NFM | Basingstoke | Police Ch.13 |
| 451.47500 | 465.37500 | NFM | Billericay | Police |
| 451.47500 | 465.37500 | NFM | Birmingham | Police |
| 451.47500 | 465.37500 | NFM | Bridgwater | Police (Golf control) |
| 451.47500 | 465.37500 | NFM | Brighton | Crown Court |
| 451.47500 | 465.37500 | NFM | Burnham | Police (CC) |
| 451.47500 | 465.37500 | NFM | Campsfield | Campsfield Ho Detention |
| 451.47500 | 465.37500 | NFM | Cleveland, Eston | Police |
| 451.47500 | 465.37500 | NFM | England | General Fire Incidents Ch 4 |
| 451.47500 | 465.37500 | NFM | England & Wales | Police Channel 13 |
| 451.47500 | 465.37500 | NFM | Erlestoke | HM Prison  Erlestoke |
| 451.47500 | 465.37500 | NFM | Greyshott | Police |
| 451.47500 | 465.37500 | NFM | Harrogate | Police |
| 451.47500 | 465.37500 | NFM | Hull | Police (HA) Ch.13 |
| 451.47500 | 465.37500 | NFM | Ilkley | Police |
| 451.47500 | 465.37500 | NFM | Isle of Wight | Police Relay |
| 451.47500 | 465.37500 | NFM | Keighley | Police Ch.13 |
| 451.47500 | 465.37500 | NFM | London | HM Prison  Wandsworth |
| 451.47500 | 465.37500 | NFM | Maidenhead | Police (M2CG) |
| 451.47500 | 465.37500 | NFM | Manchester, Chadderton | Police |
| 451.47500 | 465.37500 | NFM | Manchester, Failsworth | Police |
| 451.47500 | 465.37500 | NFM | Manchester, Royton | Police |
| 451.47500 | 465.37500 | NFM | Manchester, Uppermill | Police |
| 451.47500 | 465.37500 | NFM | Newcastle | Police |
| 451.47500 | 465.37500 | NFM | Northampton | Police Ch 4 |
| 451.47500 | 465.37500 | NFM | Oldham | Police (Q1) Ch.13 |
| 451.47500 | 465.37500 | NFM | Petersfield | Police (OSCAR 1) Ch.13 |
| 451.47500 | 465.37500 | NFM | Ripley | Police |
| 451.47500 | 465.37500 | NFM | South Godstone | Police |
| 451.47500 | 465.37500 | NFM | Southend | Police |
| 451.47500 | 465.37500 | NFM | Statford upon Avon | Police |
| 451.47500 | 465.37500 | NFM | Thames Valley | Police |
| 451.47500 | 465.37500 | NFM | Thorne, South Yorkshire | Police (A2) Ch.13 |
| 451.47500 | 465.37500 | NFM | Tonbridge | Police (CC) Ch.14 |
| 451.47500 | 465.37500 | NFM | Torquay | Police (EC) |
| 451.47500 | 465.37500 | NFM | Uttoxeter | Police |
| 451.47500 | 465.37500 | NFM | Wakefield | HM Prison  Wakefield |
| 451.47500 | 465.37500 | NFM | Wallsend | Police (M2LBC3)/(I1) |
| 451.47500 | 465.37500 | NFM | Walsall | Police (M2YMHX) Ch.13 |
| 451.47500 | 465.37500 | NFM | Wickford | Police |
| 451.50000 | 465.40000 | NFM | Eccleshill | Police Ch.14 |
| 451.50000 | 465.40000 | NFM | Edinburgh, Fettes | Police (ZH) Ch.1 |
| 451.50000 | | NFM | England & Wales | Police Channel 14 |
| 451.50000 | 465.40000 | NFM | London | British Transport Police Ch.14 |
| 451.50000 | 465.40000 | NFM | London | Police Special Branch Ch 14 (RANGER) |
| 451.52500 | 465.42500 | NFM | Adwick | Police |
| 451.52500 | 465.42500 | NFM | Basildon | Police |
| 451.52500 | 465.42500 | NFM | Birkenhead | Police (A2) |
| 451.52500 | 465.42500 | NFM | Birmingham | Police (RD) Ch.15 |
| 451.52500 | 465.42500 | NFM | Birmingham, Solihull | Police (M2YML) |
| 451.52500 | 465.42500 | NFM | Birtley | Police (K2) |
| 451.52500 | 465.42500 | NFM | Blaydon | Police (K3) |
| 451.52500 | 465.42500 | NFM | Bradford, Laisterdyke | Police |
| 451.52500 | 465.42500 | NFM | Bristol | Traffic Wardens |
| 451.52500 | 465.42500 | NFM | Cardiff Central | Police (WY) |
| 451.52500 | 465.42500 | NFM | Carterton | Police (FJ) |

| Base | Mobile | Mode | Location | User and Notes |
|------|--------|------|----------|----------------|
| 451.52500 | 465.42500 | NFM | Chelmsford | Police (CT) Ch.15 |
| 451.52500 | 465.42500 | NFM | Dudley | Police (WO) Ch.13 |
| 451.52500 | 465.42500 | NFM | Dudley Hill | Police (GB) Ch.13 |
| 451.52500 | 465.42500 | NFM | Eastchurch | HM Prison Elmley |
| 451.52500 | 465.42500 | NFM | England & Wales | Fire Breathing Apparatus Ch6 |
| 451.52500 | 465.42500 | NFM | England & Wales | Police Channel 15 |
| 451.52500 | 465.42500 | NFM | Essex | Police |
| 451.52500 | 465.42500 | NFM | Exeter | Police Ch 15 (EV) |
| 451.52500 | 465.42500 | NFM | Faringdon | Police |
| 451.52500 | 465.42500 | NFM | Farncombe | Police |
| 451.52500 | 465.42500 | NFM | Godalming | Police (WO) |
| 451.52500 | 465.42500 | NFM | Grays | Police |
| 451.52500 | 465.42500 | NFM | Hazelmere | Police (WO) |
| 451.52500 | 465.42500 | NFM | Huntingdon | Police |
| 451.52500 | 465.42500 | NFM | Long Eaton | Police |
| 451.52500 | 465.42500 | NFM | Malvern | Police |
| 451.52500 | 465.42500 | NFM | Manchester, Ancoats | Police |
| 451.52500 | 465.42500 | NFM | Manchester, Blackley | Police |
| 451.52500 | 465.42500 | NFM | Manchester, Bradford | Police |
| 451.52500 | 465.42500 | NFM | Manchester, Cheetham Hill | Police |
| 451.52500 | 465.42500 | NFM | Manchester, Collyhurst | Police (B2) Ch.15 |
| 451.52500 | 465.42500 | NFM | Manchester, Harpurhey | Police |
| 451.52500 | 465.42500 | NFM | Manchester, Newton Heath | Police |
| 451.52500 | 465.42500 | NFM | Mexborough | Police (A3)Ch.15 |
| 451.52500 | 465.42500 | NFM | Miles Platting | Police |
| 451.52500 | 465.42500 | NFM | Milton Keynes | HM Prison Woodhill (HM) Ch.15 |
| 451.52500 | 465.42500 | NFM | Newcastle | Police |
| 451.52500 | 465.42500 | NFM | Nottingham | Police |
| 451.52500 | 465.42500 | NFM | Oldhill | Police |
| 451.52500 | 465.42500 | NFM | Oxford | Police |
| 451.52500 | 465.42500 | NFM | Plymouth | Police VHF-UHF Repeater |
| 451.52500 | 465.42500 | NFM | Poole | Police |
| 451.52500 | 465.42500 | NFM | Shearness | HM Prison Elmley (M2KE) |
| 451.52500 | 465.42500 | NFM | Shirley | Police |
| 451.52500 | 465.42500 | NFM | Solihull | Police (L1) |
| 451.52500 | 465.42500 | NFM | Southampton | Police (WHISKY 1) Ch.15 |
| 451.52500 | 465.42500 | NFM | Stafford | Police |
| 451.52500 | 465.42500 | NFM | Thames Valley | Police |
| 451.52500 | 465.42500 | NFM | West Bridgford | Police |
| 451.52500 | 465.42500 | NFM | West Midlands | Police, Birmingham Rd |
| 451.52500 | 465.42500 | NFM | Weymouth | Police |
| 451.52500 | 465.42500 | NFM | Whickham | Police (K1) |
| 451.52500 | 465.42500 | NFM | Windsor | Castle (RAPIER CHARLIE) |
| 451.52500 | 465.42500 | NFM | Wirral | Police |
| 451.52500 | 465.42500 | NFM | Wisley | Police (FI) |
| 451.52500 | 465.42500 | NFM | Witney | Police |
| 451.52500 | 465.42500 | NFM | Wolverhampton | Police (RD) encrypted Ch.15 |
| 451.53750 | 465.43750 | NFM | Merseyside | Police (Encrypted) |
| 451.55000 | 465.45000 | NFM | Accrington | Police |
| 451.55000 | 465.45000 | NFM | Bradford Central | Police |
| 451.55000 | 465.45000 | NFM | Brierley Hill | Police |
| 451.55000 | 465.45000 | NFM | Bristol | Police (M2QP) |
| 451.55000 | 465.45000 | NFM | Castleford | Police |
| 451.55000 | 465.45000 | NFM | Cleveland | HM Prison Kirklevington |
| 451.55000 | 465.45000 | NFM | Doncaster | HM Prison Lindholme |
| 451.55000 | 465.45000 | NFM | Dover | Dover Detention Centre |

| Base | Mobile | Mode | Location | User and Notes |
|---|---|---|---|---|
| 451.55000 | 465.45000 | NFM | Dudley | Police (M2YMJ) |
| 451.55000 | 465.45000 | NFM | Eastleigh | Police |
| 451.55000 | 465.45000 | NFM | England & Wales | Police Channel 16 |
| 451.55000 | 465.45000 | NFM | Evesham | HM Prison  Long Lartin |
| 451.55000 | 465.45000 | NFM | Faringdon | Police (M2FE) |
| 451.55000 | 465.45000 | NFM | Farnham | Police (WF) |
| 451.55000 | 465.45000 | NFM | Garstang | Police |
| 451.55000 | 465.45000 | NFM | Gosforth | Police (M2LBB5) |
| 451.55000 | 465.45000 | NFM | Haslingden | Police |
| 451.55000 | 465.45000 | NFM | Jesmond | Police |
| 451.55000 | 465.45000 | NFM | Kenton | Police (G3) |
| 451.55000 | 465.45000 | NFM | Lancaster | Police |
| 451.55000 | 465.45000 | NFM | Liverpool | HM Prison |
| 451.55000 | 465.45000 | NFM | London | HM Prison  Pentonville |
| 451.55000 | 465.45000 | NFM | London | Police Buckingham Palace Ch1 (RAPIER BRAVO) |
| 451.55000 | 465.45000 | NFM | London | Police Diplomatic Protection |
| 451.55000 | 465.45000 | NFM | Milton Keynes | HM Prison  Woodhill |
| 451.55000 | 465.45000 | NFM | Ranby | HM Prison |
| 451.55000 | 465.45000 | NFM | Richmond | HM Prison Latchmere House |
| 451.55000 | 465.45000 | NFM | Rochester | Borstal |
| 451.55000 | 465.45000 | NFM | Romsey | Police |
| 451.55000 | 465.45000 | NFM | Saltash | Police |
| 451.55000 | 465.45000 | NFM | Sedgeley | Police |
| 451.55000 | 465.45000 | NFM | Somerset | Police |
| 451.55000 | 465.45000 | NFM | Southampton (West) | Police |
| 451.55000 | 465.45000 | NFM | Swindon | Police |
| 451.55000 | 465.45000 | NFM | Taunton | Police |
| 451.55000 | 465.45000 | NFM | Telford | Police |
| 451.55000 | 465.45000 | NFM | Tetbury | Police Special Branch Highgrove House Ch.6 |
| 451.55000 | 465.45000 | NFM | Thames Valley | Police |
| 451.55000 | 465.45000 | NFM | Torpoint | Police B Division |
| 451.55000 | 465.45000 | NFM | Walton | HM Prison |
| 451.55000 | 465.45000 | NFM | Wantage | Police (FF) |
| 451.55000 | 465.45000 | NFM | Warrington | Police (D2) |
| 451.55000 | 465.45000 | NFM | Wellingborough | HM Prison |
| 451.55000 | 465.45000 | NFM | Whitehaven | Police |
| 451.55000 | 465.45000 | NFM | Yorkshire (M62) | Police |
| 451.57500 | 465.47500 | NFM | Accrington | Police |
| 451.57500 | 465.47500 | NFM | Bradford | Police (GA) Ch.17 |
| 451.57500 | 465.47500 | NFM | Bristol | Police (M2QP) Ch.17 |
| 451.57500 | 465.47500 | NFM | Bristol, Southlea | Police (FF) Ch.17 |
| 451.57500 | 465.47500 | NFM | Bristol, Staplehill | Police (FF) Ch.17 |
| 451.57500 | 465.47500 | NFM | Brough | HM Prison Evanthorpe Ch.17 |
| 451.57500 | 465.47500 | NFM | Castleford | Police (DC) Ch.17 |
| 451.57500 | 465.47500 | NFM | Dudley | Police (M2YMJ) Ch.17 |
| 451.57500 | 465.47500 | NFM | Eastleigh | Police |
| 451.57500 | 465.47500 | NFM | England & Wales | Police Channel 17 |
| 451.57500 | 465.47500 | NFM | Fallham | Police (WF) Ch.17 |
| 451.57500 | 465.47500 | NFM | Faringdon | Police (M2FE) Ch.17 |
| 451.57500 | 465.47500 | NFM | Garstang | Police |
| 451.57500 | 465.47500 | NFM | Gosforth | Police (M2LBB5) Ch.17 |
| 451.57500 | 465.47500 | NFM | Haslingden | Police |
| 451.57500 | 465.47500 | NFM | Huntington | Police Special Branch at John Major's house Ch.17 |
| 451.57500 | 465.47500 | NFM | Jesmond | Police |

| Base | Mobile | Mode | Location | User and Notes |
|------|--------|------|----------|----------------|
| 451.57500 | 465.47500 | NFM | Kenton | Police (G3) |
| 451.57500 | 465.47500 | NFM | Lancaster | Police |
| 451.57500 | 465.47500 | NFM | Newton Abbot | Police (TB) Ch.17 |
| 451.57500 | 465.47500 | NFM | Normanton | Police (DB) Ch.17 |
| 451.57500 | 465.47500 | NFM | Northampton | Police Ch 17 (EQ/NQ) |
| 451.57500 | 465.47500 | NFM | Reading | HM Prison (M2AY) Ch.17 |
| 451.57500 | 465.47500 | NFM | Riston Filton | Police (FF) Ch.17 |
| 451.57500 | 465.47500 | NFM | Romsey | Police |
| 451.57500 | 465.47500 | NFM | Saltash | Police |
| 451.57500 | 465.47500 | NFM | Sedgeley | Police |
| 451.57500 | 465.47500 | NFM | Somerset | Police |
| 451.57500 | 465.47500 | NFM | Southampton, west | Police |
| 451.57500 | 465.47500 | NFM | Swindon | Police |
| 451.57500 | 465.47500 | NFM | Taunton | Police |
| 451.57500 | 465.47500 | NFM | Telford | Police |
| 451.57500 | 465.47500 | NFM | Thames Valley | Police |
| 451.57500 | 465.47500 | NFM | Torpoint | Police B division |
| 451.57500 | 465.47500 | NFM | Wantage | Police (FF) |
| 451.57500 | 465.47500 | NFM | Warrington | Police (B1) Ch.17 |
| 451.57500 | 465.47500 | NFM | Whitehaven | Police |
| 451.57500 | 465.47500 | NFM | Yorkshire, M62 | Police |
| 451.57500 | 465.67500 | NFM | Cleveland | HM Prison Kirlevington |
| 451.57500 | 465.67500 | NFM | Dover | Police Detention Centre Ch.17 |
| 451.57500 | 465.67500 | NFM | Eavesham | HM Prison Long Lartin (JZ) Ch.17 |
| 451.57500 | 465.67500 | NFM | London | HM Prison Pentonville |
| 451.57500 | 465.67500 | NFM | Milton Keynes | HM Prison Woodhill |
| 451.57500 | 465.67500 | NFM | Ranby | HM Prison |
| 451.57500 | 465.67500 | NFM | Richmond | HM Prison Latchmere House |
| 451.57500 | 465.67500 | NFM | Rochester | Borstal |
| 451.57500 | 465.67500 | NFM | Walton | HM Prison |
| 451.57500 | 465.67500 | NFM | Wellingborough | HM Prison |
| 451.58750 | 465.48750 | NFM | Borth | Police |
| 451.58750 | 465.48750 | NFM | London | Police divisions P/R/N and part of Z trunked |
| 451.60000 | 465.50000 | NFM | Addlestone | Police (NA) Ch.18 |
| 451.60000 | 465.50000 | NFM | Avon | Police support and tactical assault Ch.18 |
| 451.60000 | 465.50000 | NFM | Birmingham | Police Central (M2YMF) |
| 451.60000 | 465.50000 | NFM | Birmingham, Digbeth | Police Ch.18 |
| 451.60000 | 465.50000 | NFM | Boston | HM Prison North Sea Camp Ch.18 |
| 451.60000 | 465.50000 | NFM | Cheltenham | Police |
| 451.60000 | 465.50000 | NFM | Cradley Heath | Police |
| 451.60000 | 465.50000 | NFM | Doncaster | HM Prison |
| 451.60000 | 465.50000 | NFM | England & Wales | Police Channel 18 |
| 451.60000 | 465.50000 | NFM | Gipton | Police (BB) |
| 451.60000 | 465.50000 | NFM | Ipswich | Police Ch.18 links to Ch.47 |
| 451.60000 | 465.50000 | NFM | Lancaster | Police |
| 451.60000 | 465.50000 | NFM | London | Police |
| 451.60000 | 465.50000 | NFM | Maidstone | Police (CZ) Ch.18 |
| 451.60000 | 465.50000 | NFM | Mallington | Police (CZ) Ch.18 |
| 451.60000 | 465.50000 | NFM | Manchester, Altrincham | Police |
| 451.60000 | 465.50000 | NFM | Manchester, Sale | Police |
| 451.60000 | 465.50000 | NFM | Manchester, Stretford | Police (M1) Ch.18 |
| 451.60000 | 465.50000 | NFM | Manchester, Trafford | Police |
| 451.60000 | 465.50000 | NFM | Manchester, Urmston | Police |
| 451.60000 | 465.50000 | NFM | Middlesborough | Police |
| 451.60000 | 465.50000 | NFM | Nottingham | HM Prison |
| 451.60000 | 465.50000 | NFM | Oldham | Police |

| Base | Mobile | Mode | Location | User and Notes |
|------|--------|------|----------|----------------|
| 451.60000 | 465.50000 | NFM | Preston | Police |
| 451.60000 | 465.50000 | NFM | Ramsgate | Police |
| 451.60000 | 465.50000 | NFM | Rushton | Police Ch.18 |
| 451.60000 | 465.50000 | NFM | Sale | Police |
| 451.60000 | 465.50000 | NFM | South Yorkshire | Police Ch.18 for special use |
| 451.60000 | 465.50000 | NFM | Southwick | Police (M1) Encrypted |
| 451.60000 | 465.50000 | NFM | Southwood | Police (F3) |
| 451.60000 | 465.50000 | NFM | Sunderland | Police (M2LBF3) |
| 451.60000 | 465.50000 | NFM | W. Midlands, Steelhouse La | Police |
| 451.60000 | 465.50000 | NFM | Wellingborough | Police Ch 18 |
| 451.60000 | 465.50000 | NFM | West Midlands, Bradford St | Police |
| 451.61250 | 465.51250 | NFM | England & Wales | Fire Breathing Apparatus Ch2 |
| 451.61250 | 465.51250 | NFM | London | Police division X |
| 451.61250 | 465.51250 | NFM | Plymouth Airport | Fire Appliance |
| 451.62500 | 465.52500 | NFM | Birmingham | Police (NEC Motor Show) |
| 451.62500 | 465.52500 | NFM | Blackpool | Police Football Control |
| 451.62500 | 465.52500 | NFM | Brighton | Police Special Ops |
| 451.62500 | 465.52500 | NFM | Cambridge | Police Football Control |
| 451.62500 | 465.52500 | NFM | Cardiff | Police |
| 451.62500 | 465.52500 | NFM | Co Durham | Police (LA) |
| 451.62500 | 465.52500 | NFM | Conway | Police Mobile Repeater |
| 451.62500 | 465.52500 | NFM | Derby | Police Derby City Football Club /Vice Squad |
| 451.62500 | 465.52500 | NFM | Dover | Police Operations Centre |
| 451.62500 | 465.52500 | NFM | Dyfed | Police Helicopter (X99) |
| 451.62500 | 465.52500 | NFM | England & Wales | Police Channel 19 |
| 451.62500 | 465.52500 | NFM | Essex | Police |
| 451.62500 | 465.52500 | NFM | Guernsey | Police Channel 2 |
| 451.62500 | 465.52500 | NFM | Ipswich | Police special events & football control Ch.19 |
| 451.62500 | 465.52500 | NFM | Kendal | Police |
| 451.62500 | 465.52500 | NFM | Leicester | Police |
| 451.62500 | 465.52500 | NFM | London | Police Special Branch Ch 19 |
| 451.62500 | 465.52500 | NFM | London, Gatwick | Police M2KB (GatPol) Special Ch.19 |
| 451.62500 | 465.52500 | NFM | Manchester | Police Surveillance (Part Time) |
| 451.62500 | 465.52500 | NFM | Nationwide | CID Use/National Emergencies |
| 451.62500 | 465.52500 | NFM | Northampton | Police Ch 19 |
| 451.62500 | 465.52500 | NFM | Nottingham | Police covering The Goose Fair |
| 451.62500 | 465.52500 | NFM | Peterborough | Police Ops |
| 451.62500 | 465.52500 | NFM | Slough | Police |
| 451.62500 | 465.52500 | NFM | Stoke on Trent | Police |
| 451.62500 | 465.52500 | NFM | Tenterden | Police |
| 451.62500 | 465.52500 | NFM | Thames Valley | Police Special Events |
| 451.62500 | 465.52500 | NFM | West Sussex | Police Emergency Use |
| 451.62500 | 465.52500 | NFM | Yorkshire | Police Football Control |
| 451.63750 | 465.53750 | NFM | Oxford | Police |
| 451.65000 | 465.55000 | NFM | Bagshot | Police |
| 451.65000 | 465.55000 | NFM | Birmingham | Police |
| 451.65000 | 465.55000 | NFM | Cambridge | Police Mobile Repeater |
| 451.65000 | 465.55000 | NFM | Caterham | Police |
| 451.65000 | 465.55000 | NFM | Chiddingfold | Police |
| 451.65000 | 465.55000 | NFM | City of London | Police |
| 451.65000 | 465.55000 | NFM | Cornwall | Police Mobile Repeater |
| 451.65000 | 465.55000 | NFM | Devon | Police Mobile Repeater |
| 451.65000 | 465.55000 | NFM | England & Wales | Police Mobile Repeaters Ch. 20 |
| 451.65000 | 465.55000 | NFM | Exeter | Police Ch.20 |
| 451.65000 | 465.55000 | NFM | Flint | Police |
| 451.65000 | 465.55000 | NFM | Hertfordshire | Police Mobile Repeater |

| Base | Mobile | Mode | Location | User and Notes |
|------|--------|------|----------|----------------|
| 451.65000 | 465.55000 | NFM | Humberside | Police Mobile Repeater |
| 451.65000 | 465.55000 | NFM | Leeds | Police Force Control |
| 451.65000 | 465.55000 | NFM | Leeds | HM Prison Armley |
| 451.65000 | 465.55000 | NFM | Lincolnshire | Police Mobile Repeater |
| 451.65000 | 465.55000 | NFM | Lowestoft | Police |
| 451.65000 | 465.55000 | NFM | Merseyside | Police Mobile Repeater |
| 451.65000 | 465.55000 | NFM | Milton Keynes | Police Ch 20 (TS/NG) |
| 451.65000 | 465.55000 | NFM | Northumberland | Police Repeaters |
| 451.65000 | 465.55000 | NFM | Nottinghamshire | Police Mobile Repeater |
| 451.65000 | 465.55000 | NFM | Poole | Police RCS Encrypted Cougar |
| 451.65000 | 465.55000 | NFM | Shirehall | Police Link |
| 451.65000 | 465.55000 | NFM | South Cumbria | Police Repeater |
| 451.65000 | 465.55000 | NFM | South Wales | Police Mobile Repeater |
| 451.65000 | 465.55000 | NFM | South Yorkshire | Police Mobile Repeater |
| 451.65000 | 465.55000 | NFM | Southend | Police Ch.4 |
| 451.65000 | 465.55000 | NFM | St Ives | Police |
| 451.65000 | 465.55000 | NFM | Staffordshire | Police Mobile Repeater |
| 451.65000 | 465.55000 | NFM | Thames Valley | Police Mobile Repeater |
| 451.65000 | 465.55000 | NFM | Tyne and Wear | Police Repeaters |
| 451.65000 | 465.55000 | NFM | Ulverstone | Police |
| 451.65000 | 465.55000 | NFM | West Mercia | Police |
| 451.65000 | 465.55000 | NFM | West Midlands | Police Repeater |
| 451.65000 | 465.55000 | NFM | West Sussex | Police Mobile Repeater |
| 451.65000 | 465.55000 | NFM | West Yorkshire | Police Mobile Repeater |
| 451.65000 | 465.55000 | NFM | Weybridge | Police |
| 451.65000 | 465.55000 | NFM | Wrexham | Police |
| 451.67500 | 465.57500 | NFM | Anglesey | Police |
| 451.67500 | 465.57500 | NFM | Barnsley | Police Ch.21 |
| 451.67500 | 465.57500 | NFM | Benfleet | Police (JD) Ch.21 |
| 451.67500 | 465.57500 | NFM | Birmingham | Police |
| 451.67500 | 465.57500 | NFM | Bishop Stortford | Police (ABS) Ch.21 |
| 451.67500 | 465.57500 | NFM | Bradford | Police |
| 451.67500 | 465.57500 | NFM | Buxton | Police |
| 451.67500 | 465.57500 | NFM | Canvey Island | Police relay (JC) Ch.21 |
| 451.67500 | 465.57500 | NFM | Canvey Island | Police |
| 451.67500 | 465.57500 | NFM | Cardiff Central | Police |
| 451.67500 | 465.57500 | NFM | Cheltenham | Police (MIKE VICTOR) Ch.21 |
| 451.67500 | 465.57500 | NFM | Chipping Norton | Police |
| 451.67500 | 465.57500 | NFM | City of London | Police Channel 2 (AJ) |
| 451.67500 | 465.57500 | NFM | Cornwall | Police (Mobile Repeater) |
| 451.67500 | 465.57500 | NFM | Cosham | Police |
| 451.67500 | 465.57500 | NFM | Devon | Police Mobile Repeater |
| 451.67500 | 465.57500 | NFM | England & Wales | Police Channel 21 |
| 451.67500 | 465.57500 | NFM | Gateshead (South) | Police |
| 451.67500 | 465.57500 | NFM | Glossop | Police |
| 451.67500 | 465.57500 | NFM | Hadleigh | Police (JD) Ch.21 |
| 451.67500 | 465.57500 | NFM | Havant | Police |
| 451.67500 | 465.57500 | NFM | Henley | Police (M2EE) |
| 451.67500 | 465.57500 | NFM | Hertfordshire | Police Mobile Repeater (VH) |
| 451.67500 | 465.57500 | NFM | Kettering | Police (CB) Ch.21 |
| 451.67500 | 465.57500 | NFM | Kirky in Ashfield | Police |
| 451.67500 | 465.57500 | NFM | Leicester | Police |
| 451.67500 | 465.57500 | NFM | Liverpool | Police |
| 451.67500 | 465.57500 | NFM | Mansfield | Police |
| 451.67500 | 465.57500 | NFM | Matlock | Police |
| 451.67500 | 465.57500 | NFM | Merseyside | Police HQ Div A (Encrypted) |

| Base | Mobile | Mode | Location | User and Notes |
|---|---|---|---|---|
| 451.67500 | 465.57500 | NFM | Newcastle | Police (M2LBB3)/(F1) |
| 451.67500 | 465.57500 | NFM | Northampton | Police Ch 21 |
| 451.67500 | 465.57500 | NFM | Northwich | Police (E1) |
| 451.67500 | 465.57500 | NFM | Pangbourne | Police |
| 451.67500 | 465.57500 | NFM | Portsmouth | Police |
| 451.67500 | 465.57500 | NFM | Reading | Police (EG) Ch.21 |
| 451.67500 | 465.57500 | NFM | Redditch | Police |
| 451.67500 | 465.57500 | NFM | Shinfield | Police |
| 451.67500 | 465.57500 | NFM | Stoke on Trent | Police |
| 451.67500 | 465.57500 | NFM | Sutton | Police |
| 451.67500 | 465.57500 | NFM | Sutton in Ashfield | Police |
| 451.67500 | 465.57500 | NFM | Tamworth | Police (MASC) Ch.21 |
| 451.67500 | 465.57500 | NFM | Theale | Police |
| 451.67500 | 465.57500 | NFM | Twyford | Police |
| 451.67500 | 465.57500 | NFM | Waterloo, Hants | Police (CHARLIE 1) Ch.21 |
| 451.67500 | 465.57500 | NFM | Welwyn Garden City | Police |
| 451.67500 | 465.57500 | NFM | Wokingham | Police |
| 451.67500 | 465.57500 | NFM | Woodley | Police (EB) |
| 451.68750 | 465.58750 | NFM | Kent | Police Ch.14 |
| 451.70000 | 465.60000 | NFM | Arnold | Police |
| 451.70000 | 465.60000 | NFM | Ashford | Police |
| 451.70000 | 465.60000 | NFM | Birmingham, Bourneville | Police (M2YMB) |
| 451.70000 | 465.60000 | NFM | Bitterne | Police |
| 451.70000 | 465.60000 | NFM | Bournville | Police Ch.22 |
| 451.70000 | 465.60000 | NFM | Burscough | Police |
| 451.70000 | 465.60000 | NFM | Chandlers Ford | Police (WHISKY 1) Ch.22 |
| 451.70000 | 465.60000 | NFM | Chorley | Police |
| 451.70000 | 465.60000 | NFM | Coppull | Police |
| 451.70000 | 465.60000 | NFM | Dorking | Police (ED) Ch.22 |
| 451.70000 | 465.60000 | NFM | Durham | Police (BD) |
| 451.70000 | 465.60000 | NFM | England & Wales | Police Channel 22 |
| 451.70000 | 465.60000 | NFM | Folkestone | Police (DC) Ch.22 |
| 451.70000 | 465.60000 | NFM | Folkestone | Police |
| 451.70000 | 465.60000 | NFM | Gillingham | Police (BB) Ch.22 |
| 451.70000 | 465.60000 | NFM | Hackenthorpe | Police Ch.22 |
| 451.70000 | 465.60000 | NFM | Leatherhead | Police (EL) |
| 451.70000 | 465.60000 | NFM | Manchester International | Police Ch.22 |
| 451.70000 | 465.60000 | NFM | Manchester, Broughton | Police |
| 451.70000 | 465.60000 | NFM | Manchester, Eccles | Police |
| 451.70000 | 465.60000 | NFM | Manchester, Little Hulton | Police |
| 451.70000 | 465.60000 | NFM | Manchester, Pendleton | Police |
| 451.70000 | 465.60000 | NFM | Manchester, Salford | Police |
| 451.70000 | 465.60000 | NFM | Manchester, Swinton | Police |
| 451.70000 | 465.60000 | NFM | Manchester, Walkden | Police |
| 451.70000 | 465.60000 | NFM | Nottinghamshire | Police MASC Ch.22 |
| 451.70000 | 465.60000 | NFM | Rainham | Police (BB) Ch.22 |
| 451.70000 | 465.60000 | NFM | Sheffield | Police (E1) |
| 451.70000 | 465.60000 | NFM | South Yorkshire | Police emergency communications van Ch.22 |
| 451.70000 | 465.60000 | NFM | Southampton | Police |
| 451.70000 | 465.60000 | NFM | Thames Valley | Police |
| 451.70000 | 465.60000 | NFM | Westbury | Police (CB/ CW /CM) Ch.22 |
| 451.71250 | 465.61250 | NFM | London | Police central security network trunked |
| 451.72500 | 465.62500 | NFM | Ammanford | Police |
| 451.72500 | 465.62500 | NFM | Birmingham | Police NEC Security |
| 451.72500 | 465.62500 | NFM | Blackpool | Police |
| 451.72500 | 465.62500 | NFM | Brighton | Police Conference Security |

| Base | Mobile | Mode | Location | User and Notes |
|---|---|---|---|---|
| 451.72500 | 465.62500 | NFM | Cardiff | Police Special Events |
| 451.72500 | 465.62500 | NFM | Cheadle Hulme | Police |
| 451.72500 | 465.62500 | NFM | Cromer | Police (N) Ch.23 |
| 451.72500 | 465.62500 | NFM | England & Wales | Police Channel 23 |
| 451.72500 | 465.62500 | NFM | Humberside | Police Football Control |
| 451.72500 | 465.62500 | NFM | Leicester | Police (encrypted) Ch.23 |
| 451.72500 | 465.62500 | NFM | London | Police Notting Hill Carnival 3 |
| 451.72500 | 465.62500 | NFM | Manchester | Police |
| 451.72500 | 465.62500 | NFM | Northumberland | Police Mobile (M2LBX+Y) |
| 451.72500 | 465.62500 | NFM | Suffolk | Police Special Events |
| 451.72500 | 465.62500 | NFM | Thames Valley | Police |
| 451.72500 | 465.62500 | NFM | Wakefield | Police HQ |
| 451.75000 | 465.65000 | NFM | Birmingham, Ward End | Police (M2YME) |
| 451.75000 | 465.65000 | NFM | Blackpool | Police |
| 451.75000 | 465.65000 | NFM | Boscombe | Police |
| 451.75000 | 465.65000 | NFM | Bournemouth | Police |
| 451.75000 | 465.65000 | NFM | Bramford | Police |
| 451.75000 | 465.65000 | NFM | Burnley | Police |
| 451.75000 | 465.65000 | NFM | Bury | Police |
| 451.75000 | 465.65000 | NFM | Cardiff | Police L Division (WY) |
| 451.75000 | 465.65000 | NFM | Croxteth | Police (C1) |
| 451.75000 | 465.65000 | NFM | Ely | Police |
| 451.75000 | 465.65000 | NFM | England & Wales | Police Channel 24 |
| 451.75000 | 465.65000 | NFM | Flint | Police |
| 451.75000 | 465.65000 | NFM | Hinckley | Police (WEST DECK) Ch.24 |
| 451.75000 | 465.65000 | NFM | Kirkham | Police |
| 451.75000 | 465.65000 | NFM | Liverpool, Huyton | Police Ch.24 |
| 451.75000 | 465.65000 | NFM | London | Police Special Branch surveillance Ch.24 |
| 451.75000 | 465.65000 | NFM | Lytham | Police |
| 451.75000 | 465.65000 | NFM | Manchester, Birch | Police |
| 451.75000 | 465.65000 | NFM | Manchester, Motorway | Police |
| 451.75000 | 465.65000 | NFM | Manchester, Prestwich | Police |
| 451.75000 | 465.65000 | NFM | Manchester, Radcliffe | Police |
| 451.75000 | 465.65000 | NFM | Manchester, Ramsbottom | Police |
| 451.75000 | 465.65000 | NFM | Manchester, Whitefield | Police |
| 451.75000 | 465.65000 | NFM | Market Harborough | Police |
| 451.75000 | 465.65000 | NFM | Melksham | Police |
| 451.75000 | 465.65000 | NFM | Merseyside | Police HQ Div D (Encrypted) |
| 451.75000 | 465.65000 | NFM | Middleton | Police |
| 451.75000 | 465.65000 | NFM | Peterlee | Police (BE) |
| 451.75000 | 465.65000 | NFM | Retford | Police (MASC) Ch.24 |
| 451.75000 | 465.65000 | NFM | Rochford | Police Ch.24 |
| 451.75000 | 465.65000 | NFM | Salisbury | HM Prison  Salisbury |
| 451.75000 | 465.65000 | NFM | Skegness | Police |
| 451.75000 | 465.65000 | NFM | Southend | Police |
| 451.75000 | 465.65000 | NFM | St Annes | Police |
| 451.75000 | 465.65000 | NFM | Thames Valley | Police |
| 451.75000 | 465.65000 | NFM | Warton | Police |
| 451.75000 | 465.65000 | NFM | Weeton | Police |
| 451.75000 | 465.65000 | NFM | Workington | Police |
| 451.75000 | 465.65000 | NFM | Worksop | Police |
| 451.76250 | 465.66250 | NFM | London | Police central security network trunked |
| 451.77500 | 465.67500 | NFM | Blackpool | Police Conference Security |
| 451.77500 | 465.67500 | NFM | Brighton | Brighton Crown Court |
| 451.77500 | 465.67500 | NFM | Cambridge | Police Special Branch |
| 451.77500 | 465.67500 | NFM | Cardiff | Police CID |

| Base | Mobile | Mode | Location | User and Notes |
|---|---|---|---|---|
| 451.77500 | 465.67500 | NFM | England & Wales | Fire Breathing Apparatus |
| 451.77500 | 465.67500 | NFM | England & Wales | Police Channel 25 |
| 451.77500 | 465.67500 | NFM | Farnborough | Police Air Show Security Ch.25 |
| 451.77500 | 465.67500 | NFM | Hull | Police Football Control |
| 451.77500 | 465.67500 | NFM | Lancashire | Police Emergency Channel |
| 451.77500 | 465.67500 | NFM | Leicester | Police |
| 451.77500 | 465.67500 | NFM | Lincoln | Police |
| 451.77500 | 465.67500 | NFM | London | Police Notting Hill Carnival 5 |
| 451.77500 | 465.67500 | NFM | Maidstone | Police |
| 451.77500 | 465.67500 | NFM | Manchester | Police Surveillance (Part Time) |
| 451.77500 | 465.67500 | NFM | Merseyside | Police HQ Div F (Encrypted) |
| 451.77500 | 465.67500 | NFM | Northumberland | Police Mobile (M2LBX+Y) |
| 451.77500 | 465.67500 | NFM | Rotherham | Police Football Control |
| 451.77500 | 465.67500 | NFM | Southend/Westcliff | Ch.25 Special Constables |
| 451.77500 | 465.67500 | NFM | Southport | Police football control |
| 451.77500 | 465.67500 | NFM | Suffolk | Police FHQ Repeater |
| 451.77500 | 465.67500 | NFM | Sunninghill | Police |
| 451.77500 | 465.67500 | NFM | Thames Valley | Police Special Events |
| 451.77500 | 465.67500 | NFM | USAF Lakenheath | Police Base Security |
| 451.77500 | 465.67500 | NFM | York | Police (KY) Ch.25 |
| 451.80000 | 465.70000 | NFM | Ainsdale | Police |
| 451.80000 | 465.70000 | NFM | Birmingham, Acock's Green | Police (M2YME) |
| 451.80000 | 465.70000 | NFM | Bolton | Police |
| 451.80000 | 465.70000 | NFM | Bootle | Police (B1) |
| 451.80000 | 465.70000 | NFM | Burton on Trent | Police (MASC) Ch.25 |
| 451.80000 | 465.70000 | NFM | Cheltenham | Police (DELTA) Ch.26 |
| 451.80000 | 465.70000 | NFM | Crosby | Police |
| 451.80000 | 465.70000 | NFM | England & Wales | Police Channel 26 |
| 451.80000 | 465.70000 | NFM | Felling | Police (M2LBD2)/(J2) |
| 451.80000 | 465.70000 | NFM | Formby | Police |
| 451.80000 | 465.70000 | NFM | Gateshead | Police Stadium Area |
| 451.80000 | 465.70000 | NFM | Gipton | Police Ch.26 |
| 451.80000 | 465.70000 | NFM | Gloucester | Police |
| 451.80000 | 465.70000 | NFM | Hemel Hempstead | Police (DH) Ch.26 |
| 451.80000 | 465.70000 | NFM | Lancashire | Police Radio & Vehicle Maintenance |
| 451.80000 | 465.70000 | NFM | Leeds, Gipton | Police |
| 451.80000 | 465.70000 | NFM | Leeds, Killingbeck | Police |
| 451.80000 | 465.70000 | NFM | Liverpool, Marsh Lane | Police |
| 451.80000 | 465.70000 | NFM | London | Police Special Branch Ch 26 |
| 451.80000 | 465.70000 | NFM | London | Police Special Branch Kensington Palace (RAPIER KILO) Ch.2 |
| 451.80000 | 465.70000 | NFM | Lymington | Police (WHISKY 1) Ch.26 |
| 451.80000 | 465.70000 | NFM | Manchester Airport | Police |
| 451.80000 | 465.70000 | NFM | Manchester, Astley Bridge | Police |
| 451.80000 | 465.70000 | NFM | Manchester, Breightmet | Police |
| 451.80000 | 465.70000 | NFM | Manchester, Farnworth | Police |
| 451.80000 | 465.70000 | NFM | Manchester, Horwich | Police |
| 451.80000 | 465.70000 | NFM | Manchester, Middle Hulton | Police |
| 451.80000 | 465.70000 | NFM | Manchester, Westhoughton | Police |
| 451.80000 | 465.70000 | NFM | Merseyside | Police HQ Div B (Encrypted) |
| 451.80000 | 465.70000 | NFM | New Forest | Police |
| 451.80000 | 465.70000 | NFM | Oldbury | Police |
| 451.80000 | 465.70000 | NFM | Ringwood | Police |
| 451.80000 | 465.70000 | NFM | Salisbury | Police Ch.26 |
| 451.80000 | 465.70000 | NFM | Seacroft | Police |
| 451.80000 | 465.70000 | NFM | Southampton, Totton | Police |

| Base | Mobile | Mode | Location | User and Notes |
|------|--------|------|----------|----------------|
| 451.80000 | 465.70000 | NFM | Southport | Police (B2) Ch.26 |
| 451.80000 | 465.70000 | NFM | Tetford | Police Ch.26 |
| 451.80000 | 465.70000 | NFM | Thames Valley | Police |
| 451.80000 | 465.70000 | NFM | Wallington | Police |
| 451.80000 | 465.70000 | NFM | Windsor | Police Castle (RAPIER LIMA) Ch.26 |
| 451.80000 | 465.70000 | FM | Wisbech | Police |
| 451.80000 | 466.70000 | NFM | Eastbourne | Police PR (EE) |
| 451.82500 | 465.72500 | NFM | Abingdon | Police |
| 451.82500 | 465.72500 | NFM | Ashford | Police Sandgate Centre |
| 451.82500 | 465.72500 | NFM | Barry | Police |
| 451.82500 | 465.72500 | NFM | Bispham | Police |
| 451.82500 | 465.72500 | NFM | Blyth | Police (M2LBC5) |
| 451.82500 | 465.72500 | NFM | Bristol | Police CID |
| 451.82500 | 465.72500 | NFM | Cambridgeshire | Police Ch.27 |
| 451.82500 | 465.72500 | NFM | Canning | Police |
| 451.82500 | 465.72500 | NFM | Canterbury | HM Prison Canterbury |
| 451.82500 | 465.72500 | NFM | Cleveleys | Police |
| 451.82500 | 465.72500 | NFM | Clitheroe | Police |
| 451.82500 | 465.72500 | NFM | Corringham | Police |
| 451.82500 | 465.72500 | NFM | Cowley | Police (BC) |
| 451.82500 | 465.72500 | NFM | Devon | Police Ch.27 |
| 451.82500 | 465.72500 | NFM | Eastchurch | HM Prison Swaleside Ch.27 |
| 451.82500 | 465.72500 | NFM | Eastleigh | Police (WHISKY 1) Ch.27 |
| 451.82500 | 465.72500 | NFM | Eccleshall | Police |
| 451.82500 | 465.72500 | NFM | Egham | Police |
| 451.82500 | 465.72500 | NFM | England & Wales | Police Channel 27 |
| 451.82500 | 465.72500 | NFM | Epping | Police |
| 451.82500 | 465.72500 | NFM | Fleetwood | Police |
| 451.82500 | 465.72500 | NFM | Frampton Cotterill | Police |
| 451.82500 | 465.72500 | NFM | Gloucester | Police |
| 451.82500 | 465.72500 | NFM | Grays, Essex | Police (FD) Ch.27 |
| 451.82500 | 465.72500 | NFM | Harlow | Police (GX) Ch.27 |
| 451.82500 | 465.72500 | NFM | Kempston | Police Ch.27 |
| 451.82500 | 465.72500 | NFM | Kenilworth | Police Ch.27 |
| 451.82500 | 465.72500 | NFM | Langley | Police (CE) |
| 451.82500 | 465.72500 | NFM | Malvern | Police (CA) Ch.27 |
| 451.82500 | 465.72500 | NFM | Manchester, Heywood | Police |
| 451.82500 | 465.72500 | NFM | Manchester, Kirkholt | Police |
| 451.82500 | 465.72500 | NFM | Manchester, Littleborough | Police |
| 451.82500 | 465.72500 | NFM | Manchester, Middleton | Police |
| 451.82500 | 465.72500 | NFM | Manchester, Milnrow | Police |
| 451.82500 | 465.72500 | NFM | Neath | Police |
| 451.82500 | 465.72500 | NFM | Nelson Colne | Police |
| 451.82500 | 465.72500 | NFM | Newcastle | Police |
| 451.82500 | 465.72500 | NFM | Nottingham | Police (NH) |
| 451.82500 | 465.72500 | NFM | Oxford | Police (BA) |
| 451.82500 | 465.72500 | NFM | Pendle | Police |
| 451.82500 | 465.72500 | NFM | Port Talbot | Police |
| 451.82500 | 465.72500 | NFM | Poulton le Fyde | Police |
| 451.82500 | 465.72500 | NFM | Rochdale | Police |
| 451.82500 | 465.72500 | NFM | Salisbury | Police (AT) Ch.27 |
| 451.82500 | 465.72500 | NFM | Slough | Police HQ (CA) Ch.27 |
| 451.82500 | 465.72500 | NFM | South Ockendon | Police |
| 451.82500 | 465.72500 | NFM | Spennymoor | Police (AL) |
| 451.82500 | 465.72500 | NFM | Stratford-Upon-Avon | Police |
| 451.82500 | 465.72500 | NFM | Tadcaster | Police |

| Base | Mobile | Mode | Location | User and Notes |
|------|--------|------|----------|----------------|
| 451.82500 | 465.72500 | NFM | Thames Valley | Police |
| 451.82500 | 465.72500 | NFM | West Midlands | Police Ch.27 |
| 451.82500 | 465.72500 | NFM | Wigan | Police |
| 451.82500 | 465.72500 | NFM | Woking | HM Prison Coldingley Ch.27 |
| 451.82500 | 465.72500 | NFM | Wombourne | Police |
| 451.82500 | 465.72500 | NFM | Woodsetts | Police Ch.27 |
| 451.82500 | 465.72500 | NFM | Yate | Police |
| 451.83750 | 465.73750 | NFM | London | Police divisions G/ H/ J/ K |
| 451.85000 | 465.75000 | NFM | Amersham | Police |
| 451.85000 | 465.75000 | NFM | Aylesbury | Police |
| 451.85000 | 465.75000 | NFM | Beaconsfield | Police (AC) |
| 451.85000 | 465.75000 | NFM | Birmingham | Police |
| 451.85000 | 465.75000 | NFM | Bletchley | Police (DG) |
| 451.85000 | 465.75000 | NFM | Bristol | Police |
| 451.85000 | 465.75000 | NFM | Buckingham | Police (DB) |
| 451.85000 | 465.75000 | NFM | Congleton | Police |
| 451.85000 | 465.75000 | NFM | Corby | Police Ch 28 (XM/DS) |
| 451.85000 | 465.75000 | NFM | Doncaster | Thorne Young Offenders Centre |
| 451.85000 | 465.75000 | NFM | England & Wales | Police Channel 28 |
| 451.85000 | 465.75000 | NFM | Gerrards Cross | Police (AC) |
| 451.85000 | 465.75000 | NFM | Grays | Police Ch.28 |
| 451.85000 | 465.75000 | NFM | Havant | Police (CHARLIE 1) Ch.28 |
| 451.85000 | 465.75000 | NFM | Horndean | Police |
| 451.85000 | 465.75000 | NFM | Leeds | HM Prison  Armley Ch.28 |
| 451.85000 | 465.75000 | NFM | Lincoln | HM Prison  Morton Hall Ch.28 |
| 451.85000 | 465.75000 | NFM | Lincoln | Police |
| 451.85000 | 465.75000 | NFM | London | Police Notting Hill Carnival 6 |
| 451.85000 | 465.75000 | NFM | Macclesfield | Police (C1) |
| 451.85000 | 465.75000 | NFM | Manchester | Police |
| 451.85000 | 465.75000 | NFM | Milton Keynes | Police |
| 451.85000 | 465.75000 | NFM | Nottingham | HM Prison |
| 451.85000 | 465.75000 | NFM | Oldbury | Police Ch.28 |
| 451.85000 | 465.75000 | NFM | Ormskirk | Police |
| 451.85000 | 465.75000 | NFM | Smethwick | Police |
| 451.85000 | 465.75000 | NFM | Southend | Police |
| 451.85000 | 465.75000 | NFM | Stanley | Police (CH) |
| 451.85000 | 465.75000 | NFM | Thames Valley | Police |
| 451.85000 | 465.75000 | NFM | Waterlooville | Police |
| 451.85000 | 465.75000 | NFM | Wednesbury | Police (M2YMK) |
| 451.85000 | 466.75000 | NFM | Northamptonshire | Police MASC Ch.27 |
| 451.86250 | 465.76250 | NFM | London | Police divisions P/ R/ M and part of Z |
| 451.87500 | 465.77500 | NFM | Birmingham | Police |
| 451.87500 | 465.77500 | NFM | Boroughbridge | Police |
| 451.87500 | 465.77500 | NFM | Bournemouth | Police Football Security |
| 451.87500 | 465.77500 | NFM | Cambridge | Police Cambridge United Football Club Ch.29 |
| 451.87500 | 465.77500 | NFM | City of London | Police |
| 451.87500 | 465.77500 | NFM | Cosham | Police |
| 451.87500 | 465.77500 | NFM | England & Wales | Police Channel 29 |
| 451.87500 | 465.77500 | NFM | Farnborough | Police Air Show Security |
| 451.87500 | 465.77500 | NFM | Gloucester | Police |
| 451.87500 | 465.77500 | NFM | Kent | Police SOS N. Ireland Residence Ch.29 |
| 451.87500 | 465.77500 | NFM | Lakenheath | Police |
| 451.87500 | 465.77500 | NFM | Lancashire | Police Emergency Channel |
| 451.87500 | 465.77500 | NFM | Leeds | Police Observation |
| 451.87500 | 465.77500 | NFM | Leicester, Wigston | Police |
| 451.87500 | 465.77500 | NFM | Liverpool | Police Hooligan Van |

| Base | Mobile | Mode | Location | User and Notes |
|------|--------|------|----------|----------------|
| 451.87500 | 465.77500 | NFM | Northumberland | Police Mobile (M2LBX+Y) |
| 451.87500 | 465.77500 | NFM | Peterborough | Police Crowd Control |
| 451.87500 | 465.77500 | NFM | Portsmouth | Police |
| 451.87500 | 465.77500 | NFM | Rayleigh | Police Ch.1 |
| 451.87500 | 465.77500 | NFM | Southend | Police |
| 451.87500 | 465.77500 | NFM | Southsea | Police |
| 451.87500 | 465.77500 | NFM | Suffolk | Police Special Events |
| 451.87500 | 465.77500 | NFM | Thames Valley | Police |
| 451.87500 | 465.77500 | NFM | Warwickshire | Police (YJ) |
| 451.87500 | 465.77500 | NFM | Wigston | Police (CA/W) |
| 451.87500 | 465.77500 | NFM | Wolverhampton | Police |
| 451.90000 | 465.80000 | NFM | Bury | Police |
| 451.90000 | 465.80000 | NFM | Camberley | Police (NC) Ch.30 |
| 451.90000 | 465.80000 | NFM | Colchester | Military Prison |
| 451.90000 | 465.80000 | NFM | Coventry South | Police PNC checks (M2YMM) |
| 451.90000 | 465.80000 | NFM | Cwmbran, Gwent | Police - Bravo 3 Section |
| 451.90000 | 465.80000 | NFM | Darlington | Police |
| 451.90000 | 465.80000 | NFM | Dover | Police Special Branch (OSCAR) Ch 30 |
| 451.90000 | 465.80000 | NFM | Egham | Police (NE) |
| 451.90000 | 465.80000 | NFM | England & Wales | Police Channel 30 |
| 451.90000 | 465.80000 | NFM | Fletchamstead | Police |
| 451.90000 | 465.80000 | NFM | Folkestone | Police Special Branch |
| 451.90000 | 465.80000 | NFM | Holywell | Police |
| 451.90000 | 465.80000 | NFM | Horsforth | Police (AB) |
| 451.90000 | 465.80000 | NFM | Horsforth | Police Ch.30 |
| 451.90000 | 465.80000 | NFM | Kirkby | Police (E3) Ch.30 |
| 451.90000 | 465.80000 | NFM | Leeds Horsforth | Police |
| 451.90000 | 465.80000 | NFM | Liverpool Kirby | Police |
| 451.90000 | 465.80000 | NFM | London | HM Prison Holloway |
| 451.90000 | 465.80000 | NFM | London | HM Prison Pentonville (JP) Ch.30 |
| 451.90000 | 465.80000 | NFM | Manchester, Birch | Police |
| 451.90000 | 465.80000 | NFM | Manchester, Motorway Post | Police |
| 451.90000 | 465.80000 | NFM | Manchester, Prestwich | Police |
| 451.90000 | 465.80000 | NFM | Manchester, Radcliffe | Police |
| 451.90000 | 465.80000 | NFM | Manchester, Ramsbottom | Police |
| 451.90000 | 465.80000 | NFM | Manchester, Whitefield | Police |
| 451.90000 | 465.80000 | NFM | Medway | Police (DZ/ BA/ BC) Ch.30 |
| 451.90000 | 465.80000 | NFM | Melton Mowbray | Police Ch.30 |
| 451.90000 | 465.80000 | NFM | Mostyn | Police |
| 451.90000 | 465.80000 | NFM | Newcastle | Police |
| 451.90000 | 465.80000 | NFM | Ormskirk | Police |
| 451.90000 | 465.80000 | NFM | Portsmouth, central | Police Scrambled Ch.30 |
| 451.90000 | 465.80000 | NFM | Southend | Police |
| 451.90000 | 465.80000 | NFM | Thames Valley | Police |
| 451.90000 | 465.80000 | NFM | Wednesfield | Police (M2YMG) |
| 451.90000 | 465.80000 | NFM | Wolverhampton | Police (GX) Ch.30 |
| 451.92500 | 465.82500 | NFM | Bedford | Police Ch 31 (C/G) |
| 451.92500 | 465.82500 | NFM | Birmingham | Police |
| 451.92500 | 465.82500 | NFM | Blackpool | Police Divisional HQ |
| 451.92500 | 465.82500 | NFM | Bracknell | Police (M2CH) |
| 451.92500 | 465.82500 | NFM | Braintree | Police |
| 451.92500 | 465.82500 | NFM | Buckingham | Police (DB) |
| 451.92500 | 465.82500 | NFM | Buckley | Police |
| 451.92500 | 465.82500 | NFM | Caergwrle | Police |
| 451.92500 | 465.82500 | NFM | Coalville | Police (NORTH DESK) Ch.31 |
| 451.92500 | 465.82500 | NFM | Crowthorne | Police (M2CF) |

| Base | Mobile | Mode | Location | User and Notes |
|------|--------|------|----------|----------------|
| 451.92500 | 465.82500 | NFM | Dorchester | Police |
| 451.92500 | 465.82500 | NFM | Dorking | Police |
| 451.92500 | 465.82500 | NFM | Downham Market | Police (SIERRA) Ch.31 |
| 451.92500 | 465.82500 | NFM | Ely | Police |
| 451.92500 | 465.82500 | NFM | England & Wales | Police Channel 31 |
| 451.92500 | 465.82500 | NFM | Hackenthorpe | Police (E1) |
| 451.92500 | 465.82500 | NFM | Hatfield | Police (BHA) Ch.31 |
| 451.92500 | 465.82500 | NFM | Holbeck | Police (CA) Ch.31 |
| 451.92500 | 465.82500 | NFM | Hungerford | Police (FB) |
| 451.92500 | 465.82500 | NFM | Kirby | Police |
| 451.92500 | 465.82500 | NFM | Lancaster | HM Prison |
| 451.92500 | 465.82500 | NFM | Langley | Police |
| 451.92500 | 465.82500 | NFM | Loughborough | Police (NORTH PARK)Ch.31 |
| 451.92500 | 465.82500 | NFM | Manchester, Eccles | Police |
| 451.92500 | 465.82500 | NFM | Manchester, Hr. Broughton | Police |
| 451.92500 | 465.82500 | NFM | Manchester, Little Hulton | Police |
| 451.92500 | 465.82500 | NFM | Manchester, Pendleton | Police |
| 451.92500 | 465.82500 | NFM | Manchester, Salford | Police |
| 451.92500 | 465.82500 | NFM | Manchester, Swinton | Police |
| 451.92500 | 465.82500 | NFM | Manchester, Walkden | Police |
| 451.92500 | 465.82500 | NFM | Milton Keynes | Police |
| 451.02600 | 465.82500 | NFM | Morley | Police (CC) Ch.31 |
| 451.92500 | 465.82500 | NFM | Newbury (FA) | Police |
| 451.92500 | 465.82500 | NFM | Newcastle | Police (M2LBB1) |
| 451.92500 | 465.82500 | NFM | Newport Pagnell | Police (DD) |
| 451.92500 | 465.82500 | NFM | Northallerton | Police |
| 451.92500 | 465.82500 | NFM | Redhill | Police (ER) |
| 451.92500 | 465.82500 | NFM | Reigate | Police (ER) Ch.31 |
| 451.92500 | 465.82500 | NFM | Saxmundham | Police (G8C) Ch.31 |
| 451.92500 | 465.82500 | NFM | Southend | Police relay (HD) Ch.31 |
| 451.92500 | 465.82500 | NFM | Stafford | Police Ch.31 |
| 451.92500 | 465.82500 | NFM | Thatcham | Police |
| 451.92500 | 465.82500 | NFM | Welwyn Garden City | Police |
| 451.92500 | 465.82500 | NFM | Wolverton | Police |
| 451.93750 | 465.83750 | NFM | London | Police divisions G/ H/ J/ K trunked |
| 451.95000 | 465.85000 | NFM | Aldershot | Police |
| 451.95000 | 465.85000 | NFM | Ash | Police |
| 451.95000 | 465.85000 | NFM | Bewdley | Police |
| 451.95000 | 465.85000 | NFM | Birmingham, Kings Heath | Police |
| 451.95000 | 465.85000 | NFM | Blackpool | Police |
| 451.95000 | 465.85000 | NFM | Bournemouth | Police |
| 451.95000 | 465.85000 | NFM | Brownhills | Police |
| 451.95000 | 465.85000 | NFM | Dorset | Police (QC) Ch.32 |
| 451.95000 | 465.85000 | NFM | Douglas, Strathclyde | Police |
| 451.95000 | 465.85000 | NFM | Ely | Police Ch.32 |
| 451.95000 | 465.85000 | NFM | England & Wales | Police Channel 32 |
| 451.95000 | 465.85000 | NFM | Exeter | Police CID Ch 32 |
| 451.95000 | 465.85000 | NFM | Farnborough | Police Air Show Security |
| 451.95000 | 465.85000 | NFM | Forest Hill | Police (M2LBC4)/(I2) |
| 451.95000 | 465.85000 | NFM | Garforth | Police Ch.32 |
| 451.95000 | 465.85000 | NFM | Hitchin | Police MASC in clear (GH) Ch.32 |
| 451.95000 | 465.85000 | NFM | Kings Heath | Police MASC (M2YMB) Ch.32 |
| 451.95000 | 465.85000 | NFM | Lancashire | Police Spare Channel |
| 451.95000 | 465.85000 | NFM | Lichfield | Police MASC Ch.32 |
| 451.95000 | 465.85000 | NFM | Long Benton | Police |
| 451.95000 | 465.85000 | NFM | March | Police Ch.32 |

| Base | Mobile | Mode | Location | User and Notes |
|---|---|---|---|---|
| 451.95000 | 465.85000 | NFM | Mytchett | Police |
| 451.95000 | 465.85000 | NFM | Newark | Police MASC Ch.32 |
| 451.95000 | 465.85000 | NFM | Plymouth | Police Response Team (JULIET) Ch.32 |
| 451.95000 | 465.85000 | NFM | Portsmouth | HM Prison Kingston (M2PZ) |
| 451.95000 | 465.85000 | NFM | Redditch | Police Ch.32 |
| 451.95000 | 465.85000 | NFM | Southend | Police |
| 451.95000 | 465.85000 | NFM | Stourport | Police |
| 451.95000 | 465.85000 | NFM | Thames Valley | Police |
| 451.95000 | 465.85000 | NFM | Wetherby | Police Ch.32 |
| 451.95000 | 465.85000 | NFM | Whittlesey | Police Ch.32 |
| 451.95000 | 465.85000 | NFM | Widnes | Police (D1) |
| 451.96250 | 465.86200 | NFM | London | Police divisions P/ R/ M and part of Z |
| 451.97500 | 456.87500 | NFM | Manchester | Police (C3) Ch.9 |
| 451.97500 | 456.87500 | NFM | Nationwide | Local Authorities Emergency Network |
| 451.97500 | 465.87500 | NFM | Burnley | Police |
| 452.00000 | | NFM | Derbyshire | Police air support unit (HO88) Ch.95 |
| 452.00000 | | NFM | England & Wales | Police helicopter air/ground Ch.95 |
| 452.00000 | | NFM | Leyland | Police |
| 452.00000 | | NFM | Nottinghamshire | Police air support unit (HO88) Ch.95 |
| 452.00000 | | NFM | Thames Valley | Police air support unit (XA97 & XA99) covering Herts & Beds Ch.95 |
| 452.02500 | 465.92500 | NFM | Nationwide | Local Authorities Emergency Network |
| 452.05000 | | NFM | Avon | Police air support unit (QP99) Ch.96 |
| 452.05000 | | NFM | Derbyshire | Police air support unit (HO88) Ch.96 |
| 452.05000 | | NFM | England & Wales | Police helicopter air/ground Ch.96 |
| 452.05000 | 456.95000 | NFM | Nationwide | Local Authorities Emergency Network |
| 452.05000 | | NFM | Nottinghamshire | Police air support unit (HO88) Ch.96 |
| 452.05000 | | NFM | Thames Valley | Police air support unit (XA97 & XA99) covering Herts & Beds Ch.96 |
| 452.05000 | 465.95000 | NFM | Birmingham | Police |
| 452.05000 | 465.95000 | NFM | Skelmersdale | Police |
| 452.07500 | 465.97500 | NFM | Gloucester | Police |
| 452.07500 | 456.97500 | NFM | Humberside | Prison vans mobile/mobile |
| 452.10000 | 466.00000 | NFM | England & Wales | Police helicopter air/ground |
| 452.10000 | 466.00000 | NFM | Hampshire | Police air support (Boxer 10 Optica plane) air/ground links Ch.94 |
| 452.10000 | 466.00000 | NFM | Nationwide | Local Authorities Emergency Network |
| 452.10000 | 466.00000 | NFM | West Yorkshire | Police Helicopter (XRAY 99) |
| 452.12500 | 466.02500 | NFM | Nationwide | Local Authorities Emergency Network |
| 452.15000 | 466.05000 | NFM | Birmingham | Police |
| 452.15000 | 466.05000 | NFM | Brentwood | Police |
| 452.15000 | 466.05000 | NFM | London | Police air support unit (INDIA 98 /99) Ch.93 |
| 452.15000 | 466.05000 | NFM | Morecambe Bay | Police |
| 452.15000 | 466.05000 | NFM | Nationwide | Local Authorities Emergency Network |
| 452.15000 | 466.05000 | NFM | Sywell, Northants | Police Ch 93 (X55) |
| 452.15000 | 466.05000 | NFM | Thames Valley | Police Special Use |
| 452.15000 | 466.05000 | NFM | Warwickshire | Police air support unit (X55) Ch.93 |
| 452.16250 | 466.06250 | NFM | Hendon | Police Training College |
| 452.17500 | 466.07500 | NFM | Nationwide | Local Authorities Emergency Network |
| 452.17500 | 466.07500 | NFM | Preston | Police |
| 452.20000 | 466.10000 | NFM | Nationwide | Local Authorities Emergency Network |
| 452.22500 | 466.12500 | NFM | Blackburn | Police |
| 452.22500 | 466.12500 | NFM | Hendon | Police Training Centre (S) |
| 452.25000 | 466.15000 | NFM | England & Wales | Police Channel 73 |
| 452.25000 | 466.15000 | NFM | Reading | HM Remand Centre |
| 452.26250 | 466.16250 | NFM | Basildon | Police |

| Base | Mobile | Mode | Location | User and Notes |
|------|--------|------|----------|----------------|
| 452.26250 | 466.17250 | NFM | London | Police division X |
| 452.27500 | 465.17500 | NFM | Belper | Police Ch.57 |
| 452.27500 | 465.17500 | NFM | Droitwich | Police (CA) |
| 452.27500 | 465.17500 | NFM | England & Wales | Police Channel 57 |
| 452.27500 | 465.17500 | NFM | England & Wales | Police Reserve Channel A |
| 452.27500 | 465.17500 | NFM | Manchester, Chadderton | Police |
| 452.27500 | 465.17500 | NFM | Manchester, Failsworth | Police |
| 452.27500 | 465.17500 | NFM | Manchester, Royton | Police |
| 452.27500 | 465.17500 | NFM | Manchester, Uppermill | Police |
| 452.27500 | 465.17500 | NFM | Merseyside | Police armed (TH) |
| 452.27500 | 465.17500 | NFM | Oldham | Police |
| 452.27500 | 465.17500 | NFM | Thames Valley | Police |
| 452.30000 | 466.20000 | NFM | Bridgenorth | Police |
| 452.30000 | 466.20000 | NFM | England & Wales | Police Channel 60 |
| 452.30000 | 466.20000 | NFM | Manchester | Police |
| 452.30000 | 466.20000 | NFM | Northwich | Police |
| 452.30000 | 466.20000 | NFM | Nuneaton | Police Ch 60 |
| 452.30000 | 466.20000 | NFM | Portsmouth | Police Diplomatic Protection & Navy docks Ch.60 |
| 452.30000 | 466.20000 | NFM | Rayleigh | Police (JD) Ch.60 |
| 452.30000 | 466.20000 | NFM | Silverstone | David Coulthard to pits |
| 452.30000 | 466.20000 | NFM | Thames Valley | Police |
| 452.30000 | 466.20000 | NFM | Winsford | Police |
| 452.31250 | 466.21250 | NFM | London | Police divisions T/X |
| 452.31250 | 466.21250 | NFM | Southend | Police |
| 452.32500 | 466.22500 | NFM | Darwin | Police |
| 452.32500 | 466.22500 | NFM | England & Wales | Police Channel 74 |
| 452.32500 | 466.22500 | NFM | England & Wales | Police Radio Engineers |
| 452.32500 | 466.22500 | NFM | Manchester | Police |
| 452.32500 | 466.22500 | NFM | Thames Valley | Police Support Units |
| 452.33750 | 466.23750 | NFM | Kent | Police Ch.16 |
| 452.35000 | 466.25000 | NFM | Cannock | Police MASC Ch.59 |
| 452.35000 | 466.25000 | NFM | England & Wales | Police Channel 59 |
| 452.35000 | 466.25000 | NFM | Houghton | Police (O2) Encrypted |
| 452.35000 | 466.25000 | NFM | London | Police divisions T/X |
| 452.35000 | 466.25000 | NFM | Manchester, Ashton-U-Lyme | Police |
| 452.35000 | 466.25000 | NFM | Manchester, Denton | Police |
| 452.35000 | 466.25000 | NFM | Manchester, Droylsden | Police |
| 452.35000 | 466.25000 | NFM | Manchester, Hyde | Police |
| 452.35000 | 466.25000 | NFM | Manchester, Mottram | Police |
| 452.35000 | 466.25000 | NFM | Manchester, Stalybridge | Police |
| 452.35000 | 466.25000 | NFM | Newhaven | Police Ch.59 |
| 452.35000 | 466.25000 | NFM | Southend | Police |
| 452.35000 | 466.25000 | NFM | Thames Valley | Police |
| 452.35000 | 466.25000 | NFM | Thameside | Police |
| 452.36250 | 452.26250 | NFM | England & Wales | Fire Services Channel 2 |
| 452.37500 | 446.27500 | NFM | England & Wales | Police Tactical Firearms Unit Ch.76 |
| 452.37500 | 452.37500 | NFM | England & Wales | Police Tactical Firearms Unit Ch.75 |
| 452.37500 | 452.37500 | NFM | Jersey | Police Tactical Firearms Unit Ch 1 |
| 452.37500 | 452.37500 | NFM | Jersey | Police Tactical Firearms Unit Ch 3 |
| 452.37500 | 452.37500 | NFM | Scarborough | Police CID |
| 452.37500 | 466.27500 | NFM | City of London | Police tactical firearms units Ch.19 |
| 452.37500 | 466.27500 | NFM | County Durham | HM Prison  Frankland |
| 452.37500 | 466.27500 | NFM | England & Wales | Police Channel 76 |
| 452.37500 | 466.27500 | NFM | Jersey | Police Tactical Firearms Unit Ch 2 |
| 452.37500 | 466.27500 | NFM | London | Police Tactical Firearms Unit Ch.77 |

| Base | Mobile | Mode | Location | User and Notes |
|---|---|---|---|---|
| 452.40000 | 466.30000 | NFM | Allestree | Police (OSCAR 3) Ch.33 |
| 452.40000 | 466.30000 | NFM | Arundel | HM Prison Ford (open prison) Ch.33 |
| 452.40000 | 466.30000 | NFM | Attercliffe | Police Ch.33 |
| 452.40000 | 466.30000 | NFM | Birmingham | HM Prison Digbeth |
| 452.40000 | 466.30000 | NFM | Birmingham Airport | Police |
| 452.40000 | 466.30000 | NFM | Birmingham Central | Police (M2YMF) Ch.33 |
| 452.40000 | 466.30000 | NFM | Bolton | Police |
| 452.40000 | 466.30000 | NFM | Bootle | Police (B1) Ch.33 |
| 452.40000 | 466.30000 | NFM | Bungay | Police (C8B) Ch.33 |
| 452.40000 | 466.30000 | NFM | Burnley | Police |
| 452.40000 | 466.30000 | NFM | Cambridge | Police |
| 452.40000 | 466.30000 | NFM | Canterbury | HM Prison Canterbury Ch.33 |
| 452.40000 | 466.30000 | NFM | Crosby | Police (B3) |
| 452.40000 | 466.30000 | NFM | Derby | Police (OSCAR 3) Ch.33 |
| 452.40000 | 466.30000 | NFM | Dereham | Police (M) Ch.33 |
| 452.40000 | 466.30000 | NFM | East Dereham | Police |
| 452.40000 | 466.30000 | NFM | East Sussex | HM Prison |
| 452.40000 | 466.30000 | NFM | England & Wales | Police Channel 33 |
| 452.40000 | 466.30000 | NFM | Epping | Police (GE) Ch.33 |
| 452.40000 | 466.30000 | NFM | Exeter | Police (Delta Control) |
| 452.40000 | 466.30000 | NFM | Gloucester | Police |
| 452.40000 | 466.30000 | NFM | Great Yarmouth | Police Ch.33 |
| 452.40000 | 466.30000 | NFM | Harpenden | Police (BHN) Ch.33 |
| 452.40000 | 466.30000 | NFM | Hebburn | Police (L4) |
| 452.40000 | 466.30000 | NFM | Holmfirth | Police Ch.33 |
| 452.40000 | 466.30000 | NFM | Huddersfield | Police (EA) Ch.33 |
| 452.40000 | 466.30000 | NFM | Hull | Police Ch.33 |
| 452.40000 | 466.30000 | NFM | Humberside | Police |
| 452.40000 | 466.30000 | NFM | Hunstanton | Police (INDIA) Ch.33 |
| 452.40000 | 466.30000 | NFM | Huntingdon | Police |
| 452.40000 | 466.30000 | NFM | Jarrow | Police (M2LBE2) |
| 452.40000 | 466.30000 | NFM | Lancashire | Police Drug Squad |
| 452.40000 | 466.30000 | NFM | Lancaster | HM Prison |
| 452.40000 | 466.30000 | NFM | Leicester | HM Prison (OJ) Ch.33 |
| 452.40000 | 466.30000 | NFM | Lewes | HM Prison Lewes Ch.33 |
| 452.40000 | 466.30000 | NFM | Liverpool Marsh Lane | Police |
| 452.40000 | 466.30000 | NFM | London | HM Prison Wormwood Scrubs |
| 452.40000 | 466.30000 | NFM | London | Police House of Commons (PATRIOT) Ch.33 |
| 452.40000 | 466.30000 | NFM | Maghull | Police |
| 452.40000 | 466.30000 | NFM | Manchester, Arndale Centre | Police |
| 452.40000 | 466.30000 | NFM | Manchester, Bootle Street | Police |
| 452.40000 | 466.30000 | NFM | Manchester, City Centre | Police |
| 452.40000 | 466.30000 | NFM | Manchester, Newton Street | Police |
| 452.40000 | 466.30000 | NFM | March | HM Prison Whitemoor (VX) Ch.33 |
| 452.40000 | 466.30000 | NFM | Merseyside | Police HQ Div B (Encrypted) |
| 452.40000 | 466.30000 | NFM | Needham Market | Police Ch.33 |
| 452.40000 | 466.30000 | NFM | Neots | Police |
| 452.40000 | 466.30000 | NFM | Newcastle | Police |
| 452.40000 | 466.30000 | NFM | Norwich | Police |
| 452.40000 | 466.30000 | NFM | Padiham | Police |
| 452.40000 | 466.30000 | NFM | Pickering | Police |
| 452.40000 | 466.30000 | NFM | Plymouth | Traffic Wardens (EXETER DELTA) Ch.33 |
| 452.40000 | 466.30000 | NFM | Portland Bill | HM Borstal |
| 452.40000 | 466.30000 | NFM | Portsmouth | Police (Encrypted) |
| 452.40000 | 466.30000 | NFM | Sheffield Attercliffe | Police (F3) |
| 452.40000 | 466.30000 | NFM | Sheringham | Police Ch.33 |

| Base | Mobile | Mode | Location | User and Notes |
|------|--------|------|----------|----------------|
| 452.40000 | 466.30000 | NFM | Shipley | Police |
| 452.40000 | 466.30000 | NFM | Southend | Police |
| 452.40000 | 466.30000 | NFM | St Albans | Police |
| 452.40000 | 466.30000 | NFM | Stafford | HM Prison |
| 452.40000 | 466.30000 | NFM | Swansea | HM Prison |
| 452.40000 | 466.30000 | NFM | Swindon | Police |
| 452.40000 | 466.30000 | NFM | Thames Valley | Police |
| 452.40000 | 466.30000 | NFM | Thetford | Police Ch.33 |
| 452.40000 | 466.30000 | NFM | Woodbridge | Police (W8A) Ch.33 |
| 452.40000 | 466.30000 | NFM | York | Police (AY) and Traffic Wardens Ch.33 |
| 452.40000 | 466.40000 | NFM | St Austell | Police |
| 452.40000 | 466.40000 | NFM | Windermere | Police |
| 452.42500 | 466.32000 | NFM | London | Notting Hill Carnival 7 |
| 452.42500 | 466.32500 | NFM | Bedworth | Police |
| 452.42500 | 466.32500 | NFM | Botesdale | Police (D8B) Ch.34 |
| 452.42500 | 466.32500 | NFM | Bradford, Queensberry | Police |
| 452.42500 | 466.32500 | NFM | Braintree | Police |
| 452.42500 | 466.32500 | NFM | Bridgend | Police |
| 452.42500 | 466.32500 | NFM | Channel Tunnel | French Police Ch.34 |
| 452.42500 | 466.32500 | NFM | Clare | Police Ch.34 |
| 452.42500 | 466.32500 | NFM | Derby, South West | Police (O2) |
| 452.42500 | 466.32500 | NFM | Eccleshall | Police (HA) Ch.34 |
| 452.42500 | 466.32500 | NFM | Ebbw Vale | Police (E) Ch.34 |
| 452.42500 | 466.32500 | NFM | England & Wales | Police Channel 34 |
| 452.42500 | 466.32500 | NFM | Fareham | Police (CH) Ch.34 |
| 452.42500 | 466.32500 | NFM | Gosport | Police |
| 452.42500 | 466.32500 | NFM | Hadleigh | Police (U8A) Ch.34 |
| 452.42500 | 466.32500 | NFM | Ipswich | Police Ipswich Football Club Ch.34 |
| 452.42500 | 466.32500 | NFM | Lakenheath | Police Ch.34 |
| 452.42500 | 466.32500 | NFM | Leyland | Police |
| 452.42500 | 466.32500 | NFM | Littleover | Police (OSCAR) Ch.34 |
| 452.42500 | 466.32500 | NFM | London | HM Prison  Wormwood Scrubs |
| 452.42500 | 466.32500 | NFM | Malton | Police |
| 452.42500 | 466.32500 | NFM | Manchester, Altrincham | Police |
| 452.42500 | 466.32500 | NFM | Manchester, Sale | Police |
| 452.42500 | 466.32500 | NFM | Manchester, Stretford | Police |
| 452.42500 | 466.32500 | NFM | Manchester, Trafford | Police (M2) Ch.34 |
| 452.42500 | 466.32500 | NFM | Manchester, Urmston | Police |
| 452.42500 | 466.32500 | NFM | Manningham | Police |
| 452.42500 | 466.32500 | NFM | Peartree | Police (OSCAR) Ch.34 |
| 452.42500 | 466.32500 | NFM | Portsmouth | Police |
| 452.42500 | 466.32500 | NFM | Preston | Police Ch.34 |
| 452.42500 | 466.32500 | NFM | Preston HQ | Police (BD) |
| 452.42500 | 466.32500 | NFM | Scarborough | Police (DS) Ch.34 |
| 452.42500 | 466.32500 | NFM | Stockton on Tees | Police |
| 452.42500 | 466.32500 | NFM | Swadlincote | Police (OSCAR 2) Ch.34 |
| 452.42500 | 466.32500 | NFM | Thames Valley | Police |
| 452.42500 | 466.32500 | NFM | Wombwell | Police (B2) |
| 452.43750 | 466.33750 | NFM | Biggin Hill | Police Ch.34 |
| 452.43750 | 466.33750 | NFM | Chislehurst | Police Ch.34 |
| 452.43750 | 466.33750 | NFM | Orpington | Police Ch.34 |
| 452.45000 | 466.35000 | NFM | Amersham | Police (AD) |
| 452.45000 | 466.35000 | NFM | Birmingham | Police Ch.35 |
| 452.45000 | 466.35000 | NFM | Birmingham, Northfield | Police MASC Ch.35 |
| 452.45000 | 466.35000 | NFM | Boroughbridge | Police |
| 452.45000 | 466.35000 | NFM | Bradford, Odsall | Police |

| Base | Mobile | Mode | Location | User and Notes |
|------|--------|------|----------|----------------|
| 452.45000 | 466.35000 | NFM | Bridgend | Police |
| 452.45000 | 466.35000 | NFM | Bridlington | Police |
| 452.45000 | 466.35000 | NFM | Cheltenham | Police (A) Ch.35 |
| 452.45000 | 466.35000 | NFM | Chesham | Police (AH) |
| 452.45000 | 466.35000 | NFM | Colwyn Bay | Police |
| 452.45000 | 466.35000 | NFM | Deal | Police |
| 452.45000 | 466.35000 | NFM | Derby, Central | Police |
| 452.45000 | 466.35000 | NFM | Digbeth | Police |
| 452.45000 | 466.35000 | NFM | Dorking | Police (ED) |
| 452.45000 | 466.35000 | NFM | Dover | Police |
| 452.45000 | 466.35000 | NFM | Eastbourne | Police (M2KBEO+EE) Ch.35 |
| 452.45000 | 466.35000 | NFM | Egbaston | Police (M2YMB) Ch.35 |
| 452.45000 | 466.35000 | NFM | Ely | Police |
| 452.45000 | 466.35000 | NFM | England & Wales | Police Channel 35 |
| 452.45000 | 466.35000 | NFM | Exeter | Police Ch.35 |
| 452.45000 | 466.35000 | NFM | Exmouth | Police |
| 452.45000 | 466.35000 | NFM | Farnborough | Police |
| 452.45000 | 466.35000 | NFM | Farringdon | Police (N1) Encrypted |
| 452.45000 | 466.35000 | NFM | Fleet | Police |
| 452.45000 | 466.35000 | NFM | Folkestone | Police |
| 452.45000 | 466.35000 | NFM | Frome | Police |
| 452.45000 | 466.35000 | NFM | Gorleston-on-Sea | Police Ch.35 |
| 452.45000 | 466.35000 | NFM | Great Yarmouth | Police |
| 452.45000 | 466.35000 | NFM | Halewood | Police |
| 452.45000 | 466.35000 | NFM | Herefordshire | Police Ch.35 links 155.125 Ch.2 |
| 452.45000 | 466.35000 | NFM | Hillsborough | Police |
| 452.45000 | 466.35000 | NFM | Hull | Police |
| 452.45000 | 466.35000 | NFM | Huntingdon | Police Ch.35 |
| 452.45000 | 466.35000 | NFM | Isle of Grain | Police (BA) Ch.35 |
| 452.45000 | 466.35000 | NFM | Knutsford | Police |
| 452.45000 | 466.35000 | NFM | Leatherhead | Police (EL) |
| 452.45000 | 466.35000 | NFM | Liverpool | Police Ch.35 |
| 452.45000 | 466.35000 | NFM | London, Chequers | Police (AZ) |
| 452.45000 | 466.35000 | NFM | Manchester, Heywood | Police |
| 452.45000 | 466.35000 | NFM | Manchester, Kirkholt | Police |
| 452.45000 | 466.35000 | NFM | Manchester, Littleborough | Police |
| 452.45000 | 466.35000 | NFM | Manchester, Middleton | Police |
| 452.45000 | 466.35000 | NFM | Manchester, Milnrow | Police |
| 452.45000 | 466.35000 | NFM | Medway | Police |
| 452.45000 | 466.35000 | NFM | Medway Towns | Police |
| 452.45000 | 466.35000 | NFM | North Wales | Police |
| 452.45000 | 466.35000 | NFM | Norwich Rural | Police |
| 452.45000 | 466.35000 | NFM | Nottingham, Radford Rd | Police |
| 452.45000 | 466.35000 | NFM | Odsal | Police (GC) Ch.35 |
| 452.45000 | 466.35000 | NFM | Rochdale | Police |
| 452.45000 | 466.35000 | NFM | Rochester | Police (BA) Ch.35 |
| 452.45000 | 466.35000 | NFM | Ruabon | Police |
| 452.45000 | 466.35000 | NFM | Ryhope | Police (N2) Encrypted |
| 452.45000 | 466.35000 | NFM | Salisbury | Police Ch.35 |
| 452.45000 | 466.35000 | NFM | Sheffield, Hammerton Rd | Police (F1) |
| 452.45000 | 466.35000 | NFM | Speke | Police (F1) Ch.35 |
| 452.45000 | 466.35000 | NFM | Stroud | Police |
| 452.45000 | 466.35000 | NFM | Sunderland | Police (M2LBF2) |
| 452.45000 | 466.35000 | NFM | Thirsk | Police |
| 452.45000 | 466.35000 | NFM | Westbury | Police |
| 452.45000 | 466.35000 | NFM | Wilmslow | Police (C2) |

| Base | Mobile | Mode | Location | User and Notes |
|------|--------|------|----------|----------------|
| 452.45000 | 466.35000 | NFM | Wisbech | Police Ch.35 |
| 452.45000 | 466.35000 | NFM | Worcester | Police |
| 452.45000 | 466.35000 | NFM | Workington | Police |
| 452.45000 | 466.35000 | NFM | Wymondham | Police Ch.35 |
| 452.46250 | 466.36250 | NFM | London | Police division X |
| 452.46250 | 466.36250 | NFM | Northumbria | Police Car-Car (M2LB) |
| 452.47500 | 466.37500 | NFM | Beumont Leys | Police |
| 452.47500 | 466.37500 | NFM | Bieleys | Police (W) |
| 452.47500 | 466.37500 | NFM | Birmingham, Brierley Hill | Police (M2YMJ) |
| 452.47500 | 466.37500 | NFM | Bootle | Police |
| 452.47500 | 466.37500 | NFM | Brierley Hill | Police |
| 452.47500 | 466.37500 | NFM | Brighton | Police (M2KBCO+CB) |
| 452.47500 | 466.37500 | NFM | Broadmoor | Secure Prison Hospital Ch.36 |
| 452.47500 | 466.37500 | NFM | Caterham | Police (EC) Ch.36 |
| 452.47500 | 466.37500 | NFM | Chelmsley Wood | Police |
| 452.47500 | 466.37500 | NFM | Durham | HM Prison  Frankland (M2NE) |
| 452.47500 | 466.37500 | NFM | England & Wales | Police Channel 36 |
| 452.47500 | 466.37500 | NFM | Farnborough | Police Air Show Security |
| 452.47500 | 466.37500 | NFM | Hotley | HM Prison Bullwood Hall (KH) Ch.36 |
| 452.47500 | 466.37500 | NFM | Kingswinford | Police |
| 452.47500 | 466.37500 | NFM | Leicester | Police Ch.36 relaying 451.175 |
| 452.47500 | 466.37500 | NFM | New Forest | Police |
| 452.47500 | 466.37500 | NFM | North Watford | Police |
| 452.47500 | 466.37500 | NFM | Ormskirk | Police |
| 452.47500 | 466.37500 | NFM | Oxley | Police |
| 452.47500 | 466.37500 | NFM | Oxted | Police |
| 452.47500 | 466.37500 | NFM | Rawmarsh | Police Ch.36 |
| 452.47500 | 466.37500 | NFM | Shrewsbury | Police |
| 452.47500 | 466.37500 | NFM | Skelmersdale | Police |
| 452.47500 | 466.37500 | NFM | Thames Valley | Police |
| 452.47500 | 466.37500 | NFM | Watford, west | Police (CN) Ch.36 |
| 452.50000 | 446.40000 | NFM | Aldershot | Police (OSCAR 1) Ch.37 |
| 452.50000 | 466.40000 | NFM | Ashford | HM Remand Centre (JC) Ch.37 |
| 452.50000 | 466.40000 | NFM | Barton on Humber | Police |
| 452.50000 | 466.40000 | NFM | Bicester | HM Prison  Bullingdon |
| 452.50000 | 466.40000 | NFM | Birmingham | Police |
| 452.50000 | 466.40000 | NFM | Bishop Auckland | Police (AA) |
| 452.50000 | 466.40000 | NFM | Braintree | Police |
| 452.50000 | 466.40000 | NFM | Brighton | Police |
| 452.50000 | 466.40000 | NFM | Bristol | Police (BSI) Ch.37 |
| 452.50000 | 466.40000 | NFM | Byker | Police (E1) |
| 452.50000 | 466.40000 | NFM | Cardiff | Police radio engineers test channel |
| 452.50000 | 466.40000 | NFM | Carmarthen | Police |
| 452.50000 | 466.40000 | NFM | Chelmsford | HM Prison  Chelmsford (PG) |
| 452.50000 | 466.40000 | NFM | Chevening, Kent | Police Foreign Secretary' Residence Ch.37 |
| 452.50000 | 466.40000 | NFM | Clacton-on-Sea | Police (EN) Ch.37 |
| 452.50000 | 466.40000 | NFM | Colchester | Prison |
| 452.50000 | 466.40000 | NFM | Colney Heath, Herts | Police (FLC) Ch.37 |
| 452.50000 | 466.40000 | NFM | Dartford | Police (CB) Ch.37 |
| 452.50000 | 466.40000 | NFM | East Grinstead | Police (NE) Ch.37 |
| 452.50000 | 466.40000 | NFM | England & Wales | Police Channel 37 |
| 452.50000 | 466.40000 | NFM | England & Wales | Police Special Use Channel 88 |
| 452.50000 | 466.40000 | NFM | Exeter | Police CID Ch 37 |
| 452.50000 | 466.40000 | NFM | Farnborough | Police |
| 452.50000 | 466.40000 | NFM | Fleet | Police (OSCAR 1) Ch.37 |
| 452.50000 | 466.40000 | NFM | Framlingham | Police (J8F) Ch.37 |

| Base | Mobile | Mode | Location | User and Notes |
|------|--------|------|----------|----------------|
| 452.50000 | 466.40000 | NFM | Great Yarmouth | Police Ch.37 |
| 452.50000 | 466.40000 | NFM | Hailsham | Police (M2KBEO+EA) Ch.37 |
| 452.50000 | 466.40000 | NFM | Harbourne | Police (M2YMC) Ch.37 |
| 452.50000 | 466.40000 | NFM | Harpenden | Police |
| 452.50000 | 466.40000 | NFM | Haverfordwest | Police |
| 452.50000 | 466.40000 | NFM | Heaton | Police (E3) |
| 452.50000 | 466.40000 | NFM | Hedingley | Police |
| 452.50000 | 466.40000 | NFM | Hove | Police (M2KBCO+CH) |
| 452.50000 | 466.40000 | NFM | Kirkdale | Police |
| 452.50000 | 466.40000 | NFM | Ladywood | Police |
| 452.50000 | 466.40000 | NFM | Lancashire | Police Spare Channel |
| 452.50000 | 466.40000 | NFM | Leeds, Westwood | Police |
| 452.50000 | 466.40000 | NFM | Leicester, city centre | Police covert - private CCTV operators |
| 452.50000 | 466.40000 | NFM | Letchwood | Police |
| 452.50000 | 466.40000 | NFM | Liverpool, City Centre | Police (CI) Ch.37 |
| 452.50000 | 466.40000 | NFM | London | HM Prison  Brixton (JX) |
| 452.50000 | 466.40000 | NFM | Longsight | Police |
| 452.50000 | 466.40000 | NFM | Loughborough | Police (B/L) Ch.37 |
| 452.50000 | 466.40000 | NFM | Manchester | Police |
| 452.50000 | 466.40000 | NFM | Manchester Airport | Police |
| 452.50000 | 466.40000 | NFM | Manchester, Baguley | Police |
| 452.50000 | 466.40000 | NFM | Manchester, Benchill | Police |
| 452.50000 | 466.40000 | NFM | Manchester, Chorlton | Police |
| 452.50000 | 466.40000 | NFM | Manchester, Didsbury | Police |
| 452.50000 | 466.40000 | NFM | Manchester, Northenden | Police |
| 452.50000 | 466.40000 | NFM | Manchester, Northern Moor | Police |
| 452.50000 | 466.40000 | NFM | Manchester, Rusholme | Police (D1) Ch.37 |
| 452.50000 | 466.40000 | NFM | Manchester, Withington | Police |
| 452.50000 | 466.40000 | NFM | March | Police |
| 452.50000 | 466.40000 | NFM | Market Drayton | Police (JH) |
| 452.50000 | 466.40000 | NFM | Merseyside | Police HQ Div A (Encrypted) |
| 452.50000 | 466.40000 | NFM | Nationwide | Police Airborne |
| 452.50000 | 466.40000 | NFM | Nationwide | Police Special Use |
| 452.50000 | 466.40000 | NFM | Newcastle | Police (M2LBB2) |
| 452.50000 | 466.40000 | NFM | Newport | Police Ch 2 |
| 452.50000 | 466.40000 | NFM | Newtown | Police |
| 452.50000 | 466.40000 | NFM | Northampton | Police Ch 37 |
| 452.50000 | 466.40000 | NFM | Preston | HM Prison |
| 452.50000 | 466.40000 | NFM | Redcar | Police |
| 452.50000 | 466.40000 | NFM | Ross on Wye | Police Ch.37 |
| 452.50000 | 466.40000 | NFM | South Killingholme | Police |
| 452.50000 | 466.40000 | NFM | Sowerby Bridge | Police Ch.37 |
| 452.50000 | 466.40000 | NFM | St Albans | Police (FH) Ch.37 |
| 452.50000 | 466.40000 | NFM | Stockport | Police |
| 452.50000 | 466.40000 | NFM | Swaffham | Police (J) Ch.37 |
| 452.50000 | 466.40000 | NFM | Swanley | Police (CB) Ch.37 |
| 452.50000 | 466.40000 | NFM | Swanscombe | Police |
| 452.50000 | 466.40000 | NFM | Tenby | Police control Ch.37 |
| 452.50000 | 466.40000 | NFM | Thames Valley | Police |
| 452.50000 | 466.40000 | NFM | Todmorden | Police (FD) Ch.37 |
| 452.50000 | 466.40000 | NFM | Walker | Police (E2) |
| 452.50000 | 466.40000 | NFM | Walton | Police (C4) |
| 452.50000 | 466.40000 | NFM | Warminster | Police Ch.37 |
| 452.50000 | 466.40000 | NFM | Weetwood | Police (AA) Ch.37 |
| 452.50000 | 466.40000 | NFM | Wellington | Police (JA) |
| 452.50000 | 466.40000 | NFM | Wem | Police (JF) |

| Base | Mobile | Mode | Location | User and Notes |
|------|--------|------|----------|----------------|
| 452.50000 | 466.40000 | NFM | West Kingsdown | Police |
| 452.50000 | 466.40000 | NFM | Weymouth | Police |
| 452.50000 | 466.40000 | NFM | Whitchurch | Police (JG) |
| 452.50000 | 466.40000 | NFM | Winterton | Police |
| 452.50000 | 466.40000 | NFM | Worcester | Police (CA) Ch.37 |
| 452.52500 | 466.42500 | NFM | Birmingham | Police |
| 452.52500 | 466.42500 | NFM | England & Wales | Police Channel 38 |
| 452.52500 | 466.42500 | NFM | Leeds | Police CID |
| 452.52500 | 466.42500 | NFM | Tetbury | Police Ch.38 |
| 452.53750 | 466.43750 | NFM | England & Wales | Fire/Police Link Repeater Ch 8 |
| 452.53750 | 466.43750 | NFM | London | Police divisions L/V trunked |
| 452.55000 | 466.45000 | NFM | Banbury | Police (BD) Ch.39 |
| 452.55000 | 466.45000 | NFM | Barnstable | Police |
| 452.55000 | 466.45000 | NFM | Benfleet | Police (JD) Ch.39 |
| 452.55000 | 466.45000 | NFM | Bicester | Police (BE) Ch.39 |
| 452.55000 | 466.45000 | NFM | Birmingham | Police |
| 452.55000 | 466.45000 | NFM | Canvey Island | Police (JC) Ch.36 |
| 452.55000 | 466.45000 | NFM | Carlisle | Police Encrypted |
| 452.55000 | 466.45000 | NFM | Carlton | Police |
| 452.55000 | 466.45000 | NFM | Dalton | Police |
| 452.55000 | 466.45000 | NFM | Dishforth | Police |
| 452.55000 | 466.45000 | NFM | Ditton Marsh | Police Ch.39 |
| 452.55000 | 466.45000 | NFM | England & Wales | Police Channel 39 |
| 452.55000 | 466.45000 | NFM | Hadleigh | Police (JD) Ch.39 |
| 452.55000 | 466.45000 | NFM | Hanley | Police |
| 452.55000 | 466.45000 | NFM | Helmsley | Police (FH) Ch.39 |
| 452.55000 | 466.45000 | NFM | Hessle | Police Ch.39 |
| 452.55000 | 466.45000 | NFM | Hull | Police |
| 452.55000 | 466.45000 | NFM | Keswick | Police |
| 452.55000 | 466.45000 | NFM | Kings Lynn | Police (D) Ch.39 |
| 452.55000 | 466.45000 | NFM | Leeds, Millgarth | Police (BA) Ch.39 |
| 452.55000 | 466.45000 | NFM | Liverpool | Police |
| 452.55000 | 466.45000 | NFM | Luton | Police Ch.39 |
| 452.55000 | 466.45000 | NFM | Luton Airport | Police |
| 452.55000 | 466.45000 | NFM | Manchester, Ashton-U-Lyme | Police |
| 452.55000 | 466.45000 | NFM | Manchester, Denton | Police (G2) Ch.39 |
| 452.55000 | 466.45000 | NFM | Manchester, Droylsden | Police |
| 452.55000 | 466.45000 | NFM | Manchester, Hyde | Police |
| 452.55000 | 466.45000 | NFM | Manchester, Mottram | Police |
| 452.55000 | 466.45000 | NFM | Manchester, Stalybridge | Police |
| 452.55000 | 466.45000 | NFM | March | Police |
| 452.55000 | 466.45000 | NFM | Merseyside | Police HQ Div  D |
| 452.55000 | 466.45000 | NFM | Milford Haven | Police |
| 452.55000 | 466.45000 | NFM | Millgarth | Police |
| 452.55000 | 466.45000 | NFM | Newport | Police Ch 1 |
| 452.55000 | 466.45000 | NFM | Newton Abbot | Police (TV) Ch39 |
| 452.55000 | 466.45000 | NFM | Newton Aycliffe | Police (AK) |
| 452.55000 | 466.45000 | NFM | Norwich | British Transport Police |
| 452.55000 | 466.45000 | NFM | Norwich | Police (B) Ch.39 |
| 452.55000 | 466.45000 | NFM | Nottingham | Police MASC Ch.39 |
| 452.55000 | 466.45000 | NFM | Rhos | Police |
| 452.55000 | 466.45000 | NFM | Rotherham | Police (C1) Ch.39 |
| 452.55000 | 466.45000 | NFM | Ryton | Police Training College Ch.39 |
| 452.55000 | 466.45000 | NFM | Smethwick | Police (M2YMK) Ch.39 |
| 452.55000 | 466.45000 | NFM | Southampton City | Police CID |
| 452.55000 | 466.45000 | NFM | Southend | Police |

| Base | Mobile | Mode | Location | User and Notes |
|------|--------|------|----------|----------------|
| 452.55000 | 466.45000 | NFM | Swindon | Police |
| 452.55000 | 466.45000 | NFM | Thames Valley | Police |
| 452.55000 | 466.45000 | NFM | Thameside | Police |
| 452.55000 | 466.45000 | NFM | Trowbridge | Police (CT) Ch.33 |
| 452.55000 | 466.45000 | NFM | Tuebrook | Police (C3) Ch.39 |
| 452.55000 | 466.45000 | NFM | Uckfield | Police (M2KBCU+NU) Ch.39 |
| 452.55000 | 466.45000 | NFM | Westbury | Police Ch.39 |
| 452.55000 | 466.45000 | NFM | Whitby | Police |
| 452.55000 | 466.45000 | NFM | Whitby | Police |
| 452.55000 | 466.45000 | NFM | Whitehaven | Police |
| 452.55000 | 466.45000 | NFM | Wilmslow | Police |
| 452.55000 | 466.45000 | NFM | Windermere | Police |
| 452.55000 | 466.45000 | NFM | Woking | Police (NW) Ch.39 |
| 452.56250 | 466.46250 | NFM | Derbyshire | Prison vans on M1 |
| 452.56250 | 466.46250 | NFM | London | HM Prison Wormwood Scrubs (JS) |
| 452.57500 | 466.47500 | NFM | Bacup | Police |
| 452.57500 | 466.47500 | NFM | Basildon | Police (BD) relay Ch.40 |
| 452.57500 | 466.47500 | NFM | Basingstoke | Police (O 1) Ch.40 |
| 452.57500 | 466.47500 | NFM | Billericay | Police |
| 452.57500 | 466.47500 | NFM | Bradford, Toller Lane | Police |
| 452.57500 | 466.47500 | NFM | Canterbury | Police |
| 452.57500 | 466.47500 | NFM | Edenbridge | Police (CC) Ch.40 |
| 452.57500 | 466.47500 | NFM | England & Wales | Police Channel 40 |
| 452.57500 | 466.47500 | NFM | Gosport | Police |
| 452.57500 | 466.47500 | NFM | Hexham | Police (B1) |
| 452.57500 | 466.47500 | NFM | Lancaster | Police |
| 452.57500 | 466.47500 | NFM | Leeds, Queens Rd | Police (HB) |
| 452.57500 | 466.47500 | NFM | Manchester ,Standish | Police |
| 452.57500 | 466.47500 | NFM | Manchester ,Tyldesley | Police |
| 452.57500 | 466.47500 | NFM | Manchester, Ashton-in-M'field | Police |
| 452.57500 | 466.47500 | NFM | Manchester, Hindley | Police |
| 452.57500 | 466.47500 | NFM | Manchester, Leigh | Police (L1) Ch.40 |
| 452.57500 | 466.47500 | NFM | Manchester, Lower Ince | Police |
| 452.57500 | 466.47500 | NFM | Manchester, Pemberton | Police |
| 452.57500 | 466.47500 | NFM | Morecambe | Police |
| 452.57500 | 466.47500 | NFM | Morpeth | Police (M2LBA1) |
| 452.57500 | 466.47500 | NFM | Nationwide | British Transport Police |
| 452.57500 | 466.47500 | NFM | Newhaven | Police Special Branch Ch.40 |
| 452.57500 | 466.47500 | NFM | Portsmouth | MoD Police Navy docks and launches Ch.40 |
| 452.57500 | 466.47500 | NFM | Portsmouth Docks | Police |
| 452.57500 | 466.47500 | NFM | Rawtenstall | Police |
| 452.57500 | 466.47500 | NFM | Rossendale | Police |
| 452.57500 | 466.47500 | NFM | Sevenoaks | Police (CC) Ch.40 |
| 452.57500 | 466.47500 | NFM | Southend | Police |
| 452.57500 | 466.47500 | NFM | Stockton-on-Tees | Police |
| 452.57500 | 466.47500 | NFM | Thames Valley | Police |
| 452.57500 | 466.47500 | NFM | Waterfoot | Police |
| 452.57500 | 466.47500 | NFM | Welwyn Garden City | Police (BWG) Ch.40 |
| 452.57500 | 466.47500 | NFM | Wickford | Police |
| 452.57500 | 466.47500 | NFM | Wickham | Police (CHARLIE 1) Ch.40 |
| 452.57500 | 466.47500 | NFM | Wigan | Police |
| 452.60000 | 466.50000 | NFM | Alnwick | Police (M2LBA3) |
| 452.60000 | 466.50000 | NFM | Ascot | Police (M2CB) |
| 452.60000 | 466.50000 | NFM | Beccles | Police (C8A) Ch.41 |
| 452.60000 | 466.50000 | NFM | Berkhamstead | Police (DB) Ch.41 |
| 452.60000 | 466.50000 | NFM | Birmingham, West Bromwich | Police (M2YMK) |

| Base | Mobile | Mode | Location | User and Notes |
|---|---|---|---|---|
| 452.60000 | 466.50000 | NFM | Bognor Regis | Police (WO) |
| 452.60000 | 466.50000 | NFM | Bristol | Police (C) Ch.41 |
| 452.60000 | 466.50000 | NFM | Bromsgrove | Police |
| 452.60000 | 466.50000 | NFM | Buckinghamshire | HM Prison Grendon |
| 452.60000 | 466.50000 | NFM | Bury St Edmunds | Police |
| 452.60000 | 466.50000 | NFM | Canterbury | Police |
| 452.60000 | 466.50000 | NFM | Cardiff | Police |
| 452.60000 | 466.50000 | NFM | Carmarthen | Police control Ch.41 |
| 452.60000 | 466.50000 | NFM | Chichester | Police (WC) Ch.41 |
| 452.60000 | 466.50000 | NFM | Crewe | Police (B1) |
| 452.60000 | 466.50000 | NFM | Darlington | Police (DJ) Encrypted |
| 452.60000 | 466.50000 | NFM | Derby | Police |
| 452.60000 | 466.50000 | NFM | Droitwich | Police |
| 452.60000 | 466.50000 | NFM | England & Wales | Police Channel 41 |
| 452.60000 | 466.50000 | NFM | Exeter | Police Ch.41 |
| 452.60000 | 466.50000 | NFM | Fallowfields | Police |
| 452.60000 | 466.50000 | NFM | Felixstowe | Police (F8A) Ch.41 |
| 452.60000 | 466.50000 | NFM | Fulwood | Police |
| 452.60000 | 466.50000 | NFM | Glenfield | Police |
| 452.60000 | 466.50000 | NFM | Gravesend | Police |
| 452.60000 | 466.50000 | NFM | Grimsby | Police |
| 452.60000 | 466.50000 | NFM | Hamilton | Police (ECHO) |
| 452.60000 | 466.50000 | NFM | Hastings | Police (M2KBEO+EH) Ch.41 |
| 452.60000 | 466.50000 | NFM | Haverhill | Police (H8A) Ch.41 |
| 452.60000 | 466.50000 | NFM | Hemel Hempstead | Police |
| 452.60000 | 466.50000 | NFM | Hertford | Police (AHE) Ch.41 |
| 452.60000 | 466.50000 | NFM | Holmfirth | Police |
| 452.60000 | 466.50000 | NFM | Hook | Police |
| 452.60000 | 466.50000 | NFM | Leamington Spa | Police |
| 452.60000 | 466.50000 | NFM | Leicester | Police Ch.41 |
| 452.60000 | 466.50000 | NFM | Leiston | Police (G8A) Ch.41 |
| 452.60000 | 466.50000 | NFM | London | Police Clarence House Special Branch (RAPIER SIERRA) Ch 41 |
| 452.60000 | 466.50000 | NFM | London | Police St James Palace (RAPIER SIERRA) Ch.41 |
| 452.60000 | 466.50000 | NFM | Maldon | Police (CM) Ch.41 |
| 452.60000 | 466.50000 | NFM | Manchester, Gorton | Police |
| 452.60000 | 466.50000 | NFM | Manchester, Greenheys | Police |
| 452.60000 | 466.50000 | NFM | Manchester, Leverhulme | Police |
| 452.60000 | 466.50000 | NFM | Manchester, Longsight | Police |
| 452.60000 | 466.50000 | NFM | Manchester, Moss Side | Police (C2) Ch.41 |
| 452.60000 | 466.50000 | NFM | Manchester, Whalley Range | Police |
| 452.60000 | 466.50000 | NFM | Midhurst | Police (M2KBWO/C/M) Ch.41 |
| 452.60000 | 466.50000 | NFM | Mildenhall | Police (Y8A) Ch.41 |
| 452.60000 | 466.50000 | NFM | Nantwich | Police |
| 452.60000 | 466.50000 | NFM | Northfleet | Police |
| 452.60000 | 466.50000 | NFM | Northhamptonshire | Police Ch 41 |
| 452.60000 | 466.50000 | NFM | Petworth | Police (M2KBWO/ WP) Ch.41 |
| 452.60000 | 466.50000 | NFM | Preston | Police |
| 452.60000 | 466.50000 | NFM | Rubery | Police |
| 452.60000 | 466.50000 | NFM | Scunthorpe | Police |
| 452.60000 | 466.50000 | NFM | Seaham | Police (BF) |
| 452.60000 | 466.50000 | NFM | Selsey | Police (M2KBWO, C) |
| 452.60000 | 466.50000 | NFM | Stavely | Police |
| 452.60000 | 466.50000 | NFM | Stow | Police (S8A) Ch.41 |
| 452.60000 | 466.50000 | NFM | Swansea | Police |

| Base | Mobile | Mode | Location | User and Notes |
|------|--------|------|----------|----------------|
| 452.60000 | 466.50000 | NFM | Syston | Police (B/S) |
| 452.60000 | 466.50000 | NFM | Thames Valley | Police |
| 452.60000 | 466.50000 | NFM | Tring | Police (DT) Ch.41 |
| 452.60000 | 466.50000 | NFM | Wallasey | Police |
| 452.60000 | 466.50000 | NFM | Ware | Police |
| 452.60000 | 466.50000 | NFM | West Bromwich | Police Ch.41 |
| 452.60000 | 466.50000 | NFM | Windsor | Police (CD) |
| 452.60000 | 466.50000 | NFM | Worksop | Police |
| 452.62500 | 466.52500 | NFM | Barrow-in-Furness | Police (BB) |
| 452.62500 | 466.52500 | NFM | Benwell | Police (F1) |
| 452.62500 | 466.52500 | NFM | Birmingham | Police |
| 452.62500 | 466.52500 | NFM | Buntingford | Police (ABU) Ch.42 |
| 452.62500 | 466.52500 | NFM | Canterbury | Police (FZ) Ch.42 |
| 452.62500 | 466.52500 | NFM | Carlisle | Police |
| 452.62500 | 466.52500 | NFM | Chichester | Police (M2KBWO, C) |
| 452.62500 | 466.52500 | NFM | England & Wales | Police Channel 42 |
| 452.62500 | 466.52500 | NFM | Erdington | Police (M2YMD) |
| 452.62500 | 466.52500 | NFM | Harborough | Police |
| 452.62500 | 466.52500 | NFM | Henley on Thames | HM Young Offenders Institution Huntercombe (NI) Ch.42 |
| 452.62500 | 466.52500 | NFM | Herne Bay | Police (FZ) Ch.42 |
| 452.62500 | 466.52500 | NFM | Hove | Police (CO) Ch.42 |
| 452.62500 | 466.52500 | NFM | Immingham | Police |
| 452.62500 | 466.52500 | NFM | Kendal | Police |
| 452.62500 | 466.52500 | NFM | Lancashire | Police |
| 452.62500 | 466.52500 | NFM | Leicester, City Centre | Police |
| 452.62500 | 466.52500 | NFM | Malvern | Police |
| 452.62500 | 466.52500 | NFM | Manchester, Eccles | Police |
| 452.62500 | 466.52500 | NFM | Manchester, Hr. Broughton | Police |
| 452.62500 | 466.52500 | NFM | Manchester, Little Hulton | Police |
| 452.62500 | 466.52500 | NFM | Manchester, Pendleton | Police |
| 452.62500 | 466.52500 | NFM | Manchester, Salford | Police |
| 452.62500 | 466.52500 | NFM | Manchester, Swinton | Police |
| 452.62500 | 466.52500 | NFM | Manchester, Walkden | Police |
| 452.62500 | 466.52500 | NFM | Mansfield | Police Encrypted |
| 452.62500 | 466.52500 | NFM | Newburn | Police (M2LBB4) |
| 452.62500 | 466.52500 | NFM | Newcastle | Police |
| 452.62500 | 466.52500 | NFM | Penrith | Police |
| 452.62500 | 466.52500 | NFM | Scotswood | Police (F1) |
| 452.62500 | 466.52500 | NFM | Shoreham-by-Sea | Police Ch 5 (CO) |
| 452.62500 | 466.52500 | NFM | South Lakes, Cumbria | Police (BB) |
| 452.62500 | 466.52500 | NFM | Stoke on Trent | Police |
| 452.62500 | 466.52500 | NFM | Swinton | Police (K2) |
| 452.62500 | 466.52500 | NFM | Tamworth | Police |
| 452.62500 | 466.52500 | NFM | Thames Valley | Police |
| 452.62500 | 466.52500 | NFM | Whitstable | Police (FZ) Ch.42 |
| 452.62500 | 466.52500 | NFM | Wigston | Police (CA) |
| 452.62500 | 466.52500 | NFM | Wolverhampton | Police |
| 452.62500 | 466.52500 | NFM | Yorkshire | Police Techn. Support Units |
| 452.63750 | 466.53750 | NFM | Biggin Hill | Police |
| 452.63750 | 466.53750 | NFM | Chislehurst | Police |
| 452.63750 | 466.53750 | NFM | Farnborough | Police |
| 452.63750 | 466.53750 | NFM | Orpington | Police |
| 452.63750 | 466.53750 | NFM | St Mary Cray | Police |
| 452.65000 | 466.55000 | NFM | Ambleside | Police |
| 452.65000 | 466.55000 | NFM | Arundel | Police (WA) Ch.43 |

| Base | Mobile | Mode | Location | User and Notes |
|------|--------|------|----------|----------------|
| 452.65000 | 466.55000 | NFM | Basingstoke | Police |
| 452.65000 | 466.55000 | NFM | Bedford | Police Ch.43 |
| 452.65000 | 466.55000 | NFM | Bexhill | Police (EB) Ch.43 |
| 452.65000 | 466.55000 | NFM | Birmingham, Aldridge & Bnhills | Police (M2YMH) |
| 452.65000 | 466.55000 | NFM | Blackburn | Police |
| 452.65000 | 466.55000 | NFM | Bodmin | Police |
| 452.65000 | 466.55000 | NFM | Bootle | HM Prison |
| 452.65000 | 466.55000 | NFM | Brentwood | Police (FB) Ch.43 |
| 452.65000 | 466.55000 | NFM | Bridgend | Police |
| 452.65000 | 466.55000 | NFM | Bridgnorth | Police |
| 452.65000 | 466.55000 | NFM | Brighton | Police HQ |
| 452.65000 | 466.55000 | NFM | Bristol | Police |
| 452.65000 | 466.55000 | NFM | Cambourne | Police |
| 452.65000 | 466.55000 | NFM | Chaddesden | Police (OSCAR 1) Ch.43 |
| 452.65000 | 466.55000 | NFM | Chapeltown | Police (AC) Ch.43 |
| 452.65000 | 466.55000 | NFM | Chapeltown | Police (AC) |
| 452.65000 | 466.55000 | NFM | Chelmsford | Police |
| 452.65000 | 466.55000 | NFM | Chester | Police (A1) |
| 452.65000 | 466.55000 | NFM | Christchurch | Police |
| 452.65000 | 466.55000 | NFM | Colchester | Police (ED) Ch.43 |
| 452.65000 | 466.55000 | NFM | Coventry | Police |
| 452.65000 | 166.55000 | NFM | Crowborough | Police (M2KBNR) Ch.43 |
| 452.65000 | 466.55000 | NFM | Derby, City Centre | Police(O3) |
| 452.65000 | 466.55000 | NFM | Durham | HM Prison Durham (M2MW) |
| 452.65000 | 466.55000 | NFM | Ely | Police |
| 452.65000 | 466.55000 | NFM | England & Wales | Police Channel 43 |
| 452.65000 | 466.55000 | NFM | Gateshead, Metro Centre | Police (M2LBD1)/(J1) |
| 452.65000 | 466.55000 | NFM | Gosport | Police |
| 452.65000 | 466.55000 | NFM | Hagley | Police |
| 452.65000 | 466.55000 | NFM | Hartlepool | Police |
| 452.65000 | 466.55000 | NFM | Helston | Police |
| 452.65000 | 466.55000 | NFM | Hemel Hempstead | Police |
| 452.65000 | 466.55000 | NFM | Hoddesdon | Police (AHO) Ch.43 |
| 452.65000 | 466.55000 | NFM | Kidderminster | Police Ch.43 |
| 452.65000 | 466.55000 | NFM | Leicester | Police (452.8750MHz alternate) |
| 452.65000 | 466.55000 | NFM | Lewes | Police HQ |
| 452.65000 | 466.55000 | NFM | Lincoln | HM Prison (M2JB) Ch.43 |
| 452.65000 | 466.55000 | NFM | Liskeard | Police Town Net |
| 452.65000 | 466.55000 | NFM | Littlehampton | Police (M2KBWO, WL) Ch.43 |
| 452.65000 | 466.55000 | NFM | Liverpool | HM Prison Liverpool |
| 452.65000 | 466.55000 | NFM | London | HM Prison Holloway |
| 452.65000 | 466.55000 | NFM | Longbridge | Police |
| 452.65000 | 466.55000 | NFM | Longton | Police |
| 452.65000 | 466.55000 | NFM | Luton | Police Ch 43 (BL) |
| 452.65000 | 466.55000 | NFM | Manchester | HN Prison Strangeways Ch.43 |
| 452.65000 | 466.55000 | NFM | Maryport | Police |
| 452.65000 | 466.55000 | NFM | Merthyr Tydfil | Police (E) 43 |
| 452.65000 | 466.55000 | NFM | Millom | Police |
| 452.65000 | 466.55000 | NFM | Morpeth | Police |
| 452.65000 | 466.55000 | NFM | New Town | Police |
| 452.65000 | 466.55000 | NFM | Newcastle | Police |
| 452.65000 | 466.55000 | NFM | Norwich | Police Ch.43 |
| 452.65000 | 466.55000 | NFM | Nuneaton | Police (M2YJN) |
| 452.65000 | 466.55000 | NFM | Portland | Prison |
| 452.65000 | 466.55000 | NFM | Portsmouth | Police |
| 452.65000 | 466.55000 | NFM | Preston | Police |

| Base | Mobile | Mode | Location | User and Notes |
|---|---|---|---|---|
| 452.65000 | 466.55000 | NFM | Rhymney Valley | Police |
| 452.65000 | 466.55000 | NFM | Sheffield | Police |
| 452.65000 | 466.55000 | NFM | Shrewsbury | HM Prison Shrewsbury (M2JY) |
| 452.65000 | 466.55000 | NFM | Stratford-Upon-Avon | Police Ch.43 |
| 452.65000 | 466.55000 | NFM | Swansea | Police |
| 452.65000 | 466.55000 | NFM | Telford | Police |
| 452.65000 | 466.55000 | NFM | Thames Valley | Police |
| 452.65000 | 466.55000 | NFM | Truro | Police |
| 452.65000 | 466.55000 | NFM | Walsall | Police |
| 452.65000 | 466.55000 | NFM | Ware | Police (AW) Ch.43 |
| 452.65000 | 466.55000 | NFM | West Bar | Police (E3) Ch.43 |
| 452.65000 | 466.55000 | NFM | West Sussex | Police HQ |
| 452.65000 | 466.55000 | NFM | West Yorkshire | Police Mobile Repeaters |
| 452.65000 | 466.55000 | NFM | Weston Super Mere | Police (MIKE CONTROL) Ch.43 |
| 452.65000 | 466.55000 | NFM | Wigton | Police |
| 452.65000 | 466.55000 | NFM | Woodbridge | Police |
| 452.66250 | 466.56250 | NFM | London | Police divisions P/R/M and part of Z trunked |
| 452.67500 | 466.57500 | NFM | Ashington | Police (M2LBA6) |
| 452.67500 | 466.57500 | NFM | Aston | Police MASC (M2YMD1) Ch.44 |
| 452.67500 | 466.57500 | NFM | Basingstoke | Police |
| 452.67500 | 466.57500 | NFM | Birmingham, Stoney Stanton | Police |
| 452.67500 | 466.57500 | NFM | Coventry, east | Police (MZ/MX) Ch.44 |
| 452.67500 | 466.57500 | NFM | Coventry, north | Police (M2YMM) Ch.44 |
| 452.67500 | 466.57500 | NFM | Debenham | Police (J8D) Ch.44 |
| 452.67500 | 466.57500 | NFM | Dover | Police Special Branch |
| 452.67500 | 466.57500 | NFM | England & Wales | Police Channel 44 |
| 452.67500 | 466.57500 | NFM | England & Wales | Prison emergency reserve Ch.44 |
| 452.67500 | 466.57500 | NFM | Grantham | Police |
| 452.67500 | 466.57500 | NFM | Hollbeach | Police |
| 452.67500 | 466.57500 | NFM | Maltby | Police (C3) Ch.44 |
| 452.67500 | 466.57500 | NFM | Manchester Airport | Police |
| 452.67500 | 466.57500 | NFM | Manchester, Baguley | Police |
| 452.67500 | 466.57500 | NFM | Manchester, Benchill | Police |
| 452.67500 | 466.57500 | NFM | Manchester, Chorlton | Police |
| 452.67500 | 466.57500 | NFM | Manchester, Didsbury | Police |
| 452.67500 | 466.57500 | NFM | Manchester, Northenden | Police (D2) Ch.44 |
| 452.67500 | 466.57500 | NFM | Manchester, Northern Moor | Police |
| 452.67500 | 466.57500 | NFM | Manchester, Rusholme | Police |
| 452.67500 | 466.57500 | NFM | Manchester, Withington | Police |
| 452.67500 | 466.57500 | NFM | Martlesham | Police (W8A) Ch.33 |
| 452.67500 | 466.57500 | NFM | Merseyside | Police (Encrypted) |
| 452.67500 | 466.57500 | NFM | Middlesborough | Police (M2) |
| 452.67500 | 466.57500 | NFM | Newbury | Police (G2) |
| 452.67500 | 466.57500 | NFM | Norwich | HM Prison Norwich (PO) Ch.44 |
| 452.67500 | 466.57500 | NFM | Oxford | HM Prison Oxford (M2PC) Ch.44 |
| 452.67500 | 466.57500 | NFM | Rotherham | Police |
| 452.67500 | 466.57500 | NFM | Royston | Police (G4/GR) Ch.44 |
| 452.67500 | 466.57500 | NFM | Shipley | Police (HC) Ch.44 |
| 452.67500 | 466.57500 | NFM | Telford | Police |
| 452.67500 | 466.57500 | NFM | Thames Valley | Police |
| 452.68750 | 466.58750 | NFM | Basildon | Police |
| 452.68750 | 466.58750 | NFM | London | Police Division X |
| 452.70000 | 466.60000 | NFM | Barrow in Furness | Police |
| 452.70000 | 466.60000 | NFM | Battle | Police (ET) Ch.45 |
| 452.70000 | 466.60000 | NFM | Bilston | Police |
| 452.70000 | 466.60000 | NFM | Birmingham | Police |

| Base | Mobile | Mode | Location | User and Notes |
|------|--------|------|----------|----------------|
| 452.70000 | 466.60000 | NFM | Bognor Regis | Police (M2KBNO) Ch.45 |
| 452.70000 | 466.60000 | NFM | Boston | Police |
| 452.70000 | 466.60000 | NFM | Bristol | Police |
| 452.70000 | 466.60000 | NFM | Burgess Hill | Police (NB) Ch.45 |
| 452.70000 | 466.60000 | NFM | Cambridge | Police |
| 452.70000 | 466.60000 | NFM | Cheshire | Police |
| 452.70000 | 466.60000 | NFM | Chippenham | Police |
| 452.70000 | 466.60000 | NFM | Chipping Norton | Police (BF) |
| 452.70000 | 466.60000 | NFM | Clifton | Police (DR) Ch.45 |
| 452.70000 | 466.60000 | NFM | Congleton | Police (B2) |
| 452.70000 | 466.60000 | NFM | Doncaster | Police Ch.45 |
| 452.70000 | 466.60000 | NFM | Dover | HM Immigration |
| 452.70000 | 466.60000 | NFM | Dunstable | Police Ch.45 |
| 452.70000 | 466.60000 | NFM | Easingwold | Police |
| 452.70000 | 466.60000 | NFM | England & Wales | Police Channel 45 |
| 452.70000 | 466.60000 | NFM | Essex | Police |
| 452.70000 | 466.60000 | NFM | Flint | Police |
| 452.70000 | 466.60000 | NFM | Grays | Police (FD) Ch.45 |
| 452.70000 | 466.60000 | NFM | Guildford | Police (WG) Ch.45 |
| 452.70000 | 466.60000 | NFM | Halesowen & Stourbridge | Police (M2YMJ) |
| 452.70000 | 466.60000 | NFM | Halifax | Police (FA) Ch.45 |
| 452.70000 | 466.60000 | NFM | Harrogate | Police (BH) Ch.45 |
| 452.70000 | 466.60000 | NFM | Haywards Heath | Police (M2KBNO, NA) Ch.45 |
| 452.70000 | 466.60000 | NFM | Hucknall | Police MASC Ch.45 |
| 452.70000 | 466.60000 | NFM | Hull, central | Police Ch.45 |
| 452.70000 | 466.60000 | NFM | Irby | Police (A3) |
| 452.70000 | 466.60000 | NFM | Kettering | Police |
| 452.70000 | 466.60000 | NFM | Knaresborough | Police |
| 452.70000 | 466.60000 | NFM | Lancing | Police |
| 452.70000 | 466.60000 | NFM | Langholm | Police |
| 452.70000 | 466.60000 | NFM | Leighton Buzzard | Police |
| 452.70000 | 466.60000 | NFM | Longtown, Cumbria | Police |
| 452.70000 | 466.60000 | NFM | Louth | Police Ch.45 |
| 452.70000 | 466.60000 | NFM | Manchester, Rainhill | Police (E1) Ch.45 |
| 452.70000 | 466.60000 | NFM | Merseyside | Police HQ Div E (Encrypted) |
| 452.70000 | 466.60000 | NFM | Morpeth | Police |
| 452.70000 | 466.60000 | NFM | Newark | Police |
| 452.70000 | 466.60000 | NFM | Peterborough | Police Ch.45 |
| 452.70000 | 466.60000 | NFM | Rugby | Police Ch.45 |
| 452.70000 | 466.60000 | NFM | Salisbury | Police |
| 452.70000 | 466.60000 | NFM | Scarborough | Police |
| 452.70000 | 466.60000 | NFM | Shoreham | Police |
| 452.70000 | 466.60000 | NFM | South Shields | Police (M2LBE1)/(L1) |
| 452.70000 | 466.60000 | NFM | Stockton | Police |
| 452.70000 | 466.60000 | NFM | Sutton Coldfield | Police (M2YMD) Ch.45 |
| 452.70000 | 466.60000 | NFM | Thames Valley | Police |
| 452.70000 | 466.60000 | NFM | Ulverston | Police |
| 452.70000 | 466.60000 | NFM | West Midlands | Police (M2KBNO, B) |
| 452.70000 | 466.60000 | NFM | Whitehaven | Police |
| 452.70000 | 466.60000 | NFM | Woodstock | Police |
| 452.70000 | 466.60000 | NFM | Worthing | Police |
| 452.71250 | 466.61250 | NFM | London | Police divisions P/R/M and part of Z trunked |
| 452.72500 | 446.62500 | NFM | Heckmondwyke | Police (EB) Ch.46 |
| 452.72500 | 466.62500 | NFM | Accrington | Police Ch.46 |
| 452.72500 | 466.62500 | NFM | Batley | Police (EB) Ch.46 |
| 452.72500 | 466.62500 | NFM | Birmingham | Police |

| Base | Mobile | Mode | Location | User and Notes |
|------|--------|------|----------|----------------|
| 452.72500 | 466.62500 | NFM | Bloxwich | Police (M2YMH) |
| 452.72500 | 466.62500 | NFM | Broadmoor | HM Prison Broadmoor |
| 452.72500 | 466.62500 | NFM | Brownhills | Police (M2YMHX) |
| 452.72500 | 466.62500 | NFM | Cleckheaton | Police |
| 452.72500 | 466.62500 | NFM | Cleethorpes | Police Ch.46 |
| 452.72500 | 466.62500 | NFM | Coventry, central | Police MASC (M2YMM) Ch.46 |
| 452.72500 | 466.62500 | NFM | Coventry, east | Police (MZ/ MX) Ch.46 |
| 452.72500 | 466.62500 | NFM | Cowes | Police |
| 452.72500 | 466.62500 | NFM | Darlaston | Police (M2YMHX) |
| 452.72500 | 466.62500 | NFM | England & Wales | Police Channel 46 |
| 452.72500 | 466.62500 | NFM | Grimsby | Police Ch.46 |
| 452.72500 | 466.62500 | NFM | Guernsey | HM Prison Les Nicholles |
| 452.72500 | 466.62500 | NFM | Horsham | Police (M2KBNO/NH) Ch.46 |
| 452.72500 | 466.62500 | NFM | Houghton le Spring | Police |
| 452.72500 | 466.62500 | NFM | Isle of Sheppy | Police (EZ) Ch.46 |
| 452.72500 | 466.62500 | NFM | Isle of Wight | Police |
| 452.72500 | 466.62500 | NFM | Keswick | Police |
| 452.72500 | 466.62500 | NFM | Liverpool Toxteth | Police |
| 452.72500 | 466.62500 | NFM | Manchester | HM Prison Strangeways |
| 452.72500 | 466.62500 | NFM | Mold | Police |
| 452.72500 | 466.62500 | NFM | Pulborough | Police (NP) Ch.46 |
| 452.72500 | 466.62500 | NFM | Ryde | Police |
| 452.72500 | 466.62500 | NFM | Sittingbourne | Police (EZ) Ch.46 |
| 452.72500 | 466.62500 | NFM | Southend | Police |
| 452.72500 | 466.62500 | NFM | Stechford | Police |
| 452.72500 | 466.62500 | NFM | Stockport | Police |
| 452.72500 | 466.62500 | NFM | Storrington | Police (NS) Ch.46 |
| 452.72500 | 466.62500 | NFM | Swale | Police (EZ) Ch.46 |
| 452.72500 | 466.62500 | NFM | Thames Valley | Police |
| 452.72500 | 466.62500 | NFM | Tunstall | Police |
| 452.72500 | 466.62500 | NFM | Warrington | HM Prison Risley |
| 452.72500 | 466.62500 | NFM | Washington | Police (M2LBF4) Encrypted |
| 452.72500 | 466.62500 | NFM | Wednesbury | Police |
| 452.72500 | 466.62500 | NFM | Willenhall | Police MASC (M2YMHX) Ch.46 |
| 452.72500 | 466.62500 | NFM | Wrexham | Police (C2) Ch.46 |
| 452.73750 | 466.63750 | NFM | London | Police division P trunked |
| 452.73750 | 466.63750 | NFM | Oxford | Police Oxford United Football Club |
| 452.73750 | 466.63750 | NFM | Westerham | Police |
| 452.75000 | 466.65000 | NFM | Arundel | Police |
| 452.75000 | 466.65000 | NFM | Baldock | Police (GB) Ch.47 |
| 452.75000 | 466.65000 | NFM | Baldock | Police (GB) Ch.47 |
| 452.75000 | 466.65000 | NFM | Bangor | Police Ch.47 |
| 452.75000 | 466.65000 | NFM | Basildon | Police |
| 452.75000 | 466.65000 | NFM | Bath | Police Ch.47 |
| 452.75000 | 466.65000 | NFM | Beeston | Police |
| 452.75000 | 466.65000 | NFM | Beverley | Police Ch.47 |
| 452.75000 | 466.65000 | NFM | Birkenhead | Police |
| 452.75000 | 466.65000 | NFM | Birmingham, Yardley | Police (M2YME) |
| 452.75000 | 466.65000 | NFM | Blackwater | Police |
| 452.75000 | 466.65000 | NFM | Boston | Police |
| 452.75000 | 466.65000 | NFM | Brandon | Police (Y8B) Ch.47 |
| 452.75000 | 466.65000 | NFM | Bridgeford | Police |
| 452.75000 | 466.65000 | NFM | Bridlington | Police (CB) Ch.47 |
| 452.75000 | 466.65000 | NFM | Brighton | Police CID |
| 452.75000 | 466.65000 | NFM | Bristol | Police |
| 452.75000 | 466.65000 | NFM | Burslem | Police |

| Base | Mobile | Mode | Location | User and Notes |
|---|---|---|---|---|
| 452.75000 | 466.65000 | NFM | Bury St Edmunds | Police (V8A) Ch.47 |
| 452.75000 | 466.65000 | NFM | Caernarfon | Police Ch.47 |
| 452.75000 | 466.65000 | NFM | Camberley | Police (NC) |
| 452.75000 | 466.65000 | NFM | Cardiff | Police and Pubwatch |
| 452.75000 | 466.65000 | NFM | Castleford | Police (DC) Ch.47 |
| 452.75000 | 466.65000 | NFM | Chelmsford | Police (CD) Ch.47 |
| 452.75000 | 466.65000 | NFM | Dartford | Police (CB) Ch.47 |
| 452.75000 | 466.65000 | NFM | Deal | Police (DB) Ch.47 |
| 452.75000 | 466.65000 | NFM | Dewsbury | Police |
| 452.75000 | 466.65000 | NFM | Dover | Police (DB) Ch.47 |
| 452.75000 | 466.65000 | NFM | Egham | Police (NE) |
| 452.75000 | 466.65000 | NFM | Ellesmere Port | Police (A2) |
| 452.75000 | 466.65000 | NFM | England & Wales | Police Channel 47 |
| 452.75000 | 466.65000 | NFM | Goole | Police |
| 452.75000 | 466.65000 | NFM | Guernsey | Police (M2GY) |
| 452.75000 | 466.65000 | NFM | Hadleigh | Police |
| 452.75000 | 466.65000 | NFM | Halesworth | Police (J8A) Ch.47 |
| 452.75000 | 466.65000 | NFM | Halifax | Police |
| 452.75000 | 466.65000 | NFM | Handsworth | Police (M2YMC) |
| 452.75000 | 466.65000 | NFM | Hitchin | Police |
| 452.75000 | 466.65000 | NFM | Holyhead | Police Ch.47 |
| 452.75000 | 466.65000 | NFM | Ilkley | Police (HD) Ch.47 |
| 452.75000 | 466.65000 | NFM | Ipswich | Police Div HQ (I8A) Ch.47 |
| 452.75000 | 466.65000 | NFM | Jonnstown | Police |
| 452.75000 | 466.65000 | NFM | Keighley | Police (HD) Ch.47 |
| 452.75000 | 466.65000 | NFM | Lancing | Police |
| 452.75000 | 466.65000 | NFM | Leicester | Police |
| 452.75000 | 466.65000 | NFM | Letchworth | Police (GL) Ch.47 |
| 452.75000 | 466.65000 | NFM | Lewes | Police (M2KBEO/ EL) Ch.47 |
| 452.75000 | 466.65000 | NFM | Littlehampton | Police |
| 452.75000 | 466.65000 | NFM | Llandudno | Police Ch.47 |
| 452.75000 | 466.65000 | NFM | London, Gatwick | Police - GatPol (GB) Ch.47 |
| 452.75000 | 466.65000 | NFM | Lowestoft | Police (Q8A) Ch.47 |
| 452.75000 | 466.65000 | NFM | Manchester Ringway | Police |
| 452.75000 | 466.65000 | NFM | Manchester, Bredbury | Police |
| 452.75000 | 466.65000 | NFM | Manchester, Brinnington | Police |
| 452.75000 | 466.65000 | NFM | Manchester, Cheadle | Police |
| 452.75000 | 466.65000 | NFM | Manchester, Cheadle Hulme | Police |
| 452.75000 | 466.65000 | NFM | Manchester, Hazel Grove | Police |
| 452.75000 | 466.65000 | NFM | Manchester, Marple | Police |
| 452.75000 | 466.65000 | NFM | Manchester, Reddish | Police |
| 452.75000 | 466.65000 | NFM | Merseyside | Police (Encrypted) |
| 452.75000 | 466.65000 | NFM | Mexborough | Police |
| 452.75000 | 466.65000 | NFM | Needham Market | Police |
| 452.75000 | 466.65000 | NFM | Newmarket | Police (N8A) Ch.47 |
| 452.75000 | 466.65000 | NFM | Nottingham | Police |
| 452.75000 | 466.65000 | NFM | Ossett | Police (DC) Ch.47 |
| 452.75000 | 466.65000 | NFM | Oxhey | Police |
| 452.75000 | 466.65000 | NFM | Paddock Wood | Police (AC) Ch.47 |
| 452.75000 | 466.65000 | NFM | Pitsea | Police |
| 452.75000 | 466.65000 | NFM | Pontypool, Gwent | Police - Bravo 1 Section |
| 452.75000 | 466.65000 | NFM | Redcar | Police |
| 452.75000 | 466.65000 | NFM | Rickmansworth | Police (C3 /C2) Ch.47 |
| 452.75000 | 466.65000 | NFM | Ripon | Police |
| 452.75000 | 466.65000 | NFM | Royston | Police |
| 452.75000 | 466.65000 | NFM | Sheerness | Police |

| Base | Mobile | Mode | Location | User and Notes |
|------|--------|------|----------|----------------|
| 452.75000 | 466.65000 | NFM | Shoreham | Police (WS) Ch.47 |
| 452.75000 | 466.65000 | NFM | Somerset | Police Ch.47 |
| 452.75000 | 466.65000 | NFM | Stevenage | Police (GL) Ch.47 |
| 452.75000 | 466.65000 | NFM | Stockport | Police (J1) Ch.47 |
| 452.75000 | 466.65000 | NFM | Sudbury | Police (Z8A) Ch.47 |
| 452.75000 | 466.65000 | NFM | Sullbridge | Police (F1) |
| 452.75000 | 466.65000 | NFM | Sunderland | Police (M2LBF1) Encrypted |
| 452.75000 | 466.65000 | NFM | Swanley | Police (CB) Ch.47 |
| 452.75000 | 466.65000 | NFM | Swansea | Police |
| 452.75000 | 466.65000 | NFM | Thames Valley | Police |
| 452.75000 | 466.65000 | NFM | Tipton | Police |
| 452.75000 | 466.65000 | NFM | Tunbridge Wells | Police (AC) Ch.47 |
| 452.75000 | 466.65000 | NFM | Wakefield | Police MASC (DA) Ch.47 |
| 452.75000 | 466.65000 | NFM | Wallsey | Police |
| 452.75000 | 466.65000 | NFM | Wellingborough | Police Ch 47 (WV) |
| 452.75000 | 466.65000 | NFM | West Midlands, Thornhill Rd | Police |
| 452.75000 | 466.65000 | NFM | Worthing | Police (M2KBWO, WW) Ch.47 |
| 452.76200 | 446.66250 | NFM | Birmingham | Police |
| 452.76250 | 466.66250 | NFM | London | Police divisions P/R/M and part Z trunked |
| 452.77500 | 466.67500 | NFM | Basildon | Police (BD) Ch.48 |
| 452.77500 | 466.67500 | NFM | Birmingham | Police |
| 452.77500 | 466.67500 | NFM | Brighouse | Police (FB) Ch.48 |
| 452.77500 | 466.67500 | NFM | Cambridge | Police Ch.48 |
| 452.77500 | 466.67500 | NFM | England & Wales | Police Channel 48 |
| 452.77500 | 466.67500 | NFM | Nottingham | Police (NH) |
| 452.80000 | 466.70000 | NFM | Abingdon | Police (FH) |
| 452.80000 | 466.70000 | NFM | Aldeburgh | Police Ch.49 (G8B link to G8A Ch.41) |
| 452.80000 | 466.70000 | NFM | Attleborough | Police Ch.49 |
| 452.80000 | 466.70000 | NFM | Beeston | Police |
| 452.80000 | 466.70000 | NFM | Berwick-upon-Tweed | Police (M2LBA2) |
| 452.80000 | 466.70000 | NFM | Blundiston | HM Prison |
| 452.80000 | 466.70000 | NFM | Brighouse | Police (FB) Ch.49 |
| 452.80000 | 466.70000 | NFM | Bristol | HM Prison  Horfield |
| 452.80000 | 466.70000 | NFM | Camborne | Police |
| 452.80000 | 466.70000 | NFM | Chelmsford | Police Ch.43 |
| 452.80000 | 466.70000 | NFM | Chester le Street | Police (CG) |
| 452.80000 | 466.70000 | NFM | City of London | Police Ch.1 |
| 452.80000 | 466.70000 | NFM | Cornwall | Police |
| 452.80000 | 466.70000 | NFM | Crawley | Police (M2KBNO/ NC) Ch.49 |
| 452.80000 | 466.70000 | NFM | Daventry | Police Ch.49 |
| 452.80000 | 466.70000 | NFM | Didcot | Police (M2 football clubs) |
| 452.80000 | 466.70000 | NFM | Dyfed | Police |
| 452.80000 | 466.70000 | NFM | Eastbourne | Police EO (EE) |
| 452.80000 | 466.70000 | NFM | England & Wales | Police Channel 49 |
| 452.80000 | 466.70000 | NFM | Evesham | Police |
| 452.80000 | 466.70000 | NFM | Eye | Police (J8E) Ch.49 |
| 452.80000 | 466.70000 | NFM | Falmouth | Police |
| 452.80000 | 466.70000 | NFM | Gloucester | Police |
| 452.80000 | 466.70000 | NFM | Grantham | Police |
| 452.80000 | 466.70000 | NFM | Hailsham | Police (EA) |
| 452.80000 | 466.70000 | NFM | Harwich | Police Ch.49 |
| 452.80000 | 466.70000 | NFM | Hastings | Police PR (EH) |
| 452.80000 | 466.70000 | NFM | Haverfordwest | Police |
| 452.80000 | 466.70000 | NFM | Hayle | Police |
| 452.80000 | 466.70000 | NFM | Hemsworth | Police |
| 452.80000 | 466.70000 | NFM | Horsham | Police |

| Base | Mobile | Mode | Location | User and Notes |
|------|--------|------|----------|----------------|
| 452.80000 | 466.70000 | NFM | Hull | HM Prison Hull (HO) Ch.49 |
| 452.80000 | 466.70000 | NFM | Ipswich | Police |
| 452.80000 | 466.70000 | NFM | Ladywood | Police (M2YMC) |
| 452.80000 | 466.70000 | NFM | Leicester, Beumont Leys | Police (A/B) |
| 452.80000 | 466.70000 | NFM | Lewes | Police CO (EL) |
| 452.80000 | 466.70000 | NFM | Llanelli | Police control Ch.49 |
| 452.80000 | 466.70000 | NFM | Louth | Police |
| 452.80000 | 466.70000 | NFM | Lowestoft | HM Prison Blundeston Ch.49 |
| 452.80000 | 466.70000 | NFM | Maidstone | HM Prison Maidstone (KM) Ch.49 |
| 452.80000 | 466.70000 | NFM | Manchester, Salford West | Police (F1) encrypted |
| 452.80000 | 466.70000 | NFM | Merseyside | Police HQ Div C (Encrypted) |
| 452.80000 | 466.70000 | NFM | New Quay | Police |
| 452.80000 | 466.70000 | NFM | Newbury | Police |
| 452.80000 | 466.70000 | NFM | Newcastle | Police |
| 452.80000 | 466.70000 | NFM | Newhaven | Police (M2KBEO/ EN) Ch.49 |
| 452.80000 | 466.70000 | NFM | North Shields | Police (M2LBC1) |
| 452.80000 | 466.70000 | NFM | Norwich | HM Prison |
| 452.80000 | 466.70000 | NFM | Penry | Police |
| 452.80000 | 466.70000 | NFM | Penzance | Police |
| 452.80000 | 466.70000 | NFM | Plymouth | Police (ECHO & SIERRA VICTOR) Ch.49 |
| 452.80000 | 466.70000 | NFM | Polegate | Police Traffic (TP) |
| 152.80000 | 466.70000 | NFM | Pontefract | Police |
| 452.80000 | 466.70000 | NFM | Powys | Police |
| 452.80000 | 466.70000 | NFM | Preston | HM Prison |
| 452.80000 | 466.70000 | NFM | Rhyl | Police |
| 452.80000 | 466.70000 | NFM | Risca Area, Gwent | Police (CHARLIE 2) Ch.49 |
| 452.80000 | 466.70000 | NFM | Salford | Police MASC Ch.49 |
| 452.80000 | 466.70000 | NFM | Seaford | Police (ES) Ch.49 |
| 452.80000 | 466.70000 | NFM | Skipton | Police |
| 452.80000 | 466.70000 | NFM | St Ives | Police |
| 452.80000 | 466.70000 | NFM | Stevenage | Police (ES) Ch.49 |
| 452.80000 | 466.70000 | NFM | Stoke on Trent | Police |
| 452.80000 | 466.70000 | NFM | Stradishall | HM Prison Highpoint Ch.49 |
| 452.80000 | 466.70000 | NFM | Telford | Police |
| 452.80000 | 466.70000 | NFM | Thames Valley | Police |
| 452.80000 | 466.70000 | NFM | Todmorden | Police (XW) Ch5 |
| 452.80000 | 466.70000 | NFM | Truro | Police |
| 452.80000 | 466.70000 | NFM | Wallingford | Police |
| 452.80000 | 466.70000 | NFM | Walton, Merseyside | Police (C4) Ch.49 |
| 452.80000 | 466.70000 | NFM | Warton | Police |
| 452.80000 | 466.70000 | NFM | Watford | Police (CW) Ch.49 |
| 452.80000 | 466.70000 | NFM | Wellington | Police |
| 452.80000 | 466.70000 | NFM | Willenhall | Police |
| 452.80000 | 466.70000 | NFM | Witham | Police (CW) Ch.49 |
| 452.82500 | 466.67500 | NFM | Jersey | HM Prison La Moye Ch 1 |
| 452.82500 | 466.72500 | NFM | England & Wales | Police Channel 50 |
| 452.82500 | 466.72500 | NFM | Nationwide | Police Vehicle Trackers |
| 452.85000 | 466.75000 | NFM | Altrincham | Police |
| 452.85000 | 466.75000 | NFM | Birmingham | Police |
| 452.85000 | 466.75000 | NFM | Bromborough | Police |
| 452.85000 | 466.75000 | NFM | England & Wales | Police Channel 51 |
| 452.85000 | 466.75000 | NFM | England & Wales | Police Vehicle Trackers |
| 452.85000 | 466.75000 | NFM | Jersey | Police Special Events |
| 452.85000 | 466.75000 | NFM | Witham | Police |
| 452.87500 | 466.77500 | NFM | Basildon | Police |
| 452.87500 | 466.77500 | NFM | Birmingham | Police |

| Base | Mobile | Mode | Location | User and Notes |
|------|--------|------|----------|----------------|
| 452.87500 | 466.77500 | NFM | Bolton | Police (K2) Ch.52 |
| 452.87500 | 466.77500 | NFM | Chelmsley Wood | Police (M2YML) |
| 452.87500 | 466.77500 | NFM | Christchurch | Police |
| 452.87500 | 466.77500 | NFM | Coventry | Police |
| 452.87500 | 466.77500 | NFM | Dyfed | Police Ch.52 |
| 452.87500 | 466.77500 | NFM | England & Wales | Police Channel 52 |
| 452.87500 | 466.77500 | NFM | Farnworth | Police |
| 452.87500 | 466.77500 | NFM | Gloucester | Police air support unit - HQ & force comms. link to Ch.52 |
| 452.87500 | 466.77500 | NFM | Leicester, central | Police (C/A) Ch.52 |
| 452.87300 | 466.77500 | NFM | Manchester Westhoughton | Police |
| 452.87500 | 466.77500 | NFM | Manchester. Astley Bridge | Police |
| 452.87500 | 466.77500 | NFM | Manchester. Breightmet | Police |
| 452.87500 | 466.77500 | NFM | Manchester. Farnworth | Police |
| 452.87500 | 466.77500 | NFM | Manchester. Horwich | Police |
| 452.87500 | 466.77500 | NFM | Manchester. Middle Hulton | Police |
| 452.87500 | 466.77500 | NFM | North Yorkshire | Police Link to Ravenscar Ch 4 |
| 452.87500 | 466.77500 | NFM | Poole | Police Encrypted |
| 452.87500 | 466.77500 | NFM | Rayleigh | Police |
| 452.87500 | 466.77500 | NFM | Southend on Sea | Police (HD) Ch.52 |
| 452.87500 | 466.77500 | NFM | Thames Valley | Police |
| 452.87500 | 466.77500 | NFM | Winchester | Police (OSCAR 1) Ch.52 |
| 452.87500 | 466.77500 | NFM | Wombwell | Police Ch.52 |
| 452.88750 | 466.78750 | NFM | London | Police division P/R/M and part of Z trunked |
| 452.90000 | 466.80000 | NFM | Barrow In Furness | Police |
| 452.90000 | 466.80000 | NFM | Bedfordshire | Fire Brigade VHF to UHF Ch.53 |
| 452.90000 | 466.80000 | NFM | Birmingham | Police |
| 452.90000 | 466.80000 | NFM | Birmingham, | HM Prison, Winston Green (JG) Ch.53 |
| 452.90000 | 466.80000 | NFM | Burton Down | Police |
| 452.90000 | 466.80000 | NFM | Chester le Street | Police (CG) |
| 452.90000 | 466.80000 | NFM | England & Wales | Police Channel 53 |
| 452.90000 | 466.80000 | NFM | Gloucester | Police |
| 452.90000 | 466.80000 | NFM | London, Heathrow | Police Special Branch (SV/ SB) Ch.53 |
| 452.90000 | 466.80000 | NFM | Manchester ,Standish | Police |
| 452.90000 | 466.80000 | NFM | Manchester, Ashton-in-M'field | Police |
| 452.90000 | 466.80000 | NFM | Manchester, Hindley | Police |
| 452.90000 | 466.80000 | NFM | Manchester, Leigh | Police (L2) Ch.53 |
| 452.90000 | 466.80000 | NFM | Manchester, Lower Ince | Police |
| 452.90000 | 466.80000 | NFM | Manchester, Pemberton | Police |
| 452.90000 | 466.80000 | NFM | Manchester, Tyldesley | Police |
| 452.90000 | 466.80000 | NFM | Mid Glamorgan | Police |
| 452.90000 | 466.80000 | NFM | Thames Valley | Police |
| 452.90000 | 466.80000 | NFM | Wigan | Police |
| 452.91250 | 466.81250 | NFM | London | Police central security network trunked |
| 452.92500 | 466.77500 | NFM | Jersey | Traffic Wardens |
| 452.92500 | 466.82500 | NFM | Chelmsford | Police (GOLF TANGO) Ch.43 |
| 452.92500 | 466.82500 | NFM | Christchurch | Police |
| 452.92500 | 466.82500 | NFM | Derby | Police |
| 452.92500 | 466.82500 | NFM | Ely | Police |
| 452.92500 | 466.82500 | NFM | England & Wales | Police VHF-UHF repeater Ch.54 |
| 452.92500 | 466.82500 | NFM | Essex | Police |
| 452.92500 | 466.82500 | NFM | Ipswich | Police |
| 452.92500 | 466.82500 | NFM | Leicester | Police |
| 452.92500 | 466.82500 | NFM | Lincolnshire | Police Mobile Repeater |
| 452.92500 | 466.82500 | NFM | Lyme | Police |
| 452.92500 | 466.82500 | NFM | Newport Area, Gwent | Police - (WO) Traffic Ch |

| Base | Mobile | Mode | Location | User and Notes |
|---|---|---|---|---|
| 452.92500 | 466.82500 | NFM | North Cumbria | Police Mobile Repeaters |
| 452.92500 | 466.82500 | NFM | South Hams | Police VHF-UHF Repeater |
| 452.92500 | 466.82500 | NFM | South Yorkshire | Police Mobile Repeater |
| 452.92500 | 466.82500 | NFM | Thames Valley | Police |
| 452.92500 | 466.82500 | NFM | Warrington | Police |
| 452.92500 | 466.82500 | NFM | Warwickshire | Police Mobile Repeater |
| 452.92500 | 466.82500 | NFM | West Mercia | Police |
| 452.95000 | 466.85000 | NFM | Badsworth | Police |
| 452.95000 | 466.85000 | NFM | England & Wales | Police Channel 55 |
| 452.95000 | 466.85000 | NFM | Kidsgrove | Police |
| 452.95000 | 466.85000 | NFM | Minsthorpe | Police |
| 452.95000 | 466.85000 | NFM | Newport | Police traffic |
| 452.95000 | 466.85000 | NFM | North Yorkshire | Police Link to Ravenscar Ch 2 |
| 452.95000 | 466.85000 | NFM | Nottinghamshire | Police MASC Ch.55 |
| 452.95000 | 466.85000 | NFM | Pontefract | Police (DC) Ch.55 |
| 452.95000 | 466.85000 | NFM | Runcorn | Police (E2) |
| 452.95000 | 466.85000 | NFM | South Yorkshire | Police Mobile Repeater |
| 452.95000 | 466.85000 | NFM | Thames Valley | Police |
| 452.95000 | 466.85000 | NFM | Widnes | Police |
| 452.95000 | 466.85000 | NFM | Wiltshire | Fire Brigade VHF-UHF repeater (M2QM) Ch.55 |
| 452.96250 | 466.86250 | NFM | London | Police central security network trunked |
| 452.97500 | 466.82500 | NFM | Jersey | Police Tactical Firearms Unit Ch 3 |
| 452.97500 | 466.87500 | NFM | Blyth | Police (M2LBC5) |
| 452.97500 | 466.87500 | NFM | Bolton | Police (K1) Ch 2 |
| 452.97500 | 466.87500 | NFM | Broadstairs | Police (GZ) Ch.56 |
| 452.97500 | 466.87500 | NFM | Cardiff | British Transport Police |
| 452.97500 | 466.87500 | NFM | Crook Weardale | Police (AB) |
| 452.97500 | 466.87500 | NFM | England & Wales | Police Channel 56 |
| 452.97500 | 466.87500 | NFM | Gloucester | Police Ch.56 |
| 452.97500 | 466.87500 | NFM | Horwich | Police |
| 452.97500 | 466.87500 | NFM | Jersey | HM Prison La Moye Ch 2 |
| 452.97500 | 466.87500 | NFM | Manchester, Astley Bridge | Police |
| 452.97500 | 466.87500 | NFM | Manchester, Breightmet | Police |
| 452.97500 | 466.87500 | NFM | Manchester, Farnworth | Police |
| 452.97500 | 466.87500 | NFM | Manchester, Horwich | Police |
| 452.97500 | 466.87500 | NFM | Manchester, Middle Hulton | Police |
| 452.97500 | 466.87500 | NFM | Manchester, Westhoughton | Police |
| 452.97500 | 466.87500 | NFM | Margate | Police (GZ) Ch.56 |
| 452.97500 | 466.87500 | NFM | Ramsgate | Police (GZ) Ch.56 |
| 452.97500 | 466.87500 | NFM | Scarborough | Police |
| 452.97500 | 466.87500 | NFM | Thames Valley | Police |

### 453.0000 - 454.0000 MHz  PMR Mobile Band 12.5 kHz
### (Mobiles +6.5 MHz)

| Base | Mobile | Mode | Location | User and Notes |
|---|---|---|---|---|
| 453.00000 | 459.50000 | NFM | Nationwide | British Transport Police |
| 453.02500 | 459.52500 | NFM | Bath | National Car Parks maintenance |
| 453.02500 | 459.52500 | NFM | Birmingham | Shopwatch. |
| 453.02500 | 459.52500 | NFM | Bolton | C&A Store Security |
| 453.02500 | 459.52500 | NFM | Bolton | Shopping Centre Security |
| 453.02500 | 459.52500 | NFM | Bristol | City CCTV System |
| 453.02500 | 459.52500 | NFM | Coventry | Burger King Drive Thru Central 6 |
| 453.02500 | 459.52500 | NFM | Croydon | Shopwatch |
| 453.02500 | 459.52500 | NFM | Croydon | Tavener Security |
| 453.02500 | 459.52500 | NFM | Dagenham | Ford Motor Plant |
| 453.02500 | 459.52500 | NFM | Dover | Hoverspeed |
| 453.02500 | 459.52500 | NFM | Edinburgh | Waverley Market Security |

| Base | Mobile | Mode | Location | User and Notes |
|------|--------|------|----------|----------------|
| 453.02500 | 459.52500 | NFM | Felixstowe | Harbour Channel |
| 453.02500 | 459.52500 | NFM | Gloucestershire Airport | Ground Control |
| 453.02500 | 459.52500 | NFM | Guernsey | Harbour Channel |
| 453.02500 | 459.52500 | NFM | Harwich | Harbour Channel |
| 453.02500 | 459.52500 | NFM | Jersey | Shell Aviation Fuel Supplies |
| 453.02500 | 459.52500 | NFM | Leatherhead | Oil Co. |
| 453.02500 | 459.52500 | NFM | Leicester | Shopping Centre Security |
| 453.02500 | 459.52500 | NFM | London | Borough of Croydon Repeater |
| 453.02500 | 459.52500 | NFM | London | Heathrow Airport Skyline Hotel. |
| 453.02500 | 459.52500 | NFM | London | Houses of Parliament |
| 453.02500 | 459.52500 | NFM | London, Covent Garden | Command Security |
| 453.02500 | 459.52500 | NFM | London, Heathrow | Skyline Hotel |
| 453.02500 | 459.52500 | NFM | London, Putney | Exchange Shops Security |
| 453.02500 | 459.52500 | NFM | London, Wood Green | Shop Watch Scheme Ch 2 |
| 453.02500 | 459.52500 | NFM | Manchester | International Airport |
| 453.02500 | 459.52500 | NFM | Middlesborough | BSC Ros Railways |
| 453.02500 | 459.52500 | NFM | Moray Firth | Beatrice Alpha Platform |
| 453.02500 | 459.52500 | NFM | Newcastle | Metro Net - emergency use only |
| 453.02500 | 459.52500 | NFM | Nigg Bay | BP Oil Terminal Control |
| 453.02500 | 459.52500 | NFM | North Sea | Amoco NW Hutton |
| 453.02500 | 459.52500 | NFM | North Sea | Amoco North Everest |
| 453.02500 | 459.52500 | NFM | North Sea | Beatrice A BP |
| 453.02500 | 459.52500 | NFM | North Sea | Beryl B Mobil Temp. Const. Facility |
| 453.02500 | 459.52500 | NFM | North Sea | Lomond Amoco |
| 453.02500 | 459.52500 | NFM | North Sea | Shell Fulmar FSU |
| 453.02500 | 459.52500 | NFM | Stansted | Ground Repeater |
| 453.02500 | 459.52500 | NFM | Staverton | Staverton Airport Ground |
| 453.02500 | 459.52500 | NFM | Teesside | British Steel trains |
| 453.02500 | 459.52500 | NFM | Warwick | Castle staff Ch 2 |
| 453.03750 | 459.53750 | NFM | Glasgow | Sports Connection |
| 453.03750 | 459.53750 | NFM | London, Heathrow | Airline & BAA Ops |
| 453.05000 | 459.55000 | NFM | Blackpool | Trams mainly data |
| 453.05000 | 459.55000 | NFM | Bournemouth | Winfaith Security |
| 453.05000 | 459.55000 | NFM | Brighton | American Express |
| 453.05000 | 459.55000 | NFM | Brighton | Shop Security |
| 453.05000 | 459.55000 | NFM | Bristol | BAE Filton Security |
| 453.05000 | 459.55000 | NFM | Burnley | Burnley & Pendle Buses |
| 453.05000 | 459.55000 | NFM | Coventry | City Centre Car Parks |
| 453.05000 | 459.55000 | NFM | Edinburgh | Royal Infirmary Porters |
| 453.05000 | 459.55000 | NFM | Guernsey | Princess Elizabeth Hospital |
| 453.05000 | 459.55000 | NFM | Hull | Royal Infirmary Porters & Security |
| 453.05000 | 459.55000 | NFM | Immingham | Coal Products Docking |
| 453.05000 | 459.55000 | NFM | Kings Lynn | Shopwatch |
| 453.05000 | 459.55000 | NFM | Leicester | Bradgate & Brecon Park Rangers |
| 453.05000 | 459.55000 | NFM | London, Heathrow | Airline & BAA Ops |
| 453.05000 | 459.55000 | NFM | Luton | Airport Alpha Flight Catering |
| 453.05000 | 459.55000 | NFM | Luton Airport | Alpha Catering |
| 453.05000 | 459.55000 | NFM | Nationwide | Air Rangers |
| 453.05000 | 459.55000 | NFM | Nationwide | R.R. Security |
| 453.05000 | 459.55000 | NFM | Nationwide | Shopping Centre Security |
| 453.05000 | 459.55000 | NFM | North Sea | Chevron Alba ANP PABX Interface - Mobiles |
| 453.05000 | 459.55000 | NFM | North Sea | Shell Brent Spar |
| 453.05000 | 459.55000 | NFM | Oxford | City centre store detectives |
| 453.05000 | 459.55000 | NFM | Oxford | College security |
| 453.05000 | 459.55000 | NFM | Peterborough | Peter Brotherhood |
| 453.05000 | 459.55000 | NFM | Rhyl | Security |

| Base | Mobile | Mode | Location | User and Notes |
|------|--------|------|----------|----------------|
| 453.05000 | 459.55000 | NFM | Sheffield | Council emergency glaziers |
| 453.05000 | 459.55000 | NFM | Stevenage | Glaxo Security |
| 453.05000 | 459.55000 | NFM | Stoke On Trent | Roebuck Centre |
| 453.05000 | 467.55000 | NFM | Magor | Whitbread Beer Security |
| 453.06250 | 459.56250 | NFM | Barrow | Debenhams Security |
| 453.06250 | 459.56250 | NFM | Chatham | Shopwatch scheme |
| 453.06250 | 459.56250 | NFM | Croyde | Ruda Holiday Park |
| 453.06250 | 459.56250 | NFM | Croydon | Goodenough Bryans Food Manufacturer |
| 453.06250 | 459.56250 | NFM | Edinburgh | Store detectives and CCTV |
| 453.06250 | 459.56250 | NFM | Hull | Shopwatch. |
| 453.06250 | 459.56250 | NFM | Kent | Medway Shop Security |
| 453.06250 | 459.56250 | NFM | London, Heathrow | Quantas Airline Ops |
| 453.06250 | 459.56250 | NFM | Luton | Car Assembly Plant |
| 453.06250 | 459.56250 | NFM | Manchester | Springfield Hospital Porters |
| 453.06250 | 459.56250 | NFM | Romford | Liberty 2 Shopping Centre Shopwatch |
| 453.06250 | 459.56250 | NFM | York | Shopwatch |
| 453.07500 | 459.57500 | NFM | Barnet | Barnet General Hospital |
| 453.07500 | 459.57500 | NFM | Barnet | Queen Elizabeth Girls School |
| 453.07500 | 459.57500 | NFM | Billingham | ICI |
| 453.07500 | 459.57500 | NFM | Bristol | Portland Dock Control |
| 453.07500 | 459.57500 | NFM | Carnforth | Wimpey Quarry |
| 453.07500 | 459.57500 | NFM | Coryton | Shell Haven Oil Refinery |
| 453.07500 | 459.57500 | NFM | Dover | Docks security |
| 453.07500 | 459.57500 | NFM | Edinburgh | Dynamic Earth |
| 453.07500 | 459.57500 | NFM | Felixstowe | Quay Shipping |
| 453.07500 | 459.57500 | NFM | Harwich | Quay Shipping |
| 453.07500 | 459.57500 | NFM | Jersey | Harbour/Marina Ch 2 |
| 453.07500 | 459.57500 | NFM | London | Olympia Complex Maintenance Engineers |
| 453.07500 | 459.57500 | NFM | London | Royal Festival Hall |
| 453.07500 | 459.57500 | NFM | London | Savoy Hotel |
| 453.07500 | 459.57500 | NFM | London, Heathrow | Airline & BAA Ops |
| 453.07500 | 459.57500 | NFM | London, Oxford Street | Mount Royal Hotel |
| 453.07500 | 459.57500 | NFM | Manchester | Aircraft Fitters |
| 453.07500 | 459.57500 | NFM | Manchester | Airport Motor Pool Maintenance |
| 453.07500 | 459.57500 | NFM | March | March Ground Services |
| 453.07500 | 459.57500 | NFM | Middlesborough | ICI Ammonia Base |
| 453.07500 | 459.57500 | NFM | North Sea | Amoco Bacton |
| 453.07500 | 459.57500 | NFM | North Sea | Amoco Montrose A |
| 453.07500 | 459.57500 | NFM | North Sea | Amoco NW Hutton |
| 453.07500 | 459.57500 | NFM | Oxford | University Science Area |
| 453.07500 | 459.57500 | NFM | Teddington | National Physical Laboratory |
| 453.07500 | 459.57500 | NFM | Tilbury | Container Port. |
| 453.08750 | 459.58750 | NFM | Brighton | Churchill Square Shopping Centre Security |
| 453.08750 | 459.58750 | NFM | Cambridge | Shopwatch |
| 453.08750 | 459.58750 | NFM | Chatham | World Naval Base Admin/Security Ch 1 |
| 453.08750 | 459.58750 | NFM | Coventry | Coal Authority |
| 453.08750 | 459.58750 | NFM | Hull | Royal Infirmary Security |
| 453.08750 | 459.58750 | NFM | London | Courtaulds Coatings Silvertown |
| 453.08750 | 459.58750 | NFM | London | Selfridges |
| 453.08750 | 459.58750 | NFM | London, Kensington | British Home Stores |
| 453.08750 | 459.58750 | NFM | London, Kensington | River Island |
| 453.08750 | 459.58750 | NFM | London, Oxford Street | D H Evans security |
| 453.08750 | 459.58750 | NFM | Luton | Shopwatch |
| 453.08750 | 459.58750 | NFM | Reading | Primary Shopwatch |
| 453.08750 | 459.58750 | NFM | Watford | Shopwatch and C&A Ch 3 |
| 453.10000 | 456.60000 | NFM | Tyneside | Metro Repairs |

| Base | Mobile | Mode | Location | User and Notes |
|------|--------|------|----------|----------------|
| 453.10000 | 459.60000 | NFM | Beeston | Boots |
| 453.10000 | 459.60000 | NFM | Belfast | Queen's University Security |
| 453.10000 | 459.60000 | NFM | Blackpool | Local Health Authority |
| 453.10000 | 459.60000 | NFM | Blackpool | Tramcar Inspectors |
| 453.10000 | 459.60000 | NFM | Brighton | Hotel |
| 453.10000 | 459.60000 | NFM | Cowley | Rover Plant Channel 1 |
| 453.10000 | 459.60000 | NFM | Edinburgh | Rocksteady Security |
| 453.10000 | 459.60000 | NFM | Fleetwood | Tram Inspectors |
| 453.10000 | 459.60000 | NFM | Glasgow | Ibrox Match Control |
| 453.10000 | 459.60000 | NFM | Keynsham | Fry's Chocolate |
| 453.10000 | 459.60000 | NFM | London | Docklands Security |
| 453.10000 | 459.60000 | NFM | London | Lawn Tennis Association Repeater |
| 453.10000 | 459.60000 | NFM | London | Victoria and Albert Museum |
| 453.10000 | 459.60000 | NFM | London, Gatwick | Airline ops. |
| 453.10000 | 459.60000 | NFM | London, Heathrow | Indian Language Channel |
| 453.10000 | 459.60000 | NFM | London, Knightsbridge | Shopwatch |
| 453.10000 | 459.60000 | NFM | London, Wimbledon | Lawn Tennis Association |
| 453.10000 | 459.60000 | NFM | Maltby | Buttlers Roadstone |
| 453.10000 | 459.60000 | NFM | Manchester | International Airport |
| 453.10000 | 459.60000 | NFM | Manchester Airport | Boarding control |
| 453.10000 | 459.60000 | NFM | Manchester, Piccadilly | Storewatch Ch.1 |
| 453.10000 | 459.60000 | NFM | Moray Firth | Beatrice Bravo Platform |
| 453.10000 | 459.60000 | NFM | Newcastle | Tyne & Wear Metro |
| 453.10000 | 459.60000 | NFM | North Sea | BP Beatrice B |
| 453.10000 | 459.60000 | NFM | North Sea | Unocal Heather A |
| 453.10000 | 459.60000 | NFM | Oldham | Building Site Security |
| 453.10000 | 459.60000 | NFM | Peterborough | Queensgate Shopping Cent. |
| 453.10000 | 459.60000 | NFM | South Walden | Schering Agrochemicals |
| 453.10000 | 459.60000 | NFM | Southampton | Hospital Transport Ch 1 |
| 453.10000 | 459.60000 | NFM | Telford | Docks security |
| 453.10000 | 459.60000 | NFM | Telford | Shopping Centre Security |
| 453.10000 | 459.60000 | NFM | Watford | John Lewis Store |
| 453.11250 | 459.61250 | NFM | Guildford | Royal Victoria Shopping Centre Security |
| 453.11250 | 459.61250 | NFM | Ipswich | Action For Community in Rural England |
| 453.11250 | 459.61250 | NFM | Leicester | Royal Infirmary Porters |
| 453.11250 | 459.61250 | NFM | London | Brent Cross Shopping Centre security control |
| 453.11250 | 459.61250 | NFM | London | Earls Court Centre |
| 453.11250 | 459.61250 | NFM | London, Gatwick | Cleaning Service |
| 453.11250 | 459.61250 | NFM | Manchester | Council |
| 453.11250 | 459.61250 | NFM | Manchester, Piccadilly | Storewatch Ch.2 |
| 453.11250 | 459.61250 | NFM | Peterborough | Industrial Use |
| 453.11250 | 459.61250 | NFM | Skipton | Shopwatch. |
| 453.11250 | 459.61250 | NFM | Tunbridge Wells | Royal Victoria Place shops |
| 453.11250 | 459.61250 | NFM | Watford | C&A Ch 1 |
| 453.12500 | 459.62500 | NFM | Coventry | Jaguar Cars Ltd. Security |
| 453.12500 | 459.62500 | NFM | Coventry | Orchards Security |
| 453.12500 | 459.62500 | NFM | Cowley | Rover Plant Channel 4 |
| 453.12500 | 459.62500 | NFM | Dover | Western Docks Jetfoil |
| 453.12500 | 459.62500 | NFM | East Midlands Airport | British Midland |
| 453.12500 | 459.62500 | NFM | Edinburgh Airport | British Midland |
| 453.12500 | 459.62500 | NFM | Felixstowe | Docks |
| 453.12500 | 459.62500 | NFM | Glasgow | British Midland |
| 453.12500 | 459.62500 | NFM | Guernsey | St. Sampson's Harbour |
| 453.12500 | 459.62500 | NFM | Harwich | Carless Solvents |
| 453.12500 | 459.62500 | NFM | Harwich | Port loaders |
| 453.12500 | 459.62500 | NFM | Immingham | Conoco Oil Refinery |

| Base | Mobile | Mode | Location | User and Notes |
|------|--------|------|----------|----------------|
| 453.12500 | 459.62500 | NFM | Jersey Airport | British Midland Handling |
| 453.12500 | 459.62500 | NFM | London | Borough of Fulham and Hammersmith. |
| 453.12500 | 459.62500 | NFM | London | City Airport |
| 453.12500 | 459.62500 | NFM | London, Heathrow | Airline & BAA Ops |
| 453.12500 | 459.62500 | NFM | Manchester | International Airport |
| 453.12500 | 459.62500 | NFM | Newhaven | Port & Property Services |
| 453.12500 | 459.62500 | NFM | Nigg Bay | BP Oil Terminal Fire Channel |
| 453.12500 | 459.62500 | NFM | North Sea | Conoco Murchison |
| 453.12500 | 459.62500 | NFM | North Sea | Conoco Viking Field |
| 453.12500 | 459.62500 | NFM | Norwich | Colmans Foods |
| 453.12500 | 459.62500 | NFM | Oldham | Garforth Glass |
| 453.12500 | 459.62500 | NFM | Oxted | Surrey Leisure Site. |
| 453.12500 | 459.62500 | NFM | Sheffield | Stockbridge Engineering Steels |
| 453.12500 | 459.62500 | NFM | Speke | Halewood Ford Plant Sec. |
| 453.12500 | 459.62500 | NFM | Stevenage | ICL Computers Security Ch |
| 453.12500 | 459.62500 | NFM | Teddington | Studios Security. |
| 453.12500 | 459.62500 | NFM | Woodbridge | Tannington Pea Harvesting |
| 453.13750 | 459.63750 | NFM | Birmingham | Hyatt Regency Hotel Security |
| 453.13750 | 459.63750 | NFM | London | Police Dartford Tunnel |
| 453.13750 | 459.63750 | NFM | Manchester | Data Link |
| 453.13750 | 459.63750 | NFM | Morecambe | Data Link |
| 453.15000 | 460.65000 | NFM | Aston under Lyme | Shopping Security |
| 453.15000 | 459.65000 | NFM | Birmingham International | Ops |
| 453.15000 | 459.65000 | NFM | Bradford | Kirkgate Shopping Centre security |
| 453.15000 | 459.65000 | NFM | Coventry | Hillfield flats security |
| 453.15000 | 459.65000 | NFM | Edinburgh | City Centre Couriers |
| 453.15000 | 459.65000 | NFM | Fleetwood | P & O Security |
| 453.15000 | 459.65000 | NFM | London | Bermondsey Traffic Wardens |
| 453.15000 | 459.65000 | NFM | London | City Security |
| 453.15000 | 459.65000 | NFM | London | Metro Bus Orpington |
| 453.15000 | 459.65000 | NFM | London, Heathrow | Airline & BAA Ops |
| 453.15000 | 459.65000 | NFM | Sheffield | Council Cleansing Dept. |
| 453.15000 | 459.65000 | NFM | Stansted Airport | El-Al Security |
| 453.15000 | 459.65000 | NFM | Swansea | Storenet Security |
| 453.15000 | 459.65000 | NFM | Swindon | Council Maintenance |
| 453.15000 | 459.65000 | NFM | Whittlesey | McCain International |
| 453.15000 | 459.65000 | NFM | Wigan | Central Park Rugby Grnd OB |
| 453.15000 | 459.65000 | NFM | Wiltshire | Reading Cable TV |
| 453.15050 | 459.65000 | NFM | Coventry | Hillfields Flat Complex Security. |
| 453.16250 | 459.66250 | NFM | Aberdyfi | Lifeboat |
| 453.16250 | 459.66250 | NFM | Oldham | Two Counties |
| 453.17500 | 459.67500 | NFM | Bedford | 3M UK |
| 453.17500 | 459.67500 | NFM | Billingham | ICI |
| 453.17500 | 459.67500 | NFM | Brighton | On Site Nr Railway Station |
| 453.17500 | 459.67500 | NFM | Bristol | Badger Line Bus Inspectors |
| 453.17500 | 459.67500 | NFM | Cardiff | Docks Security |
| 453.17500 | 459.67500 | NFM | Chelmsford | McDonalds Drive Thru |
| 453.17500 | 459.67500 | NFM | City of London | Central Criminal Court Old Bailey Repeater |
| 453.17500 | 459.67500 | NFM | Coventry | Courtaulds Security |
| 453.17500 | 459.67500 | NFM | Croydon | Drummonds Shopping Centre |
| 453.17500 | 459.67500 | NFM | Dagenham | Ford Motor Plant Repeater |
| 453.17500 | 459.67500 | NFM | Edinburgh | Royal Infirmary Security |
| 453.17500 | 459.67500 | NFM | Essex | County Council |
| 453.17500 | 459.67500 | NFM | Grimsby | Tioxide UK Chemical Plant |
| 453.17500 | 459.67500 | NFM | Harwich | Car Park |
| 453.17500 | 459.67500 | NFM | Ipswich | Copdock Burger King Drive Thru |

| Base | Mobile | Mode | Location | User and Notes |
|------|--------|------|----------|----------------|
| 453.17500 | 459.67500 | NFM | Ipswich | Docks Security |
| 453.17500 | 459.67500 | NFM | London | Grays Inn Gardens Repeater |
| 453.17500 | 459.67500 | NFM | London | Heathrow Transport Repeater |
| 453.17500 | 459.67500 | NFM | London | Stratford Container Terminal |
| 453.17500 | 459.67500 | NFM | London, Heathrow | Airline ops. |
| 453.17500 | 459.67500 | NFM | Luton | Airport Station Coach Service |
| 453.17500 | 459.67500 | NFM | Manchester | Airport (IVORY) |
| 453.17500 | 459.67500 | NFM | Manchester North | Security Firm |
| 453.17500 | 459.67500 | NFM | Moray Firth | Beatrice Alpha Platform |
| 453.17500 | 459.67500 | NFM | Nationwide | Railtrack |
| 453.17500 | 459.67500 | NFM | Newcastle | Tyne & Wear Metro |
| 453.17500 | 459.67500 | NFM | North Sea | Amoco Lomond |
| 453.17500 | 459.67500 | NFM | North Sea | Amoco NW Hutton |
| 453.17500 | 459.67500 | NFM | North Sea | Amoco North Everest |
| 453.17500 | 459.67500 | NFM | North Sea | BP Beatrice A |
| 453.17500 | 459.67500 | NFM | North Sea | Shell Bacton |
| 453.17500 | 459.67500 | NFM | North Sea | Shell Inde J |
| 453.17500 | 459.67500 | NFM | North Sea | Shell Inde K |
| 453.17500 | 459.67500 | NFM | North Sea | Shell Leman B |
| 453.17500 | 459.67500 | NFM | North Sea | Shell St. Fergus |
| 453.17500 | 459.67500 | NFM | Oxford | Shopwatch |
| 453.17500 | 459.67500 | NFM | Peterborough | Shopwatch |
| 453.17500 | 459.67500 | NFM | Sheffield | City Parks Security |
| 453.17500 | 459.67500 | NFM | Stevenage | Knebworth House Security and Staff |
| 453.17500 | 459.67500 | NFM | Suffolk | County Council |
| 453.17500 | 459.67500 | NFM | Tendering | District Council |
| 453.17500 | 459.67500 | NFM | Watford | Harlequin Shopping Centre Repeater |
| 453.17500 | 459.67500 | NFM | Weybridge | Warren Pond Tennis Courts |
| 453.18750 | 459.68750 | NFM | London | Millenium Dome trunked netwoork |
| 453.20000 | 459.70000 | NFM | Birmingham | Taxi Co |
| 453.20000 | 459.70000 | NFM | Boston | Acorn Cabs |
| 453.20000 | 459.70000 | NFM | Dartford | Borough Council Parking Enforcement |
| 453.20000 | 459.70000 | NFM | Enfield | Police chase cars |
| 453.20000 | 459.70000 | NFM | Felixstowe | Docks |
| 453.20000 | 459.70000 | NFM | Fleetwood | Plumbers |
| 453.20000 | 459.70000 | NFM | Glasgow | City Centre Council Patrol |
| 453.20000 | 459.70000 | NFM | Hants | Sewage Works (V) |
| 453.20000 | 459.70000 | NFM | Hull | Hospital Porters |
| 453.20000 | 459.70000 | NFM | Ipswich | Transport Police |
| 453.20000 | 459.70000 | NFM | Jersey Harbour | Shell Fuel Supplies |
| 453.20000 | 459.70000 | NFM | London | Glaxo Security Ch1 |
| 453.20000 | 459.70000 | NFM | London | Linkcars Belsize Rd NW6 (LINK) |
| 453.20000 | 459.70000 | NFM | London, Heathrow | Passenger transport |
| 453.20000 | 459.70000 | NFM | Milton Keynes | MK Security |
| 453.20000 | 459.70000 | NFM | North Sea | Conoco Murchison |
| 453.20000 | 459.70000 | NFM | Plymouth | City Bus Inspectors |
| 453.20000 | 459.70000 | NFM | Portsmouth | Taxis |
| 453.20000 | 459.70000 | NFM | Ramsbottom | Civic Private Hire |
| 453.20000 | 459.70000 | NFM | Rotherham | Bus Inspectors |
| 453.20000 | 459.70000 | NFM | Sheffield | Main line trains maintenance |
| 453.20000 | 459.70000 | NFM | Snodland | Smurfitt,Townsend Hook Paper Mill |
| 453.20000 | 459.70000 | NFM | Stevenage | Glaxo Security Ch 1 |
| 453.21250 | 459.71250 | NFM | Dundee | Data Link |
| 453.21250 | 459.71250 | NFM | Morecambe | Data Link |
| 453.22500 | 459.72500 | NFM | Alba Chevron | FSU Shuttle Operations |
| 453.22500 | 459.72500 | NFM | Felixstowe | Docks |

| Base | Mobile | Mode | Location | User and Notes |
|------|--------|------|----------|----------------|
| 453.22500 | 459.72500 | NFM | Jersey | Harbour Ch 1 |
| 453.22500 | 459.72500 | NFM | London, Heathrow | Airline & BAA Ops Terminal 3 |
| 453.22500 | 459.72500 | NFM | North Sea | Chevron Ninian South |
| 453.22500 | 459.72500 | NFM | North Sea | Shell Eider |
| 453.22500 | 459.72500 | NFM | Peterborough | Aggregate Company |
| 453.22500 | 459.72500 | NFM | Tilbury | Rover Security |
| 453.25000 | 459.75000 | NFM | Belfast | Ulster Folk & Transport Museum Security |
| 453.25000 | 459.75000 | NFM | Bradford | BRI Security Ch.2 |
| 453.25000 | 459.75000 | NFM | Forest Hill | Taxi |
| 453.25000 | 459.75000 | NFM | Hull | Docks |
| 453.25000 | 459.75000 | NFM | Leeds | Leeds General Infirmary security |
| 453.25000 | 459.75000 | NFM | Leeds | Traffic Wardens |
| 453.25000 | 459.75000 | NFM | Leicester | Council |
| 453.25000 | 459.75000 | NFM | London | Borough of Merton Parking Control Repeater |
| 453.25000 | 459.75000 | NFM | London | Central Middx Hospital Repeater |
| 453.25000 | 459.75000 | NFM | London, Central | Traffic Wardens |
| 453.25000 | 459.75000 | NFM | London, Gatwick | Airline & BAA Ops (ground repeater) |
| 453.25000 | 459.75000 | NFM | London, Heathrow | Airline & BAA Ops |
| 453.25000 | 459.75000 | NFM | Manchester | Taxi |
| 453.25000 | 459.75000 | NFM | North Sea | BP Clyde A |
| 453.25000 | 459.75000 | NFM | North Sea | Conoco Murchison |
| 453.25000 | 459.75000 | NFM | North Sea | Marathon Brae N |
| 453.25000 | 459.75000 | NFM | Reading | Council (RC) |
| 453.25000 | 459.75000 | NFM | Whiston | Whiston Hospital Security |
| 453.26250 | 459.76250 | NFM | Newcastle | Data Link |
| 453.26250 | 459.76250 | NFM | Oldham | Courier |
| 453.27500 | 459.77500 | NFM | Humberside | Ambulance handhelds UHF to VHF link |
| 453.27500 | 459.77500 | NFM | Lincolnshire | Council |
| 453.27500 | 459.77500 | NFM | London, Heathrow | Airline & BAA Ops (ground repeater) |
| 453.27500 | 459.77500 | NFM | Middlesborough | British Steel Medics |
| 453.27500 | 459.77500 | NFM | Nationwide | Ambulance Ch.1 (VHF/UHF repeater for hand held) |
| 453.27500 | 459.77500 | NFM | North Sea | Shell Base Leman BH |
| 453.27500 | 459.77500 | NFM | North Sea | Shell Brent B |
| 453.30000 | 459.80000 | NFM | Bradford | BRI Security Ch.1 |
| 453.30000 | 459.80000 | NFM | Harwich | Port Authority Ch.1 |
| 453.30000 | 459.80000 | NFM | Humberside | Lindsey Oil Refinery |
| 453.30000 | 459.80000 | NFM | Lindsey | Oil Refinery |
| 453.30000 | 459.80000 | NFM | Liverpool | Buses |
| 453.30000 | 459.80000 | NFM | Liverpool | Merseybus Inspectors |
| 453.30000 | 459.80000 | NFM | London | Chevron Oil International Security |
| 453.30000 | 459.80000 | NFM | London, Gatwick | Airline ops. |
| 453.30000 | 459.80000 | NFM | London, Heathrow | Airport. |
| 453.30000 | 459.80000 | NFM | North Sea | Amoco Lomond |
| 453.30000 | 459.80000 | NFM | North Sea | Amoco Montrose A |
| 453.30000 | 459.80000 | NFM | North Sea | Amoco NW Hutton |
| 453.30000 | 459.80000 | NFM | North Sea | Amoco North Everest |
| 453.30000 | 459.80000 | NFM | North Sea | BP Magnus |
| 453.30000 | 459.80000 | NFM | North Sea | Marathon Brae N |
| 453.30000 | 459.80000 | NFM | Stevenage | Pulse Disco & Vogue Nightclub |
| 453.31250 | 459.81250 | NFM | Perth | Data Link |
| 453.32500 | 459.77500 | NFM | England and Wales | Ambulance Ch.1 |
| 453.32500 | 459.82500 | NFM | Avon | Ambulance Ch.2 |
| 453.32500 | 459.82500 | NFM | Cheltenham | Hospital Porters |
| 453.32500 | 459.82500 | NFM | East Sussex | Ambulance Ch.2and Incident Vehicle |
| 453.32500 | 459.82500 | NFM | Gloucester | Royal General Hospital Porters |
| 453.32500 | 459.82500 | NFM | Kent | Ambulance Ch.2 |

| Base | Mobile | Mode | Location | User and Notes |
|------|--------|------|----------|----------------|
| 453.32500 | 459.82500 | NFM | London | Ambulance Ch.2 |
| 453.32500 | 459.82500 | NFM | London, Heathrow | Ground Repeater |
| 453.32500 | 459.82500 | NFM | Lytham | Health Centre |
| 453.32500 | 459.82500 | NFM | Manchester | Doctors on Call |
| 453.32500 | 459.82500 | NFM | March | St Mary's Hospital Security |
| 453.32500 | 459.82500 | NFM | Stansted | Ground Repeater |
| 453.35000 | 459.85000 | NFM | Humberside | Ambulance handhelds UHF to VHF link |
| 453.35000 | 459.85000 | NFM | Humberside Airport | Bond Helicopters |
| 453.35000 | 459.85000 | NFM | Langley, Bucks | Industrial Coatings |
| 453.35000 | 459.85000 | NFM | London | Borough of Croydon Park Wardens |
| 453.35000 | 459.85000 | NFM | London | Security Co. |
| 453.35000 | 459.85000 | NFM | London , Gerrard Place | Masterpark |
| 453.35000 | 459.85000 | NFM | London, Portland Place | Masterpark |
| 453.35000 | 459.85000 | NFM | Manchester | International Airport |
| 453.35000 | 459.85000 | NFM | North Sea | Conoco Murchison |
| 453.35000 | 459.85000 | NFM | North Sea | Marathon Brae N |
| 453.35000 | 459.85000 | NFM | Nottingham | City Engineers |
| 453.35000 | 459.85000 | NFM | Reading | Courage Brewery |
| 453.35000 | 459.85000 | NFM | Stevenage | Town Car Park Security and Staff |
| 453.35000 | 459.85000 | NFM | Walsall | Council Works Yard |
| 453.36250 | 459.85000 | NFM | Nationwide | DSS |
| 453.37500 | 459.87500 | NFM | Cambridge | Addenbrokes Hospital Porters |
| 453.37500 | 459.87500 | NFM | Cambridge | Addenbrokes Hospital porters |
| 453.37500 | 459.87500 | NFM | City of London | Stock Exchange |
| 453.37500 | 459.87500 | NFM | Coventry | Walsgrave Hospital |
| 453.37500 | 459.87500 | NFM | Cowley | Rover Plant Channel 2 |
| 453.37500 | 459.87500 | NFM | Dartford | Stone Marshes Construction Work Repeater |
| 453.37500 | 459.87500 | NFM | Immingham | Conoco Oil Refinery Fire & Sec. |
| 453.37500 | 459.87500 | NFM | Immingham | Lindsey Oil Fire Service |
| 453.37500 | 459.87500 | NFM | Leatherhead | Construction Work Repeater |
| 453.37500 | 459.87500 | NFM | Leeds | Hospital security |
| 453.37500 | 459.87500 | NFM | Liverpool | All docks handhelds |
| 453.37500 | 459.87500 | NFM | London | Borough of Walthamstow Repeater |
| 453.37500 | 459.87500 | NFM | London | Brent Cross Shopping Centre Repeater |
| 453.37500 | 459.87500 | NFM | London | Charing Cross Hospital Repeater |
| 453.37500 | 459.87500 | NFM | London | Richmond Park Staff Repeater |
| 453.37500 | 459.87500 | NFM | London | Westminster QE 2 Conference Centre Repeater |
| 453.37500 | 459.87500 | NFM | London, Heathrow | Security Repeater |
| 453.37500 | 459.87500 | NFM | Luton Airport | Buses & Luggage Handlers Ch 5 |
| 453.37500 | 459.87500 | NFM | Nationwide | DSS |
| 453.37500 | 459.87500 | NFM | Port Talbot | BP Works |
| 453.38750 | 459.88750 | NFM | Nationwide | DSS |
| 453.40000 | 459.90000 | NFM | City of London | Barbican Centre Staff |
| 453.40000 | 459.90000 | NFM | Cliffe | Conoco Oil |
| 453.40000 | 459.90000 | NFM | Glasgow | Prince's Sq. Shopping Mall Sec. |
| 453.40000 | 459.90000 | NFM | Hull | City Council |
| 453.40000 | 459.90000 | NFM | Hull | Prospect Shopping Centre Security. |
| 453.40000 | 459.90000 | NFM | Ipswich | Port Authority |
| 453.40000 | 459.90000 | NFM | Jersey Airport | Esso Refuelling |
| 453.40000 | 459.90000 | NFM | London, Gatwick | Ground Repeater |
| 453.40000 | 459.90000 | NFM | London, Heathrow | Airline & BAA Ops Terminal 3 |
| 453.40000 | 459.90000 | NFM | Nigg Bay | BP Oil Terminal Maintenance |
| 453.40000 | 459.90000 | NFM | North Sea | Chevron Ninian North |
| 453.40000 | 459.90000 | NFM | North Sea | Marathon Brae N, S |
| 453.40000 | 459.90000 | NFM | North Sea | Shell St. Fergus |
| 453.40000 | 459.90000 | NFM | Nottingham | Formans |

| Base | Mobile | Mode | Location | User and Notes |
|---|---|---|---|---|
| 453.40000 | 459.90000 | NFM | Oxford | University Science Area |
| 453.40000 | 459.90000 | NFM | Ridham | Docks |
| 453.40000 | 459.90000 | NFM | Sizewell | Power Station work teams Ch.2 |
| 453.40000 | 459.90000 | NFM | West Midlands | Bus Route 52 |
| 453.41250 | 459.91250 | NFM | London, Wimbledon | Lawn Tennis Association |
| 453.42500 | 459.92500 | NFM | Alba Chevron | FSU Maintenance |
| 453.42500 | 459.92500 | NFM | Eastbourne | Debenhams |
| 453.42500 | 459.92500 | NFM | Felixstowe | Docks |
| 453.42500 | 459.92500 | NFM | Immingham | Conoco Oil Refinery |
| 453.42500 | 459.92500 | NFM | London, Gatwick | Ground Repeater |
| 453.42500 | 459.92500 | NFM | London, Heathrow | Ground Repeater |
| 453.42500 | 459.92500 | NFM | Lutterworth | Asda Distribution Depot |
| 453.42500 | 459.92500 | NFM | Manchester | International Airport B.P. Aviation Fuel |
| 453.42500 | 459.92500 | NFM | Middlesborough | British Steel Security |
| 453.42500 | 459.92500 | NFM | North Sea | BP Buchan |
| 453.42500 | 459.92500 | NFM | North Sea | BP Clyde A |
| 453.42500 | 459.92500 | NFM | North Sea | BP Magnus |
| 453.42500 | 459.92500 | NFM | Swansea | DVLA |
| 453.43750 | 459.93750 | NFM | Luton Airport | Data Command Ch |
| 453.45000 | 459.95000 | NFM | Basildon | Shopwatch Security |
| 453.45000 | 459.95000 | NFM | Brentford | Sky TV Studios. |
| 453.45000 | 459.95000 | NFM | Cardiff | Inland Revenue Security |
| 453.45000 | 459.95000 | NFM | Cowley | Rover Plant Channel 3 |
| 453.45000 | 459.95000 | NFM | Felixstowe | Docks |
| 453.45000 | 459.95000 | NFM | Guernsey | HM Customs & Excise |
| 453.45000 | 459.95000 | NFM | Harwich | Port |
| 453.45000 | 459.95000 | NFM | Leicester | Haymarket Centre Security |
| 453.45000 | 459.95000 | NFM | Leicester | Universities of Christian Fellowship |
| 453.45000 | 459.95000 | NFM | Llantrisant | Royal Mint Security |
| 453.45000 | 459.95000 | NFM | London | Borough of Hammersmith & Fulham repeater |
| 453.45000 | 459.95000 | NFM | London | Borough of Haringay |
| 453.45000 | 459.95000 | NFM | London | St Katharines Dock Taylor Woodrow Security |
| 453.45000 | 459.95000 | NFM | London, Gatwick | Ground Repeater |
| 453.45000 | 459.95000 | NFM | London, Gower Street | London School of Hygiene & Tropical Medicine |
| 453.45000 | 459.95000 | NFM | London, Heathrow | Ground Repeater |
| 453.45000 | 459.95000 | NFM | Nationwide | BAA Police |
| 453.45000 | 459.95000 | NFM | North Sea | Shell Dunlin |
| 453.45000 | 459.95000 | NFM | Nuneaton | Mira Car Research |
| 453.45000 | 459.95000 | NFM | Stoke-on-Trent | Police |
| 453.45000 | 459.95000 | NFM | Welwyn Garden City | Rank Xerox |
| 453.46250 | 459.96250 | NFM | Brighton | Inland Revenue Security |
| 453.46250 | 459.96250 | NFM | London | Mellenium Dome trunked network |
| 453.46250 | 459.96250 | NFM | London, Wimbledon | Lawn Tennis Association |
| 453.46250 | 459.96250 | NFM | Nationwide | Inland Revenue Security |
| 453.47500 | 459.97500 | NFM | Ayr | Hannah Research Institute |
| 453.47500 | 459.97500 | NFM | Birmingham | Airport Security |
| 453.47500 | 459.97500 | NFM | Bishopton | Compaq Security |
| 453.47500 | 459.97500 | NFM | Cambridge | Girton College |
| 453.47500 | 459.97500 | NFM | Coventry | Shopwatch |
| 453.47500 | 459.97500 | NFM | Croydon | Allders Dept Store Security |
| 453.47500 | 459.97500 | NFM | Dover | Harbour Board Police |
| 453.47500 | 459.97500 | NFM | Flint | CBM Security |
| 453.47500 | 459.97500 | NFM | Grimsby | Council |
| 453.47500 | 459.97500 | NFM | Guernsey | HM Customs Surveillance |
| 453.47500 | 459.97500 | NFM | Harwich | Stena Sealink staff |
| 453.47500 | 459.97500 | NFM | London, Gatwick | Airline & BAA Ops |

| Base | Mobile | Mode | Location | User and Notes |
|------|--------|------|----------|----------------|
| 453.47500 | 459.97500 | NFM | London, Heathrow | Airlines ops. Terminal 3 |
| 453.47500 | 459.97500 | NFM | London, Hyde Park | Staff Security |
| 453.47500 | 459.97500 | NFM | London, Royal Parks | Staff Serco Hyde Park |
| 453.47500 | 459.97500 | NFM | Luton Airport | Arrivals/Departures Ch 3 |
| 453.47500 | 459.97500 | NFM | Manchester | Arndale Shopping Centre Sec. |
| 453.47500 | 459.97500 | NFM | Manchester | Manchester University Security |
| 453.47500 | 459.97500 | NFM | Nationwide | CAA Ground Movements |
| 453.47500 | 459.97500 | NFM | Newcastle | Metro Centre |
| 453.47500 | 459.97500 | NFM | North Kent | National Grid Sub Station |
| 453.47500 | 459.97500 | NFM | North Sea | BP Buchan |
| 453.47500 | 459.97500 | NFM | North Sea | Conoco Murchison |
| 453.47500 | 459.97500 | NFM | Peterborough | Football Club stewards |
| 453.47500 | 459.97500 | NFM | Richmond | Richmond Park staff |
| 453.47500 | 459.97500 | NFM | Rotherham | Council |
| 453.47500 | 459.97500 | NFM | Sheffield | Council emergency plumbers |
| 453.47500 | 459.97500 | NFM | Stansted | Security |
| 453.47500 | 459.97500 | NFM | Stevenage | ICL Computers Ch.3 |
| 453.47500 | 459.97500 | NFM | Swindon | Austin Rover Security |
| 453.47500 | 459.97500 | NFM | Tyneside | Tyne & Wear Metro |
| 453.47500 | 459.97500 | NFM | Walthamstow | Town Hall |
| 453.47500 | 460.97500 | NFM | Mansfield | Four Seasons Shopping Centre |
| 453.47850 | 459.98750 | NFM | Wolverhampton | Shopwatch Security |
| 453.48750 | 459.98750 | NFM | East Midlands Airport | Airport Fire |
| 453.48750 | 459.98750 | NFM | London, Wimbledon | Lawn Tennis Association |
| 453.50000 | 460.00000 | NFM | Belfast | Castlecourt Shopping Centre |
| 453.50000 | 460.00000 | NFM | Farnborough Airshow | Society of British Aerospace Companies |
| 453.50000 | 460.00000 | NFM | Folkestone | Stena Sealink |
| 453.50000 | 460.00000 | NFM | Harwich | Docks and Port Security |
| 453.50000 | 460.00000 | NFM | Harwich | Stena Sealink |
| 453.50000 | 460.00000 | NFM | Lancaster | Community Radio stores link |
| 453.50000 | 460.00000 | NFM | London | Bush House B.B.C. World Service Sigma Security |
| 453.50000 | 460.00000 | NFM | London | Docklands Light Railway |
| 453.50000 | 460.00000 | NFM | London, Gatwick | Airline & BAA Ops |
| 453.50000 | 460.00000 | NFM | London, Heathrow | British Midland |
| 453.50000 | 460.00000 | NFM | Manchester | Trafford Centre Ch.1 (LIMA) |
| 453.50000 | 460.00000 | NFM | Nationwide | Railtrack Security |
| 453.50000 | 460.00000 | NFM | Newcastle | Metro - Data Command Ch |
| 453.50000 | 460.00000 | NFM | Newport | Raitrack Security |
| 453.50000 | 460.00000 | NFM | North Sea | Shell Eider |
| 453.50000 | 460.00000 | NFM | Prestwick | Data |
| 453.50000 | 460.00000 | NFM | Salford | Keys Security Co |
| 453.50000 | 460.00000 | NFM | Sheffield | Council Markets Security (Ester) |
| 453.50000 | 460.00000 | NFM | Southampton | General Hospital Car Parks/Porters. |
| 453.50000 | 460.00000 | NFM | Southampton | Sealink |
| 453.50000 | 460.00000 | NFM | Stansted | Airline & BAA Ops |
| 453.50000 | 460.00000 | NFM | Stockley Park | Repeater |
| 453.50000 | 460.00000 | NFM | Tyne & Wear | Metro |
| 453.50000 | 460.00000 | NFM | Wigan | Factory Repeater |
| 453.52500 | 460.02500 | NFM | Brighton | British Rail Transport Police |
| 453.52500 | 460.02500 | NFM | Bristol | BAE Filton Ops |
| 453.52500 | 460.02500 | NFM | East Midlands Airport | Fire Channel 1 |
| 453.52500 | 460.02500 | NFM | Ellesmere Port | Shell Security |
| 453.52500 | 460.02500 | NFM | Felixstowe | Docks, Trinity Terminal |
| 453.52500 | 460.02500 | NFM | Havering | College. |
| 453.52500 | 460.02500 | NFM | Hull | City Council Housing |
| 453.52500 | 460.02500 | NFM | Ipswich | Railtrack |

| Base | Mobile | Mode | Location | User and Notes |
|------|--------|------|----------|----------------|
| 453.52500 | 460.02500 | NFM | Jersey | Harbour Ch 2 |
| 453.52500 | 460.02500 | NFM | Langley, Bucks | Total Oil Depot |
| 453.52500 | 460.02500 | NFM | Leicester | Leicester Polytechnic Security |
| 453.52500 | 460.02500 | NFM | London | East India Dock Teleservice. |
| 453.52500 | 460.02500 | NFM | London | Leicester Square Leisure User. |
| 453.52500 | 460.02500 | NFM | Nationwide | Transport Police |
| 453.52500 | 460.02500 | NFM | Nigg Bay | Oil Terminal Security |
| 453.52500 | 460.02500 | NFM | North Sea | Alba Chevron ANP East Crane |
| 453.52500 | 460.02500 | NFM | North Sea | Chevron Ninian North |
| 453.52500 | 460.02500 | NFM | Orpington | Property Investment Co. |
| 453.52500 | 460.02500 | NFM | Sheffield | City Council Gas Fitters |
| 453.52500 | 460.02500 | NFM | Sheffield | Council emergency gas fitters |
| 453.52500 | 460.02500 | NFM | Sizewell | Power Station work teams Ch.2 |
| 453.55000 | 460.05000 | NFM | Aberdeen | Railtrack |
| 453.55000 | 460.05000 | NFM | Barrow in Furness | Railtrack |
| 453.55000 | 460.05000 | NFM | Bedford | Railtrack |
| 453.55000 | 460.05000 | NFM | Birmingham | Railtrack Birmingham New St. |
| 453.55000 | 460.05000 | NFM | Blackpool | Railtrack |
| 453.55000 | 460.05000 | NFM | Bletchley | Railtrack Bletchley Yard |
| 453.55000 | 460.05000 | NFM | Brentwood | Railtrack Shenfield |
| 453.55000 | 460.05000 | NFM | Brighton | Railtrack (Brighton Depot) |
| 453.55000 | 480.05000 | NFM | Cardiff | Great Western Railway |
| 453.55000 | 460.05000 | NFM | Carlisle | Railtrack |
| 453.55000 | 460.05000 | NFM | Chester | Railtrack |
| 453.55000 | 460.05000 | NFM | Coventry | Railtrack |
| 453.55000 | 460.05000 | NFM | Crewe | Railtrack |
| 453.55000 | 460.05000 | NFM | Croydon | Railtrack, Selhurst Railway Depot |
| 453.55000 | 460.05000 | NFM | Doncaster | Railtrack |
| 453.55000 | 460.05000 | NFM | Eastbourne | Railtrack Eastbourne Station |
| 453.55000 | 460.05000 | NFM | Edinburgh | Railtrack, Edinburgh Waverley |
| 453.55000 | 460.05000 | NFM | Ely | Railtrack |
| 453.55000 | 460.05000 | NFM | England, North West | BR Track Workers to Trains Ch 1 |
| 453.55000 | 460.05000 | NFM | Glasgow | Railtrack, Glasgow Queen Street |
| 453.55000 | 460.05000 | NFM | Harwich | International Station Railtrack Staff |
| 453.55000 | 460.05000 | NFM | Harwich | Railtrack, Parkeston Yard |
| 453.55000 | 460.05000 | NFM | Heathrow | Airport B-Line Tugs Movements |
| 453.55000 | 460.05000 | NFM | Hull | Railtrack, Hull Station |
| 453.55000 | 460.05000 | NFM | Ipswich | Railtrack |
| 453.55000 | 460.05000 | NFM | Leeds | Railtrack |
| 453.55000 | 460.05000 | NFM | Leicester | Railtrack |
| 453.55000 | 460.05000 | NFM | London | Cricklewood Railtrack Shunting Ops |
| 453.55000 | 460.05000 | NFM | London | Fenchurch St Station Lts Line |
| 453.55000 | 460.05000 | NFM | London | Railtrack (Cannon Street) |
| 453.55000 | 460.05000 | NFM | London | Railtrack (Clapham Junction Yard) |
| 453.55000 | 460.05000 | NFM | London | Railtrack (East Croydon) |
| 453.55000 | 460.05000 | NFM | London | Railtrack (Fenchurch Street) |
| 453.55000 | 460.05000 | NFM | London | Railtrack (Ilford Car Sheds) |
| 453.55000 | 460.05000 | NFM | London | Railtrack (Liverpool Street) |
| 453.55000 | 460.05000 | NFM | London | Railtrack (Paddington) |
| 453.55000 | 460.05000 | NFM | London | Railtrack (Slade Green Depot) |
| 453.55000 | 460.05000 | NFM | London | Railtrack (Waterloo) |
| 453.55000 | 460.05000 | NFM | London | Railtrack (Wimbledon Park) |
| 453.55000 | 460.05000 | NFM | London, Heathrow | B-Line Tug Movements |
| 453.55000 | 460.05000 | NFM | Manchester | Railtrack (Manchester Piccadilly) |
| 453.55000 | 460.05000 | NFM | Nationwide | Railtrack Stations Channel 1 |
| 453.55000 | 460.05000 | NFM | Newcastle | Railway Station |

| 453.55000 | 460.05000 | NFM | North Sea | Chevron Alba ANP Construction |
| 453.55000 | 460.05000 | NFM | North Sea | Chevron Ninian South |
| 453.55000 | 460.05000 | NFM | Norwich | Railtrack (Norwich Crown Point) |
| 453.55000 | 460.05000 | NFM | Nottingham | City Council |
| 453.55000 | 460.05000 | NFM | Penzance | Railtrack |
| 453.55000 | 460.05000 | NFM | Preston | Railtrack |
| 453.55000 | 460.05000 | NFM | Preston | Train guards |
| 453.55000 | 460.05000 | NFM | Reading | Railtrack |
| 453.55000 | 460.05000 | NFM | Salford | Railtrack |
| 453.55000 | 460.05000 | NFM | Selhurst Junction | Railtrack |
| 453.55000 | 460.05000 | NFM | Sheffield | Railtrack |
| 453.55000 | 460.05000 | NFM | Shrewsbury | Railtrack |
| 453.55000 | 460.05000 | NFM | Slade Green Depot | Railtrack |
| 453.55000 | 460.05000 | NFM | Stansted | Railtrack |
| 453.55000 | 460.05000 | NFM | Stratford-Upon-Avon | Railtrack |
| 453.55000 | 460.05000 | NFM | Wigan | Railtrack |
| 453.55000 | 460.05000 | NFM | Woking | Railtrack |
| 453.55000 | 460.05000 | NFM | Wolverhampton | Railtrack |
| 453.55000 | 460.05000 | NFM | York | Railtrack |
| 453.56000 | 460.06000 | NFM | London, Heathrow | Data |
| 453.56250 | 460.06250 | NFM | Nationwide | Railtrack |
| 453.56250 | 460.06250 | NFM | Swansea To Cork | Ferry Service |
| 453.57500 | 460.07500 | NFM | Dagenham | Ford Car plant engineering |
| 453.57500 | 460.07500 | NFM | Debden | Debden Playing Fields. |
| 453.57500 | 460.07500 | NFM | Enfield | Palace Gardens suppliers |
| 453.57500 | 460.07500 | NFM | Felixstowe | Freightliners |
| 453.57500 | 460.07500 | NFM | Immingham | Conoco Oil Refinery |
| 453.57500 | 460.07500 | NFM | Ipswich | Docks |
| 453.57500 | 460.07500 | NFM | London | Covent Garden security |
| 453.57500 | 460.07500 | NFM | Nationwide | British Airways |
| 453.57500 | 460.07500 | NFM | North Sea | BP Buchan |
| 453.57500 | 460.07500 | NFM | North Sea | BP Magnus |
| 453.57500 | 460.07500 | NFM | Southampton | Airport Ford Transit Factory |
| 453.57500 | 460.07500 | NFM | Southampton | Ford Transit Plant (W) |
| 453.57500 | 460.07500 | NFM | Whipsnade | Whipsnade Zoo |
| 453.57500 | 460.07500 | NFM | Worksop | Tesco |
| 453.58750 | 460.08750 | NFM | Newcastle | Data Link |
| 453.60000 | 460.10000 | NFM | Accrington | Nori Brick Works |
| 453.60000 | 460.10000 | NFM | Avonmouth | Docks (RED) |
| 453.60000 | 460.10000 | NFM | Bristol | Debenhams Security |
| 453.60000 | 460.10000 | NFM | Coventry | Shops Radio Link to Police |
| 453.60000 | 460.10000 | NFM | Cowley | Rover Assembly |
| 453.60000 | 460.10000 | NFM | Dagenham | Rhone Poulenc Chemicals |
| 453.60000 | 460.10000 | NFM | Humberside | County Council |
| 453.60000 | 460.10000 | NFM | Leeds | Shopwatch |
| 453.60000 | 460.10000 | NFM | London | Australian High Commission |
| 453.60000 | 460.10000 | NFM | London | Docklands Light Railway depot |
| 453.60000 | 460.10000 | NFM | London | Olympia Exhibition security |
| 453.60000 | 460.10000 | NFM | London, Gatwick | Ground Repeater |
| 453.60000 | 460.10000 | NFM | London, Heathrow | Airline & BAA Ops |
| 453.60000 | 460.10000 | NFM | London, Piccadilly | Regent Palace Hotel |
| 453.60000 | 460.10000 | NFM | Newport | Godings Steel Holdings |
| 453.60000 | 460.10000 | NFM | North Sea | Amoco N W Hutton |
| 453.60000 | 460.10000 | NFM | North Sea | Texaco Tartan |
| 453.60000 | 460.10000 | NFM | Prestatyn | Ship Technicians |
| 453.60000 | 460.10000 | NFM | Stansted | Ground Repeater |

| Base | Mobile | Mode | Location | User and Notes |
|------|--------|------|----------|----------------|
| 453.60000 | 460.10000 | NFM | Stevenage | Kentucky Fried Chicken Drive Thru |
| 453.60000 | 460.10000 | NFM | Teesside | British Steel trains |
| 453.61250 | 460.11250 | NFM | Cambridge | Station Railtrack |
| 453.61250 | 460.11250 | NFM | Cardiff | Railtrack |
| 453.61250 | 460.11250 | NFM | England, South East | Network South East trains |
| 453.61250 | 460.11250 | NFM | London | Euston Station Virgin and Intercity |
| 453.61250 | 460.11250 | NFM | Manchester | Piccadilly Station Staff |
| 453.61250 | 460.11250 | NFM | Wimbledon | Station Network Southwest Trains |
| 453.62500 | 460.12500 | NFM | Catford | Running Track. |
| 453.62500 | 460.12500 | NFM | Croydon | Selhurst railway depot |
| 453.62500 | 460.12500 | NFM | Denham | Bucks Food Co. |
| 453.62500 | 460.12500 | NFM | Doncaster | Doncaster Cable |
| 453.62500 | 460.12500 | NFM | Duxworth | Imperial War Museum security |
| 453.62500 | 460.12500 | NFM | England, South East | Network South East trains |
| 453.62500 | 460.12500 | NFM | Greenfood | Food Manufacturer. |
| 453.62500 | 460.12500 | NFM | Harwich | Docks Parkestone Quay |
| 453.62500 | 460.12500 | NFM | Immingham | Tioxide Chemicals |
| 453.62500 | 460.12500 | NFM | Jersey | British Airways Handling |
| 453.62500 | 460.12500 | NFM | London | Imperial War Museum Staff |
| 453.62500 | 460.12500 | NFM | London | St James Park Staff. |
| 453.62500 | 460.12500 | NFM | London | Stratford Anthonys Metals Ltd. |
| 453.62500 | 460.12500 | NFM | London , Acton | B.B.C. Site Security |
| 453.62500 | 460.12500 | NFM | London, Kingsway | CAA Headquarters |
| 453.62500 | 460.12500 | NFM | London, Trocadero | Funland |
| 453.62500 | 460.12500 | NFM | Milford Haven | Refinery |
| 453.62500 | 460.12500 | NFM | North Sea | Chevron Alba FSU General Ops. |
| 453.62500 | 460.12500 | NFM | Stanmore | Canons Park School |
| 453.62500 | 460.12500 | NFM | Stratford | Metal recycling plant |
| 453.62500 | 460.12500 | NFM | Sunbury | Planner Products Ltd. |
| 453.62500 | 460.12500 | NFM | Swansea Docks | Cargo Handlers |
| 453.65000 | 460.15000 | NFM | Dartford | Europort |
| 453.65000 | 460.15000 | NFM | Edinburgh | Lothian Regional Transport Ch.4 |
| 453.65000 | 460.15000 | NFM | Leicester | Fosse Park Car Park Security |
| 453.65000 | 460.15000 | NFM | London | Port Authority |
| 453.65000 | 460.15000 | NFM | London, Heathrow | Airline & BAA Ops |
| 453.65000 | 460.15000 | NFM | London, Southbank | LWT security |
| 453.65000 | 460.15000 | NFM | Newmarket | Race course security |
| 453.65000 | 460.15000 | NFM | Newport | Godings Workers Handhelds |
| 453.65000 | 460.15000 | NFM | North Sea | Shell Leman AK |
| 453.65000 | 460.15000 | NFM | North Sea | Texaco Tartan |
| 453.65000 | 460.15000 | NFM | York | Refuse collection |
| 453.65000 | 460.15000 | NFM | York | York Council Car Parks |
| 453.67500 | 460.17500 | NFM | Ascot | Race Course Management. |
| 453.67500 | 460.17500 | NFM | Avonmouth | Docks |
| 453.67500 | 460.17500 | NFM | Bletchley | Leisure Centre |
| 453.67500 | 460.17500 | NFM | Channel Tunnel | Trains |
| 453.67500 | 460.17500 | NFM | Edinburgh | Lothian Regional Transport |
| 453.67500 | 460.17500 | NFM | Liverpool | Stanlow Oil Refinery |
| 453.67500 | 460.17500 | NFM | London | Docklands Light Railway |
| 453.67500 | 460.17500 | NFM | Stallingbough | SCM |
| 453.70000 | 460.20000 | NFM | Barnet | General Hospital Porters/ Security |
| 453.70000 | 460.20000 | NFM | Bedford | College Security |
| 453.70000 | 460.20000 | NFM | Bristol | Bristol Intercity (Security) |
| 453.70000 | 460.20000 | NFM | Bristol | Galleries Shopping Centre Cleaners |
| 453.70000 | 460.20000 | NFM | Canvey Island | Oil Refinery |
| 453.70000 | 460.20000 | NFM | Coventry | Dunlop Security |

| Base | Mobile | Mode | Location | User and Notes |
|------|--------|------|----------|----------------|
| 453.70000 | 460.20000 | NFM | Dover | Eastern Docks Port Ops |
| 453.70000 | 460.20000 | NFM | Hull | Stagecoach Buses |
| 453.70000 | 460.20000 | NFM | London | Barnet General Hospital Repeater |
| 453.70000 | 460.20000 | NFM | London, Gatwick | Airline & BAA Ops |
| 453.70000 | 460.20000 | NFM | Manchester Shaw | Aerial Company |
| 453.70000 | 460.20000 | NFM | Middlesborough | Cleveland Centre Security |
| 453.70000 | 460.20000 | NFM | Milton Keynes | John Lewis store |
| 453.70000 | 460.20000 | NFM | Newcastle | The Metro Centre Paging |
| 453.70000 | 460.20000 | NFM | North Sea | Alba Chevron FSU Crane Operations |
| 453.70000 | 460.20000 | NFM | North Sea | Chevron Ninian North |
| 453.70000 | 460.20000 | NFM | North Sea | Shell North Cormorant |
| 453.70000 | 460.20000 | NFM | Oldham | Austin Timber Security |
| 453.70000 | 460.20000 | NFM | Sevenoaks | Shopwatch |
| 453.70000 | 460.20000 | NFM | Sheffield | Sheffield Wednesday Football Club stewards |
| 453.70000 | 460.20000 | NFM | Stockport | Merseybus Inspectors |
| 453.71250 | 460.21250 | NFM | Immingham | Conoco Oil Maintenance |
| 453.72500 | 460.22500 | NFM | Dartford | Bluewater Shopping Centre House of Fraser Security |
| 453.72500 | 460.22500 | NFM | Leicester | Shires Centre Surveillance |
| 453.72500 | 460.22500 | NFM | Morecambc Bay | BGE&P |
| 453.72500 | 460.22500 | NFM | North Sea | Alba Chevron ANP Production - Mobiles |
| 453.72500 | 460.22500 | NFM | North Sea | Chevron Ninian Central |
| 453.72500 | 460.22500 | NFM | Oldham | Royal Oldham Hospital |
| 453.72500 | 460.22500 | NFM | West Midlands | Engineering Town Planning |
| 453.72500 | 460.72500 | NFM | Manchester | Hospital porters |
| 453.75000 | 460.25000 | NFM | Aberdeen (Dyce Airport) | Staff |
| 453.75000 | 460.25000 | NFM | Bournemouth | Repeater |
| 453.75000 | 460.25000 | NFM | Brighton | American Express |
| 453.75000 | 460.25000 | NFM | Brighton | Conference Centre |
| 453.75000 | 460.25000 | NFM | Channel Tunnel | Trains |
| 453.75000 | 460.25000 | NFM | Gloucestershire | Great Western Security |
| 453.75000 | 460.25000 | NFM | Heyes | Heinz |
| 453.75000 | 460.25000 | NFM | London | Grosvenor House Hotel |
| 453.75000 | 460.25000 | NFM | London | Hotel Earls Court. |
| 453.75000 | 460.25000 | NFM | London | New Parliament Building builders |
| 453.75000 | 460.25000 | NFM | London | Wood Green Shopping Centre security |
| 453.75000 | 460.25000 | NFM | London, Brent Cross | Marks & Spencer security |
| 453.75000 | 460.25000 | NFM | London, Gatwick | Airline & BAA Ops |
| 453.75000 | 460.25000 | NFM | London, Gatwick | Airline ops. |
| 453.75000 | 460.25000 | NFM | London, Greenwich | Roans School |
| 453.75000 | 460.25000 | NFM | London, Greenwich Park | Roans School. |
| 453.75000 | 460.25000 | NFM | London, Mayfair | Grosvenor Hotel. |
| 453.75000 | 460.25000 | NFM | Luton | Vauxhall Motors |
| 453.75000 | 460.25000 | NFM | Manchester | Telford Centre security Ch.2 |
| 453.75000 | 460.25000 | NFM | Newport | Godings Security |
| 453.75000 | 460.25000 | NFM | North Sea | Amoco Bacton |
| 453.75000 | 460.25000 | NFM | North Sea | Amoco Lomond |
| 453.75000 | 460.25000 | NFM | North Sea | Amoco NW Hutton |
| 453.75000 | 460.25000 | NFM | North Sea | Amoco North Everest |
| 453.75000 | 460.25000 | NFM | Oldham | The Spindlers Security |
| 453.75000 | 460.25000 | NFM | Stowmarket | ICI Paints Fire/Medics |
| 453.75000 | 460.25000 | NFM | Wiltshire | Great Western Security |
| 453.77500 | 460.27500 | NFM | Avonmouth | Dock crane operators and stevedores |
| 453.77500 | 460.27500 | NFM | Barrow In Furness | Shopwatch Security |
| 453.77500 | 460.27500 | NFM | Birkenhead | Pyramid Shopping Centre Sec. |
| 453.77500 | 460.27500 | NFM | Bournemouth | C&A security |
| 453.77500 | 460.27500 | NFM | Cambridge | City Centre Security |

| Base | Mobile | Mode | Location | User and Notes |
|------|--------|------|----------|----------------|
| 453.77500 | 460.27500 | NFM | Channel Tunnel | Trains |
| 453.77500 | 460.27500 | NFM | Culham | UKAEA |
| 453.77500 | 460.27500 | NFM | Harwich | International Port Maintenance |
| 453.77500 | 460.27500 | NFM | Hatfield | Galleria Shopping Centre Sec. |
| 453.77500 | 460.27500 | NFM | Kings Lynn | Crest Petroleum |
| 453.77500 | 460.27500 | NFM | Leicester | Fosse Park Shop Security |
| 453.77500 | 460.27500 | NFM | Liverpool | St Johns Shopping Centre Sec. |
| 453.77500 | 460.27500 | NFM | London, Gatwick | Ground Repeater |
| 453.77500 | 460.27500 | NFM | London, Heathrow | Ground Repeater |
| 453.77500 | 460.27500 | NFM | Luton | Arndale Shopping Centre, Reliance Security |
| 453.77500 | 460.27500 | NFM | Newcastle Airport | Airline Ops |
| 453.77500 | 460.27500 | NFM | North Sea | Phillips Maureen telemetry |
| 453.77500 | 460.27500 | NFM | Northampton | C & A Security |
| 453.77500 | 460.27500 | NFM | Northampton | Debenhams Security |
| 453.77500 | 460.27500 | NFM | Northampton | Grosvenor Centre Security |
| 453.77500 | 460.27500 | NFM | Retford | Shoplink |
| 453.77500 | 460.27500 | NFM | Runcorn | Shopping Centre Security |
| 453.77500 | 460.27500 | NFM | Southampton | Hospital Transport Ch 2 |
| 453.77500 | 460.27500 | NFM | Stansted | Light Railway |
| 453.78750 | 460.28750 | NFM | Southampton | Meridian T.V Link Feed |
| 453.80000 | 453.80000 | NFM | North Sea | Amoco Lomond |
| 453.80000 | 460.30000 | NFM | Brighton | Brighton & Hove Bus & Coach |
| 453.80000 | 460.30000 | NFM | Cheltenham | Regent Arcade Security |
| 453.80000 | 460.30000 | NFM | Coventry | Warwick University |
| 453.80000 | 460.30000 | NFM | Hull | City centre bases |
| 453.80000 | 460.30000 | NFM | London, Gatwick | Ground Repeater |
| 453.80000 | 460.30000 | NFM | London, Heathrow | Airline & BAA Ops |
| 453.80000 | 460.30000 | NFM | Luton Airport | Reed Aviation |
| 453.80000 | 460.30000 | NFM | Maltby | Tarmac |
| 453.80000 | 460.30000 | NFM | Manchester | Trafford Park Factory Loading Bay |
| 453.80000 | 460.30000 | NFM | Milford Haven | Refinery |
| 453.80000 | 460.30000 | NFM | Newmarket | The Jockey Club |
| 453.80000 | 460.30000 | NFM | North Sea | Amoco North Everest |
| 453.80000 | 460.30000 | NFM | North Sea | Chevron Ninian South |
| 453.80000 | 460.30000 | NFM | North Sea | Shell Tem |
| 453.82500 | 460.32500 | NFM | Bury | Premier Cars |
| 453.82500 | 460.32500 | NFM | Channel Tunnel | Trains |
| 453.82500 | 460.32500 | NFM | Doncaster | Frenchgate Centre |
| 453.82500 | 460.32500 | NFM | Glasgow | Lloyds TSB Head Office |
| 453.82500 | 460.32500 | NFM | Ipswich | Cranfield Bros. |
| 453.82500 | 460.32500 | NFM | London | National Gallery |
| 453.82500 | 460.32500 | NFM | London, Bethnal Green | Traffic Wardens |
| 453.82500 | 460.32500 | NFM | London, Gatwick | Airline. ops |
| 453.82500 | 460.32500 | NFM | London, Heathrow | Godfrey Davis Eurocar |
| 453.82500 | 460.32500 | NFM | London, Heathrow | Ground Repeater |
| 453.82500 | 460.32500 | NFM | New Holland | Howarth Timber |
| 453.82500 | 460.32500 | NFM | North Sea | Amoco Lomond |
| 453.82500 | 460.32500 | NFM | North Sea | Amoco North Everest |
| 453.85000 | 460.35000 | NFM | Aberdeen | Hospital |
| 453.85000 | 460.35000 | NFM | Beaulieu | Motor Museum Security |
| 453.85000 | 460.35000 | NFM | Belfast | Ulsterbus |
| 453.85000 | 460.35000 | NFM | Bellingham | ICI |
| 453.85000 | 460.35000 | NFM | Brighton | Buses |
| 453.85000 | 460.35000 | FM | Cambridge | College Security |
| 453.85000 | 460.35000 | NFM | England, South East | Network South East trains |
| 453.85000 | 460.35000 | NFM | Hampshire | Buses |

| Base | Mobile | Mode | Location | User and Notes |
|------|--------|------|----------|----------------|
| 453.85000 | 460.35000 | NFM | Lancaster | University security and porters |
| 453.85000 | 460.35000 | NFM | London | Colindale A-Kwika Car Service |
| 453.85000 | 460.35000 | NFM | London | Elgro Girton |
| 453.85000 | 460.35000 | NFM | London, Arnos Grove | Ace Radio Cars |
| 453.85000 | 460.35000 | NFM | London, Gatwick | Ground Repeater |
| 453.85000 | 460.35000 | NFM | London, Heathrow | Ground Repeater |
| 453.85000 | 460.35000 | NFM | Luton Airport | Car Parks Ch 6 |
| 453.85000 | 460.35000 | NFM | Manchester | International Airport |
| 453.85000 | 460.35000 | NFM | Merseyside | Merseyside Electric |
| 453.85000 | 460.35000 | NFM | Newmarket | Security |
| 453.85000 | 460.35000 | NFM | Newport | Docks |
| 453.85000 | 460.35000 | NFM | Norfolk | Norwich & Norfolk Hospital |
| 453.85000 | 460.35000 | NFM | North Sea | BP Forties E |
| 453.85000 | 460.35000 | NFM | Rochdale | Queensway Private Hire |
| 453.85000 | 460.35000 | NFM | Sheffield | Forge Alert Security |
| 453.85000 | 460.35000 | NFM | Stansted | Catering |
| 453.85000 | 460.35000 | NFM | Wirral | Merseybus Inspectors |
| 453.87500 | 460.37500 | NFM | Aberdeen | Dyce Airport, Staff |
| 453.87500 | 460.37500 | NFM | Dartford | Engineering |
| 453.87500 | 460.37500 | NFM | Edinburgh | Lothian Regional Transport |
| 453.87500 | 460.37500 | NFM | Harrage | Port Authority Ch.2 |
| 453.87500 | 460.37500 | NFM | Kew | Royal Botanic Gardens |
| 453.87500 | 460.37500 | NFM | London | Charing Cross Hotel |
| 453.87500 | 460.37500 | NFM | London | Courtaulds Coatings Repeater |
| 453.87500 | 460.37500 | NFM | London | Covent Garden Leisure |
| 453.87500 | 460.37500 | NFM | London | Dalston Cross Shopping Centre Security & Cleaners |
| 453.87500 | 460.37500 | NFM | London | Elephant and Castle Hotel |
| 453.87500 | 460.37500 | NFM | London | St Johns Wood Education |
| 453.87500 | 460.37500 | NFM | London, Gatwick | Airline & BAA Ops |
| 453.87500 | 460.37500 | NFM | Luton Airport | Airlines ops/fire |
| 453.87500 | 460.37500 | NFM | Luton Airport | Monarch Airlines |
| 453.87500 | 460.37500 | NFM | Manchester | Freightliners Supervisors |
| 453.87500 | 460.37500 | NFM | Manchester | Trafford Centre |
| 453.87500 | 460.37500 | NFM | North Sea | Chevron Alba Field Safety |
| 453.87500 | 460.37500 | NFM | North sea | Chevron Ninian Central |
| 453.87500 | 460.37500 | NFM | Slough | Factory |
| 453.87500 | 460.37500 | NFM | Waltham Abbey | Manufacturer |
| 453.88750 | 460.38750 | NFM | London | Dalston Cross Shopping Centre Security |
| 453.90000 | 460.40000 | NFM | Ascot | Railtrack Station Staff. |
| 453.90000 | 460.40000 | NFM | Ashford | Railtrack |
| 453.90000 | 460.40000 | NFM | Barry | Docks Security |
| 453.90000 | 460.40000 | NFM | Birmingham | Railtrack Birmingham International |
| 453.90000 | 460.40000 | NFM | Bristol | Railtrack |
| 453.90000 | 460.40000 | NFM | Dartford | Connex Rail staff |
| 453.90000 | 460.40000 | NFM | Derby | Railtrack |
| 453.90000 | 460.40000 | NFM | Doncaster | Railtrack |
| 453.90000 | 460.40000 | NFM | Edinburgh | ScotRail Haymarket Depot |
| 453.90000 | 460.40000 | NFM | Glasgow | ScotRail Glasgow Central |
| 453.90000 | 460.40000 | NFM | Guildford | Railtrack |
| 453.90000 | 460.40000 | NFM | Hoo Junction Deport | Railtrack |
| 453.90000 | 460.40000 | NFM | Hull | Railtrack Paragon Signal Box |
| 453.90000 | 460.40000 | NFM | Killingholme | Railtrack/Oil Refineries |
| 453.90000 | 460.40000 | NFM | Liverpool | Railtrack Liverpool Lime Street |
| 453.90000 | 460.40000 | NFM | London | Charing Cross Railtrack Staff |
| 453.90000 | 460.40000 | NFM | London | Railtrack (Barking) |
| 453.90000 | 460.40000 | NFM | London | Railtrack (Charing Cross) |

| Base | Mobile | Mode | Location | User and Notes |
|---|---|---|---|---|
| 453.90000 | 460.40000 | NFM | London | Railtrack (Euston) |
| 453.90000 | 460.40000 | NFM | London | Railtrack (Gatwick Airport) |
| 453.90000 | 460.40000 | NFM | London | Railtrack (Kings Cross) |
| 453.90000 | 460.40000 | NFM | London | Railtrack (Victoria) |
| 453.90000 | 460.40000 | NFM | London | Railtrack (Waterloo City) |
| 453.90000 | 460.40000 | NFM | London | Railtrack (Willesden Yard) |
| 453.90000 | 460.40000 | NFM | London Bridge | Railtrack Station Staff |
| 453.90000 | 460.40000 | NFM | Manchester | Railtrack (Heaton Depot) |
| 453.90000 | 460.40000 | NFM | Nationwide | Railtrack Stations |
| 453.90000 | 460.40000 | NFM | Newport | Railtrack Porters |
| 453.90000 | 460.40000 | NFM | North Sea | Shell Cormorant A |
| 453.90000 | 460.40000 | NFM | Norwich | Railtrack (Norwich Crown Point) |
| 453.90000 | 460.40000 | NFM | Nottingham | Railtrack |
| 453.90000 | 460.40000 | NFM | Perth | ScotRail |
| 453.90000 | 460.40000 | NFM | Peterborough | Railtrack Station Staff |
| 453.90000 | 460.40000 | NFM | Ramsgate | Railtrack Station & Depot |
| 453.90000 | 460.40000 | NFM | Reading | Railtrack |
| 453.90000 | 460.40000 | NFM | Sheffield | Railtrack Tensley Hill marshalling yard |
| 453.90000 | 460.40000 | NFM | Thames | RailtrackTurbo Workshop |
| 453.90000 | 460.40000 | NFM | Watford | Railtrack (Watford Junction) |
| 453.91750 | 460.41750 | NFM | Machynlleth | Railtrack |
| 453.92500 | 460.02500 | NFM | London, Heathrow | Airline Ops trunked. |
| 453.92500 | 460.42500 | NFM | Birmingham | Airport Airline Ops |
| 453.92500 | 460.42500 | NFM | Bristol | Car Park Security (SE) |
| 453.92500 | 460.42500 | NFM | County Durham | Security Firm |
| 453.92500 | 460.42500 | NFM | Edinburgh | Ambulance Service |
| 453.92500 | 460.42500 | NFM | Leicester | Shires Centre Security Ch 1 |
| 453.92500 | 460.42500 | NFM | Lindsey | Oil Refinery |
| 453.92500 | 460.42500 | NFM | London | Docklands Light Railway |
| 453.92500 | 460.42500 | NFM | London, Gatwick | Airline & BAA Ops |
| 453.92500 | 460.42500 | NFM | London, Heathrow | Airline & BAA Ops |
| 453.92500 | 460.42500 | NFM | Manchester | International Airport |
| 453.92500 | 460.42500 | NFM | Mansfield | Shopwatch |
| 453.92500 | 460.42500 | NFM | Milford Haven | Refinery |
| 453.92500 | 460.42500 | NFM | Newport | Patent Office Security |
| 453.92500 | 460.42500 | NFM | North Sea | BP Forties E |
| 453.92500 | 460.42500 | NFM | Rhyl | Shop security with CCTV & Shopwatch |
| 453.92500 | 460.42500 | NFM | Stansted | Loading |
| 453.92500 | 460.42500 | NFM | Swindon | Austin Rover Security |
| 453.92500 | 460.42500 | NFM | Worcester | Shopwatch |
| 453.93750 | 460.43750 | NFM | Edinburgh | ScotRail Data Links |
| 453.93750 | 460.43750 | NFM | Glasgow | ScotRail Data Links |
| 453.93750 | 460.43750 | NFM | Perth | ScotRail Data Links |
| 453.95000 | 460.45000 | NFM | Channel Tunnel | Trains |
| 453.95000 | 460.45000 | NFM | Immingham | Conoco Oil Refinery |
| 453.95000 | 460.45000 | NFM | London, Heathrow | Airport Terminal 2 |
| 453.95000 | 460.45000 | NFM | London, Heathrow | Airline Ops trunked |
| 453.95000 | 460.45000 | NFM | Newport | Spencer & Llanwern Docks |
| 453.95000 | 460.45000 | NFM | North Sea | Chevron Alba ANP Maintenance |
| 453.95000 | 460.45000 | NFM | North Sea | Chevron Ninian Central |
| 453.95000 | 460.45000 | NFM | North Sea | Marathon Brae North |
| 453.95000 | 460.45000 | NFM | Southampton | Factory |
| 453.96250 | 460.45000 | NFM | London | London Taxis |
| 453.96250 | 460.46250 | NFM | Brighton | Council |
| 453.96250 | 460.46250 | NFM | Portsmouth | Parking Enforcement. |
| 453.96250 | 460.46250 | NFM | Stevenage | Sovereign Coach & Buss Company |

| Base | Mobile | Mode | Location | User and Notes |
|---|---|---|---|---|
| 453.96250 | 463.46250 | NFM | London | Digital Protection traffic |
| 453.97500 | 460.47500 | NFM | Barrow in Furness | Taxi |
| 453.97500 | 460.47500 | NFM | Bath | University Security |
| 453.97500 | 460.47500 | NFM | Cowley | Rover Security Channel 7 |
| 453.97500 | 460.47500 | NFM | Kingston Upon Thames | Parking Wardens control |
| 453.97500 | 460.47500 | NFM | Leicester | Road Contractors |
| 453.97500 | 460.47500 | NFM | Liverpool | John Moore University Security |
| 453.97500 | 460.47500 | NFM | London | Kodak |
| 453.97500 | 460.47500 | NFM | London | Silver Town |
| 453.97500 | 460.47500 | NFM | London, Heathrow | Airline & BAA Ops |
| 453.97500 | 460.47500 | NFM | London, Notting Hill | Lucky Cabs |
| 453.97500 | 460.47500 | NFM | Luton | Vauxhall Motors |
| 453.97500 | 460.47500 | NFM | North Sea | BP Forties E |
| 453.97500 | 460.47500 | NFM | Nuneaton | Mira Car Research |
| 453.97500 | 460.47500 | NFM | Sheffield | Stockbridge Steels Engineering |
| 453.97500 | 460.47500 | NFM | Sizewell | Power Station work teams Ch.3 |
| 453.97500 | 460.47500 | NFM | Stansted | Airport Ops |
| 453.97500 | 460.47500 | NFM | Stansted Airport | Ramp Ch 1 |
| 453.97500 | 460.47500 | NFM | Windsor | Caterers for Royal Wedding |
| 453.97500 | 460.48750 | NFM | Channel Tunnel | Trains |

## 454.0125 - 454.8375 MHz    WIDE AREA PAGING 25 kHz

| Base | Mobile | Mode | Location | User and Notes |
|---|---|---|---|---|
| 454.02500 | | NFM | Birmingham | Heartlands Hospital voice paging |
| 454.02500 | | NFM | Birmingham | QE Hospital Pagers |
| 454.02500 | | NFM | London | Hammersmith Area Mosque |
| 454.02500 | | NFM | London | Regents Park Mosque |
| 454.02500 | | NFM | London | US Embassy |
| 454.02500 | | NFM | Nationwide | Hospital Voice Paging |
| 454.02500 | | NFM | Newcastle | Hospital Emerg. Voice Paging |
| 454.02500 | | NFM | Ninian North | Chevron |
| 454.02500 | | NFM | North Sea | Elf Enterprise Claymore A |
| 454.02500 | | NFM | North Sea | Elf Enterprise Piper |
| 454.02500 | | NFM | Wakefield | Clayton Hospital |
| 454.05000 | | NFM | North Sea | Chevron Ninian North |
| 454.05000 | | NFM | North Sea | Elf Enterprise Claymore A |
| 454.05000 | | NFM | North Sea | Elf Enterprise Piper |
| 454.06250 | | NFM | Channel Tunnel | Trains |
| 454.07500 | | NFM | London | Kings College Hospital voice pagers |
| 454.07500 | | NFM | North Sea | Amoco Bacton Paging System |
| 454.07500 | 447.57500 | NFM | Nationwide | Aircall Voice Paging |
| 454.10000 | | NFM | Birmingham | Newcross Hospital voice paging |
| 454.10000 | | NFM | London | Golders Green Shree Swaminarayan Temple |
| 454.10000 | | NFM | London | Wembley Area Mosque |
| 454.10000 | | NFM | Manchester | Hospital Pager |
| 454.10000 | | NFM | North Sea | Shell Brent B |
| 454.10000 | | NFM | Whiston | Hospital Voice Paging |
| 454.12500 | | NFM | Bradford | Mosque |
| 454.12500 | | NFM | London | Voice paging Thames Coastguard to RNLI |
| 454.12500 | | NFM | North Sea | Chevron Ninian North |
| 454.12500 | | NFM | North Sea | Elf Enterprise Claymore A |
| 454.12500 | | NFM | North Sea | Elf Enterprise Piper |
| 454.15000 | | NFM | London | Silvertown Mosque. |
| 454.16250 | | NFM | North Sea | Chevron Ninian Central |
| 454.17500 | | NFM | Cambridge | Addenbrookes Hospital Paging |
| 454.17500 | | NFM | Leeds | General Infirmary voice pager |
| 454.17500 | | NFM | Leeds, Killingbeck | Pager Calls |

| Base | Mobile | Mode | Location | User and Notes |
|------|--------|------|----------|----------------|
| 454.17500 | | NFM | Nationwide | Hospital Voice Paging |
| 454.17500 | | NFM | Newcastle | Hospital Emerg. Voice Paging |
| 454.17500 | | NFM | Ninian South | Chevron |
| 454.17500 | | NFM | Sheffield | Royal Hallamshire Hospital Pager |
| 454.17500 | | NFM | Stevenage | Lister Hospital Pagers |
| 454.20000 | | NFM | Derbyshire | Centracom Doctors Paging |
| 454.20000 | | NFM | Manchester | Hospital Pager |
| 454.20000 | | NFM | Nationwide | Medical Pagers |
| 454.20000 | | NFM | Nationwide | Sky Sports crew |
| 454.22500 | | NFM | Nationwide | Sky Sports crew |
| 454.22500 | | NFM | Risley | UK AEA |
| 454.25000 | | NFM | Milton Keynes | Hospital Pagers |
| 454.25000 | | NFM | Nationwide | Sky Sports crew |
| 454.27500 | | NFM | North Sea | Alba Chevron ANP West Crane |
| 454.27500 | | NFM | North Sea | Chevron Ninian South |
| 454.27500 | | NFM | North Sea | Elf Enterprise Claymore A |
| 454.27500 | | NFM | North Sea | Elf Enterprise Piper |
| 454.30000 | | NFM | Edinburgh Airport | Radiopagers Channel 9 |
| 454.30000 | | NFM | Merseyside | Hospital Voice Pagers |
| 454.31250 | | NFM | Nationwide | Ligier Formula One Team |
| 454.31250 | 459.31250 | NFM | Castle Donington | Grand Prix Team |
| 454.32500 | | NFM | Basildon | Hospital Data/Paging |
| 454.32500 | | NFM | County Durham | Hospital Emerg. Voice Paging |
| 454.32500 | | NFM | North Sea | Elf Enterprise Claymore A |
| 454.32500 | | NFM | North Sea | Elf Enterprise Piper |
| 454.32500 | | NFM | Oxford | Medical Paging |
| 454.35000 | | NFM | North Sea | Chevron Ninian Central |
| 454.37500 | | NFM | Jersey | King Street Department Store |
| 454.40000 | | NFM | North Sea | Chevron Alba ANP Drilling |
| 454.40000 | | NFM | North Sea | Chevron Ninian South |
| 454.40000 | 468.40000 | NFM | North Sea | BP Forties A |
| 454.42500 | | NFM | North Sea | Chevron Ninian Central |
| 454.45000 | | NFM | North Sea | Elf Enterprise Claymore A |
| 454.45000 | | NFM | North Sea | Elf Enterprise Piper |
| 454.46250 | | NFM | Channel Tunnel | Trains |
| 454.47500 | | NFM | Southampton | AirCall Pagers |
| 454.50000 | | NFM | Nationwide | UK Atomic Energy Authority |
| 454.57500 | | NFM | Guernsey | HM Customs & Excise |
| 454.57500 | 460.07500 | NFM | North Sea | BP Magnus |
| 454.62500 | | NFM | Newport | Royal Gwent Hospital Pagers |
| 454.67500 | | NFM | Nationwide | Hutchison Paging |
| 454.67500 | | NFM | Nationwide | Millicomm Paging |
| 454.68750 | | NFM | London, Heathrow | Airline & BAA Ops |
| 454.70000 | | NFM | Bromley | Bromley Health Pagers |
| 454.75000 | | NFM | Jersey Airport | British Airways |
| 454.77500 | | NFM | Hull | Air Call Paging |
| 454.77500 | | NFM | Nationwide | AirCall Paging |
| 454.80000 | | NFM | Southampton | Meridian Pagers |
| 454.82500 | | NFM | Machynlleth | Hospital Paging |
| 454.82500 | | NFM | Nationwide | Page Boy Paging |
| 454.85000 | | NFM | Glasgow | Paging |

## 454.8375 - 454.9875 MHz    PMR RAILWAYS

| Base | Mobile | Mode | Location | User and Notes |
|------|--------|------|----------|----------------|
| 454.84375 | | NFM | Channel Tunnel | Trains |
| 454.84375 | 448.34375 | NFM | Nationwide | Railcab Radio Ch. I |
| 454.85000 | | NFM | London | Railtrack Operations (Wimbledon) |
| 454.85000 | | NFM | Stevenage | Railtrack Operations |
| 454.85625 | | NFM | Nationwide | Rail Cab Radio Data Signalling Ch.2 |
| 454.86875 | 448.36875 | NFM | Nationwide | Rail Cab Radio Ch.3 |
| 454.87500 | | NFM | Baldock | Railtrack |
| 454.88125 | 448.38125 | NFM | Nationwide | Rail Cab Radio Ch.4 |
| 454.88750 | | NFM | Bishopton | Railtrack Operations |
| 454.88750 | | NFM | Gidea Park | Railtrack Operations |
| 454.88750 | | NFM | Liverpool | Railtrack Operations |
| 454.88750 | | NFM | London | Railtrack Operations (Waterloo) |
| 454.88750 | | NFM | Reedham | Railtrack Operations |
| 454.89375 | 448.39375 | NFM | Nationwide | Rail Cab Radio Ch.5 |
| 454.90000 | | NFM | Ayr | ScotRail and SPT on board handhelds |
| 454.90000 | | NFM | England, South East | Network South East trains |
| 454.90000 | | NFM | Kilmarnock | ScotRail and SPT on board handhelds |
| 454.90000 | | NFM | London | Railtrack Operations (Alexandra Palace) |
| 454.90000 | | NFM | London | Railtrack Operations (Stratford) |
| 454.90000 | | NFM | Paisley | ScotRail and SPT on board handhelds |
| 454.90000 | | NFM | Selhurst | Railtrack Operations |
| 454.90625 | 448.40625 | NFM | Nationwide | Rail Cab Radio Ch.6 |
| 454.91875 | 448.41875 | NFM | London, Waterloo | Connex Rail cab radio |
| 454.91875 | 448.41875 | NFM | Nationwide | Rail Cab Radio Ch.7 |
| 454.91875 | 448.41875 | NFM | Rainham | London Transport train cab radios |
| 454.92500 | | NFM | Hitchin | Railtrack |
| 454.92500 | | NFM | Largs | ScotRail and SPT on board handhelds |
| 454.92500 | | NFM | Paisley | ScotRail and SPT on board handhelds |
| 454.92500 | | NFM | Threebridges | Railtrack Operations |
| 454.93125 | 448.43125 | NFM | Nationwide | Rail Cab Radio Ch.8 |
| 454.93750 | | NFM | Motherwell | Railtrack Operations |
| 454.93750 | | NFM | Threebridges | Railtrack Operations |
| 454.94000 | | NFM | Surrey | Trains comms to Victoria signal box |
| 454.94375 | 448.44375 | NFM | Nationwide | Rail Cab Radio Ch.9 |
| 454.95000 | | NFM | Burgess Hill | Railtrack Operations |
| 454.95625 | | NFM | England, South East | Network South East trains |
| 454.95625 | 448.45625 | NFM | Nationwide | Rail Cab Radio Ch.10 |
| 454.96250 | | NFM | Motherwell | Railtrack Operations |
| 454.96250 | 454.96250 | NFM | London | Railtrack Operations (Victoria) |
| 454.96875 | | NFM | England, South East | Network South East trains |
| 454.96875 | 448.46875 | NFM | Nationwide | Rail Cab Radio Ch.11 |
| 454.97500 | | NFM | Jordanhill | Railtrack Operations |
| 454.97500 | | NFM | Letchworth | Railtrack |
| 454.97500 | | NFM | London | Railtrack Operations (Victoria) |
| 454.97500 | | NFM | Redhill | Railtrack Operations |
| 454.98125 | | NFM | England, South East | Network South East trains |
| 454.98125 | 448.48125 | NFM | Nationwide | Rail Cab Radio Ch.12 |
| 454.98750 | | NFM | Motherwell | Railtrack Operations |
| 454.98750 | | NFM | Stoke On Trent | Stoke City Video Surveillance |

| Base | Mobile | Mode | Location | User and Notes |
|------|--------|------|----------|----------------|

**455.0000 - 467.7500 MHz**   IRISH POLICE BASE 25kHz

| Base | Mobile | Mode | Location | User and Notes |
|------|--------|------|----------|----------------|
| 455.0000 | 469.0000 | NFM | Dublin | Police O |
| 455.0250 | 469.0250 | NFM | Dublin | Police O |
| 455.0500 | 469.0500 | NFM | Dublin | Police O |
| 455.0750 | 469.0750 | NFM | Dublin | Police O |
| 455.1000 | 469.1000 | NFM | Dublin | Police O |
| 455.1250 | 469.1250 | NFM | Dublin | Police T (Traffic) |
| 455.1500 | 469.1500 | NFM | Dublin | Police T (Traffic) |
| 455.1750 | 469.1750 | NFM | Dublin | Police W |
| 455.2000 | 469.2000 | NFM | Dublin | Police N |
| 455.2250 | 469.2250 | NFM | Dublin | Police F |
| 455.2500 | 469.2500 | NFM | Dublin | Police F |
| 455.2750 | 469.2750 | NFM | Dublin | Police P |
| 455.3000 | 469.3000 | NFM | Dublin | Police M |
| 455.3250 | | NFM | Dublin | Police L/B/A |
| 455.3500 | | NFM | Dublin | Police G |
| 455.3750 | | NFM | Dublin | Police G |
| 455.4000 | 469.4000 | NFM | Dublin | Police E |
| 455.4250 | | NFM | Dublin | Police A |
| 455.4500 | | NFM | Dublin | Police B |
| 455.4750 | 469.4750 | NFM | Dublin | Police B |
| 455.5000 | 469.5000 | NFM | Dublin | Police J |
| 455.5250 | 469.5250 | NFM | Dublin | Police R |
| 455.5500 | 469.5500 | NFM | Dublin | Police K |
| 455.5750 | 469.5750 | NFM | Dublin | Police H |
| 455.6000 | 469.6000 | NFM | Dublin | Police H |
| 455.6250 | 469.6250 | NFM | Dublin | Police C |
| 455.6500 | 469.6500 | NFM | Dublin | Police U |
| 455.6750 | 469.6750 | NFM | Dublin | Police D |
| 455.7250 | 469.7250 | NFM | Dublin | Police W/N/T |
| 455.7500 | 469.7500 | NFM | Dublin | Police D/U/C |
| 455.7750 | 469.7750 | NFM | Dublin | Police R/H/J/K |
| 455.8000 | 469.8000 | NFM | Dublin | Police E/B/A |
| 455.8250 | 469.8250 | NFM | Dublin | Police L/M/G/P |

**455.0000 - 455.4500 MHz**   BROADCASTING LINKS AND
FORMULA ONE RACING

| Base | Mobile | Mode | Location | User and Notes |
|------|--------|------|----------|----------------|
| 454.99250 | | NFM | Edinburgh | Grampian TV O/B Talkback |
| 454.99250 | | NFM | Glasgow | Grampian TV O/B Talkback |
| 454.99250 | | NFM | Perth | Grampian TV O/B Talkback |
| 454.99350 | | NFM | East Anglia | Anglia TV Talkback |
| 454.99350 | | NFM | Nationwide | ITV O/B |
| 454.99375 | 468.36875 | NFM | Nationwide | JFMG Short Term Talkback |
| 454.99500 | | NFM | Liverpool | Granada TV Talkback |
| 455.00000 | | WFM | Nationwide | Central TV O/B |
| 455.00000 | | NFM | Southampton | Meridian TV O/B |
| 455.00625 | 468.38125 | NFM | Nationwide | JFMG Short Term Talkback |
| 455.01200 | | NFM | Kempton Park | Channel 4 TV Racing sound link |
| 455.01250 | | NFM | Nationwide | Australian TV O/B |
| 455.01250 | | NFM | Wales | S4C O/B Unit |
| 455.01250 | 468.05000 | NFM | Jersey | Channel TV O/B |
| 455.01875 | 468.04375 | NFM | Nationwide | JFMG Short Term Talkback |
| 455.02500 | | NFM | Midlands | BBC O/B |
| 455.02500 | | WFM | Nationwide | Central TV O/B |
| 455.03125 | | NFM | London | Independent TV Talkback |

| Base | Mobile | Mode | Location | User and Notes |
|------|--------|------|----------|----------------|
| 455.03125 | 468.05625 | NFM | Nationwide | JFMG Short Term Talkback |
| 455.06250 | | NFM | Capenhurst | UK AEA (HC/LH) |
| 455.06250 | | NFM | Dorset | 2CR Eye-In-The-Sky |
| 455.06250 | | NFM | Edinburgh | Forth AM O/B |
| 455.06250 | | NFM | London | BBC South East |
| 455.06250 | | NFM | Southampton | Ocean Sound Helicopter |
| 455.06250 | | NFM | Stoke on Trent | Signal Radio O/B Link |
| 455.07500 | | NFM | London | Capital Radio Flying Eye |
| 455.09375 | 468.39375 | NFM | Nationwide | JFMG Short Term Talkback |
| 455.09400 | | WFM | Nationwide | CTV Outside Broadcast |
| 455.10000 | | NFM | Cardiff | HTV O/B |
| 455.10000 | | NFM | Nottingham | BBC Radio Nottingham |
| 455.10625 | | WFM | London | BBC-TV London Marathon |
| 455.10625 | 468.40625 | NFM | Nationwide | JFMG Short Term Talkback |
| 455.11875 | 468.41875 | NFM | Nationwide | JFMG Short Term Talkback |
| 455.12500 | | NFM | Liverpool | Granada TV Talkback |
| 455.12500 | 468.39000 | NFM | Jersey | Channel TV O/B |
| 455.13125 | 468.43125 | NFM | Nationwide | JFMG Short Term Talkback |
| 455.13200 | | NFM | Edinburgh | Grampian TV O/B Talkback |
| 455.13200 | | NFM | Glasgow | Grampian TV O/B Talkback |
| 455.13200 | | WFM | Perth | Grampian TV O/B Talkback |
| 455.13260 | | NFM | Nationwide | BBC TV Sports Commentary |
| 455.13750 | | WFM | Nationwide | Central TV Outside Broadcast |
| 455.15000 | | NFM | Anglia | Anglia TV Studio Producer |
| 455.15000 | | NFM | Manchester | Piccadilly Eye in the Sky |
| 455.16250 | | NFM | Birmingham | 96.4 FM BRMB/Extra AM Flying Eye talkback |
| 455.16250 | | NFM | Dorset | 2CR Outside Broadcast Feeder |
| 455.16250 | | NFM | London | BBC South East |
| 455.16250 | | NFM | Manchester | Radio Piccadilly Eye In Sky |
| 455.16250 | | NFM | Milton Keynes | Chilton Radio OB |
| 455.16250 | | NFM | Oxfordshire | Chilton Radio Heli Traffic Reports |
| 455.16250 | | NFM | Stoke on Trent | Signal Radio O/B Link |
| 455.18750 | | NFM | Midlands | BBC O/B |
| 455.18750 | | NFM | Stoke on Trent | Stock City O/B Microphones |
| 455.19375 | 468.01875 | NFM | Nationwide | JFMG Short Term Talkback |
| 455.20000 | | NFM | Kempton Park | Channel 4 TV Racing talkback |
| 455.20000 | | NFM | Nationwide | Radio Investigations Service |
| 455.20000 | | WFM | Nationwide | Central TV O/B |
| 455.20000 | | NFM | Newmarket | Channel 4 Racing O/B |
| 455.20625 | 468.03125 | NFM | Nationwide | JFMG Short Term Talkback |
| 455.21875 | 468.49375 | NFM | Nationwide | JFMG Short Term Talkback |
| 455.22500 | | NFM | Burnley | Granada TV OB |
| 455.22500 | | NFM | Manchester | ITN O/B Studio Link |
| 455.22500 | | NFM | Nationwide | Radio Investigations Service |
| 455.22500 | | WFM | Nationwide | Central TV O/B |
| 455.22500 | | NFM | Newmarket | Channel 4 Racing O/B |
| 455.23125 | 468.50625 | NFM | Nationwide | JFMG Short Term Talkback |
| 455.23500 | | NFM | Grand Prix Circuits | Ferrari Team Voice Link |
| 455.24000 | | WFM | Leicester | BBC East Midlands O/B |
| 455.24370 | 468.16870 | NFM | Belfry (Ryder Cup) | BBC TV OB |
| 455.24375 | 468.16875 | NFM | Nationwide | JFMG Short Term Talkback |
| 455.24500 | | NFM | Birmingham | ITN camera crew |
| 455.25000 | | NFM | Nationwide | Radio Investigations Service |
| 455.25620 | 468.19370 | NFM | Nationwide | BBC TV O/B Talkback |
| 455.25625 | 468.19375 | NFM | Nationwide | JFMG Short Term Talkback |
| 455.26870 | | WFM | London | BBC TV London Marathon |

| Base | Mobile | Mode | Location | User and Notes |
|------|--------|------|----------|----------------|
| 455.26875 | 468.18125 | NFM | Nationwide | JFMG Short Term Talkback |
| 455.28000 | | WFM | Leicester | BBC East Midlands O/B |
| 455.28000 | | WFM | Portsmouth | BBC1 OB |
| 455.28120 | 468.29370 | NFM | Belfry (Ryder Cup) | BBC TV |
| 455.28125 | 468.29375 | NFM | Nationwide | JFMG Short Term Talkback |
| 455.28500 | | NFM | Edinburgh | BBC Scotland O/B |
| 455.28500 | | NFM | Glasgow | BBC Scotland O/B |
| 455.28500 | | WFM | Perth | BBC Scotland O/B |
| 455.28750 | | NFM | Goodwood | BBC Goodwood OB |
| 455.31000 | | NFM | Blyth | O/B Football (Saturdays) |
| 455.31200 | | WFM | Salisbury | BBC Wiltshire Sound |
| 455.31250 | | NFM | Belfry (Ryder Cup) | BBC Radio 5 |
| 455.31250 | | WFM | Jersey | BBC Jersey O/B |
| 455.31250 | | NFM | Nationwide | BBC Radio 1 O/B |
| 455.31250 | 469.11250 | WFM | Salisbury | BBC Wiltshire Sound |
| 455.36250 | | NFM | Belfry (Ryder Cup) | BBC Radio 5 |
| 455.36250 | | NFM | Bristol | Radio Bristol (O) |
| 455.36250 | | NFM | Carlisle | BBC Radio Cumbria OB |
| 455.36250 | | WFM | Jersey | BBC Jersey O/B |
| 455.36250 | | NFM | Nationwide | BBC Radio 1 O/B |
| 455.36500 | | WFM | Hampshire | BBC Radio Solent Radio Car |
| 455.39370 | | NFM | Belfry (Ryder Cup) | BBC TV |
| 455.39370 | | NFM | Nationwide | BBC TV O/B Talkback |
| 455.39375 | 468.33125 | NFM | Nationwide | JFMG Short Term Talkback |
| 455.40000 | | NFM | Farnborough | BBC Talkback (RAE Airfield) |
| 455.40625 | 468.20625 | NFM | Nationwide | JFMG Short Term Talkback |
| 455.41870 | | NFM | Belfry (Ryder Cup) | BBC TV |
| 455.41875 | 468.30625 | NFM | Nationwide | JFMG Short Term Talkback |
| 455.42500 | | NFM | Cumbria, south | Data Link |
| 455.43120 | | NFM | Belfry (Ryder Cup) | BBC TV |
| 455.43125 | 468.31875 | NFM | Nationwide | JFMG Short Term Talkback |
| 455.43750 | | NFM | Preston | Radio Lancashire O/B |
| 455.44375 | | NFM | Nationwide | JFMG Short Term Talkback |
| 455.44500 | | NFM | Leicester | Radio Leicester O/B Ch 2 |

### 455.46875 - 455.85625 MHz  PMR Airport Security, Ground Repeaters and Limited PMR in Scotland

| Base | Mobile | Mode | Location | User and Notes |
|------|--------|------|----------|----------------|
| 455.46250 | 469.90000 | NFM | London | BBC Eastenders Production |
| 455.47500 | 460.77500 | NFM | Birmingham Airport | Ground Ch.1 |
| 455.47500 | 460.77500 | NFM | London, Gatwick | Tower Re-Broardcast |
| 455.47500 | 460.77500 | NFM | Woodford Airfield | Crash Ops |
| 455.48750 | 461.78750 | NFM | Bournemouth (Hurn) | Tower Repeater |
| 455.48750 | 461.78750 | NFM | East Midlands Airport | Ground |
| 455.48750 | 461.78750 | NFM | Liverpool Airport | Apron Supervisor |
| 455.48750 | 461.78750 | NFM | London, Heathrow | Police Armed (HUNTER DELTA) |
| 455.50000 | 460.80000 | NFM | Guernsey | Tower Rebroadcast |
| 455.50000 | 460.80000 | NFM | USAF Fairford | IAT Medical Control |
| 455.51250 | | NFM | Duxford | Data Link |
| 455.51250 | 455.51250 | NFM | Cranfield Airport | Fire Services |
| 455.51250 | 455.51250 | NFM | Glasgow | BT Police (BX) |
| 455.51250 | 455.51250 | NFM | Nationwide | Transport Police (BRAVO XRAY) |
| 455.52500 | 460.82500 | NFM | Bristol Airport | HM Customs & Excise |
| 455.52500 | 460.82500 | NFM | Manchester International | HM Customs & Exercise |
| 455.52500 | 460.82500 | NFM | Nationwide | HM Customs & Excise |
| 455.52500 | 461.17500 | NFM | Cranfield Airfield | Fire & Security |
| 455.52500 | 461.17500 | NFM | East Midlands Airport | Fire Service |

| Base | Mobile | Mode | Location | User and Notes |
|------|--------|------|----------|----------------|
| 455.52500 | 461.17500 | NFM | Farnborough Airshow | Transport Control |
| 455.52500 | 461.17500 | NFM | London, Heathrow | Tower Rebroadcast from 118.50MHz |
| 455.52500 | 461.17500 | NFM | Manchester | International Airport Crash Ops / Fire |
| 455.52500 | 461.17500 | NFM | Nationwide | Airport Customs |
| 455.53750 | 460.53750 | NFM | Birmingham International | Ground Control |
| 455.53750 | 460.53750 | NFM | Luton Airport | Maintenance |
| 455.53750 | 460.53750 | NFM | USAF Fairford | IAT |
| 455.55000 | 461.20000 | NFM | Stansted | Tower and Ground Repeater |
| 455.55000 | 461.85000 | NFM | Leeds Airport | Security/Fire |
| 455.55000 | 461.85000 | NFM | London, Heathrow | Aircraft tugs |
| 455.55000 | 461.85000 | NFM | London, Heathrow | Ground Repeater (121.9 MHz AM rebroadcast) |
| 455.55000 | 461.85000 | NFM | Manchester Airport | Tower Repeater |
| 455.56250 | 455.56250 | NFM | Stansted | Crash Vehicles |
| 455.57500 | | NFM | USAF Fairford | IAT Barriers |
| 455.57500 | | NFM | Various Airports | Fire Services |
| 455.57500 | | NFM | Woodford Airfield | Tower-Ground |
| 455.57500 | 461.22500 | NFM | BAe Woodford | Tower Link |
| 455.57500 | 461.22500 | NFM | Birmingham International | Fire Ch.2 |
| 455.57500 | 461.22500 | NFM | London, Heathrow | Passport Control |
| 455.58750 | 449.08750 | NFM | London, Heathrow | Airport Express Trains |
| 455.58750 | 449.08750 | NFM | Nationwide | Rail Cab Radio Ch.14 |
| 455.59375 | | NFM | England, South East | Network South East trains |
| 455.60000 | | NFM | Filton (BAe), Bristol | Security |
| 455.60000 | | NFM | Jersey Airport | Securicor |
| 455.60000 | | NFM | Larne | Post Office security |
| 455.60000 | | NFM | London, Gatwick | Airline & BAA Ops |
| 455.60000 | 455.60000 | NFM | Blackpool | Ground |
| 455.60000 | 460.90000 | NFM | East Midlands Airport | Terminal Security |
| 455.60000 | 469.00000 | NFM | North Sea | BP Forties C |
| 455.61250 | | NFM | Leeds Bradford Airport | Ground Staff/Fire |
| 455.61250 | | NFM | USAF Fairford | IAT |
| 455.61250 | 461.91250 | NFM | London, Heathrow | Ground |
| 455.62500 | | NFM | Glasgow | Cargo Handlers |
| 455.62500 | | NFM | Jersey | Airport Ground |
| 455.62500 | | NFM | Prestwick Airport | Ground Ops Link |
| 455.62500 | | NFM | Prestwick Airport | Tower Rebroadcasts Ch.5 |
| 455.62500 | 460.92500 | NFM | Nationwide | Red Devil Parachute Team |
| 455.63750 | | NFM | London, Gatwick | Crash Ops |
| 455.63750 | | NFM | London, Heathrow | Airline & BAA Ops |
| 455.63750 | | NFM | Luton Airport | Crash Ops Ch 2 |
| 455.63750 | | NFM | Stansted | Maintenance |
| 455.63750 | | NFM | USAF Fairford | IAT Transport Control |
| 455.63750 | 460.93750 | NFM | Liverpool Airport | Ground Movement Control |
| 455.65000 | | NFM | Edinburgh Airport | BAA Engineering Ch.6 |
| 455.65000 | | NFM | London, Heathrow | Crash Ops |
| 455.65000 | | NFM | Manchester Airport | Ground Repeater |
| 455.65000 | | NFM | MoD Airfields | Fire Control |
| 455.65000 | | NFM | Newcastle Airport | Grass Cutting |
| 455.65000 | | NFM | Stansted | Crash Ops |
| 455.65000 | | NFM | USAF Fairford | IAT Fire Control |
| 455.65000 | 460.85000 | NFM | Birmingham International | Airway Crossing/Security |
| 455.67500 | 455.67500 | NFM | Norwich | HM Customs & Excise |
| 455.68750 | 460.98750 | NFM | Ronaldsway Airport | Tower-Ground |
| 455.70000 | | NFM | Bournemouth (Hurn) | Ground Services |
| 455.70000 | | NFM | Cardiff | Airport Security |
| 455.70000 | | NFM | Edinburgh Airport | Security Ch.5/25 |

| Base | Mobile | Mode | Location | User and Notes |
|------|--------|------|----------|----------------|
| 455.70000 | | NFM | Hawarden Airfield | Ground |
| 455.70000 | | NFM | London, Heathrow | Tower Rebroadcast |
| 455.70000 | | NFM | London,Gatwick | BAA Ops |
| 455.70000 | | NFM | Prestwick | Fire Ch.2 (RED) |
| 455.70000 | | NFM | USAF Fairford | IAT Engineering |
| 455.70000 | 461.00000 | NFM | Birmingham International | Apron Ch 4 |
| 455.71250 | | NFM | East Midlands Airport | Fire Service |
| 455.71250 | | NFM | London, Docklands | Ground Control |
| 455.71250 | | NFM | London, Heathrow | Weather Information Relay |
| 455.71250 | | NFM | Manchester Airport | Ground Handling |
| 455.72500 | 461.02500 | NFM | Edinburgh Airport | Channel 3/23 |
| 455.72500 | 461.02500 | NFM | London, Heathrow | Police Armed (Hunter Whiskey) |
| 455.72500 | 461.02500 | NFM | Nationwide | Airport Tower Rebroadcasts |
| 455.72500 | 461.02500 | NFM | Woodford Airfield | Fuel & Maintenance |
| 455.73750 | 461.03750 | NFM | Coventry Airport | Ground Ops |
| 455.73750 | 461.03750 | NFM | London, Gatwick | BAA Ops |
| 455.73750 | 461.03750 | NFM | Manchester Airport | Coach Ops |
| 455.73750 | 461.03750 | NFM | Newcastle Airport | Tower Repeater |
| 455.73750 | 461.03750 | NFM | RAE Farnborough | Maintenance/Fuel |
| 455.73750 | 461.03750 | NFM | USAF Fairford | IAT Speedbird |
| 455.75000 | | NFM | Heathrow | Airport trunked |
| 455.75000 | 461.05000 | NFM | Newcastle Airport | Tower Repeater |
| 455.75000 | 469.75000 | NFM | Prestwick | Ground ops. Ch.3 |
| 455.76250 | 461.03750 | NFM | Birmingham International | Ground Staff |
| 455.76250 | 461.03750 | NFM | Liverpool Airport | Security |
| 455.76250 | 461.03750 | NFM | USAF Fairford | IAT (ZODIAC BASE) |
| 455.77500 | | NFM | Nationwide (Airports) | HM Customs |
| 455.77500 | 461.07500 | NFM | Edinburgh Airport | Fire Service (handhelds) Channel 2/22 |
| 455.77500 | 461.07500 | NFM | London, Gatwick | Ground Control Link |
| 455.77500 | 461.07500 | NFM | London, Heathrow | Police Armed (HUNTER WHISKY) |
| 455.78750 | | NFM | Manchester Airport | Car Park Security |
| 455.80000 | 461.10000 | NFM | Birmingham International | Baggage Handlers |
| 455.80000 | 461.10000 | NFM | USAF Fairford | IAT Emergency Control |
| 455.80000 | 461.10000 | NFM | Weston-Super-Mare | Airport Security |
| 455.81250 | 461.11250 | NFM | Aberdeen (Dyce Airport) | Ground |
| 455.81250 | 461.11250 | NFM | Edinburgh Airport | PMR Channel 4 |
| 455.81250 | 461.11250 | NFM | London, Heathrow | Seagull & Checker |
| 455.81250 | 461.11250 | NFM | Manchester Airport | Ground Handling |
| 455.81250 | 461.11250 | NFM | Newcastle Airport | Baggage Handling |
| 455.81250 | 461.11250 | NFM | Stansted | Security Ops |
| 455.82500 | 461.12500 | NFM | Birmingham International | Maglev |
| 455.82500 | 461.12500 | NFM | Birmingham International | Maintenance |
| 455.82500 | 461.12500 | NFM | East Midlands Airport | Maintenance |
| 455.82500 | 461.12500 | NFM | London, Gatwick | Data |
| 455.82500 | 461.12500 | NFM | Luton Airport | Ground Movements Ch1 |
| 455.82500 | 461.12500 | NFM | Luton Airport | MacAlpine Aviation |
| 455.82500 | 461.12500 | NFM | Luton Airport | Magec Ops |
| 455.82500 | 461.12500 | NFM | Nationwide (Airports) | HM Customs |
| 455.82500 | 461.12500 | NFM | Stansted | Tower |
| 455.82500 | 461.12500 | NFM | USAF Fairford | IAT Message Centre |
| 455.83750 | 461.13750 | NFM | Edinburgh Airport | Tower/Ground Rebroadcasts Ch.1 |
| 455.83750 | 461.13750 | NFM | Glasgow | Baggage Handlers |
| 455.83750 | 461.13750 | NFM | Liverpool Airport | Fire Control |
| 455.83750 | 461.13750 | NFM | Lydd Airfield | Ground Repeater |
| 455.85000 | 461.15000 | NFM | London, Gatwick | Baggage Handlers |
| 455.85000 | 461.15000 | NFM | Nationwide (Airports) | HM Customs |

| Base | Mobile | Mode | Location | User and Notes |
|------|--------|------|----------|----------------|
| 455.85000 | 461.15000 | NFM | USAF Fairford | IAT Security Control |
| 455.85000 | 461.15000 | NFM | Woodford Airfield | VIP & Crew Bus |

## 455.8750 - 456.0000 MHz  EMERGENCY SERVICES 12.5 KHz NFM

| Base | Mobile | Mode | Location | User and Notes |
|------|--------|------|----------|----------------|
| 455.98750 | | NFM | Edinburgh | Fire Brigade |
| 455.98750 | | NFM | Fife | Fire Brigade Ch 7 |
| 455.98750 | | NFM | Glasgow | Fire Brigade |
| 455.98750 | | NFM | Leeds | Fire/Police Inter Agency |
| 455.98750 | | NFM | London, Heathrow | Airline & BAA Ops |
| 455.98750 | | NFM | Nationwide | Airfield Fire Channel |
| 455.98750 | | NFM | Southampton | Securicor |
| 455.98750 | | NFM | St. Fergus | Shell |
| 455.98750 | | NFM | West Yorkshire | Fire/Police Inter Agency |

## 456.000 - 457.000 MHz  PMR 12.5kHz (Split +5.5)
### FORMULA ONE RACING TEAMS LINKS

| Base | Mobile | Mode | Location | User and Notes |
|------|--------|------|----------|----------------|
| 455.95000 | 461.45000 | NFM | North London | DVP Traffic |
| 455.98750 | 461.48750 | NFM | Jersey | Securicor Handhelds |
| 455.98750 | 461.48750 | NFM | Nationwide | Interagency Liaison |
| 456.00000 | 461.50000 | NFM | Colchester | Play Group |
| 456.00000 | 461.50000 | NFM | Farnborough Airshow | Securicor guarding for this event |
| 456.00000 | 461.50000 | NFM | London | Fleet St. security |
| 456.01250 | 461.51250 | NFM | Essex, SE | Several Users Construction Workers, Shop Staff and Shop Security |
| 456.01250 | 461.51250 | NFM | London, Heathrow | Terminal 1 |
| 456.02500 | 461.52500 | NFM | Birmingham, Solihull | Land Rover Security |
| 456.02500 | 461.52500 | NFM | Blackpool | Spectrum Security |
| 456.02500 | 461.52500 | NFM | Clacton | Shopwatch |
| 456.02500 | 461.52500 | NFM | Coventry | Race Track |
| 456.02500 | 461.52500 | NFM | Dartford | Bluewater Shopping Centre, Marks & Spencers |
| 456.02500 | 461.52500 | NFM | Dover | Docks security |
| 456.02500 | 461.52500 | NFM | Gaydon | Rover Test Track |
| 456.02500 | 461.52500 | NFM | Havant | Xyratex Hardware Security |
| 456.02500 | 461.52500 | NFM | Immingham | DFDS Transport |
| 456.02500 | 461.52500 | NFM | London | Hamley's Toy Shop Security |
| 456.02500 | 461.52500 | NFM | London, Gatwick | Security |
| 456.02500 | 461.52500 | NFM | London, Heathrow | Ground Repeater |
| 456.02500 | 461.52500 | NFM | London, Marble Arch | Marks and Spencers Maintenance. |
| 456.02500 | 461.52500 | NFM | London, Queensway | Whiteley Shopping Centre security |
| 456.02500 | 461.52500 | NFM | Luton | Vauxhall Motors |
| 456.02500 | 461.52500 | NFM | Manchester | Airport Ground Services |
| 456.02500 | 461.52500 | NFM | Middlesborough | ICI |
| 456.02500 | 461.52500 | NFM | Nottingham | Streamline Taxis |
| 456.02500 | 461.52500 | NFM | Sidcup | Queens Marys Hospital |
| 456.02500 | 461.52500 | NFM | Stansted | Aviation Traders |
| 456.02500 | 461.52500 | NFM | Swansea City | Quadrant Shopping Centre Sec. |
| 456.02500 | 461.52500 | NFM | West Midlands | Fire Alarms |
| 456.02500 | 461.52500 | NFM | Windsor | Shopwatch |
| 456.03750 | 461.53750 | NFM | Oldham | Delivery Company |
| 456.03750 | 461.53750 | NFM | Stansted | Air UK Flight Despatch |
| 456.05000 | 461.55000 | NFM | Birmingham | Flightlink Coaches |
| 456.05000 | 461.55000 | NFM | Blackpool | Trams |
| 456.05000 | 461.55000 | NFM | Bristol | Parking Enforcement |
| 456.05000 | 461.55000 | NFM | Bristol | UKAEA Power Station Security |
| 456.05000 | 461.55000 | NFM | Grays Thurrock | Council Refuse Collection |

| Base | Mobile | Mode | Location | User and Notes |
|------|--------|------|----------|----------------|
| 456.05000 | 461.55000 | NFM | Hull | Oil Jetty |
| 456.05000 | 461.55000 | NFM | London | Police Ch.2 Wandsworth Parks and Traffic Wardens |
| 456.05000 | 461.55000 | NFM | London, Gatwick | Airline ops. |
| 456.05000 | 461.55000 | NFM | London, Heathrow | Airline & BAA Ops |
| 456.05000 | 461.55000 | NFM | Maidstone | Shop Watch Scheme |
| 456.05000 | 461.55000 | NFM | North Sea | BGE&P Rough A |
| 456.05000 | 461.55000 | NFM | North Sea | Marathon Brae South |
| 456.05000 | 461.55000 | NFM | North Sea | Shell Brent D |
| 456.05000 | 461.55000 | NFM | North Sea | Shell N. Cormorant |
| 456.05000 | 461.55000 | NFM | Oxford | Store detectives |
| 456.05000 | 461.55000 | NFM | Oxford | University Parks patrol |
| 456.05000 | 461.55000 | NFM | Sheffield | Meadowhall Centre |
| 456.05000 | 461.55000 | NFM | St Albans | Parking Enforcement |
| 456.05000 | 461.55000 | NFM | Stevenage | Grocers Shop Delivery Service |
| 456.05000 | 461.55000 | NFM | York | Council car parks |
| 456.06250 | 461.56250 | NFM | London, Heathrow | Airline & BAA Ops |
| 456.07500 | 461.57500 | NFM | Belfast | City Hospital Security |
| 456.07500 | 461.57500 | NFM | London | St. James Park Staff |
| 456.07500 | 461.57500 | NFM | London, Heathrow | Airline & BAA Ops |
| 456.08750 | 461.58750 | NFM | Jersey | Airport Ground Services |
| 456.08750 | 461.58750 | NFM | Leiston | Sizewell A Security |
| 456.08750 | 461.58750 | NFM | Nationwide | National Power |
| 456.10000 | 461.60000 | NFM | Belfast | Musgrave Park Hospital security |
| 456.10000 | 461.60000 | NFM | London, Heathrow | Airline & BAA Ops |
| 456.10000 | 461.60000 | NFM | Manchester Airport | Tugs |
| 456.10000 | 461.60000 | NFM | North Sea | BGE&P Rough A |
| 456.10000 | 461.60000 | NFM | North Sea | Marathon Brae S |
| 456.10000 | 461.60000 | NFM | Southampton | National Power |
| 456.11250 | 461.61250 | NFM | Barrow in Furness | Gas Terminal Maintenance |
| 456.12500 | 461.62500 | NFM | Birmingham | City Council |
| 456.12500 | 461.62500 | NFM | Cemaes Bay | Wylfa Power Station |
| 456.12500 | 461.62500 | NFM | Edinburgh | Scottish Hydro Electric |
| 456.12500 | 461.62500 | NFM | Edinburgh | United Artist Cable Layers |
| 456.12500 | 461.62500 | NFM | Leiston | Sizewell Power Station |
| 456.12500 | 461.62500 | NFM | London | Trunked Network |
| 456.12500 | 461.62500 | NFM | North Sea | BP Sulair Magnus |
| 456.12500 | 461.62500 | NFM | Salford | Hospital Trust Managers. |
| 456.12500 | 461.62500 | NFM | The Port of Heysham | Isle of Man Steam Packet |
| 456.13750 | 461.63750 | NFM | London | Vediotron Ltd |
| 456.13750 | 461.63750 | NFM | Newcastle Airport | Stores Department |
| 456.15000 | 461.65000 | NFM | London | London Electric |
| 456.15000 | 461.65000 | NFM | Manchester | Sub Station Audio Alarm |
| 456.15250 | 456.15250 | NFM | Dover | Harbour security |
| 456.16250 | 461.66250 | NFM | London | Electricity Board |
| 456.16250 | 461.66250 | NFM | London | Victoria Coach Station |
| 456.17500 | 461.67500 | NFM | Alwyn | Total |
| 456.17500 | 461.67500 | NFM | Calverton | National Coal Board |
| 456.17500 | 461.67500 | NFM | Dungeness | Power Station |
| 456.17500 | 461.67500 | NFM | Heysham | Power Station |
| 456.17500 | 461.67500 | NFM | Nationwide | National Power Operations |
| 456.17500 | 461.67500 | NFM | Oldham | Pizza Delivery |
| 456.18750 | 461.68750 | NFM | Atwick | British Gas |
| 456.18750 | 461.68750 | NFM | Atwick | Underground storage |
| 456.18750 | 461.68750 | NFM | Lichfield | Intruder Alert |
| 456.18750 | 461.68750 | NFM | London | Electricity Engineers |
| 456.18750 | 461.68750 | NFM | Morecambe | Voice Alarm |

| Base | Mobile | Mode | Location | User and Notes |
|------|--------|------|----------|----------------|
| 456.20000 | 461.70000 | NFM | Belfast | City Bus Channel 1 |
| 456.20000 | 461.70000 | NFM | Berkeley | BNFL Command & Control |
| 456.20000 | 461.70000 | NFM | Leicester | British Gas Security |
| 456.20000 | 461.70000 | NFM | North Sea | Shell Auk |
| 456.20000 | 461.70000 | NFM | North Sea | Shell Brent A |
| 456.20000 | 461.70000 | NFM | North Sea | Shell Dunlin |
| 456.21250 | 461.71250 | NFM | Kingsnorth | Power Station |
| 456.21250 | 461.71250 | NFM | London | Electricity Engineers |
| 456.21250 | 461.71250 | NFM | Surrey | Electricity Engineers |
| 456.22500 | 461.72500 | NFM | Leiston | Sizewell Power Station |
| 456.22500 | 461.72500 | NFM | Morecambe | Data Link |
| 456.22500 | 461.72500 | NFM | Nationwide | National Power Maintenance |
| 456.22500 | 461.72500 | NFM | North Sea | BGE&P Rough A |
| 456.22500 | 461.72500 | NFM | North Sea | Shell Dunfin |
| 456.23750 | 461.73750 | NFM | Coventry | Coal Authority |
| 456.23750 | 461.73750 | NFM | London | London Electric |
| 456.25000 | 461.75000 | NFM | Berkeley | BNFL Command & Control |
| 456.25000 | 461.75000 | NFM | Cardiff | Millennium Stadium builders |
| 456.25000 | 461.75000 | NFM | Manchester | British Transport Police |
| 456.25000 | 461.75000 | NFM | Warwick | Warwick Technology Park (CW) |
| 456.26250 | 461.76250 | NFM | Barrow in Furness | VSEL Test Engineers |
| 456.26250 | 461.76250 | NFM | Canvey Island | British Gas |
| 456.26250 | 461.76250 | NFM | London, Heathrow | Catering |
| 456.27500 | 461.77500 | NFM | Doncaster | Power Station |
| 456.27500 | 461.77500 | NFM | Dungeness | Power Station |
| 456.27500 | 461.77500 | NFM | London | London Electric |
| 456.27500 | 461.77500 | NFM | Nationwide | National Power Operations tones |
| 456.27500 | 461.77500 | NFM | North Sea | Shell Brent D |
| 456.27500 | 461.77500 | NFM | North Sea | Shell N Cormorant |
| 456.30000 | 461.80000 | NFM | Barrow in Furness | VSEL Security |
| 456.30000 | 461.80000 | NFM | Easington | British Gas Terminal |
| 456.30000 | 461.80000 | NFM | London, Heathrow | Airline & BAA Ops |
| 456.30000 | 461.80000 | NFM | North Sea | Marathon Brae N |
| 456.31250 | 461.81250 | NFM | London | Eastern Electricity |
| 456.32500 | 461.82500 | NFM | Dungeness | Power Station |
| 456.32500 | 461.82500 | NFM | London, Heathrow | General Purpose Channel |
| 456.32500 | 461.82500 | NFM | North Sea | Shell Brent B |
| 456.32500 | 461.82500 | NFM | North Sea | Shell Cormorant A |
| 456.33750 | 461.83750 | NFM | Nationwide | British Rail Transport Police |
| 456.35000 | 461.85000 | NFM | Aberdeen | City Buses |
| 456.35000 | 461.85000 | NFM | Brighton | Queens Hotel |
| 456.35000 | 461.85000 | NFM | Brighton | Royal Pavilion |
| 456.35000 | 461.85000 | NFM | Cheltenham | Water Company Engineering Dept |
| 456.35000 | 461.85000 | NFM | Dartford | Bluewater Shopping Centre security |
| 456.35000 | 461.85000 | NFM | Eastbourne | City Buses |
| 456.35000 | 461.85000 | NFM | London | Brent Cross Shopping Centre storewatch scheme |
| 456.35000 | 461.85000 | NFM | London | Euston Station Post Office sorting depot |
| 456.35000 | 461.85000 | NFM | London | Westham Parcelforce sorting depot |
| 456.35000 | 461.85000 | NFM | London, Gatwick | Cleaners, Cargo Loaders & Apron Movements |
| 456.35000 | 461.85000 | NFM | London, Gatwick | Apron Movements |
| 456.35000 | 461.85000 | NFM | London, Heathrow | Airline & BAA Ops |
| 456.35000 | 461.85000 | NFM | London, Marylebone | Bakers Street Post Office sorting Depot |
| 456.35000 | 461.85000 | NFM | Moray Firth | Beatrice Bravo Platform |
| 456.35000 | 461.85000 | NFM | North Sea | BP Beatrice B |
| 456.35000 | 461.85000 | NFM | Nottingham | City Engineers |
| 456.35000 | 461.85000 | NFM | Perivale | Distribution |

| Base | Mobile | Mode | Location | User and Notes |
|------|--------|------|----------|----------------|
| 456.35000 | 461.85000 | NFM | Reading | Courage Brewery |
| 456.35000 | 461.85000 | NFM | Reading | Police parks |
| 456.35000 | 461.85000 | NFM | Romford | Security |
| 456.35000 | 461.85000 | NFM | Saltend | BP Oil Refinery |
| 456.35000 | 461.85000 | NFM | Stansted | Airport Ops |
| 456.35000 | 461.85000 | NFM | Woodford, Essex | Print Finishers |
| 456.35000 | 462.85000 | NFM | Billingham | ICI |
| 456.36250 | 461.86250 | NFM | London | British Transport Police relay |
| 456.37500 | 461.87500 | NFM | Birmingham | Transport Police Ch 2 |
| 456.37500 | 461.87500 | NFM | Cleveland | DSS Dole Frauds Ch 8 |
| 456.37500 | 461.87500 | NFM | Doncaster | DSS |
| 456.37500 | 461.87500 | NFM | Doncaster | Transport Police Channel 2 |
| 456.37500 | 461.87500 | NFM | Exeter | Transport Police Channel 2 |
| 456.37500 | 461.87500 | NFM | Herefordshire | British Transport Police Ch.74 |
| 456.37500 | 461.87500 | NFM | Kew Gardens | Police |
| 456.37500 | 461.87500 | NFM | Lewisham | DSS Fraud team's aerial site (30 handheld) |
| 456.37500 | 461.87500 | NFM | London | Docks Light Railway Ch 10 |
| 456.37500 | 461.87500 | NFM | London | Mount Pleasant Post Office |
| 456.37500 | 461.87500 | NFM | London | Tower Bridge Staff |
| 456.37500 | 461.87500 | NFM | London | Tower of London |
| 456.37500 | 461.87500 | NFM | London | Westminster Abbey |
| 456.37500 | 461.87500 | NFM | London, N17 | DSS Fraud team's aerial site (50 handheld) |
| 456.37500 | 461.87500 | NFM | Nationwide | British Transport Police |
| 456.37500 | 461.87500 | NFM | Nationwide | Transport Police Channel 2 |
| 456.37500 | 461.87500 | NFM | Sheffield | Transport Police Channel 2 |
| 456.37500 | 461.87500 | NFM | Yorkshire | DSS Fraud teams |
| 456.38750 | 461.88750 | NFM | Canvey Island | PMR Engineers |
| 456.38750 | 461.88750 | NFM | Canvey Island | Waterside 98 Concert 19/9/98 Main Control Ch |
| 456.38750 | 461.88750 | NFM | Edinburgh Airport | Servisair |
| 456.38750 | 461.88750 | NFM | Farnborough Airshow | British Aerospace security at Aerospace Village |
| 456.38750 | 461.88750 | WFM | Framlingham | Richard Weston Trailers |
| 456.38750 | 461.88750 | NFM | Hitchin | Shopwatch |
| 456.38750 | 461.88750 | NFM | Kendall | Shopwatch. |
| 456.38750 | 461.88750 | NFM | London | 02 Centre Security (OSCAR) |
| 456.38750 | 461.88750 | NFM | London | BAFTA Awards Production |
| 456.38750 | 461.88750 | NFM | London | Hammersmith Riverside Studios Staff |
| 456.38750 | 461.88750 | NFM | London | Islington & Chelsea Council Trading Standards (A) |
| 456.38750 | 461.88750 | NFM | London | Old Bailey Crown Court |
| 456.38750 | 461.88750 | NFM | London | Pickets Lock Centre Security |
| 456.38750 | 461.88750 | NFM | London | Westland/GKN Heliport Marshallers |
| 456.38750 | 461.88750 | NFM | London, Oxford St | Marks & Spencer Food Hall |
| 456.38750 | 461.88750 | NFM | London, Piccadilly | Sega Mega World Staff |
| 456.38750 | 461.88750 | NFM | London, Woodgreen | Shopwatch |
| 456.38750 | 461.88750 | NFM | Manchester | International Airport |
| 456.38750 | 461.88750 | NFM | National | Boys Own Band Stage Crew |
| 456.38750 | 461.88750 | NFM | National | Scottish T.V Production Mccullam |
| 456.38750 | 461.88750 | NFM | National | Zenith Film/T.V Production Ch 1 |
| 456.38750 | 461.88750 | NFM | Northampton | Santa Pod Race Way Ch 3 |
| 456.38750 | 461.88750 | NFM | Purfleet | Esso Oil Storage Depot. |
| 456.38750 | 461.88750 | NFM | Romford | Quadrant Shopping Centre Security |
| 456.38750 | 461.88750 | NFM | Rugby | Christian Salvesen Ch.3 |
| 456.38750 | 461.88750 | NFM | Southend | QD Supermarket Staff |
| 456.40000 | 461.40000 | NFM | Rowhampton | Bank of England sportsground security |
| 456.40000 | 461.90000 | NFM | Blackpool | CAA Repeater |
| 456.40000 | 461.90000 | NFM | City of London | Bank of England security |
| 456.40000 | 461.90000 | NFM | Cleveland | DSS Dole Frauds Ch 9 |

| Base | Mobile | Mode | Location | User and Notes |
|------|--------|------|----------|----------------|
| 456.40000 | 461.90000 | NFM | Grays, Essex | DSS Fraud teams |
| 456.40000 | 461.90000 | NFM | Lewisham | DSS Fraud teams aerial site |
| 456.40000 | 461.90000 | NFM | London | Bank of England bullion movement |
| 456.40000 | 461.90000 | NFM | London, Crayford | British Telecoms |
| 456.40000 | 461.90000 | NFM | London, N17 | DSS Fraud teams aerial site |
| 456.40000 | 461.90000 | NFM | London, North Woolwich | British Telecoms Satellite Earth Station |
| 456.40000 | 461.90000 | NFM | Luton Airport | HM Customs & Excise |
| 456.40000 | 461.90000 | NFM | M1 | Bullion Movements |
| 456.40000 | 461.90000 | NFM | Manchester Airport | HM Customs & Excise |
| 456.40000 | 461.90000 | NFM | Martlesham Heath | British Telecoms Research Centre |
| 456.40000 | 461.90000 | NFM | Nationwide | HM Customs & Excise surveillance |
| 456.40000 | 461.90000 | NFM | Nationwide | HM Customs (Airport) |
| 456.40000 | 461.90000 | NFM | Nationwide | Royal Mail Police |
| 456.40000 | 461.90000 | NFM | Nationwide Rail Stations | Post Offices |
| 456.40000 | 461.90000 | NFM | Sheffield | City Buses |
| 456.40000 | 461.90000 | NFM | Thornton | ICI Emergency |
| 456.41250 | 461.91250 | NFM | London, N17 | DSS Fraud teams aerial site |
| 456.42500 | 461.92500 | NFM | Belfast | Shorts Ch 1. |
| 456.42500 | 461.92500 | NFM | Birmingham | Transport Police |
| 456.42500 | 461.92500 | NFM | Doncaster | Transport Police |
| 456.42500 | 461.92500 | NFM | Edinburgh | Transport Police |
| 456.42500 | 461.92500 | NFM | Glasgow | Transport Police |
| 456.42500 | 461.92500 | NFM | Herefordshire | Transport Police Ch.73 |
| 456.42500 | 461.92500 | NFM | Hull | Docks Police |
| 456.42500 | 461.92500 | NFM | Leeds | Transport Police |
| 456.42500 | 461.92500 | NFM | Liverpool | Transport Police |
| 456.42500 | 461.92500 | NFM | London | Her Majesty's Theatre backstage |
| 456.42500 | 461.92500 | NFM | London | Police Royal Parks (relayed 165.6375) Ch.1 |
| 456.42500 | 461.92500 | NFM | London | Transport Police (LT) |
| 456.42500 | 461.92500 | NFM | London, Gatwick | Ground Control Link |
| 456.42500 | 461.92500 | NFM | London, Heathrow | Airline & BAA Ops |
| 456.42500 | 461.92500 | NFM | Nationwide | Transport Police Ch. 3 |
| 456.42500 | 461.92500 | NFM | Preston | Transport Police |
| 456.42500 | 461.92500 | NFM | Sheffield | Council Works Department |
| 456.45000 | 461.95000 | NFM | Aberdeen | City Buses |
| 456.45000 | 461.95000 | NFM | Brighton | Buses |
| 456.45000 | 461.95000 | NFM | Bury | Council |
| 456.45000 | 461.95000 | NFM | Cambridge | National Car Parks |
| 456.45000 | 461.95000 | NFM | Coventry | Council Ch 4 |
| 456.45000 | 461.95000 | NFM | Coventry | Skip Hire |
| 456.45000 | 461.95000 | NFM | Dartford | Imperial War Museum Ch1 |
| 456.45000 | 461.95000 | NFM | Duxford | Security |
| 456.45000 | 461.95000 | NFM | Leicester | City Council Cleansing |
| 456.45000 | 461.95000 | NFM | London | Borough of Brent Parking Enforcement |
| 456.45000 | 461.95000 | NFM | London, Southwark | Parking Wardens |
| 456.45000 | 461.95000 | NFM | Maidstone | Borough Council Parking Enforcement (RP) |
| 456.45000 | 461.95000 | NFM | Newcastle Airport | Engine fitters |
| 456.45000 | 461.95000 | NFM | North Sea | Phillips Bacton |
| 456.45000 | 461.95000 | NFM | North Sea | Shell Brent B |
| 456.45000 | 461.95000 | NFM | North Sea | Shell Cormorant A |
| 456.45000 | 461.95000 | NFM | North Sea | Shell Dunlin |
| 456.45000 | 461.95000 | NFM | Norwich | Car parks |
| 456.45000 | 461.95000 | NFM | Nottingham | Traffic Light Repairs |
| 456.45000 | 461.95000 | NFM | Rotherham | Council |
| 456.45000 | 461.95000 | NFM | Sheffield | Council 24 hour repairs |
| 456.45000 | 461.95000 | NFM | Sullom Voe | Shell |

| Base | Mobile | Mode | Location | User and Notes |
|------|--------|------|----------|----------------|
| 456.45000 | 461.95000 | NFM | Thamesmead | Caretakers & Lift Ops |
| 456.45000 | 461.95000 | NFM | Wembley | Parking enforcement |
| 456.46250 | 461.96250 | NFM | Cleethorpes | Ross Young Fish Factory |
| 456.46250 | 461.96250 | NFM | Nationwide | Royal Jordanian Airforce Falklands display team ground crew |
| 456.47500 | 461.97500 | NFM | Barrow | Cartmel Priory Shopping Centre Security |
| 456.47500 | 461.97500 | NFM | Birmingham | Safari Park Control |
| 456.47500 | 461.97500 | NFM | Birmingham | University Security |
| 456.47500 | 461.97500 | NFM | Clayton | Maynes Buses |
| 456.47500 | 461.97500 | NFM | Duxford | Management/Maintenance |
| 456.47500 | 461.97500 | NFM | Edinburgh | St James Centre Security |
| 456.47500 | 461.97500 | NFM | Glasgow | Baggage Handlers |
| 456.47500 | 461.97500 | NFM | Grimsby | Appleby's Coaches |
| 456.47500 | 461.97500 | NFM | Immingham | Exxtor Shipping |
| 456.47500 | 461.97500 | NFM | Immingham | Tor Line Docks |
| 456.47500 | 461.97500 | NFM | Lancashire | Maynes Coaches |
| 456.47500 | 461.97500 | NFM | Leicester | Security |
| 456.47500 | 461.97500 | NFM | Leicester | Woods Coaches Ch2 |
| 456.47500 | 461.97500 | NFM | Liverpool | Dockside Crane Control |
| 456.47500 | 461.97500 | NFM | London | Greenwich District Hospital |
| 456.47500 | 461.97500 | NFM | London | Hammersmith Hospital |
| 456.47500 | 461.97500 | NFM | London | QEII Conference Centre |
| 456.47500 | 461.97500 | NFM | London, Gatwick | Airline, BAA Ops. & Aircraft tugs |
| 456.47500 | 461.97500 | NFM | London, Heathrow | Airline & BAA Ops |
| 456.47500 | 461.97500 | NFM | London, Heathrow | Crew and Passenger Coaches |
| 456.47500 | 461.97500 | NFM | London, Heathrow | Europe Car courtesy bus |
| 456.47500 | 461.97500 | NFM | London, Oxford Street | Marks & Spencer |
| 456.47500 | 461.97500 | NFM | Luton | Vauxhall Motors |
| 456.47500 | 461.97500 | NFM | Middleton | Diamond Cars |
| 456.47500 | 461.97500 | NFM | Nationwide | Federal Express |
| 456.47500 | 461.97500 | NFM | Nationwide | HM Customs & Excise |
| 456.47500 | 461.97500 | NFM | Nationwide | Independent Coach Ops |
| 456.47500 | 461.97500 | NFM | North Welsh Coast | ESSO Rig |
| 456.47500 | 461.97500 | NFM | Norwich Airport | Ground Movements |
| 456.47500 | 461.97500 | NFM | Oxford | Classic Tour Bus |
| 456.47500 | 461.97500 | NFM | Preston | Skips & Bottle Banks |
| 456.47500 | 461.97500 | NFM | Sheffield | Crystal Peaks security |
| 456.47500 | 461.97500 | NFM | Sidcup | Sidcup Station |
| 456.47500 | 461.97500 | NFM | Stockport | TNT Carriers |
| 456.47500 | 461.97500 | NFM | Stowmarket | Agricultural User |
| 456.47500 | 461.97500 | NFM | Stowmarket | ICI Paints Security/Staff |
| 456.47500 | 461.97500 | NFM | Thistle A | BP |
| 456.47500 | 461.97500 | NFM | Wilton | ICI Fire & Security |
| 456.50000 | 462.00000 | NFM | Blackburn | Council base |
| 456.50000 | 462.00000 | NFM | Bradford | Security company |
| 456.50000 | 462.00000 | NFM | Bristol | Police Link |
| 456.50000 | 462.00000 | NFM | Colchester | Securicor Guarding Shopping Centres |
| 456.50000 | 462.00000 | NFM | Dungeness | Power Station |
| 456.50000 | 462.00000 | NFM | Duxford | Imperial War Museum management |
| 456.50000 | 462.00000 | NFM | London | London Docklands Corp |
| 456.50000 | 462.00000 | NFM | London, Gatwick | Airline ops. |
| 456.50000 | 462.00000 | NFM | London, Heathrow | Eurocar Car Hire Ltd. |
| 456.50000 | 462.00000 | NFM | Manchester | International Airport Catering Airside |
| 456.50000 | 462.00000 | NFM | Sheffield | City centre store detectives (TRACK) |
| 456.50000 | 462.00000 | NFM | York | OAP warden services |
| 456.52500 | 462.02200 | NFM | London Waterloo | Euro Star Staff and Security |

| Base | Mobile | Mode | Location | User and Notes |
|------|--------|------|----------|----------------|
| 456.52500 | 462.02500 | NFM | Ashford | Eurostar staff |
| 456.52500 | 462.02500 | NFM | Billingham | ICI |
| 456.52500 | 462.02500 | NFM | Birmingham International | HM Customs & Excise |
| 456.52500 | 462.02500 | NFM | Birmingham International | Ops |
| 456.52500 | 462.02500 | NFM | Bradford | Shop lifting squad |
| 456.52500 | 462.02500 | NFM | Bristol | Galleries Shopping Centre Control |
| 456.52500 | 462.02500 | NFM | Bristol Airport | Ground Repeater |
| 456.52500 | 462.02500 | NFM | Coventry | West Orchards Shopping Centre |
| 456.52500 | 462.02500 | NFM | Gateshead | Metro Centre Security |
| 456.52500 | 462.02500 | NFM | Halifax | Mackintoshes Security |
| 456.52500 | 462.02500 | NFM | Immingham | Docks/Repairs |
| 456.52500 | 462.02500 | NFM | Ipswich | Port Authority |
| 456.52500 | 462.02500 | NFM | Leicester | Leicester City Football Club stewards |
| 456.52500 | 462.02500 | NFM | London, Gatwick | Aircraft Tugs |
| 456.52500 | 462.02500 | NFM | Manchester | International Airport |
| 456.52500 | 462.02500 | NFM | Nationwide | HM Customs & Excise |
| 456.52500 | 462.02500 | NFM | North Sea | Shell Brent C |
| 456.52500 | 462.02500 | NFM | Salisbury | Hospital Emergency/Security |
| 456.52500 | 462.02500 | NFM | Saltend | BP Oil Refinery |
| 456.52500 | 462.02500 | NFM | Sheffield | Sheffield University Channel A (CAMPUS) |
| 456.52500 | 462.02500 | NFM | Stansted | Ground Repeater |
| 456.52500 | 462.02500 | NFM | Stoke-on-Trent | Police |
| 456.52500 | 462.02500 | NFM | York | Hospital patient transport |
| 456.55000 | 462.05000 | NFM | Brighton | Royal Sussex County Hospital |
| 456.55000 | 462.05000 | NFM | Bristol | Federal Express |
| 456.55000 | 462.05000 | NFM | Coventry | Rolls Royce Ltd. Security |
| 456.55000 | 462.05000 | NFM | Filton | BAe Security |
| 456.55000 | 462.05000 | NFM | Hull | Docks |
| 456.55000 | 462.05000 | NFM | Hull | University Security |
| 456.55000 | 462.05000 | NFM | Immingham | Railtrack |
| 456.55000 | 462.05000 | NFM | Lancashire | 24Hr Vehicle Recovery |
| 456.55000 | 462.05000 | NFM | Leeds | City centre store detectives |
| 456.55000 | 462.05000 | NFM | London, Gatwick | Ground Control Link |
| 456.55000 | 462.05000 | NFM | London, Heathrow | Aircraft Maintenance |
| 456.55000 | 462.05000 | NFM | London, Heathrow | Passenger Transport, Airline & BAA Ops. |
| 456.55000 | 462.05000 | NFM | Morecambe | Parcel Service |
| 456.55000 | 462.05000 | NFM | Newcastle | Eldon Shopping Centre Security |
| 456.55000 | 462.05000 | NFM | Nottingham | Cap Count Victoria Centre |
| 456.55000 | 462.05000 | NFM | Nottinghamshire | Lex Wilkinson |
| 456.55000 | 462.05000 | NFM | Perth | Telewest Cable Company |
| 456.55000 | 462.05000 | NFM | Poole | Borough Council |
| 456.55000 | 462.05000 | NFM | Stirling | Scottish Hydro Electric Engineers |
| 456.55000 | 462.05000 | NFM | Stoke-on-Trent | Potteries Shopping Centre |
| 456.55000 | 462.05000 | NFM | Watford | Capital & Counties Car Parking Services |
| 456.57500 | 456.57500 | NFM | Nationwide | D.O.T Motorcycle Tests |
| 456.57500 | 462.07500 | NFM | Ashford | Learner Motor Cycles |
| 456.57500 | 462.07500 | NFM | Beeston | Boots |
| 456.57500 | 462.07500 | NFM | Brighton | British Home Stores Security |
| 456.57500 | 462.07500 | NFM | Brighton | Shopwatch |
| 456.57500 | 462.07500 | NFM | Bristol | University of West of England Security |
| 456.57500 | 462.07500 | NFM | Coryton | Conoco Oil Refinery Ch 1 |
| 456.57500 | 462.07500 | NFM | Felixstowe | Docks |
| 456.57500 | 462.07500 | NFM | Hants | Water Sewage Works |
| 456.57500 | 462.07500 | NFM | Hull | Hull University |
| 456.57500 | 462.07500 | NFM | Immingham | Associated Petroleum Terminals |
| 456.57500 | 462.07500 | NFM | Jersey | Servisair Handling |

| Base | Mobile | Mode | Location | User and Notes |
|---|---|---|---|---|
| 456.57500 | 462.07500 | NFM | London | DSS Fraud teams |
| 456.57500 | 462.07500 | NFM | London | St. James Park wardens Ch 1 |
| 456.57500 | 462.07500 | NFM | London, Covent Garden | Walkabout Bar |
| 456.57500 | 462.07500 | NFM | London, Heathrow | Ground Repeater |
| 456.57500 | 462.07500 | NFM | Nationwide | Dept.of Transport Motorcycle Tests |
| 456.57500 | 462.07500 | NFM | Newtown | MotorcycleTests |
| 456.57500 | 462.07500 | NFM | North Sea | BP Mille |
| 456.57500 | 462.07500 | NFM | North Sea | Shell Auk |
| 456.57500 | 462.07500 | NFM | North Sea | Shell Brent A |
| 456.57500 | 462.07500 | NFM | North Sea | Shell Dunlin |
| 456.57500 | 462.07500 | NFM | Norwich | University of East Anglia Security |
| 456.57500 | 462.07500 | NFM | Poole | Toys R Us security |
| 456.57500 | 462.07500 | NFM | Sizewell | Power station work teams Ch.4 |
| 456.57500 | 462.07500 | NFM | Southampton | ESSO Fawley (CCR3) |
| 456.57500 | 462.07500 | NFM | Swansea | Motorcycle Training |
| 456.57500 | 462.07500 | NFM | Tilbury | Container Port. |
| 456.57500 | 462.07500 | NFM | Walthamstow | Dog Track Stadium Security |
| 456.57500 | 462.07500 | NFM | Weston Super Mare | Motor Cycle Instructors |
| 456.60000 | 462.10000 | NFM | Aberdeen | Dyce Airport Loading |
| 456.60000 | 462.10000 | NFM | Belfast Airport | Airline ops. |
| 456.60000 | 462.10000 | NFM | Birmingham | Massey Ferguson Security |
| 456.00000 | 462.10000 | NFM | Bristol | Broadmead Store Detectives |
| 456.60000 | 462.10000 | NFM | Bristol Filton | Ground Repeater |
| 456.60000 | 462.10000 | NFM | Cardiff | RadioNet Shop Security |
| 456.60000 | 462.10000 | NFM | Coventry | Massey Ferguson Security |
| 456.60000 | 462.10000 | NFM | Dover | Shopwatch |
| 456.60000 | 462.10000 | NFM | Garve | Scottish Roads |
| 456.60000 | 462.10000 | NFM | Halifax | Buses |
| 456.60000 | 462.10000 | NFM | Heathrow | Airport BAA Management/Engineers |
| 456.60000 | 462.10000 | NFM | Hull | British Petroleum Saltend Ch 2 |
| 456.60000 | 462.10000 | NFM | Leeds | First Bus Company buses |
| 456.60000 | 462.10000 | NFM | Leicester | Shires Sopping Centre Security |
| 456.60000 | 462.10000 | NFM | London | Docklands Light Railway Repeater |
| 456.60000 | 462.10000 | NFM | London | Heathrow Airport Catering |
| 456.60000 | 462.10000 | NFM | London | Newham General Hospital |
| 456.60000 | 462.10000 | NFM | London | Olympia Exhibition Repeater |
| 456.60000 | 462.10000 | NFM | London | Regent Palace Hotel Repeater |
| 456.60000 | 462.10000 | NFM | London, Blackfriars | The Exchange Building |
| 456.60000 | 462.10000 | NFM | London, Heathrow | Airline catering |
| 456.60000 | 462.10000 | NFM | London, Heathrow | BAA Management and Engineering |
| 456.60000 | 462.10000 | NFM | London, Merton | Sainsburys Savacentre |
| 456.60000 | 462.10000 | NFM | London, Nine Elms | New Covent Garden Market security |
| 456.60000 | 462.10000 | NFM | London, Pentonville Road. | Engineering |
| 456.60000 | 462.10000 | NFM | London, WC1 | Library Security |
| 456.60000 | 462.10000 | NFM | Luton Airport | Car Parks replacing 453.300 |
| 456.60000 | 462.10000 | NFM | Manchester | Trafford Centre |
| 456.60000 | 462.10000 | NFM | Manchester Airport | Aircraft Cleaners |
| 456.60000 | 462.10000 | NFM | North Sea | Phillips Maureen |
| 456.60000 | 462.10000 | NFM | Norwich | Airport Departures and Arrivals |
| 456.60000 | 462.10000 | NFM | Saltend | BP Oil Refinery Ch2 |
| 456.60000 | 462.10000 | NFM | Southampton | Container Port Crane Ops. |
| 456.60000 | 462.10000 | NFM | Thornton | ICI |
| 456.60000 | 462.10000 | NFM | Warwick | Warwick Technology Park (CW) |
| 456.61250 | 462.11250 | NFM | Newcastle Airport | Tower |
| 456.61500 | 462.11500 | NFM | Grand Prix Circuits | Ferrari Team Voice Link |
| 456.62500 | 462.12500 | NFM | Barrow in Furness | VSEL Traffic Department |

| Base | Mobile | Mode | Location | User and Notes |
| --- | --- | --- | --- | --- |
| 456.62500 | 462.12500 | NFM | Birmingham | Birmingham University Security |
| 456.62500 | 462.12500 | NFM | Cardiff | Bus Co |
| 456.62500 | 462.12500 | NFM | Cardiff | Buses |
| 456.62500 | 462.12500 | NFM | Cardiff | Cardiff Council |
| 456.62500 | 462.12500 | NFM | Cleethorpes | Ross Young Fish Factory |
| 456.62500 | 462.12500 | NFM | Coventry | Warwick University Security |
| 456.62500 | 462.12500 | NFM | Croydon | Drummond Shopping Centre |
| 456.62500 | 462.12500 | NFM | Duxford | Fire Control |
| 456.62500 | 462.12500 | NFM | Harwich | Docks |
| 456.62500 | 462.12500 | NFM | Ipswich | Port Ch 1 |
| 456.62500 | 462.12500 | NFM | Jersey Airport | Ground |
| 456.62500 | 462.12500 | NFM | London | Victoria Coach Station |
| 456.62500 | 462.12500 | NFM | London, Aldgate | Building maintenance. |
| 456.62500 | 462.12500 | NFM | London, Gatwick | Ground Control Link |
| 456.62500 | 462.12500 | NFM | London, Gatwick | Car Hire Service |
| 456.62500 | 462.12500 | NFM | London, Sewardstone | Hannah Nursery Plants |
| 456.62500 | 462.12500 | NFM | London, Wandsworth | King George Park |
| 456.62500 | 462.12500 | NFM | London, White City | BBC Worldwide Sales Ch 2 |
| 456.62500 | 462.12500 | NFM | Manchester Airport | Airline Ops |
| 456.62500 | 462.12500 | NFM | North Sea | Shell Brent C |
| 456.62500 | 462.12500 | NFM | North Sea | Shell Fulmar A |
| 456.62500 | 462.12500 | NFM | Oxford | Clarendon Centre |
| 456.62500 | 462.12500 | NFM | Peterborough | Security Company |
| 456.62500 | 462.12500 | NFM | Southampton | ESSO Fawley |
| 456.63000 | 462.13000 | NFM | North Sea | Shell North Cormorant |
| 456.65000 | 462.15000 | NFM | Coventry | Warwick University Conference Rooms |
| 456.65000 | 462.15000 | NFM | Edinburgh Airport | PMR Channel 6 |
| 456.65000 | 462.15000 | NFM | Felixstowe | Docks |
| 456.65000 | 462.15000 | NFM | Glasgow | Ground |
| 456.65000 | 462.15000 | NFM | Hull | North Sea Ferries Ch 1 |
| 456.65000 | 462.15000 | NFM | Ipswich | Docks |
| 456.65000 | 462.15000 | NFM | London | Colnbrook Retail. |
| 456.65000 | 462.15000 | NFM | London | Doctors Scheme |
| 456.65000 | 462.15000 | NFM | London | Hetzlah Paramedic Ambulance Service |
| 456.65000 | 462.15000 | NFM | London | Jewish doctors scheme |
| 456.65000 | 462.15000 | NFM | London | London Electricity |
| 456.65000 | 462.15000 | NFM | London | Mayfair Locksmiths. |
| 456.65000 | 462.15000 | NFM | London | British Library |
| 456.65000 | 462.15000 | NFM | London, Colindale Ave. | British Library |
| 456.65000 | 462.15000 | NFM | London, Gatwick | Aviation Fuel |
| 456.65000 | 462.15000 | NFM | London, Heathrow | Ground Staff Terminal 1 |
| 456.65000 | 462.15000 | NFM | London, Villiers Street | Price, Waterhouse, Coopers |
| 456.65000 | 462.15000 | NFM | Manchester | International Airport Servisair |
| 456.65000 | 462.15000 | NFM | Manchester Airport | Ground Control |
| 456.65000 | 462.15000 | NFM | North Sea | BP Miller |
| 456.65000 | 462.15000 | NFM | Nuneaton | Retail Security Link |
| 456.65000 | 462.15000 | NFM | Reading | Shopwatch |
| 456.65000 | 462.15000 | NFM | Sandwich | Pfizers |
| 456.65000 | 462.15000 | NFM | Sheffield | Meadowhall Shopping Centre |
| 456.65000 | 462.15000 | NFM | Sidcup | Queen Mary Hospital |
| 456.65000 | 462.15000 | NFM | Southampton | ESSO Fawley (PET-M) |
| 456.65000 | 462.15000 | NFM | Stansted | Airport Cleaners |
| 456.65000 | 462.15000 | NFM | Stansted | Long Term Car Park |
| 456.66250 | 462.16250 | NFM | Newcastle Airport | Stand Services |
| 456.67500 | 462.17500 | NFM | Aberdeen | Dyce Airport Staff |
| 456.67500 | 462.17500 | NFM | Ashford | Shop Watch Scheme |

| Base | Mobile | Mode | Location | User and Notes |
|------|--------|------|----------|----------------|
| 456.67500 | 462.17500 | NFM | Billingham | ICI |
| 456.67500 | 462.17500 | NFM | Chorlton | Detention centre |
| 456.67500 | 462.17500 | NFM | City of London | Broad Street Halifax Building Society offices |
| 456.67500 | 462.17500 | NFM | Liverpool | Medic Control |
| 456.67500 | 462.17500 | NFM | London | British Library |
| 456.67500 | 462.17500 | NFM | London | North Thames Electricity |
| 456.67500 | 462.17500 | NFM | London | Securicor |
| 456.67500 | 462.17500 | NFM | London, Broad Street | Halifax plc offices |
| 456.67500 | 462.17500 | NFM | London, E12 | Cemetery |
| 456.67500 | 462.17500 | NFM | London, Heathrow | Air France Passenger Services |
| 456.67500 | 462.17500 | NFM | London, NW10 | North Pole Rail Depot |
| 456.67500 | 462.17500 | NFM | Luton Airport | Debonair arrivals & departures |
| 456.67500 | 462.17500 | NFM | Luton Airport | Ryan Air arrivals & departures |
| 456.67500 | 462.17500 | NFM | Manchester | City Centre Vehicle Clamping |
| 456.67500 | 462.17500 | NFM | Manchester | Paramedic Teams |
| 456.67500 | 462.17500 | NFM | North Sea | BP Miller |
| 456.67500 | 462.17500 | NFM | North Sea | Shell Brent D |
| 456.67500 | 462.17500 | NFM | North Sea | Shell North Cormorant |
| 456.67500 | 462.17500 | NFM | Nottingham | J. Player & Son |
| 456.67500 | 462.17500 | NFM | Oldbury | BNFL Backup Channel |
| 456.67500 | 462.17500 | NFM | Oldham | Minicabs |
| 456.67500 | 462.17500 | NFM | Oldham | VNFL Security |
| 456.67500 | 462.17500 | NFM | Rotherhithe | Mail Newspapers |
| 456.67500 | 462.17500 | NFM | Salisbury | Shopwatch. |
| 456.67500 | 462.17500 | NFM | Southampton | ESSO Fawley (Lubes) |
| 456.67500 | 462.17500 | NFM | Stoke-on-Trent | Police |
| 456.67500 | 462.17500 | NFM | Warton | Fence Security |
| 456.67500 | 462.17500 | NFM | Windsor | Windsor Castle Wardens |
| 456.67500 | 462.17500 | NFM | Woburn | Woburn Abbey Wildlife Park |
| 456.68750 | 456.68750 | NFM | Morecambe | Parcel Service |
| 456.70000 | 456.20000 | NFM | Nationwide | Marconi Communications |
| 456.70000 | 462.20000 | NFM | Basildon | Eastgate Centre security |
| 456.70000 | 462.20000 | NFM | Dartford | Europort |
| 456.70000 | 462.20000 | NFM | Felixstowe | Docks |
| 456.70000 | 462.20000 | NFM | Grays | Lakeside Centre Car Park |
| 456.70000 | 462.20000 | NFM | Great Coates | Courtaulds |
| 456.70000 | 462.20000 | NFM | Killingholme | Lindsey Oil Refinery |
| 456.70000 | 462.20000 | NFM | Lancaster | Lancaster University Security |
| 456.70000 | 462.20000 | NFM | Leeds | Leeds University security |
| 456.70000 | 462.20000 | NFM | London | BR Signal Engineers |
| 456.70000 | 462.20000 | NFM | London | Brent Cross Shopping Centre Security |
| 456.70000 | 462.20000 | NFM | London, Canary Wharf | Security (I) |
| 456.70000 | 462.20000 | NFM | London, Heathrow | Passenger ops. (ground repeater) |
| 456.70000 | 462.20000 | NFM | London, Heathrow | Passenger Ops |
| 456.70000 | 462.20000 | NFM | London, Wood Green | Shopwatch |
| 456.70000 | 462.20000 | NFM | Nationwide | Motorola |
| 456.70000 | 462.20000 | NFM | North Sea | Shell Brent C |
| 456.70000 | 462.20000 | NFM | North Sea | Shell Fulmar A |
| 456.70000 | 462.20000 | NFM | Perth | Car Park Security |
| 456.70000 | 462.20000 | NFM | Rugby | Cement Works |
| 456.70000 | 462.20000 | NFM | Saltend | BP Oil Refinery, Ch 1 fire |
| 456.70000 | 462.20000 | NFM | Sheffield | University security (CAMPUS) |
| 456.70000 | 462.20000 | NFM | Southampton | ESSO Fawley (RED) Fire |
| 456.70000 | 462.20000 | NFM | Ullapool | Scottish Roads |
| 456.70000 | 462.20000 | NFM | Wakefield | Security company |
| 456.70000 | 462.20000 | NFM | Welwyn Garden City | Cereal Partners |

| Base | Mobile | Mode | Location | User and Notes |
|------|--------|------|----------|----------------|
| 456.70000 | 462.20000 | NFM | West Midlands | Country Park (ALPHA) |
| 456.70000 | 462.20000 | NFM | York | University |
| 456.72500 | 462.22500 | NFM | Canvey Island | Texaco Oil Refinery |
| 456.72500 | 462.22500 | NFM | Coventry | Peugeot Talbot Works |
| 456.72500 | 462.22500 | NFM | Cowley | Rover Plant Channel 5 |
| 456.72500 | 462.22500 | NFM | Edinburgh | Herriot Watt Univ. Security |
| 456.72500 | 462.22500 | NFM | Gairloch | Scottish Roads |
| 456.72500 | 462.22500 | NFM | Harwich | Port Reception Staff. |
| 456.72500 | 462.22500 | NFM | Hull | North Sea Ferries Ch 2 |
| 456.72500 | 462.22500 | NFM | Jersey | Dock Crane Operators |
| 456.72500 | 462.22500 | NFM | Leeds | City centre store detectives |
| 456.72500 | 462.22500 | NFM | Leeds | Shop lifting squad |
| 456.72500 | 462.22500 | NFM | Leicester | Council Roads Dept |
| 456.72500 | 462.22500 | NFM | London, Gatwick | Avionics Maintenance |
| 456.72500 | 462.22500 | NFM | London, Heathrow | Airport trunked Airline & BAA ops. |
| 456.72500 | 462.22500 | NFM | Luton Airport | Security & Maintenance Ops. |
| 456.72500 | 462.22500 | NFM | Nationwide | UHF Demonstration Ch 99 |
| 456.72500 | 462.22500 | NFM | North Sea | BP SMV |
| 456.72500 | 462.22500 | NFM | Norwich | Lotus Motor Plant |
| 456.72500 | 462.22500 | NFM | Peterborough | City Council |
| 456.72500 | 462.22500 | NFM | Southampton | ESSO Fawley (OMES) |
| 456.72500 | 462.22500 | NFM | Southend-on-Sea | Store Security |
| 456.72500 | 462.22500 | NFM | Stevenston | ICI Security and Fire Service |
| 456.72500 | 462.22500 | NFM | Swansea Docks | Shipping Pilots |
| 456.72500 | 462.22500 | NFM | Ulverston | Glaxo UK |
| 456.75000 | 462.25000 | NFM | Aberdeen (Dyce Airport) | Loading |
| 456.75000 | 462.25000 | NFM | Barrow | VSEL Fire & Nuclear Incidents |
| 456.75000 | 462.25000 | NFM | Coventry | Warwick University |
| 456.75000 | 462.25000 | NFM | Glasgow | Cargo Handlers |
| 456.75000 | 462.25000 | NFM | Harwich | Port and Stena Sealink |
| 456.75000 | 462.25000 | NFM | London | Bexley Heath Shopping Cen Sec |
| 456.75000 | 462.25000 | NFM | Luton Airport | Debon Air and Ryan Air |
| 456.75000 | 462.25000 | NFM | Skelmersdale | Town Centre Security |
| 456.77500 | 462.27500 | NFM | Aberdeen | BP |
| 456.77500 | 462.27500 | NFM | Blackpool | Blackpool Pleasure Beach |
| 456.77500 | 462.27500 | NFM | Bradford | College security |
| 456.77500 | 462.27500 | NFM | Eastham | Manchester Ship Canal |
| 456.77500 | 462.27500 | NFM | Glasgow | Police |
| 456.77500 | 462.27500 | NFM | Hants | Water company |
| 456.77500 | 462.27500 | NFM | Harwich | Trinity House |
| 456.77500 | 462.27500 | NFM | Hull | Docks Cranes/Loading |
| 456.77500 | 462.27500 | NFM | Leicester | Area Traffic Control |
| 456.77500 | 462.27500 | NFM | Liverpool | Manchester Ship Canal (Eastham) |
| 456.77500 | 462.27500 | NFM | London, Gatwick | Ground Repeater |
| 456.77500 | 462.27500 | NFM | London, Heathrow | Kuwaiti Airlines |
| 456.77500 | 462.27500 | NFM | Manchester Shaw | Security |
| 456.77500 | 462.27500 | NFM | Millbrook | Test Track |
| 456.77500 | 462.27500 | NFM | Nuneaton | George Elliot Hosp. Security |
| 456.77500 | 462.27500 | NFM | Redditch | Kingfisher Shopping Centre |
| 456.77500 | 462.27500 | NFM | Southampton | ESSO Fawley (Chemicals) |
| 456.77500 | 462.27500 | NFM | Stansted Airport | Data Command Ch |
| 456.77500 | 462.27500 | NFM | Tilbury | Town. |
| 456.78750 | 462.28750 | NFM | London | Museum of Moving Images |
| 456.80000 | 462.30000 | NFM | Beeston | Boots |
| 456.80000 | 462.30000 | NFM | Guildford | Army & Navy Stores |
| 456.80000 | 462.30000 | NFM | London | Courtaulds Gallery and Institute Security. |

| Base | Mobile | Mode | Location | User and Notes |
|------|--------|------|----------|----------------|
| 456.80000 | 462.30000 | NFM | London | Madame Tassauds |
| 456.80000 | 462.30000 | NFM | London, Gatwick | Aviation Fuel |
| 456.80000 | 462.30000 | NFM | London, Heathrow | Airport Security |
| 456.80000 | 462.30000 | NFM | Luton Airport | Security |
| 456.80000 | 462.30000 | NFM | North Sea | Chevron Drilling Ninian Central & South |
| 456.80000 | 462.30000 | NFM | Peterborough | East of England Show Ground Security |
| 456.80000 | 462.30000 | NFM | Tilbury | Container Port. |
| 456.82500 | 462.32500 | NFM | Bath | University Security |
| 456.82500 | 462.32500 | NFM | Billingham | ICI |
| 456.82500 | 462.32500 | NFM | Borehamwood | Warehouse. |
| 456.82500 | 462.32500 | NFM | Bournemouth | Chase Manhattan Bank |
| 456.82500 | 462.32500 | NFM | Brighton | Sussex University Security |
| 456.82500 | 462.32500 | NFM | Cardiff | Shopping centre security |
| 456.82500 | 462.32500 | NFM | Cheltenham | Shop Security Network |
| 456.82500 | 462.32500 | NFM | Coventry | Warwick University Maintenance |
| 456.82500 | 462.32500 | NFM | Dover | Coastguard Cliff Rescue |
| 456.82500 | 462.32500 | NFM | Immingham | British Sugar |
| 456.82500 | 462.32500 | NFM | Immingham | Docks |
| 456.82500 | 462.32500 | NFM | London, Heathrow | Airline & BAA Ops |
| 456.82500 | 462.32500 | NFM | Luton Airport | Airlines Ops. |
| 456.82500 | 462.32500 | NFM | Manchester Airport | Airline Ops |
| 456.82500 | 462.32500 | NFM | Nationwide | NCB & Docks |
| 456.82500 | 462.32500 | NFM | Nottingham | Patent Brick |
| 456.82500 | 462.32500 | NFM | Sandwich | Pfizers |
| 456.82500 | 462.32500 | NFM | Southampton | ESSO Fawley CCR1 |
| 456.82500 | 462.32500 | NFM | St Helens | Pilkingtons Security |
| 456.82500 | 462.32500 | NFM | Stansted | Telephone Ops |
| 456.82500 | 462.32500 | NFM | Tamworth | Borough Council |
| 456.82500 | 462.32500 | NFM | Woburn | Woburn Abbey Wildlife Park |
| 456.85000 | 462.35000 | NFM | Colchester | Shopwatch |
| 456.85000 | 462.35000 | NFM | Coventry | Community Nurses |
| 456.85000 | 462.35000 | NFM | Coventry | Social Services |
| 456.85000 | 462.35000 | NFM | Cowley | Rover Plant |
| 456.85000 | 462.35000 | NFM | Ely | Storeys Coaches |
| 456.85000 | 462.35000 | NFM | Greenford | Radio Cars |
| 456.85000 | 462.35000 | NFM | Ipswich | Docks |
| 456.85000 | 462.35000 | NFM | Leicester | Council Road Dept |
| 456.85000 | 462.35000 | NFM | London | Greenwich Maritime |
| 456.85000 | 462.35000 | NFM | London, Heathrow | Airline & BAA Ops |
| 456.85000 | 462.35000 | NFM | Manchester | P055 Factory |
| 456.85000 | 462.35000 | NFM | Manchester | Taxis |
| 456.85000 | 462.35000 | NFM | Nationwide | J Sisk & Son (Construction) Ch1 |
| 456.85000 | 462.35000 | NFM | Nationwide | National Coach Company |
| 456.85000 | 462.35000 | NFM | Nottingham | Mapperly Hospital |
| 456.85000 | 462.35000 | NFM | Skelmersdale | Taxis |
| 456.85000 | 462.35000 | NFM | Stansted | Airport Ops |
| 456.85000 | 462.35000 | NFM | Stansted | Long Term Car Park |
| 456.85000 | 462.35000 | NFM | Tilbury | Docks Security |
| 456.85000 | 462.35000 | NFM | Wansford | Nene Valley Railway |
| 456.85000 | 462.35000 | NFM | Wigan | Taxis |
| 456.85000 | 462.35000 | NFM | Worthing | Taxi |
| 456.86250 | 462.36250 | NFM | Canvey Island | Safeways Supermarket Maintenance |
| 456.86250 | 462.36250 | NFM | Coventry | Call Security |
| 456.86250 | 462.36250 | NFM | Coventry | Delphi Packard security |
| 456.86250 | 462.36250 | NFM | Eastbourne | Pier |
| 456.86250 | 462.36250 | NFM | Edinburgh | Teviot House Security |

| Base | Mobile | Mode | Location | User and Notes |
|---|---|---|---|---|
| 456.86250 | 462.36250 | NFM | Heathrow | Airport Contractors |
| 456.86250 | 462.36250 | NFM | Ipswich | Nighthawk Security |
| 456.86250 | 462.36250 | NFM | Lakeside Thurrock | Police Shoplifters Surveillance |
| 456.86250 | 462.36250 | NFM | London | Alexandra Palace exhibitions |
| 456.86250 | 462.36250 | NFM | London | BAFTA Awards Production |
| 456.86250 | 462.36250 | NFM | London | Bayleys Nightclub doorman |
| 456.86250 | 462.36250 | NFM | London | Wembley Stadium VIP Catering |
| 456.86250 | 462.36250 | NFM | London, Heathrow | Passenger courtesy bus |
| 456.86250 | 462.36250 | NFM | London, Kings Cross | Holiday Inn Hotel |
| 456.86250 | 462.36250 | NFM | London, Leicester Square | Odeon, Premiere Security |
| 456.86250 | 462.36250 | NFM | London, Piccadilly | Sega Mega World |
| 456.86250 | 462.36250 | NFM | London, Regent Street | British Airways Travel Office |
| 456.86250 | 462.36250 | NFM | London, Regent Street | Warner Bros Store Net |
| 456.86250 | 462.36250 | NFM | Maidstone | Borough Council |
| 456.86250 | 462.36250 | NFM | National | ITV The Bill Production Team |
| 456.86250 | 462.36250 | NFM | National | Whitby Davies Productions |
| 456.86250 | 462.36250 | NFM | Nationwide | BBC filming production unit |
| 456.86250 | 462.36250 | NFM | Nationwide | Short Term Hire |
| 456.86250 | 462.36250 | NFM | RAE Farnborough | British Aerospace highway security |
| 456.86250 | 462.36250 | NFM | Reading | Grocers Shop/Delivery Service |
| 456.86250 | 462.36250 | NFM | River Thames | Ship On-Board Comms |
| 456.86250 | 462.36250 | NFM | Rugby | Christian Salvesen Ch.7 |
| 456.86250 | 462.36250 | NFM | Sheffield | Schools security |
| 456.86250 | 462.36250 | NFM | Suffolk | Redlands Stop/Go traffic control |
| 456.86250 | 462.36250 | NFM | Warwick | Aviation Executive Bodyguards |
| 456.86250 | 462.36250 | NFM | Woodford Airfield | BAe Security |
| 456.87500 | 462.37500 | NFM | Birmingham International | Midland Airport Services |
| 456.87500 | 462.37500 | NFM | City of London | Blackfriars The Salvation Army HQ |
| 456.87500 | 462.37500 | NFM | Cowdenbeath | Mossmorran Complex |
| 456.87500 | 462.37500 | NFM | Fairlop | Leisure Site Repeater |
| 456.87500 | 462.37500 | NFM | Grays | Lakeside Centre Security |
| 456.87500 | 462.37500 | NFM | Guernsey | Esso |
| 456.87500 | 462.37500 | NFM | Hayes | Factory Security Repeater |
| 456.87500 | 462.37500 | NFM | Hull | Football Stewards/Rugby Stewards, Sharks. |
| 456.87500 | 462.37500 | NFM | Jersey Airport | Jersey Air Commodore Ops |
| 456.87500 | 462.37500 | NFM | Lancashire | Vanguard Couriers |
| 456.87500 | 462.37500 | NFM | London | Belvedere Factory Security Repeater |
| 456.87500 | 462.37500 | NFM | London | Blackwall Newspaper Production Repeater |
| 456.87500 | 462.37500 | NFM | London | Brent Cross Security User Repeater |
| 456.87500 | 462.37500 | NFM | London | Hampton Court Palace Staff Repeater |
| 456.87500 | 462.37500 | NFM | London | Heathrow Airport Transport User Repeater |
| 456.87500 | 462.37500 | NFM | London | Mayfair Oil Co Repeater |
| 456.87500 | 462.37500 | NFM | London | Mile End Queenmary and Westfield College |
| 456.87500 | 462.37500 | NFM | London | Northfields London Underground Repeater |
| 456.87500 | 462.37500 | NFM | London, South Bermondsey | British Gas Site Repeater |
| 456.87500 | 462.37500 | NFM | London | South Kensington Hotel |
| 456.87500 | 462.37500 | NFM | London | Temple Construction Co |
| 456.87500 | 462.37500 | NFM | London, Gatwick | Handling |
| 456.87500 | 462.37500 | NFM | London, Hammersmith | Broadway Shopping Centre |
| 456.87500 | 462.37500 | NFM | Luton | Airport |
| 456.87500 | 462.37500 | NFM | Manchester | International Airport Catering |
| 456.87500 | 462.37500 | NFM | North Sea | Shell Auk |
| 456.87500 | 462.37500 | NFM | North Sea | Shell Brent A |
| 456.87500 | 462.37500 | NFM | North Sea | Shell Dunlin |
| 456.87500 | 462.37500 | NFM | Nottingham | Esso Colwick |
| 456.87500 | 462.37500 | NFM | Purfleet | Gulf Oil UK Ltd Repeater |

| Base | Mobile | Mode | Location | User and Notes |
|---|---|---|---|---|
| 456.87500 | 462.37500 | NFM | Southampton | ESSO Fawley Jetty |
| 456.87500 | 462.37500 | NFM | Stevenston | ICI Acid Plant Maintenance |
| 456.87500 | 462.37500 | NFM | Swansea | Docks Security |
| 456.87500 | 462.37500 | NFM | Warwick | Castle staff Ch 1 |
| 456.87500 | 462.37500 | NFM | Welsh North Coast | ESSO Rig |
| 456.90000 | 462.40000 | NFM | Ashford | Welsh School |
| 456.90000 | 462.40000 | NFM | Barrow | VSEL Works Security Control |
| 456.90000 | 462.40000 | NFM | Bexley | Hospital |
| 456.90000 | 462.40000 | NFM | Biggleswade | Jordans Cereals Ch 2 |
| 456.90000 | 462.40000 | NFM | Borehamwood | BBC Elstree Studios |
| 456.90000 | 462.40000 | NFM | Bournemouth | Bournemouth Zoo |
| 456.90000 | 462.40000 | NFM | City of London | Stockbrokers |
| 456.90000 | 462.40000 | NFM | Dartford, Kent | Bexley Hospital |
| 456.90000 | 462.40000 | NFM | East Midlands Airport | Servisair |
| 456.90000 | 462.40000 | NFM | Edinburgh Airport | Baggage Handlers |
| 456.90000 | 462.40000 | NFM | Glasgow | Ops |
| 456.90000 | 462.40000 | NFM | Greenwich, Tunnel Avenue | Tavern Snacks |
| 456.90000 | 462.40000 | NFM | Ipswich | Port |
| 456.90000 | 462.40000 | NFM | Liverpool Airport | Servisair |
| 456.90000 | 462.40000 | NFM | London | Whitehall Education Dept. |
| 456.90000 | 462.40000 | NFM | London, Gatwick | Servisair |
| 456.90000 | 462.40000 | NFM | London, Heathrow | Tower Rebroadcast |
| 456.90000 | 462.40000 | NFM | London, Queen Annes Street | Banking |
| 456.90000 | 462.40000 | NFM | Manchester Airport | Aircraft Tugs |
| 456.90000 | 462.40000 | NFM | Newcastle Airport | Refuelling |
| 456.90000 | 462.40000 | NFM | Saltend | Oil terminal |
| 456.90000 | 462.40000 | NFM | West Drayton | Retail |
| 456.92500 | 462.42500 | NFM | Ayr | Shop to Shop Security |
| 456.92500 | 462.42500 | NFM | Basildon | Alders of Basildon |
| 456.92500 | 462.42500 | NFM | Blackpool | Store Detectives |
| 456.92500 | 462.42500 | NFM | Boscombe | Sovereign Shopping Centre Security |
| 456.92500 | 462.42500 | NFM | Brentwood | Retail Park security |
| 456.92500 | 462.42500 | NFM | Burnley | Asda |
| 456.92500 | 462.42500 | NFM | Cowley | Rover Plant Channel 6 |
| 456.92500 | 462.42500 | NFM | Ealing | Shopping Centre |
| 456.92500 | 462.42500 | NFM | Grays | Council |
| 456.92500 | 462.42500 | NFM | Lea Valley | Leisure Centre |
| 456.92500 | 462.42500 | NFM | Leeds | HMV security |
| 456.92500 | 462.42500 | NFM | London | Wembley Stadium VIP Catering |
| 456.92500 | 462.42500 | NFM | London | Wood Green Shopping Centre |
| 456.92500 | 462.42500 | NFM | London, Finchley | Warner Bros Cinema |
| 456.92500 | 462.42500 | NFM | London, Heathrow | Ground Repeater |
| 456.92500 | 462.42500 | NFM | London, Oxford Street | Virgin Megastore staff |
| 456.92500 | 462.42500 | NFM | London, Piccadilly | Cafe de Paris |
| 456.92500 | 462.42500 | NFM | London, Piccadilly | Waxy O'Connon's Irish Pubs |
| 456.92500 | 462.42500 | NFM | London, Whitehall | Government department |
| 456.92500 | 462.42500 | NFM | Milton Keynes | Bowl Car Park Staff |
| 456.92500 | 462.42500 | NFM | National | Boys Own Band Stage Crew |
| 456.92500 | 462.42500 | NFM | National | Lewis Outside Catering Special Events |
| 456.92500 | 462.42500 | NFM | Nationwide | BAA Airport Security |
| 456.92500 | 462.42500 | NFM | Nationwide | BBC filming production unit |
| 456.92500 | 462.42500 | NFM | Nationwide | Power Station Security |
| 456.92500 | 462.42500 | NFM | Nationwide | Short Term Hire |
| 456.92500 | 462.42500 | NFM | Nationwide | UHF Demonstration Channel |
| 456.92500 | 462.42500 | NFM | Reading | Centre Crane Ops |
| 456.92500 | 462.42500 | NFM | Sellafield | Security |

| Base | Mobile | Mode | Location | User and Notes |
|------|--------|------|----------|----------------|
| 456.92500 | 462.42500 | NFM | Stansted | Airport |
| 456.92500 | 462.42500 | NFM | Stowmarket | Shopwatch |
| 456.92500 | 462.42500 | NFM | West Midlands | Short term hire mobiles |
| 456.92500 | 462.42500 | NFM | Wigan | Galleries Shopping Centre Sec. |
| 456.93750 | 462.43750 | NFM | London | Sega World Ch 1 |
| 456.95000 | 462.45000 | NFM | Birmingham International | Ops |
| 456.95000 | 462.45000 | NFM | Bournemouth | Repeater |
| 456.95000 | 462.45000 | NFM | Brighton | Royal Sussex Hospital Porters |
| 456.95000 | 462.45000 | NFM | Gillingham | Shopwatch |
| 456.95000 | 462.45000 | NFM | Halewood | Ford Plant Shop Stewards |
| 456.95000 | 462.45000 | NFM | Leamington | Shopmet |
| 456.95000 | 462.45000 | NFM | Liverpool | Cherry Tree Shopping Cent Sec. |
| 456.95000 | 462.45000 | NFM | London, Gatwick | Airline & BAA Ops |
| 456.95000 | 462.45000 | NFM | London, Heathrow | Virgin Airlines |
| 456.95000 | 462.45000 | NFM | Preston | Store detectives |
| 456.95000 | 462.45000 | NFM | RAE Farnborough | British Aerospace transport |
| 456.95000 | 462.45000 | NFM | Southampton | ESSO Fawley Chemicals |
| 456.95000 | 462.45000 | NFM | Wilmslow | Taxi |
| 456.96250 | 462.46250 | NFM | Basildon | Allders staff net |
| 456.97500 | 462.47500 | NFM | Birmingham | Shop Watch Security Fort Retail Park |
| 456.97500 | 462.47500 | NFM | Birmingham, Longbridge | Rover Group Ltd. Security & Fire |
| 456.97500 | 462.47500 | NFM | City of London | Leadenhall Street Market security |
| 456.97500 | 462.47500 | NFM | Doncaster | Winifreda Coach Co. |
| 456.97500 | 462.47500 | NFM | Flitwick | Buffalo Bus Co. |
| 456.97500 | 462.47500 | NFM | Humberside | Appleby's Coaches |
| 456.97500 | 462.47500 | NFM | Leamington Spa | British Leyland |
| 456.97500 | 462.47500 | NFM | Leicester | Woods Coaches Ch1 |
| 456.97500 | 462.47500 | NFM | Nationwide | Bus & Coach Operators |
| 456.97500 | 462.47500 | NFM | Nationwide | Formula One Racing Team Links |
| 456.97500 | 462.47500 | NFM | Newcastle Airport | Britannia Airways |
| 456.97500 | 462.47500 | NFM | Newport | New Borough Transport |
| 456.97500 | 462.47500 | NFM | North Sea | North Denes Oil Rig |
| 456.97500 | 462.47500 | NFM | Rochdale | Buses |
| 456.97500 | 462.47500 | NFM | Stansted | Stansted Cars |
| 456.97500 | 462.47500 | NFM | Stevenage | Sovereign Coach & Bus |
| 456.97500 | 462.47500 | NFM | Teddington | National Physical Labs Repeater |
| 456.98750 | 462.48750 | NFM | Barking | Vicarage Fields Shopping Centre |
| 456.98750 | 462.48750 | NFM | Brighton | Columbia Pictures End of the Affair filming |
| 456.98750 | 462.48750 | NFM | Brighton | Royal Sussex County Hospital |
| 456.98750 | 462.48750 | NFM | Bristol | Pinkerton Security Services |
| 456.98750 | 462.48750 | NFM | Coventry | Comtel Cable T.V. |
| 456.98750 | 462.48750 | NFM | Duxford | Imperial War Museum car parks |
| 456.98750 | 462.48750 | NFM | Jersey | Community Repeater |
| 456.98750 | 462.48750 | NFM | London | Oxford St Boarders Book Shop Staff |
| 456.98750 | 462.48750 | NFM | London, Garrick Street | The 38 Club |
| 456.98750 | 462.48750 | NFM | London, Heathrow | Airline & BAA Ops |
| 456.98750 | 462.48750 | NFM | London, Kensington High Street | Gap Store Staff Net |
| 456.98750 | 462.48750 | NFM | National | Tescos Hot Air Balloon Team Air to Ground |
| 456.98750 | 462.48750 | NFM | Nationwide | Christian Salvesen Ch.4 |
| 456.98750 | 462.48750 | NFM | Nationwide | Short Term Hire |
| 456.98750 | 462.48750 | NFM | Nationwide | Tescos Hot Air Balloon Team |
| 456.98750 | 462.48750 | NFM | Southend | Illegal Use By Local Family |
| 456.98750 | 462.48750 | NFM | Southend | Seafront Watch For Clubs/Pubs Etc |
| 456.98750 | 462.48750 | NFM | Sussex, SE | Security Patrol |
| 456.98750 | 462.48750 | NFM | Tamworth | Ankerside Car Park Security. |
| 456.98750 | 462.48750 | NFM | Tunbridge Wells | Tour de France Barrier Erectors |

## 457.000 - 457.250 MHz    FIRE BRIGADES MOBILE LINKS 12.5 KHZ
### SIMPLEX & DUPLEX BASE (SPLIT + 5.5 MHZ)

| Base | Mobile | Mode | Location | User and Notes |
|---|---|---|---|---|
| 457.00000 | 462.50000 | NFM | Doncaster | Fire Brigade handhelds |
| 457.01250 | 462.51250 | NFM | Edinburgh | Fire Brigade |
| 457.01250 | 462.51250 | NFM | Glasgow | Fire Brigade |
| 457.01250 | 462.51250 | NFM | London | Fire Brigade |
| 457.01250 | 462.51250 | NFM | Nationwide | Fire Brigade Ch.3 |
| 457.01250 | 462.51250 | NFM | Suffolk | Fire Brigade Ch.3 (BA) |
| 457.03750 | 462.53750 | NFM | Cumbria | Fire Brigade Portables |
| 457.03750 | 462.53750 | NFM | Doncaster | Fire Brigade handhelds |
| 457.03750 | 462.53750 | NFM | Dyfed | Fire Motorola Ascom Ch 1 |
| 457.03750 | 462.53750 | NFM | Edinburgh | Fire Brigade |
| 457.03750 | 462.53750 | NFM | Fife | Fire Brigade Ch 1 |
| 457.03750 | 462.53750 | NFM | Glasgow | Fire Brigade |
| 457.03750 | 462.53750 | NFM | Halifax | Fire Brigade Ch 1 |
| 457.03750 | 462.53750 | NFM | Harwick | Fire Brigade handhelds |
| 457.03750 | 462.53750 | NFM | Humberside | Fire Brigade handhelds |
| 457.03750 | 462.53750 | NFM | Langholm | Fire Brigade handhelds |
| 457.03750 | 462.53750 | NFM | London | Fire Brigade |
| 457.03750 | 462.53750 | NFM | London | Fire Brigade Ch.1 (main firefighters channel) |
| 457.03750 | 462.53750 | NFM | Merseyside | Fire Brigade Ch 1 |
| 457.03750 | 462.53750 | NFM | Nationwide | Airfield Fire Channel 1 |
| 457.03750 | 462.53750 | NFM | Nationwide | Fire Brigade Ch.1 |
| 457.03750 | 462.53750 | NFM | Perth | Fire Brigade Portable to Tender |
| 457.03750 | 462.53750 | NFM | West Midlands | Fire on Site handhelds Ch 1 |
| 457.03750 | 462.53750 | NFM | West Yorkshire | Fire Brigade handhelds and training |
| 457.08750 | 462.58750 | NFM | Dyfed | Fire Motorola Ascom Ch 2 |
| 457.08750 | 462.58750 | NFM | Edinburgh | Fire Brigade |
| 457.08750 | 462.58750 | NFM | Farnborough Airshow | Hampshire Fire Service |
| 457.08750 | 462.58750 | NFM | Glasgow | Fire Brigade |
| 457.08750 | 462.58750 | NFM | London | Fire Brigade |
| 457.08750 | 462.58750 | NFM | Nationwide | Fire Brigade Ch.2 |
| 457.10000 | 462.60000 | NFM | England & Wales | Police Channel 92 |
| 457.13750 | 462.63750 | FM | Cambridgeshire | Fire Bridge (VC) Hand helds |
| 457.13750 | 462.63750 | NFM | Edinburgh | Fire Brigade |
| 457.13750 | 462.63750 | NFM | Glasgow | Fire Brigade |
| 457.13750 | 462.63750 | NFM | London | Fire Brigade |
| 457.13750 | 462.63750 | NFM | London | Fire Brigade Ch.5 |
| 457.13750 | 462.63750 | NFM | London, Gatwick | Fire Brigade |
| 457.13750 | 462.63750 | NFM | Nationwide | Fire Brigade Ch.5 |
| 457.18750 | 462.68750 | NFM | Edinburgh | Fire Brigade |
| 457.18750 | 462.68750 | NFM | Fife | Fire Brigade Ch 4 |
| 457.18750 | 462.68750 | NFM | Glasgow | Fire Brigade |
| 457.18750 | 462.68750 | NFM | London | Fire Brigade |
| 457.18750 | 462.68750 | NFM | London | Fire Brigade Ch.4 instant incident command channel |
| 457.18750 | 462.68750 | NFM | Nationwide | Fire Brigade Ch.4 |
| 457.18750 | 462.68750 | NFM | Perth | Fire Brigade CFO/Handhelds |
| 457.18750 | 462.68750 | NFM | RAF Valley | Fire Brigade Ch.4 |
| 457.22500 | 462.72500 | NFM | Ipswich | Data Traffic |
| 457.23750 | 462.73750 | NFM | Cumbria | Fire Brigade Portables |
| 457.23750 | 462.73750 | NFM | Edinburgh | Fire Brigade |
| 457.23750 | 462.73750 | NFM | Fife | Fire Brigade Ch 6 |
| 457.23750 | 462.73750 | NFM | Glasgow | Fire Brigade |
| 457.23750 | 462.73750 | NFM | London | Fire Brigade |
| 457.23750 | 462.73750 | NFM | Nationwide | Fire Brigade Ch.6 |

## 457.250 -457.500 MHz — RADIO MICROPHONES AND BROADCASTING LINKS

| Base | Mobile | Mode | Location | User and Notes |
|------|--------|------|----------|----------------|
| 457.25625 | 462.75625 | NFM | London, Southbank | National Theatre |
| 457.25625 | 467.30625 | NFM | Nationwide | JFMG Short Term Talkback |
| 457.25750 | 457.25750 | NFM | West Midlands | Fire on Site handhelds Ch 37 |
| 457.26875 | 467.31875 | NFM | Nationwide | JFMG Short Term Talkback |
| 457.28125 | 467.29375 | NFM | London | Palace Theatre - "Les Miserables" |
| 457.28125 | 467.29375 | NFM | Nationwide | JFMG Short Term Talkback |
| 457.29375 | 467.40625 | NFM | Nationwide | JFMG Short Term Talkback |
| 457.30000 | | NFM | Nationwide | SIS link Racetech (Ch4 Racing & Racing Channel O/B) |
| 457.30625 | 462.80625 | NFM | Warwick | Racecourse Technical Services O/B |
| 457.30625 | 467.36875 | NFM | Nationwide | JFMG Short Term Talkback |
| 457.31250 | | NFM | Grand Prix Circuits | Ligier Team Voice Link |
| 457.31875 | 467.48125 | NFM | Nationwide | JFMG Short Term Talkback |
| 457.32500 | | NFM | Glasgow | SkyTV Ibrox Park |
| 457.33125 | 467.44375 | NFM | Nationwide | JFMG Short Term Talkback |
| 457.34375 | 467.38125 | NFM | Nationwide | JFMG Short Term Talkback |
| 457.35625 | 467.33125 | NFM | Nationwide | JFMG Short Term Talkback |
| 457.36875 | 467.35625 | NFM | Nationwide | JFMG Short Term Talkback |
| 457.39375 | 467.39375 | NFM | Nationwide | JFMG Short Term Talkback |
| 457.40625 | 467.34375 | NFM | Nationwide | JFMG Short Term Talkback |
| 457.41875 | 467.49375 | NFM | Nationwide | JFMG Short Term Talkback |
| 457.42500 | | NFM | Manchester | Sky Sport O/B from Old Trafford |
| 457.43125 | 467.46875 | NFM | Nationwide | JFMG Short Term Talkback |
| 457.44375 | 462.94375 | NFM | Warwick | Racecourse Technical Services O/B |
| 457.44375 | 467.53125 | NFM | Nationwide | JFMG Short Term Talkback |
| 457.45625 | 467.51875 | NFM | Nationwide | JFMG Short Term Talkback |
| 457.46875 | 467.50625 | NFM | Nationwide | JFMG Short Term Talkback |

## 457.50625 - 458.49375 MHz — FIXED SCAN TELEMETRY LINKS

| Base | Mobile | Mode | Location | User and Notes |
|------|--------|------|----------|----------------|
| 457.55000 | 463.05000 | NFM | Morecambe | Data Link |
| 457.55000 | 463.05000 | NFM | Newmarket | Scan Data Link |
| 457.56250 | 463.06250 | NFM | Newmarket | Data Link |
| 457.65000 | | NFM | Newmarket | Digital Paging |
| 457.66250 | | NFM | Newcastle | Data Link |
| 457.67500 | | NFM | Newmarket | Data Link |
| 457.76250 | | NFM | Stirling | Data Link |
| 457.77500 | 463.27500 | NFM | Fulmar FSU | Shell telemetry |
| 457.80000 | 463.30000 | NFM | Birmingham | West Midlands GA Data Link |
| 457.85000 | 463.35000 | NFM | Viking Field | Conoco telemetry |
| 457.87500 | 463.37500 | NFM | North Sea | BP Buchan |
| 457.87500 | 463.37500 | NFM | North Sea | BP Forties D |
| 457.93750 | | NFM | Stirling | Data Link |
| 457.95000 | | NFM | Newcastle | Data Link |
| 458.00000 | | NFM | Lincoln | Data Link |
| 458.02500 | | NFM | Law | Railway Telemetry |
| 458.02500 | 463.52500 | NFM | Newcastle | Data Link |
| 458.05000 | 463.55000 | NFM | Beryl A | Mobil Telemetry |
| 458.24375 | | NFM | West Cumbria | Water Telemetry |
| 458.27000 | | NFM | Carlisle | Railway Telemetry |
| 458.36250 | | NFM | Dundee | Data Link |
| 458.36250 | | NFM | Morecambe | Data Link |
| 458.41875 | | NFM | North Sea | Chevron Alba FSU Shuttle Green Line Data |
| 458.45625 | | NFM | North Sea | Chevron Alba ANP Data |

| Base | Mobile | Mode | Location | User and Notes |
|------|--------|------|----------|----------------|

**457.525 - 457.575 MHz**    INTETATIONAL MARIME ON-BOARD HANDHELP
TRANSCEIVERS 12.5 kHz

| Base | Mobile | Mode | Location | User and Notes |
|------|--------|------|----------|----------------|
| 457.52500 | 462.97500 | NFM | Dover | P & O (on board handhelds) |
| 457.52500 | 462.97500 | NFM | Fishguard | Sealink (on board handhelds) |
| 457.52500 | 462.97500 | NFM | Nationwide | BT Marine Cable Laying |
| 457.52500 | 462.97500 | NFM | North Sea | Balmoral Sun Oil Portables |
| 457.52500 | 462.97500 | NFM | North Sea | Elf Frigg Field |
| 457.52500 | 462.97500 | NFM | Ramsgate | Sally Line (on board handhelds) |
| 457.52500 | 462.97500 | NFM | Rosslare | Sealink (on board handhelds) |
| 457.53120 | 463.03120 | NFM | Maritime | Ship handheld Ch 3 |
| 457.54370 | 463.04370 | NFM | Maritime | Ship handheld Ch 4 |
| 457.55000 | 463.05000 | NFM | Dover | P & O (on board handhelds) |
| 457.55000 | 463.05000 | NFM | Dover | P & O (on board handhelds) |
| 457.55000 | 463.05000 | NFM | Fishguard | Sealink (on board handhelds) |
| 457.55000 | 463.05000 | NFM | Maritime | Ship handheld Ch.5 |
| 457.55000 | 463.05000 | NFM | Nationwide | BT Marine Cable Laying |
| 457.55000 | 463.05000 | NFM | North Sea | Balmoral Field Sun Oil Portables |
| 457.55000 | 463.05000 | NFM | North Sea | Elf Frigg Field |
| 457.55000 | 463.05000 | NFM | Ramsgate | Sally Line (on board handhelds) |
| 457.55000 | 463.05000 | NFM | Rosslare | Sealink (on board handhelds) |
| 457.55000 | 463.05000 | NFM | Southampton | P&O Marine |
| 457.56250 | 463.06250 | NFM | Marine | Ship's handheld Ch.5 |
| 457.57500 | 463.07500 | NFM | Dover | P & O (on board handhelds) |
| 457.57500 | 463.07500 | NFM | Dover | P & O (on board handhelds) |
| 457.57500 | 463.07500 | NFM | Maritime | Ship handheld Ch.6 |
| 457.57500 | 463.07500 | NFM | Montrose Docks | Big Orange XVIII |
| 457.57500 | 463.07500 | NFM | North Sea | BP Lolair |
| 457.57500 | 463.07500 | NFM | North Sea | Elf Frigg Field |
| 457.57500 | 463.07500 | NFM | Ramsgate | Sally Line (on board handhelds) |
| 457.57500 | 463.07500 | NFM | Southampton | P&O Marine |
| 457.57500 | 467.57500 | NFM | North Sea | Sun Oil Balmoral |
| 457.60000 | 463.10000 | NFM | Maritime | Ship Communications |

**458.500 - 459.500 MHz**    SHORT RANGE DEVICES, TELEMETRY, ALAMS,
VEHICLE PAGING, RADIO KEYS, MEDICAL AND
BIOLOGICAL EQUIPMENT

| Base | Mobile | Mode | Location | User and Notes |
|------|--------|------|----------|----------------|
| 458.50000 | | NFM | Flimby | Factory Telemetry |
| 458.50000 | | NFM | Nationwide | Telemetry |
| 458.51250 | | NFM | Nationwide | Telemetry |
| 458.52500 | | NFM | Jersey | BGS Seismic Telemetry |
| 458.52500 | | NFM | Morecambe | Data Link |
| 458.55000 | 458.50000 | NFM | Edinburgh Airport | Telemetry Channel 8 |
| 458.62500 | | NFM | Stevenage | ICL Computers telemetry |
| 458.65000 | | NFM | Nationwide | Telemetry |
| 458.67500 | | NFM | Jersey | BGS Seismic Telemetry |
| 458.67500 | | NFM | Nationwide | Shell Geophysical |
| 458.70000 | | NFM | Nationwide | Telemetry |
| 458.72500 | | NFM | Jersey | BGS Seismic Telemetry |
| 458.80000 | | NFM | Jersey | BGS Seismic Telemetry |
| 458.90000 | | NFM | Flimby | Factory Telemetry |
| 458.95000 | | NFM | Bassenthwaite | Lake Telemetry |
| 459.02500 | | NFM | Jersey | BGS Seismic Telemetry |

## 458.8375 - 459.4875 MHz ON SITE PAGING AND LOCAL COMMUNICATIONS

| Base | Mobile | Mode | Location | User and Notes |
|------|--------|------|----------|----------------|
| 458.83750 | | NFM | Nationwide | Transportable & Mobile Alarm |
| 458.85000 | | NFM | Jersey | Paging Queens Valley Area |
| 458.85000 | | NFM | Magnus | BP Paging-Base |
| 458.90000 | | NFM | Nationwide | Car Theft Alarm Paging |
| 458.97500 | | NFM | North Sea | Mobil Statfjord A |
| 459.00000 | | NFM | Nationwide | Medical & Biological Telemetry |
| 459.00000 | | NFM | North Sea | Mobil Statfjord A |
| 459.02500 | | NFM | North Sea | Mobil Statfjord A |
| 459.05000 | | NFM | North Sea | Conoco Murchison |
| 459.07500 | | NFM | North Sea | Conoco Murchison |
| 459.07500 | | NFM | North Sea | Mobil Statfjord B |
| 459.07500 | 453.47500 | NFM | North Sea | BP Buchan |
| 459.10000 | | NFM | North Sea | Mobil Statfjord B |
| 459.10500 | 161.00000 | NFM | Nationwide | Paging |
| 459.12500 | | NFM | London | Science Museum pagers |
| 459.12500 | | NFM | North Sea | Mobil Statfjord B |
| 459.15000 | | NFM | Jersey | Paging Fort Regent |
| 459.15000 | | NFM | North Sea | Mobil Statfjord C |
| 459.15000 | 161.02500 | NFM | Nationwide | Marina Paging |
| 459.17500 | | NFM | Perth | Paging |
| 459.20000 | | NFM | Leicester | Mackro Centre paging |
| 459.20000 | | NFM | North Sea | Mobil Statfjord C |
| 459.22500 | | NFM | Colchester | Voice Pagers |
| 459.25000 | | NFM | Earls Court | Voice Pagers |
| 459.25000 | | NFM | North Sea | Mobil Statfjord C |
| 459.25000 | | NFM | North Sea | Phillips Edda |
| 459.25000 | 161.05000 | NFM | Nationwide | Paging |
| 459.27500 | | NFM | North Sea | Mobil Statfjord A tankers |
| 459.27500 | | NFM | West Midlands | Paging Systems |
| 459.30000 | | NFM | London | Two Way Tone Paging |
| 459.32500 | | NFM | Scarborough | Voice Paging |
| 459.32500 | 161.01250 | NFM | Cambridge | Voice pagers |
| 459.32500 | 161.01250 | NFM | Heysham Power Station | Ops |
| 459.32500 | 161.01250 | NFM | Leicester | Holiday Inn voice paging |
| 459.32500 | 161.01250 | NFM | London | Silver Town Pager |
| 459.32500 | 161.01250 | NFM | London, Brent Cross | Fenwicks |
| 459.32500 | 161.01250 | NFM | Nationwide | Paging |
| 459.32500 | 161.01250 | NFM | North Sea | Chevron Alba ANP Paging |
| 459.32500 | 161.01250 | NFM | Romford | Tesco Staff Paging |
| 459.32500 | 161.01250 | NFM | Worcester | Voice Pager |
| 459.35000 | | NFM | North Sea | Marathon Brae South Paging |
| 459.35000 | | NFM | North Sea | Mobil Brett 2,1 A Paging |
| 459.35000 | 161.02500 | NFM | London | Old Bailey Voice Paging |
| 459.35000 | 161.02500 | NFM | Nationwide | Paging |
| 459.37500 | | NFM | Dartford | John Lewis voice pager |
| 459.37500 | | NFM | London | Selfridges voice pager |
| 459.37500 | | NFM | London, Marble Arch | Littlewoods voice pager |
| 459.37500 | | NFM | London, Sloane Square | Voice Pager Peter Jones Ltd |
| 459.37500 | | NFM | North Sea | Mobil ALP Statfjord C |
| 459.37500 | | NFM | Romford | BAC Staff Paging |
| 459.37500 | | NFM | Slough | Voice pagers |
| 459.37500 | | NFM | Thornton | Multitone ICI |
| 459.37500 | | NFM | Wirral | Mobil Oil Security |
| 459.37500 | 161.03750 | NFM | Basildon | Hospital Porters Paging |

| Base | Mobile | Mode | Location | User and Notes |
|---|---|---|---|---|
| 459.37500 | 161.03750 | NFM | Dumfries | Gates Rubber Company |
| 459.37500 | 161.03750 | NFM | Nationwide | Paging |
| 459.40000 | | NFM | London | Earls Court Voice Pagers |
| 459.40000 | | NFM | North Sea | Phillips Ekofisk Senter |
| 459.40000 | | NFM | Wembley | Wembley Conference Centre pager |
| 459.40000 | 161.05000 | NFM | Nationwide | Paging |
| 459.41250 | | NFM | Colchester | Garrison Meeanne Barracks Constant Carrier. |
| 459.42500 | | NFM | Bridgend | Ford engine plant pager |
| 459.42500 | | NFM | Coventry | Pagers |
| 459.42500 | | NFM | Heysham Power Station | Ops |
| 459.42500 | | NFM | North Sea | BP Clyde A Paging |
| 459.42500 | | NFM | North Sea | Mobil Statfjord B |
| 459.42500 | 161.06250 | NFM | London | BBC Bush House Pagers |
| 459.43750 | | NFM | Watford | Pager |
| 459.45000 | | NFM | Heysham Power Station | Ops |
| 459.45000 | | NFM | Manchester | Paging |
| 459.45000 | | NFM | North Sea | Mobil Statfjord C |
| 459.45000 | 161.10000 | NFM | Nationwide | Paging |
| 459.47500 | | NFM | Luton | Arndale Shopping Centre |
| 459.47500 | | NFM | Romford | BHS Staff Paging |
| 459.47500 | | NFM | Sleaford | Padleys Poultry (PAPA BASE) |
| 459.47500 | | NFM | Wirral | Sainsbury's |
| 459.47500 | 161.11250 | NFM | Eastbourne | Store Paging |
| 459.47500 | 161.11250 | NFM | Nationwide | Paging |

**459.500 - 460.500 MHz     PMR (MOBILES -6.5 MHZ)**

| Base | Mobile | Mode | Location | User and Notes |
|---|---|---|---|---|
| 459.50000 | 453.00000 | NFM | North Sea | Mobil A.L.P.Statfjord A |
| 459.50000 | 453.00000 | NFM | North Sea | Phillips Albuskjell A |
| 459.50000 | 454.00000 | NFM | Blackpool | Tower Ascent |
| 459.52500 | 453.02500 | NFM | Felixstowe | Docks security |
| 459.52500 | 453.02500 | NFM | North Sea | BP Beatrice A |
| 459.52500 | 453.02500 | NFM | North Sea | Mobil A. L. P. Statfjord B |
| 459.52500 | 453.02500 | NFM | North Sea | Mobil Beryl B Temp. Const. Facility |
| 459.52500 | 453.02500 | NFM | North Sea | Phillips Albuskjell F |
| 459.52500 | 453.02500 | NFM | Portsmouth | Allders Super Store |
| 459.52500 | 453.02500 | NFM | Stansted | Telephone Ops |
| 459.54500 | 453.04500 | NFM | Glasgow | Versace Collection |
| 459.55000 | 453.05000 | NFM | Doncaster | Peglers Security |
| 459.55000 | 453.05000 | NFM | London, Oxford Street | West 1 Shopping Centre |
| 459.55000 | 453.05000 | NFM | North Sea | Chevron Alba ANP PABX Interface |
| 459.57500 | 453.07500 | NFM | Dagenham | Ford Motor Plant |
| 459.57500 | 453.07500 | NFM | Kingswood | Warren Tadworth BBC Site |
| 459.57500 | 453.07500 | NFM | London | Aldwych Bush House B.B.C. Security |
| 459.57500 | 453.07500 | NFM | London | Brent Trading Estate |
| 459.57500 | 453.07500 | NFM | London | Coliseum |
| 459.57500 | 453.07500 | NFM | London | Gunnersbury London Underground Works |
| 459.57500 | 453.07500 | NFM | London | Hammersmith Hospital |
| 459.57500 | 453.07500 | NFM | London | The City University |
| 459.57500 | 453.07500 | NFM | London, Aldwych | London School of Economics |
| 459.57500 | 453.07500 | NFM | Montrose Basin | Rangers |
| 459.57500 | 453.07500 | NFM | North Sea | Amoco Bacton |
| 459.57500 | 453.07500 | NFM | North Sea | Total Frigg Field |
| 459.57500 | 453.07500 | NFM | Sizewell | Power station work teams Ch.5 |
| 459.57500 | 453.07500 | NFM | Twickenham | Richmond Upon Thames College |
| 459.60000 | 453.10000 | NFM | Blackpool | Train and Bus Inspectors |
| 459.60000 | 453.10000 | NFM | Ibrox | Ground staff |

| Base | Mobile | Mode | Location | User and Notes |
|------|--------|------|----------|----------------|
| 459.60000 | 453.10000 | NFM | North Sea | BP Beatrice B |
| 459.60000 | 453.10000 | NFM | North Sea | BP Clyde A |
| 459.60000 | 453.10000 | NFM | North Sea | Total Frigg Field |
| 459.60000 | 453.10000 | NFM | North Sea | Unocol Heather A |
| 459.62500 | 453.12500 | NFM | London | Police Dartford Tunnel |
| 459.62500 | 453.12500 | NFM | North Sea | Conoco Viking Field |
| 459.62500 | 453.12500 | NFM | North Sea | Total Frigg Field |
| 459.62500 | 453.12500 | NFM | Sizewell | Power station work teams Ch.6 |
| 459.65000 | 453.15000 | NFM | North Sea | Total Frigg Field |
| 459.65000 | 453.15000 | NFM | Nottingham | Boots Broadmarch Shopping Cn |
| 459.67500 | 453.17500 | NFM | North Sea | Shell Bacton |
| 459.67500 | 453.17500 | NFM | North Sea | Shell Indefatigable J |
| 459.67500 | 453.17500 | NFM | North Sea | Shell Indefatigable K |
| 459.67500 | 453.17500 | NFM | North Sea | Shell Leman B |
| 459.67500 | 453.17500 | NFM | North Sea | Shell St. Fergus |
| 459.67500 | 453.17500 | NFM | North Sea | Total Frigg Field |
| 459.70000 | 453.20000 | NFM | Bristol | HTV Television |
| 459.70000 | 453.20000 | NFM | Cambridge | Coach Services |
| 459.70000 | 453.20000 | NFM | London, Gatwick | Ground Repeater |
| 459.70000 | 453.20000 | NFM | North Sea | BP Magnus |
| 459.70000 | 453.20000 | NFM | North Sea | Total Frigg Field |
| 459.72500 | 453.22500 | NFM | Coventry | City Allders Dept Store Security |
| 459.72500 | 453.22500 | NFM | England & Wales | Police and Fire Channel |
| 459.72500 | 453.22500 | NFM | Guernsey | Fuel Supplies |
| 459.72500 | 453.22500 | NFM | North Sea | Chevron Ninian South |
| 459.72500 | 453.22500 | NFM | North Sea | Phillips Tor |
| 459.72500 | 453.22500 | NFM | North Sea | Shell Eider |
| 459.72500 | 453.22500 | NFM | North Sea | Total Frigg Field |
| 459.72500 | 455.22500 | NFM | Felixstowe | Docks fire brigade |
| 459.75000 | 453.25000 | NFM | North Sea | Conoco Murchison |
| 459.75000 | 453.25000 | NFM | North Sea | Marathon Brae South |
| 459.75000 | 453.25000 | NFM | North Sea | Phillips Ekofisk Centre to Ekofisk B |
| 459.77500 | 453.27500 | NFM | Jersey | Health Authority |
| 459.77500 | 453.27500 | NFM | London | Ambulance handhelds Ch 1 |
| 459.77500 | 453.27500 | NFM | Nationwide | Ambulance UHF to VHF |
| 459.77500 | 453.27500 | NFM | Nationwide | Philips Security |
| 459.77500 | 453.27500 | NFM | North Sea | Phillips Eldfisk B to Ekofisk Center |
| 459.77500 | 453.27500 | NFM | North Sea | Shell Cormorant A |
| 459.77500 | 453.27500 | NFM | North Sea | Shell Leman BH Portables |
| 459.77500 | 453.27500 | NFM | North Sea | Total Frigg Field |
| 459.77500 | 453.27500 | NFM | Strathclyde | Ambulance handhelds |
| 459.77500 | 453.27500 | NFM | Tilbury | Container Port |
| 459.80000 | 453.30000 | NFM | Milford Haven | Texaco Refinery Control |
| 459.80000 | 453.30000 | NFM | North Sea | BP Magnus |
| 459.80000 | 453.30000 | NFM | North Sea | Marathon Brae South |
| 459.80000 | 453.30000 | NFM | North Sea | Phillips Ekofisk Senter |
| 459.80000 | 453.30000 | NFM | North Sea | Total Frigg Field |
| 459.80000 | 453.30000 | NFM | Sizewell | Power stations work teams Ch.7 |
| 459.80000 | 453.30000 | NFM | Southend | Police |
| 459.80000 | 453.30000 | NFM | Waddington | BAE ACMI |
| 459.82500 | 453.32500 | NFM | Hampshire | Ambulance Pagers |
| 459.82500 | 453.32500 | NFM | Lincolnshire | Ambulance |
| 459.82500 | 453.32500 | NFM | London | Ambulance handhelds Ch 2 |
| 459.82500 | 453.32500 | NFM | West Yorkshire | Ambulance Service |
| 459.83750 | 453.33750 | NFM | Swindon | Brunel Security |
| 459.85000 | 453.35000 | NFM | Harrow on the Hill | St Anne's Shopping Centre |

| Base | Mobile | Mode | Location | User and Notes |
|------|--------|------|----------|----------------|
| 459.85000 | 453.35000 | NFM | Harwich | Stena Sealink Loaders |
| 459.85000 | 453.35000 | NFM | Jersey | Alpha Airport Catering Service |
| 459.85000 | 453.35000 | NFM | Morecambe Bay | BGE&P |
| 459.85000 | 453.35000 | NFM | Nationwide | Ambulance UHF to VHF |
| 459.85000 | 453.35000 | NFM | North Sea | Conoco Murchison |
| 459.85000 | 453.35000 | NFM | North Sea | Marathon Brae South |
| 459.85000 | 453.35000 | NFM | Swindon | Brunel Security |
| 459.87500 | 453.37500 | NFM | Salisbury | Hospital Security |
| 459.90000 | 453.40000 | NFM | North Sea | Chevron Ninian North |
| 459.90000 | 453.40000 | NFM | North Sea | Marathon Brae N, S |
| 459.90000 | 453.40000 | NFM | North Sea | Shell St. Fergus |
| 459.90000 | 453.40000 | NFM | Sizewell | Power stations work teams Ch.8 |
| 459.90000 | 453.40000 | NFM | Tilbury | Container Port |
| 459.92500 | 453.42500 | NFM | North Sea | BP Buchan |
| 459.92500 | 453.42500 | NFM | North Sea | BP Magnus |
| 459.92500 | 453.42500 | NFM | North Sea | Chevron Alba FSU Maintenance |
| 459.95000 | 435.45000 | NFM | London, Regent Street | Jaeger security |
| 459.95000 | 453.45000 | NFM | Bournemouth Airport | Ground Services |
| 459.95000 | 453.45000 | NFM | City of London | Lloyds of London. |
| 459.95000 | 453.45000 | NFM | Jersey | HM Customs & Excise |
| 459.95000 | 453.45000 | NFM | London, Gatwick | Messages for Captains |
| 459.95000 | 453.45000 | NFM | Morecambe Bay | BGE&P |
| 459.95000 | 453.45000 | NFM | Prestwick | Passenger handling and check-ins Ch.4 |
| 459.95000 | 453.45000 | NFM | Tilbury | Container Port |
| 459.95000 | 453.45000 | NFM | Twickenham | House. |
| 459.95000 | 453.45000 | NFM | Weybridge | Brooklands Technical College. |
| 459.97500 | 453.47500 | NFM | Dorset | BP Wytch Farm |
| 459.97500 | 453.47500 | NFM | Mutchison | Conoco |
| 459.97500 | 453.47500 | NFM | North Sea | BP Buchan |
| 459.97500 | 453.47500 | NFM | North Sea | Shell St. Fergus |
| 459.97500 | 453.47500 | NFM | Sizewell | Power stations work teams Ch.9 |
| 459.98750 | 453.48750 | NFM | London | Fleet St/Strand Unid Site Security |
| 460.00000 | 453.50000 | NFM | North Sea | Shell Eider |
| 460.01500 | 453.51500 | NFM | North Sea | Chevron Ninian North |
| 460.02500 | 453.52500 | NFM | Ascot | Race Course. |
| 460.02500 | 453.52500 | NFM | London | Southwark Council |
| 460.02500 | 453.52500 | NFM | London, Edgware | Council offices |
| 460.02500 | 453.52500 | NFM | London, Hampstead | Royal Free Hospital |
| 460.02500 | 453.52500 | NFM | London, Leicester Square | Voodoo Lounge |
| 460.02500 | 453.52500 | NFM | London, Oxford Street | D H Evans, Sabre Watch Security |
| 460.02500 | 453.52500 | NFM | London, Piccadilly | The Body Shop |
| 460.02500 | 453.52500 | NFM | London, Stockley Park | Securiplan Security |
| 460.02500 | 453.52500 | NFM | London, Wood Green | Pearsons Department Store security |
| 460.02500 | 453.52500 | NFM | Morecambe Bay | BGE&P |
| 460.02500 | 453.52500 | NFM | Northumberland | Geological Surveys |
| 460.02500 | 453.52500 | NFM | Romford | Tetley Carlsberg Brewery |
| 460.02500 | 453.52500 | NFM | Southend-On-Sea | Odeon Cinema staff |
| 460.02500 | 453.52500 | NFM | Stevenage | Kings Leisure Site Midas Security. |
| 460.02500 | 453.52500 | NFM | Tilbury | Container Port |
| 460.05000 | 453.55000 | NFM | Cardiff, Central Station | Great Western Trains |
| 460.05000 | 453.55000 | NFM | North Sea | Chevron Alba ANP Construction |
| 460.05000 | 453.55000 | NFM | North Sea | Chevron Ninian South |
| 460.07500 | 453.57500 | NFM | London | Canary Wharf Credit Suisse Bank Boston |
| 460.07500 | 453.57500 | NFM | London | Heathrow Airport Cargo Terminal Security. |
| 460.07500 | 453.57500 | NFM | London, Heathrow | Cargo Terminal |
| 460.07500 | 453.57500 | NFM | Morecambe Bay | BGE&P |

| Base | Mobile | Mode | Location | User and Notes |
|------|--------|------|----------|----------------|
| 460.07500 | 453.57500 | NFM | Nationwide | Safeways Supermarkets |
| 460.07500 | 453.57500 | NFM | North Sea | BP Buchan |
| 460.07500 | 453.57500 | NFM | North Sea | BP Magnus |
| 460.07500 | 453.57500 | NFM | Sunbury | Oil Co. |
| 460.07500 | 453.57500 | NFM | Watford | Newspaper Printers. |
| 460.10000 | 453.60000 | NFM | Beckenham | Kent Food Manufacturing Eden Park |
| 460.10000 | 453.60000 | NFM | Bedford | Debenhams Security |
| 460.10000 | 453.60000 | NFM | Birmingham | Debenhams Security |
| 460.10000 | 453.60000 | NFM | Bridlington | Leisure World Entertainment Complex |
| 460.10000 | 453.60000 | NFM | Cambridge | Debenhams Security |
| 460.10000 | 453.60000 | NFM | Derby | Debenhams Security |
| 460.10000 | 453.60000 | NFM | Folkestone | Debenhams Security |
| 460.10000 | 453.60000 | NFM | Manchester | Debenhams |
| 460.10000 | 453.60000 | NFM | North Sea | Amoco N W Hutton |
| 460.10000 | 453.60000 | NFM | North Sea | Texaco Tartan |
| 460.10000 | 453.60000 | NFM | Sizewell | Power station management Ch.10 |
| 460.10000 | 460.10000 | NFM | Plymouth | Debenhams Store Detectives |
| 460.11250 | 453.61250 | NFM | Doncaster | Railtrack |
| 460.11250 | 453.61250 | NFM | London | British Rail (Richmond) |
| 460.11250 | 453.61250 | NFM | Newcastle Airport | Passenger Information |
| 460.12500 | 453.62500 | NFM | Bromley | Church House Gardens. |
| 460.12500 | 453.62500 | NFM | Coventry | Central Library |
| 460.12500 | 453.62500 | NFM | London, Finsbury Park | Michael Sobell Sports Centre. |
| 460.12500 | 453.62500 | NFM | London, Knightsbridge | Harrods security. |
| 460.12500 | 453.62500 | NFM | London, Oxford Circus | Top Shop |
| 460.12500 | 453.62500 | NFM | Manchester | Top Shop staff |
| 460.12500 | 453.62500 | NFM | North Sea | Chevron Alba FSU General Ops |
| 460.12500 | 453.62500 | NFM | Swansea | University Security |
| 460.15000 | 453.65000 | NFM | Dartford | Dartford Engineering |
| 460.15000 | 453.65000 | NFM | North Sea | Shell Brent C |
| 460.15000 | 453.65000 | NFM | North Sea | Shell TCM |
| 460.15000 | 453.65000 | NFM | Peterborough | Quo Vadis Club |
| 460.20000 | 453.70000 | NFM | London, Langham Place | BBC Radio |
| 460.20000 | 453.70000 | NFM | North Sea | Chevron Ninian North |
| 460.20000 | 453.70000 | NFM | North Sea | Shell Eider |
| 460.20000 | 453.70000 | NFM | North Sea | Shell Leman A portables |
| 460.20000 | 453.70000 | NFM | Rugb, Swift Valley Induct. Est. | Christian Salvessen |
| 460.20000 | 453.70000 | NFM | Sizewell | Power station management Ch.11 |
| 460.20000 | 453.70000 | NFM | Tilbury | Container Port |
| 460.22500 | 453.72500 | NFM | Isle of Grain | Security |
| 460.22500 | 453.72500 | NFM | Morecambe Bay | BGE&P |
| 460.22500 | 453.72500 | NFM | North Sea | Chevron Alba ANP Production |
| 460.22500 | 453.72500 | NFM | North Sea | Chevron Ninian North |
| 460.22500 | 453.72500 | NFM | Sizewell | Power station management Ch.12 |
| 460.25000 | 453.75000 | NFM | Bradford | Allied Colloids Chemicals |
| 460.25000 | 453.75000 | NFM | Nottingham | Formans |
| 460.27500 | 453.77500 | NFM | Culham | UKAEA Laboratory Fire Team |
| 460.27500 | 453.77500 | NFM | North Sea | Phillips Maureen telemetry |
| 460.30000 | 453.80000 | NFM | Cardiff | Millennium Stadium builders |
| 460.30000 | 453.80000 | NFM | London, Piccadilly | Callaghans Irish Bar |
| 460.30000 | 453.80000 | NFM | Newmarket | Community Repeater |
| 460.30000 | 453.80000 | NFM | North Sea | Amoco Lomond |
| 460.30000 | 453.80000 | NFM | North Sea | Amoco North Everest |
| 460.30000 | 453.80000 | NFM | North Sea | Chevron Ninian South |
| 460.30000 | 453.80000 | NFM | North Sea | Shell TCM |
| 460.30000 | 453.80000 | NFM | Sizewell | Power station management Ch.13 |

| Base | Mobile | Mode | Location | User and Notes |
|------|--------|------|----------|----------------|
| 460.32500 | 453.82500 | NFM | Grand Prix Circuits | Lotus Team Voice Link |
| 460.32500 | 453.82500 | NFM | Plymouth | Debenhams Maintenance |
| 460.35000 | 453.85000 | NFM | Bradford | Allied Colloids Chemicals |
| 460.35000 | 453.85000 | NFM | County Durham | Taxis |
| 460.35000 | 453.85000 | NFM | North Sea | BP Forties E |
| 460.35000 | 453.85000 | NFM | North Sea | BP Magnus |
| 460.35000 | 453.85000 | NFM | North Sea | Shell TCM |
| 460.36250 | 453.86250 | NFM | Bristol | Pinkerton Security Services |
| 460.37000 | 453.87000 | NFM | City of London | London Wall Engineering |
| 460.37500 | 453.87500 | NFM | City of London | Banking |
| 460.37500 | 453.87500 | NFM | Dagenham | Checkers Lane Engineering |
| 460.37500 | 453.87500 | NFM | London, Kensington | Campden Hill School |
| 460.37500 | 453.87500 | NFM | London, Kensington | Kempton Hill School |
| 460.37500 | 453.87500 | NFM | London, Marble Arch | Mount Charlotte Hotel. |
| 460.37500 | 453.87500 | NFM | London, North | Hoxton School |
| 460.37500 | 453.87500 | NFM | North Sea | Chevron Alba Field Safety |
| 460.37500 | 453.87500 | NFM | North Sea | Chevron Ninian Central |
| 460.37500 | 453.87500 | NFM | Sizewell | Power station work teams Ch.14 |
| 460.37500 | 453.87500 | NFM | Staines | Retail Use. |
| 460.37500 | 453.87500 | NFM | Waltham Cross | Education Supplier. |
| 460.37500 | 453.87500 | NFM | Watford | Communication Studio |
| 460.40000 | 453.90000 | NFM | Bristol | Railtrack Bristol Temple Meads |
| 460.40000 | 453.90000 | NFM | Doncaster | Railtrack Doncaster Yard |
| 460.40000 | 453.90000 | NFM | London | Railtrack (Euston) |
| 460.40000 | 453.90000 | NFM | London | Railtrack (Gatwick Airport) |
| 460.40000 | 453.90000 | NFM | London | Railtrack (Hornsey Depot) |
| 460.40000 | 453.90000 | NFM | London | Railtrack (Marylebone) |
| 460.40000 | 453.90000 | NFM | London | Railtrack (Victoria) |
| 460.40000 | 453.90000 | NFM | London, Upminster | Station Staff LTS Line. |
| 460.40000 | 453.90000 | NFM | North Sea | Shell Brent C |
| 460.40000 | 453.90000 | NFM | Poole | Flight Refuelling Ltd |
| 460.42500 | 453.92500 | NFM | London, Neasden | Ikea |
| 460.42500 | 453.92500 | NFM | North Sea | BP Forties E |
| 460.42500 | 453.92500 | NFM | North Sea | BP Magnus |
| 460.42500 | 453.92500 | NFM | Sizewell | Power station management Ch.15 |
| 460.45000 | 453.95000 | NFM | Aldermaston | Atomic weapons establishment services/contractors (WE) |
| 460.45000 | 453.95000 | NFM | Glasgow | Virgin Records Security |
| 460.45000 | 453.95000 | NFM | North Sea | Chevron Alba ANP Maintenance |
| 460.45000 | 453.95000 | NFM | North Sea | Chevron Ninian Central |
| 460.45000 | 453.95000 | NFM | North Sea | Marathon Brae North |
| 460.45200 | 453.95200 | NFM | Cardiff | Millennium Stadium builders |
| 460.47500 | 453.97500 | NFM | London | HMV Shop Security |
| 460.47500 | 453.97500 | NFM | Manchester | HMV Records security |
| 460.47500 | 453.97500 | NFM | North Sea | BP Forties E |
| 460.47500 | 453.97500 | NFM | North Sea | BP Magnus |
| 460.47500 | 453.97500 | NFM | Sizewell | Power station management Ch.17 |

| 460.500 - 460.750 MHz | | | EMERGENCY SERVICES, UHF POINT TO POINT LINKS 25 kHz, BROADCASTING LINKS (SPLIT+6.5MHz) | |
|------|--------|------|----------|----------------|
| 460.47500 | 453.97500 | NFM | USAF Croughton | Police |
| 460.50620 | 454.00620 | NFM | Belfry (Ryder Cup) | US TV Talkback |
| 460.50620 | 467.00620 | NFM | Nationwide | Sky TV O/B Talkback |
| 460.52500 | 467.02500 | NFM | Bristol | HM Prison (MY) |
| 460.52500 | 467.02500 | NFM | Carstairs | HM Prison Hospital (YX) |

| Base | Mobile | Mode | Location | User and Notes |
|------|--------|------|----------|----------------|
| 460.52500 | 467.02500 | NFM | Didcot | Power Station staff |
| 460.52500 | 467.02500 | NFM | London | HM Prison Pentonville (JP) |
| 460.52500 | 467.02500 | NFM | March, Cambs | HM Prison Whitemoor |
| 460.52500 | 467.02500 | NFM | Rochester | Construction Work |
| 460.52500 | 467.02500 | NFM | Rochester | HM Borstal (PR) |
| 460.52500 | 467.02500 | NFM | Wakefield | Prison Training College |
| 460.53120 | 454.03120 | NFM | Castle Donington | US TV Talkback |
| 460.53750 | 467.03750 | NFM | Aylesbury | HM Prison (M2PA) |
| 460.53750 | 467.03750 | NFM | Banstead | HM Prison (M2KI) |
| 460.53750 | 467.03750 | NFM | Brixton | HM Prison (JX) |
| 460.55000 | 454.05000 | NFM | Kent | Southern Gas |
| 460.55000 | 454.05000 | NFM | London | Holloway (MJ) |
| 460.55000 | 454.05000 | NFM | Nationwide | Sky TV Talkback |
| 460.55000 | 467.05000 | NFM | Jersey Airport | Air Traffic Control Link |
| 460.55000 | 467.05000 | NFM | Swaleside, Kent | HM Prison (KS) |
| 460.56250 | 454.06850 | NFM | Falkirk | Police (G) |
| 460.56850 | 454.06850 | NFM | Castle Donington | Japanese TV Talkback |
| 460.57500 | 454.07500 | NFM | Avon | Health Authority |
| 460.57500 | 454.07500 | NFM | Cornwall | Health Authority |
| 460.57500 | 454.07500 | NFM | Devon | Health Authority |
| 460.57500 | 454.07500 | NFM | East Hertfordshire | Health Authority |
| 460.57500 | 454.07500 | NFM | Gloucester | Health Authority |
| 460.57500 | 454.07500 | NFM | Nationwide | Sky TV OB |
| 460.57500 | 454.07500 | NFM | North Bedfordshire | Health Authority |
| 460.57500 | 454.07500 | NFM | Scilly Isles | Health Authority |
| 460.57500 | 454.07500 | NFM | Somerset | Health Authority |
| 460.57500 | 454.07500 | NFM | Wales | BBC Wales Talkback |
| 460.58125 | 454.08125 | NFM | Belfry (Ryder Cup) | German TV Talkback |
| 460.58125 | 454.08125 | NFM | Castle Donington | Japanese TV Talkback |
| 460.58375 | 454.08375 | NFM | Nationwide | Sky TV OB Talkback |
| 460.58750 | 454.08750 | NFM | Wales | BBC Wales Talkback |
| 460.59375 | 454.09375 | NFM | Belfry (Ryder Cup) | US TV Talkback |
| 460.60000 | 454.10000 | NFM | Buckinghamshire | Health Authority |
| 460.60000 | 454.10000 | NFM | Northamptonshire | Health Authority |
| 460.60000 | 454.10000 | NFM | Oxford | Health Authority |
| 460.60000 | 454.10000 | NFM | West Berkshire | Health Authority |
| 460.60000 | 467.10000 | NFM | Eastchurch | HM Prison (M2PE) |
| 460.61870 | 467.11870 | NFM | Belfry (Ryder Cup) | German TV Talkback |
| 460.62500 | 454.12500 | NFM | Buckinghamshire | Health Authority |
| 460.62500 | 454.12500 | NFM | Cleveland | Health Authority |
| 460.62500 | 454.12500 | NFM | Cumbria | Health Authority |
| 460.62500 | 454.12500 | NFM | Durham | Health Authority |
| 460.62500 | 454.12500 | NFM | North Sea | Mobil Statfjord A,B,C |
| 460.62500 | 454.12500 | NFM | Northamptonshire | Health Authority |
| 460.62500 | 454.12500 | NFM | Northumbria | Health Authority |
| 460.62500 | 454.12500 | NFM | Oxford | Health Authority |
| 460.62500 | 454.12500 | NFM | Wales | BBC Wales Announcer |
| 460.62500 | 454.12500 | NFM | West Berkshire | Health Authority |
| 460.62500 | 467.12500 | NFM | London | HM Prison Wormwood Scrubs (M2JS) |
| 460.62500 | 467.12500 | NFM | Shearness | HM Prison Emley (M2KE) |
| 460.64370 | 454.14370 | NFM | Belfry (Ryder Cup) | US TV Talkback |
| 460.65000 | 454.15000 | NFM | Wales | Health Authority |
| 460.66250 | 467.16250 | NFM | Bedford | HM Prison |
| 460.66250 | 467.16250 | NFM | London | HM Prison Belmarsh (MB) |
| 460.66250 | 467.16250 | NFM | Woodbridge | HM Prison Hollesey Bay colony |
| 460.67500 | 467.17500 | NFM | Cleveland | Health Authority |

| Base | Mobile | Mode | Location | User and Notes |
|------|--------|------|----------|----------------|
| 460.67500 | 467.17500 | NFM | Cumbria | Health Authority |
| 460.67500 | 467.17500 | NFM | Durham | Health Authority |
| 460.67500 | 467.17500 | NFM | East Yorkshire | Health Authority |
| 460.67500 | 467.17500 | NFM | Humberside | Health Authority |
| 460.67500 | 467.17500 | NFM | Manchester | Strangeways Prison |
| 460.67500 | 467.17500 | NFM | Northumbria | Health Authority |
| 460.67500 | 467.17500 | NFM | Silverstone | French TV Talkback |
| 460.68750 | 454.18750 | NFM | Wales | BBC Wales Studio Controller |
| 460.70000 | 454.20000 | NFM | Dublin | Fire Service |
| 460.70000 | 467.20000 | NFM | Kent | Prison (KV/KB) |
| 460.70620 | 454.20620 | NFM | Nationwide | Sky TV Talkback |
| 460.72500 | 467.22500 | NFM | Avon | Health Authority |
| 460.72500 | 467.22500 | NFM | Cornwall | Health Authority |
| 460.72500 | 467.22500 | NFM | Devon | Health Authority |
| 460.72500 | 467.22500 | NFM | Doncaster | HM Prison (M2XD) |
| 460.72500 | 467.22500 | NFM | Doncaster | HM Prison (XD) |
| 460.72500 | 467.22500 | NFM | Gloucester | Health Authority |
| 460.72500 | 467.22500 | NFM | Nationwide | Sky TV OB |
| 460.72500 | 467.22500 | NFM | Scilly Isles | Health Authority |
| 460.72500 | 467.22500 | NFM | Somerset | Health Authority |
| 460.72500 | 467.22500 | NFM | Warrington | HM Young Offenders Institution Thorn Cross (BO) |
| 460.73750 | 454.23750 | NFM | Rugby | Swift Valley Industrial Estate. |
| 460.74370 | 454.24370 | NFM | Nationwide | BBC TV O/B Production |
| 460.75000 | 454.25000 | NFM | Cleveland | Health Authority |
| 460.75000 | 454.25000 | NFM | Cumbria | Health Authority |
| 460.75000 | 454.25000 | NFM | Durham | Health Authority |
| 460.75000 | 454.25000 | NFM | Northumbria | Health Authority |

### 460.76875 - 461.23125 MHzPMR (Airport and North Sea Rigs)

| Base | Mobile | Mode | Location | User and Notes |
|------|--------|------|----------|----------------|
| 460.77000 | 467.27000 | NFM | Birmingham International | Airport Marshalls |
| 460.77500 | 467.27500 | NFM | Manchester | Air Frame Ground Staff |
| 460.78750 | 467.28750 | NFM | Nationwide | National Air Traffic Service |
| 460.85000 | 467.35000 | NFM | North Sea | Shell TCM |
| 460.92500 | 467.42500 | NFM | Newcastle Airport | Airport Mobiles |
| 460.95000 | 467.42500 | NFM | Edinburgh Airport | PMR Channel 7 |
| 461.00000 | 467.50000 | NFM | Edinburgh Airport | Channel 35 |
| 461.00000 | 467.50000 | NFM | Edinburgh Airport | PMR Channel 15 |
| 461.00000 | 467.50000 | NFM | Filton (BAe), Bristol | Ground Crews |
| 461.00000 | 467.50000 | NFM | Nationwide | RAF Falcons Display Team |
| 461.02500 | 455.72500 | NFM | Edinburgh Airport | PMR Channel 13 |
| 461.02500 | 461.02500 | NFM | Edinburgh Airport | Channel 33 |
| 461.02500 | 467.52500 | NFM | Cardiff | Air Traffic Control |
| 461.02500 | 467.52500 | NFM | Cleveland | Health Authority |
| 461.02500 | 467.52500 | NFM | Cumbria | Health Authority |
| 461.02500 | 467.52500 | NFM | Durham | Health Authority |
| 461.02500 | 467.52500 | NFM | Easington | BP To West Sole A |
| 461.02500 | 467.52500 | NFM | Nationwide | National Air Traffic Service |
| 461.02500 | 467.52500 | NFM | North Sea | Shell Brent B |
| 461.02500 | 467.52500 | NFM | North Sea | Shell Brent D |
| 461.02500 | 467.52500 | NFM | North Sea | Shell Brent Spar |
| 461.05000 | 467.55000 | NFM | North Sea | Shell Fulmar A |
| 461.07500 | 455.77500 | NFM | Edinburgh Airport | Channel 12 |
| 461.07500 | 461.07500 | NFM | Edinburgh Airport | Channel 32 |
| 461.07500 | 467.57500 | NFM | Easington | BP to West Sole A |
| 461.10000 | 467.60000 | NFM | Newcastle Airport | Tower & Following |
| 461.10000 | 467.60000 | NFM | North Sea | Shell Fulmar A |

| Base | Mobile | Mode | Location | User and Notes |
|------|--------|------|----------|----------------|
| 461.11250 | 467.61250 | NFM | Newcastle Airport | Luggage Control |
| 461.16250 | 467.66250 | NFM | Newcastle Airport | Baggage Handling |
| 461.20000 | 467.70000 | NFM | London, Heathrow | Ground Staff |

**461.250 - 462.500 MHz        PMR**

| Base | Mobile | Mode | Location | User and Notes |
|------|--------|------|----------|----------------|
| 461.21500 | 467.71500 | NFM | London, Brent Cross | C & A staff |
| 461.21650 | 467.71650 | NFM | London, Finchley | Waitrose staff |
| 461.23750 | 468.52500 | NFM | Manchester | Manchester United FC O/B |
| 461.23750 | 468.52500 | NFM | Nationwide | JFMG Short Term Talkback |
| 461.25000 | 468.53750 | NFM | Manchester | Sky Sport O/B from Old Trafford |
| 461.25000 | 468.53750 | NFM | Nationwide | JFMG Short Term Talkback |
| 461.26250 | | NFM | Ayr | Gaiety Theatre |
| 461.26250 | | NFM | Basildon | Eastgate Shopping Centre maintenance |
| 461.26250 | | NFM | Basildon | Robins Cinema Staff. |
| 461.26250 | | NFM | Canvey Island | Kings Club Night Club Security |
| 461.26250 | | NFM | Chelmsford | Benson Motorcycle Training |
| 461.26250 | | NFM | Chelmsford | Shopping Centre, HMV Security |
| 461.26250 | | NFM | Coventry | Index Catalogue Shop |
| 461.26250 | | NFM | Dartford | Bluewater Shopping Centre, JD Casuals Staff |
| 461.26250 | | NFM | Dartford | JJD Sports, Bluewater Centre |
| 461.26250 | | NFM | Faversham | Kent Shopwatch |
| 461.26250 | | NFM | Hull | Go Karting Track. |
| 461.26250 | | NFM | Liverpool | Mecca Bingo security Ch.1 |
| 461.26250 | | NFM | London | Capital Radio Restaurant doorman |
| 461.26250 | | NFM | London | Finsbury Park Cil Ltd. |
| 461.26250 | | NFM | London | Sainsburys Check Out/Help Staff |
| 461.26250 | | NFM | London, Oxford St | Dolcis Shoes (Sabrewatch Security) |
| 461.26250 | | NFM | London, Oxford Street | Border Bookshop security |
| 461.26250 | | NFM | London, Oxford Street | Dolcis Shoes |
| 461.26250 | | NFM | London, Raynes Park | David Lloyd Leisure Club |
| 461.26250 | | NFM | London, Raynes Park | Rutlish School |
| 461.26250 | | NFM | London, Stratford | JJD Sports |
| 461.26250 | | NFM | Nationwide | Motorola Business Radios Ch 1 |
| 461.26250 | | NFM | Peterborough | College Arms Pub. |
| 461.26250 | | NFM | Wimbledon | Centre Court Shopping Centre Cleaners |
| 461.26250 | | NFM | Woodbridge | Farlingaye High School Teachers |
| 461.26250 | | NFM | Worcester | Town Centre. |
| 461.27500 | | NFM | Cardiff | Millennium Stadium builders |
| 461.27500 | | NFM | North Sea | Shell Brent A |
| 461.27850 | | NFM | London White City | BBC Worldwide Ch1 |
| 461.28750 | | NFM | Ascot | Race Course Bookies |
| 461.28750 | | NFM | Ayr | Asda |
| 461.28750 | | NFM | Ayrshire | Motorbike instructors |
| 461.28750 | | NFM | Cheltenham | Race Course Car Park |
| 461.28750 | | NFM | Coventry | Central 6 Retail Park Security |
| 461.28750 | | NFM | Coventry | Unid Security City Centre |
| 461.28750 | | NFM | Fife Council | Scotland |
| 461.28750 | | NFM | Guernsey | Brock Fireworks |
| 461.28750 | | NFM | Guernsey | Performing Arts Handhelds |
| 461.28750 | | NFM | London | Borough of Brent Trading Standards Inspectors |
| 461.28750 | | NFM | London | Paramount Pictures Sleepy Hollow film. |
| 461.28750 | | NFM | London | Walthemstow DSS |
| 461.28750 | | NFM | London, Stratford | Motor cycle training |
| 461.28750 | | NFM | Manchester | Asda staff and security |
| 461.28750 | | NFM | Manchester | Centre Construction |
| 461.28750 | | NFM | Manchester | DSS Ch.1 |

| Base | Mobile | Mode | Location | User and Notes |
|------|--------|------|----------|----------------|
| 461.28750 | | NFM | Manchester | Trafford Centre Unid User |
| 461.28750 | | NFM | National | British Telecom Engineers |
| 461.28750 | | NFM | National | Fantastic Firework Displays |
| 461.28750 | | NFM | Nationwide | Rock Steady Event safety Ch.3 |
| 461.28750 | | NFM | Sheffield | Sheffield Arena security |
| 461.28750 | | NFM | Tamworth | Asda. |
| 461.30000 | | NFM | Ayrshire | Motorbike instructors |
| 461.30000 | | NFM | Bedfordshire | Health Authority |
| 461.30000 | | NFM | Berkshire | Health Authority |
| 461.30000 | | NFM | Buckinghamshire | Health Authority |
| 461.30000 | | NFM | Doncaster | Tickhill Garden Centre |
| 461.30000 | | NFM | East Hertfordshire | Health Authority |
| 461.30000 | | NFM | Eastbourne | Health Authority |
| 461.30000 | | NFM | Essex | Health Authority |
| 461.30000 | | NFM | Humberside | Health Authority |
| 461.30000 | | NFM | Kent | Health Authority |
| 461.30000 | | NFM | Liverpool | Mecca Bingo security Ch.2 |
| 461.30000 | | NFM | Medway | Health Authority |
| 461.30000 | | NFM | Nationwide | Motorola Business Radios Ch 2 |
| 461.30000 | | NFM | Northamptonshire | Health Authority |
| 461.30000 | | NFM | Oxford | Health Authority |
| 461.30000 | | NFM | Surrey | Health Authority |
| 461.30000 | | NFM | West Sussex | Health Authority |
| 461.30000 | | NFM | Yorkshire | Health Authority |
| 461.31250 | | NFM | Ashford | County Square Security |
| 461.31250 | | NFM | Brentford | Factory Security |
| 461.31250 | | NFM | Chadwell Heath | Music Distributor |
| 461.31250 | | NFM | Coventry | CW Electronics |
| 461.31250 | | NFM | Coventry | Geest Bananas Walsgrave |
| 461.31250 | | NFM | Dartford | Manufacturing Co |
| 461.31250 | | NFM | Drayton Green | School |
| 461.31250 | | NFM | Eastbourne | Theatre |
| 461.31250 | | NFM | Felixstowe | Spa Pavilion Theatre |
| 461.31250 | | NFM | London | Brent Cross Shopping Centre security |
| 461.31250 | | NFM | London | Edgware Road Construction Co |
| 461.31250 | | NFM | London | Hanover Square Security |
| 461.31250 | | NFM | London | Harrow Weald Manufacturing |
| 461.31250 | | NFM | London | Hayes Town Distribution |
| 461.31250 | | NFM | London | Heathrow Cargo Handling Unit |
| 461.31250 | | NFM | London | Kensington College |
| 461.31250 | | NFM | London | Kentish Town Leisure |
| 461.31250 | | NFM | London | Park Royal Construction Co |
| 461.31250 | | NFM | London | Rock Circus staff |
| 461.31250 | | NFM | London | St James Square Property Management |
| 461.31250 | | NFM | London | Upton Plashet Road Retail Outlet |
| 461.31250 | | NFM | London | West India Docks Engineering Co |
| 461.31250 | | NFM | London | West London Shooting Ground |
| 461.31250 | | NFM | Nationwide | TNT Loaders Channel 1 |
| 461.31250 | | NFM | Sheffield | Sheffield Arena security |
| 461.31250 | | NFM | Tamworth | TNT Loading Bays. |
| 461.31250 | | NFM | Warwick | Warwick Castle staff Ch.2 |
| 461.31250 | | NFM | Watford | High Street Retail Outlet |
| 461.31250 | | NFM | West Thurrock | Tunnel Estate Warehouse Distribution |
| 461.31250 | | NFM | Wilmslow | Top Shop staff |
| 461.32500 | | NFM | Ashington | Wansbeck General Hospital Car Park |
| 461.32500 | | NFM | Buckinghamshire | Health Authority |

| Base | Mobile | Mode | Location | User and Notes |
|------|--------|------|----------|----------------|
| 461.32500 | | NFM | Chatham | World Naval Base Admin Ch 2 |
| 461.32500 | | NFM | Cheltenham | Shopping Arcade Security |
| 461.32500 | | NFM | Doncaster | DMBC Security |
| 461.32500 | | NFM | Elm Park | Retail Outlet |
| 461.32500 | | NFM | Ipswich | Docks |
| 461.32500 | | NFM | Jersey | General Hospital |
| 461.32500 | | NFM | London | Barbican Theatre production comms. |
| 461.32500 | | NFM | London | Barking Retail Outlet |
| 461.32500 | | NFM | London | Blackwell Cleaning Co |
| 461.32500 | | NFM | London | Colindale Retail Outlet |
| 461.32500 | | NFM | London | County Hall F.A. Premier Hall of Fame |
| 461.32500 | | NFM | London | Edmonton Retail Outlet |
| 461.32500 | | NFM | London | Heathrow Taxi&Car Hire |
| 461.32500 | | NFM | London | Marylebone Medical |
| 461.32500 | | NFM | London | Norwood Retail Outlet |
| 461.32500 | | NFM | London | Old Bond St Retail Outlet |
| 461.32500 | | NFM | London | Victoria Retail Outlet |
| 461.32500 | | NFM | London, Oxford Street | CLH staff |
| 461.32500 | | NFM | Nationwide | British Aerospace |
| 461.32500 | | NFM | Northamptonshire | Health Authority |
| 461.32500 | | NFM | Oxford | Health Authority |
| 461.32500 | | NFM | Retford | Halcroft Industrial Estate CCTV |
| 461.32500 | | NFM | Sheffield | Sheffield Arena security |
| 461.32500 | | NFM | Waltham Cross | Works Engineering |
| 461.32500 | | NFM | Watford | Retail Outlet |
| 461.32500 | | NFM | West Berkshire | Health Authority |
| 461.33700 | | NFM | Southampton | Sealink Car Ferries |
| 461.33700 | | NFM | Tamworth | Ankerside Shopping Centre |
| 461.33750 | | NFM | Barnstaple | Green Lanes Shopping Centre |
| 461.33750 | | NFM | Biggleswade | Jordans Cereals Ch.3 |
| 461.33750 | | NFM | Burton upon Trent | Shopping Centre Security |
| 461.33750 | | NFM | Chatham | Shop Security. |
| 461.33750 | | NFM | Cheadle | Top Shop staff |
| 461.33750 | | NFM | Doncaster | Warner Bros. Cinema |
| 461.33750 | | NFM | East Molesey | Field Common Construction Co |
| 461.33750 | | NFM | London | Covent Garden Hotel |
| 461.33750 | | NFM | London | Piccadilly Circus Retail Outlet |
| 461.33750 | | NFM | London | St Pauls Cray Manufacturing Works |
| 461.33750 | | NFM | London | Wandsworth Retail Outlet |
| 461.33750 | | NFM | London, Oxford Street | Top Shop |
| 461.33750 | | NFM | Luton Airport | Alpha Flight Catering outlets |
| 461.33750 | | NFM | Nationwide | TNT Parcels Channel 2 |
| 461.33750 | | NFM | Newmilns | Vesuvius office staff |
| 461.33750 | | NFM | Northamptonshire | Ambulance Service |
| 461.33750 | | NFM | Oxford | Ambulance Service |
| 461.33750 | | NFM | Sheffield | Sheffield Arena security |
| 461.33750 | | NFM | Tamworth | Ankerside Shopping Centre Security. |
| 461.33750 | | NFM | West Croydon | Retail Outlet |
| 461.33750 | | NFM | Widnes | Widnes Leisure Centre |
| 461.34250 | | NFM | Richmond Upon Thames | Retail Outlet |
| 461.35000 | | NFM | Borehamwood | Retail Outlet |
| 461.35000 | | NFM | Brooklands Ind Park | Retail Outlet |
| 461.35000 | | NFM | Chatham | World Naval Base Security Ch 4 |
| 461.35000 | | NFM | Cheshunt | Retail Outlet |
| 461.35000 | | NFM | Coventry | Cathedral Lane Shopping Centre |
| 461.35000 | | NFM | Eastbourne | Arndale Security |

| Base | Mobile | Mode | Location | User and Notes |
|------|--------|------|----------|----------------|
| 461.35000 | | NFM | Jersey | Builders (On-Site Radios) |
| 461.35000 | | NFM | London | Bowes Park Security User |
| 461.35000 | | NFM | London | Bromley Retail Outlet |
| 461.35000 | | NFM | London | LI Hospital |
| 461.35000 | | NFM | London | Marylebone Hotel |
| 461.35000 | | NFM | London, Heathrow | Airline ops. |
| 461.35000 | | NFM | London, Swiss Cottage | Government dept. |
| 461.35000 | | NFM | Moor Park | Works |
| 461.35000 | | NFM | Romford | Crown Court Security |
| 461.35000 | | NFM | Romford | Super Store |
| 461.35000 | | NFM | Sheffield | William Brothers |
| 461.35000 | | NFM | Stevenage | ICL Computers Ch.1 |
| 461.35000 | | NFM | Sunbury | Security User |
| 461.35000 | | NFM | Sutton | Retail Outlet |
| 461.35000 | | NFM | Tamworth | Snowdome Staff. |
| 461.35000 | | NFM | Waltham Abbey | Retail Outlet |
| 461.35000 | | NFM | Waltham Cross | Retail Outlet |
| 461.35000 | | NFM | Wirral | Emergency Doctors |
| 461.35050 | | NFM | Coventry | Cathedral Lane Shopping Centre security |
| 461.36250 | | NFM | Ashford | Shop Security |
| 461.36250 | | NFM | Borehamwood | Works Security |
| 461.36250 | | NFM | Coventry | B&Q Warehouse |
| 461.36250 | | NFM | Harrow on the Hill | St Georges's Shopping Centre security |
| 461.36250 | | NFM | Hersham | Charity User |
| 461.36250 | | NFM | London | Bakers St Security Co |
| 461.36250 | | NFM | London | Bayswater Queens Ice Rink |
| 461.36250 | | NFM | London | Heathrow Telephone Co |
| 461.36250 | | NFM | London | Islington Leisure |
| 461.36250 | | NFM | London | Oxford Circus Topshop Staff |
| 461.36250 | | NFM | London | Victoria Security |
| 461.36250 | | NFM | London | Willesden Junction Builders Merchant |
| 461.36250 | | NFM | Manchester | Marks & Spencer plainclothes security |
| 461.36250 | | NFM | Morden | Charity |
| 461.36250 | | NFM | Peterborough | Chicago Cafe |
| 461.36250 | | NFM | Portsmouth | Guildhall Security |
| 461.36250 | | NFM | Southampton | Lowe Security |
| 461.36250 | | NFM | St Albans | Works |
| 461.36250 | | NFM | Stowmarket | Stowmarket Country Farms |
| 461.36250 | | NFM | Waltham Cross | Works Engineering |
| 461.36250 | | NFM | Watford | Leisure User |
| 461.36250 | | NFM | Worcester | Crowngate Shopping Centre |
| 461.37500 | | NFM | Ascot | Race Course Staff. |
| 461.37500 | | NFM | Basildon | Hospital car park security |
| 461.37500 | | NFM | Berkshire | Health Authority |
| 461.37500 | | NFM | Buckinghamshire | Health Authority |
| 461.37500 | | NFM | Cardiff | Millennium Stadium builders |
| 461.37500 | | NFM | Cheltenham | Race Court Tic Tac Men |
| 461.37500 | | NFM | Coventry | Virgin Megastore Security |
| 461.37500 | | NFM | Dartford | Bluewater Shopping Centre contractors |
| 461.37500 | | NFM | Dartford | Virgin Megastore, Bluewater Shopping Centre |
| 461.37500 | | NFM | Leicester | Virgin Megastore Security |
| 461.37500 | | NFM | Liverpool | Virgin Megastore |
| 461.37500 | | NFM | London | Construction 02 Leisure Complex Swiss Cottage |
| 461.37500 | | NFM | London | Paramount Pictures Sleepy Hollow filming |
| 461.37500 | | NFM | London | Scorpion Security |
| 461.37500 | | NFM | London, Haymarket | Sports Cafe |

| Base | Mobile | Mode | Location | User and Notes |
|------|--------|------|----------|----------------|
| 461.37500 | | NFM | Manchester | Centre Virgin Mega Store |
| 461.37500 | | NFM | Manchester | Virgin Megastore staff & security |
| 461.37500 | | NFM | Nationwide | Sky TV Engineers |
| 461.37500 | | NFM | North Sea | Shell Brent B |
| 461.37500 | | NFM | Northamptonshire | Health Authority |
| 461.37500 | | NFM | Oxford | Health Authority |
| 461.37500 | | NFM | Sheffield | Sheffield Arena security (LINK) |
| 461.37500 | | NFM | Southend on Sea | Government agency (TARGET) |
| 461.37500 | | NFM | Southend on Sea | Job Centre Staff |
| 461.38750 | | NFM | Ascot | Race Course Grandstand staff |
| 461.38750 | | NFM | Ashford | Middx Manor Golf Club |
| 461.38750 | | NFM | City of London | Blackfriars Post office |
| 461.38750 | | NFM | Coventry | Midland Lewis Woodyard |
| 461.38750 | | NFM | Dover | P & O Ferries |
| 461.38750 | | NFM | Eastbourne | Sovereign Leisure and Swimming Pool |
| 461.38750 | | NFM | Elstree | Lister Institute |
| 461.38750 | | NFM | Essex | Trading Standards |
| 461.38750 | | NFM | Heston | Harlequin Centre |
| 461.38750 | | NFM | Kilmarnock | Galleon Centre (GOLF) |
| 461.38750 | | NFM | Kingston Upon Thames | University |
| 461.38750 | | NFM | London | Arnos Grove School |
| 461.38750 | | NFM | London | Bakers St University |
| 461.38750 | | NFM | London | Bond St Versace Couture |
| 461.38750 | | NFM | London | Eltham School |
| 461.38750 | | NFM | London, golders Green | St. Edward The Confessor Catholic Church |
| 461.38750 | | NFM | London | Hillangdon Warren Road School |
| 461.38750 | | NFM | London | Islington Business Design Centre |
| 461.38750 | | NFM | London | Paramount Pictures security. |
| 461.38750 | | NFM | London | Russell Square Hotel |
| 461.38750 | | NFM | London | Totteridge South Herts Golf Club |
| 461.38750 | | NFM | London | Wandsworth The Arndale Centre |
| 461.38750 | | NFM | London, Bond Street | Versace Couture security |
| 461.38750 | | NFM | Mainningtree | ICI Factory Staff. |
| 461.38750 | | NFM | Newmilns | Vesuvius maintenance engineers |
| 461.38750 | | NFM | Purfleet | UK Petroleum Products Ltd |
| 461.38750 | | NFM | Richmond Upon Thames | School |
| 461.38750 | | NFM | Surrey | Woldingham Garden Village |
| 461.40000 | | NFM | Bushey | Moor Park Golf Course |
| 461.40000 | | NFM | Dagenham | Dagenham Town Football Club stewards |
| 461.40000 | | NFM | Dartford | Central Park Retail User |
| 461.40000 | | NFM | Eastbourne | Hospital Porters |
| 461.40000 | | NFM | Elstree | Works Security |
| 461.40000 | | NFM | Harrow on the Hill | The Edge Cafe |
| 461.40000 | | NFM | Harwich | Scandinavian Seaways staff |
| 461.40000 | | NFM | Hitchin | Wilkinson Home & Garden Store security |
| 461.40000 | | NFM | Jersey | PMR |
| 461.40000 | | NFM | Kingston Upon Thames | Retail Outlet |
| 461.40000 | | NFM | Liverpool | Mecca Bingo security Ch.3 |
| 461.40000 | | NFM | London | Burnt Oak Security Co |
| 461.40000 | | NFM | London | Her Majesty's Theatre |
| 461.40000 | | NFM | London | Hounslow Retail Outlet |
| 461.40000 | | NFM | London | Kew Gardens Retail Outlet |
| 461.40000 | | NFM | London | Kings Road Retail Outlet |
| 461.40000 | | NFM | London | Pimlico Security Co |
| 461.40000 | | NFM | London | Regents Park Hotel |
| 461.40000 | | NFM | London | Regents Park Retail Outlet |

| Base | Mobile | Mode | Location | User and Notes |
|------|--------|------|----------|----------------|
| 461.40000 | | NFM | London | Twickenham Retail Outlet |
| 461.40000 | | NFM | London | Walthamstow Retail Outlet |
| 461.40000 | | NFM | London | Woolwich Arsenal Retail Outlet |
| 461.40000 | | NFM | London, Brent Cross | Holiday Inn Hotel |
| 461.40000 | | NFM | London, Knightsbridge | The Chelsea Hotel |
| 461.40000 | | NFM | Snaresbrook | Crown Court |
| 461.40000 | | NFM | Southend on Sea | Victoria Plaza |
| 461.40000 | | NFM | Warwick | Warwick Castle staff Ch.3 |
| 461.40000 | | NFM | Weybridge | Paper Merchant |
| 461.42500 | 467.92500 | NFM | Altrincham | Marks & Spencer Sabrewatch Security |
| 461.42500 | 467.92500 | NFM | London, Gatwick | Cellular Link |
| 461.42500 | 467.92500 | NFM | North Sea | Shell Auk A to ELSBM |
| 461.42500 | 467.92500 | NFM | North Sea | Shell Brent D |
| 461.43750 | 467.93750 | NFM | Farnborough Airshow | Scaffolding Co on site |
| 461.45000 | 467.95000 | NFM | Altrincham | C&A Sabrewatch Security |
| 461.45000 | 467.95000 | NFM | Ascot | Race Course |
| 461.45000 | 467.95000 | NFM | Ashford | Shop Security |
| 461.45000 | 467.95000 | NFM | Basildon | Hospital car park security |
| 461.45000 | 467.95000 | NFM | Canvey Island | Cater and Ward Construction. |
| 461.45000 | 467.95000 | NFM | City of London | Cannon St Laing Construction |
| 461.45000 | 467.95000 | NFM | Jersey | C.A. Mauger Builders |
| 461.45000 | 467.95000 | NFM | Leicester | D&J Event Caterers |
| 461.45000 | 467.95000 | NFM | Liverpool | Mecca Bingo security Ch.4 |
| 461.45000 | 467.95000 | NFM | London | Lord Mayors firework display |
| 461.45000 | 467.95000 | NFM | London | Sainsburys Sabrewatch Security |
| 461.45000 | 467.95000 | NFM | London | Waterloo Imax Cinema Builders |
| 461.45000 | 467.95000 | NFM | London, Oxford Street | CLH staff |
| 461.45000 | 467.95000 | NFM | Reading | Wimpey Construction |
| 461.46250 | 467.96250 | NFM | Ascot | Race Course Staff. |
| 461.46250 | 467.96250 | NFM | Chadwell Heath | Manufacturing Co |
| 461.46250 | 467.96250 | NFM | City of London | Bank Area Construction Co |
| 461.46250 | 467.96250 | NFM | Coventry | Pool Meadow Bus Depot |
| 461.46250 | 467.96250 | NFM | Coventry, Walsgrave Triangle | Hilton Hotel |
| 461.46250 | 467.96250 | NFM | Coventry, Walsgrave Triangle | Trusthouse Forte Hotel. |
| 461.46250 | 467.96250 | NFM | Dagenham | Ford Motor Co. |
| 461.46250 | 467.96250 | NFM | Dartford | Ford Motor - Security and Works Dept Ch4 |
| 461.46250 | 467.96250 | NFM | Doncaster | Traffic Wardens |
| 461.46250 | 467.96250 | NFM | Duxford | Security (OSCAR BASE) |
| 461.46250 | 467.96250 | NFM | East Ham | London Borough of Newham |
| 461.46250 | 467.96250 | NFM | Garston Nr Watford | Retail Outlet |
| 461.46250 | 467.96250 | NFM | Hull | Princes Quay Shopping Centre |
| 461.46250 | 467.96250 | NFM | Lewisham | Lewisham College |
| 461.46250 | 467.96250 | NFM | London | Belgravia Square Hotel |
| 461.46250 | 467.96250 | NFM | London | Belsize Park Engineering Co |
| 461.46250 | 467.96250 | NFM | London | Cavendish Square Drinks Co |
| 461.46250 | 467.96250 | NFM | London | Covent Garden Medical |
| 461.46250 | 467.96250 | NFM | London | Cricklewood Government |
| 461.46250 | 467.96250 | NFM | London | Dagenham East Factory Security |
| 461.46250 | 467.96250 | NFM | London | Fortnum & Masons |
| 461.46250 | 467.96250 | NFM | London | Greenwich Engineering Co |
| 461.46250 | 467.96250 | NFM | London | Heathrow Hotel |
| 461.46250 | 467.96250 | NFM | London | Hurlingham Construction Co |
| 461.46250 | 467.96250 | NFM | London | Inner Temple |
| 461.46250 | 467.96250 | NFM | London | North Acton Food Factory |
| 461.46250 | 467.96250 | NFM | London | Odeon Cinemas Ltd. |
| 461.46250 | 467.96250 | NFM | London | Old Kent Road Construction Co |

| Base | Mobile | Mode | Location | User and Notes |
|------|--------|------|----------|----------------|
| 461.46250 | 467.96250 | NFM | London | Old Kent Road Hotel |
| 461.46250 | 467.96250 | NFM | London | Regent Street Hotel |
| 461.46250 | 467.96250 | NFM | London | Twickenham Charity |
| 461.46250 | 467.96250 | NFM | London | Walthamstow Engineering Co |
| 461.46250 | 467.96250 | NFM | London, Buckingham Palace Rd | National Audit Commission |
| 461.46250 | 467.96250 | NFM | London, Fleet St | Law Courts |
| 461.46250 | 467.96250 | NFM | London, Grays Inn Road | National Advisory Council for Education & Training Standards |
| 461.46250 | 467.96250 | NFM | London, Heathrow | Sterling Hotel |
| 461.46250 | 467.96250 | NFM | Nationwide | DSS |
| 461.46250 | 467.96250 | NFM | Nationwide | Dept. of Employment |
| 461.46250 | 467.96250 | NFM | Nationwide | National Audit Office |
| 461.46250 | 467.96250 | NFM | Peterborough | 5th Avenue |
| 461.46250 | 467.96250 | NFM | St Albans | Works |
| 461.46250 | 467.96250 | NFM | Stockport | Top Shop security |
| 461.46250 | 467.96250 | NFM | Walthamstow | Hawker Siddeley Transformer |
| 461.46250 | 467.96250 | NFM | West Thurrock | Factory |
| 461.46250 | 467.96250 | NFM | Windsor | Royal Station Shopping Mall Staff & Cleaners |
| 461.46250 | 467.96250 | NFM | Woodbridge | Farlingaye High School Caretakers |
| 461.46250 | 467.96250 | NFM | Worcester | Lychgate Shopping Centre |
| 461.47500 | 467.97500 | NFM | Ayr | Citadel Leisure Centre |
| 461.47500 | 467.97500 | NFM | Ayr | Harbour coal depot |
| 461.47500 | 467.97500 | NFM | Ayr, Lawson Street | Costcutters |
| 461.47500 | 467.97500 | NFM | Birmingham | JJD Sports Fort Retail Park |
| 461.47500 | 467.97500 | NFM | Bridlington | Boyes Dept. Store staff |
| 461.47500 | 467.97500 | NFM | Cardiff | Millennium Stadium builders |
| 461.47500 | 467.97500 | NFM | Dartford | Bluewater Shopping Centre Contractors |
| 461.47500 | 467.97500 | NFM | Dartford | John Lewis, Bluewater Shopping Centre |
| 461.47500 | 467.97500 | NFM | Devon | Highways surveyors |
| 461.47500 | 467.97500 | NFM | Essex | Cable TV engineers |
| 461.47500 | 467.97500 | NFM | Farnborough Airshow | Catering |
| 461.47500 | 467.97500 | NFM | Ipswich | Vodka Bar Doormen |
| 461.47500 | 467.97500 | NFM | Letchworth | Morrisons Superstore, Sabre Security |
| 461.47500 | 467.97500 | NFM | London, Barnes | St. Paul's School staff |
| 461.47500 | 467.97500 | NFM | London, Oxford Street | Borders Book Store security |
| 461.47500 | 467.97500 | NFM | London, Oxford Street | John Lewis, security |
| 461.47500 | 467.97500 | NFM | Nationwide | Marks & Spencer Security |
| 461.47500 | 467.97500 | NFM | Nationwide | Motorola Business Radios Ch 3 |
| 461.47500 | 467.97500 | NFM | North Sea | Shell Auk A to ELSBM |
| 461.47500 | 467.97500 | NFM | North Weald | Furniture Shop. |
| 461.47500 | 467.97500 | NFM | Peterborough | Break/Boarder Club. |
| 461.47500 | 467.97500 | NFM | Peterborough | The Academy Bar |
| 461.47500 | 467.97500 | NFM | Preston | Sharoe Green Hospital |
| 461.47500 | 467.97500 | NFM | Prestwick | Centrum Arena |
| 461.47500 | 467.97500 | NFM | Rugby | Swift Valley Industrial Estate. |
| 461.47500 | 467.97500 | NFM | Scotland | Scottish Football Association |
| 461.47500 | 467.97500 | NFM | Southend-On-Sea | Never Never Land. |
| 461.47500 | 467.97500 | NFM | Tilbury | Container Port |
| 461.47500 | 467.97500 | NFM | Windsor | Royal Station Staff. |
| 461.47500 | 467.97500 | NFM | Woodbridge | Farlingaye High School Teachers |
| 461.47500 | 467.97500 | NFM | Worthing | Motor Cycle Driving Test Instructor |
| 461.48750 | 467.98750 | NFM | Ascot | Race Course Bookies |
| 461.48750 | 467.98750 | NFM | Ashford | Marks & Spencer Sabrewatch security |
| 461.48750 | 467.98750 | NFM | Ayr | Index |
| 461.48750 | 467.98750 | NFM | Bedworth | Food Giant |
| 461.48750 | 467.98750 | NFM | Blackpool | Pub/Restaurant |

| Base | Mobile | Mode | Location | User and Notes |
|------|--------|------|----------|----------------|
| 461.48750 | 467.98750 | NFM | Bridlington | Shopwatch |
| 461.48750 | 467.98750 | NFM | Canvey Island | Cornelius Vermugden School |
| 461.48750 | 467.98750 | NFM | Coventry | Hilton Hotel |
| 461.48750 | 467.98750 | NFM | Coventry | Orchard Retailpark |
| 461.48750 | 467.98750 | NFM | Dartford, Bluewater Centre | John Lewis Shop Staff |
| 461.48750 | 467.98750 | NFM | Etonbury | School |
| 461.48750 | 467.98750 | NFM | Farnborough Airshow | Sabreguard Security |
| 461.48750 | 467.98750 | NFM | Halifax | Swimming Pools staff |
| 461.48750 | 467.98750 | NFM | Hawick | Hotel staff |
| 461.48750 | 467.98750 | NFM | Hull | Rugby Ground. |
| 461.48750 | 467.98750 | NFM | Ipswich | Railtrack Station Staff. |
| 461.48750 | 467.98750 | NFM | Irvine | Index |
| 461.48750 | 467.98750 | NFM | London | Museum of The Moving Image. |
| 461.48750 | 467.98750 | NFM | London, Barnes | St. Paul's School porters & security |
| 461.48750 | 467.98750 | NFM | London, Oxford Street | Dolcis Shoes |
| 461.48750 | 467.98750 | NFM | London, Oxford Street | JJD Sports |
| 461.48750 | 467.98750 | NFM | London, Waterloo | Imax Cinema Staff |
| 461.48750 | 467.98750 | NFM | Manchester | Arndale Centre JJB Sports |
| 461.48750 | 467.98750 | NFM | Nationwide | Motorola Business Radios Ch 4 |
| 461.48750 | 467.98750 | NFM | Poole | Pub/Club |
| 461.48750 | 467.98750 | NFM | Reading | Centre JJB Sports Ltd |
| 461.48750 | 467.98750 | NFM | Southend | C & A staff |
| 461.48750 | 467.98750 | NFM | Woodbridge | Farlingaye High School Teachers |
| 461.48750 | 467.98750 | NFM | Worthing | Motor Cycle Driving Test Instructor |
| 461.85000 | 467.35000 | NFM | Sizewell | Power station management Ch.16 |

## 461.500 - 462.500 MHz          PMR (Mobiles -5.5 MHz)

| Base | Mobile | Mode | Location | User and Notes |
|------|--------|------|----------|----------------|
| 461.50000 | 456.00000 | NFM | Lancaster | St Nicholas Arcade security Ch.2 |
| 461.50000 | 456.00000 | NFM | Leicester | City Council Repairs |
| 461.50000 | | NFM | London, Millennium Dome | Group 4 Total Security Ltd |
| 461.50000 | 456.00000 | NFM | Penzance | Railway repair contractor |
| 461.50000 | 456.00000 | NFM | Southampton | Group 4 Security |
| 461.50000 | 456.00000 | NFM | Southend-On-Sea | Wilkinsons Store Security |
| 461.52500 | 456.02500 | NFM | North Sea | Total Alwyn |
| 461.54000 | 456.04000 | NFM | London, Brent Cross | C & A security |
| 461.55000 | 456.05000 | NFM | Brae South | Marathon |
| 461.55000 | 456.05000 | NFM | Jersey | La Collette Power Station |
| 461.55000 | 456.05000 | NFM | North Sea | BGE&P Rough A |
| 461.55000 | 456.05000 | NFM | North Sea | BGE&P Rough B |
| 461.55000 | 456.05000 | NFM | North Sea | Total Alwyn |
| 461.57500 | 456.07500 | NFM | Bath | SW Electricity Disconnections |
| 461.57500 | 456.07500 | NFM | Nationwide | NCB Security |
| 461.57500 | 456.07500 | NFM | Northampton | Santa Pod Race Way Ch 4 |
| 461.60000 | 456.10000 | NFM | North Sea | BGE&P Rough B |
| 461.60000 | 456.10000 | NFM | North Sea | Marathon Brae S |
| 461.62500 | 456.11500 | NFM | Nationwide | Simply Red Crew |
| 461.62500 | 456.11500 | NFM | North Sea | BP Sulair Magnus |
| 461.67500 | 456.17500 | NFM | North Sea | Total Alwyn |
| 461.70000 | 456.20000 | NFM | North Sea | Shell Dunlin A |
| 461.70000 | 456.20000 | NFM | North Sea | Total MCP-01 |
| 461.72500 | 456.22500 | NFM | North Sea | BGE&P Rough B |
| 461.77500 | 456.27500 | NFM | North Sea | Shell Brent D |
| 461.77500 | 456.27500 | NFM | North Sea | Shell Cormorant N |
| 461.77500 | 456.27500 | NFM | Nottingham | Esso Colwick |
| 461.80000 | 456.30000 | NFM | North Sea | Marathon Brae North |
| 461.85000 | 456.35000 | NFM | Nottingham | Technical Services |

| Base | Mobile | Mode | Location | User and Notes |
|---|---|---|---|---|
| 461.87500 | 456.37500 | NFM | Essex | DSS Fraud teams |
| 461.87500 | 456.37500 | NFM | Sheffield | DSS Fraud teams |
| 461.88750 | 456.38750 | NFM | Birmingham | Sonic Communications P055 DCS tones. |
| 461.88750 | 456.38750 | NFM | Canvey Island | Sound/Lighting Crew |
| 461.88750 | 456.38750 | NFM | Coventry | Britannia Hotel |
| 461.88750 | 456.38750 | NFM | Hitchin | Loft Night Club |
| 461.88750 | 456.38750 | NFM | London | Palace Theatre |
| 461.88750 | 456.38750 | NFM | London | Paramount Pictures Sleepy Hollow filming |
| 461.88750 | 456.38750 | NFM | Rugby | Christian Salvesen Ch.6 |
| 461.90000 | 456.40000 | NFM | Essex | DSS (using MASC in clear) |
| 461.90000 | 456.40000 | NFM | London | HM Customs & Excise/DSS (using MASC in clear) |
| 461.90000 | 456.40000 | NFM | M1 | HM Customs & Excise surveillance |
| 461.90000 | 456.40000 | NFM | Nationwide | HM Customs Covert Repeater |
| 461.90000 | 456.40000 | NFM | Nationwide | HM Customs Surveillance |
| 461.90000 | 456.40000 | NFM | North Sea | Total Alwyn |
| 461.90000 | 456.40000 | NFM | Southend | Victoria Plaza Car Park security |
| 461.91250 | 456.41250 | NFM | Chesterfield | DSS (W) using MASC in clear |
| 461.91250 | 456.41250 | NFM | Chesterfield | DSS (W) using MASC in clear |
| 461.91250 | 456.41250 | NFM | East Midlands | Government surveillance using MASC encryption |
| 461.91250 | 456.41250 | NFM | London | DSS Ch.2 |
| 461.91250 | 456.41250 | NFM | Manchester | DSS Ch.2 |
| 461.92500 | 456.42500 | NFM | Manchester | British Rail Security |
| 461.92500 | 456.42500 | NFM | Nationwide | British Telecom Police Security |
| 461.92500 | 456.42500 | NFM | North Sea | BP Thistle A |
| 461.95000 | 456.45000 | NFM | Birmingham | RSPCA |
| 461.95000 | 456.45000 | NFM | Duxford Aerodrome | Imperial War Museum Security |
| 461.95000 | 456.45000 | NFM | North Sea | BP SMV |
| 461.95000 | 456.45000 | NFM | North Sea | Shell Brent B |
| 461.95000 | 456.45000 | NFM | North Sea | Shell Cormorant A |
| 461.95000 | 456.45000 | NFM | Sullom Voe | Shell |
| 461.97500 | 456.47500 | NFM | London, Heathrow | Hertz courtesy bus |
| 461.97500 | 456.47500 | NFM | North Sea | BP Thistle A |
| 461.97500 | 456.47500 | NFM | North Sea | BP Thistle A |
| 462.00000 | 456.50000 | NFM | Doncaster | Tesco Supermarket |
| 462.00000 | 456.50000 | NFM | Duxford Aerodrome | Imperial War Museum Gnd Mmnt |
| 462.00000 | 456.50000 | NFM | Nationwide | Securicor Datatrak System |
| 462.01250 | 456.51250 | NFM | London | Taxis |
| 462.02500 | 456.52500 | NFM | London | Taxis |
| 462.02500 | 456.52500 | NFM | National | Quayle digital headsets |
| 462.02500 | 456.52500 | NFM | North Sea | Shell Brent C |
| 462.05000 | 456.55000 | NFM | Ascot | Race Course Contractors |
| 462.05000 | 456.55000 | NFM | Ayr | Tesco |
| 462.05000 | 456.55000 | NFM | Bridlington | Tesco |
| 462.05000 | 456.55000 | NFM | Eastbourne | Tesco Supermarket |
| 462.05000 | 456.55000 | NFM | London | Cable & Wireless |
| 462.05000 | 456.55000 | NFM | London, Brent Cross | Marks & Spencer security |
| 462.05000 | 456.55000 | NFM | London, Brent Cross | W H Smith |
| 462.05000 | 456.55000 | NFM | London, Oxford St | John Lewis |
| 462.05000 | 456.55000 | NFM | Milton Keynes | W H Smith Ltd. |
| 462.05000 | 456.55000 | NFM | Nationwide | Tesco Supermarkets |
| 462.05000 | 456.55000 | NFM | Peterborough | Tesco's |
| 462.05000 | 456.55000 | NFM | Rochester | Furniture Shop. |
| 462.05000 | 456.55000 | NFM | Stirling | Castle security |
| 462.05000 | 462.05000 | NFM | North Sea | BP Thistle A |
| 462.05000 | 462.05000 | NFM | Stockport | WH Smith staff & security |
| 462.05000 | 462.05000 | NFM | Stretford | Tesco staff & security |

| Base | Mobile | Mode | Location | User and Notes |
|------|--------|------|----------|----------------|
| 462.07500 | 453.57500 | NFM | London, Heathrow | BP |
| 462.07500 | 456.57500 | NFM | London | Paddington Station Renovation Construction Crews |
| 462.07500 | 456.57500 | NFM | Luton Airport | Reed Aviation |
| 462.07500 | 456.57500 | NFM | North Sea | BP Buchan |
| 462.07500 | 456.57500 | NFM | North Sea | BP Darlington |
| 462.07500 | 456.57500 | NFM | North Sea | BP Easington |
| 462.07500 | 456.57500 | NFM | North Sea | BP Miller |
| 462.07500 | 456.57500 | NFM | North Sea | Shell Auk |
| 462.07500 | 456.57500 | NFM | North Sea | Shell Brent A |
| 462.07500 | 456.57500 | NFM | North Sea | Shell Dunlin |
| 462.07500 | 456.57500 | NFM | Sizewell | Power station management Ch.18 |
| 462.09500 | 456.59500 | NFM | Girton | Tarmac Quarries |
| 462.10000 | 456.60000 | NFM | Brentwood | Sainsburys Savacentre security. |
| 462.10000 | 456.60000 | NFM | Manchester | Littlewoods Sabrewatch Security |
| 462.10000 | 456.60000 | NFM | Nationwide | Visual Comm. Systems Engineers |
| 462.10000 | 456.60000 | NFM | North Sea | Total Alwyn |
| 462.10000 | 456.60000 | NFM | Welton | BP |
| 462.12500 | 456.62500 | NFM | Duxford Aerodrome | Imperial War Museum Fire |
| 462.12500 | 456.62500 | NFM | London | North Greenwich Engineering Works |
| 462.12500 | 456.62500 | NFM | London, Wembley | White Arrow Express Couriers |
| 462.12500 | 456.62500 | NFM | London, Wembley Park | Parcel Service |
| 462.12500 | 456.62500 | NFM | North Sea | Shell Fulmar A |
| 462.12500 | 456.62500 | NFM | North Sea | Total St. Fergus |
| 462.12500 | 456.62500 | NFM | Portsmouth | Ferry Port |
| 462.12500 | 456.62500 | NFM | Tilbury | Container Port. |
| 462.12500 | 456.62500 | NFM | Uxbridge | Factory |
| 462.15000 | 456.65000 | NFM | North Sea | BP Miller |
| 462.16250 | 456.66250 | NFM | Cheshire | Haulage |
| 462.17500 | 456.67500 | NFM | London, Heathrow | Ground Staff |
| 462.17500 | 456.67500 | NFM | North Sea | BP Miller |
| 462.17500 | 456.67500 | NFM | North Sea | Shell Brent D |
| 462.17500 | 456.67500 | NFM | North Sea | Shell North Cormorant |
| 462.20000 | 456.67500 | FM | Nationwide | John Sisk & Son Construction Ch 2 |
| 462.20000 | 456.67500 | NFM | North Sea | Shell Auk |
| 462.22500 | 456.72500 | NFM | Hull | Docks |
| 462.22500 | 456.72500 | NFM | London | Oxford Circus Store Net |
| 462.22500 | 456.72500 | NFM | London | Sloane Square National Army Museum Security |
| 462.22500 | 456.72500 | NFM | London | Tooting St Georges Hospital |
| 462.22500 | 456.72500 | NFM | London Chelsea | National Army Museum |
| 462.22500 | 456.72500 | NFM | Manchester | Marks & Spencer Sabrewatch Security |
| 462.22500 | 456.72500 | NFM | North Sea | BP Miller |
| 462.22500 | 456.72500 | NFM | North Sea | BP SMV |
| 462.22500 | 456.72500 | NFM | Rainham | Construction Co |
| 462.22500 | 456.72500 | NFM | Teddington | National Physical Laboratory |
| 462.25000 | 456.75000 | NFM | Altrincham | Littlewoods Sabrewatch Security |
| 462.25000 | 456.75000 | NFM | Barrow in Furness | VSEL Nuclear Incident Channel |
| 462.25000 | 456.75000 | NFM | Blackpool | Security |
| 462.25000 | 456.75000 | NFM | Bournemouth | Marks & Spencer Security |
| 462.25000 | 456.75000 | NFM | Coventry | Marks & Spencer Security |
| 462.25000 | 456.75000 | NFM | Doncaster | Marks & Spencer (M) |
| 462.25000 | 456.75000 | NFM | Ipswich | Littlewoods |
| 462.25000 | 456.75000 | NFM | Kirkby | Gala Bingo security Ch.1 |
| 462.25000 | 456.75000 | NFM | Kirkcaldy | Marks & Spencers Security |
| 462.25000 | 456.75000 | NFM | London, Heathrow | Ground Staff |
| 462.25000 | 456.75000 | NFM | London, Oxford Street | D.H. Evans Staff. |
| 462.25000 | 456.75000 | NFM | Peterborough | Marks & Spencer Security |

| Base | Mobile | Mode | Location | User and Notes |
|------|--------|------|----------|----------------|
| 462.25000 | 456.75000 | NFM | Stevenage | Marks & Spencer Security |
| 462.26250 | 456.76250 | NFM | Morecambe | Christie Park |
| 462.27500 | 456.77500 | NFM | Aberdeen, Dyce Airport | BP |
| 462.27500 | 456.77500 | NFM | Blackpool | Pleasure Beach Patrol |
| 462.27500 | 456.77500 | NFM | Dartford | Europort loaders |
| 462.27500 | 456.77500 | NFM | Hull | Docks |
| 462.27500 | 456.77500 | NFM | Nationwide | John Sisk & Son Construction Ch 1 |
| 462.27500 | 456.77500 | NFM | Portsmouth | Ferry Port |
| 462.30000 | 456.80000 | NFM | Blackpool | Security Town Centre Stores |
| 462.30000 | 456.80000 | NFM | Brent B | Shell PMR |
| 462.30000 | 456.80000 | NFM | Cormorant A | Shell PMR |
| 462.30000 | 456.80000 | NFM | Fulmar | Shell PMR |
| 462.30000 | 456.80000 | NFM | North Sea | Total MCP-01 |
| 462.30000 | 456.80000 | NFM | North Sea | Total St. Fergus |
| 462.30000 | 456.80000 | NFM | Slough | Coopers-Payen Ltd Security |
| 462.30000 | 456.80000 | NFM | Windsor and Eton | Riverside Station Staff. |
| 462.32500 | 456.82500 | NFM | Harrow on the Hill | St Georges's Shopping Centre |
| 462.32500 | 456.82500 | NFM | Ipswich | Port Authority Channel 4 |
| 462.32500 | 456.82500 | NFM | Kirkby | Gala Bingo security Ch.2 |
| 462.32500 | 456.82500 | NFM | London | Earls Court & Olympia Security |
| 462.35000 | 462.42500 | NFM | Hull | Docks |
| 462.36250 | 456.86250 | NFM | Ascot | Race Course Staff Security and Catering |
| 462.36250 | 456.86250 | NFM | Ayr | Race Course officials |
| 462.36250 | 456.86250 | NFM | Ayr | Somerset Park stewards (AYR) |
| 462.36250 | 456.86250 | NFM | Dartford | Bluewater Shopping Centre |
| 462.36250 | 456.86250 | NFM | Gt Yarmouth | Go Karting Circuit |
| 462.36250 | 456.86250 | NFM | Jersey | PMR |
| 462.36250 | 456.86250 | NFM | Kirkby | Gala Bingo security Ch.3 |
| 462.36250 | 456.86250 | NFM | London | Greys Advertising |
| 462.36250 | 456.86250 | NFM | London | Mallinson T.V Productions |
| 462.36250 | 456.86250 | NFM | London | Whiteleys |
| 462.36250 | 456.86250 | NFM | London, Leicester Square | Planet Hollywood staff |
| 462.36250 | 456.86250 | NFM | London, Queensway | Marks & Spencer Foodhall staff |
| 462.36250 | 456.86250 | NFM | Nationwide | Rock Steady Event safety Ch.1 |
| 462.36250 | 456.86250 | NFM | Nationwide | Short Term Hire |
| 462.36250 | 456.86250 | NFM | Northampton | Santa Pod Race Way Ch 1 |
| 462.36250 | 456.86250 | NFM | Prestwick | Centrum Arena stewards (CENTRUM) |
| 462.36250 | 456.86250 | NFM | Rugby | Christian Salvesen Ch.2 |
| 462.37500 | 456.87500 | NFM | Basildon | Town Centre Boots Chemist Store Detectives P055 Securicor Guardian |
| 462.37500 | 456.87500 | NFM | Doncaster | Car Park Security |
| 462.37500 | 456.87500 | NFM | London, Bond Street | Tommy Hilfiger security |
| 462.37500 | 456.87500 | NFM | London, Knightsbridge | Tommy Hilfiger security |
| 462.37500 | 456.87500 | NFM | London, WC1 | Gucci |
| 462.37500 | 456.87500 | NFM | North Sea | Shell Auk |
| 462.37500 | 456.87500 | NFM | North Sea | Shell Brent A |
| 462.37500 | 456.87500 | NFM | North Sea | Shell Dunlin |
| 462.37500 | 456.87500 | NFM | Peterborough | Boots Security |
| 462.38750 | 456.88750 | NFM | London, central | Black Taxi control |
| 462.40000 | 456.90000 | NFM | Borehamwood | Council Services |
| 462.40000 | 456.90000 | NFM | Chelmsford | Chelmer Shopping Centre Security |
| 462.40000 | 456.90000 | NFM | Chelmsford | Town Centre Security |
| 462.40000 | 456.90000 | NFM | City of London | Tower Hill Security |
| 462.40000 | 456.90000 | NFM | Hayes | Food Manufacturing |
| 462.40000 | 456.90000 | NFM | London | Corporation of London |
| 462.40000 | 456.90000 | NFM | London | Piccadilly Hotel |

| Base | Mobile | Mode | Location | User and Notes |
|------|--------|------|----------|----------------|
| 462.40000 | 456.90000 | NFM | London | Stratford Container Terminal |
| 462.40000 | 456.90000 | NFM | London, Wapping | World Trade Centre |
| 462.40000 | 456.90000 | NFM | North Sea | BP SMV |
| 462.40000 | 456.90000 | NFM | North Sea | Total Alwyn |
| 462.40000 | 456.90000 | NFM | North Sea | Total St. Fergus |
| 462.40000 | 456.90000 | NFM | Stevenage | ICL security |
| 462.40000 | 456.90000 | NFM | Stevenage | North Herts College security |
| 462.42500 | 456.92500 | NFM | Ascot | Race Course |
| 462.42500 | 456.92500 | NFM | Bristol | Zoo |
| 462.42500 | 456.92500 | NFM | Dartford | Bluewater Shopping Centre, John Lewis Maintenance |
| 462.42500 | 456.92500 | NFM | Grand Prix Circuits | Lotus Team Voice Link |
| 462.42500 | 456.92500 | NFM | Hull | Docks |
| 462.42500 | 456.92500 | NFM | Jersey | Short Term Hire Radios |
| 462.42500 | 456.92500 | NFM | London | TV Programme 'The Bill' |
| 462.42500 | 456.92500 | NFM | London, Oxford Street | JJB Sports |
| 462.42500 | 456.92500 | NFM | London, Piccadilly | Trocadero James Bond Attraction |
| 462.42500 | 456.92500 | NFM | London, Swiss Cottage | O'Henerys Bar Staff |
| 462.42500 | 456.92500 | NFM | Nationwide | Short Term Hire |
| 462.42500 | 456.92500 | NFM | North Sea | BP Welton |
| 462.42500 | 456.92500 | NFM | Sheffield | Sheffield Arena |
| 462.42500 | 456.92500 | NFM | Southend-on-Sea | Victoria Circus Precinct Security |
| 462.47500 | 456.97500 | NFM | Ashford | Shop Security |
| 462.47500 | 456.97500 | NFM | Canvey Island | Waterside Sports Centre. |
| 462.47500 | 456.97500 | NFM | Doncaster | RJB Mining |
| 462.47500 | 456.97500 | NFM | Ipswich | Dragon Boat Racing Rescue/Marshalls |
| 462.47500 | 456.97500 | NFM | Jersey | Short Term Hire Radios |
| 462.47500 | 456.97500 | NFM | London | Guardian Angels Patrols London Underground Etc. |
| 462.47500 | 456.97500 | NFM | London | Horse Guards Parade security |
| 462.47500 | 456.97500 | NFM | London | Paramount Pictures *Sleepy Hollow* film production |
| 462.47500 | 456.97500 | NFM | London | Sogo Japanese Department Store |
| 462.47500 | 456.97500 | NFM | London | Sound Republic staff |
| 462.47500 | 456.97500 | NFM | London | TV Programme 'The Bill' |
| 462.47500 | 456.97500 | NFM | London | Venture Security |
| 462.47500 | 456.97500 | NFM | London, Oxford Street | British Home Stores security |
| 462.47500 | 456.97500 | NFM | Nationwide | Short Term Hire Equipment |
| 462.47500 | 456.97500 | NFM | North Sea | Shell St. Fergus |
| 462.47500 | 456.97500 | NFM | Northampton | Santa Pod Race Way Ch |
| 462.47500 | 456.97500 | NFM | Peterborough | The Solstice Broadways Club |
| 462.47500 | 456.97500 | NFM | Poole | Flight Refuelling Ltd |
| 462.47500 | 456.97500 | NFM | Rugby | Christian Salvesen Ch.1 |
| 462.47500 | 456.97500 | NFM | Rugby | Christian Salvesen Ch.8 |
| 462.47500 | 456.97500 | NFM | Shire Oaks | Shire Oaks Colliery NCB Security |
| 462.48750 | 456.98750 | NFM | Ascot | Race Course Bookies |
| 462.48750 | 456.98750 | NFM | Brighton, Marina | Asda Supermarket |
| 462.48750 | 456.98750 | NFM | Coventry | Comtel Cable T.V. |
| 462.48750 | 456.98750 | NFM | Doncaster | Clarks Shoes |
| 462.48750 | 456.98750 | NFM | London | Callaghans Irish Bar |
| 462.48750 | 456.98750 | NFM | London, Oxford Street | Benneton Store |
| 462.48750 | 456.98750 | NFM | Nationwide | Short Term Hire Radios |
| 462.48750 | 456.98750 | NFM | Rugby | Christian Salvesen Ch.5 |
| 462.50000 | 457.00000 | NFM | London | Doctors |

| Base | Mobile | Mode | Location | User and Notes |
|------|--------|------|----------|----------------|

## 462.500 - 462.750 MHz    EMERGENCY SERVICES 12.5 kHz

| Base | Mobile | Mode | Location | User and Notes |
|------|--------|------|----------|----------------|
| 462.53750 | | NFM | Fife | Fire Brigade Ch 8 |
| 462.57500 | 457.07500 | NFM | Aberdeen | Scottish Hydro Electric |
| 462.58750 | | NFM | Fife | Fire Brigade Ch 2 |
| 462.62500 | | NFM | Nationwide | Red Devils Parachute Team |
| 462.62750 | | NFM | Fife | Fire Brigade Ch 5 |
| 462.65000 | 466.55000 | NFM | Poole | Police |
| 462.68750 | 457.1875 | NFM | Manchester | Volunteer doctors service ch.4 |

## 462.75625 - 464.000 MHz    FIXED LINKS, TELEMETRY AND PMR

| Base | Mobile | Mode | Location | User and Notes |
|------|--------|------|----------|----------------|
| 462.75625 | | NFM | Nationwide | JFGM long term fixed talkback TX |
| 462.75625 | | NFM | Nationwide | JFGM long term paired with 469.49375 long term |
| 462.75625 | 469.61875 | NFM | London | Dominion Theatre |
| 462.75625 | 469.61875 | NFM | London | Palladium Theatre Talkback Link. |
| 462.76875 | | NFM | Nationwide | JFGM long term fixed talkback TX |
| 462.77500 | | NFM | Ipswich | Data Traffic |
| 462.77500 | 458.27500 | NFM | North Sea | Conoco Murchison DKN |
| 462.78125 | | NFM | Nationwide | JFGM long term fixed talkback TX |
| 462.78750 | 467.28750 | NFM | Poole | Point-to-Point Link |
| 462.79375 | | NFM | Nationwide | JFGM long term fixed talkback TX |
| 462.80625 | | NFM | Nationwide | JFGM long term fixed talkback TX |
| 462.81875 | | NFM | Nationwide | JFGM long term fixed talkback TX |
| 462.83125 | | NFM | London | Prince of Wales Theatre |
| 462.83125 | | NFM | Nationwide | JFGM long term fixed talkback TX |
| 462.83125 | 469.56875 | NFM | London | Prince Edward Theatre Talkback |
| 462.84375 | | NFM | Nationwide | JFGM long term fixed talkback TX |
| 462.84375 | 469.66875 | NFM | London | Whitehall Theatre Ch5 TV productions |
| 462.85625 | | NFM | Nationwide | JFGM long term fixed talkback TX |
| 462.86875 | | NFM | Nationwide | JFGM long term fixed talkback TX |
| 462.86875 | 469.66875 | NFM | London | Whitehall Theatre Ch5 TV productions |
| 462.88125 | | NFM | London, Islington | Sadlers Wells Theatre talkback |
| 462.88125 | | NFM | Nationwide | JFGM long term fixed talkback TX |
| 462.89375 | | NFM | Nationwide | JFGM long term fixed talkback TX |
| 462.90625 | | NFM | Nationwide | JFGM long term fixed talkback TX |
| 462.91875 | | NFM | London | The Palace Theatre directions |
| 462.91875 | | NFM | Nationwide | JFGM long term fixed talkback TX |
| 462.92500 | | NFM | Cambridgeshire | Health Authority |
| 462.92500 | | NFM | Norfolk | Health Authority |
| 462.92500 | | NFM | Suffolk | Health Authority |
| 462.93125 | | NFM | Nationwide | JFGM long term fixed talkback TX |
| 462.94375 | | NFM | Nationwide | JFGM long term fixed talkback TX |
| 462.95000 | | NFM | Cleveland | Health Authority |
| 462.95000 | | NFM | Cumbria | Health Authority |
| 462.95000 | | NFM | Durham | Health Authority |
| 462.95000 | | NFM | East Dorset | Health Authority |
| 462.95000 | | NFM | Hampshire | Health Authority |
| 462.95000 | | NFM | Isle of Wight | Health Authority |
| 462.95000 | | NFM | Northumbria | Health Authority |
| 462.95625 | | NFM | Nationwide | JFGM long term fixed talkback TX |
| 462.96875 | | NFM | Nationwide | JFGM long term fixed talkback TX |
| 462.97500 | | NFM | Cambridgeshire | Health Authority |
| 462.97500 | | NFM | Norfolk | Health Authority |
| 462.97500 | | NFM | Suffolk | Health Authority |
| 462.98125 | | NFM | Nationwide | JFGM long term fixed talkback TX |
| 462.99375 | | NFM | Nationwide | JFGM long term fixed talkback TX |

| Base | Mobile | Mode | Location | User and Notes |
|---|---|---|---|---|
| 462.99375 | | NFM | Nationwide | Talkback Output London Dominion Theatre |
| 463.05000 | | NFM | Buckinghamshire | Health Authority |
| 463.05000 | | NFM | Northamptonshire | Health Authority |
| 463.05000 | | NFM | Oxford | Health Authority |
| 463.05000 | | NFM | West Berkshire | Health Authority |
| 463.05500 | | NFM | Tamworth | BT data |
| 463.05500 | 461.37500 | NFM | North Sea | Shell Fulmar A to Auk-A |
| 463.07500 | | NFM | Cambridgeshire | Health Authority |
| 463.07500 | | NFM | Norfolk | Health Authority |
| 463.07500 | | NFM | Suffolk | Health Authority |
| 463.10000 | | NFM | Cleveland | Health Authority |
| 463.10000 | | NFM | Cumbria | Health Authority |
| 463.10000 | | NFM | Durham | Health Authority |
| 463.10000 | | NFM | Northumbria | Health Authority |
| 463.10000 | | NFM | Wales | Health Authority |
| 463.15000 | | NFM | Cleveland | Health Authority |
| 463.15000 | | NFM | Cumbria | Health Authority |
| 463.15000 | | NFM | Durham | Health Authority |
| 463.15000 | | NFM | Northumbria | Health Authority |
| 463.15000 | | NFM | Wales | Health Authority |
| 463.22500 | | NFM | Wales | Health Authority |
| 463.25000 | | AM | Birmingham International | HM Customs & Excise |
| 463.25000 | | NFM | Cambridgeshire | Health Authority |
| 463.25000 | | NFM | Norfolk | Health Authority |
| 463.25000 | | NFM | Suffolk | Health Authority |
| 463.27500 | 457.77500 | NFM | Fulmar | FSU Shell telemetry |
| 463.27500 | 463.37500 | NFM | Cheshire | Plant Maintenance |
| 463.35000 | 457.85000 | NFM | North Sea | Conoco Viking Field |
| 463.37500 | 457.87500 | NFM | North Sea | BP ESV III |
| 463.37500 | 457.87500 | NFM | North Sea | BP Forties D to Forties Kiwi |
| 463.37500 | 463.37500 | NFM | North Sea | BP Buchan |
| 463.50000 | | NFM | East Dorset | Health Authority |
| 463.50000 | | NFM | Hampshire | Health Authority |
| 463.50000 | | NFM | Isle of Wight | Health Authority |
| 463.52500 | | NFM | Cambridgeshire | Health Authority |
| 463.52500 | | NFM | Cleveland | Health Authority |
| 463.52500 | | NFM | Cumbria | Health Authority |
| 463.52500 | | NFM | Durham | Health Authority |
| 463.52500 | | NFM | Norfolk | Health Authority |
| 463.52500 | | NFM | Northumbria | Health Authority |
| 463.52500 | | NFM | Suffolk | Health Authority |
| 463.55000 | | NFM | Wales | Health Authority |
| 463.60000 | | NFM | East Dorset | Health Authority |
| 463.60000 | | NFM | Hampshire | Health Authority |
| 463.60000 | | NFM | Isle of Wight | Health Authority |
| 463.60000 | | NFM | Wales | Health Authority |
| 463.62500 | | NFM | Cleveland | Health Authority |
| 463.62500 | | NFM | Cumbria | Health Authority |
| 463.62500 | | NFM | Durham | Health Authority |
| 463.62500 | | NFM | East Dorset | Health Authority |
| 463.62500 | | NFM | Hampshire | Health Authority |
| 463.62500 | | NFM | Isle of Wight | Health Authority |
| 463.62500 | | NFM | Northumbria | Health Authority |
| 463.65000 | | NFM | East Hertfordshire | Health Authority |
| 463.65000 | | NFM | Eastbourne | Health Authority |
| 463.65000 | | NFM | Kent | Health Authority |

| Base | Mobile | Mode | Location | User and Notes |
|------|--------|------|----------|----------------|
| 463.65000 | | NFM | Medway | Health Authority |
| 463.65000 | | NFM | Mid Essex | Health Authority |
| 463.65000 | | NFM | Mid Surrey | Health Authority |
| 463.65000 | | NFM | North Bedfordshire | Health Authority |
| 463.65000 | | NFM | West Sussex | Health Authority |
| 463.70000 | | NFM | Mid Staffordshire | Health Authority |
| 463.70000 | | NFM | Salop | Health Authority |
| 463.70000 | | NFM | South Warwickshire | Health Authority |
| 463.70000 | | NFM | Worcestershire | Health Authority |
| 463.72500 | 458.22500 | NFM | North Sea | Conoco Murchison |
| 463.72500 | 458.22500 | NFM | North Sea | Shell Brent A PLIS backup to Dunlin A |
| 463.72500 | 458.22500 | NFM | North Sea | Shell Brent B PLIS backup to Dunlin A |
| 463.72500 | 458.22500 | NFM | North Sea | Shell Brent C PLIS backup to Dunlin A |
| 463.72500 | 458.22500 | NFM | North Sea | Shell Brent D |
| 463.72500 | 458.22500 | NFM | North Sea | Shell Brent Spar |
| 463.72500 | 458.22500 | NFM | North Sea | Shell Cormorant A |
| 463.72500 | 458.22500 | NFM | North Sea | Shell N. Cormorant |
| 463.75000 | | NFM | East Dorset | Health Authority |
| 463.75000 | | NFM | Hampshire | Health Authority |
| 463.75000 | | NFM | Isle of Wight | Health Authority |
| 463.75000 | | NFM | Mid Staffordshire | Health Authority |
| 463.75000 | | NFM | Salop | Health Authority |
| 463.75000 | | NFM | South Warwickshire | Health Authority |
| 463.75000 | | NFM | Worcestershire | Health Authority |
| 463.82500 | | NFM | Cumbria | Health Authority |
| 463.82500 | | NFM | Durham | Health Authority |
| 463.82500 | | NFM | North Sea | Conoco Murchison |
| 463.82500 | | NFM | Northumbria | Health Authority |
| 463.82500 | | NFM | Wales | Health Authority |
| 463.82500 | 458.32500 | NFM | Cleveland | Health Authority |
| 463.85000 | | NFM | Cleveland | Health Authority |
| 463.85000 | | NFM | Cumbria | Health Authority |
| 463.85000 | | NFM | Durham | Health Authority |
| 463.85000 | | NFM | Northumbria | Health Authority |
| 463.85000 | | NFM | Wales | Health Authority |
| 463.90000 | | NFM | Bedfordshire | Health Authority |
| 463.90000 | | NFM | East Hertfordshire | Health Authority |
| 463.90000 | | NFM | Eastbourne | Health Authority |
| 463.90000 | | NFM | Essex | Health Authority |
| 463.90000 | | NFM | Kent | Health Authority |
| 463.90000 | | NFM | Medway | Health Authority |
| 463.90000 | | NFM | Surrey | Health Authority |
| 463.90000 | | NFM | West Sussex | Health Authority |
| 463.90620 | 458.45620 | NFM | North Sea | FSU Chevron Alba to ANP, FSD data |
| 463.91870 | 458.41870 | NFM | North Sea | Shell Kittiwake Loading Buoy |
| 463.91870 | 458.41870 | NFM | North Sea | Shell Stadfill Cormorant A |
| 463.92500 | | NFM | Cleveland | Health Authority |
| 463.92500 | | NFM | Cumbria | Health Authority |
| 463.92500 | | NFM | Durham | Health Authority |
| 463.92500 | | NFM | Northumbria | Health Authority |
| 463.92500 | | NFM | Wales | Health Authority |
| 463.93120 | 458.43120 | NFM | North Sea | Shell Kittiwake Tanker Loading Buoy |
| 463.95000 | | NFM | Dorset | Health Authority |
| 463.95000 | | NFM | Eastbourne | Health Authority |
| 463.95000 | | NFM | Essex | Health Authority |
| 463.95000 | | NFM | Hampshire | Health Authority |

| Base | Mobile | Mode | Location | User and Notes |
|---|---|---|---|---|
| 463.95000 | | NFM | Hertfordshire | Health Authority |
| 463.95000 | | NFM | Isle of Wight | Health Authority |
| 463.95000 | | NFM | Kent | Health Authority |
| 463.95000 | | NFM | Medway | Health Authority |
| 463.95000 | | NFM | North Bedfordshire | Health Authority |
| 463.95000 | | NFM | Salop | Health Authority |
| 463.95000 | | NFM | South Warwickshire | Health Authority |
| 463.95000 | | NFM | Staffordshire | Health Authority |
| 463.95000 | | NFM | Surrey | Health Authority |
| 463.95000 | | NFM | West Sussex | Health Authority |
| 463.95000 | | NFM | Worcestershire | Health Authority |
| 463.95000 | 458.43120 | NFM | Murchison | Conoco |
| 463.95000 | 458.43120 | NFM | North Sea | Shell Brent B PEL Backup to Dunlin A |
| 463.95000 | 458.43120 | NFM | North Sea | Shell Brent C PEL Backup to Dunlin A |
| 463.95000 | 458.43120 | NFM | North Sea | Shell Brent D PEL Backup to Dunlin A |
| 463.95000 | 458.43120 | NFM | North Sea | Shell Brent Spar |
| 463.95000 | 458.43120 | NFM | North Sea | Shell Cormorant N |
| 463.95000 | 458.45000 | NFM | North Sea | Shell Brent A |
| 463.97500 | | NFM | Salop | Health Authority |
| 463.97500 | | NFM | South Warwickshire | Health Authority |
| 463.97500 | | NFM | Staffordshire | Health Authority |
| 463.97500 | | NFM | Worcestershire | Health Authority |
| 464.02500 | | NFM | North Sea | Shell N. Cormorant |

### 465.0000 - 467.0000 MHz   POLICE AND AMBULANCE PR BASE AND REPEATER SYSTEM SCOTLAND. LIMITED USE IN ENGLAND.

| Base | Mobile | Mode | Location | User and Notes |
|---|---|---|---|---|
| 464.025 | 450.025 | NFM | Edinburgh | Police Hibs Football Club Control |
| 464.075 | 450.075 | NFM | Edinburgh | Police Tynecastle Match Control |
| 464.125 | 464.125 | NFM | Bishop Auckland | Police Football Security |
| 464.175 | 451.175 | NFM | Largs | Police (UL) |
| 464.175 | 451.175 | NFM | Saltcoats | Police (UB) |
| 464.175 | 451.175 | NFM | Skelmorlie | Police (UL) |
| 464.200 | 450.200 | NFM | Cumbernauld | Police Ch 15 (N) |
| 464.225 | 450.225 | NFM | Ayr | Police (RA) |
| 464.250 | | NFM | England & Wales | Army Para team Red Devils dropzone air/ground Ch.1 |
| 464.350 | 450.350 | NFM | Edinburgh | Police Special Events |
| 464.375 | 450.375 | NFM | Edinburgh | Police Special Events |
| 464.400 | 450.400 | NFM | Edinburgh | Police Special Events |
| 464.450 | 450.450 | NFM | Edinburgh | Police Special Events |
| 464.500 | 450.500 | NFM | Edinburgh | Police Special Events |
| 464.550 | | NFM | England & Wales | Army Para team Red Devils dropzone air/ground Ch.2 |
| 464.600 | | NFM | England & Wales | Benetton Formula 1 Racing Team Alessi |
| 464.675 | 450.675 | NFM | Edinburgh | Police Special Events |
| 464.725 | 450.725 | NFM | Edinburgh | Police Special Events |
| 464.750 | 450.750 | NFM | Edinburgh | Police Special Events |
| 464.775 | 450.775 | NFM | Edinburgh | Police Special Events |
| 464.800 | 450.800 | NFM | Edinburgh | Police Special Events |
| 464.825 | 450.825 | NFM | Edinburgh | Police Special Events |
| 464.875 | 450.875 | NFM | Nationwide | Police reverse working channel Ch.91 |
| 465.000 | 451.000 | NFM | Edinburgh | Police |
| 465.000 | 451.000 | NFM | Musselburgh | Police |
| 465.025 | 451.025 | NFM | East Lothian | Police (N) Ch.16 |
| 465.050 | 451.050 | NFM | Bristol | Private Traffic Wardens |
| 465.050 | 451.050 | NFM | Dalkeith | Police |

| Base | Mobile | Mode | Location | User and Notes |
|------|--------|------|----------|----------------|
| 465.050 | 451.050 | NFM | Lothian and Borders | Police |
| 465.100 | 451.100 | NFM | Broxburn | Police (F) |
| 465.100 | 451.100 | NFM | Hawick | Police (ZH) |
| 465.125 | 451.125 | NFM | Edinburgh | Police |
| 465.150 | 451.150 | NFM | South Queensferry | Police (F) Ch.27 repeater |
| 465.175 | 451.175 | NFM | Garnock Valley | Police |
| 465.175 | 451.175 | NFM | Irvine | Police (UA) |
| 465.175 | 451.175 | NFM | Kilbirnie | Police (UG) |
| 465.175 | 451.175 | NFM | Kilwinning | Police |
| 465.250 | 451.250 | NFM | Bristol | Transport Police (Temple Meads) |
| 465.250 | 451.250 | NFM | Edinburgh, Corstorphine | Police (CV)  Ch.7 repeater |
| 465.275 | 451.275 | NFM | Edinburgh, Westerhailes | Police (CH) |
| 465.300 | 451.300 | NFM | Ayrshire, east | Police |
| 465.300 | 451.300 | NFM | Denny | Police Ch 7 (F) |
| 465.300 | 451.300 | NFM | Fife | Police |
| 465.300 | 451.300 | NFM | Galston | Police (UE) |
| 465.300 | 451.300 | NFM | Kilmarnock | Police (UC) |
| 465.300 | 451.300 | NFM | Troon | Police |
| 465.325 | 451.325 | NFM | Hawick | Police |
| 465.325 | 451.325 | NFM | Perth | Police (W) |
| 465.375 | 451.375 | NFM | Cumnock | Police (RB) |
| 465.375 | 451.375 | NFM | Mauchline | Police |
| 465.425 | 451.425 | NFM | Fife | Police |
| 465.425 | 465.425 | NFM | Dubly Hill | Police (GB) |
| 465.450 | 451.450 | NFM | Ballantrae | Police |
| 465.450 | 451.450 | NFM | Girvan | Police (RA) |
| 465.475 | 451.475 | NFM | Brechin | Police |
| 465.475 | 451.475 | NFM | Montrose | Police |
| 465.500 | 451.500 | NFM | Edinburgh | Police (ZH) Ch.1 |
| 465.600 | 451.600 | NFM | Bonnyrigg | Police |
| 465.600 | 451.600 | NFM | Glasgow | Police |
| 465.600 | 451.600 | NFM | Larkhall | Police |
| 465.600 | 451.600 | NFM | Penicuik | Police |
| 465.625 | 451.625 | NFM | Bristol | City Line Buses |
| 465.625 | 451.625 | NFM | Edinburgh | Police Special Events  Ch.33 |
| 465.625 | 451.625 | NFM | Falkirk | Falkirk Football Square |
| 465.625 | 451.625 | NFM | Glasgow | Police Special Events |
| 465.625 | 451.625 | NFM | Hawick | Police (ZH) |
| 465.625 | 451.625 | NFM | Langholm | Police Ch.13 |
| 465.625 | 451.625 | NFM | Perth | Police Special Events |
| 465.650 | 451.650 | NFM | East Lothian | Police (N) Ch.16 |
| 465.650 | 451.650 | NFM | Edinburgh | Police |
| 465.650 | 451.650 | NFM | Hamilton | Police |
| 465.650 | 465.650 | NFM | Glasgow | Police |
| 465.675 | 451.675 | NFM | Edinburgh | Police Special Events  Ch.34 |
| 465.675 | 451.675 | NFM | Glasgow | Police Special Events |
| 465.675 | 451.675 | NFM | Perth | Party Conference (L Control) |
| 465.675 | 451.700 | NFM | Motherwell | Police |
| 465.725 | 451.725 | NFM | Edinburgh | Police (ZH) Ch.35 |
| 465.725 | 451.725 | NFM | Edinburgh | Shoplifting Squad |
| 465.725 | 451.725 | NFM | Glasgow | Police Special Events |
| 465.725 | 451.725 | NFM | Hawick | Police (ZH) |
| 465.725 | 451.725 | NFM | Perth | Party Conference (S Control) |
| 465.750 | 451.750 | NFM | Wishaw | Police |
| 465.775 | 451.775 | NFM | Edinburgh | Police Special Events Ch.36 |
| 465.775 | 451.775 | NFM | Glasgow | Police Special Events |

| Base | Mobile | Mode | Location | User and Notes |
|---|---|---|---|---|
| 465.775 | 451.775 | NFM | Perth | Party Conference (C Control) |
| 465.775 | 451.775 | NFM | Yorkshire | Police Command Vehicle |
| 465.800 | 451.800 | NFM | Dunbar | Police |
| 465.800 | 451.800 | NFM | Edinburgh | Police |
| 465.875 | 465.875 | NFM | Midlands | Police Helicopter (Air 1) |
| 465.900 | 465.900 | NFM | West Midlands | Police Helicopter Ch 2 |
| 465.925 | 451.825 | NFM | Glasgow | Police |
| 466.025 | 452.025 | NFM | Stirling | Police |
| 466.100 | 452.100 | NFM | Nationwide | Local Authority emergency communications network |
| 466.175 | 452.175 | NFM | Lancashire | Police Ch9 |
| 466.225 | 452.225 | NFM | Nationwide | Local Authority emergency communications network |
| 466.250 | 452.250 | NFM | Aberdeen | Police |
| 466.250 | 452.250 | NFM | Ayr | Police |
| 466.250 | 452.250 | NFM | Dalkeith | Police |
| 466.250 | 452.250 | NFM | Dumfries &Galloway | Police |
| 466.250 | 452.250 | NFM | Edinburgh | Police Firearms Support Group Div HQ (B) |
| 466.250 | 452.250 | NFM | Edinburgh | St Leonards Div HQ (B) Ch. 2 |
| 466.250 | 452.250 | NFM | Glasgow | Police Firearms Support Group |
| 466.250 | 452.250 | NFM | Lanark | Police |
| 466.275 | 452.275 | NFM | Aberdeen | Police |
| 466.275 | 452.275 | NFM | Ayr | Traffic Wardens (TW) |
| 466.275 | 452.275 | NFM | Dumfries & Galloway | Police |
| 466.275 | 452.275 | NFM | Edinburgh | Police (C) Edinburgh Tattoo |
| 466.275 | 452.275 | NFM | Edinburgh | Traffic Wardens (TW and TM) Ch.15 |
| 466.275 | 452.275 | NFM | Glasgow | Traffic Wardens (TW) |
| 466.275 | 452.275 | NFM | Lanark | Traffic Wardens (TW) |
| 466.275 | 452.275 | NFM | Perth | Police (Racecourse Control) |
| 466.275 | 452.275 | NFM | Perth | Traffic Wardens (TW) |
| 466.300 | 452.300 | NFM | Fife | Traffic Wardens |
| 466.325 | 452.325 | NFM | Dumbarton | Police (L) |
| 466.325 | 452.325 | NFM | Edinburgh, Oxgangs | Police (CO) |
| 466.325 | 452.325 | NFM | Edinburgh, Westerhailes | Police (CH) Ch.6 |
| 466.350 | 451.350 | NFM | Glasgow | Police (E ) |
| 466.375 | 452.375 | NFM | Edinburgh | Police |
| 466.375 | 452.375 | NFM | Glasgow, Barrhead | Police (K) |
| 466.400 | 451.400 | NFM | Aberdeen | HM Prison  Aberdeen |
| 466.400 | 451.400 | NFM | Bedford | HM Prison Ch.33 |
| 466.400 | 451.400 | NFM | Dumfries | HM Young Offenders Institution |
| 466.400 | 451.400 | NFM | Edinburgh | HM Prison  Saughton |
| 466.400 | 451.400 | NFM | Forfar | HM Prison  Noranside |
| 466.400 | 451.400 | NFM | Glasgow | HM Prison  Barlinnie |
| 466.400 | 451.400 | NFM | Lothian and Borders | Police (E) |
| 466.400 | 451.400 | NFM | Perth | HM Prison  Friarton |
| 466.400 | 451.400 | NFM | St Andrews | Traffic Wardens |
| 466.400 | 451.400 | NFM | Stirling | HM Prison  Cornton Vale (Control) |
| 466.425 | 452.425 | NFM | Edinburgh | Police |
| 466.425 | 452.425 | NFM | Peebles | Police |
| 466.450 | 452.450 | NFM | Dundee | Police (ZS) |
| 466.450 | 452.450 | NFM | Glasgow | Police North (C) |
| 466.475 | 452.475 | NFM | Dumfries & Galloway | Police |
| 466.500 | 452.500 | NFM | Alloa | Police Ch 6 (A) |
| 466.500 | 452.500 | NFM | Arbroath | Police |
| 466.500 | 452.500 | NFM | Argyll | Police (A) |
| 466.500 | 452.500 | NFM | Dalbeattie | Police |
| 466.500 | 452.500 | NFM | Dumfries & Galloway | Police |
| 466.500 | 452.500 | NFM | Edinburgh | Police |

| Base | Mobile | Mode | Location | User and Notes |
|------|--------|------|----------|----------------|
| 466.500 | 452.500 | NFM | Forfar | Police |
| 466.500 | 452.500 | NFM | Glasgow | Police Central (A) |
| 466.500 | 452.500 | NFM | Kirkcudbright | Police |
| 466.500 | 452.500 | NFM | Langholm | Police |
| 466.500 | 452.500 | NFM | Moffat | Police |
| 466.500 | 452.500 | NFM | Perth | Police (W) |
| 466.500 | 452.500 | NFM | Stirling | Police |
| 466.525 | 452.525 | NFM | Edinburgh | Police City Centre Ch.1 |
| 466.525 | 452.525 | NFM | Perth | Police Football Club |
| 466.525 | 452.525 | NFM | Selkirk | Police |
| 466.550 | 452.550 | NFM | Argyll | Police (B) |
| 466.550 | 452.550 | NFM | Glasgow | Police West (B) |
| 466.550 | 452.550 | NFM | Inverness | Police |
| 466.550 | 452.550 | NFM | Irvine | Police (U) |
| 466.550 | 452.550 | NFM | Kilbirnie | Police (G) |
| 466.550 | 452.550 | NFM | Kilmarnock | Police (U) |
| 466.550 | 452.550 | NFM | Kilwinning | Police (U) |
| 466.550 | 452.550 | NFM | Stirling | Police Ch 5 (S) |
| 466.575 | 452.575 | NFM | Edinburgh | Police West End Div HQ (C) Ch.4 |
| 466.600 | 452.600 | NFM | Aberdeen | Police |
| 466.600 | 452.600 | NFM | Angus | Police |
| 466.600 | 452.600 | NFM | Cupar | Police |
| 466.600 | 452.600 | NFM | Glasgow | Police Easterhill (D) |
| 466.600 | 452.600 | NFM | Kilmarnock | Police |
| 466.625 | 452.625 | NFM | Aberdeen | Police |
| 466.625 | 452.625 | NFM | Edinburgh | Police Gayfield (BG) Ch.3 |
| 466.625 | 452.625 | NFM | Fort William | Police |
| 466.625 | 452.625 | NFM | Thurso | Police (M2URCE) |
| 466.650 | 452.650 | NFM | Aberdeen | Police |
| 466.650 | 452.650 | NFM | Ayr | Police (R) |
| 466.650 | 452.650 | NFM | Ballater | Police (UBK5) |
| 466.650 | 452.650 | NFM | Edinburgh | Police Drylaw (DR ) Ch.10 |
| 466.650 | 452.650 | NFM | Edinburgh | Police Royston (Encrypted) |
| 466.650 | 452.650 | NFM | Glasgow | Police Kilpatrick (M) |
| 466.650 | 452.650 | NFM | Glasgow | Police South/East (F) |
| 466.675 | 452.675 | NFM | Edinburgh | Police Portobello |
| 466.675 | 452.675 | NFM | Portobello | Police (DJ & DN) |
| 466.700 | 452.700 | NFM | Ayr | Police (X) |
| 466.700 | 452.700 | NFM | Edinburgh | Police |
| 466.700 | 452.700 | NFM | Musselburgh | Police |
| 466.700 | 452.700 | NFM | Strathclyde | Police Helicopter |
| 466.725 | 452.725 | NFM | Livingston | Police (F) |
| 466.740 | 452.740 | NFM | Falkirk | Police Ch 3 (F) |
| 466.750 | 452.750 | NFM | Falkirk | Police |
| 466.750 | 452.750 | NFM | Glasgow | Police Ibrox (G) |
| 466.750 | 452.750 | NFM | Stirling | Police |
| 466.775 | 452.775 | NFM | Glasgow | Police Hamilton (Q) |
| 466.775 | 452.775 | NFM | Grangemouth | Police Ch 4 (G) |
| 466.775 | 452.775 | NFM | Hamilton | Police (Q) |
| 466.800 | 452.800 | NFM | Edinburgh | Police Firearms Support Group |
| 466.800 | 452.800 | NFM | Glasgow | Police Firearms Support Group |
| 466.800 | 452.900 | NFM | Truleigh Hill | Fire Brigade |
| 466.825 | 452.825 | NFM | Airdrie | Police |
| 466.825 | 452.825 | NFM | Edinburgh | Police Leith Ch.9 |
| 466.825 | 452.825 | NFM | Lanark | Police (N) |
| 466.825 | 452.825 | NFM | Leith | Police (D) Division HQ |

| Base | Mobile | Mode | Location | User and Notes |
|---|---|---|---|---|
| 466.825 | 452.825 | NFM | Nationwide | Army Air Corps Parachute Team Loader |
| 466.875 | 452.875 | NFM | Galashiels | Police |
| 466.900 | 452.900 | NFM | Edinburgh | Police Firearms Support Group |
| 466.900 | 452.900 | NFM | Glasgow | Police Firearms Support Group |
| 466.925 | | NFM | Abington | Police Repeater |
| 466.975 | | NFM | Enniskillen | Military Data Link |

### 467.29375 - 470.0000 MHz — BROADCASTING LINKS AND NORTH SEA FIXED LINKS

| Base | Mobile | Mode | Location | User and Notes |
|---|---|---|---|---|
| 467.29375 | | NFM | London | BBC Radio News Talk Back London |
| 467.30000 | | NFM | Nationwide | BBC Radio 5 O/B |
| 467.42370 | | NFM | London | BBC Radio 5 Talkback |
| 467.42500 | | NFM | London | BBC Radio Engineers |
| 467.47500 | | NFM | Burnley | Granada TV OB |
| 467.49370 | | NFM | London | Carlton TV Talkback |
| 467.49370 | | NFM | London | ITV Weather |
| 467.49375 | | NFM | London | Carlton TV London Tonight Link |
| 467.52500 | 461.02500 | NFM | North Sea | BP West Sole A to Easington |
| 467.53125 | | NFM | London | Japanese Family Radio |
| 467.55000 | | NFM | North Sea | BP Thistle A |
| 467.55000 | | NFM | North Sea | Unocol Heather A |
| 467.55000 | 461.05000 | NFM | North Sea | Stiell Brent A |
| 467.56250 | | NFM | Nationwide | Jordan Formula 1 Racing Team Brundle |
| 467.57500 | | NFM | Belfast | Downtown Radio O/B |
| 467.57500 | | NFM | North Sea | BP Thistle A |
| 467.57500 | | NFM | North Sea | Sun Oil Balmoral portables |
| 467.57500 | 461.07500 | NFM | North Sea | BP West Sole A to Easington |
| 467.61250 | | NFM | Belfast | Downtown Radio Belfast |
| 467.61250 | | NFM | Glasgow | Radio Clyde |
| 467.61250 | | NFM | Hereford | Radio Wyvern |
| 467.61250 | | NFM | London | Capital Radio 95.8 |
| 467.61250 | | WFM | Salisbury | Spire FM O/B |
| 467.62500 | 461.12500 | NFM | North Sea | FSU Shell Fulmar |
| 467.66250 | | NFM | Ayr | West Sound Radio |
| 467.66250 | | NFM | Cardiff | CBC Radio |
| 467.66250 | | NFM | Coventry | Mercia Sound Outside Broadcast |
| 467.66250 | | NFM | Ipswich | SGRFM Radio |
| 467.66250 | | NFM | Manchester | Piccadilly Radio |
| 467.66250 | | NFM | Teesside | Radio Tees |
| 467.66250 | | NFM | Wiltshire | Radio |
| 467.66250 | 467.61250 | NFM | London | Capital Radio Flying Eye |
| 467.67500 | 461.17500 | NFM | North Sea | Phillips Hewett Field to Great Yarmouth |
| 467.71250 | | NFM | Aberdeen | North Sound Radio |
| 467.71250 | | WFM | Berkshire | Radio 210 Outside Broadcasts |
| 467.71250 | | NFM | Glasgow | Radio Clyde |
| 467.71250 | | NFM | Gloucester | Severn Radio |
| 467.71250 | | WFM | Hampshire | Radio 210 Outside Broadcasts |
| 467.71250 | | NFM | London | Virgin Radio OB Link |
| 467.71250 | | NFM | Plymouth | Sound |
| 467.71250 | | NFM | Southend | Essex Radio |
| 467.71250 | | NFM | Swansea | Swansea Sound O/B |
| 467.72500 | | NFM | Nationwide | Grand Prix Benetton Team |
| 467.72500 | 462.25000 | NFM | Castle Donington | Grand Prix Team |
| 467.77500 | | NFM | North Sea | Shell Brent A |
| 467.77500 | | NFM | Wales | Health Authority |
| 467.80000 | | NFM | Maritime | Ship Communications |

| Base | Mobile | Mode | Location | User and Notes |
|---|---|---|---|---|
| 467.80000 | | NFM | Wales | Health Authority |
| 467.82500 | | NFM | Wales | Health Authority |
| 467.86250 | | NFM | Nationwide | Jordan Formula 1 Racing Team Barrichello |
| 467.87500 | | NFM | North Sea | Shell Brent A |
| 467.87500 | 461.37500 | NFM | North Sea | Shell Brent Spar |
| 467.87500 | 461.87500 | NFM | Nationwide | Pye Telecom Mobiles |
| 467.90000 | | NFM | Wales | Health Authority |
| 467.91500 | | NFM | North Sea | Shell N. Cormorant |
| 467.92500 | | NFM | Wales | Health Authority |
| 467.92500 | 461.42500 | NFM | North Sea | Shell to Auk-A |
| 467.92500 | 461.92500 | NFM | Nationwide | Pye Telecom Mobiles |
| 467.95000 | | NFM | Dublin | Police L/M/G/P |
| 467.95000 | 461.95000 | NFM | Derby | County Council |
| 467.95000 | 462.95000 | NFM | Castle Donington | Grand Prix Team |
| 467.97500 | 461.47500 | NFM | North Sea | Shell To Auk-A |
| 467.99375 | | NFM | Nationwide | Sky TV OB Sound Gallery |
| 468.00000 | 141.00000 | NFM | London | LWT |
| 468.01875 | | NFM | Nationwide | Anglia TV OB Camera Link |
| 468.02500 | | NFM | London | Police Dartford Tunnel |
| 468.02500 | | NFM | North Sea | Chevron Ninian South |
| 468.05000 | | NFM | Jersey | Channel TV Talkback |
| 468.05000 | | NFM | North Sea | Chevron Ninian South |
| 468.05625 | | NFM | Nationwide | BBC TV OB Link |
| 468.06250 | | NFM | East Sussex | Fire Brigade |
| 468.07500 | | NFM | Kent | Invicta Radio |
| 468.08750 | | NFM | Exeter | Devonair Radio |
| 468.08750 | | NFM | Guildford | County Sound Radio |
| 468.08750 | | NFM | Inverness | Moray Firth Radio |
| 468.08750 | | NFM | Leeds | Radio Aire |
| 468.08750 | | NFM | Leicester | Park Security |
| 468.08750 | | NFM | Leicester | Sunrise Radio O/B |
| 468.08750 | | NFM | Tayside | Radio Tay Talkback |
| 468.08750 | | NFM | Wrexham | Marcher Sound |
| 468.08750 | | NFM | York | Great Yorkshire Gold c/b |
| 468.08750 | 141.18000 | NFM | Kent | Heli-Teli Radio Uplink |
| 468.12500 | | NFM | North Sea | Chevron Ninian South |
| 468.13670 | | NFM | London | Spectrum Radio Flying Eye |
| 468.13750 | | NFM | London | Sunrise Radio OB Link |
| 468.13750 | | NFM | Sussex | Local Radio Flying Eye |
| 468.13750 | 141.08750 | NFM | Manchester | Key 103 Eye in the Sky |
| 468.15000 | | NFM | Castle Donington | Italian TV Talkback |
| 468.15000 | | NFM | Nationwide | BBC Radio 1 Roadshow O/B |
| 468.16250 | | NFM | North Sea | Chevron Ninian South |
| 468.25000 | | NFM | Nationwide | BBC Radio 1 O/B |
| 468.27500 | | NFM | Nationwide | BBC Radio 1 O/B |
| 468.31250 | | NFM | Nationwide | Anglia TV OB Camera Link |
| 468.31250 | | NFM | Newmarket | Community Repeater |
| 468.33750 | | NFM | Peterborough | Herewood Fm Spotter Plane |
| 468.35000 | | NFM | Ninian South | Chevron |
| 468.37500 | | NFM | Nationwide | ITV Cameras |
| 468.39000 | | NFM | Jersey | Channel TV Talkback |
| 468.40000 | 454.40000 | NFM | North Sea | BP Forties A |
| 468.42500 | | NFM | England | Central TV Base Link Input |
| 468.42500 | | NFM | North Sea | Chevron Ninian South |
| 468.45625 | | NFM | London | Capital Radio Gold OB |
| 468.46250 | | NFM | Bristol | Radio West |

| Base | Mobile | Mode | Location | User and Notes |
|------|--------|------|----------|----------------|
| 468.46250 | | NFM | Crawley | Oak Ridge Radio |
| 468.46250 | | NFM | Edinburgh | Radio Forth |
| 468.46250 | | NFM | Inverness | Moray Firth Radio O/B |
| 468.46250 | | NFM | Nottingham | Radio Trent |
| 468.46250 | | NFM | Tyne & Wear | Metro Radio |
| 468.46250 | | NFM | Wolverhampton | Beacon Radio |
| 468.47500 | | NFM | Nationwide | IBA Riggers |
| 468.48750 | | NFM | Nationwide | Formula 1 Racing Feam |
| 468.50000 | | NFM | Nationwide | ITV O/B |
| 468.58750 | | WFM | Yorkshire | Flying Eye traffic reports |
| 468.59375 | | NFM | London | Virgin Radio Chopper OB |
| 468.60000 | | WFM | Yorkshire | Flying Eye traffic reports |
| 468.64375 | | NFM | Leeds | Flying Eye for Magic 828, Hallam FM & Viking AM |
| 468.65000 | | WFM | Yorkshire | Flying Eye traffic reports |
| 468.68750 | | NFM | Herts/Beds | Chiltern Radio |
| 468.69375 | | NFM | Manchester | Piccadilly Radio Eye In The Sky |
| 468.70000 | | NFM | London | Ch. 4 Wanted Program WFM |
| 468.74375 | | NFM | Manchester | Red Rose Radio Eye In The Sky |
| 468.78750 | | NFM | Peterborough | Herewood FM Spotter Plane |
| 468.79375 | | NFM | Doncaster | Radio Eye In The Sky |
| 468.79375 | | NFM | Manchester | Radio City Eye In The Sky |
| 468.79375 | | NFM | West Country | Severn Sound Radio Air-Ground Talk Back |
| 468.80000 | | NFM | Bristol | Seven Sound FM Flying Eye |
| 468.83750 | | NFM | Peterborough | Herewood FM spotter plane |
| 468.94375 | | NFM | West Country | GWR Radio Air-Ground Talk Back |
| 468.95000 | | NFM | Bristol | Talk Radio Travel Eyewitness |
| 468.95625 | | NFM | London | BBC/LTV Air-Ground |
| 469.00000 | 455.60000 | NFM | North Sea | BP Forties C |
| 469.00000 | 455.60000 | NFM | Preston | Radio Lancashire O/B |
| 469.01250 | | NFM | Berkshire | BBC Radio Berkshire Radio Car |
| 469.01250 | | NFM | Humberside | BBC Radio Humberside O/B |
| 469.01250 | | NFM | Shropshire | BBC Radio Shropshire O/B |
| 469.06250 | | NFM | Nationwide | BBC Radio 5 O/B |
| 469.11250 | | NFM | Lincoln | BBC Radio Lincolnshire O/B |
| 469.11250 | | NFM | London | BBC Radio 5 Talkback |
| 469.11250 | | NFM | London | Choice FM Flying Eye |
| 469.11250 | | NFM | London | Jazz FM Flying Eye |
| 469.11250 | | NFM | London | Star FM Flying Eye |
| 469.11250 | | NFM | Wiltshire | BBC Wiltshire Sound |
| 469.11250 | | NFM | York | BBC Radio York |
| 469.16250 | | NFM | Nationwide | BBC Radios OB. |
| 469.21250 | | NFM | Blackpool | Red Rose Rock FM Flying Eye |
| 469.21250 | | NFM | Kent | Invicta FM Radio OB |
| 469.21250 | | NFM | London | Evening Standard Sky Patrol |
| 469.21250 | | NFM | London | Jazz Radio OB |
| 469.21250 | | NFM | Midlands | Gem AM Radio OB |
| 469.21250 | | NFM | Midlands | Ram FM Radio OB |
| 469.21250 | | NFM | Nationwide | BBC Radio 5 O/B |
| 469.22500 | | NFM | Nationwide | Formula 1 Racing Team |
| 469.24000 | | NFM | London | Executive Buses |
| 469.26250 | | NFM | Aberdeen | North Sound Radio |
| 469.26250 | | NFM | Ayr | West Sound Radio |
| 469.26250 | | NFM | Liverpool | Radio City Talkback |
| 469.26250 | | NFM | London | AA Skywatch OB |
| 469.26250 | | NFM | London | LBC FM Flying Eye |
| 469.26250 | 455.16250 | NFM | Norfolk | Radio Broadland OB |

| Base | Mobile | Mode | Location | User and Notes |
|---|---|---|---|---|
| 469.31250 | | NFM | Ayr | Radio Clyde Super Scoreboard talkback |
| 469.31250 | | NFM | Cardiff | CBC Radio |
| 469.31250 | | NFM | East Sussex | Radio Mercury |
| 469.31250 | | NFM | Swindon | Wiltshire Radio |
| 469.31250 | | NFM | Teesside | Radio Tees |
| 469.31250 | 467.66250 | NFM | Ipswich | SGRFM Radio OB |
| 469.35000 | | NFM | Essex | Radio OB |
| 469.35000 | | NFM | Kent | Invicta Fm Radio OB |
| 469.36250 | | NFM | Berkshire | Radio 210 Outside Broadcasts |
| 469.36250 | | NFM | Essex | Radio OB |
| 469.36250 | | NFM | Glasgow | Radio Clyde Traffic Helicopter |
| 469.36250 | | NFM | Gloucester | Severn Radio |
| 469.36250 | | NFM | Hampshire | Radio 210 Outside Broadcasts |
| 469.36250 | | NFM | Plymouth | Plymouth Sound |
| 469.36250 | | NFM | Swansea | Swansea Sound O/B |
| 469.36250 | | NFM | Wrexham | Marcher Gold Talkback |
| 469.36975 | | NFM | Essex | BBC Radio Essex Flying Eye |
| 469.37500 | | NFM | Manchester | BBC Radio O/B |
| 469.41250 | | NFM | Essex | Saxon Radio |
| 469.41250 | | NFM | London | LBC Aircraft Downlink |
| 469.41250 | | NFM | Londonderry | North Side Sound Radio |
| 469.41250 | | NFM | Medway | North Down Radio Medway |
| 469.41250 | 468.08750 | NFM | Bury St. Edmunds | SGRFM Radio OB |
| 469.46250 | | NFM | Exeter | Devonair Radio |
| 469.46250 | | NFM | Guildford | County Sound |
| 469.46250 | | NFM | Kent | Invicta Heli-Radio Uplink |
| 469.46250 | | NFM | London | Kiss FM Flying Eye |
| 469.46250 | | NFM | London | Spectrum Radio OB |
| 469.46250 | | NFM | London | Sunrise Radio OB |
| 469.46250 | 141.18750 | NFM | Cowley | Fox FM Flying Eye Downlink |
| 469.49375 | | NFM | Nationwide | JFGM long term fixed talkback RX |
| 469.49375 | | NFM | Nationwide | JFGM long term paired with 462.75625 |
| 469.50625 | | NFM | Nationwide | JFGM long term fixed talkback RX |
| 469.51875 | | NFM | Nationwide | JFGM long term fixed talkback RX |
| 469.53125 | | NFM | Nationwide | JFGM long term fixed talkback RX |
| 469.54375 | | NFM | Nationwide | JFGM long term fixed talkback RX |
| 469.55625 | | NFM | Nationwide | JFGM long term fixed talkback RX |
| 469.56875 | | NFM | Nationwide | JFGM long term fixed talkback RX |
| 469.57500 | | NFM | Doncaster | Continental Landscapes Ltd |
| 469.58125 | | NFM | Nationwide | JFGM long term fixed talkback RX |
| 469.59375 | | NFM | Nationwide | JFGM long term fixed talkback RX |
| 469.60625 | | NFM | Nationwide | JFGM long term fixed talkback RX |
| 469.61875 | | NFM | Nationwide | JFGM long term fixed talkback RX |
| 469.63125 | | NFM | Nationwide | JFGM long term fixed talkback RX |
| 469.64375 | | NFM | Nationwide | JFGM long term fixed talkback RX |
| 469.65625 | | NFM | Nationwide | JFGM long term fixed talkback RX |
| 469.66250 | | NFM | Manchester | Piccadilly Radio Programme link |
| 469.66875 | | NFM | Nationwide | JFGM long term fixed talkback RX |
| 469.66875 | | NFM | Nationwide | JFGM long term fixed talkback RX |
| 469.68125 | | NFM | Nationwide | JFGM long term fixed talkback RX |
| 469.69375 | | NFM | Nationwide | JFGM long term fixed talkback RX |
| 469.70625 | | NFM | Nationwide | JFGM long term fixed talkback RX |
| 469.71875 | | NFM | Nationwide | JFGM long term fixed talkback RX |
| 469.73125 | | NFM | Nationwide | JFGM long term fixed talkback RX |
| 469.74375 | | NFM | Nationwide | JFGM long term fixed talkback RX |
| 469.75000 | | NFM | Castle Donington | French TV Talkback |

| Base | Mobile | Mode | Location | User and Notes |
|------|--------|------|----------|----------------|
| 469.75000 | | NFM | North Sea | Phillips EkoFisk-B |
| 469.75625 | | NFM | Nationwide | JFGM long term fixed talkback RX |
| 469.76875 | | NFM | Nationwide | JFGM long term fixed talkback RX |
| 469.78125 | | NFM | Nationwide | JFGM long term fixed talkback RX |
| 469.79375 | | NFM | Nationwide | JFGM long term fixed talkback RX |
| 469.80625 | | NFM | Nationwide | JFGM long term fixed talkback RX |
| 469.81875 | | NFM | Nationwide | JFGM long term fixed talkback RX |
| 469.83125 | | NFM | Nationwide | JFGM long term fixed talkback RX |
| 469.84375 | | NFM | Nationwide | JFGM long term fixed talkback RX |
| 469.85625 | | NFM | Nationwide | JFGM long term fixed talkback RX |
| 469.86875 | | NFM | Nationwide | JFGM long term fixed talkback RX |

**470.0000 - 855.0000 MHz**  UK TV CHANNELS (SOUND/VIDEO)
LOCAL RADIO TALKBACK AND
THEATRE RADIOMICROPHONES (10MW MAX)

## UK Television

### UHF Band IV

| Ch. | Vision | Sound | Ch. | Vision | Sound |
|-----|--------|-------|-----|--------|-------|
| 21 | 471.25 | 477.25 | 30 | 543.25 | 549.25 |
| 22 | 479.25 | 485.25 | 31 | 551.25 | 557.25 |
| 23 | 487.25 | 493.25 | 32 | 559.25 | 565.25 |
| 24 | 495.25 | 501.25 | 33 | 567.25 | 573.25 |
| 25 | 503.25 | 509.25 | 34 | 575.25 | 581.25 |
| 26 | 511.25 | 517.25 | 35 | 583.25 | 589.25 Channel 5 |
| 27 | 519.25 | 525.25 | 36 | 591.25 | 597.25 |
| 28 | 527.25 | 533.25 | 37 | 599.25 | 605.25 Channel 5 |
| 29 | 535.25 | 541.25 | 38 | 607.25 | 613.25 |

### UHF Band V

| Ch. | Vision | Sound | Ch. | Vision | Sound |
|-----|--------|-------|-----|--------|-------|
| 39 | 615.25 | 621.25 | 54 | 735.25 | 741.25 |
| 40 | 623.36 | 629.25 | 55 | 743.25 | 749.25 |
| 41 | 631.25 | 627.25 | 56 | 751.25 | 757.25 |
| 42 | 629.25 | 645.25 | 57 | 759.25 | 765.25 |
| 43 | 647.25 | 653.25 | 58 | 767.25 | 773.25 |
| 44. | 655.25 | 661.25 | 59 | 775.25 | 781.25 |
| 45 | 663.25 | 669.25 | 60 | 783.25 | 789.25 |
| 46 | 671.25 | 677.25 | 61 | 791.25 | 797.25 |
| 47 | 679.25 | 685.25 | 62 | 799.25 | 805.25 |
| 48 | 687.25 | 693.26 | 62 | 807.25 | 813.25 |
| 49 | 695.25 | 701.25 | 64 | 815.25 | 821.25 |
| 50 | 703.25 | 709.25 | 65 | 823.25 | 829.25 |
| 51 | 711.25 | 717.25 | 66 | 831.26 | 837.25 |
| 52 | 711.25 | 717.25 | 66 | 831.25 | 837.25 |
| 52 | 719.25 | 725.25 | 67 | 839.25 | 845.25 |
| 53 | 727.26 | 733.25 | 68 | 847.25 | 853.25 |

## UK Television Channels

| | BBC1 | BBC2 | ITV | CH4 | | BBC1 | BBC2 | ITV | CH4 |
|---|---|---|---|---|---|---|---|---|---|
| **SCOTLAND** | | | | | | | | | |
| Aberfoyle | 58 | 64 | 61 | 54 | Abington | 57 | 63 | 60 | 53 |
| Acharacle | 40 | 46 | 43 | 50 | Angus | 57 | 63 | 60 | 53 |
| Ardentinny | 39 | 45 | 49 | 52 | Ardintoul | 39 | 45 | 49 | 42 |
| Ardnadam | 51 | 44 | 41 | 47 | Arisaig | 33 | 26 | 23 | 29 |
| Arrochar | 21 | 27 | 24 | 31 | Attadale | 22 | 28 | 25 | 32 |
| Auchmore Wood | 22 | 28 | 25 | 32 | Auchtermuchty | 39 | 45 | 49 | 42 |
| Aviemore | 22 | 28 | 25 | 32 | Avoch | 63 | 57 | 53 | 60 |
| Ayr South | 51 | 44 | 41 | 47 | Badachro | 40 | 46 | 43 | 50 |
| Balblair Wood | 55 | 62 | 59 | 65 | Balgownie | 40 | 46 | 43 | 50 |
| Ballachulish | 33 | 26 | 23 | 29 | Balmullo | 39 | 45 | 49 | 42 |
| Balnaguard | 42 | 49 | 39 | 45 | Baltasound | 39 | 45 | 42 | 49 |
| Banff | 39 | 45 | 42 | 49 | Bellanoch | 39 | 45 | 42 | 49 |
| Ben Tongue | 39 | 45 | 49 | 42 | Biggar | 22 | 28 | 25 | 32 |
| Black Hill | 40 | 46 | 43 | 50 | Blackwaterfoot | 49 | 46 | 43 | 50 |
| Blair Atholl | 40 | 46 | 43 | 50 | Boddam | 39 | 45 | 42 | 49 |
| Borve | 22 | 28 | 32 | 25 | Bowmore | 39 | 45 | 49 | 42 |
| Braemar | 39 | 45 | 42 | 49 | Brechin | 40 | 46 | 43 | 50 |
| Bressay | 22 | 28 | 25 | 32 | Bridge of Allan | 33 | 26 | 23 | 29 |
| Broughton | 21 | 27 | 24 | 31 | Bruernish | 40 | 46 | 43 | 50 |
| Burgar Hill | 21 | 27 | 24 | 31 | Cairndon | 21 | 27 | 24 | 31 |
| Callander | 22 | 28 | 25 | 32 | Campbeltown | 57 | 63 | 60 | 53 |
| Camperdown | 33 | 26 | 23 | 29 | Canongate | 58 | 64 | 61 | 54 |
| Carie | 21 | 27 | 24 | 31 | Carradale | 51 | 44 | 41 | 47 |
| Castlebay | 21 | 27 | 24 | 31 | Cathcart | 57 | 63 | 60 | 53 |
| Catrine | 55 | 62 | 59 | 65 | Clachan | 40 | 46 | 43 | 50 |
| Claonaig | 55 | 62 | 59 | 65 | Clettraval | 51 | 44 | 41 | 47 |
| Clovenfords | 21 | 27 | 24 | 31 | Clovenfords Village | 39 | 45 | 49 | 42 |
| Collafirth Hill | 51 | 44 | 41 | 47 | Cow Hill (Fort William) | 40 | 46 | 43 | 50 |
| Craigellachie | 57 | 63 | 60 | 53 | Craigkelly | 31 | 27 | 24 | 21 |
| Crieff | 33 | 26 | 23 | 29 | Cromarty | 22 | 28 | 25 | 32 |
| Cumbernauld Village | 58 | 64 | 61 | 54 | Cupar | 51 | 44 | 41 | 47 |
| Daliburgh | 57 | 63 | 60 | 53 | Dalmally | 51 | 44 | 41 | 47 |
| Darvel | 33 | 26 | 23 | 29 | Deanston | 53 | 60 | 63 | 57 |
| Dollar | 58 | 64 | 61 | 54 | Duncraig | 51 | 44 | 41 | 47 |
| Dunkeld | 51 | 44 | 41 | 47 | Dunure | 40 | 46 | 43 | 50 |
| Durness | 57 | 63 | 53 | 60 | Durris | 22 | 28 | 25 | 32 |
| Dychliemore | 22 | 28 | 25 | 32 | Easdale | 39 | 45 | 49 | 42 |
| Eitshal (Lewis) | 33 | 26 | 23 | 29 | Ellon | 39 | 45 | 49 | 42 |
| Fetlar | 40 | 46 | 43 | 50 | Fintry | 34 | 27 | 24 | 31 |
| Fitful Head | 39 | 45 | 42 | 49 | Fiunary | 40 | 46 | 43 | 50 |
| Fodderty | 57 | 62 | 60 | 53 | Fort Augustus | 33 | 26 | 23 | 29 |
| Garelochhead | 51 | 44 | 41 | 47 | Gartly Moor | 58 | 64 | 61 | 54 |
| Gigha Island | 51 | 44 | 41 | 47 | Girvan | 55 | 62 | 59 | 65 |
| Glasgow (W Central) | 68 | 62 | 56 | 66 | Glen Urquhart | 51 | 44 | 41 | 47 |
| Glenconvinth | 33 | 26 | 23 | 29 | Glengorm | 56 | 52 | 48 | 54 |
| Glespin | 58 | 64 | 61 | 54 | Gourdon | 55 | 62 | 65 | 59 |
| Grandtully | 58 | 64 | 61 | 54 | Grangemouth | 57 | 63 | 60 | 53 |
| Grantown | 51 | 44 | 41 | 47 | Haddington | 58 | 64 | 61 | 54 |
| High Keil | 51 | 44 | 47 | 41 | Holmhead | 51 | 44 | 41 | 47 |
| Inverarish | 40 | 46 | 43 | 50 | Inverness | 55 | 62 | 65 | 59 |

| Base | Mobile | Mode | Location | | | User and Notes | | | |
|------|--------|------|----------|---|---|----------------|---|---|---|

| | BBC1 | BBC2 | ITV | CH4 | | | BBC1 | BBC2 | ITV | CH4 |
|---|------|------|-----|-----|---|---|------|------|-----|-----|
| **SCOTLAND** (cont.) | | | | | | | | | | |
| Keelylang Hill | 40 | 46 | 43 | 50 | | Kelvindale | 34 | 52 | 30 | 48 |
| Kenmore | 33 | 26 | 23 | 29 | | Kilbride (South Mist) | 39 | 45 | 49 | 42 |
| Killin | 39 | 45 | 49 | 42 | | Kilmacolm | 21 | 27 | 42 | 31 |
| Kilmelford | 55 | 62 | 59 | 65 | | Kingussie | 40 | 46 | 43 | 50 |
| Kinlochleven | 55 | 62 | 59 | 65 | | Kinross | 61 | 67 | 64 | 54 |
| Kintraw | 40 | 46 | 43 | 50 | | Kirkconnel | 58 | 64 | 61 | 54 |
| Kirkfieldbank | 57 | 63 | 60 | 53 | | Kirkmichael | 39 | 45 | 49 | 52 |
| Kirkoswald | 22 | 28 | 25 | 32 | | Knock More | 33 | 26 | 23 | 29 |
| Kylerhea | 51 | 44 | 41 | 47 | | Lairg | 51 | 44 | 41 | 47 |
| Largs | 39 | 45 | 42 | 49 | | Leadhills | 58 | 64 | 61 | 54 |
| Lethanhill | 57 | 63 | 60 | 53 | | Lindores | 40 | 46 | 43 | 50 |
| Loch Feochan | 58 | 64 | 61 | 68 | | Lochearnhead | 58 | 64 | 61 | 54 |
| Lochgoilhead | 57 | 63 | 53 | 60 | | Lochinver | 40 | 46 | 43 | 50 |
| Lochmaddy | 22 | 28 | 25 | 32 | | Lochwinnoch | 57 | 63 | 60 | 53 |
| Lumphanan | 49 | 42 | 39 | 45 | | Mallaig | 43 | 46 | 40 | 50 |
| Melvich | 51 | 44 | 41 | 47 | | Methven | 22 | 28 | 25 | 32 |
| Millburn Muir | 39 | 52 | 42 | 49 | | Millport | 58 | 64 | 61 | 54 |
| Muirkirk | 51 | 44 | 41 | 47 | | Ness of Lewis | 51 | 44 | 41 | 47 |
| Netherton Braes | 22 | 28 | 25 | 32 | | New Cumnock | 40 | 46 | 43 | 50 |
| Newbattle | 55 | 62 | 59 | 65 | | Oban | 51 | 44 | 41 | 47 |
| Onich | 59 | 64 | 61 | 54 | | Penicuik | 58 | 64 | 61 | 54 |
| Penifiler | 39 | 45 | 49 | 42 | | Perth | 39 | 45 | 49 | 42 |
| Peterhead | 55 | 62 | 59 | 65 | | Pierowall | 33 | 26 | 23 | 29 |
| Pitlochry | 22 | 28 | 25 | 32 | | Poolewe | 51 | 44 | 47 | 41 |
| Pornahaven | 33 | 26 | 23 | 29 | | Port Ellen | 22 | 28 | 25 | 32 |
| Ravenscraig | 21 | 27 | 24 | 31 | | Rosehearty | 51 | 44 | 41 | 47 |
| Rosemarkie | 39 | 45 | 49 | 42 | | Rosneath | 58 | 64 | 61 | 54 |
| Rothesay | 22 | 28 | 25 | 32 | | Rothesay Town | 55 | 62 | 59 | 65 |
| Rumster Forest | 31 | 26 | 24 | 21 | | Scalloway | 55 | 62 | 59 | 65 |
| Scoval | 55 | 62 | 59 | 65 | | Skriaig (Skye) | 21 | 27 | 24 | 31 |
| Sorn | 40 | 46 | 43 | 50 | | South Knapdale | 57 | 63 | 60 | 53 |
| Spean Bridge | 21 | 27 | 24 | 31 | | St. Fillans | 51 | 44 | 47 | 41 |
| Staffin | 39 | 45 | 49 | 42 | | Strachur | 33 | 26 | 23 | 29 |
| Strathallan | 39 | 45 | 49 | 42 | | Strathblane | 21 | 27 | 24 | 31 |
| Strathyre | 21 | 27 | 24 | 31 | | Strathyre Link | 40 | 46 | 43 | 50 |
| Strontian | 42 | 49 | 39 | 45 | | Swinister | 55 | 62 | 59 | 65 |
| Tarbert (Harris) | 39 | 45 | 49 | 52 | | Tarbert (Loch Fyne) | 21 | 27 | 24 | 31 |
| Tay Bridge | 51 | 44 | 41 | 47 | | Taynuilt | 40 | 46 | 43 | 50 |
| Tayvallich | 40 | 46 | 43 | 50 | | Thurso | 57 | 63 | 60 | 53 |
| Tighnabruaich | 39 | 45 | 49 | 42 | | Tillicoultry | 57 | 63 | 60 | 53 |
| Tomatin | 22 | 28 | 25 | 32 | | Tomich | 21 | 27 | 24 | 31 |
| Tomich Link | 39 | 45 | 49 | 42 | | Tomintoul | 40 | 46 | 43 | 50 |
| Torosay | 22 | 28 | 25 | 32 | | Troon | 58 | 64 | 61 | 54 |
| Tullich | 55 | 62 | 59 | 65 | | Tummel Bridge | 39 | 45 | 49 | 42 |
| Twechar | 22 | 28 | 25 | 32 | | Uig | 53 | 46 | 53 | 50 |
| Ullapool | 39 | 45 | 49 | 52 | | Uplawmoor | 58 | 64 | 61 | 54 |
| Voe | 57 | 62 | 60 | 53 | | Wanlockhead | 51 | 44 | 47 | 41 |
| Weisdale | 58 | 64 | 61 | 54 | | West Kilbride | 51 | 44 | 41 | 47 |
| West Linton | 33 | 26 | 23 | 29 | | Wester Erchite | 21 | 27 | 24 | 31 |

| | BBC1 | BBC2 | ITV | CH4 | | BBC1 | BBC2 | ITV | CH4 |
|---|---|---|---|---|---|---|---|---|---|
| **Borders and Northern England** | | | | | | | | | |
| Addingham | 40 | 46 | 43 | 50 | Ainstable | 52 | 45 | 42 | 49 |
| Aislaby | 39 | 45 | 52 | 49 | Allenheads | 21 | 27 | 31 | 24 |
| Alston | 52 | 45 | 49 | 42 | Armitage Bridge | 58 | 64 | 61 | 54 |
| Austwick | 39 | 45 | 49 | 42 | Backbarro W | 57 | 63 | 60 | 50 |
| Bacup | 40 | 46 | 43 | 53 | Bainbridge | 57 | 62 | 60 | 53 |
| Ballantrae | 58 | 64 | 61 | 54 | Barrow Town Hall | 51 | 44 | 67 | 47 |
| Barskeoch Hill | 55 | 62 | 59 | 65 | Bassenthwaite | 52 | 45 | 49 | 42 |
| Batley | 57 | 623 | 60 | 67 | Beary Peark (IoM) | 40 | 46 | 43 | 50 |
| Beecroft Hill (Leeds) | 55 | 62 | 59 | 65 | Bellingham | 21 | 27 | 24 | 31 |
| Belmont | 22 | 28 | 25 | 32 | Berwick-on-Tweed | 21 | 27 | 24 | 31 |
| Bidston | 51 | 44 | 30 | 47 | Bilsdale (W Moor) | 33 | 26 | 29 | 23 |
| Birch Vale | 40 | 46 | 43 | 53 | Blackburn | 51 | 44 | 41 | 31 |
| Blackburn in Rother'm | 57 | 63 | 60 | 53 | Blaydon | 51 | 44 | 41 | 47 |
| Bleachgreen | 57 | 62 | 60 | 53 | Bollington | 21 | 27 | 24 | 31 |
| Bonchester Bridge | 39 | 45 | 49 | 42 | Bradford West | 57 | 62 | 49 | 67 |
| Brinscall | 27 | 21 | 24 | 31 | Broadbottom | 39 | 45 | 42 | 49 |
| Brockwell | 66 | 39 | 68 | 49 | Brook Bottom | 58 | 64 | 61 | 68 |
| Burbage | 44 | 51 | 41 | 47 | Buxton | 21 | 27 | 24 | 31 |
| Byrness | 21 | 27 | 31 | 24 | Caldbeck | 30 | 44 | 28 | 32 |
| Calver Peak | 39 | 45 | 49 | 42 | Cambret Hill | 44 | 51 | 41 | 47 |
| Cartmel | 22 | 28 | 25 | 32 | Castleton | 55 | 62 | 59 | 65 |
| Catton Beacon | 40 | 46 | 43 | 50 | Chaigley | 21 | 27 | 24 | 31 |
| Chatburn | 33 | 26 | 23 | 29 | Chatton | 39 | 45 | 49 | 42 |
| Chesterfield | 33 | 26 | 23 | 29 | Chinley | 57 | 64 | 61 | 67 |
| Cleckheaton | 55 | 62 | 59 | 65 | Congleton | 51 | 44 | 41 | 47 |
| Conisbrough | 57 | 63 | 60 | 53 | Coniston High Man | 21 | 27 | 24 | 31 |
| Cop Hill | 22 | 28 | 25 | 32 | Copley | 55 | 62 | 59 | 65 |
| Cornholme | 58 | 64 | 61 | 54 | Cowling | 40 | 46 | 43 | 50 |
| Cragg Vale | 58 | 64 | 61 | 54 | Creeetown | 58 | 64 | 61 | 54 |
| Crosby Ravensworth | 57 | 62 | 60 | 53 | Crosthwaite | 57 | 63 | 60 | 53 |
| Cullingworth | 66 | 39 | 49 | 68 | Dalton | 40 | 46 | 43 | 53 |
| Darwen | 39 | 45 | 49 | 42 | Delph | 33 | 26 | 23 | 29 |
| Dentdale | 57 | 63 | 60 | 53 | Dog Hill | 40 | 46 | 43 | 53 |
| Douglas (IoM) | 68 | 66 | 48 | 56 | Dronfield | 55 | 62 | 59 | 65 |
| Dumfries South | 40 | 48 | 46 | 50 | Durham | 40 | 46 | 43 | 50 |
| Edale | 57 | 63 | 60 | 53 | Elland | 58 | 64 | 61 | 54 |
| Elton | 21 | 27 | 24 | 31 | Emley Moor | 44 | 52 | 47 | 41 |
| Esh | 39 | 45 | 49 | 42 | Eskdale Green | 22 | 28 | 25 | 32 |
| Eston Nab | 40 | 46 | 43 | 50 | Eyemouth | 33 | 26 | 23 | 29 |
| Falstone | 51 | 44 | 41 | 47 | Far Highfield | 48 | 66 | 56 | 68 |
| Felling | 52 | 50 | 46 | 66 | Fenham | 21 | 27 | 24 | 31 |
| Foxdale | 33 | 26 | 23 | 29 | Galashield | 68 | 44 | 41 | 47 |
| Glencoyne | 21 | 27 | 24 | 31 | Glenluce | 58 | 64 | 61 | 54 |
| Glenmaye (IoM) | 58 | 64 | 61 | 54 | Glenridding | 60 | 53 | 57 | 63 |
| Glossop | 22 | 28 | 25 | 32 | Gosforth | 58 | 64 | 61 | 54 |
| Grasmere | 57 | 63 | 60 | 53 | Grassington | 33 | 26 | 23 | 29 |
| Greystoke | 57 | 63 | 60 | 53 | Grimsby | 39 | 45 | 42 | 49 |
| Grinton Lodge | 40 | 46 | 43 | 50 | Guisborough | 57 | 63 | 60 | 53 |
| Hagg Wood | 55 | 62 | 59 | 65 | Halifax | 21 | 27 | 24 | 31 |
| Haltwhistle | 55 | 62 | 59 | 65 | Hasland | 57 | 63 | 60 | 53 |
| Haslingden | 33 | 26 | 23 | 29 | Haughton Green | 40 | 46 | 43 | 53 |
| Hawick | 33 | 26 | 23 | 29 | Hawkshead | 33 | 26 | 23 | 29 |
| Haydon Bridge | 51 | 44 | 41 | 47 | Headingley | 58 | 64 | 61 | 54 |
| Hebden Bridge | 22 | 28 | 25 | 32 | Hedleyhyope | 40 | 46 | 43 | 50 |

## Borders and Northern England (cont.)

| Location | BBC1 | BBC2 | ITV | CH4 | Location | BBC1 | BBC2 | ITV | CH4 |
|----------|------|------|-----|-----|----------|------|------|-----|-----|
| Heyshaw | 57 | 63 | 60 | 53 | Holmfield | 55 | 62 | 59 | 65 |
| Holmfirth | 49 | 66 | 56 | 68 | Hope | 22 | 28 | 25 | 32 |
| Hulme | 51 | 44 | 41 | 47 | Humshaugh | 39 | 45 | 49 | 42 |
| Hunmanby | 40 | 46 | 43 | 50 | Idle | 21 | 27 | 24 | 31 |
| Innerleithen | 58 | 64 | 61 | 54 | Ireshopeburn | 55 | 62 | 59 | 65 |
| Jedburgh | 68 | 44 | 41 | 47 | Keighley | 58 | 64 | 61 | 54 |
| Keighley Town | 33 | 26 | 23 | 29 | Kendal | 58 | 64 | 61 | 54 |
| Kendal Fell | 40 | 46 | 43 | 50 | Keswick | 21 | 27 | 24 | 31 |
| Kettlewell | 49 | 42 | 39 | 45 | Kielder | 33 | 26 | 23 | 29 |
| Kimmeragh (IoM) | 57 | 63 | 60 | 53 | Kirkby Stephen | 57 | 63 | 60 | 53 |
| Kirkcudbright | 21 | 27 | 24 | 31 | Ladder Hill | 33 | 26 | 23 | 29 |
| Lancaster | 31 | 27 | 24 | 21 | Langholm | 57 | 62 | 60 | 53 |
| Langley | 21 | 27 | 24 | 31 | Lauder | 22 | 28 | 25 | 32 |
| Laxey | 58 | 64 | 61 | 54 | Lees | 22 | 28 | 32 | 25 |
| Limber Hill | 40 | 46 | 43 | 50 | Lincoln Central | 39 | 45 | 42 | 52 |
| Littleborough | 21 | 27 | 24 | 31 | Longwood Edge | 55 | 62 | 59 | 65 |
| Lorton | 57 | 63 | 60 | 53 | Lowther Valley | 48 | 40 | 46 | 50 |
| Luddenden | 57 | 63 | 60 | 67 | Lydgate | 33 | 26 | 23 | 28 |
| Macclesfield | 22 | 28 | 25 | 32 | Melling | 57 | 62 | 60 | 53 |
| Middleton | 67 | 34 | 30 | 31 | Millhouse Green | 58 | 64 | 61 | 54 |
| Millom Park | 22 | 28 | 25 | 32 | Millthrop | 48 | 66 | 56 | 68 |
| Minnigaff | 33 | 26 | 29 | 23 | Moffar | 52 | 45 | 42 | 49 |
| Morpeth | 22 | 28 | 25 | 32 | Moss Bank | 21 | 27 | 24 | 31 |
| Mottram | 40 | 46 | 43 | 53 | New Galloway | 33 | 26 | 23 | 29 |
| Newchurch | 27 | 21 | 24 | 31 | Newton | 33 | 26 | 23 | 29 |
| Norden | 34 | 67 | 30 | 57 | North Oldham | 21 | 27 | 24 | 31 |
| Oakenhead | 51 | 44 | 41 | 47 | Olivers Mount | 57 | 63 | 60 | 53 |
| Orton | 40 | 46 | 43 | 50 | Oughtibridge | 55 | 62 | 59 | 65 |
| Over Biddulph | 34 | 67 | 30 | 48 | Oxenhope | 22 | 28 | 25 | 32 |
| Parbold | 51 | 44 | 41 | 47 | Peebles | 22 | 28 | 25 | 32 |
| Pendle Forest | 22 | 28 | 25 | 32 | Penny Bridge | 33 | 26 | 23 | 29 |
| Peterlee | 45 | 52 | 49 | 39 | Pinwherry | 22 | 28 | 25 | 32 |
| Pontop Pike | 58 | 64 | 61 | 54 | Pooley Bridge | 48 | 40 | 46 | 50 |
| Port St Mary (IoM) | 58 | 64 | 61 | 54 | Portpatrick | 58 | 64 | 61 | 54 |
| Portwood | 22 | 28 | 32 | 25 | Prestbury | 40 | 46 | 43 | 50 |
| Primrose Hill | 57 | 62 | 60 | 67 | Ramsbotton | 58 | 66 | 56 | 68 |
| Ravenscar | 58 | 64 | 61 | 54 | Ravenstonedale | 57 | 62 | 60 | 53 |
| Ribblesdale | 51 | 44 | 41 | 47 | Ripponden | 58 | 64 | 61 | 54 |
| Romaldkirk | 51 | 44 | 41 | 47 | Romiley | 51 | 44 | 41 | 47 |
| Rookhope | 40 | 46 | 43 | 50 | Roose | 26 | 33 | 29 | 39 |
| Rosedale Abbey | 40 | 46 | 43 | 50 | Rothbury | 55 | 62 | 65 | 59 |
| Saddleworth | 52 | 45 | 49 | 42 | Sandale | 22 | 67 | - | - |
| Seaham | 51 | 44 | 41 | 47 | Sedbergh | 40 | 46 | 43 | 50 |
| Selkirk | 55 | 62 | 59 | 65 | Shatton Edge | 52 | 58 | 48 | 54 |
| Sheffield | 31 | 27 | 24 | 21 | Shotleyfield | 22 | 28 | 25 | 32 |
| Skinningrove | 40 | 46 | 43 | 50 | Skipton | 39 | 45 | 49 | 42 |
| Skipton Town | 21 | 27 | 24 | 31 | St. Bees | 58 | 64 | 61 | 54 |
| Staithes | 51 | 44 | 41 | 47 | Staveley-in-Cartmel | 40 | 46 | 43 | 53 |
| Stockport | 27 | 24 | 21 | 31 | Stocksbridge | 58 | 64 | 61 | 54 |
| Storeton | 22 | 28 | 25 | 32 | Stow | 33 | 26 | 23 | 29 |
| Stranraer | 57 | 63 | 60 | 53 | Sunderland | 40 | 46 | 43 | 50 |
| Sutton-in-Craven | 33 | 26 | 23 | 29 | Thornhill | 57 | 63 | 60 | 53 |
| Threlkeld | 57 | 63 | 60 | 53 | Tideswell Moor | 56 | 63 | 60 | 66 |

## Borders and Northern England (cont.)

| Location | BBC1 | BBC2 | ITV | CH4 | Location | BBC1 | BBC2 | ITV | CH4 |
|---|---|---|---|---|---|---|---|---|---|
| Todmorden | 39 | 45 | 49 | 42 | Totley Rise | 39 | 45 | 49 | 42 |
| Trawden | 57 | 63 | 60 | 67 | Union Mills (IoM) | 39 | 45 | 52 | 42 |
| Urswick | 51 | 44 | 41 | 47 | Wall | 40 | 46 | 43 | 50 |
| Walsden | 57 | 62 | 60 | 67 | Walsden South | 40 | 46 | 43 | 53 |
| Walton-le-Dale | 21 | 27 | 24 | 31 | Wardle | 22 | 28 | 25 | 32 |
| Weardale | 44 | 51 | 41 | 47 | Weaverthorpe | 55 | 62 | 59 | 65 |
| West Burton | 40 | 46 | 43 | 50 | West Kirby | 34 | 27 | 24 | 31 |
| Whaley Bridge | 39 | 45 | 49 | 52 | Whalley | 40 | 46 | 43 | 53 |
| Wharfedale | 22 | 28 | 25 | 32 | Wheatley | 58 | 64 | 61 | 54 |
| Whitaside | 51 | 44 | 41 | 47 | Whitby | 55 | 62 | 59 | 65 |
| Whitehaven | 40 | 46 | 43 | 50 | Whitewell | 57 | 63 | 60 | 67 |
| Whitworth | 22 | 28 | 25 | 32 | Wincobank | 55 | 62 | 59 | 65 |
| Windermere | 51 | 44 | 41 | 47 | Winter Hill | 55 | 62 | 59 | 65 |
| Woodnook | 39 | 45 | 49 | 52 | Wooler | 22 | 28 | 25 | 32 |
| Workington | 58 | 64 | 61 | 54 | Yetholm | 51 | 44 | 41 | 47 |

## Midlands and Eastern England

| Location | BBC1 | BBC2 | ITV | CH4 | Location | BBC1 | BBC2 | ITV | CH4 |
|---|---|---|---|---|---|---|---|---|---|
| Aldeburgh | 33 | 26 | 23 | 30 | Allesley Park | 22 | 28 | 25 | 32 |
| Ambergate | 22 | 28 | 25 | 32 | Andoversford | 55 | 62 | 59 | 65 |
| Ascott ud. Wychwood | 21 | 27 | 24 | 31 | Ashbourne | 22 | 28 | 25 | 32 |
| Ashford-in-Water | 33 | 26 | 23 | 29 | Belper | 66 | 56 | 68 | 62 |
| Birchover | 39 | 45 | 49 | 42 | Bolehill | 63 | 57 | 53 | 60 |
| Brailes | 30 | 52 | 34 | 59 | Bramford | 21 | 27 | 24 | 31 |
| Bretch Hill | 65 | 48 | 55 | 67 | Bridgnorth | 62 | 68 | 56 | 66 |
| Brierley Hill | 57 | 63 | 60 | 53 | Bromsgrove | 31 | 27 | 24 | 21 |
| Bucknell | 39 | 45 | 49 | 42 | Burnham | 41 | - | 46 | - |
| Bury St Edmunds | 22 | 28 | 25 | 32 | Charlbury | 51 | 44 | 41 | 47 |
| Cheadle | 48 | 66 | 56 | 68 | Clun | 55 | 62 | 59 | 65 |
| Coalbrookdale | 51 | 44 | 47 | 41 | Creake | 39 | 45 | 49 | 42 |
| Dallington Park | 66 | 62 | 56 | 68 | Darley Dale | 30 | 48 | 34 | 52 |
| Derby | - | - | 30 | - | Eardiston | 58 | 64 | 61 | 54 |
| Earl Sterndale | 58 | 64 | 61 | 54 | Eastwood | 33 | 26 | 23 | 29 |
| Edgbaston | 21 | 27 | 24 | 31 | Ewyas Harold | 51 | 44 | 67 | 47 |
| Felixstowe | 31 | 63 | 60 | 67 | Fenton | 31 | 27 | 24 | 21 |
| Garth Hill | 57 | 63 | 60 | 53 | Gib Heath | 56 | 66 | 62 | 68 |
| Gorleston | 33 | 26 | 23 | 39 | Gravelly Hill | 66 | 56 | 62 | 68 |
| Guiting Power | 51 | 44 | 41 | 47 | Haden Hill | 39 | 52 | 49 | 42 |
| Halesowen | 58 | 64 | 61 | 54 | Hamstead | 21 | 27 | 24 | 31 |
| Harborne | 30 | 48 | 34 | 67 | Hartington | 66 | 48 | 56 | 68 |
| Hazler Hill | 51 | 44 | 41 | 47 | Hereford | 51 | 44 | 41 | 47 |
| Hope Under Dinmore | 63 | 57 | 60 | 53 | Icomb Hill | 22 | 28 | 25 | 32 |
| Ipstones Edge | 57 | 63 | 60 | 53 | Ipswich | 22 | 28 | 25 | 32 |
| Ironbridge | 58 | 64 | 61 | 54 | Kenilworth | 57 | 63 | 60 | 53 |
| Kidderminster | 58 | 64 | 61 | 54 | Kimpton | 45 | 56 | 52 | 48 |
| King's Lynn | 48 | - | 52 | - | Kington | 39 | 45 | 49 | 42 |
| Kinver | 66 | 48 | 56 | 68 | Knucklas | 39 | 45 | 42 | 49 |
| Lark Stoke | 33 | 26 | 23 | 29 | Leamington Spa | 56 | 62 | 66 | 68 |
| Leek | 22 | 28 | 25 | 32 | Leicester City | 22 | 28 | 25 | 32 |
| Linnet Valley | 33 | 26 | 23 | 29 | Little Eaton | 33 | 26 | 23 | 29 |
| Little Walsingham | 51 | 44 | 41 | 47 | Long Compton | 22 | 28 | 25 | 32 |
| Ludlow | 39 | 45 | 42 | 49 | Luton | 55 | 62 | 59 | 65 |
| Malvern | 56 | 62 | 66 | 68 | Matlock | 21 | 27 | 24 | 31 |
| New Radnor | 51 | 44 | 41 | 47 | Norwich (Central) | 39 | 45 | 49 | 42 |

## Midlands and Eastern England (cont.)

| Location | BBC1 | BBC2 | ITV | CH4 | Location | BBC1 | BBC2 | ITV | CH4 |
|---|---|---|---|---|---|---|---|---|---|
| Nottingham | 21 | 27 | 24 | 31 | Oakamoor | 21 | 27 | 24 | 31 |
| Oakeley Mynd | 39 | 45 | 49 | 42 | Over Norton | 65 | 48 | 55 | 67 |
| Overstrand | 51 | 44 | 41 | 47 | Oxford | 57 | 63 | 60 | 53 |
| Parwich | 21 | 27 | 24 | 31 | Perry Beaches | 22 | 28 | 25 | 32 |
| Peterchurch | 57 | 62 | 60 | 53 | Presteigne | 48 | 56 | 52 | 66 |
| Questlett | 58 | 64 | 61 | 54 | Redditch | 22 | 28 | 25 | 32 |
| Repton | 48 | 68 | 56 | 66 | Ridge Hill | 22 | 28 | 25 | 32 |
| Ross-on-Wye | 55 | 62 | 65 | 59 | Rugeley | 66 | 48 | 56 | 68 |
| Sandy Heath | 31 | 27 | 24 | 21 | Somersham | 22 | 28 | 25 | 32 |
| St. Briavels | 40 | 46 | 43 | 50 | Stamford | 39 | 45 | 49 | 42 |
| Stanton Moor | 55 | 62 | 59 | 65 | Sudbury | 51 | 44 | 41 | 47 |
| Sutton Coldfield | 46 | 40 | 43 | 50 | Tacolneston | 62 | 55 | 59 | 65 |
| Tenbury Wells | 57 | 63 | 60 | 53 | The Wrekin | 26 | 33 | 23 | 29 |
| Thetford | 33 | 26 | 23 | 29 | Turves Green | 56 | 66 | 62 | 68 |
| Upper Soudley | 40 | 46 | 43 | 50 | Waltham | 58 | 64 | 61 | 54 |
| Wells-next-the-Sea | 43 | - | 50 | - | West Runton | 33 | 26 | 23 | 29 |
| Whittingslow | 57 | 63 | 60 | 53 | Winchcombe | 58 | 64 | 61 | 54 |
| Winshill | 66 | 48 | 56 | 68 | Wivenhoe Park | 58 | 64 | 61 | 54 |
| Woodbridge | 58 | 64 | 61 | 54 | Woodford Halse | 22 | 28 | 25 | 32 |

## Southern England

| Location | BBC1 | BBC2 | ITV | CH4 | Location | BBC1 | BBC2 | ITV | CH4 |
|---|---|---|---|---|---|---|---|---|---|
| Aldbourne | 21 | 27 | 24 | 31 | Alderney | 58 | 64 | 61 | 68 |
| Alexandra Palace | 58 | 64 | 61 | 54 | Alton | 49 | 62 | 59 | 52 |
| Alverton | 21 | 27 | 24 | 31 | Ashburton | 21 | 27 | 24 | 31 |
| Assendon | 55 | 68 | 58 | 65 | Avening | 51 | 44 | 41 | 47 |
| Aveton Gifford | 51 | 44 | 66 | 47 | Backwell | 22 | 28 | 25 | 32 |
| Bampton | 39 | 49 | 45 | 52 | Barnstaple | 40 | 46 | 43 | 30 |
| Bath | 22 | 28 | 25 | 32 | Beacon Hill | 57 | 63 | 60 | 53 |
| Beaminster | 55 | 62 | 59 | 65 | Beer | 55 | 62 | 59 | 65 |
| Berrynarbor | 22 | 28 | 25 | 32 | Bevendean | 40 | 46 | 43 | 29 |
| Biggin Hill | 45 | 52 | 49 | 67 | Bincombe Hill | 55 | 62 | 59 | 65 |
| Bishop's Stortford | 55 | 62 | 59 | 49 | Blakeney | 21 | 27 | 24 | 31 |
| Bluebell Hill | 40 | 46 | 43 | 65 | Bnruton | 40 | 46 | 43 | 50 |
| Boscastle | 33 | 26 | 23 | 29 | Bossiney | 58 | 64 | 61 | 54 |
| Bovey Tracey | 39 | 45 | 49 | 42 | Bovington | 51 | 44 | 41 | 47 |
| Box | 40 | 46 | 43 | 50 | Brading | 51 | 44 | 41 | 47 |
| Branscombe | 51 | 44 | 47 | 41 | Braunton | 39 | 45 | 49 | 42 |
| Bridport | 51 | 44 | 41 | 47 | Brighstone | 51 | 44 | 41 | 47 |
| Brighton (Central) | 39 | 45 | 41 | 47 | Brighton (Whiteh'k Hl) | 57 | 62 | 60 | 53 |
| Bristol Barton House | 21 | 27 | 24 | 31 | Bristol Warmley | 66 | 49 | 39 | 68 |
| Brixham | 40 | 46 | 43 | 50 | Brushford | 21 | 27 | 24 | 31 |
| Buckfastleigh | 51 | 44 | 41 | 47 | Burrington | 55 | 62 | 59 | 65 |
| Calne | 21 | 27 | 24 | 31 | Cane Hill | 61 | 54 | 58 | 68 |
| Canford Heath | 39 | 45 | 68 | 42 | Caradon Hill | 22 | 28 | 25 | 32 |
| Carhampton | 21 | 27 | 24 | 31 | Caterham | 55 | 62 | 59 | 65 |
| Cerne Abbas | 22 | 28 | 25 | 32 | Chagford | 21 | 27 | 24 | 31 |
| Chalford | 21 | 27 | 24 | 31 | Chalford Vale | 68 | 46 | 43 | 50 |
| Chambercombe | 21 | 27 | 24 | 31 | Charmouth | 51 | 44 | 41 | 47 |
| Chartham | 21 | 27 | 24 | 31 | Chatham Town | 58 | 68 | 61 | 54 |
| Chepping Wycombe | 51 | 44 | 41 | 47 | Chepstow | 21 | 27 | 24 | 31 |
| Cheselbourne | 57 | 63 | 53 | 60 | Chesham | 40 | 46 | 43 | 50 |
| Chideock | 49 | 45 | 39 | 42 | Chilfrome | 39 | 49 | 45 | 52 |
| Chingford | 56 | 50 | 52 | 48 | Chisbury | 55 | 62 | 59 | 52 |

**Southern England** (cont.)

| Location | BBC1 | BBC2 | ITV | CH4 | Location | BBC1 | BBC2 | ITV | CH4 |
|---|---|---|---|---|---|---|---|---|---|
| Chiseldon | 30 | 49 | 34 | 67 | Chitterne | 40 | 46 | 43 | 50 |
| Chudleigh | 51 | 44 | 41 | 47 | Cirencester | 33 | 26 | 23 | 29 |
| Clearwell | 66 | 48 | 68 | 56 | Clennon Valley | 39 | 45 | 49 | 42 |
| Coldean | 65 | 42 | 44 | 68 | Coleford | 42 | 52 | 45 | 39 |
| Combe Martin | 39 | 45 | 49 | 42 | Compton | 51 | 44 | 68 | 47 |
| Coombe | 21 | 27 | 24 | 31 | Corfe Castle | 51 | 44 | 41 | 47 |
| Corsham | 51 | 44 | 41 | 47 | Countisbury | 39 | 66 | 49 | 68 |
| Creditor | 40 | 46 | 43 | 50 | Crewkerne | 40 | 46 | 43 | 50 |
| Crockerton | 51 | 44 | 41 | 47 | Croyde | 51 | 44 | 41 | 47 |
| Croydon (Old Town) | 49 | 56 | 52 | 67 | Crystal Palace | 26 | 33 | 23 | 30 |
| Culm Valley | 39 | 45 | 49 | 42 | Dartmouth | 51 | 44 | 41 | 47 |
| Dawlich | 55 | 62 | 59 | 65 | Donhead | 51 | 44 | 41 | 47 |
| Dorking | 51 | 44 | 41 | 47 | Dover | 50 | 56 | 66 | 53 |
| Dover Town | 33 | 26 | 23 | 30 | Downderry | 55 | 62 | 59 | 65 |
| Dunsford | 45 | 67 | 39 | 49 | Dursley | 40 | 46 | 43 | 50 |
| East Dean | 62 | 44 | 54 | 42 | East Grinstead | 40 | 56 | 46 | 59 |
| Eastbourne | 33 | 26 | 23 | 30 | Eastbourne | 40 | 46 | 43 | 58 |
| Easter Compton | 57 | 63 | 60 | 53 | Edginswell | 39 | 49 | 45 | 67 |
| Edmonton | 57 | 42 | 60 | 53 | Elham | 33 | 26 | 23 | 30 |
| Exford | 51 | 44 | 41 | 47 | Farleigh | 28 | 57 | 21 | 54 |
| Faversham | 22 | 28 | 25 | 32 | Ferningham | 48 | 56 | 50 | 58 |
| Finchley | 52 | 56 | 49 | 67 | Findon | 51 | 44 | 41 | 47 |
| Folkstone | 33 | 26 | 23 | 30 | Forest Row | 48 | 54 | 62 | 66 |
| Fowey | 58 | 64 | 61 | 54 | Fremont Point | 51 | 44 | 41 | 47 |
| Frome | 21 | 27 | 24 | 31 | Gorey | 54 | 26 | 23 | 29 |
| Gravesend | 55 | 62 | 59 | 49 | Great Missenden | 58 | 64 | 61 | 54 |
| Great Torrington | 39 | 45 | 49 | 42 | Greenwich | 56 | 50 | 52 | 48 |
| Guildford | 40 | 46 | 43 | 50 | Gulval | 33 | 26 | 23 | 29 |
| Gunnislake | 40 | 46 | 43 | 50 | Hammersmith | 48 | 62 | 59 | 65 |
| Hampstead Heath | 51 | 44 | 47 | 41 | Hangleton | 39 | 45 | 49 | 42 |
| Hannington | 39 | 45 | 42 | 66 | Harbertonford | 39 | 45 | 49 | 42 |
| Harmstreet | 33 | 26 | 23 | 30 | Hartland | 48 | 56 | 52 | 66 |
| Haslemere | 22 | 28 | 25 | 32 | Hastings | 22 | 25 | 28 | 32 |
| Hastings Old Town | 45 | 39 | 42 | 55 | Hatch Bottom | - | - | 49 | - |
| Haywards Heath | 39 | 45 | 43 | 41 | Heathfield | 49 | 52 | 64 | 67 |
| Hele | 40 | 46 | 43 | 50 | Helston | 58 | 64 | 61 | 54 |
| Hemel Hempstead | 51 | 44 | 47 | 41 | Hemel Hempstead | 58 | 63 | 61 | 54 |
| Henley-on-Thames | 48 | 64 | 67 | 54 | Herndean | 49 | 52 | 56 | 59 |
| Hertford | 58 | 64 | 61 | 54 | High Wycombe | 55 | 62 | 59 | 65 |
| Hollington Park | 45 | 39 | 42 | 55 | Honiton | 49 | 39 | 52 | 45 |
| Horn Street | 58 | 44 | 41 | 47 | Horndean | 56 | 64 | 52 | 62 |
| Hughenden | 40 | 46 | 43 | 50 | Huntshaw Cross | 55 | 62 | 59 | 65 |
| Hurstbourne Tarrant | 22 | 28 | 32 | 25 | Hutton | 49 | 66 | 39 | 68 |
| Hythe | 21 | 27 | 24 | 31 | Hythe (Hants) | - | - | 59 | - |
| Ilchester Crescent | 40 | 46 | 43 | 50 | Ilfracombe | 58 | 65 | 61 | 54 |
| Isles of Scilly | 21 | 27 | 24 | 31 | Ivybridge | 39 | 45 | 42 | 49 |
| Kenley | 40 | 46 | 43 | 50 | Kensal Town | 56 | 49 | 52 | 67 |
| Kewstoke | 40 | 46 | 43 | 50 | Kilve | 49 | 66 | 39 | 68 |
| Kings Weston Hill | 45 | 48 | 42 | 52 | Kingsbridge | 40 | 46 | 43 | 50 |
| Kingskerswell | 55 | 68 | 48 | 65 | Lamberhurst | 54 | 60 | 62 | 58 |
| Lambourn | 55 | 62 | 59 | 52 | Lea Bridge | 55 | 62 | 39 | 59 |
| Les Toillets | 56 | 48 | 54 | 52 | Lewes | 22 | 28 | 25 | 32 |
| Liverton | 55 | 68 | 48 | 65 | Looe | 40 | 46 | 43 | 50 |

| Base | Mobile | Mode | Location | | User and Notes | | | |
|------|--------|------|----------|--|----------------|--|--|--|

| | BBC1 | BBC2 | ITV | CH4 | | BBC1 | BBC2 | ITV | CH4 |
|---|---|---|---|---|---|---|---|---|---|
| **Southern England** (cont.) | | | | | | | | | |
| Lostwithiel | 40 | 46 | 43 | 50 | Luccombe | 56 | 62 | 59 | 37 |
| Lulworth | 55 | 62 | 59 | 65 | Luscombe Valley | 39 | 45 | 49 | 42 |
| Lydbrook | 40 | 46 | 43 | 50 | Lydden | 42 | 68 | 39 | 64 |
| Lyminge | 22 | 28 | 25 | 32 | Margate | 22 | 28 | 25 | 32 |
| Marlborough | 22 | 28 | 25 | 32 | Marlow Bottom | 58 | 64 | 61 | 54 |
| Marystow | 39 | 45 | 49 | 42 | Mendip | 58 | 64 | 61 | 54 |
| Mevagissey | 40 | 46 | 43 | 50 | Micklefield | 54 | 64 | 57 | 67 |
| Micleham | 61 | 55 | 58 | 68 | Midhurst | 61 | 55 | 58 | 68 |
| Millbrook | 51 | 44 | 41 | 47 | Modbury | 55 | 62 | 59 | 54 |
| Monksilver | 45 | 48 | 52 | 42 | Montpelier | 33 | 26 | 23 | 29 |
| Mountfield | 21 | 27 | 24 | 31 | Muddiford | 51 | 44 | 41 | 47 |
| Nailsworth | 33 | 26 | 23 | 29 | New Addington | 64 | 48 | 54 | 68 |
| New Barnet | 55 | 62 | 59 | 48 | Newhaven | 39 | 45 | 43 | 41 |
| Newnham (Kent) | 21 | 27 | 24 | 31 | Newton Abbot | 40 | 46 | 43 | 50 |
| Newton Ferrers | 55 | 62 | 59 | 54 | North Bovey | 40 | 46 | 43 | 50 |
| North Hessary Tor | 55 | 62 | 59 | 54 | North Winchester | - | - | 52 | - |
| Occombe Valley | 21 | 27 | 24 | 31 | Ogbourne St. George | 40 | 46 | 43 | 50 |
| Okehampton | 39 | 45 | 49 | 42 | Old Coulsdon | 48 | 64 | 45 | 66 |
| Orpington | 55 | 62 | 59 | 66 | Otford | 57 | 63 | 60 | 53 |
| Ovingdean | 65 | 42 | 44 | 68 | Parkend | 51 | 44 | 41 | 47 |
| Patcham | 46 | 40 | 43 | 50 | Penaligon Downs | 39 | 45 | 49 | 42 |
| Penryn | 55 | 62 | 59 | 54 | Pensylvania | 58 | 64 | 61 | 54 |
| Perranporth | 55 | 62 | 59 | 65 | Piddletrenthide | 39 | 45 | 49 | 42 |
| Pillowell | 40 | 46 | 43 | 50 | Plymouth North Rd | 40 | 46 | 43 | 50 |
| Plympton | 58 | 64 | 61 | 54 | Polperry | 57 | 63 | 60 | 53 |
| Poole | 57 | 63 | 60 | 53 | Poplar | 45 | 66 | 49 | 68 |
| Porlock | 48 | 46 | 42 | 52 | Port Isaac | 55 | 62 | 65 | 59 |
| Porthleven | 33 | 26 | 23 | 29 | Porthtowan | 21 | 27 | 24 | 31 |
| Portishead | 66 | 39 | 49 | 68 | Portreath | 33 | 26 | 23 | 29 |
| Portslade | 51 | 44 | 41 | 47 | Poulner | 39 | 45 | 68 | 42 |
| Preston | 58 | 64 | 61 | 54 | Praa Sands | 55 | 62 | 59 | 65 |
| Rampisham | 40 | 46 | 43 | 50 | Ramsgate | 33 | 26 | 23 | 30 |
| Redbrook | 39 | 45 | 42 | 52 | Redcliff Bay | 57 | 63 | 60 | 53 |
| Redruth | 51 | 44 | 41 | 47 | Reigate | 57 | 63 | 60 | 53 |
| Roadwater | 21 | 27 | 24 | 31 | Rowridge | 31 | 24 | 27 | 21 |
| Rye | 58 | 44 | 41 | 47 | Salcombe | 51 | 41 | 44 | 30 |
| Salisbury | 57 | 63 | 60 | 53 | Saltdean | 51 | 66 | 55 | 47 |
| Seagry Crt, Swindon | 44 | 51 | 41 | 47 | Sedlescombe | 33 | 26 | 23 | 30 |
| Shrewton | 51 | 44 | 41 | 47 | Sidmouth | 39 | 49 | 45 | 67 |
| Singleton | 51 | 44 | 41 | 47 | Siston | 31 | 24 | 34 | 21 |
| Skirmett | 51 | 44 | 41 | 47 | Slad | 33 | 26 | 23 | 29 |
| Slapton | 48 | 66 | 55 | 68 | South Brent | 40 | 46 | 43 | 50 |
| Southway | 55 | 62 | 59 | 65 | St. Albans | 49 | 63 | 57 | 67 |
| St. Anthony Roseland | 33 | 26 | 23 | 29 | St. Austell | 55 | 62 | 59 | 65 |
| St. Brelades | 57 | 62 | 67 | 53 | St. Helier | 55 | 62 | 59 | 65 |
| St. Just | 58 | 64 | 61 | 54 | St. Marks | 57 | 63 | 60 | 53 |
| St. Neot | 39 | 42 | 49 | 45 | St. Peter Port | 21 | 27 | 24 | 31 |
| St. Thomas (Exeter) | 51 | 44 | 41 | 47 | Steyning | 45 | 59 | 62 | 56 |
| Stockland Hill | 33 | 25 | 23 | 29 | Stokeinteignhead | 51 | 44 | 41 | 47 |
| Stroud | 48 | 45 | 42 | 52 | Sutton | 55 | 62 | 59 | 65 |
| Sutton Row | 22 | 28 | 25 | 32 | Swimbridge | 33 | 26 | 23 | 29 |
| Tavistock | 57 | 63 | 60 | 53 | Tedburn St. Mary | 42 | 48 | 52 | 31 |
| Teignmouth | 39 | 49 | 45 | 67 | The Bournes | 47 | 51 | 59 | 49 |
| Tidworth | 22 | 28 | 32 | 25 | Till Valley | 46 | 40 | 43 | 50 |

| Base | Mobile | Mode | Location | User and Notes |
|------|--------|------|----------|----------------|

| | BBC1 | BBC2 | ITV | CH4 | | BBC1 | BBC2 | ITV | CH4 |
|---|------|------|-----|-----|---|------|------|-----|-----|
| **Southern England** (cont.) | | | | | | | | | |
| Tintern | 21 | 27 | 24 | 31 | Tiverton | 40 | 46 | 43 | 50 |
| Torquay Town | 51 | 44 | 41 | 47 | Torteval | 50 | 40 | 46 | 66 |
| Totnes | 21 | 27 | 24 | 31 | Truro | 58 | 64 | 61 | 54 |
| Tunbridge Wells | 51 | 44 | 41 | 47 | Turnpike Hill | 58 | 44 | 41 | 47 |
| Ubley | 21 | 27 | 24 | 31 | Upavon | 33 | 25 | 23 | 29 |
| Vewntnor | 39 | 45 | 49 | 42 | Walthamstow North | 45 | 66 | 49 | 68 |
| Washford | 49 | 66 | 39 | 68 | Welwyn | 40 | 46 | 43 | 50 |
| West Lavington | 21 | 27 | 24 | 31 | West Wycombe | 40 | 46 | 43 | 67 |
| Westbourne | 51 | 44 | 41 | 47 | Weston Mill | 49 | 42 | 39 | 45 |
| Westward Ho! | 21 | 27 | 24 | 31 | Westwood | 40 | 46 | 43 | 50 |
| Weymouth | 40 | 46 | 43 | 50 | Wid'combe in Moor | 40 | 46 | 43 | 50 |
| Winterbourne Stapletn | 39 | 42 | 45 | 66 | Winterbourne Sticklnd | 40 | 46 | 43 | 50 |
| Wonersh | 48 | 65 | 52 | 67 | Wooburn | 49 | 52 | 56 | 68 |
| Woodcombe | 57 | 62 | 60 | 53 | Woolacombe | 39 | 45 | 42 | 49 |
| Woolwich | 57 | 63 | 60 | 67 | Wootton Courtenay | 22 | 28 | 25 | 32 |
| Worlds End | 43 | 50 | 46 | 68 | Wye (Ashford) | 22 | 28 | 25 | 32 |
| | | | | | | | | | |
| **Northern Ireland** | | | | | | | | | |
| Armagh | 39 | 45 | 49 | 42 | Ballintoy | 39 | 45 | 49 | 42 |
| Ballycastle | 39 | 45 | 49 | 42 | Banbridge | 44 | 48 | 46 | 50 |
| Bangor | 62 | 55 | 69 | 65 | Belcoo | 51 | 44 | 41 | 47 |
| Bellair | 48 | 56 | 52 | 67 | Benagh | 22 | 28 | 25 | 32 |
| Black Mountain | 39 | 45 | 49 | 42 | Brougher Mountain | 22 | 28 | 25 | 32 |
| Buckna | 51 | 44 | 41 | 47 | Bushmills | 51 | 44 | 41 | 47 |
| Carnmoney Hill | 40 | 46 | 43 | 50 | Castlederg | 55 | 62 | 65 | 59 |
| Claudy | 57 | 63 | 60 | 53 | Conlig | 39 | 45 | 49 | 42 |
| Cushendall | 40 | 46 | 43 | 50 | Cushendun | 22 | 28 | 32 | 25 |
| Derrygonnelly | 51 | 44 | 47 | 66 | Divis | 31 | 27 | 24 | 21 |
| Draperstown | 39 | 45 | 49 | 42 | Dromore | 58 | 64 | 61 | 54 |
| Ederny | 65 | 59 | 62 | 55 | Glenariff | 58 | 64 | 61 | 54 |
| Glenelly Valley | 33 | 26 | 23 | 29 | Glynn | 58 | 64 | 61 | 54 |
| Gornalee | 21 | 27 | 24 | 31 | Gortnageeragh | 39 | 45 | 42 | 49 |
| Kilkeel | 39 | 45 | 49 | 42 | Killowen Mountain | 31 | 27 | 24 | 21 |
| Larne | 39 | 45 | 49 | 42 | Leitrim | 57 | 63 | 60 | 53 |
| Limavady | 55 | 62 | 59 | 65 | Lisbellaw | 55 | 62 | 59 | 65 |
| Londonderry | 51 | 44 | 41 | 47 | Moneymore | 39 | 45 | 49 | 42 |
| Muldonagh | 22 | 28 | 32 | 25 | Newcastle (NI) | 55 | 62 | 59 | 65 |
| Newry North | 51 | 44 | 41 | 47 | Newry South | 39 | 45 | 49 | 42 |
| Newtownards | 58 | 64 | 61 | 54 | Plumbridge | 52 | 66 | 56 | 68 |
| Rostrevor Forest | 48 | 40 | 46 | 50 | Strabane | 39 | 45 | 49 | 42 |
| Whitehead | 48 | 56 | 51 | 67 | | | | | |
| | | | | | | | | | |
| **Wales** | | | | | | | | | |
| Aberbeeg | 40 | 46 | 43 | 50 | Abercraf | 22 | 28 | 25 | 32 |
| Abercynon | 64 | 66 | 58 | 54 | Aberdare | 21 | 27 | 24 | 31 |
| Abergavenny | 39 | 45 | 49 | 42 | Abergwynfi | 21 | 27 | 24 | 31 |
| Abertillery | 22 | 28 | 25 | 32 | Abertridwr | 57 | 63 | 60 | 54 |
| Aberystwyth | 58 | 64 | 61 | 54 | Afon Dyfi | 22 | 28 | 25 | 32 |
| Alltwen | 40 | 46 | 43 | 50 | Amlwch | 22 | 28 | 25 | 32 |
| Arfon | 51 | 44 | 41 | 47 | Bagillt | 43 | - | - | 40 |
| Bala | 33 | 26 | 23 | 29 | Bargoed | 21 | 27 | 24 | 31 |
| Beddgelert | 55 | 62 | 59 | 65 | Bedlinog | 21 | 27 | 24 | 31 |
| Bethesda | 57 | 63 | 60 | 53 | Bethesda North | 28 | 22 | 25 | 32 |

| | BBC1 | BBC2 | ITV | CH4 | | BBC1 | BBC2 | ITV | CH4 |
|---|---|---|---|---|---|---|---|---|---|
| **Wales** (cont.) | | | | | | | | | |
| Betws-y-Coed | 21 | 27 | 24 | 31 | Betws-yn-Rhos | 21 | 27 | 24 | 31 |
| Blackmill | 22 | 28 | 25 | 32 | Blaenau Gwent | 57 | 63 | 60 | 53 |
| Blaenavon | 57 | 63 | 60 | 53 | Blaenllechau | 21 | 27 | 24 | 31 |
| Blaenplwyf | 31 | 27 | 24 | 21 | Blaina | 40 | 46 | 43 | 50 |
| Bow Street | 51 | 44 | 41 | 47 | Brechfa | 21 | 27 | 31 | 24 |
| Brecon | 58 | 64 | 61 | 54 | Briton Ferry | 46 | 40 | 43 | 50 |
| Broadhaven | 58 | 64 | 61 | 54 | Broeirion | 33 | 26 | 29 | 23 |
| Bronwydd Arms | 21 | 27 | 31 | 24 | Builth Wells | 22 | 28 | 25 | 32 |
| Burry Port | 58 | 64 | 61 | 54 | Caergybi | 21 | 27 | 24 | 31 |
| Caernarfron | 21 | 27 | 24 | 31 | Carmel | 57 | 62 | 60 | 53 |
| Carno | 21 | 27 | 24 | 31 | Castle Caereinion | 40 | 46 | 43 | 50 |
| Cefn-Mawr | 51 | 44 | 41 | 47 | Cemaes | 40 | 46 | 43 | 50 |
| Cerrigydrudion | 33 | 26 | 23 | 29 | Cilfrew | 39 | 45 | 49 | 52 |
| Cilycym | 21 | 27 | 31 | 24 | Clydach | 33 | 26 | 23 | 29 |
| Clyro | 51 | 44 | 41 | 47 | Coed Derw | 51 | 44 | 41 | 47 |
| Conway | 40 | 46 | 43 | 50 | Corris | 39 | 45 | 49 | 42 |
| Corwen | 22 | 28 | 25 | 32 | Craig-Cefn-Parc | 46 | 40 | 43 | 50 |
| Crickhowell | 21 | 27 | 24 | 31 | Croeserw | 58 | 64 | 61 | 54 |
| Crucorney | 21 | 27 | 24 | 31 | Crumlin | 56 | 66 | 60 | 68 |
| Cwm Ffrwd-oer | 39 | 46 | 43 | 50 | Cwm Twrch | 21 | 27 | 24 | 31 |
| Cwmafon | 21 | 27 | 24 | 31 | Cwmaman | 39 | 45 | 49 | 42 |
| Cwmferlinfach | 52 | 45 | 48 | 42 | Cwmgors | 21 | 27 | 24 | 31 |
| Cwrtnewydd | 51 | 44 | 41 | 47 | Cyffylliog | 22 | 28 | 25 | 32 |
| Cynwyl Elfed | 22 | 28 | 25 | 32 | Deiniolen | 22 | 28 | 25 | 32 |
| Deri | 22 | 28 | 25 | 32 | Dolgellau | 55 | 62 | 59 | 65 |
| Dolwyddelan | 51 | 44 | 41 | 47 | Dolybont | 58 | 64 | 61 | 54 |
| Dowlais | 58 | 64 | 61 | 54 | Duffryn | 22 | 28 | 25 | 32 |
| Ebbw Vale | 55 | 62 | 59 | 65 | Efail Fach | 39 | 45 | 49 | 52 |
| Erwood | 57 | 62 | 60 | 53 | Evvw Vale South | 27 | 21 | 24 | 31 |
| Ferndale | 57 | 63 | 60 | 53 | Fernhill | 55 | 62 | 59 | 65 |
| Ferryside | 21 | 27 | 24 | 31 | Ffestiniog | 22 | 28 | 25 | 32 |
| Fishguard | 58 | 64 | 61 | 54 | Flint | 46 | - | - | 53 |
| Gelli-fendigaid | 55 | 62 | 59 | 65 | Gilfach | 21 | 27 | 24 | 31 |
| Glyn Ceiriog | 58 | 64 | 61 | 54 | Glyncorrwg | 39 | 45 | 49 | 42 |
| Glyndyfrdwy | 55 | 62 | 59 | 65 | Greenhill | 21 | 27 | 24 | 31 |
| Gronant | 26 | 33 | 29 | 23 | Haverfordwest | 52 | 66 | 56 | 68 |
| Holywell | 57 | - | - | 67 | Kerry | 21 | 27 | 24 | 31 |
| Kilvey Hill | 33 | 26 | 23 | 29 | Llanarmon-yn-Ial | 21 | 27 | 24 | 31 |
| Llanbrynmair | 22 | 28 | 25 | 32 | Llandderfel | 55 | 62 | 65 | 59 |
| Llanddona | 57 | 63 | 60 | 53 | Llanddulas | 33 | 26 | 23 | 29 |
| Llandecwyn | 58 | 64 | 61 | 54 | Llandinam | 44 | 51 | 41 | 47 |
| Llandrindod Wells | 39 | 45 | 49 | 42 | Llandyfriog | 22 | 28 | 25 | 32 |
| Llandysul | 57 | 63 | 60 | 53 | Llanengan | 58 | 64 | 61 | 54 |
| Llanfach | 57 | 63 | 60 | 53 | Llanfoist | 57 | 63 | 60 | 53 |
| Llanfyllin | 22 | 28 | 25 | 32 | Llangadfan | 22 | 28 | 25 | 32 |
| Llangbi | 22 | 28 | 25 | 32 | Llangeinor | 55 | 62 | 59 | 65 |
| Llangernyw | 22 | 28 | 32 | 25 | Llangollen | 57 | 63 | 60 | 53 |
| Llangranog | 22 | 28 | 25 | 32 | Llangurig | 33 | 26 | 23 | 29 |
| Llangynog | 55 | 62 | 65 | 59 | Llanharan | 21 | 27 | 24 | 31 |
| Llanhilleth | 39 | 45 | 49 | 42 | Llanidloes | 22 | 28 | 25 | 32 |
| Llanrhaeadr ym-Mocht | 39 | 45 | 49 | 42 | Llansawel | 22 | 28 | 32 | 25 |
| Llanuwchilyn | 40 | 46 | 43 | 50 | Llanwrtyd Wells | 21 | 27 | 24 | 31 |
| Llenelli | 39 | 45 | 49 | 67 | Llsywen | 21 | 27 | 24 | 31 |
| Llyn Onn | 22 | 28 | 25 | 32 | Long Mountin | 58 | 64 | 61 | 54 |

| Base | Mobile | Mode | Location | | | | User and Notes | | | |
|------|--------|------|----------|---|---|---|----------------|---|---|---|
| | | | BBC1 | BBC2 | ITV | CH4 | | BBC1 | BBC2 | ITV | CH4 |

**Wales** (cont.)

| Location | BBC1 | BBC2 | ITV | CH4 | Location | BBC1 | BBC2 | ITV | CH4 |
|----------|------|------|-----|-----|----------|------|------|-----|-----|
| Machen Uppwer | 55 | 65 | 62 | 68 | Machynlleth | 57 | 62 | 60 | 53 |
| Maentwrog | 40 | 46 | 43 | 50 | Maesteg | 22 | 28 | 25 | 32 |
| Merthyr Tydfil | 22 | 28 | 25 | 32 | Mochdre | 33 | 26 | 23 | 29 |
| Moel-y-Parc | 52 | 45 | 49 | 42 | Moel-y-Sant | 34 | 27 | 24 | 31 |
| Monmouth | 55 | 62 | 59 | 65 | Morfa Nefyn | 22 | 28 | 25 | 32 |
| Mynydd Bach | 58 | 64 | 61 | 54 | Mynydd Emroch | 40 | 46 | 43 | 50 |
| Mynydd Machen | 33 | 26 | 23 | 29 | Mynydd Pencarreg | 58 | 64 | 61 | 54 |
| Nant-y-Moel | 21 | 27 | 31 | 24 | Nantyglo | 57 | 63 | 60 | 53 |
| Neath Abbey | 66 | 48 | 42 | 56 | Newport Bay | 57 | 63 | 60 | 67 |
| Ogmore Vale | 57 | 63 | 60 | 53 | Pembroke Dokc | 58 | 64 | 61 | 54 |
| Pen-y-Banc | 21 | 27 | 24 | 31 | Pencader | 33 | 26 | 23 | 29 |
| Penderyn | 39 | 45 | 49 | 42 | Penmaen Rhos | 22 | 28 | 25 | 32 |
| Pennar | 40 | 46 | 43 | 50 | Pennorth | 33 | 26 | 23 | 29 |
| Penrhiwceiber | 57 | 63 | 53 | 60 | Penryhn-Coch | 55 | 62 | 59 | 65 |
| Pontardawe | 58 | 64 | 61 | 68 | Pontfadog | 22 | 28 | 25 | 32 |
| Pontypool | 21 | 27 | 24 | 31 | Pontypridd | 22 | 28 | 25 | 32 |
| Porth | 40 | 46 | 43 | 50 | Presely | 46 | 40 | 43 | 50 |
| Pwil-glas | 33 | 26 | 23 | 29 | Rhayader | 33 | 26 | 23 | 29 |
| Rheola | 55 | 62 | 59 | 65 | Rhondda | 33 | 26 | 23 | 29 |
| Rhondda B | 66 | 39 | 49 | 68 | Rhondda Fach | 22 | 28 | 25 | 32 |
| Rhymney | 57 | 63 | 60 | 53 | Risca | 40 | 46 | 43 | 50 |
| Sennybridge | 40 | 46 | 43 | 50 | South Maesteg | 55 | 62 | 59 | 65 |
| South Tredegar | 52 | 45 | 49 | 39 | St. Davids | 33 | 26 | 23 | 29 |
| St. Dogmaels | 33 | 26 | 23 | 29 | Taffs Well | 55 | 62 | 59 | 65 |
| Talley | 39 | 45 | 49 | 42 | Tenby | 39 | 45 | 49 | 42 |
| Ton Pentre | 58 | 64 | 61 | 54 | Tonypandy | 55 | 62 | 59 | 65 |
| Tonyrefail | 55 | 62 | 59 | 65 | Trebanog | 21 | 27 | 24 | 34 |
| Trecastle | 22 | 28 | 25 | 32 | Trefechan | 39 | 45 | 42 | 49 |
| Trefilan | 57 | 63 | 60 | 53 | Trefin | 22 | 28 | 25 | 32 |
| Trefor | 39 | 45 | 49 | 42 | Tregaron | 62 | 68 | 56 | 66 |
| Tregynon | 22 | 28 | 25 | 32 | Treharris | 56 | 48 | 52 | 68 |
| Tynewydd | 55 | 62 | 59 | 65 | Upper Killay | 21 | 27 | 24 | 31 |
| Van Terrace | 39 | 45 | 49 | 42 | Wattsville | 63 | 57 | 60 | 53 |
| Waunfawr | 22 | 28 | 25 | 32 | Wenvoe | 44 | 51 | 41 | 47 |
| Wrexham-Rhos | 39 | - | 32 | 67 | Ynys Owen | 55 | 62 | 59 | 65 |
| Ynys-Pennal | 51 | 44 | 41 | 47 | Ystalyfera | 39 | 45 | 49 | 42 |
| Ystumtuen | 39 | 45 | 49 | 42 | | | | | |

**Channel 5**

| Location | | Location | | Location | | Location | |
|----------|----|----------|----|----------|----|----------|----|
| Belmont | 56 | Bilsdale | 35 | Black Hill | 37 | Black Mountain | 37 |
| Blaen Plwyf | 56 | Burnhope | 68 | Caldbeck | 56 | Cambret Hill | 37 |
| Cambridge | 34 | Chelmsford | 63 | Churchdown Hill | 48 | Craigkelly | 48 |
| Croydon | 37 | Darvel | 35 | Durris | 67 | Emley Moor | 37 |
| Fawley | 34 | Fenham | 56 | Fenton | 35 | Hannington | 35 |
| Huntshaw Cross | 67 | Kilvey Hill | 35 | Lichfield | 37 | Londonderry | 31 |
| Mendip | 37 | Mounteagle | 67 | Norwich Central | 33 | Nottingham | 34 |
| Olivers Mount | 66 | Oxford | 49 | Perth | 55 | Peterhead | 68 |
| Plympton | 30 | Presely | 37 | Redruth | 37 | Ridge Hill | 35 |
| Sandy Heath | 39 | Selkirk | 52 | Sheffield | 67 | Storeton | 39 |
| Sudbury | 35 | Tacolneston | 52 | Tay Bridge | 34 | The Wrekin | 35 |
| Waltham | 35 | Winter Hill | 48 | | | | |

## Local Radio and TV Talkback, Links and Theatre Radiomicrophones

| Base | Mobile | Mode | Location | User and Notes |
|---|---|---|---|---|
| 470.50650 | | NFM | Nationwide | British Telecom |
| 471.66250 | | NFM | Nationwide | Benetton Formula 1 Racing Team Berger |
| 471.92500 | 459.77500 | NFM | Nationwide | Ligier Formula 1 Racing Team |
| 473.68750 | | NFM | London | R.Mic Canadian Broadcast CBC |
| 473.95000 | | NFM | Newcastle Upon Tyne | Metro Radio talkback |
| 474.05000 | | NFM | Norwich | Anglia TV Ch 1 |
| 474.10000 | | NFM | Norwich | Anglia TV Ch 2 |
| 474.20000 | | NFM | Norwich | Anglia TV Ch 3 |
| 474.40000 | | NFM | Norwich | Anglia TV Ch 4 |
| 474.75000 | | NFM | London | BBC OB Producers Link |
| 476.46250 | | NFM | Tyneside | Metro Radio Starbust 1 helicopter downlink |
| 476.47500 | | NFM | London | Capital Radio Flying Eye |
| 476.95000 | | NFM | London | U.S. Secret Service DVP Al Gore visit |
| 476.97500 | | NFM | England, South West | BBC Southeast TV OB |
| 477.05000 | | NFM | London | U.S. Secret Service DVP Al Gore visit |
| 477.20000 | | NFM | London | U.S. Secret Service DVP Al Gore visit |
| 478.00000 | | NFM | London | Radio London |
| 478.70000 | | NFM | Nationwide | Theatre Radiomicrophone |
| 479.03750 | | NFM | London | U.S. Secret Service DVP Al Gore visit |
| 479.65000 | | NFM | London | Her Majesty's Theatre |
| 479.65000 | | NFM | Nationwide | Theatre Radiomicrophone |
| 479.95000 | | NFM | London | Her Majesty's Theatre |
| 480.20000 | | NFM | London | Her Majesty's Theatre |
| 480.20000 | | NFM | Nationwide | Theatre Radiomicrophone |
| 480.40000 | | NFM | Nationwide | Theatre Radiomicrophone |
| 483.75000 | | NFM | London | Prince Edward Theatre Radio Mic |
| 488.82500 | | NFM | London | Talking Clock |
| 495.56750 | 479.67500 | NFM | Glasgow | Victorias Nite Club microphones |
| 497.50000 | | NFM | Nationwide | Theatre Radiomicrophone |
| 497.70000 | | NFM | Nationwide | Theatre Radiomicrophone |
| 498.48000 | | NFM | Nationwide | Theatre Radiomicrophone |
| 498.78000 | | NFM | Nationwide | Theatre Radiomicrophone |
| 498.82500 | | NFM | London | Prince Edward Theatre Radio Mic |
| 499.61000 | | NFM | Nationwide | Theatre Radiomicrophone |
| 500.28000 | | NFM | Nationwide | Theatre Radiomicrophone |
| 502.44000 | | NFM | Nationwide | Theatre Radiomicrophone |
| 502.69000 | | NFM | Nationwide | Theatre Radiomicrophone |
| 583.69000 | | NFM | Nationwide | Theatre Radiomicrophone |
| 584.15000 | | NFM | Nationwide | Theatre Radiomicrophone |
| 590.00000 | | NFM | Nationwide | JFGM radio microphone Ch.36 |
| 598.00000 | | NFM | Nationwide | JFGM radio microphone Ch.36 |
| 598.00000 | | NFM | Nationwide | JFGM radio microphone Ch.37 |
| 606.00000 | | NFM | Nationwide | JFGM radio microphone Ch.37 |
| 606.00000 | | NFM | Nationwide | JFGM radio microphone Ch.38 |
| 614.00000 | | NFM | Nationwide | JFGM radio microphone Ch.38 |

**477.00 - 854.00 MHz**      IRISH TELEVISION CHANNELS

| Sound | Video | | | |
|--------|--------|------|-------------|-----------|
| 477.250 | 471.250 | WFM | Ballybofey | RTE 1 |
| | | WFM | Cahir | RTE 1 |
| | | WFM | Stranolar | RTE 1 |
| 485.250 | 479.250 | WFM | Kerry | RTE 1 |
| | | WFM | Malin | RTE 1 |
| 493.250 | | WFM | Dingle | RTE 1 |
| 493.250 | | WFM | Donegal | RTE 1 |
| 501.250 | | WFM | Cahir | Network 2 |
| 509.250 | | WFM | Kerry | Network 2 |
| | | WFM | Malin | Network 2 |
| 511.250 | | WFM | Dingle | Network 2 |
| | | WFM | Donegal | Network 2 |
| 519.250 | | WFM | Clonmel | RTE 1 |
| 541.250 | | WFM | Co. Cork | RTE 1 |
| | | WFM | Dublin | RTE 1 |
| 549.250 | | WFM | Youghal | RTE 1 |
| 549.259 | | WFM | Bandon | RTE 1 |
| | | WFM | Knockmoyle | RTE 1 |
| 557.250 | | WFM | Ballybofey | Network 2 |
| | | WFM | Clonmel | Network 2 |
| | | WFM | Stranolar | Network 2 |
| 573.250 | | WFM | Co. Cork | Network 2 |
| | | WFM | Dublin | Network 2 |
| 581.250 | | WFM | Bandon | Network 2 |
| | | WFM | Knockmoyle | Network 2 |
| | | WFM | Youghal | Network 2 |
| 621.250 | | WFM | Bantry | RTE 1 |
| | | WFM | Cork City | RTE 1 |
| | | WFM | Glenbeigh | RTE 1 |
| 629.250 | | WFM | Dunquin | RTE 1 |
| | | WFM | Longford | RTE 1 |
| 645.250 | | WFM | Glenbeigh | Network 2 |
| | | WFM | Dunquin | Network 2 |
| | | WFM | Longford | Network 2 |
| 693.250 | | WFM | Limerick City | RTE 1 |
| 701.250 | | WFM | Bantry | Network 2 |
| | | WFM | Cork City | Network 2 |
| 725.250 | | WFM | Limerick City | Network 2 |
| | | WFM | Louth | RTE 1 |
| 733.250 | | WFM | Inistioge | RTE 1 |
| 749.250 | | WFM | Crosshaven | RTE 1 |
| 757.250 | | WFM | Louth | Network 2 |
| 765.250 | | WFM | Inistioge | Network 2 |
| 781.250 | | WFM | Crosshaven | Network 2 |
| 797.250 | | WFM | Carlingford | RTE 1 |
| 845.250 | | WFM | Carlingford | Network 2 |

**500.00000**            AM NATIONWIDE NATO MAYDAY DISCRETE

**590.0000 - 598.0000 MHz**     CIVIL & DEFENCE RADAR

**606.0000 - 614.0000 MHz**     RADIO ASTRONOMY

**854.500 - 855.250 MHz**    RADIO MICROPHONES AND
BROADCASTING LINKS

| Base | Mobile | Mode | Location | User and Notes |
|------|--------|------|----------|----------------|
| 854.50000 | | WFM | Ipswich | BBC Look-East London Studio |
| 854.50000 | | WFM | Sutton Coldfield | BBC O/B Link |
| 854.75000 | | WFM | Nationwide | Channel 1 |
| 854.75000 | 856.00000 | NFM | Nationwide | JFMG Airborne Use |
| 854.77500 | | WFM | Nationwide | Channel 2 |
| 854.77500 | | NFM | Nationwide | JFMG mono high power O/B sound link |
| 854.80000 | | WFM | Nationwide | Channel 3 |
| 854.82500 | | WFM | Nationwide | Channel 4 |
| 854.85000 | | WFM | Nationwide | Channel 5 |
| 854.87500 | | WFM | Nationwide | Channel 6 |
| 854.90000 | | NFM | Nationwide | JFMG radio mic. mobile Ch.ML4 |
| 854.90000 | | WFM | Nationwide | Channel 7 |
| 854.92500 | | WFM | Nationwide | Channel 8 |
| 854.95000 | | WFM | Nationwide | Channel 9 |
| 854.97500 | | WFM | Nationwide | Channel 10 |
| 855.00000 | | WFM | Nationwide | Channel 11 |
| 855.02500 | | WFM | Nationwide | Channel 12 |
| 855.05000 | | WFM | Nationwide | Channel 13 |
| 855.07500 | | NFM | Nationwide | JFMG mono high power sound link |
| 855.07500 | | NFM | Nationwide | JFMG set radio mic co-ord Ch.68 |
| 855.07500 | | WFM | Nationwide | Channel 14 |
| 855.10000 | | WFM | Nationwide | Channel 15 |
| 855.12500 | | WFM | Nationwide | Channel 16 |
| 855.15000 | | WFM | Nationwide | Channel 17 |
| 855.17500 | | WFM | Nationwide | Channel 18 |
| 855.20000 | | WFM | Nationwide | Channel 19 |
| 855.22500 | | WFM | Nationwide | Channel 20 |
| 855.27500 | | NFM | London | Prince Edward Theatre Radio Mic |
| 855.27500 | | NFM | London | Prince of Wales Theatre Radio Mic |
| 855.27500 | | NFM | Nationwide | JFMG radio mic. mobile Ch.ML5 |
| 855.40000 | | NFM | Nationwide | JFMG mono low power sound link |
| 855.45000 | | NFM | Nationwide | JFMG mono low power sound link |
| 855.47500 | | NFM | Nationwide | JFMG mono low power sound link |
| 855.47500 | | NFM | Nationwide | JFMG set 1 radio mic co-ord Ch.68 |
| 855.50000 | | NFM | Nationwide | JFMG mono low power sound link |
| 855.55000 | | NFM | Nationwide | JFMG mono low power sound link |
| 855.60000 | | NFM | Nationwide | JFMG mono low power sound link |
| 855.65000 | | NFM | Nationwide | JFMG mono low power sound link |
| 855.67500 | | NFM | Nationwide | JFMG set 1 radio mic co-ord Ch.68 |
| 855.67500 | | NFM | Nationwide | JFMG stereo low power sound link |
| 855.70000 | | NFM | Nationwide | JFMG mono low power sound link |
| 855.75000 | | NFM | Nationwide | JFMG mono low power sound link |
| 855.90000 | | NFM | London | Noels House Party Radio Mic High Power |
| 855.90000 | | NFM | Nationwide | JFMG radio mic mobile Ch.M116 |
| 855.90000 | | NFM | London | Prince Edward Theatre Radio Mic |
| 856.17500 | | NFM | Nationwide | JFMG radio mic mobile Ch.M120 |
| 856.25000 | | WFM | London | Cable News Engineer Radio Mic |
| 856.30000 | | NFM | Nationwide | JFMG mono low power sound link |
| 856.35000 | | NFM | Nationwide | JFMG mono low power sound link |
| 856.37500 | | NFM | Nationwide | JFMG set 1 radio mic co-ord Ch.68 |
| 856.37500 | | NFM | Nationwide | JFMG stereo low power sound link |
| 856.40000 | | NFM | Nationwide | JFMG mono low power sound link |
| 856.45000 | | NFM | Nationwide | JFMG mono low power sound link |

| Base | Mobile | Mode | Location | User and Notes |
| --- | --- | --- | --- | --- |
| 856.50000 | | NFM | Nationwide | JFMG radio mic set 2 co-ord Ch.68 |
| 856.57500 | | NFM | Nationwide | JFMG radio mic mobile Ch.ML21 |
| 856.72500 | | NFM | Nationwide | JFMG mono low power sound link |
| 856.77500 | | NFM | Nationwide | JFMG mono low power sound link |
| 856.80000 | | NFM | Nationwide | JFMG set 1 radio mic co-ord Ch.68 |
| 856.80000 | | NFM | Nationwide | JFMG stereo low power sound link |
| 856.82500 | | NFM | Nationwide | JFMG mono low power sound link |
| 856.87500 | | NFM | Nationwide | JFMG mono low power sound link |
| 857.02500 | | NFM | Nationwide | JFMG radio mic set 2 co-ord Ch.68 |
| 857.35000 | | NFM | Nationwide | JFMG mono low power O/B sound link |
| 857.40000 | | NFM | Nationwide | JFMG mono low power O/B sound link |
| 857.42500 | | NFM | Nationwide | JFMG set 1 radio mic co-ord Ch.68 |
| 857.42500 | | NFM | Nationwide | JFMG stereo High/Low power alternate |
| 857.45000 | | NFM | Nationwide | JFMG mono low power O/B sound link |
| 857.50000 | | NFM | Nationwide | JFMG mono low power O/B sound link |
| 857.50000 | | NFM | Nationwide | JFMG radio mic set 2 co-ord Ch.68 |
| 857.62500 | | NFM | Nationwide | JFMG radio mic mobile Ch.M122 |
| 857.77500 | | NFM | Nationwide | JFMG set 3 radio mic co-ord Ch.68 |
| 857.95000 | | NFM | Nationwide | JFMG radio mic mobile Ch.ML22 |
| 858.20000 | | NFM | London | Prince Edward Theatre Radio Mic |
| 858.20000 | | NFM | Nationwide | JFMG radio mic mobile Ch.M124 |
| 858.25000 | | NFM | Nationwide | JFMG radio mic set 2 co-ord Ch.68 |
| 858.37500 | | NFM | Nationwide | JFMG set 3 radio mic co-ord Ch.68 |
| 858.65000 | | NFM | Nationwide | JFMG radio mic mobile Ch.M125 |
| 858.70000 | | NFM | Nationwide | JFMG radio mic set 2 co-ord Ch.68 |
| 859.10000 | | NFM | Nationwide | JFMG radio mic set 2 co-ord Ch.68 |
| 859.52500 | | NFM | Nationwide | JFMG radio mic set 2 co-ord Ch.68 |
| 859.80000 | | WFM | Sutton Coldfield | BBC O/B Link |

## 860.2500 - 860.7500 MHz    Radio Microphones

| Base | Mobile | Mode | Location | User and Notes |
| --- | --- | --- | --- | --- |
| 860.25000 | | WFM | Nationwide | Channel 1 |
| 860.25000 | 862.25000 | NFM | Nationwide | JFMG Airborne Use |
| 860.27500 | | NFM | Nationwide | JFMG mono low power O/B sound link |
| 860.27500 | | WFM | Nationwide | Channel 2 |
| 860.30000 | | WFM | Nationwide | Channel 3 |
| 860.32500 | | WFM | Nationwide | Channel 4 |
| 860.35000 | | WFM | Nationwide | Channel 5 |
| 860.37500 | | WFM | Nationwide | Channel 6 |
| 860.40000 | | NFM | Nationwide | JFMG mono high power O/B sound link |
| 860.40000 | | WFM | Nationwide | Channel 7 |
| 860.42500 | | WFM | Nationwide | Channel 8 |
| 860.45000 | | WFM | Nationwide | Channel 9 |
| 860.47500 | | WFM | Nationwide | Channel 10 |
| 860.50000 | | WFM | Nationwide | Channel 11 |
| 860.52500 | | NFM | Nationwide | JFMG mono high power O/B sound link |
| 860.52500 | | NFM | Nationwide | JFMG mono low power O/B sound link |
| 860.52500 | | WFM | Nationwide | Channel 12 |
| 860.55000 | | WFM | Nationwide | Channel 13 |
| 860.57500 | | NFM | Nationwide | JFMG mono high power O/B sound link |
| 860.57500 | | NFM | Nationwide | JFMG mono low power O/B sound link |
| 860.57500 | | WFM | Nationwide | Channel 14 |
| 860.60000 | | NFM | Nationwide | JFMG mono high power O/B sound link |
| 860.60000 | | NFM | Nationwide | JFMG mono low power O/B sound link |
| 860.60000 | | NFM | Nationwide | JFMG set 1 radio mic co-ord Ch.68 |
| 860.60000 | | NFM | Nationwide | JFMG stereo high power sound link |

| Base | Mobile | Mode | Location | User and Notes |
|---|---|---|---|---|
| 860.60000 | | WFM | Nationwide | Channel 15 |
| 860.62500 | | NFM | Nationwide | JFMG mono high power O/B sound link |
| 860.62500 | | NFM | Nationwide | JFMG mono low power O/B sound link |
| 860.62500 | | WFM | Nationwide | Channel 16 |
| 860.65000 | | WFM | Nationwide | Channel 17 |
| 860.67500 | | NFM | Nationwide | JFMG mono high power O/B sound link |
| 860.67500 | | NFM | Nationwide | JFMG mono low power O/B sound link |
| 860.67500 | | WFM | Nationwide | Channel 18 |
| 860.70000 | | WFM | Nationwide | Channel 19 |
| 860.72500 | | NFM | Nationwide | JFMG mono high power sound link |
| 860.72500 | | NFM | Nationwide | JFMG set 3 radio mic co-ord Ch.68 |
| 860.72500 | | WFM | Nationwide | Channel 20 |
| 860.90000 | | NFM | Nationwide | JFMG radio mic mobile Ch.M118 |
| 861.17500 | | NFM | London | Prince of Wales Theatre Radio Mic |
| 861.20000 | | NFM | London | Prince of Wales Theatre Radio Mic |
| 861.20000 | | NFM | Nationwide | JFMG radio mic mobile Ch.M126 |
| 861.37500 | | NFM | Nationwide | JFMG set 3 radio mic co-ord Ch.68 |
| 861.55000 | | NFM | Nationwide | JFMG radio mic mobile Ch.ML27 |
| 861.75000 | | NFM | Nationwide | JFMG radio mic mobile Ch.ML19 |
| 861.92500 | | NFM | Nationwide | JFMG set 3 radio mic co-ord Ch.68 |
| 863.70000 | | NFM | Nationwide | Senhthser Headphones/Ross Wireless Speakers |
| 863.72500 | | WFM | Nationwide | Senhthser Headphones/Ross Wireless Speakers |
| 863.77500 | | WFM | Nationwide | Senhthser Headphones/Ross Wireless Speakers |
| 863.80000 | | WFM | Nationwide | Senhthser Headphones/Ross Wireless Speakers |
| 863.82500 | | WFM | Nationwide | Senhthser Headphones/Ross Wireless Speakers |
| 863.85000 | | WFM | Nationwide | Senhthser Headphones/Ross Wireless Speakers |
| 863.87500 | | WFM | Nationwide | Senhthser Headphones/Ross Wireless Speakers |
| 863.97500 | | WFM | Nationwide | Senhthser Headphones/Ross Wireless Speakers |
| 864.00000 | | WFM | Nationwide | Senhthser Headphones/Ross Wireless Speakers |
| 870.02500 | | NFM | Bournemouth | BBC O/B Link |
| 875.00000 | | WFM | Nationwide | WFM BBC Music Link |
| 880.00000 | | WFM | Nationwide | WFM BBC Music Link |

## 917.0125 - 949.9875 MHz   UHF Cellular ETACS (Extended Total Access Communications System)
### Telephone Nodes

| Base | Mobile | Mode | Location | User and Notes |
|---|---|---|---|---|
| 917.01250 | 872.01250 | NFM | Nationwide | Vodafone Channel 1329 |
| 917.03750 | 872.03750 | NFM | Nationwide | Vodafone Channel 1330 |
| 917.06250 | 872.06250 | NFM | Nationwide | Vodafone Channel 1331 |
| 917.08750 | 872.08750 | NFM | Nationwide | Vodafone Channel 1332 |
| 917.16250 | 872.16250 | NFM | Nationwide | Vodafone Channel 1335 |
| 917.21250 | 872.21250 | NFM | Nationwide | Vodafone Channel 1337 |
| 917.26250 | 872.26250 | NFM | Nationwide | Vodafone Channel 1339 |
| 917.31250 | 872.31250 | NFM | Nationwide | Vodafone Channel 1341 |
| 917.33750 | 872.33750 | NFM | Nationwide | Vodafone Channel 1342 |
| 917.36250 | 872.36250 | NFM | Nationwide | Vodafone Channel 1343 |
| 917.38750 | 872.38750 | NFM | Nationwide | Vodafone Channel 1344 |
| 917.41250 | 872.41250 | NFM | Nationwide | Vodafone Channel 1345 |
| 917.43750 | 872.43750 | NFM | Nationwide | Vodafone Channel 1346 |
| 917.46250 | 872.46250 | NFM | Nationwide | Vodafone Channel 1347 |
| 917.48750 | 872.48750 | NFM | Nationwide | Vodafone Channel 1348 |
| 917.51250 | 872.51250 | NFM | Nationwide | Vodafone Channel 1349 |
| 917.53750 | 872.53750 | NFM | Nationwide | Vodafone Channel 1350 |
| 917.56250 | 872.56250 | NFM | Nationwide | Vodafone Channel 1351 |
| 917.58750 | 872.58750 | NFM | Nationwide | Vodafone Channel 1352 |

| Base | Mobile | Mode | Location | User and Notes |
|------|--------|------|----------|----------------|
| 917.61250 | 872.61250 | NFM | Nationwide | Vodafone Channel 1353 |
| 917.68750 | 872.68750 | NFM | Nationwide | Vodafone Channel 1356 |
| 917.73750 | 872.73750 | NFM | Nationwide | Vodafone Channel 1358 |
| 917.78750 | 872.78750 | NFM | Nationwide | Vodafone Channel 1360 |
| 917.83750 | 872.83750 | NFM | Nationwide | Vodafone Channel 1362 |
| 917.86250 | 872.86250 | NFM | Nationwide | Vodafone Channel 1363 |
| 917.88750 | 872.88750 | NFM | Nationwide | Vodafone Channel 1364 |
| 917.91250 | 872.91250 | NFM | Nationwide | Vodafone Channel 1365 |
| 917.93750 | 872.93750 | NFM | Nationwide | Vodafone Channel 1366 |
| 917.96250 | 872.96250 | NFM | Nationwide | Vodafone Channel 1367 |
| 918.01250 | 873.01250 | NFM | Nationwide | Vodafone Channel 1369 |
| 918.03750 | 873.03750 | NFM | Nationwide | Vodafone Channel 1370 |
| 918.06250 | 873.06250 | NFM | Nationwide | Vodafone Channel 1371 |
| 918.08750 | 873.08750 | NFM | Nationwide | Vodafone Channel 1372 |
| 918.11250 | 873.11250 | NFM | Nationwide | Vodafone Channel 1373 |
| 918.13750 | 873.13750 | NFM | Nationwide | Vodafone Channel 1374 |
| 918.21250 | 873.21250 | NFM | Nationwide | Vodafone Channel 1377 |
| 918.26250 | 873.26250 | NFM | Nationwide | Vodafone Channel 1379 |
| 918.31250 | 873.31250 | NFM | Nationwide | Vodafone Channel 1381 |
| 918.36250 | 873.36250 | NFM | Nationwide | Vodafone Channel 1383 |
| 918.38750 | 873.38750 | NFM | Nationwide | Vodafone Channel 1384 |
| 918.41250 | 873.41250 | NFM | Nationwide | Vodafone Channel 1385 |
| 918.43750 | 873.43750 | NFM | Nationwide | Vodafone Channel 1386 |
| 918.48750 | 873.48750 | NFM | Nationwide | Vodafone Channel 1388 |
| 918.51250 | 873.51250 | NFM | Nationwide | Vodafone Channel 1389 |
| 918.53750 | 873.53750 | NFM | Nationwide | Vodafone Channel 1390 |
| 918.56250 | 873.56250 | NFM | Nationwide | Vodafone Channel 1391 |
| 918.58750 | 873.58750 | NFM | Nationwide | Vodafone Channel 1392 |
| 918.61250 | 873.61250 | NFM | Nationwide | Vodafone Channel 1393 |
| 918.63750 | 873.63750 | NFM | Nationwide | Vodafone Channel 1394 |
| 918.66250 | 873.66250 | NFM | Nationwide | Vodafone Channel 1395 |
| 918.73750 | 873.73750 | NFM | Nationwide | Vodafone Channel 1398 |
| 918.78750 | 873.78750 | NFM | Nationwide | Vodafone Channel 1400 |
| 918.83750 | 873.83750 | NFM | Nationwide | Vodafone Channel 1402 |
| 918.88750 | 873.88750 | NFM | Nationwide | Vodafone Channel 1404 |
| 918.91250 | 873.91250 | NFM | Nationwide | Vodafone Channel 1405 |
| 918.93750 | 873.93750 | NFM | Nationwide | Vodafone Channel 1406 |
| 918.96250 | 873.96250 | NFM | Nationwide | Vodafone Channel 1407 |
| 919.01250 | 874.01250 | NFM | Nationwide | Vodafone Channel 1409 |
| 919.06250 | 874.06250 | NFM | Nationwide | Vodafone Channel 1411 |
| 919.08750 | 874.08750 | NFM | Nationwide | Vodafone Channel 1412 |
| 919.11250 | 874.11250 | NFM | Nationwide | Vodafone Channel 1413 |
| 919.13750 | 874.13750 | NFM | Nationwide | Vodafone Channel 1414 |
| 919.16250 | 874.16250 | NFM | Nationwide | Vodafone Channel 1415 |
| 919.18750 | 874.18750 | NFM | Nationwide | Vodafone Channel 1416 |
| 919.23750 | 874.23750 | NFM | Nationwide | Vodafone Channel 1418 |
| 919.26250 | 874.26250 | NFM | Nationwide | Vodafone Channel 1419 |
| 919.31250 | 874.31250 | NFM | Nationwide | Vodafone Channel 1421 |
| 919.36250 | 874.36250 | NFM | Nationwide | Vodafone Channel 1423 |
| 919.41250 | 874.41250 | NFM | Nationwide | Vodafone Channel 1425 |
| 919.43750 | 874.43750 | NFM | Nationwide | Vodafone Channel 1426 |
| 919.46250 | 874.46250 | NFM | Nationwide | Vodafone Channel 1427 |
| 919.48750 | 874.48750 | NFM | Nationwide | Vodafone Channel 1428 |
| 919.53750 | 874.53750 | NFM | Nationwide | Vodafone Channel 1430 |
| 919.56250 | 874.56250 | NFM | Nationwide | Vodafone Channel 1431 |
| 919.58750 | 874.58750 | NFM | Nationwide | Vodafone Channel 1432 |

| Base | Mobile | Mode | Location | User and Notes |
|------|--------|------|----------|----------------|
| 919.61250 | 874.61250 | NFM | Nationwide | Vodafone Channel 1433 |
| 919.63750 | 874.63750 | NFM | Nationwide | Vodafone Channel 1434 |
| 919.66250 | 874.66250 | NFM | Nationwide | Vodafone Channel 1435 |
| 919.68750 | 874.68750 | NFM | Nationwide | Vodafone Channel 1436 |
| 919.71250 | 874.71250 | NFM | Nationwide | Vodafone Channel 1437 |
| 919.76250 | 874.76250 | NFM | Nationwide | Vodafone Channel 1439 |
| 919.78750 | 874.78750 | NFM | Nationwide | Vodafone Channel 1440 |
| 919.83750 | 874.83750 | NFM | Nationwide | Vodafone Channel 1442 |
| 919.88750 | 874.88750 | NFM | Nationwide | Vodafone Channel 1444 |
| 919.91250 | 874.91250 | NFM | Nationwide | Vodafone Channel 1445 |
| 919.93750 | 874.93750 | NFM | Nationwide | Vodafone Channel 1446 |
| 919.96250 | 874.96250 | NFM | Nationwide | Vodafone Channel 1447 |
| 919.98750 | 874.98750 | NFM | Nationwide | Vodafone Channel 1448 |
| 920.01250 | 875.01250 | NFM | Nationwide | Vodafone Channel 1449 |
| 920.06250 | 875.06250 | NFM | Nationwide | Vodafone Channel 1451 |
| 920.08750 | 875.08750 | NFM | Nationwide | Vodafone Channel 1452 |
| 920.11250 | 875.11250 | NFM | Nationwide | Vodafone Channel 1453 |
| 920.13750 | 875.13750 | NFM | Nationwide | Vodafone Channel 1454 |
| 920.16250 | 875.16250 | NFM | Nationwide | Vodafone Channel 1455 |
| 920.18750 | 875.18750 | NFM | Nationwide | Vodafone Channel 1456 |
| 920.21250 | 875.21250 | NFM | Nationwide | Vodafone Channel 1457 |
| 920.23750 | 875.23750 | NFM | Nationwide | Vodatone Channel 1458 |
| 920.31250 | 875.31250 | NFM | Nationwide | Vodafone Channel 1461 |
| 920.36250 | 875.36250 | NFM | Nationwide | Vodafone Channel 1463 |
| 920.41250 | 875.41250 | NFM | Nationwide | Vodafone Channel 1465 |
| 920.46250 | 875.46250 | NFM | Nationwide | Vodafone Channel 1467 |
| 920.48750 | 875.48750 | NFM | Nationwide | Vodafone Channel 1468 |
| 920.53750 | 875.53750 | NFM | Nationwide | Vodafone Channel 1470 |
| 920.58750 | 875.58750 | NFM | Nationwide | Vodafone Channel 1472 |
| 920.61250 | 875.61250 | NFM | Nationwide | Vodafone Channel 1473 |
| 920.63750 | 875.63750 | NFM | Nationwide | Vodafone Channel 1474 |
| 920.66250 | 875.66250 | NFM | Nationwide | Vodafone Channel 1475 |
| 920.68750 | 875.68750 | NFM | Nationwide | Vodafone Channel 1476 |
| 920.71250 | 875.71250 | NFM | Nationwide | Vodafone Channel 1477 |
| 920.73750 | 875.73750 | NFM | Nationwide | Vodafone Channel 1478 |
| 920.76250 | 875.76250 | NFM | Nationwide | Vodafone Channel 1479 |
| 920.83750 | 875.83750 | NFM | Nationwide | Vodafone Channel 1482 |
| 920.88750 | 875.88750 | NFM | Nationwide | Vodafone Channel 1484 |
| 920.93750 | 875.93750 | NFM | Nationwide | Vodafone Channel 1486 |
| 920.98750 | 875.98750 | NFM | Nationwide | Vodafone Channel 1488 |
| 921.01250 | 876.01250 | NFM | Nationwide | Vodafone Channel 1489 |
| 921.06250 | 876.06250 | NFM | Nationwide | Vodafone Channel 1491 |
| 921.11250 | 876.11250 | NFM | Nationwide | Vodafone Channel 1493 |
| 921.13750 | 876.13750 | NFM | Nationwide | Vodafone Channel 1494 |
| 921.16250 | 876.16250 | NFM | Nationwide | Vodafone Channel 1495 |
| 921.18750 | 876.18750 | NFM | Nationwide | Vodafone Channel 1496 |
| 921.21250 | 876.21250 | NFM | Nationwide | Vodafone Channel 1497 |
| 921.23750 | 876.23750 | NFM | Nationwide | Vodafone Channel 1498 |
| 921.26250 | 876.26250 | NFM | Nationwide | Vodafone Channel 1499 |
| 921.28750 | 876.28750 | NFM | Nationwide | Vodafone Channel 1500 |
| 921.36250 | 876.36250 | NFM | Nationwide | Vodafone Channel 1503 |
| 921.41250 | 876.41250 | NFM | Nationwide | Vodafone Channel 1505 |
| 921.46250 | 876.46250 | NFM | Nationwide | Vodafone Channel 1507 |
| 921.51250 | 876.51250 | NFM | Nationwide | Vodafone Channel 1509 |
| 921.53750 | 876.53750 | NFM | Nationwide | Vodafone Channel 1510 |
| 921.58750 | 876.58750 | NFM | Nationwide | Vodafone Channel 1512 |

| Base | Mobile | Mode | Location | User and Notes |
|------|--------|------|----------|----------------|
| 921.63750 | 876.63750 | NFM | Nationwide | Vodafone Channel 1514 |
| 921.66250 | 876.66250 | NFM | Nationwide | Vodafone Channel 1515 |
| 921.68750 | 876.68750 | NFM | Nationwide | Vodafone Channel 1516 |
| 921.71250 | 876.71250 | NFM | Nationwide | Vodafone Channel 1517 |
| 921.73750 | 876.73750 | NFM | Nationwide | Vodafone Channel 1518 |
| 921.76250 | 876.76250 | NFM | Nationwide | Vodafone Channel 1519 |
| 921.78750 | 876.78750 | NFM | Nationwide | Vodafone Channel 1520 |
| 921.81250 | 876.81250 | NFM | Nationwide | Vodafone Channel 1521 |
| 921.88750 | 876.88750 | NFM | Nationwide | Vodafone Channel 1524 |
| 921.93750 | 876.93750 | NFM | Nationwide | Vodafone Channel 1526 |
| 921.98750 | 876.98750 | NFM | Nationwide | Vodafone Channel 1528 |
| 922.03750 | 877.03750 | NFM | Nationwide | Vodafone Channel 1530 |
| 922.06250 | 877.06250 | NFM | Nationwide | Vodafone Channel 1531 |
| 922.08750 | 877.08750 | NFM | Nationwide | Vodafone Channel 1532 |
| 922.11250 | 877.11250 | NFM | Nationwide | Vodafone Channel 1533 |
| 922.16250 | 877.16250 | NFM | Nationwide | Vodafone Channel 1535 |
| 922.21250 | 877.21250 | NFM | Nationwide | Vodafone Channel 1537 |
| 922.23750 | 877.23750 | NFM | Nationwide | Vodafone Channel 1538 |
| 922.26250 | 877.26250 | NFM | Nationwide | Vodafone Channel 1539 |
| 922.28750 | 877.28750 | NFM | Nationwide | Vodafone Channel 1540 |
| 922.31250 | 877.31250 | NFM | Nationwide | Vodafone Channel 1541 |
| 922.33750 | 877.33750 | NFM | Nationwide | Vodafone Channel 1542 |
| 922.41250 | 877.41250 | NFM | Nationwide | Vodafone Channel 1545 |
| 922.46250 | 877.46250 | NFM | Nationwide | Vodafone Channel 1547 |
| 922.51250 | 877.51250 | NFM | Nationwide | Vodafone Channel 1549 |
| 922.56250 | 877.56250 | NFM | Nationwide | Vodafone Channel 1551 |
| 922.58750 | 877.58750 | NFM | Nationwide | Vodafone Channel 1552 |
| 922.63750 | 877.63750 | NFM | Nationwide | Vodafone Channel 1554 |
| 922.68750 | 877.68750 | NFM | Nationwide | Vodafone Channel 1556 |
| 922.73750 | 877.73750 | NFM | Nationwide | Vodafone Channel 1558 |
| 922.76250 | 877.76250 | NFM | Nationwide | Vodafone Channel 1559 |
| 922.78750 | 877.78750 | NFM | Nationwide | Vodafone Channel 1560 |
| 922.81250 | 877.81250 | NFM | Nationwide | Vodafone Channel 1561 |
| 922.83750 | 877.83750 | NFM | Nationwide | Vodafone Channel 1562 |
| 922.86250 | 877.86250 | NFM | Nationwide | Vodafone Channel 1563 |
| 922.93750 | 877.93750 | NFM | Nationwide | Vodafone Channel 1566 |
| 922.98750 | 877.98750 | NFM | Nationwide | Vodafone Channel 1568 |
| 923.03750 | 878.03750 | NFM | Nationwide | Vodafone Channel 1570 |
| 923.08750 | 878.08750 | NFM | Nationwide | Vodafone Channel 1572 |
| 923.11250 | 878.11250 | NFM | Nationwide | Vodafone Channel 1573 |
| 923.16250 | 878.16250 | NFM | Nationwide | Vodafone Channel 1575 |
| 923.21250 | 878.21250 | NFM | Nationwide | Vodafone Channel 1577 |
| 923.26250 | 878.26250 | NFM | Nationwide | Vodafone Channel 1579 |
| 923.28750 | 878.28750 | NFM | Nationwide | Vodafone Channel 1580 |
| 923.31250 | 878.31250 | NFM | Nationwide | Vodafone Channel 1581 |
| 923.36250 | 878.36250 | NFM | Nationwide | Vodafone Channel 1583 |
| 923.38750 | 878.38750 | NFM | Nationwide | Vodafone Channel 1584 |
| 923.46250 | 878.46250 | NFM | Nationwide | Vodafone Channel 1587 |
| 923.51250 | 878.51250 | NFM | Nationwide | Vodafone Channel 1589 |
| 923.56250 | 878.56250 | NFM | Nationwide | Vodafone Channel 1591 |
| 923.61250 | 878.61250 | NFM | Nationwide | Vodafone Channel 1593 |
| 923.63750 | 878.63750 | NFM | Nationwide | Vodafone Channel 1594 |
| 923.68750 | 878.68750 | NFM | Nationwide | Vodafone Channel 1596 |
| 923.71250 | 878.71250 | NFM | Nationwide | Vodafone Channel 1597 |
| 923.73750 | 878.73750 | NFM | Nationwide | Vodafone Channel 1598 |
| 923.78750 | 878.78750 | NFM | Nationwide | Vodafone Channel 1600 |

| Base | Mobile | Mode | Location | User and Notes |
|------|--------|------|----------|----------------|
| 923.83750 | 878.83750 | NFM | Nationwide | Vodafone Channel 1602 |
| 923.86250 | 878.86250 | NFM | Nationwide | Vodafone Channel 1603 |
| 923.88750 | 878.88750 | NFM | Nationwide | Vodafone Channel 1604 |
| 923.91250 | 878.91250 | NFM | Nationwide | Vodafone Channel 1605 |
| 923.98750 | 878.98750 | NFM | Nationwide | Vodafone Channel 1608 |
| 924.03750 | 879.03750 | NFM | Nationwide | Vodafone Channel 1610 |
| 924.08750 | 879.08750 | NFM | Nationwide | Vodafone Channel 1612 |
| 924.13750 | 879.13750 | NFM | Nationwide | Vodafone Channel 1614 |
| 924.16250 | 879.16250 | NFM | Nationwide | Vodafone Channel 1615 |
| 924.21250 | 879.21250 | NFM | Nationwide | Vodafone Channel 1617 |
| 924.26250 | 879.26250 | NFM | Nationwide | Vodafone Channel 1619 |
| 924.31250 | 879.31250 | NFM | Nationwide | Vodafone Channel 1621 |
| 924.33750 | 879.33750 | NFM | Nationwide | Vodafone Channel 1622 |
| 924.36250 | 879.36250 | NFM | Nationwide | Vodafone Channel 1623 |
| 924.38750 | 879.38750 | NFM | Nationwide | Vodafone Channel 1624 |
| 924.41250 | 879.41250 | NFM | Nationwide | Vodafone Channel 1625 |
| 924.43750 | 879.43750 | NFM | Nationwide | Vodafone Channel 1626 |
| 924.51250 | 879.51250 | NFM | Nationwide | Vodafone Channel 1629 |
| 924.56250 | 879.56250 | NFM | Nationwide | Vodafone Channel 1631 |
| 924.61250 | 879.61250 | NFM | Nationwide | Vodafone Channel 1633 |
| 924.66250 | 879.66250 | NFM | Nationwide | Vodafone Channel 1635 |
| 924.68750 | 879.68750 | NFM | Nationwide | Vodafone Channel 1636 |
| 924.73750 | 879.73750 | NFM | Nationwide | Vodafone Channel 1638 |
| 924.78750 | 879.78750 | NFM | Nationwide | Vodafone Channel 1640 |
| 924.83750 | 879.83750 | NFM | Nationwide | Vodafone Channel 1642 |
| 924.86250 | 879.86250 | NFM | Nationwide | Vodafone Channel 1643 |
| 924.88750 | 879.88750 | NFM | Nationwide | Vodafone Channel 1644 |
| 924.91250 | 879.91250 | NFM | Nationwide | Vodafone Channel 1645 |
| 924.93750 | 879.93750 | NFM | Nationwide | Vodafone Channel 1646 |
| 924.96250 | 879.96250 | NFM | Nationwide | Vodafone Channel 1647 |

926.0000 - 934.0000 MHz          RADIO ASTRONOMY USED FOR PULARS

935.00 - 942.00 MHz          RADIO LOCATION DEVICES

935.0000 - 950.0000 MHz          GSM CELLULAR RADIO TELEPHONES (CELLNET, VODAFONE AND EIREAN TELECOM) REPEATER SITES

### Eirean Telecom

| Base | Mobile | Mode | Location | User and Notes |
|------|--------|------|----------|----------------|
| 935.13750 | | NFM | Galway | Eirean Telecom |
| 935.18750 | | NFM | Galway | Eirean Telecom |
| 935.23750 | | NFM | Ballinrobe | Eirean Telecom |
| 935.26250 | | NFM | Galway | Eirean Telecom |
| 935.31250 | | NFM | Galway | Eirean Telecom |
| 935.43750 | | NFM | Castlebar | Eirean Telecom |
| 935.66250 | | NFM | Galway | Eirean Telecom |
| 935.81250 | | NFM | Galway | Eirean Telecom |
| 935.96250 | | NFM | Castlebar | Eirean Telecom |
| 936.01250 | | NFM | Galway | Eirean Telecom |
| 936.18750 | 891.18750 | NFM | Galway | Eirean Telecom |
| 936.23750 | 891.23750 | NFM | Galway | Eirean Telecom |
| 936.28750 | 891.28750 | NFM | Ballinrobe | Eirean Telecom |
| 936.31250 | 891.31250 | NFM | Galway | Eirean Telecom |

| Base | Mobile | Mode | Location | User and Notes |
|------|--------|------|----------|----------------|
| 936.36250 | 891.36250 | NFM | Galway | Eirean Telecom |
| 936.83750 | 891.83750 | NFM | Galway | Eirean Telecom |
| 936.88750 | 891.88750 | NFM | Galway | Eirean Telecom |
| 937.06250 | 892.06250 | NFM | Galway | Eirean Telecom |
| 937.41250 | 892.41250 | NFM | Galway | Eirean Telecom |
| 937.86250 | 892.86250 | NFM | Ballinrobe | Eirean Telecom |
| 937.88750 | 892.88750 | NFM | Galway | Eirean Telecom |
| 937.93750 | 892.93750 | NFM | Galway | Eirean Telecom |
| 938.11250 | 893.11250 | NFM | Galway | Eirean Telecom |
| 938.38750 | 893.38750 | NFM | Ballinrobe | Eirean Telecom |
| 938.41250 | 893.41250 | NFM | Galway | Eirean Telecom |
| 938.58750 | 893.58750 | NFM | Castlebar | Eirean Telecom |
| 938.63750 | 893.63750 | NFM | Galway | Eirean Telecom |
| 938.66250 | 893.66250 | NFM | Castlebar | Eirean Telecom |
| 938.91250 | 893.91250 | NFM | Ballinrobe | Eirean Telecom |
| 938.93750 | 893.93750 | NFM | Galway | Eirean Telecom |
| 938.98750 | 893.98750 | NFM | Galway | Eirean Telecom |
| 939.16250 | 894.16250 | NFM | Galway | Eirean Telecom |
| 939.33750 | 894.33750 | NFM | Galway | Eirean Telecom |
| 939.38750 | 894.38750 | NFM | Galway | Eirean Telecom |
| 939.43750 | 894.43750 | NFM | Ballinrobe | Eirean Telecom |
| 939.46250 | 894.46250 | NFM | Galway | Eirean Telecom |
| 939.68750 | 894.68750 | NFM | Galway | Eirean Telecom |
| 939.91250 | 894.91250 | NFM | Galway | Eirean Telecom |
| 939.96250 | 894.96250 | NFM | Ballinrobe | Eirean Telecom |
| 939.98750 | 894.98750 | NFM | Galway | Eirean Telecom |
| 940.03750 | 895.03750 | NFM | Galway | Eirean Telecom |
| 940.21250 | 895.21250 | NFM | Galway | Eirean Telecom |
| 940.38750 | 895.38750 | NFM | Galway | Eirean Telecom |
| 940.43750 | 895.43750 | NFM | Galway | Eirean Telecom |
| 940.48750 | 895.48750 | NFM | Ballinrobe | Eirean Telecom |
| 940.56250 | 895.56250 | NFM | Galway | Eirean Telecom |
| 940.68750 | 895.68750 | NFM | Castlebar | Eirean Telecom |
| 940.73750 | 895.73750 | NFM | Galway | Eirean Telecom |
| 941.01250 | 896.01250 | NFM | Galway | Eirean Telecom |
| 941.03750 | 896.03750 | NFM | Galway | Eirean Telecom |
| 941.08750 | 896.08750 | NFM | Galway | Eirean Telecom |
| 941.21250 | 896.21250 | NFM | Ballinrobe | Eirean Telecom |
| 941.26250 | 896.26250 | NFM | Galway | Eirean Telecom |
| 941.31250 | 896.31250 | NFM | Galway | Eirean Telecom |
| 941.56250 | 896.56250 | NFM | Galway | Eirean Telecom |
| 941.78750 | 896.78750 | NFM | Galway | Eirean Telecom |
| 941.96250 | 896.96250 | NFM | Galway | Eirean Telecom |
| 942.08750 | 897.08750 | NFM | Galway | Eirean Telecom |
| 942.48750 | 897.48750 | NFM | Galway | Eirean Telecom |
| 942.53750 | 897.53750 | NFM | Galway | Eirean Telecom |
| 942.61250 | 897.61250 | NFM | Galway | Eirean Telecom |
| 942.83750 | 897.83750 | NFM | Galway | Eirean Telecom |
| 943.13750 | 898.13750 | NFM | Galway | Eirean Telecom |
| 943.18750 | 898.18750 | NFM | Galway | Eirean Telecom |
| 943.68750 | 898.68750 | NFM | Galway | Eirean Telecom |
| 944.38750 | 899.38750 | NFM | Galway | Eirean Telecom |

## UK Mobile Telephones

| Base | Mobile | Mode | Location | User and Notes |
|------|--------|------|----------|----------------|
| 935.06250 | 890.06250 | NFM | Nationwide | Vodafone Channel 3 |
| 935.13750 | 890.13750 | NFM | Nationwide | Vodafone Channel 6 |
| 935.18750 | 890.18750 | NFM | Nationwide | Vodafone Channel 8 |
| 935.21250 | 890.21250 | NFM | Nationwide | Vodafone Channel 9 |
| 935.23750 | 890.23750 | NFM | Nationwide | Vodafone Channel 10 |
| 935.26250 | 890.26250 | NFM | Nationwide | Vodafone Channel 11 |
| 935.28750 | 890.28750 | NFM | Nationwide | Vodafone Channel 12 |
| 935.31250 | 890.31250 | NFM | Nationwide | Vodafone Channel 13 |
| 935.33750 | 890.33750 | NFM | Nationwide | Vodafone Channel 14 |
| 935.36250 | 890.36250 | NFM | Nationwide | Vodafone Channel 15 |
| 935.38750 | 890.38750 | NFM | Nationwide | Vodafone Channel 16 |
| 935.41250 | 890.41250 | NFM | Nationwide | Vodafone Channel 17 |
| 935.43750 | 890.43750 | NFM | Nationwide | Vodafone Channel 18 |
| 935.46250 | 890.46250 | NFM | Nationwide | Vodafone Channel 19 |
| 935.56250 | | NFM | Nationwide | Vodafone Data Control |
| 935.56250 | 890.56250 | NFM | Nationwide | Vodafone Channel 23 |
| 935.58750 | | NFM | Nationwide | Vodafone Data Control |
| 935.58750 | 890.58750 | NFM | Nationwide | Vodafone Channel 24 |
| 935.61250 | | NFM | Nationwide | Vodafone Data Control |
| 935.61250 | 890.61250 | NFM | Nationwide | Vodafone Channel 25 |
| 935.63750 | | NFM | Nationwide | Vodatone Data Control |
| 935.63750 | 890.63750 | NFM | Nationwide | Vodafone Channel 26 |
| 935.66250 | | NFM | Nationwide | Vodafone Data Control |
| 935.66250 | 890.66250 | NFM | Nationwide | Vodafone Channel 27 |
| 935.68750 | | NFM | Nationwide | Vodafone Data Control |
| 935.68750 | 890.68750 | NFM | Nationwide | Vodafone Channel 28 |
| 935.71250 | 890.71250 | NFM | Nationwide | Vodafone Channel 29 |
| 935.71250 | | NFM | Nationwide | Vodafone Data Control |
| 935.73750 | | NFM | Nationwide | Vodafone Data Control |
| 935.73750 | 890.73750 | NFM | Nationwide | Vodafone Channel 30 |
| 935.76250 | 890.76250 | NFM | Nationwide | Vodafone Channel 31 |
| 935.78750 | 890.78750 | NFM | Nationwide | Vodafone Channel 32 |
| 935.78750 | | NFM | Nationwide | Vodafone Data Control |
| 935.81250 | | NFM | Nationwide | Vodafone Data Control |
| 935.81250 | 890.81250 | NFM | Nationwide | Vodafone Channel 33 |
| 935.83750 | | NFM | Nationwide | Vodafone Data Control |
| 935.83750 | 890.83750 | NFM | Nationwide | Vodafone Channel 34 |
| 935.86250 | | NFM | Nationwide | Vodafone Data Control |
| 935.86250 | 890.86250 | NFM | Nationwide | Vodafone Channel 35 |
| 935.88750 | | NFM | Nationwide | Vodafone Data Control |
| 935.88750 | 890.88750 | NFM | Nationwide | Vodafone Channel 36 |
| 935.91250 | 890.91250 | NFM | Nationwide | Vodafone Channel 37 |
| 935.91250 | | NFM | Nationwide | Vodafone Data Control |
| 935.93750 | 890.93750 | NFM | Nationwide | Vodafone Channel 38 |
| 935.93750 | | NFM | Nationwide | Vodafone Data Control |
| 935.96250 | 890.96250 | NFM | Nationwide | Vodafone Channel 39 |
| 935.96250 | | NFM | Nationwide | Vodafone Data Control |
| 935.98750 | | NFM | Nationwide | Vodafone Data Control |
| 935.98750 | 890.98750 | NFM | Nationwide | Vodafone Channel 40 |
| 936.01250 | | NFM | Nationwide | Vodafone Data Control |
| 936.01250 | 891.01250 | NFM | Nationwide | Vodafone Channel 41 |
| 936.03750 | | NFM | Nationwide | Vodafone Data Control |
| 936.03750 | 891.03750 | NFM | Nationwide | Vodafone Channel 42 |
| 936.06250 | 891.06250 | NFM | Nationwide | Vodafone Channel 43 |
| 936.11250 | 891.11250 | NFM | Nationwide | Vodafone Channel 45 |

| Base | Mobile | Mode | Location | User and Notes |
|------|--------|------|----------|----------------|
| 936.18750 | 891.18750 | NFM | Nationwide | Vodafone Channel 48 |
| 936.21250 | 891.21250 | NFM | Nationwide | Vodafone Channel 49 |
| 936.23750 | 891.23750 | NFM | Nationwide | Vodafone Channel 50 |
| 936.26250 | 891.26250 | NFM | Nationwide | Vodafone Channel 51 |
| 936.28750 | 891.28750 | NFM | Nationwide | Vodafone Channel 52 |
| 936.31250 | 891.31250 | NFM | Nationwide | Vodafone Channel 53 |
| 936.33750 | 891.33750 | NFM | Nationwide | Vodafone Channel 54 |
| 936.36250 | 891.36250 | NFM | Nationwide | Vodafone Channel 55 |
| 936.38750 | 891.38750 | NFM | Nationwide | Vodafone Channel 56 |
| 936.41250 | 891.41250 | NFM | Nationwide | Vodafone Channel 57 |
| 936.51250 | 891.51250 | NFM | Nationwide | Vodafone Channel 61 |
| 936.63750 | 891.63750 | NFM | Nationwide | Vodafone Channel 66 |
| 936.68750 | 891.68750 | NFM | Nationwide | Vodafone Channel 68 |
| 936.73750 | 891.73750 | NFM | Nationwide | Vodafone Channel 70 |
| 936.76250 | 891.76250 | NFM | Nationwide | Vodafone Channel 71 |
| 936.81250 | 891.81250 | NFM | Nationwide | Vodafone Channel 73 |
| 936.83750 | 891.83750 | NFM | Nationwide | Vodafone Channel 74 |
| 936.88750 | 891.88750 | NFM | Nationwide | Vodafone Channel 76 |
| 936.93750 | 891.93750 | NFM | Nationwide | Vodafone Channel 78 |
| 937.03750 | 892.03750 | NFM | Nationwide | Vodafone Channel 82 |
| 937.06250 | 892.06250 | NFM | Nationwide | Vodafone Channel 83 |
| 937.16250 | 892.16250 | NFM | Nationwide | Vodafone Channel 87 |
| 937.26250 | 892.26250 | NFM | Nationwide | Vodafone Channel 91 |
| 937.28750 | 892.28750 | NFM | Nationwide | Vodafone Channel 92 |
| 937.31250 | 892.31250 | NFM | Nationwide | Vodafone Channel 93 |
| 937.33750 | 892.33750 | NFM | Nationwide | Vodafone Channel 94 |
| 937.41250 | 892.41250 | NFM | Nationwide | Vodafone Channel 97 |
| 937.43750 | 892.43750 | NFM | Nationwide | Vodafone Channel 98 |
| 937.46250 | 892.46250 | NFM | Nationwide | Vodafone Channel 99 |
| 937.51250 | 892.51250 | NFM | Nationwide | Vodafone Channel 101 |
| 937.56250 | 892.56250 | NFM | Nationwide | Vodafone Channel 103 |
| 937.58750 | 892.58750 | NFM | Nationwide | Vodafone Channel 104 |
| 937.66250 | 892.66250 | NFM | Nationwide | Vodafone Channel 107 |
| 937.78750 | 892.78750 | NFM | Nationwide | Vodafone Channel 112 |
| 937.86250 | 892.86250 | NFM | Nationwide | Vodafone Channel 115 |
| 937.88750 | 892.88750 | NFM | Nationwide | Vodafone Channel 116 |
| 937.93750 | 892.93750 | NFM | Nationwide | Vodafone Channel 118 |
| 937.98750 | 892.98750 | NFM | Nationwide | Vodafone Channel 120 |
| 938.01250 | 893.01250 | NFM | Nationwide | Vodafone Channel 121 |
| 938.03750 | 893.03750 | NFM | Nationwide | Vodafone Channel 122 |
| 938.08750 | 893.08750 | NFM | Nationwide | Vodafone Channel 124 |
| 938.11250 | 893.11250 | NFM | Nationwide | Vodafone Channel 125 |
| 938.13750 | 893.13750 | NFM | Nationwide | Vodafone Channel 126 |
| 938.16250 | 893.16250 | NFM | Nationwide | Vodafone Channel 127 |
| 938.18750 | 893.18750 | NFM | Nationwide | Vodafone Channel 128 |
| 938.21250 | 893.21250 | NFM | Nationwide | Vodafone Channel 129 |
| 938.31250 | 893.31250 | NFM | Nationwide | Vodafone Channel 133 |
| 938.38750 | 893.38750 | NFM | Nationwide | Vodafone Channel 136 |
| 938.41250 | 893.41250 | NFM | Nationwide | Vodafone Channel 137 |
| 938.46250 | 893.46250 | NFM | Nationwide | Vodafone Channel 139 |
| 938.51250 | 893.51250 | NFM | Nationwide | Vodafone Channel 141 |
| 938.53750 | 893.53750 | NFM | Nationwide | Vodafone Channel 142 |
| 938.56250 | 893.56250 | NFM | Nationwide | Vodafone Channel 143 |
| 938.58750 | 893.58750 | NFM | Nationwide | Vodafone Channel 144 |
| 938.61250 | 893.61250 | NFM | Nationwide | Vodafone Channel 145 |
| 938.63750 | 893.63750 | NFM | Nationwide | Vodafone Channel 146 |

| Base | Mobile | Mode | Location | User and Notes |
|------|--------|------|----------|----------------|
| 938.66250 | 893.66250 | NFM | Nationwide | Vodafone Channel 147 |
| 938.73750 | 893.73750 | NFM | Nationwide | Vodafone Channel 150 |
| 938.78750 | 893.78750 | NFM | Nationwide | Vodafone Channel 152 |
| 938.83750 | 893.83750 | NFM | Nationwide | Vodafone Channel 154 |
| 938.86250 | 893.86250 | NFM | Nationwide | Vodafone Channel 155 |
| 938.88750 | 893.88750 | NFM | Nationwide | Vodafone Channel 156 |
| 938.91250 | 893.91250 | NFM | Nationwide | Vodafone Channel 157 |
| 938.93750 | 893.93750 | NFM | Nationwide | Vodafone Channel 158 |
| 938.98750 | 893.98750 | NFM | Nationwide | Vodafone Channel 160 |
| 939.03750 | 894.03750 | NFM | Nationwide | Vodafone Channel 162 |
| 939.13750 | 894.13750 | NFM | Nationwide | Vodafone Channel 166 |
| 939.16250 | 894.16250 | NFM | Nationwide | Vodafone Channel 167 |
| 939.26250 | 894.26250 | NFM | Nationwide | Vodafone Channel 171 |
| 939.31250 | 894.31250 | NFM | Nationwide | Vodafone Channel 173 |
| 939.33750 | 894.33750 | NFM | Nationwide | Vodafone Channel 174 |
| 939.36250 | 894.36250 | NFM | Nationwide | Vodafone Channel 175 |
| 939.38750 | 894.38750 | NFM | Nationwide | Vodafone Channel 176 |
| 939.43750 | 894.43750 | NFM | Nationwide | Vodafone Channel 178 |
| 939.46250 | 894.46250 | NFM | Nationwide | Vodafone Channel 179 |
| 939.48750 | 894.48750 | NFM | Nationwide | Vodafone Channel 180 |
| | | | | |
| 939.68750 | 894.68750 | NFM | Nationwide | Cellnet Channel 188 |
| 939.76250 | 894.76250 | NFM | Nationwide | Cellnet Channel 191 |
| 939.81250 | 894.81250 | NFM | Nationwide | Cellnet Channel 193 |
| 939.86250 | 894.86250 | NFM | Nationwide | Cellnet Channel 195 |
| 939.88750 | 894.88750 | NFM | Nationwide | Cellnet Channel 196 |
| 939.91250 | 894.91250 | NFM | Nationwide | Cellnet Channel 197 |
| 939.96250 | 894.96250 | NFM | Nationwide | Cellnet Channel 199 |
| 939.98750 | 894.98750 | NFM | Nationwide | Cellnet Channel 200 |
| 940.01250 | 895.01250 | NFM | Nationwide | Cellnet Channel 201 |
| 940.03750 | 895.03750 | NFM | Nationwide | Cellnet Channel 202 |
| 940.21250 | 895.21250 | NFM | Nationwide | Cellnet Channel 209 |
| 940.23750 | 895.23750 | NFM | Nationwide | Cellnet Channel 210 |
| 940.36250 | 895.36250 | NFM | Nationwide | Cellnet Channel 215 |
| 940.38750 | 895.38750 | NFM | Nationwide | Cellnet Channel 216 |
| 940.41250 | 895.41250 | NFM | Nationwide | Cellnet Channel 217 |
| 940.43750 | 895.43750 | NFM | Nationwide | Cellnet Channel 218 |
| 940.46250 | 895.46250 | NFM | Nationwide | Cellnet Channel 219 |
| | | | | |
| 940.48750 | 895.48750 | NFM | Nationwide | (Not Used) Channel 220 |
| 940.53750 | 895.53750 | NFM | Nationwide | Vodafone Channel 222 |
| 940.56250 | 895.56250 | NFM | Nationwide | Vodafone Channel 223 |
| 940.61250 | 895.61250 | NFM | Nationwide | Vodafone Channel 225 |
| 940.63750 | 895.63750 | NFM | Nationwide | Vodafone Channel 226 |
| 940.68750 | 895.68750 | NFM | Nationwide | Vodafone Channel 228 |
| 940.71250 | 895.71250 | NFM | Nationwide | Vodafone Channel 229 |
| 940.73750 | 895.73750 | NFM | Nationwide | Vodafone Channel 230 |
| 940.83750 | 895.83750 | NFM | Nationwide | Vodafone Channel 234 |
| 940.93750 | 895.93750 | NFM | Nationwide | Vodafone Channel 238 |
| 941.01250 | 896.01250 | NFM | Nationwide | Vodafone Channel 241 |
| 941.03750 | 896.03750 | NFM | Nationwide | Vodafone Channel 242 |
| 941.06250 | 896.06250 | NFM | Nationwide | Vodafone Channel 243 |
| 941.08750 | 896.08750 | NFM | Nationwide | Vodafone Channel 244 |
| 941.13750 | 896.13750 | NFM | Nationwide | Vodafone Channel 246 |
| 941.21250 | 896.21250 | NFM | Nationwide | Vodafone Channel 249 |
| 941.23750 | 896.23750 | NFM | Nationwide | Vodafone Channel 250 |

| Base | Mobile | Mode | Location | User and Notes |
|------|--------|------|----------|----------------|
| 941.26250 | 896.26250 | NFM | Nationwide | Vodafone Channel 251 |
| 941.31250 | 896.31250 | NFM | Nationwide | Vodafone Channel 253 |
| 941.51250 | 896.51250 | NFM | Nationwide | Vodafone Channel 261 |
| 941.53750 | 896.53750 | NFM | Nationwide | Vodafone Channel 262 |
| 941.56250 | 896.56250 | NFM | Nationwide | Vodafone Channel 263 |
| 941.61250 | 896.61250 | NFM | Nationwide | Vodafone Channel 265 |
| 941.66250 | 896.66250 | NFM | Nationwide | Vodafone Channel 267 |
| 941.78750 | 896.78750 | NFM | Nationwide | Vodafone Channel 272 |
| 941.83750 | 896.83750 | NFM | Nationwide | Vodafone Channel 274 |
| 941.88750 | 896.88750 | NFM | Nationwide | Vodafone Channel 276 |
| 941.96250 | 896.96250 | NFM | Nationwide | Vodafone Channel 279 |
| 942.03750 | 897.03750 | NFM | Nationwide | Vodafone Channel 282 |
| 942.08750 | 897.08750 | NFM | Nationwide | Vodafone Channel 284 |
| 942.16250 | 897.16250 | NFM | Nationwide | Vodafone Channel 287 |
| 942.21250 | 897.21250 | NFM | Nationwide | Vodafone Channel 289 |
| 942.26250 | 897.26250 | NFM | Nationwide | Vodafone Channel 291 |
| 942.36250 | 897.36250 | NFM | Nationwide | Vodafone Channel 295 |
| 942.43750 | 897.43750 | NFM | Nationwide | Vodafone Channel 298 |
| 942.48750 | 897.48750 | NFM | Nationwide | Vodafone Channel 300 |
| | | | | |
| 942.53750 | 897.53750 | NFM | Nationwide | Cellnet Channel 302 |
| 942.56250 | 897.56250 | NFM | Nationwide | Cellnet Channel 303 |
| 942.61250 | 897.61250 | NFM | Nationwide | Cellnet Channel 305 |
| 942.76250 | 897.76250 | NFM | Nationwide | Cellnet Channel 311 |
| 942.81250 | 897.81250 | NFM | Nationwide | Cellnet Channel 313 |
| 942.83750 | 897.83750 | NFM | Nationwide | Cellnet Channel 314 |
| 942.86250 | 897.86250 | NFM | Nationwide | Cellnet Channel 315 |
| 942.96250 | 897.96250 | NFM | Nationwide | Cellnet Channel 319 |
| 943.06250 | 898.06250 | NFM | Nationwide | Cellnet Channel 323 |
| 943.08750 | 898.08750 | NFM | Nationwide | Cellnet Channel 324 |
| 943.11250 | 898.11250 | NFM | Nationwide | Cellnet Channel 325 |
| 943.13750 | 898.13750 | NFM | Nationwide | Cellnet Channel 326 |
| 943.16250 | 898.16250 | NFM | Nationwide | Cellnet Channel 327 |
| 943.18750 | 898.18750 | NFM | Nationwide | Cellnet Channel 328 |
| 943.21250 | 898.21250 | NFM | Nationwide | Cellnet Channel 329 |
| 943.23750 | 898.23750 | NFM | Nationwide | Cellnet Channel 330 |
| 943.26250 | 898.26250 | NFM | Nationwide | Cellnet Channel 331 |
| 943.28750 | 898.28750 | NFM | Nationwide | Cellnet Channel 332 |
| 943.31250 | 898.31250 | NFM | Nationwide | Cellnet Channel 333 |
| 943.33750 | 898.33750 | NFM | Nationwide | Cellnet Channel 334 |
| 943.36250 | 898.36250 | NFM | Nationwide | Cellnet Channel 335 |
| 943.38750 | 898.38750 | NFM | Nationwide | Cellnet Channel 336 |
| 943.41250 | 898.41250 | NFM | Nationwide | Cellnet Channel 337 |
| 943.43750 | 898.43750 | NFM | Nationwide | Cellnet Channel 338 |
| 943.46250 | 898.46250 | NFM | Nationwide | Cellnet Channel 339 |
| 943.48750 | 898.48750 | NFM | Nationwide | Cellnet Channel 340 |
| 943.51250 | 898.51250 | NFM | Nationwide | Cellnet Channel 341 |
| 943.53750 | 898.53750 | NFM | Nationwide | Cellnet Channel 342 |
| 943.56250 | 898.56250 | NFM | Nationwide | Cellnet Channel 343 |
| 943.63750 | 898.63750 | NFM | Nationwide | Cellnet Channel 346 |
| 943.68750 | 898.68750 | NFM | Nationwide | Cellnet Channel 348 |
| 943.78750 | 898.78750 | NFM | Nationwide | Cellnet Channel 352 |
| 943.81250 | 898.81250 | NFM | Nationwide | Cellnet Channel 353 |
| 943.96250 | 898.96250 | NFM | Nationwide | Channel 359 Data Control |
| 944.01250 | 899.01250 | NFM | Nationwide | Cellnet Channel 361 |
| 944.06250 | 899.06250 | NFM | Nationwide | Cellnet Channel 363 |

| Base | Mobile | Mode | Location | User and Notes |
|------|--------|------|----------|----------------|
| 944.11250 | 899.11250 | NFM | Nationwide | Cellnet Channel 365 |
| 44.13750 | 899.13750 | NFM | Nationwide | Cellnet Channel 366 |
| 944.18750 | 899.18750 | NFM | Nationwide | Cellnet Channel 368 |
| 944.23750 | 899.23750 | NFM | Nationwide | Cellnet Channel 370 |
| 944.38750 | 899.38750 | NFM | Nationwide | Cellnet Channel 376 |
| 944.43750 | 899.43750 | NFM | Nationwide | Cellnet Channel 378 |
| 944.46250 | 899.46250 | NFM | Nationwide | Cellnet Channel 379 |
| 944.48750 | 899.48750 | NFM | Nationwide | Cellnet Channel 380 |
| 944.51250 | 899.51250 | NFM | Nationwide | Cellnet Channel 381 |
| 944.56250 | 899.56250 | NFM | Nationwide | Cellnet Channel 383 |
| 944.61250 | 899.61250 | NFM | Nationwide | Cellnet Channel 385 |
| 944.66250 | 899.66250 | NFM | Nationwide | Cellnet Channel 387 |
| 944.83750 | 899.83750 | NFM | Nationwide | Cellnet Channel 394 |
| 944.98750 | 899.98750 | NFM | Nationwide | Cellnet Channel 400 |
| 945.03750 | 900.03750 | NFM | Nationwide | Cellnet Channel 402 |
| 945.11250 | 900.11250 | NFM | Nationwide | Cellnet Channel 405 |
| 945.16250 | 900.16250 | NFM | Nationwide | Cellnet Channel 407 |
| 945.26250 | 900.26250 | NFM | Nationwide | Cellnet Channel 411 |
| 945.63750 | 900.63750 | NFM | Nationwide | Cellnet Channel 426 |
| 945.68750 | 900.68750 | NFM | Nationwide | Cellnet Channel 428 |
| 945.76250 | 900.76250 | NFM | Nationwide | Cellnet Channel 431 |
| 945.81250 | 900.81250 | NFM | Nationwide | Cellnet Channel 433 |
| 945.86250 | 900.86250 | NFM | Nationwide | Cellnet Channel 435 |
| 946.01250 | 901.01250 | NFM | Nationwide | Cellnet Channel 441 |
| 946.11250 | 901.11250 | NFM | Nationwide | Cellnet Channel 445 |
| 946.18750 | 901.18750 | NFM | Nationwide | Cellnet Channel 448 |
| 946.23750 | 901.23750 | NFM | Nationwide | Cellnet Channel 450 |
| 946.26250 | 901.26250 | NFM | Nationwide | Cellnet Channel 451 |
| 946.28750 | 901.28750 | NFM | Nationwide | Cellnet Channel 452 |
| 946.36250 | 901.36250 | NFM | Nationwide | Cellnet Channel 455 |
| 946.46250 | 901.46250 | NFM | Nationwide | Cellnet Channel 459 |
| | | | | |
| 946.51250 | 901.51250 | NFM | Nationwide | Vodafone Channel 461 |
| 946.61250 | 901.61250 | NFM | Nationwide | Vodafone Channel 465 |
| 946.73750 | 901.73750 | NFM | Nationwide | Vodafone Channel 470 |
| 946.83750 | 901.83750 | NFM | Nationwide | Vodafone Channel 474 |
| 946.88750 | 901.88750 | NFM | Nationwide | Vodafone Channel 476 |
| 946.91250 | 901.91250 | NFM | Nationwide | Vodafone Channel 477 |
| 947.03750 | 902.03750 | NFM | Nationwide | Vodafone Channel 482 |
| 947.16250 | 902.16250 | NFM | Nationwide | Vodafone Channel 487 |
| 947.26250 | 902.26250 | NFM | Nationwide | Vodafone Channel 491 |
| 947.36250 | 902.36250 | NFM | Nationwide | Vodafone Channel 495 |
| 947.41250 | 902.41250 | NFM | Nationwide | Vodafone Channel 497 |
| 947.58750 | 902.58750 | NFM | Nationwide | Vodafone Channel 504 |
| 947.66250 | 902.66250 | NFM | Nationwide | Vodafone Channel 507 |
| 947.88750 | 902.88750 | NFM | Nationwide | Vodafone Channel 516 |
| 947.93750 | 902.93750 | NFM | Nationwide | Vodafone Channel 518 |
| 947.96250 | 902.96250 | NFM | Nationwide | Vodafone Channel 519 |
| 948.18750 | 903.18750 | NFM | Nationwide | Vodafone Channel 528 |
| 948.41250 | 903.41250 | NFM | Nationwide | Vodafone Channel 537 |
| 948.46250 | 903.46250 | NFM | Nationwide | Vodafone Channel 539 |
| 948.48750 | 903.48750 | NFM | Nationwide | Vodafone Channel 540 |
| 948.93750 | 903.93750 | NFM | Nationwide | Vodafone Channel 558 |
| 948.96250 | 903.96250 | NFM | Nationwide | Vodafone Channel 559 |
| | | | | |
| 949.03750 | 904.03750 | NFM | Nationwide | Cellnet Channel 562 |

| Base | Mobile | Mode | Location | User and Notes |
|------|--------|------|----------|----------------|
| 949.23750 | 904.23750 | NFM | Nationwide | Cellnet Channel 570 |
| 949.41250 | 904.41250 | NFM | Nationwide | Cellnet Channel 577 |
| 949.48750 | 904.48750 | NFM | Nationwide | Cellnet Channel 580 |
| 949.71250 | 904.71250 | NFM | Nationwide | Cellnet Channel 589 |
| 949.91250 | 904.91250 | NFM | Nationwide | Cellnet Channel 597 |

## JERSEY GMS

| Base | Mobile | Mode | Location | User and Notes |
|------|--------|------|----------|----------------|
| 935.2000 | 890.2000 | WFM | Five Oaks | |
| 936.4000 | 891.4000 | WFM | Fort Regent | |
| 938.6000 | 893.6000 | WFM | Springfield | |
| 939.0000 | 894.0000 | WFM | La Chasse, St Ouens | |
| 942.0000 | 897.0000 | WFM | Rozel Mill | |
| 943.6000 | 898.6000 | WFM | Five Oaks | |
| 944.0000 | 899.0000 | WFM | Near East Exchange | |
| 944.4000 | 899.4000 | WFM | St John's Parish Hall | |
| 946.6000 | 901.6000 | WFM | Gorsey | |
| 946.8000 | 901.8000 | WFM | St Helier, Jersey | |
| 947.4000 | 902.4000 | WFM | Five Oaks | |
| 949.0000 | 904.0000 | WFM | Steam Museum, Sion | |
| 950.4000 | 905.4000 | WFM | St Peter's | |
| 950.6000 | 905.6000 | WFM | Fort Regent | |
| 951.4000 | 906.4000 | WFM | La Chasse, St Ouens | |
| 952.2000 | 907.2000 | WFM | Gorey | |
| 953.0000 | 908.0000 | WFM | Le Hocq | |
| 945.0000 | 909.0000 | WFM | St Ouen's Bay | |
| 954.2000 | 909.2000 | WFM | First Tower | |
| 955.4000 | 910.4000 | WFM | Fort Regent | |
| 956.2000 | 911.2000 | WFM | La Chasse, St Ouens | |
| 956.6000 | 911.6000 | WFM | Fort Regent | |
| 957.0000 | 912.0000 | WFM | St Brelade | |
| 958.4000 | 913.4000 | WFM | St Lawrence | |
| 958.8000 | 913.8000 | WFM | St Brelade, Red Houses | |

## 959.0125 - 959.9875 MHz   New Cybernet/Uniden Cordless Telephone Base

| Base | Mobile | Mode | Location | User and Notes |
|------|--------|------|----------|----------------|
| 959.01250 | 914.01250 | NFM | Nationwide | Channel 1 |
| 959.02500 | 914.02500 | NFM | Nationwide | Channel 2 |
| 959.03750 | 914.03750 | NFM | Nationwide | Channel 3 |
| 959.05000 | 914.05000 | NFM | Nationwide | Channel 4 |
| 959.06250 | 914.06250 | NFM | Nationwide | Channel 5 |
| 959.07500 | 914.07500 | NFM | Nationwide | Channel 6 |
| 959.08750 | 914.08750 | NFM | Nationwide | Channel 7 |
| 959.10000 | 914.10000 | NFM | Nationwide | Channel 8 |
| 959.11250 | 914.11250 | NFM | Nationwide | Channel 9 |
| 959.12500 | 914.12500 | NFM | Nationwide | Channel 10 |
| 959.13750 | 914.13750 | NFM | Nationwide | Channel 11 |
| 959.15000 | 914.15000 | NFM | Nationwide | Channel 12 |
| 959.16250 | 914.16250 | NFM | Nationwide | Channel 13 |
| 959.17500 | 914.17500 | NFM | Nationwide | Channel 14 |
| 959.18750 | 914.18750 | NFM | Nationwide | Channel 15 |
| 959.20000 | 914.20000 | NFM | Nationwide | Channel 16 |
| 959.21250 | 914.21250 | NFM | Nationwide | Channel 17 |
| 959.22500 | 914.22500 | NFM | Nationwide | Channel 18 |
| 959.23750 | 914.23750 | NFM | Nationwide | Channel 19 |
| 959.25000 | 914.25000 | NFM | Nationwide | Channel 20 |
| 959.26250 | 914.26250 | NFM | Nationwide | Channel 21 |

| Base | Mobile | Mode | Location | User and Notes |
|------|--------|------|----------|----------------|
| 959.27500 | 914.27500 | NFM | Nationwide | Channel 22 |
| 959.28750 | 914.28750 | NFM | Nationwide | Channel 23 |
| 959.30000 | 914.30000 | NFM | Nationwide | Channel 24 |
| 959.31250 | 914.31250 | NFM | Nationwide | Channel 25 |
| 959.32500 | 914.32500 | NFM | Nationwide | Channel 26 |
| 959.33750 | 914.33750 | NFM | Nationwide | Channel 27 |
| 959.35000 | 914.35000 | NFM | Nationwide | Channel 28 |
| 959.36250 | 914.36250 | NFM | Nationwide | Channel 29 |
| 959.37500 | 914.37500 | NFM | Nationwide | Channel 30 |
| 959.38750 | 914.38750 | NFM | Nationwide | Channel 31 |
| 959.40000 | 914.40000 | NFM | Nationwide | Channel 32 |
| 959.41250 | 914.41250 | NFM | Nationwide | Channel 33 |
| 959.42500 | 914.42500 | NFM | Nationwide | Channel 34 |
| 959.43750 | 914.43750 | NFM | Nationwide | Channel 35 |
| 959.45000 | 914.45000 | NFM | Nationwide | Channel 36 |
| 959.46250 | 914.46250 | NFM | Nationwide | Channel 37 |
| 959.47500 | 914.47500 | NFM | Nationwide | Channel 38 |
| 959.48750 | 914.48750 | NFM | Nationwide | Channel 39 |
| 959.50000 | 914.50000 | NFM | Nationwide | Channel 40 |
| 959.51250 | 914.51250 | NFM | Nationwide | Channel 41 |
| 959.52500 | 914.52500 | NFM | Nationwide | Channel 42 |
| 959.53750 | 914.53750 | NFM | Nationwide | Channel 43 |
| 959.55000 | 914.55000 | NFM | Nationwide | Channel 44 |
| 959.56250 | 914.56250 | NFM | Nationwide | Channel 45 |
| 959.57500 | 914.57500 | NFM | Nationwide | Channel 46 |
| 959.58750 | 914.58750 | NFM | Nationwide | Channel 47 |
| 959.60000 | 914.60000 | NFM | Nationwide | Channel 48 |
| 959.61250 | 914.61250 | NFM | Nationwide | Channel 49 |
| 959.62500 | 914.62500 | NFM | Nationwide | Channel 50 |
| 959.63750 | 914.63750 | NFM | Nationwide | Channel 51 |
| 959.65000 | 914.65000 | NFM | Nationwide | Channel 52 |
| 959.66250 | 914.66250 | NFM | Nationwide | Channel 53 |
| 959.67500 | 914.67500 | NFM | Nationwide | Channel 54 |
| 959.68750 | 914.68750 | NFM | Nationwide | Channel 55 |
| 959.70000 | 914.70000 | NFM | Nationwide | Channel 56 |
| 959.71250 | 914.71250 | NFM | Nationwide | Channel 57 |
| 959.72500 | 914.72500 | NFM | Nationwide | Channel 58 |
| 959.73750 | 914.73750 | NFM | Nationwide | Channel 59 |
| 959.75000 | 914.75000 | NFM | Nationwide | Channel 60 |
| 959.76250 | 914.76250 | NFM | Nationwide | Channel 61 |
| 959.77500 | 914.77500 | NFM | Nationwide | Channel 62 |
| 959.78750 | 914.78750 | NFM | Nationwide | Channel 63 |
| 959.80000 | 914.80000 | NFM | Nationwide | Channel 64 |
| 959.81250 | 914.81250 | NFM | Nationwide | Channel 65 |
| 959.82500 | 914.82500 | NFM | Nationwide | Channel 66 |
| 959.83750 | 914.83750 | NFM | Nationwide | Channel 67 |
| 959.85000 | 914.85000 | NFM | Nationwide | Channel 68 |
| 959.86250 | 914.86250 | NFM | Nationwide | Channel 69 |
| 959.87500 | 914.87500 | NFM | Nationwide | Channel 70 |
| 959.88750 | 914.88750 | NFM | Nationwide | Channel 71 |
| 959.90000 | 914.90000 | NFM | Nationwide | Channel 72 |
| 959.91250 | 914.91250 | NFM | Nationwide | Channel 73 |
| 959.92500 | 914.92500 | NFM | Nationwide | Channel 74 |
| 959.93750 | 914.93750 | NFM | Nationwide | Channel 75 |
| 959.95000 | 914.95000 | NFM | Nationwide | Channel 76 |
| 959.96250 | 914.96250 | NFM | Nationwide | Channel 77 |

| Base | Mobile | Mode | Location | User and Notes |
|------|--------|------|----------|----------------|
| 959.97500 | 914.97500 | NFM | Nationwide | Channel 78 |
| 959.98750 | 914.98750 | NFM | Nationwide | Channel 79 |

## 962.00 - 970.00 MHz — RADIOASTRONOMY USED FOR PULSARS

## 960.0000 - 1215.0000 MHz — DME AERONAUTICAL RADIO NAVIGATION AND TRANSPONDER EQUIPMENT

| Base | Mobile | Mode | Location | User and Notes |
|------|--------|------|----------|----------------|
| 962.00000 | 1025.00000 | AM | Nationwide | DME Channel 1X Not Used |
| 963.00000 | 1026.00000 | AM | Nationwide | DME Channel 2X Not Used |
| 964.00000 | 1027.00000 | AM | Nationwide | DME Channel 3X Not Used |
| 965.00000 | 1028.00000 | AM | Nationwide | DME Channel 4X Not Used |
| 966.00000 | 1029.00000 | AM | Nationwide | DME Channel 5X Not Used |
| 967.00000 | 1030.00000 | AM | Nationwide | DME Channel 6X Not Used |
| 968.00000 | 1031.00000 | AM | Nationwide | DME Channel 7X Not Used |
| 969.00000 | 1032.00000 | AM | Nationwide | DME Channel 8X Not Used |
| 970.00000 | 1033.00000 | AM | Nationwide | DME Channel 9X Not Used |
| 971.00000 | 1034.00000 | AM | Nationwide | DME Channel 10X Not Used |
| 972.00000 | 1035.00000 | AM | Nationwide | DME Channel 11X Not Used |
| 973.00000 | 1036.00000 | AM | Nationwide | DME Channel 12X Not Used |
| 974.00000 | 1037.00000 | AM | Nationwide | DME Channel 13X Not Used |
| 975.00000 | 1038.00000 | AM | Nationwide | DME Channel 14X Not Used |
| 976.00000 | 1039.00000 | AM | Nationwide | DME Channel 15X Not Used |
| 977.00000 | 1040.00000 | AM | Nationwide | DME Channel 16X Not Used |
| 978.00000 | 1041.00000 | AM | Nationwide | DME Ch 17X (108.00 Mhz) |
| 979.00000 | 1042.00000 | AM | Dundee Airport | DME |
| 979.00000 | 1042.00000 | AM | Nationwide | DME Ch 18X (108.10 MHz) |
| 979.00000 | 1042.00000 | AM | RAF Cottesmore | TACAN |
| 980.00000 | 1043.00000 | AM | Boscombe Down (MoD) | TACAN |
| 980.00000 | 1043.00000 | AM | Nationwide | DME Ch 19X (108.20 MHz) |
| 981.00000 | 1044.00000 | AM | Nationwide | DME Ch 20X (108.30 MHz) |
| 982.00000 | 1045.00000 | AM | Nationwide | DME Ch 21X (108.40 MHz) |
| 982.00000 | 1045.00000 | AM | RAF Valley | TACAN |
| 983.00000 | 1046.00000 | AM | Nationwide | DME Ch 22X (108.50 MHz) |
| 983.00000 | 1046.00000 | AM | Sumburgh Airport | DME |
| 983.00000 | 1046.00000 | AM | Teesside Airport | DME |
| 984.00000 | 1047.00000 | AM | Kirkwall Airport | DME |
| 984.00000 | 1047.00000 | AM | Nationwide | DME Ch 23X (108.60 MHz) |
| 985.00000 | 1048.00000 | AM | Nationwide | DME Ch 24X (108.70 MHz) |
| 985.00000 | 1048.00000 | AM | Newton Point | TACAN |
| 986.00000 | 1049.00000 | AM | Nationwide | DME Ch 25X (108.80 MHz) |
| 986.00000 | 1049.00000 | AM | Weathersfield | TACAN |
| 987.00000 | 1050.00000 | AM | Edinburgh Airport | DME |
| 987.00000 | 1050.00000 | AM | Nationwide | DME Ch 26X (108.90 MHz) |
| 987.00000 | 1050.00000 | AM | Ventnor | TACAN |
| 988.00000 | 1051.00000 | AM | Nationwide | DME Ch 27X (109.00 MHz) |
| 989.00000 | 1052.00000 | AM | Nationwide | DME Ch 28X (109.10 MHz) |
| 990.00000 | 1053.00000 | AM | Inverness Airport | DME |
| 990.00000 | 1053.00000 | AM | Nationwide | DME Ch 29X (109.20 MHz) |
| 990.00000 | 1053.00000 | AM | Swansea Aerodrome | DME |
| 991.00000 | 1054.00000 | AM | Nationwide | DME Ch 30X (109.30 MHz) |
| 992.00000 | 1055.00000 | AM | Barrow Airport | DME |
| 992.00000 | 1055.00000 | AM | Nationwide | DME Ch 31X (109.40 MHz) |
| 993.00000 | 1056.00000 | AM | London, Heathrow | DME |
| 993.00000 | 1056.00000 | AM | Manchester Airport | DME |
| 993.00000 | 1056.00000 | AM | Nationwide | DME Ch 32X (109.50 MHz) |

| Base | Mobile | Mode | Location | User and Notes |
|------|--------|------|----------|----------------|
| 993.00000 | 1056.00000 | AM | Plymouth Airport | DME |
| 994.00000 | 1057.00000 | AM | Nationwide | DME Ch 33X (109.60 MHz) |
| 994.00000 | 1057.00000 | AM | RAF Linton-on-Ouse | TACAN |
| 994.00000 | 1057.00000 | AM | RAF Odiham | TACAN |
| 995.00000 | 1058.00000 | AM | Nationwide | DME Ch 34X (109.70 MHz) |
| 996.00000 | 1059.00000 | AM | Nationwide | DME Ch 35X (109.80 MHz) |
| 996.00000 | 1059.00000 | AM | RAF Kinloss | TACAN |
| 997.00000 | 1060.00000 | AM | Nationwide | DME Ch 36X (109.90 MHz) |
| 997.00000 | 1060.00000 | AM | Warton (MoD) | DME |
| 998.00000 | 1061.00000 | AM | Nationwide | DME Ch 37X (110.00 MHz) |
| 999.00000 | 1062.00000 | AM | Birmingham International | DME |
| 999.00000 | 1062.00000 | AM | Nationwide | DME Ch 38X (110.10 MHz) |
| 1000.00000 | 1063.00000 | AM | Nationwide | DME Ch 39X (110.20 MHz) |
| 1000.00000 | 1063.00000 | AM | USAF Lakenheath | TACAN |
| 1001.00000 | 1064.00000 | AM | Nationwide | DME Ch 40X (110.30 MHz) |
| 1002.00000 | 1065.00000 | AM | Bournemouth (Hurn) | DME |
| 1002.00000 | 1065.00000 | AM | Nationwide | DME Ch 41X (110.40 MHz) |
| 1003.00000 | 1066.00000 | AM | Nationwide | DME Ch 42X (110.50 MHz) |
| 1003.00000 | 1066.00000 | AM | RAF Leuchars | TACAN |
| 1003.00000 | 1066.00000 | AM | Stansted | DME |
| 1004.00000 | 1067.00000 | AM | Cardiff Airport | DME |
| 1004.00000 | 1067.00000 | AM | Carlisle Airport | DME |
| 1004.00000 | 1067.00000 | AM | London, Heathrow | DME |
| 1004.00000 | 1067.00000 | AM | Nationwide | DME Ch 43X (110.60 MHz) |
| 1005.00000 | 1068.00000 | AM | Nationwide | DME Ch 44X (110.70 MHz) |
| 1006.00000 | 1069.00000 | AM | Nationwide | DME Ch 45X (110.80 MHz) |
| 1007.00000 | 1070.00000 | AM | Jersey Airport | DME |
| 1007.00000 | 1070.00000 | AM | London, Gatwick | DME |
| 1007.00000 | 1070.00000 | AM | Nationwide | DME Ch 46X (110.90 MHz) |
| 1007.00000 | 1070.00000 | AM | Ronaldsway, Isle of Man | DME |
| 1008.00000 | 1071.00000 | AM | Nationwide | DME Ch 47X (111.00 MHz) |
| 1008.00000 | 1071.00000 | AM | RNAS Yeovilton | TACAN |
| 1009.00000 | 1072.00000 | AM | Nationwide | DME Ch 48X (111.10 MHz) |
| 1010.00000 | 1073.00000 | AM | Nationwide | DME Ch 49X (111.20 MHz) |
| 1011.00000 | 1074.00000 | AM | London, Heathrow | DME |
| 1011.00000 | 1074.00000 | AM | Nationwide | DME Ch 50X (111.30 MHz) |
| 1012.00000 | 1075.00000 | AM | Nationwide | DME Ch 51X (111.40 MHz) |
| 1012.00000 | 1075.00000 | AM | RAF Coningsby | TACAN |
| 1013.00000 | 1076.00000 | AM | London, City Airport | DME |
| 1013.00000 | 1076.00000 | AM | Nationwide | DME Ch 52X (111.50 MHz) |
| 1013.00000 | 1076.00000 | AM | Newcastle Airport | DME |
| 1013.00000 | 1076.00000 | AM | USAF Fairford | TACAN |
| 1014.00000 | 1077.00000 | AM | Nationwide | DME Ch 53X (111.60 MHz) |
| 1014.00000 | 1077.00000 | AM | RAF Chivenor | TACAN |
| 1015.00000 | 1078.00000 | AM | Nationwide | DME Ch 54X (111.70 MHz) |
| 1016.00000 | 1079.00000 | AM | Nationwide | DME Ch 55X (111.80 MHz) |
| 1017.00000 | 1080.00000 | AM | Nationwide | DME Ch 56X (111.90 MHz) |
| 1017.00000 | 1080.00000 | AM | RAF Brize Norton | TACAN |
| 1018.00000 | 1081.00000 | AM | Nationwide | DME Ch 57X (112.00 MHz) |
| 1019.00000 | 1082.00000 | AM | Nationwide | DME Ch 58X (112.10 MHz) |
| 1019.00000 | 1082.00000 | AM | Pole Hill | DME |
| 1020.00000 | 1083.00000 | AM | Nationwide | DME Ch 59X (112.20 MHz) |
| 1020.00000 | 1083.00000 | AM | Ronaldsway, Isle of Man | DME |
| 1021.00000 | 1084.00000 | AM | Nationwide | DME Ch 60X (112.30 MHz) |
| 1022.00000 | 1085.00000 | AM | Nationwide | DME Ch 61X Not Used |
| 1023.00000 | 1086.00000 | AM | Nationwide | DME Ch 62X Not Used |

| Base | Mobile | Mode | Location | User and Notes |
|------|--------|------|----------|----------------|
| 1024.00000 | 1087.00000 | AM | Nationwide | DME Ch 63X  Not Used |
| 1025.00000 | 1088.00000 | AM | Nationwide | DME Ch 64X  Not Used |
| 1026.00000 | 1089.00000 | AM | Nationwide | DME Ch 65X  Not Used |
| 1027.00000 | 1090.00000 | AM | Nationwide | DME Ch 66X  Not Used |
| 1028.00000 | 1091.00000 | AM | Nationwide | DME Ch 67X  Not Used |
| 1029.00000 | 1092.00000 | AM | Nationwide | DME Ch 68X  Not Used |
| 1030.00000 | 1090.00000 | AM | Nationwide | Transponder Interrog./Reply |
| 1030.00000 | 1093.00000 | AM | Nationwide | DME Ch 69X  Not Used |
| 1031.00000 | 1094.00000 | AM | Nationwide | DME Ch 70X  (112.30 MHz) |
| 1032.00000 | 1095.00000 | AM | Nationwide | DME Ch 71X  (112.40 MHz) |
| 1033.00000 | 1096.00000 | AM | Nationwide | DME Ch 72X  (112.50 MHz) |
| 1033.00000 | 1096.00000 | AM | St Abbs | DME |
| 1034.00000 | 1097.00000 | AM | Nationwide | DME Ch 73X  (112.60 MHz) |
| 1034.00000 | 1097.00000 | AM | RAF St Mawgan | TACAN |
| 1035.00000 | 1098.00000 | AM | Berry Head | DME |
| 1035.00000 | 1098.00000 | AM | Donegal Aerodrome | DME |
| 1035.00000 | 1098.00000 | AM | Nationwide | DME Ch 74X  (112.70 MHz) |
| 1036.00000 | 1099.00000 | AM | Gamston Aerodrome | DME |
| 1036.00000 | 1099.00000 | AM | Nationwide | DME Ch 75X  (112.80 MHz) |
| 1037.00000 | 1100.00000 | AM | Nationwide | DME Ch 76X  (112.90 MHz) |
| 1038.00000 | 1101.00000 | AM | Nationwide | DME Ch 77X  (113.00 MHz) |
| 1039.00000 | 1102.00000 | AM | Nationwide | DME Ch 78X  (113.10 MHz) |
| 1039.00000 | 1102.00000 | AM | Strumble | DME |
| 1040.00000 | 1103.00000 | AM | Nationwide | DME Ch 79X  (113.20 MHz) |
| 1040.00000 | 1103.00000 | AM | Warton (MoD) | TACAN |
| 1041.00000 | 1104.00000 | AM | Nationwide | DME Ch 80X  (113.30 MHz) |
| 1042.00000 | 1105.00000 | AM | Nationwide | DME Ch 81X  (113.40 MHz) |
| 1043.00000 | 1106.00000 | AM | Nationwide | DME Ch 82X  (113.50 MHz) |
| 1044.00000 | 1107.00000 | AM | London, Heathrow | DME |
| 1044.00000 | 1107.00000 | AM | Nationwide | DME Ch 83X  (113.60 MHz) |
| 1044.00000 | 1107.00000 | AM | Wick Aerodrome | TACAN |
| 1045.00000 | 1108.00000 | AM | Nationwide | DME Ch 84X  (113.70 MHz) |
| 1046.00000 | 1109.00000 | AM | Nationwide | DME Ch 85X  (113.80 MHz) |
| 1046.00000 | 1109.00000 | AM | Talla | DME |
| 1047.00000 | 1110.00000 | AM | Nationwide | DME Ch 86X  (113.90 MHz) |
| 1047.00000 | 1110.00000 | AM | Ottringham | DME |
| 1048.00000 | 1111.00000 | AM | Midhurst | DME |
| 1048.00000 | 1111.00000 | AM | Nationwide | DME Ch 87X  (114.00 MHz) |
| 1049.00000 | 1112.00000 | AM | Nationwide | DME Ch 88X  (114.10 MHz) |
| 1049.00000 | 1112.00000 | AM | Wallasey | DME |
| 1050.00000 | 1113.00000 | AM | Land's End Airport | DME |
| 1050.00000 | 1113.00000 | AM | Nationwide | DME Ch 89X  (114.20 MHz) |
| 1051.00000 | 1114.00000 | AM | Aberdeen (Dyce Airport) | DME |
| 1051.00000 | 1114.00000 | AM | Nationwide | DME Ch 90X  (114.30 MHz) |
| 1052.00000 | 1115.00000 | AM | Benbecula Airport | TACAN |
| 1052.00000 | 1115.00000 | AM | Nationwide | DME Ch 91X  (114.40 MHz) |
| 1053.00000 | 1116.00000 | AM | Koksijde | DME |
| 1053.00000 | 1116.00000 | AM | Nationwide | DME Ch 92X  (114.50 MHz) |
| 1054.00000 | 1117.00000 | AM | Nationwide | DME Ch 93X  (114.60 MHz) |
| 1055.00000 | 1118.00000 | AM | Nationwide | DME Ch 94X  (114.70 MHz) |
| 1056.00000 | 1119.00000 | AM | Nationwide | DME Ch 95X  (114.80 Mhz) |
| 1057.00000 | 1120.00000 | AM | Nationwide | DME Ch 96X  (114.90 MHz) |
| 1057.00000 | 1120.00000 | AM | Vallafield | TACAN |
| 1058.00000 | 1121.00000 | AM | Nationwide | DME Ch 97X  (115.00 MHz) |
| 1058.00000 | 1121.00000 | AM | Stornoway Airport | TACAN |
| 1059.00000 | 1122.00000 | AM | Biggin Hill | DME |

| Base | Mobile | Mode | Location | User and Notes |
|------|--------|------|----------|----------------|
| 1059.00000 | 1122.00000 | AM | Nationwide | DME Ch 98X (115.10 MHz) |
| 1060.00000 | 1123.00000 | AM | Dean Cross | DME |
| 1060.00000 | 1123.00000 | AM | Nationwide | DME Ch 99X (115.20 MHz) |
| 1061.00000 | 1124.00000 | AM | Nationwide | DME Ch 100X (115.30 MHz) |
| 1061.00000 | 1124.00000 | AM | Ockham | DME |
| 1062.00000 | 1125.00000 | AM | Glasgow | DME |
| 1062.00000 | 1125.00000 | AM | Nationwide | DME Ch 101X (115.40 MHz) |
| 1063.00000 | 1126.00000 | AM | Nationwide | DME Ch 102X (115.50 MHz) |
| 1064.00000 | 1127.00000 | AM | Lambourne | DME |
| 1064.00000 | 1127.00000 | AM | Nationwide | DME Ch 103X (115.60 MHz) |
| 1065.00000 | 1128.00000 | AM | Nationwide | DME Ch 104X (115.70 MHz) |
| 1065.00000 | 1128.00000 | AM | Stoke on Trent | DME |
| 1066.00000 | 1129.00000 | AM | Nationwide | DME Ch 105X (115.80 MHz) |
| 1067.00000 | 1130.00000 | AM | Nationwide | DME Ch 106X (115.90 MHz) |
| 1067.00000 | 1130.00000 | AM | USAF Mildenhall | TACAN |
| 1068.00000 | 1131.00000 | AM | Nationwide | DME Ch 107X (116.00 MHz) |
| 1069.00000 | 1132.00000 | AM | Nationwide | DME Ch 108X (116.10 MHz) |
| 1070.00000 | 1133.00000 | AM | Blackbushe | DME |
| 1070.00000 | 1133.00000 | AM | Nationwide | DME Ch 109X (116.20 MHz) |
| 1071.00000 | 1134.00000 | AM | Nationwide | DME Ch 110X (116.30 MHz) |
| 1072.00000 | 1135.00000 | AM | Daventry | DME |
| 1072.00000 | 1135.00000 | AM | Nationwide | DME Ch 111X (116.40 MHz) |
| 1073.00000 | 1136.00000 | AM | Nationwide | DME Ch 112X (116.50 MHz) |
| 1073.00000 | 1136.00000 | AM | RAF Coltishall | TACAN |
| 1074.00000 | 1137.00000 | AM | Nationwide | DME Ch 113X (116.60 MHz) |
| 1075.00000 | 1138.00000 | AM | Nationwide | DME Ch 114X (116.70 MHz) |
| 1076.00000 | 1139.00000 | AM | Nationwide | DME Ch 115X (116.80 MHz) |
| 1077.00000 | 1140.00000 | AM | Nationwide | DME Ch 116X (116.90 MHz) |
| 1078.00000 | 1141.00000 | AM | Nationwide | DME Ch 117X (117.00 MHz) |
| 1078.00000 | 1141.00000 | AM | Seaford | DME |
| 1079.00000 | 1142.00000 | AM | Nationwide | DME Ch 118X (117.10 MHz) |
| 1080.00000 | 1143.00000 | AM | Nationwide | DME Ch 119X (117.20 MHz) |
| 1081.00000 | 1144.00000 | AM | Detling | DME |
| 1081.00000 | 1144.00000 | AM | Nationwide | DME Ch 120X (117.30 MHz) |
| 1082.00000 | 1145.00000 | AM | Connaught Airport | DME |
| 1082.00000 | 1145.00000 | AM | Nationwide | DME Ch 121X (117.40 MHz) |
| 1082.00000 | 1145.00000 | AM | RAF Cranwell | TACAN |
| 1083.00000 | 1146.00000 | AM | Brookmans Park | DME |
| 1083.00000 | 1146.00000 | AM | Nationwide | DME Ch 122X (117.50 MHz) |
| 1083.00000 | 1146.00000 | AM | Turnberry | DME |
| 1084.00000 | 1147.00000 | AM | Nationwide | DME Ch 123X (117.60 MHz) |
| 1084.00000 | 1147.00000 | AM | RAF Wittering | TACAN |
| 1085.00000 | 1148.00000 | AM | Nationwide | DME Ch 124X (117.70 MHz) |
| 1085.00000 | 1148.00000 | AM | Oxford/Kidlington | DME |
| 1085.00000 | 1148.00000 | AM | Tiree | DME |
| 1086.00000 | 1149.00000 | AM | Nationwide | DME Ch 125X (117.80 MHz) |
| 1087.00000 | 1150.00000 | AM | Mayfield | DME |
| 1087.00000 | 1150.00000 | AM | Nationwide | DME Ch 126X (117.90 MHz) |
| 1088.00000 | 1025.00000 | AM | Nationwide | DME Channel 1Y  Not Used |
| 1089.00000 | 1026.00000 | AM | Nationwide | DME Channel 2Y  Not Used |
| 1090.00000 | 1027.00000 | AM | Nationwide | DME Channel 3Y  Not Used |
| 1091.00000 | 1028.00000 | AM | Nationwide | DME Channel 4Y  Not Used |
| 1092.00000 | 1029.00000 | AM | Nationwide | DME Channel 5Y  Not Used |
| 1093.00000 | 1030.00000 | AM | Nationwide | DME Channel 6Y  Not Used |
| 1094.00000 | 1031.00000 | AM | Nationwide | DME Channel 7Y  Not Used |
| 1095.00000 | 1032.00000 | AM | Nationwide | DME Channel 8Y  Not Used |

| Base | Moblle | Mode | Location | User and Notes |
|------|--------|------|----------|----------------|
| 1096.00000 | 1033.00000 | AM | Nationwide | DME Channel 9Y  Not Used |
| 1097.00000 | 1034.00000 | AM | Nationwide | DME Channel 10Y  Not Used |
| 1098.00000 | 1035.00000 | AM | Nationwide | DME Channel 11Y  Not Used |
| 1099.00000 | 1036.00000 | AM | Nationwide | DME Channel 12Y  Not Used |
| 1100.00000 | 1037.00000 | AM | Nationwide | DME Channel 13Y  Not Used |
| 1101.00000 | 1038.00000 | AM | Nationwide | DME Channel 14Y  Not Used |
| 1102.00000 | 1039.00000 | AM | Nationwide | DME Channel 15Y  Not Used |
| 1103.00000 | 1040.00000 | AM | Nationwide | DME Channel 16Y  Not Used |
| 1104.00000 | 1041.00000 | AM | Lydd Airport | DME |
| 1104.00000 | 1041.00000 | AM | Nationwide | DME Ch 17Y  (108.05 MHz) |
| 1105.00000 | 1042.00000 | AM | Blackpool | DME |
| 1105.00000 | 1042.00000 | AM | Nationwide | DME Ch 18Y  (108.15 MHz) |
| 1106.00000 | 1043.00000 | AM | Nationwide | DME Ch 19Y  (108.25 MHz) |
| 1107.00000 | 1044.00000 | AM | Nationwide | DME Ch 20Y  (108.35 MHz) |
| 1108.00000 | 1045.00000 | AM | Nationwide | DME Ch 21Y  (108.45 MHz) |
| 1109.00000 | 1046.00000 | AM | Nationwide | DME Ch 22Y  (108.55 MHz) |
| 1110.00000 | 1047.00000 | AM | Nationwide | DME Ch 23Y  (108.65 MHz) |
| 1111.00000 | 1048.00000 | AM | Humberside Airport | DME |
| 1111.00000 | 1048.00000 | AM | Nationwide | DME Ch 24Y  (108.75 MHz) |
| 1112.00000 | 1049.00000 | AM | Nationwide | DME Ch 25Y  (108.85 MHz) |
| 1113.00000 | 1050.00000 | AM | Nationwide | DME Ch26Y  (108.95 MHz) |
| 1113.00000 | 1050.00000 | AM | Woodford | DME |
| 1114.00000 | 1051.00000 | AM | Nationwide | DME Ch 27Y  (109.05 MHz) |
| 1114.00000 | 1051.00000 | AM | Yeovil Aerodrome | DME |
| 1115.00000 | 1052.00000 | AM | Luton Airport | DME |
| 1115.00000 | 1052.00000 | AM | Nationwide | DME Ch 28Y  (109.15 MHz) |
| 1116.00000 | 1053.00000 | AM | Nationwide | DME Ch 29Y  (109.25 MHz) |
| 1117.00000 | 1054.00000 | AM | Nationwide | DME Ch 30Y  (109.35 MHz) |
| 1118.00000 | 1055.00000 | AM | Nationwide | DME Ch 31Y  (109.45 MHz) |
| 1119.00000 | 1056.00000 | AM | Nationwide | DME Ch 32Y  (109.55 MHz) |
| 1120.00000 | 1057.00000 | AM | Nationwide | DME Ch 33Y  (109.65 MHz) |
| 1121.00000 | 1058.00000 | AM | Nationwide | DME Ch 34Y  (109.75 MHz) |
| 1122.00000 | 1059.00000 | AM | Fairoaks Aerodrome | DME |
| 1122.00000 | 1059.00000 | AM | Nationwide | DME Ch 35Y  (109.85 MHz) |
| 1123.00000 | 1060.00000 | AM | Nationwide | DME Ch36Y  (109.95 MHz) |
| 1124.00000 | 1061.00000 | AM | Nationwide | DME Ch 37Y  (110.05 MHz) |
| 1125.00000 | 1062.00000 | AM | Nationwide | DME Ch 38Y  (110.15 MHz) |
| 1126.00000 | 1063.00000 | AM | Nationwide | DME Ch39Y  (110.25 MHz) |
| 1127.00000 | 1064.00000 | AM | Nationwide | DME Ch 40Y  (110.35 MHz) |
| 1128.00000 | 1065.00000 | AM | Nationwide | DME Ch 41Y  (110.45 MHz) |
| 1129.00000 | 1066.00000 | AM | Nationwide | DME Ch 42Y  (110.55 MHz) |
| 1130.00000 | 1067.00000 | AM | Nationwide | DME Ch 43Y  (110.65 MHz) |
| 1131.00000 | 1068.00000 | AM | Nationwide | DME Ch 44Y  (110.75 MHz) |
| 1132.00000 | 1069.00000 | AM | Nationwide | DME Ch 45Y  (110.85 MHz) |
| 1133.00000 | 1070.00000 | AM | Nationwide | DME Ch 46Y  (110.95 MHz) |
| 1134.00000 | 1071.00000 | AM | Nationwide | DME Ch 47Y  (111.05 MHz) |
| 1135.00000 | 1072.00000 | AM | Nationwide | DME Ch 48Y  (111.15 MHz) |
| 1136.00000 | 1073.00000 | AM | Nationwide | DME Ch 49Y  (111.25 MHz) |
| 1137.00000 | 1074.00000 | AM | Nationwide | DME Ch 50Y  (111.35 MHz) |
| 1137.00000 | 1074.00000 | AM | Southend Airport | DME |
| 1138.00000 | 1075.00000 | AM | Nationwide | DME Ch 51Y  (111.45 MHz) |
| 1139.00000 | 1076.00000 | AM | Nationwide | DME Ch 52Y  (111.55 MHz) |
| 1140.00000 | 1077.00000 | AM | Nationwide | DME Ch 53Y  (111.65 MHz) |
| 1141.00000 | 1078.00000 | AM | Liverpool Airport | DME |
| 1141.00000 | 1078.00000 | AM | Nationwide | DME Ch 54Y  (111.75 MHz) |
| 1142.00000 | 1079.00000 | AM | Nationwide | DME Ch 55Y  (111.85 MHz) |

| Base | Mobile | Mode | Location | User and Notes |
|------|--------|------|----------|----------------|
| 1143.00000 | 1080.00000 | AM | Nationwide | DME Ch 56Y  (111.95 MHz) |
| 1144.00000 | 1081.00000 | AM | Nationwide | DME Ch 57Y  (112.05 MHz) |
| 1145.00000 | 1082.00000 | AM | Nationwide | DME Ch 58Y  (112.15 MHz) |
| 1146.00000 | 1083.00000 | AM | Nationwide | DME Ch 59Y  (112.25 MHz) |
| 1147.00000 | 1084.00000 | AM | Nationwide | DME Channel 60Y  Not Used |
| 1148.00000 | 1085.00000 | AM | Nationwide | DME Channel 61Y  Not Used |
| 1149.00000 | 1086.00000 | AM | Nationwide | DME Channel 62Y  Not Used |
| 1150.00000 | 1087.00000 | AM | Nationwide | DME Channel 63Y  Not Used |
| 1151.00000 | 1088.00000 | AM | Nationwide | DME Channel 64Y  Not Used |
| 1152.00000 | 1089.00000 | AM | Nationwide | DME Channel 65Y  Not Used |
| 1153.00000 | 1090.00000 | AM | Nationwide | DME Channel 66Y  Not Used |
| 1154.00000 | 1091.00000 | AM | Nationwide | DME Channel 67Y  Not Used |
| 1155.00000 | 1092.00000 | AM | Nationwide | DME Channel 68Y  Not Used |
| 1156.00000 | 1093.00000 | AM | Nationwide | DME Channel 69Y  Not Used |
| 1157.00000 | 1094.00000 | AM | Nationwide | DME Ch 70Y  (112.35 MHz) |
| 1158.00000 | 1095.00000 | AM | Nationwide | DME Ch 71Y  (112.45 MHz) |
| 1159.00000 | 1096.00000 | AM | Nationwide | DME Ch 72Y  (112.55 MHz) |
| 1160.00000 | 1097.00000 | AM | Nationwide | DME Ch 73Y  (112.65 MHz) |
| 1161.00000 | 1098.00000 | AM | Nationwide | DME Ch 74Y  (112.75 MHz) |
| 1162.00000 | 1099.00000 | AM | Nationwide | DME Ch 75Y  (112.85 MHz) |
| 1163.00000 | 1100.00000 | AM | Nationwide | DME Ch 76Y  (112.95 MHz) |
| 1164.00000 | 1101.00000 | AM | Nationwide | DME Ch 77Y  (113.05 MHz) |
| 1165.00000 | 1102.00000 | AM | Nationwide | DME Ch 78Y  (113.15 MHz) |
| 1166.00000 | 1103.00000 | AM | Nationwide | DME Ch 79Y  (113.25 MHz) |
| 1167.00000 | 1104.00000 | AM | Nationwide | DME Ch 80Y  (113.35 MHz) |
| 1168.00000 | 1105.00000 | AM | Nationwide | DME Ch 81Y  (113.45 MHz) |
| 1169.00000 | 1106.00000 | AM | Manchester Airport | DME |
| 1169.00000 | 1106.00000 | AM | Nationwide | DME Ch 82Y  (113.55 MHz) |
| 1170.00000 | 1107.00000 | AM | Honiley | DME |
| 1170.00000 | 1107.00000 | AM | Nationwide | DME Ch 83Y  (113.65 MHz) |
| 1171.00000 | 1108.00000 | AM | Bovingdon | DME |
| 1171.00000 | 1108.00000 | AM | Nationwide | DME Ch 84Y  (113.75 MHz) |
| 1172.00000 | 1109.00000 | AM | Nationwide | DME Ch 85Y  (113.85 MHz) |
| 1173.00000 | 1110.00000 | AM | Nationwide | DME Ch 86Y  (113.95 MHz) |
| 1174.00000 | 1111.00000 | AM | Nationwide | DME Ch 87Y  (114.05 MHz) |
| 1175.00000 | 1112.00000 | AM | Nationwide | DME Ch 88Y  (114.15 MHz) |
| 1176.00000 | 1113.00000 | AM | Nationwide | DME Ch 89Y  (114.25 MHz) |
| 1177.00000 | 1114.00000 | AM | Compton | DME |
| 1177.00000 | 1114.00000 | AM | Nationwide | DME Ch90Y  (114.35 MHz) |
| 1178.00000 | 1115.00000 | AM | Nationwide | DME Ch 91Y  (114.45 MHz) |
| 1179.00000 | 1116.00000 | AM | Clacton Aerodrome | DME |
| 1179.00000 | 1116.00000 | AM | Nationwide | DME Ch 92Y  (114.55 MHz) |
| 1180.00000 | 1117.00000 | AM | Nationwide | DME Ch 93Y  (114.65 MHz) |
| 1181.00000 | 1118.00000 | AM | Nationwide | DME Ch 94Y  (114.75 MHz) |
| 1182.00000 | 1119.00000 | AM | Nationwide | DME Ch 95Y  (114.85 MHz) |
| 1183.00000 | 1120.00000 | AM | Dover | DME |
| 1183.00000 | 1120.00000 | AM | Nationwide | DME Ch 96Y  (114.95 MHz) |
| 1184.00000 | 1121.00000 | AM | Nationwide | DME Ch 97Y  (115.05 MHz) |
| 1185.00000 | 1122.00000 | AM | Nationwide | DME Ch 98Y  (115.15 MHz) |
| 1186.00000 | 1123.00000 | AM | Nationwide | DME Ch 99Y  (115.25 MHz) |
| 1187.00000 | 1124.00000 | AM | Nationwide | DME Ch 100Y  (115.35 MHz) |
| 1188.00000 | 1125.00000 | AM | Nationwide | DME Ch 101Y  (115.45 MHz) |
| 1189.00000 | 1126.00000 | AM | Gloucestershire Airport | DME |
| 1189.00000 | 1126.00000 | AM | Nationwide | DME Ch 102Y  (115.55 MHz) |
| 1190.00000 | 1127.00000 | AM | Nationwide | DME Ch 103Y  (115.65 MHz) |
| 1191.00000 | 1128.00000 | AM | Nationwide | DME Ch 104Y  (115.75 MHz) |

| Base | Mobile | Mode | Location | User and Notes |
|------|--------|------|----------|----------------|
| 1192.00000 | 1129.00000 | AM | Nationwide | DME Ch 105Y (115.85 MHz) |
| 1193.00000 | 1130.00000 | AM | Nationwide | DME Ch 106Y (115.95 MHz) |
| 1194.00000 | 1131.00000 | AM | Nationwide | DME Ch 107Y (116.05 MHz) |
| 1195.00000 | 1132.00000 | AM | Nationwide | DME Ch 108Y (116.15 MHz) |
| 1196.00000 | 1133.00000 | AM | Barkway | DME |
| 1196.00000 | 1133.00000 | AM | Nationwide | DME Ch 109Y (116.25 MHz) |
| 1197.00000 | 1134.00000 | AM | Nationwide | DME Ch 110Y (116.35 MHz) |
| 1198.00000 | 1135.00000 | AM | Nationwide | DME Ch 111Y (116.45 MHz) |
| 1199.00000 | 1136.00000 | AM | Nationwide | DME Ch 112Y (116.55 MHz) |
| 1200.00000 | 1137.00000 | AM | Nationwide | DME Ch 113Y (116.65 MHz) |
| 1201.00000 | 1138.00000 | AM | Cambridge Airport | DME |
| 1201.00000 | 1138.00000 | AM | Nationwide | DME Ch 114Y (116.75 MHz) |
| 1202.00000 | 1139.00000 | AM | Nationwide | DME Ch 115Y (116.85 MHz) |
| 1203.00000 | 1140.00000 | AM | Nationwide | DME Ch 116Y (116.95 MHz) |
| 1204.00000 | 1141.00000 | AM | Nationwide | DME Ch 117Y (117.05 MHz) |
| 1205.00000 | 1142.00000 | AM | Nationwide | DME Ch 118Y (117.15 MHz) |
| 1206.00000 | 1143.00000 | AM | Nationwide | DME Ch 119Y (117.25 MHz) |
| 1207.00000 | 1144.00000 | AM | Nationwide | DME Ch 120Y (117.35 MHz) |
| 1207.00000 | 1144.00000 | AM | Sumburgh Airport | DME |
| 1208.00000 | 1145.00000 | AM | Brecon | DME |
| 1208.00000 | 1145.00000 | AM | Nationwide | DME Ch 121Y (117.45 MHz) |
| 1209.00000 | 1146.00000 | AM | Nationwide | DME Ch 122Y (117.55 MHz) |
| 1210.00000 | 1147.00000 | AM | Nationwide | DME Ch 123Y (117.65 MHz) |
| 1211.00000 | 1148.00000 | AM | Nationwide | DME Ch 124Y (117.75 MHz) |
| 1212.00000 | 1149.00000 | AM | Nationwide | DME Ch 125Y (117.85 MHz) |
| 1213.00000 | 1150.00000 | AM | Nationwide | DME Ch 126Y (117.95 MHz) |

## 1240.0000 - 1260.0000 MHz    CIVIL RADAR SYSTEMS

## 1215.0000 - 1240.0000 MHz    SATELLITE NAVIGATION SYSTEMS

| Base | Mobile | Mode | Location | User and Notes |
|------|--------|------|----------|----------------|
| 1227.60000 | | NFM | Nationwide | Military GPS Navstar |

## 1240.0000 - 1296.0000 MHz    RADIO LOCATION AND SATELLITE POSITIONING SYSTEMS

| Base | Mobile | Mode | Location | User and Notes |
|------|--------|------|----------|----------------|
| 1246.00000 | | NFM | Nationwide | Military Glonass Ch 0 |
| 1246.43750 | | NFM | Nationwide | Military Glonass Ch 1 |
| 1246.87500 | | NFM | Nationwide | Military Glonass Ch 2 |
| 1247.31250 | | NFM | Nationwide | Military Glonass Ch 3 |
| 1247.75000 | | NFM | Nationwide | Military Glonass Ch 4 |
| 1248.18750 | | NFM | Nationwide | Military Glonass Ch 5 |
| 1248.62500 | | NFM | Nationwide | Military Glonass Ch 6 |
| 1249.06250 | | NFM | Nationwide | Military Glonass Ch 7 |
| 1249.50000 | | NFM | Nationwide | Military Glonass Ch 8 |
| 1249.93750 | | NFM | Nationwide | Military Glonass Ch 9 |
| 1250.37500 | | NFM | Nationwide | Military Glonass Ch 10 |
| 1250.81250 | | NFM | Nationwide | Military Glonass Ch 11 |
| 1251.25000 | | NFM | Nationwide | Military Glonass Ch 12 |
| 1251.68750 | | NFM | Nationwide | Military Glonass Ch 13 |
| 1252.12500 | | NFM | Nationwide | Military Glonass Ch 14 |
| 1252.56250 | | NFM | Nationwide | Military Glonass Ch 15 |
| 1253.00000 | | NFM | Nationwide | Military Glonass Ch 16 |
| 1253.43750 | | NFM | Nationwide | Military Glonass Ch 17 |
| 1253.87500 | | NFM | Nationwide | Military Glonass Ch 18 |
| 1254.31250 | | NFM | Nationwide | Military Glonass Ch 19 |

| Base | Mobile | Mode | Location | User and Notes |
|------|--------|------|----------|----------------|
| 1254.75000 | | NFM | Nationwide | Military Glonass Ch 20 |
| 1255.00000 | 1255.00000 | WFM | Nationwide | Amateur TV |
| 1255.18750 | | NFM | Nationwide | Military Glonass Ch 21 |
| 1255.62500 | | NFM | Nationwide | Military Glonass Ch 22 |
| 1256.06250 | | NFM | Nationwide | Military Glonass Ch 23 |
| 1256.50000 | | NFM | Nationwide | Military Glonass Ch 24 |
| 1260.00000 | | NFM | Nationwide | German Bugging Devices |

## 1240.0000 - 1325.0000 MHz    25 cm Amateur Radio Band

| Base | Mobile | Mode | Location | User and Notes |
|------|--------|------|----------|----------------|
| 1240.150 | | SSB | Nationwide | Packet Radio |
| 1248.000 | | SSB | Nationwide | Amateur TV |
| 1248.000 | 1308.000 | NFM | High Wycombe | Repeater (GB3HV) |
| 1249.000 | 1308.000 | NFM | Hull | Repeater (GB3EY) |
| 1249.000 | 1310.000 | NFM | Eastbourne | Repeater (GB3VX) |
| 1249.000 | 1310.000 | NFM | Sheerness | Repeater (GB3KT) |
| 1249.000 | 1310.000 | NFM | Stevenage | Repeater (GB3AD) |
| 1249.000 | 1316.000 | NFM | Almwich | Repeater (GB3TM) |
| 1249.000 | 1316.000 | NFM | Brighton | Repeater (GB3VR) |
| 1249.000 | 1316.000 | NFM | Bristol | Repeater (GB3ZZ) |
| 1249.000 | 1316.000 | NFM | Cambridge | Repeater (GB3PV) |
| 1249.000 | 1316.000 | NFM | Chesterfield | Repeater (GB3TT) |
| 1249.000 | 1316.000 | NFM | Coventry | Repeater (GB3RT) |
| 1249.000 | 1316.000 | NFM | Dartmoor | Repeater (GB3WV) |
| 1249.000 | 1316.000 | NFM | Derby | Repeater (GB3DH) |
| 1249.000 | 1316.000 | NFM | Emley Moor | Repeater (GB3ET) |
| 1249.000 | 1316.000 | NFM | Fakenham | Repeater (GB3TN) |
| 1249.000 | 1316.000 | NFM | Leicestershire | Repeater (GB3GV) |
| 1249.000 | 1316.000 | NFM | Lowestoft | Repeater (GB3LO) |
| 1249.000 | 1316.000 | NFM | Northampton | Repeater (GB3MV) |
| 1249.000 | 1316.000 | NFM | Nottingham | Repeater (GB3NV) |
| 1249.000 | 1316.000 | NFM | Southampton | Repeater (GB3AT) |
| 1249.000 | 1318.500 | NFM | Dunstable | Repeater (GB3TV) |
| 1249.000 | 1318.500 | NFM | Stoke on Trent | Repeater (GB3UD) |
| 1276.000 | | AM | Nationwide | TV input |
| 1276.500 | 1311.500 | NFM | Bath | Repeater (GB3UT) |
| 1291.000 | 1297.000 | NFM | Bolton | Repeater (GB3MC) |
| 1291.000 | 1297.000 | NFM | Norwich | Repeater (GB3NO) |
| 1291.050 | 1297.050 | NFM | Farnham | Repeater (GB3FM) |
| 1291.075 | 1297.075 | NFM | Royston | Repeater (GB3PS) |
| 1291.075 | 1297.075 | NFM | Stoke on Trent | Repeater (GB3SE) |
| 1291.125 | 1297.125 | NFM | Northampton | Repeater (GB3CN) |
| 1291.150 | 1297.105 | NFM | Wolverhampton | Repeater (GB3MM) |
| 1291.375 | 1297.375 | NFM | Wakefield | Repeater (GB3WC) |
| 1296.000 | | CW | Space | Moonbounce |
| 1296.500 | | SSB | Nationwide | Slow scan television |
| 1296.600 | | SSB | Nationwide | RTTY |
| 1296.700 | | SSB | Nationwide | Fax |
| 1296.810 | | CW | Orpington | Beacon (GB3NWK) |
| 1296.830 | | CW | Martlesham | Beacon (GB3MHL) |
| 1296.850 | | CW | Farnborough | Beacon (GB3FRS) |
| 1296.860 | | CW | St. Austell | Beacon (GB3MCB) |
| 1296.875 | | CW | Bristol | Beacon (GB3USK) |
| 1296.890 | | CW | Dunstable | Beacon (GB3DUN) |
| 1296.900 | | CW | Newport, IOW | Beacon (GB3IOW) |
| 1296.910 | | CW | Clee Hill, Salop | Beacon (GB3CLE) |

| Base | Mobile | Mode | Location | User and Notes |
|------|--------|------|----------|----------------|
| 1296.930 | | CW | Emley Moor | Beacon (GB3MLE) |
| 1296.965 | | CW | Dundee | Beacon (GB3ANG) |
| 1296.990 | | CW | Edinburgh | Beacon (GB3EDN) |
| 1297.500 | | NFM | Nationwide | Channel 20 |
| 1297.525 | | NFM | Nationwide | Channel 21 |
| 1297.550 | | NFM | Nationwide | Channel 22 |
| 1297.575 | | NFM | Nationwide | Channel 23 |
| 1297.600 | | NFM | Nationwide | Channel 24 |
| 1297.625 | | NFM | Nationwide | Channel 25 |
| 1297.650 | | NFM | Nationwide | Channel 26 |
| 1297.675 | | NFM | Nationwide | Channel 27 |
| 1297.700 | | NFM | Nationwide | Channel 28 |
| 1297.725 | | NFM | Nationwide | Channel 29 |
| 1297.750 | | NFM | Nationwide | Channel 30 |
| 1299.000 | | SSB | Nationwide | Remote control |
| 1299.425 | | NFM | Nationwide | Packet Radio |

**1325.0000 - 1400.0000 MHz     POINT-TO-POINT DIGITAL MULTIPLEXED MICROWAVE LINKS**

| Base | Mobile | Mode | Location | User and Notes |
|------|--------|------|----------|----------------|
| 1328.02000 | | MUX | Poole | Bulbarrow Main Site |
| 1331.20000 | | MUX | Poole | Bulbarrow Main Site |
| 1334.00000 | | MUX | Poole | Bulbarrow Main Site |

**1362.500 MHz     MARITIME SEISMIC STEAMER TAILBOUYS**

**1394.000 MHz     CIVIL VIDEO LINKS**

**1370.000 - 1400.000 MHz     RADIO ASTRONOMY**
Used to study redshift hydron lines

**1389.500 MHz     MARITIME SEISMIC STEAMER TAILBOUYS**

**1400.000 - 1427 MHz     RADIO ASTRONOMY**
Used for hydrogen line studies, MERLIN, pulsars and mapping radio sources.

**1427.0000 - 1429.0000 MHz SATELLITE UPLINKS**

**1429.0000 - 1450.0000 MHz GOVERNMENT FIXED LINKS**
Paired with 1375 - 1400 MHz

**1450.0000 - 1530.0000 MHz     POINT-TO-POINT DIGITAL MICROWAVE LINKS**

| Base | Mobile | Mode | Location | User and Notes |
|------|--------|------|----------|----------------|
| 1450.60000 | | MUX | Poole | Bulbarrow Main Site |
| 1451.15625 | | NFM | West Midlands | 96.4 FM BRMB |
| 1455.35000 | | NFM | Merseyside | Police DCR Link |
| 1457.64000 | | MUX | Poole | 70.8625 MHz Fire Brigade |
| 1458.24750 | | NFM | Badminton | Palace Link |
| 1459.15000 | | MUX | Poole | Microwave link |
| 1460.43000 | | MUX | Poole | Microwave link |
| 1461.62500 | | NFM | Wiltshire | Fire Brigade   link |
| 1461.64000 | | MUX | Poole | Microwave link |
| 1466.87500 | 1529.37500 | NFM | Nationwide | UK Test & Development |

| Base | Mobile | Mode | Location | User and Notes |
|------|--------|------|----------|----------------|
| 1467.12500 | 1529.62500 | NFM | Nationwide | UK Test & Development |
| 1468.77000 | | MUX | Poole | Microwave Link |
| 1469.68000 | | MUX | Poole | 171.2875 MHz Feeder |
| 1470.33000 | | MUX | Poole | Bulbarrow Main Site |
| 1472.00000 | | MUX | Poole | Corfe Castle |
| 1472.65000 | | MUX | Poole | Microwave Link |
| 1472.98750 | 1492.85000 | NFM | Channel Islands | Aurigny Airlines Link |
| 1473.15000 | | MUX | Poole | Bulbarrow Main Site |
| 1492.30000 | | MUX | Poole | 454.1 MHz Paging Feeder |
| 1492.30000 | | MUX | Poole | Microwave Link |

## 1575.420 - 1616.500 MHz    RADIO LOCATION AND SATELLITE POSITIONING SYSTEMS

| Base | Mobile | Mode | Location | User and Notes |
|------|--------|------|----------|----------------|
| 1575.42000 | | NFM | Nationwide | Civilian GPS Navstar |
| 1602.00000 | | NFM | Nationwide | Civil Glonass Ch 0 |
| 1602.56250 | | NFM | Nationwide | Civil Glonass Ch 1 |
| 1603.12500 | | NFM | Nationwide | Civil Glonass Ch 2 |
| 1603.67850 | | NFM | Nationwide | Civil Glonass Ch 3 |
| 1604.25000 | | NFM | Nationwide | Civil Glonass Ch 4 |
| 1604.81250 | | NFM | Nationwide | Civil Glonass Ch 5 |
| 1605.37500 | | NFM | Nationwide | Civil Glonass Ch 6 |
| 1605.93750 | | NFM | Nationwide | Civil Glonass Ch 7 |
| 1606.50000 | | NFM | Nationwide | Civil Glonass Ch 8 |
| 1607.06250 | | NFM | Nationwide | Civil Glonass Ch 9 |
| 1607.62500 | | NFM | Nationwide | Civil Glonass Ch 10 |
| 1608.18750 | | NFM | Nationwide | Civil Glonass Ch 11 |
| 1608.75000 | | NFM | Nationwide | Civil Glonass Ch 12 |
| 1609.31250 | | NFM | Nationwide | Civil Glonass Ch 13 |
| 1609.87500 | | NFM | Nationwide | Civil Glonass Ch 14 |
| 1610.43750 | | NFM | Nationwide | Civil Glonass Ch 15 |
| 1611.00000 | | NFM | Nationwide | Civil Glonass Ch 16 |
| 1611.56250 | | NFM | Nationwide | Civil Glonass Ch 17 |
| 1612.12500 | | NFM | Nationwide | Civil Glonass Ch 18 |
| 1612.67850 | | NFM | Nationwide | Civil Glonass Ch 19 |
| 1613.25000 | | NFM | Nationwide | Civil Glonass Ch 20 |
| 1613.81250 | | NFM | Nationwide | Civil Glonass Ch 21 |
| 1614.37500 | | NFM | Nationwide | Civil Glonass Ch 22 |
| 1614.93750 | | NFM | Nationwide | Civil Glonass Ch 23 |
| 1616.50000 | | NFM | Nationwide | Civil Glonass Ch 24 |

## 1670.0000 - 1675.0000 MHz    TERRESTRIAL FLIGHT TELEPHONE SYSTEM UPLINKS

| Base | Mobile | Mode | Location | User and Notes |
|------|--------|------|----------|----------------|
| 1691.00000 | | NFM | Nationwide | Meteosat Ch A1/GOES |
| 1694.50000 | | NFM | Nationwide | Meteosat Ch A2/FAX |
| 1698.00000 | | NFM | Nationwide | NOAA-10 |
| 1707.00000 | | NFM | Nationwide | NOAA-9, 11 |

## 1800.0000 - 1805.0000 MHz    TERRESTRIAL FLIGHT TELEPHONE SYSTEM DOWNLINKS

# Part 2

# Civil Aviation Band

---

# Tuning in Air Band Communications
## by Peter G. Clark

In the world of scanning, there are few things more exciting or entertaining than listening to the civil aviation band. Whether it is in the comfort of your own home or at your local airport, civil air band listening will always have a surprise in store for you. It is probably the most visible form of the scanning hobby (look around any airport or air display and you'll see scanners by the dozen) and for all those law-abiding citizens amongst you, it is the one area that is not likely to land you in serious trouble!

Airband listening (118.000 to 136.975 MHz) is an easily accessible form of scanning with a plethora of dedicated handheld receivers on the market, but from the listeners point of view, it can often be a daunting prospect trying to understand the various terms and often confusing phrases that pilots and air traffic controllers use. So, let's take a look at airband listening, from the beginner's point of view. For this, let's assume that we are at a major airport, like London Heathrow. Of course, many of you will not live near an airport, but that shouldn't spoil your airband listening - you will still be able to hear aircraft checking in with controllers as they track although the airways. And if that isn't enough, someone once calculated that almost the entire UK population live no more than 25 miles away from an airport or aerodrome!

### Getting Started in Airband Radio

If you are a novice to the hobby then the biggest desire is to hear your first aircraft. The table below illustrates how the civil airband is broken down into several sections and lists the best frequencies to hear the action.

| | |
|---|---|
| Control Tower Frequencies | 118 - 123 MHz |
| | 118.050 MHz Birmingham Tower |
| | 118.625 MHz Manchester Tower |
| | 118.700 MHz London Heathrow Tower |
| | 118.800 MHz Glasgow Tower |
| General Airways Frequencies | 123 - 130 MHz |
| | 126.075 MHz London Control |
| | 126.600 MHz London VOLMET North |
| | 127.900 MHz Shanwick Oceanic |
| | 129.225 MHz Scottish Control |
| Company Frequencies | 130 - 132 MHz |
| | 131.050 MHz London Control |
| | 131.500 MHz British Airways |
| | 131.725 MHz ACARS Data |
| General Airways Frequencies | 132 - 136 MHz |
| | 132.150 MHz Shannon Control |
| | 133.600 MHz London Control |
| | 133.675 MHz Scottish Control |
| | 135.375 MHz London VOLMET Main |

## How far can I hear?

As you will have probably discovered by now, VHF signals do not seem to travel very far. That's because of the phenomenon known as propagation, or the natural dispersion and relay of radio signals by our atmosphere. If you have ever listened to shortwave (below 30 MHz), you will probably have heard a variety of weird and wonderful stations from all around the world. That is due to propagation: shortwave signals are bounced around the globe! VHF signals on the other hand, are pretty energetic and pass straight through the atmosphere and out into space. So, as a rule of thumb, you really need to see a VHF transmitter to hear it. If it is over the horizon, typically only 20nm away, then you can't hear it. But, aircraft fly at altitude and that means even when they are many tens of miles away, they can still be above the horizon. In fact an aircraft flying at 37,000 feet can be heard up to 240 miles away. So as you can see, airband radio opens up new possibilities in VHF listening and increases your reception range tenfold.

## What can I hear?

Find a good atlas or even local road map and search out the location of all the local airports and aerodromes In your area within a distance of about 60nm. Now, turn to pages 539 to 556 and find the frequencies for each airport. Dial the frequencies into your scanner and just wait. You may wish to programme your scanner's memories with the frequencies so that you can rapid scan a number of channels for activity, but sooner or later the scanner will stop and airband communications will pour from your scanner! But don't just limit yourself to local airports. Remember the air traffic control frequencies like London and Scottish. You might not be able to hear the ground station, but you will almost certainly hear the aircraft. Working out which frequencies are best to listen to can be easily solved with North Atlantic Flight Communications by Mike Simkins. This is an absolutely indispensable guide to airband radio on both VHF and shortwave and will help you pinpoint the best airways frequencies to tune in at your location. Recently, several magazine articles have reported on the re-structuring of the civil airband to use 8.5 kHz spacing. Although this change may occur in the future, no firm commitment has been made by the aviation industry, thus the current 25 kHz channel spacing will remain in operation for some time to come. Finally, remember that all airband communications are carried out in the AM mode.

Now, let's take a quick look at some of the more complex aspects of airband radio - understanding what pilots and air traffic controllers talk about.

## Departures

So, let's begin at the beginning, the departure. Once we passengers are loaded safely aboard and the doors are closed, that's when the pilots' job really begins. Before the aircraft can even turn a wheel, engine start, taxi and departure clearances are all required. This will generally happen on the Ground Frequency with a call like "Speedbird 175 on stand 43 request push and start." One thing you will quickly discover with airband listening is that pilots and controllers operate in a world of precision and that is very evident even in the way they speak. That short and apparently simple radio call has identified the flight as Speedbird 175, a scheduled British Airways flight from London Heathrow to New York JFK, that it is parked on Stand 43, is requesting clearance to start his engines and that the tug crew push him back onto the taxi way.  Once clearance for engine start and taxi has been received, the all important airways clearance quickly follows:

ATC:     "Speedbird 175. Clearance when you're ready."
BA175: "Go ahead."
ATC:     "Speedbird 175 is cleared to New York Kennedy via UA1 UR3 55 North. Airways frequency 133.45, and the squawk will be 4026."

That short exchange has just cleared the flight from London Heathrow to it's Oceanic entry point at 55° North 10° West, about 110nm west of Belfast via two Upper Air Routes, UA1 and UR3.  As the aircraft begins to move, it will be asked to change frequency to the Tower where it will be guided along the taxi-ways and onto the runway in use.  Once the "cleared for take-off" message is received, the aircraft will begin its acceleration run before lifting off from the runway and beginning in journey to destination.

Once airborne, the aircraft will switch frequency to the Radar Frequency and begin to follow the Standard Instrument Departure or SID in force for that day.  Like approach procedures, which we will look at later, these are a set of precise instructions that get the aircraft from the runway and onto a heading and position so that they can join the airway.

So, let's quickly recap on frequency usage at major airports: the use of three frequencies is not uncommon.  Ground is used for ground movements, Tower is responsible for getting aircraft to and from the runways and Approach or Radar takes over as soon as the flight is airborne.

More detailed information on Upper Air Routes, flight procedures and radio communications across the North Atlantic can be found in *North Atlantic Flight Communications*. This comprehensive book is accompanied by software that allows you to plot the progress of flights as they cross the "pond". See page 594.

**The Flight**
Once the flight has left the confines of the airport and has entered controlled airspace, responsibility for separation is handed to air traffic controllers who watch the progress of individual flights across various sectors of the country. During the flights of yesteryear, pilots' workload remained high for the duration of any flight.  Today, however, that is not always the case.  Certainly, flight instruments still have to be monitored and forward estimates calculated but essentially the work of flying the aircraft has been handed over to onboard computers in the form of the autopilot.

With the flight plan entered into the flight management system, pilots rarely communicate with air traffic control centres accept when checking in on a new frequency, requesting a slight course deviations to avoid CB's or Cumulo Nimbus clouds, responsible for much of the unpleasant flying weather or requesting flight level changes.

Over land, most navigation involves flying between two radio navigation beacons, such as VORs, which operate in the 108-118 MHz band and NDBs (non-directional beacons) which operate in the 283.5-435 kHz band. Coupled with some VORs are DMEs or Distance Measuring Equipment, which provide a readout on board the aircraft of their distance to run to a beacon. Over water, where beacons are not practical, aircraft rely on their internal navigation systems. Of course, where VHF radio navigation do not work, neither do VHF voice communications. The solution is to use HF or shortwave radio (3 - 30 MHz, a band that many scanners now cover and is well worth exploring), which is the main communications mode in use for flights crossing the Atlantic. If you do wish to accept the challenge and explore the world of then *North Atlantic Flight Communications* is without doubt the book to have as is another invaluable book by the same author *World Airline Fleet and Selcal Directory*. See page 595.

## Arrivals

Arriving at the destination gives us all the sigh of relief, but behind the scenes, the workload is frantic. All flights arriving at an airport must be positioned to ensure safety and flight separation. Airport approach frequencies positively buzz with instructions and clearances as pilots fly Instrument Approaches or what are known as plates; diagrams of the procedures to be flown to land safely. The plate shown here is for a VOR/DME approach onto runway 06 at Inverness and allows pilots to land their aircraft in almost zero visibility. In fact many flights end with the pilots only gaining visual contact with the runway a few hundred feet from their touchdown point. Plates form an essential part of Instrument Flying that allow pilots to fly between two airports in cloud all the way.

Adventurous readers with flight simulator software, such as *Flight Simulator 98*, might like to position themselves over any one of the reporting points and "fly the approach."

A final word on airband radio. One of the more popular airband past-times these days is tuning in air display teams like the Red Arrows. If you've never done it them there is a real treat in store for you. Just imagine being able to listen in to the same instructions the display pilots are receiving! Check out our Air Display Frequencies list on page 314. We promise you nothing but pure nail-biting excitement!

# UK and Irish Airports

| Airport | Mhz AM | Airport | MHz AM |
|---|---|---|---|
| Abbeyshrule, Eire | | Barrow (Walney Island) | |
| Air/Ground | 122.600 | Air/Ground | 123.200 |
| Aberdeen (Dyce Airport) | | Barton Aerodrome, Manchester | |
| Air UK | 130.600 | Air/Ground | 122.700 |
| Approach/Radar | 120.400 | Beccles Heliport | |
| ATIS | 121.850 | Air/Ground | 134.600 |
| Bristow Helicopters | 122.950 | Belfast (Aldergrove) | |
| British Airways Ops | 131.850 | Approach/Radar | 120.900 |
| British Airways | 122.050 | ATIS | 128.200 |
| Fire Channel | 121.600 | British Airways Ops | 131.850 |
| Granite Ops | 130.625 | British Midland | 131.575 |
| Ground Staff | 130.050 | Ground | 121.750 |
| Ground | 121.700 | Radar | 120.000 |
| Information | 135.175 | Servisair | 130.600 |
| Radar | 121.250 | Tower | 118.300 |
| Radar | 128.300 | Belfast (City) | |
| Radar | 134.100 | AFIS | 136.625 |
| Servisair | 130.600 | Approach/Radar | 130.850 |
| Tower | 118.100 | Tower | 130.750 |
| Aberporth (MoD) | | Bellarena | |
| AFIS | 122.150 | Air/Ground Gliders | 130.100 |
| Alderney | | Belmullet, Eire | |
| Aurigny Airlines | 122.300 | AFIS and Air/Ground | 123.600 |
| Approach (Guernsey) | 128.650 | Bembridge, Isle of Wight | |
| Tower | 125.350 | AFIS and Air/Ground | 123.250 |
| Trinity Lightship Heliport | 129.700 | Benbecula | |
| Andrewsfield | | Approach/Tower and FIS | 119.200 |
| Air/Ground | 130.550 | British Airways Ops | 131.850 |
| Ashcroft Farm | | Berwick-on-Tweed (Winfield) | |
| Air/Ground | 122.525 | Winfield Radio | 123.500 |
| Audley End | | Beverley (Linley Hill) | |
| Air/Ground | 122.350 | Tower | 123.050 |
| Badminton | | Biggin Hill | |
| Air/Ground | 123.175 | Approach | 129.400 |
| Bagby (Thirsk) | | ATIS | 121.875 |
| Air/Ground | 123.250 | Speedbird Ops | 120.525 |
| Baldonnel, Eire | | Srikair | 130.025 |
| Approach | 122.000 | Tower | 134.800 |
| Area Control | 122.800 | Birmingham International | |
| Ground | 123.100 | Air 2000 Ops | 131.700 |
| IAC Military Radar | 122.300 | Air Foyle | 131.775 |
| IAC Military Radar | 129.700 | Allied | 131.425 |
| Radar | 129.700 | ATIS | 126.275 |
| Tower | 123.500 | Birmingham Executive | 131.850 |
| Ballykelly | | British Airways Ops | 131.850 |
| Approach (Eglinton) ATZ | 123.625 | Fire Service | 121.600 |
| Bantry, Eire | | Ground | 121.800 |
| Air/Ground | 122.400 | Loganair | 131.575 |
| Barra, Scotland | | Lufthansa | 131.925 |
| AFIS | 118.075 | Ogden Aviation | 131.425 |

# UK and Irish Airports

| Airport | Mhz AM | Airport | MHz AM |
|---|---|---|---|
| Birmingham International (cont.) | | Tower | 133.850 |
|    Radar | 131.325 | Brittas Bay, Eire | |
|    Radar/Approach | 118.050 |    Air/Ground (Brittas Bay Radio) | 118.250 |
|    Servisair | 130.600 | Brooklands | |
|    TEA Operations | 131.575 |    Air/Ground | 122.350 |
|    Tower | 118.300 | Brough Aerodrome | |
| Birr Aerodrome, Eire | |    Tower and Air/Ground | 130.550 |
|    Air/Ground (Birr Radio) | 122.950 | Bruntingthorpe | |
| Bitteswell Aerodrome | |    Air/Ground | 122.825 |
|    Air/Ground | 122.500 | Burtonwood | |
| Blackbushe | |    US Army Helicopter Ops | 119.850 |
|    A.T.S. | 129.700 | Caernarfon Aerodrome | |
|    AFIS and Air/Ground | 122.300 |    Tower | 122.250 |
|    Air Hanson Ops | 130.370 | Cambridge Airport | |
|    Air Lynton Ops | 130.175 |    Approach | 123.600 |
| Blackpool | |    Magnet Air | 130.175 |
|    Approach | 119.950 |    Radar | 130.750 |
|    ATIS | 121.750 |    Suckling Ops | 130.175 |
|    Janes Ops | 130.175 |    Tower | 122.200 |
|    Lynton Ops | 130.175 | Campbeltown | |
|    Radar | 135.950 |    Flight Information | 125.900 |
|    Servisair | 130.600 | Canterbury | |
|    Tower | 118.400 |    Traffic information (Manston) | 126.350 |
| Bodmin | | Cardiff Airport | |
|    Tower | 122.700 |    Approach/Radar | 125.850 |
| Boscombe Down (MoD) | |    ATIS | 119.475 |
|    Radar | 126.700 |    Operations | 122.350 |
|    Radar | 130.000 |    Radar | 124.100 |
|    Tower/Ground | 130.750 |    Servisair | 130.600 |
| Bourn Aerodrome | |    Tower | 125.000 |
|    Air/Ground | 129.800 |    Tremorfa Heliport | 129.900 |
| Bournemouth (Hurn) | | Cark | |
|    Approach/Radar | 119.625 |    Cark Radio | 123.450 |
|    ATIS | 121.950 | Carlisle Airport | |
|    Channel Express | 130.600 |    Approach/Tower/Ground | 123.600 |
|    FR Aviation (Broadway Ops) | 123.650 | Castlebar, Eire | |
|    Ground | 121.700 |    Air/Ground | 122.600 |
|    Radar | 118.650 | Castleforbes, Eire | |
|    Services | 130.650 |    Air/Ground | 130.500 |
|    Tower | 125.600 | Cheltenham Racecourse | |
| Braintree Airfield | |    Heliport | 121.075 |
|    Air/Ground | 130.775 | Chester Garrison | |
| Breighton | |    Army Helicopter | 124.950 |
|    Air/Ground | 129.800 |    Army Helicopter Tower | 129.850 |
| Bristol Airport | | Chichester (Goodwood) | |
|    Approach | 128.550 |    AFIS | 122.450 |
|    ATIS | 126.025 | Chichester | |
|    Clifton Ops | 130.625 |    Military Police Helicopter Ops | 122.450 |
|    Radar | 124.350 | | |
|    Servisair | 130.600 | | |

# UK and Irish Airports

| Airport | Mhz AM | Airport | MHz AM |
|---|---|---|---|
| Clacton Aerodrome | | Donegal (Carrickfinn), Eire | |
| Air/Ground | 135.400 | Tower/AFIS | 129.800 |
| Clonbullogue, Eire | | Dornoch Aerodrome | |
| Air/Ground | 128.550 | Approach (Lossiemouth) | 119.350 |
| Colerne | | Dounreay Aerodrome | |
| AFIS | 129.900 | Tower | 122.400 |
| Compton Abbas Aerodrome | | Dublin Airport | |
| Air/Ground | 122.700 | Aer Lingus | 131.500 |
| Connaught (Knock) Airport | | Aer Turas Ops | 131.950 |
| Ground | 121.900 | Appr oach | 121.100 |
| Tower | 130.700 | Area Control (North) | 129.175 |
| Connemara, Eire | | Area Control (South) & Radar | 124.650 |
| Air/Ground | 123.000 | ATIS | 124.525 |
| Coonagh, Eire | | British Midlands Ops | 131.425 |
| Air/Ground | 129.900 | City Jet Ops | 136.825 |
| Cork Airport | | Delivery | 121.875 |
| Aer Lingus Ops | 131.500 | Director | 118.500 |
| Aer Lingus | 131.850 | Dublin Military ATC | 123.300 |
| Approach | 119.900 | Dublin VOLMET | 127.000 |
| ATIS | 120.925 | Ground | 121.800 |
| Ground | 121.800 | Park Aviation | 131.825 |
| Radar | 118.800 | Radar | 136.050 |
| Tower | 119.300 | Radar | 136.150 |
| Tower | 121.700 | Radar | 119.550 |
| Coventry Airport | | Ryanair Ops | 131.550 |
| Approach | 119.250 | Tower | 118.600 |
| Ground | 121.700 | Translift Ops | 131.475 |
| Radar | 122.000 | Dundee | |
| Tower | 124.800 | Approach/Tower | 122.900 |
| ATIS | 126.050 | Dunkeswell Aerodrome | |
| Cowden Range | | Air/Ground | 123.475 |
| Range Control | 122.750 | Dunsfold Aerodrome | |
| Cranfield | | Approach/Radar | 135.175 |
| Approach/ATIS | 121.875 | Radar | 122.550 |
| Approach | 122.850 | Tower | 124.325 |
| Tower | 134.925 | Duxford | |
| Cromer (Northrepps) | | Air Display Channel | 121.075 |
| Air/Ground (Micro) | 129.825 | Air Display Channel | 128.500 |
| Crowfield Aerodrome | | Air Display Channel | 130.675 |
| Air/Ground | 122.775 | Air Display Channel | 134.850 |
| Cumbernauld Airport | | Information | 122.075 |
| AFIS | 120.600 | Ops | 122.675 |
| Deanethorpe | | Eaglescott | |
| Approach | 127.575 | Air/Ground | 123.000 |
| Denham | | Earls Colne | |
| Air/Ground and AFIS | 130.725 | Air/Ground | 122.425 |
| Derby | | | |
| Air/Ground | 118.350 | | |
| Approach (East Midlands) | 119.65000 | | |

# UK and Irish Airports

| Airport | Mhz AM | Airport | MHz AM |
|---|---|---|---|
| **East Midlands Airport** | | **Enstone Aerodrome** | |
| Air Bridge Carriers Ops | 122.350 | Air/Ground | 129.875 |
| Approach | 119.650 | **Epson Aerodrome** | |
| ATIS | 128.225 | Tower | 123.725 |
| British Midland | 131.575 | **Errol Aerodrome** | |
| Donington Aviation Ops | 130.625 | Drop Zone Control | 123.450 |
| Donington Aviation | 130.250 | **Esholt** | |
| Excalibur Ops | 131.575 | Air/Ground (Esholt Radio) | 129.820 |
| Fire Service | 121.600 | **Exeter Airport** | |
| Ground | 121.900 | Handling | 130.175 |
| Radar | 120.125 | Markair Ops | 130.175 |
| Tower | 124.000 | Radar | 119.050 |
| UPS Ops | 131.600 | Tower | 119.800 |
| UPS Ops | 136.850 | Tower/Radar | 128.150 |
| **Edinburgh Airport** | | **Fadmoor Aerodrome** | |
| Approach (gliders) | 130.400 | Air/Ground | 123.220 |
| Approach/Radar | 121.200 | **Fair Isle** | |
| ATIS | 132.075 | Approach (Sumburgh) | 123.150 |
| British Airways | 131.800 | **Fairoaks** | |
| British Midland | 131.575 | Tower and AFIS | 123.425 |
| Execair Operations | 122.350 | **Farnborough (RAE Airfield)** | |
| Ground | 121.750 | Air Show Approach | 135.750 |
| Radar | 128.975 | Air Show Tower | 118.100 |
| Servisair | 130.600 | Approach | 134.350 |
| Tower | 118.700 | CAA Event Special use | 121.175 |
| **Eggesford Aerodrome** | | Executive Ops | 130.375 |
| Tower | 123.500 | Farnborough Tower | 134.025 |
| **Elmsett** | | HeliPad | 130.500 |
| Air/Ground (Elmsett Radio) | 130.425 | Precision Approach Radar | 130.050 |
| **Elstree Aerodrome** | | Radar | 125.250 |
| Air/Ground/AFIS | 122.400 | Tower | 122.500 |
| **English Channel** | | **Felthorpe Aerodrome** | |
| Bishops Rock Trinity Lightship | 129.700 | Tower | 123.500 |
| Casquets Trinity Lightship | 129.700 | **Fenland** | |
| Fisheries Protection | 130.800 | Air/Ground and AFIS | 122.925 |
| Flatholm Trinity Lightship | 129.700 | **Filton (BAe), Bristol** | |
| Hanois Trinity Lightship | 129.700 | Approach/Radar | 122.725 |
| Inner Dowsing Trinity Lightship | 129.700 | Approach/Radar | 124.950 |
| Longships Trinity Lightship | 129.700 | Filton Ops | 134.500 |
| Lundy South Trinity Lightship | 129.700 | Rolls Royce Ops | 129.750 |
| Round Island Trinity Lightship | 129.700 | Tower | 132.350 |
| Royal Sovereign Trinity L/ship | 129.700 | **Fishburn** | |
| Skerries Trinity Lightship | 129.700 | Air/Ground | 118.275 |
| Skokholm Trinity Lightship | 129.700 | **Flotta Airfield** | |
| Smalls Trinity Lightship | 129.700 | Tower | 122.125 |
| South Bishop Trinity Lightship | 129.700 | **Foulsham Aerodrome** | |
| St Anns Head Trinity Lightship | 129.700 | Tower | 130.650 |
| **Enniskillen (St. Angelo)** | | **Fowlemere** | |
| Air/Ground | 123.200 | Air/Ground | 120.925 |

# UK and Irish Airports

| Airport | Mhz AM | Airport | MHz AM |
|---|---|---|---|
| Full Sutton | | Hatfield Aerodrome | |
|    Air/Ground | 132.325 |    Approach | 123.350 |
| Galway, Eire | |    Hatair Ops | 123.650 |
|    A/G and AFIS | 122.500 |    Radar | 119.300 |
| Glasgow | |    Tower | 130.800 |
|    Air 2000 Ops | 131.700 | Haverfordwest Aerodrome | |
|    Air Canada | 131.375 |    Air/Ground | 122.200 |
|    Approach/Radar | 119.100 | Hawarden Aerodrome | |
|    ATIS | 129.575 |    Approach | 123.350 |
|    British Airways | 131.975 |    Radar | 130.250 |
|    Execair | 122.350 |    Tower | 124.950 |
|    Ground | 121.700 | Haydock Park | |
|    Loganair Ops | 130.650 |    Approach | 119.400 |
|    Maersk Ops | 130.650 | Hayes Heliport | |
|    Northwest | 129.700 |    A/G (Macline Hayes) | 123.650 |
|    Radar | 119.300 | Henlow | |
|    Radar | 121.300 |    Air/Ground | 121.100 |
|    Tower | 118.800 | Henstridge | |
| Glenrothes | |    Tower | 130.250 |
|    Air/Ground | 130.450 | Hethel | |
| Gloucestershire Airport | |    Air/Ground | 122.350 |
|    Approach | 125.650 | Hethersett Aerodrome | |
|    ATIS | 127.475 |    Hethersett Radio | 129.875 |
|    Radar | 120.975 | High Easter Aerodrome | |
|    Tower | 122.900 |    Approach (Stansted) | 120.625 |
| Gormanston, Eire | | Hinton in the Hedges | |
|    IAC Military Approach | 122.200 |    Air/Ground | 119.450 |
|    IAC Military Tower | 122.700 | Hitchin (Rush Green) | |
| Great Yarmouth (North Denes) | |    Air/Ground | 122.350 |
|    Approach/Tower/Ground | 123.400 | Hucknall Aerodrome | |
| Grimsby (Cuxwold) | |    Air/Ground | 130.800 |
|    Air/Ground | 122.350 | Huddersfield (Crossland Moor) | |
| Guernsey | |    Air/Ground | 122.200 |
|    Approach | 128.650 | Hull (Mount Airy) | |
|    Aurigny Air Services | 122.350 |    Approach (Humberside) | 124.670 |
|    British Midland Ops | 131.575 | Humberside Airport | |
|    Ground | 121.800 |    Approach/Radar | 124.675 |
|    Radar | 118.900 |    ATIS | 124.125 |
|    Radar | 124.500 |    Bond Helicopters | 122.375 |
|    Servisair | 130.600 |    Radar | 123.150 |
|    Tower | 119.950 |    Tower | 118.550 |
| Halfpenny Green Aerodrome | | Inisheer, Eire | |
|    FIS | 123.000 |    Air/Ground | 123.000 |
| Halton Aerodrome | | Inishman, Eire | |
|    Air/Ground | 130.425 |    Air/Ground | 123.000 |
| | | Inishmore, Eire | |
| | |    Air/Ground | 123.000 |
| | | Insch Airfield | |
| | |    Air/Ground | 129.825 |

# UK and Irish Airports

| Airport | Mhz AM | Airport | MHz AM |
|---|---|---|---|
| Inverness Airport | | Leeds/Bradford Airport | |
|    Approach/Tower | 122.600 |    Approach | 123.750 |
|    British Airways Ops | 131.850 |    ATIS | 118.025 |
| Ipswich Airport | |    Radar | 121.050 |
|    AFIS | 118.325 |    Tower | 120.300 |
| Islay Airport | | Lee-on-Solent | |
|    AFIS | 123.150 |    Tower (Fleetlands) | 135.700 |
| Jersey Airport | | Leicester Aerodrome | |
|    Air Traffic Control (Zone)/Radar | 120.450 |    Air/Ground | 122.125 |
|    Air Traffic Control (Zone)/Radar | 125.200 | Lerwick (Tingwall) | |
|    Approach | 118.550 |    Air/Ground and Air Ambulance | 122.600 |
|    Approach/Radar | 120.300 | Lewes (Deanland) | |
|    Aviation Beauport Ops | 129.700 |    Air/Ground | 129.725 |
|    British Airways Jersey Ops | 131.850 | Limerick (Coonagh) | |
|    British Midland Jersey Ops | 131.575 |    Air/Ground | 129.900 |
|    Company Ops | 130.650 | Liskeard | |
|    Company Ops | 131.825 |    Civil Heliport | 129.900 |
|    Ground | 121.900 | Little Gransden Aerodrome | |
|    Information | 129.725 |    Air/Ground | 130.850 |
|    Radar | 118.550 | Little Snoring Aerodrome | |
|    Servisair | 130.600 |    Air/Ground | 124.150 |
|    Tower | 119.450 | Little Staughton | |
| Kemble | |    Air/Ground | 123.925 |
|    Air/Ground | 118.900 | Liverpool Airport | |
|    Radar (Brize) | 134.300 |    Approach/Radar | 119.850 |
| Kent | |    Cheshire Air Training Ops | 122.350 |
|    Air Ambulance | 132.650 |    Emerald Ops | 130.175 |
| Kerry | |    Keenair Ops | 122.050 |
|    Tower | 123.325 |    Mail Flights (Air-Air) | 135.975 |
| Kilkenny | |    Radar | 118.450 |
|    Air/Ground | 122.900 |    Royal Mail Ops | 130.175 |
|    Air/Ground (Weekends) | 130.400 |    Tower | 118.100 |
| Kirkwall Airport | | Llanbedr (MoD) | |
|    Tower/Approach | 118.300 |    Tower/Radar | 122.500 |
| Kyle of Lochalsh | | Lochaber | |
|    RN Heliport | 130.650 |    Air Ambulance | 121.300 |
| Land's End (St Just) | |    PLM Helicopters | 122.350 |
|    Tower/Approach/Ground | 130.700 | London | |
| Langar Airfield | |    Air Ambulance G-HEMS | 122.950 |
|    Drop Zone | 129.900 |    Capital Radio Flying Eye Ops | 130.025 |
|    Approach | 130.200 |    Jersey Air Ops | 122.050 |
| Lasham Aerodrome | |    Special Flypasts Air/Ground | 123.100 |
|    Glider Ops | 129.900 | London, City Airport | |
|    Approach (Farnborough) | 125.250 |    Approach/Thames Radar | 132.700 |
| Lashenden (Headcorn) | |    City Jet Ops | 136.825 |
|    Air/Ground | 122.000 |    Radar/City Radar | 128.025 |
| | |    Tower | 118.075 |
| | |    Tower/ATIS | 127.950 |

# UK and Irish Airports

| Airport | Mhz AM | Airport | MHz AM |
|---|---|---|---|
| London, Gatwick | | Alitalia Ops | 131.450 |
| Air 2000 | 131.900 | All Nippon Ops | 131.475 |
| Air New Zealand Ops | 131.425 | Ambassador Ops | 130.175 |
| American Airlines | 130.650 | American Airlines Maintenance | 131.925 |
| American Airlines | 131.925 | American Ops | 131.925 |
| Approach (Director) | 126.825 | Approach (Director) | 119.725 |
| Aproach/Radar | 134.225 | Approach | 120.400 |
| ATIS | 121.025 | Approach | 127.525 |
| British Airways Maintenance | 131.475 | Approach | 134.975 |
| British Airways | 131.625 | ATIS | 123.900 |
| British Caledonian | 130.600 | Bangladesh Biman | 131.400 |
| British Caledonian | 131.625 | British Airways Ops | 131.500 |
| Caledonian Ops | 131.475 | British Airways Ops | 131.775 |
| Canadian Pacific Ops | 131.625 | British Airways Parking | 131.550 |
| China Airlines | 130.650 | British Airways Speedbird Ops | 131.900 |
| City Flyer Ops | 131.600 | British Airways Speedbird Ops | 136.975 |
| Continental | 131.750 | British Airways | 123.650 |
| Delivery | 121.950 | British Airways | 131.800 |
| Ground | 121.800 | British Midlands Ops | 131.425 |
| Handling | 130.650 | BWIA Ops | 131.450 |
| Information | 136.525 | Cathay Pacific Ops | 131.450 |
| Interflight Ops | 130.575 | Cathay Pacific Ops | 131.825 |
| Jetset Ops | 131.700 | Channnel Express Ops | 131.575 |
| Korean Airlines | 130.650 | Conair Ops | 131.900 |
| London VOLMET (Main) | 135.375 | Conair Ops | 136.975 |
| Monarch Airlines Ops | 136.875 | Corporate Jet Ops | 130.175 |
| Northwest Orient | 130.650 | Crossair Ops | 131.700 |
| Ogden Aviation Ops | 131.425 | CSA | 131.400 |
| Police Helicopter Ops | 119.800 | CSA | 131.775 |
| Radar Standby | 129.025 | Delivery | 121.975 |
| Radar Standby | 135.575 | Delta Ops | 131.700 |
| Radar | 118.950 | Departure/TMA | 132.050 |
| Servisair Ops | 130.075 | El Al | 131.575 |
| Servisair | 131.075 | El Al | 131.950 |
| Tower | 124.225 | El Al | 131.975 |
| TWA Ops | 131.600 | Emirates Ops | 130.150 |
| Virgin Ops | 131.425 | Emirates Ops | 131.850 |
| London, Heathrow | | Federal Express Ops | 131.825 |
| Aer Lingus Ops | 131.450 | Federal Express | 131.950 |
| Aer Lingus Ops | 131.750 | Fields Aviation Ops | 130.600 |
| Aeroflot | 131.775 | Fields Ops | 131.600 |
| Air 2000 Ops | 131.700 | Gama Ops | 130.175 |
| Air Canada Ops | 131.450 | GB Airways Ops | 131.475 |
| Air France Ops | 131.500 | Gibair Ops | 131.825 |
| Air India Ops | 131.925 | Ground | 121.900 |
| Air Lines Ops | 131.600 | Gulf Air Terminal 3 | 122.350 |
| Air Malta Ops | 130.075 | Huntair | 130.600 |
| Air Malta Ops | 131.450 | Iberia Airlines Ops | 131.950 |
| Air Malta Ops | 131.650 | Icelandair | 131.775 |
| Air UK | 131.750 | Iran Air Ops | 131.575 |

# UK and Irish Airports

| Airport | Mhz AM | Airport | MHz AM |
|---|---|---|---|
| London, Heathrow (cont.) | | London, Heathrow (cont.) | |
| Japan Airlines Ops | 131.650 | TAT Ops | 131.900 |
| JAT | 131.775 | TAT Ops | 136.975 |
| Kenya Airways | 131.400 | Thai Airways Ops | 131.450 |
| Kenya Airways | 131.750 | Thames Radar | 132.700 |
| KLM Ops Terminal 4 | 131.650 | Tower | 118.500 |
| KLM Ops | 131.450 | Tower | 118.700 |
| KLM | 131.700 | Trans Mediterranean | 131.400 |
| Korean Air Ops | 131.775 | TWA Ops | 131.600 |
| Kuwait Airways Ops | 131.500 | United Ops | 131.850 |
| London VOLMET (Main) | 135.375 | United Ops | 131.975 |
| London Zone | 134.450 | Viva Ops | 131.950 |
| LOT | 131.775 | Zambian Airlines | 131.400 |
| Lufthansa Ops | 131.750 | Zambian Airlines | 131.850 |
| Lufthansa | 131.925 | London, Lippits Hill | |
| Luxair Ops | 131.550 | Met Police Helicopter | 130.475 |
| Maersk Ops | 131.475 | London, Westland Heliport | |
| Malaysian Airlines | 131.850 | Tower (Battersea) | 122.900 |
| Malev | 131.775 | Londonderry | |
| Mam Aviation | 129.700 | Approach | 123.625 |
| Manx Ops | 131.575 | Tower | 134.150 |
| MEA Ops | 131.950 | Long Marston Aerodrome | |
| Medivac | 132.650 | Tower | 122.900 |
| Nigerian Airlines Ops | 131.950 | Tower | 130.100 |
| Nigerian Airlines Ops | 131.975 | Luton Airport | |
| Olympic Airways Ops | 131.950 | Air Foyle | 131.775 |
| Olympic | 131.775 | Approach/Radar | 126.725 |
| Pakistan International Ops | 131.450 | Approach/Radar | 128.750 |
| Quantas Ops | 131.875 | Approach/Radar | 129.550 |
| Radar | 119.900 | ATIS | 120.575 |
| Radar | 125.625 | BA Maintence | 131.775 |
| Royal Jordanian Ops | 131.425 | Britannia Airways | 131.675 |
| Royal Jordanian Ops | 131.625 | Ground | 121.750 |
| Ryanair Ops | 131.550 | London European Airways | 131.525 |
| Sabena | 131.475 | Magec Ops | 130.175 |
| Sabena | 131.625 | Monarch Airlines Ops | 136.875 |
| Sabena | 131.700 | Monarch Airlines | 131.525 |
| Sabena | 131.775 | Reed Aviation | 122.350 |
| SAS Ops | 131.700 | Ryan Air | 131.525 |
| Saudia Ops | 131.425 | Thames Valley Police Ops | 130.650 |
| Shell Ops | 130.575 | Tower | 132.550 |
| Singapore Airlines Ops | 131.950 | Lydd Airport | |
| South African Airlines | 131.900 | AFIS | 120.700 |
| South African Airlines | 136.975 | AFIS | 131.300 |
| Speedbird Control North | 131.475 | | |
| Springbok Ops | 131.550 | | |
| Stand-by Tower | 124.475 | | |
| Swissair Ops | 131.700 | | |
| TAP Air Portugal | 131.750 | | |
| TAT Ops | 131.475 | | |

# UK and Irish Airports

| Airport | Mhz AM | Airport | MHz AM |
|---|---|---|---|
| **Manchester Airport** | | **Marston Moor Aerodrome** | |
| Aer Lingus Ops | 130.650 | Tower | 122.975 |
| Aer Lingus Ops | 130.750 | **Middle Wallop Army Airfield** | |
| Aer Lingus Ops | 131.750 | Army Air/Ground | 126.700 |
| Air 2000 Ops | 131.700 | Tower/Approach | 122.100 |
| Air Kilroe Ops | 122.350 | **Morecambe Bay** | |
| Airport Monarch Airlines Ops | 136.875 | British Gas Helicopters | 123.375 |
| Airtours Ops | 136.800 | **Mull** | |
| American Airlines Ops | 136.825 | Mull Traffic | 123.450 |
| American Ops | 131.525 | **Nationwide** | |
| Approach/Radar (Director) | 119.400 | 100 Sqd. Air to Air | 123.450 |
| ATC arrivals | 118.575 | AAC Blue Eagles Air to Air | 131.950 |
| ATC | 123.300 | AAC Blue Eagles Ch.1 | 136.975 |
| ATIS | 128.175 | AAC Blue Eagles Display Team | 135.950 |
| British Airways Ops | 131.850 | AAC Blue Eagles Display Team | 135.975 |
| Cathay Pacific Ops | 131.425 | ACARS Frequency | 131.725 |
| Delivery/Ground | 121.700 | Aero Stars | 122.475 |
| Euro Manx Ops | 131.875 | Air Ambulance | 129.900 |
| Federal Express | 131.950 | Air Express Ops | 129.750 |
| Fire Service | 121.600 | Air France Company Channel | 129.025 |
| FLS Engineering Ops | 130.375 | Air France Company Channel | 131.950 |
| Handling | 130.650 | Air to Air Common | 131.800 |
| London VOLMET (Main) | 135.375 | Air UK Company Channel | 127.750 |
| London VOLMET (North) | 126.600 | Air-Air Common | 123.450 |
| LTU Ops | 130.650 | Air-Air Display Co-ordination | 118.000 |
| Lufthansa | 131.925 | Aircraft Exercise Frequency | 122.300 |
| Manchester Air Traffic Control | 124.200 | Airfield Fire & Rescue | 121.600 |
| Manchester Air Traffic Control | 125.100 | American Airlines Packet | 129.200 |
| Manchester Air Traffic Control | 125.950 | American Airlines Packet | 130.250 |
| Manchester Air Traffic Control | 126.650 | Aquilla Spanish Display Team | 130.500 |
| Manchester Air Traffic Control | 133.050 | Aquilla Spanish Display Team | 130.300 |
| Manchester Air Traffic Control | 133.400 | Army Air-Air | 135.975 |
| Northern Executive | 130.650 | Army Helicopter Common | 124.150 |
| Pennine Radar | 128.675 | Battle of Britain Flight | 120.800 |
| Pennine Radar | 132.900 | BMA Ops | 129.750 |
| Radar Standby | 118.575 | Britannia Ops | 129.700 |
| Radar | 121.350 | British Airways Ops | 131.850 |
| Ringway Handling | 136.650 | British Airways Packet | 131.100 |
| Ryan Air Ops | 130.175 | Brymon Airways Ops | 130.600 |
| SAS Ops | 131.700 | Brymon Airways | 122.050 |
| Servisair | 130.600 | Brymon Airways | 123.650 |
| Swissair Ops | 131.700 | Brymon Airways | 129.750 |
| Tourjet Ops | 136.800 | CAA Calibrator Aircraft | 122.275 |
| Tower | 118.625 | CAA events (rarely used) | 121.700 |
| **Manston** | | CAA Events (rarely used) | 123.775 |
| Approach/Radar (LARS/MATZ) | 126.350 | CAA Events (rarely used) | 130.825 |
| Director | 129.450 | CAA Events (rarely used) | 134.500 |
| KIA Ops | 130.600 | CAA events (rearly used) | 123.350 |
| Talkdown | 119.275 | CAA events air to ground | 121.175 |
| | | CAA Events Air/Ground | 130.500 |

# UK and Irish Airports

| Airport | Mhz AM | Airport | MHz AM |
|---|---|---|---|
| Nationwide (cont.) | | Nationwide (cont.) | |
| CAA Events Approach | 130.875 | Philips Airship Air to Ground | 130.575 |
| CAA Events Approach/Tower | 130.675 | RAC Network Q Medivac Helo | 129.900 |
| CAA Events Approach/Tower | 132.900 | RAF Common | 119.000 |
| CAA Special Events | 129.250 | RAF Flight Checker | 126.150 |
| CAA Test Flights | 127.050 | RAF Flight Checker | 134.650 |
| CAA Tests Flight | 134.975 | RAF Formation Air/Air | 129.900 |
| CAA Tests Flight | 135.000 | Red Star Racing Yaks Team | 123.350 |
| CAA Tests Flight | 135.475 | Royal Flights | 132.650 |
| CAA Tests Flight | 135.750 | Royal Navy Pussers Pair | 136.950 |
| Canadian Armed Forces | 131.475 | Ryanair (Air-Air) | 135.975 |
| Civil Aviation Distress Channel | 121.500 | SAR Incident | 130.425 |
| Civilian Air-Air | 118.000 | Search & Rescue Co-ordination | 123.100 |
| Coastguard standby | 132.650 | Search and Rescue | 123.100 |
| Crunchie Flight Team | 118.000 | Servisair | 130.600 |
| Delta Airlines Ops | 130.600 | Sharks Helicopter Displays | 136.975 |
| Delta Airlines Packet Channel | 129.500 | Trinity House Helicopters | 129.700 |
| Delta Airlines Packet Channel | 129.600 | TWA Packet Frequency | 129.625 |
| Distress & Emergency | 121.500 | US Navy C-12 Air to Air | 123.450 |
| Dollar Air Metro | 130.025 | Netheravon (Army) | |
| Dutch F-16 Display Team A/G | 122.275 | Air/Ground (Salisbury Plain) | 122.750 |
| Dutch F-16 Display Team | 130.900 | Drop Zone Radio | 128.300 |
| Dutch Ops | 136.825 | Information | 128.300 |
| Eastern Airlines Packet Ch | 128.850 | Netherthorpe | |
| Fisheries Protection | 131.800 | Air/Ground | 123.275 |
| Frecce Tricolori Display Team | 123.475 | Newcastle Airport | |
| Freemans Aviation | 122.950 | Approach/Radar | 124.375 |
| Glider Training | 130.125 | Army Tower | 128.350 |
| Gliders Channel | 130.400 | Radar | 118.500 |
| Gliders | 130.100 | Samson Ops | 130.650 |
| Gliders | 130.400 | Servisair | 130.600 |
| Gliders | 130.425 | Tower | 119.700 |
| Gliding | 129.975 | Newton | |
| Green March Moroccan Team | 135.925 | Approach/Tower | 119.120 |
| Green March Moroccan Team | 135.975 | Newtownards | |
| Hang Gliders & Balloons | 129.000 | Air/Ground | 123.500 |
| Hang Gliding | 129.900 | North Coates | |
| Helicopter DEPCON | 122.950 | Air/Ground | 120.150 |
| Helicopters Air/Air & A/G | 129.700 | Air/Ground Donna Nook Range | 122.750 |
| Hot Air Ballooning | 122.475 | | |
| Hot Air Ballooning | 129.900 | | |
| Kestrel Ops | 136.800 | | |
| Loganair Ops | 129.750 | | |
| Manx Ops | 129.750 | | |
| Marlboro Aerobatic Display | 118.000 | | |
| Microlight Common | 129.825 | | |
| Military Airfield Radar | 123.300 | | |
| Military Tower Common | 122.100 | | |
| Monarch Airlines Ops | 136.875 | | |
| Navy Gazelle Duo Air/Air | 136.975 | | |

# UK and Irish Airports

| Airport | Mhz AM | Airport | MHz AM |
|---|---|---|---|
| North Sea | | North Sea (cont.) | |
| Alba Oil Field Deck | 130.87500 | FRG/STFS Pipe | 130.725 |
| Alwyn North Oil Field log | 130.200 | Frigg Oil Field deck | 118.050 |
| Amethyst Field deck | 129.875 | Galahad Oil Field deck | 122.875 |
| Amoco Arbroath Field | 129.700 | Galleon Oil Field deck | 133.575 |
| Amoco Indefatigable Field | 123.450 | Gannet Oil Field deck | 129.700 |
| Amoco Indefatigable Field | 123.625 | Gryphon Oil Field deck | 123.025 |
| Amoco Leman Field | 123.625 | Guinevere Oil Field deck | 122.875 |
| Amoco Montrose Field | 129.700 | Hamilton Argyll Field | 122.125 |
| Amoco NW Hutton Deck | 130.800 | Hamilton Esmond Field | 122.325 |
| Amoco Vauxhall Field | 130.550 | Hamilton Forbes Field | 122.325 |
| Andrew Oil Field deck | 130.875 | Hamilton Gordon Field | 122.325 |
| Arco Thames Field | 123.225 | Hamilton Pipe Field | 122.525 |
| Barque Oil Field deck | 133.875 | Hamilton Ravenspurnn North | 123.025 |
| Beatrice Field deck | 123.650 | Helicopter Common | 129.975 |
| Bessemer Oil Field deck | 123.625 | Ivanhoe Oil Field deck | 123.000 |
| BP Buchan Field | 122.000 | Judy Oil Field deck | 122.525 |
| BP Cleeton Field deck | 129.875 | Kewanee Nordsee Field | 129.750 |
| BP Cyprus Field | 122.000 | Kittiwake Oil Field deck | 130.870 |
| BP Forties Field | 122.000 | Kotter Oil Field deck | 122.950 |
| BP Gyda Field | 122.000 | Lancelot Oil Field deck | 122.875 |
| BP Magnus Field Deck | 122.375 | Lennox Oil Field deck | 129.775 |
| BP Ravenspurn North Field deck | 129.875 | Logger Oil Field deck | 122.950 |
| BP West Sole Field deck | 129.875 | Lomond Oil Field deck | 129.700 |
| Brae Oil Field deck | 123.650 | Magnus BP | 122.395 |
| Brent Oil Field log | 123.050 | Marathon East Kinsale | 123.450 |
| British Gas Rough Field deck | 129.875 | Marathon West Kinsale | 123.450 |
| Bruce Oil Field deck | 123.225 | Markham Oil Field deck | 125.175 |
| Caister Oil Field deck | 122.000 | Maureen Oil Field deck | 123.875 |
| Camelott Oil Field deck | 123.625 | Mobil Beryl Field | 122.175 |
| Captian Oil Field deck | 123.550 | Murdoch Oil Field deck | 122.025 |
| Chevron Ninian Field log | 122.050 | Nam Nam Field | 122.950 |
| Claymore & Tartan | 122.450 | Nam Noordwinning | 122.950 |
| Clipper Oil Field deck | 133.575 | Nelson Oil Field deck | 122.650 |
| Clyde Oil Field deck | 122.525 | Ninian Field | 122.050 |
| Conoco Hutton Deck | 130.800 | Noordwinning Oil Field deck | 125.175 |
| Conoco Murchison Field Deck | 122.050 | Noordwinning/Zanddijk Field | 125.175 |
| Conoco oil rig | 129.950 | North Cormorant deck | 129.950 |
| Conoco Viking Field | 122.625 | North Cormorant log | 123.050 |
| Dab Duc Dan Field | 123.450 | North Hamilton Oil Field deck | 129.775 |
| Dab Duc Gorm Field | 123.450 | Occidental Claymore Field | 122.450 |
| Dab Duc Skjold Field | 123.400 | Oil Rig Heliport Common | 120.450 |
| Davey Oil Field deck | 123.625 | Penzoil Noordwinning | 122.950 |
| Dunbar Oil Field deck | 130.200 | Petroland Oil Field deck | 125.175 |
| East Brae Oil Field deck | 123.650 | Petroland Petroland Field | 122.950 |
| Eider Oil Field deck | 129.900 | Phillip Ekofisk Field | 122.925 |
| Eko/Tees Pip Oil Field deck | 122.950 | Phillips Albuskjell Field | 130.550 |
| Elf Aquataine Norge Frigg | 129.750 | Phillips Cod Field | 130.550 |
| Everest Oil Field deck | 129.700 | Phillips Edda Field | 130.550 |
| Excalibur Oil Field deck | 122.875 | Phillips Eko/EMB Pipe deck | 129.900 |

# UK and Irish Airports

| Airport | Mhz AM | Airport | MHz AM |
|---|---|---|---|
| **North Sea (cont.)** | | **Norwich Airport** | |
| Phillips Ekofisk Field | 130.550 | Air UK Ops | 129.750 |
| Phillips Eldfisk Field | 130.550 | Approach/Radar | 119.350 |
| Phillips Hewett Field | 122.875 | ATIS | 128.625 |
| Phillips Tor Field | 130.550 | Radar | 128.325 |
| Pickerill Oil Field deck | 120.075 | Tower | 124.250 |
| Piper Oil Field deck | 122.450 | **Nottingham Aerodrome** | |
| Placid Oil Field deck | 125.175 | Air/Ground | 122.800 |
| Placid Placid Field | 122.950 | Hutchins Crop Sprayers | 122.050 |
| Rolf Oil Field deck | 123.450 | **Nuthampstead, Royston** | |
| Saltire Oil Field deck | 122.450 | Air/Ground | 123.050 |
| Scott Oil Field deck | 122.775 | **Oaksey Park** | |
| Shell/Esso Auk Field | 122.050 | Air/Ground | 122.775 |
| Shell/Esso Brent Field | 122.250 | **Oban** | |
| Shell/Esso Dunlin field deck | 129.950 | Air/Ground | 130.100 |
| Shell/Esso Eider Field log | 123.050 | **Old Sarum** | |
| Shell/Esso Fulmar Field | 122.050 | Air/Ground | 123.200 |
| Shell/Esso Indefatigable | 123.625 | **Old Warden (Biggleswade)** | |
| Shell/Esso Kittiwake Field | 122.050 | Tower (Display days only) | 123.050 |
| Shell/Esso Leman Field | 123.625 | **Oxford (Kidlington Airport)** | |
| Shell/Esso Sean Field | 123.625 | Approach | 125.325 |
| Shell/Esso Tern field deck | 129.950 | ATIS | 121.750 |
| Shell/Esso Tern Field log | 123.050 | Ground | 121.950 |
| South Cormorant log | 123.050 | Tower/AFIS | 118.875 |
| South Cormorant oil field deck | 129.950 | **Oxford** | |
| Statfjord Oil Field deck | 129.650 | Churchill Hospital Helicopter | 132.650 |
| Sun Balmoral Field | 123.550 | **Panshanger** | |
| Texaco Tartan Field | 122.450 | Air/Ground | 120.250 |
| Thames Oil Field deck | 123.625 | **Penzance Heliport** | |
| Thistle Field Deck | 122.050 | Tower | 118.100 |
| Tiffany Oil Field deck | 123.575 | **Perranporth** | |
| Total Alwyn Field | 122.350 | Air/Ground | 119.750 |
| Total/Elf Frigg Field | 129.750 | Glider Ops | 130.100 |
| Trent Oil Field deck | 120.075 | **Perth (Scone)** | |
| Tyne Oil Field deck | 120.075 | Air/Ground and AFIS | 119.800 |
| Tyra Oil Field deck | 124.450 | **Peterborough (Conington)** | |
| Unionoil Heather Field | 122.800 | Air/Ground | 129.725 |
| Unity Oil Field deck | 122.000 | **Peterborough (Sibson)** | |
| Valhall Oil Field deck | 130.550 | Approach/Radar | 122.300 |
| Viking Oil Field log | 120.075 | MATZ and LARS | 130.200 |
| West Sole Oil Field deck | 129.875 | **Peterhead/Longside** | |
| Zanddijk | 122.950 | Air/Ground Bond Helicopters | 122.375 |
| **North Weald** | | **Plockton Airfield** | |
| Aceair Company channel | 130.175 | Air/Ground | 122.375 |
| Air/Ground | 123.525 | **Plymouth City Airport** | |
| Display Frequency | 121.175 | Approach | 133.550 |
| Fighter Grouping meet | 121.075 | Brymon | 131.575 |
| Gliders | 129.975 | Tower | 122.600 |
| **Northampton (Sywell)** | | | |
| AFIS | 122.700 | | |

# UK and Irish Airports

| Airport | Mhz AM | Airport | MHz AM |
|---|---|---|---|
| Pocklington | | Approach/Tower | 122.100 |
|     Air/Ground Glider Ops | 130.100 | Director | 125.900 |
|     Base | 129.900 | Radar | 123.300 |
| Popham Aerodrome | | RAF Coningsby | |
|     Popham Radio | 129.800 |     Approach (LARS and MATZ) | 120.800 |
| Portishead | |     Approach/Tower and Ground | 122.100 |
|     Aero Radio Telephones | 131.625 |     Radar | 123.300 |
| Prestwick Airport | |     Tower | 119.975 |
|     Air Canada Ops | 131.450 | RAF Cosford | |
|     Approach/Radar | 120.550 |     Approach/Tower | 118.925 |
|     ATIS (Information) | 127.125 |     Ground | 121.950 |
|     Eastern Airlines Ops | 131.900 | RAF Cottesmore | |
|     Flight handling | 129.700 |     Approach (LARS and MATZ) | 130.200 |
|     Highland Radar | 126.100 |     Approach/Director | 130.200 |
|     Highland Radar | 134.100 |     Talkdown | 123.300 |
|     Ogden Aviation | 129.700 |     Tower/Ground | 122.100 |
|     Radar | 119.450 | RAF Cranwell | |
|     Tower | 118.150 |     Approach | 119.375 |
|     Tower | 121.800 |     Talkdown | 123.300 |
| Punchestown | |     Tower | 122.100 |
|     Air/Ground (Parachute/Glider ops) | 130.400 | RAF Dishforth (also Army) | |
| RAF Barkston Heath | |     Air/Ground Gliders | 130.100 |
|     Tower | 120.425 |     Air/Ground | 130.100 |
| RAF Benson | |     Approach | 122.100 |
|     Approach | 122.100 |     Approach | 125.000 |
|     Approach | 127.150 |     Approach/Tower | 122.100 |
|     Centralised Approach Control | 134.300 | RAF Fairford | |
|     Radar | 123.300 |     Approach | 119.000 |
|     Tower/Zone | 130.250 |     Approach | 122.100 |
|     Zone | 120.900 |     Centralised Approach Control | 134.300 |
| RAF Boulmer | |     Chilean Air Force Display Team | 136.175 |
|     Boulmer Rescue | 123.100 |     Int. Air Tattoo Base Ops | 125.500 |
| RAF Brize Norton | |     Silver Eagles Display Team | 135.975 |
|     ATC | 123.550 |     Tower (Airshows Only) | 126.500 |
|     Brize Director | 124.275 |     Tower (Airshows Only) | 129.250 |
|     Brize Director | 133.750 |     Tower | 119.150 |
|     Brize Ops | 130.075 |     Ukraine Team SU-27 ops. | 128.500 |
|     Brize Radar | 134.300 | RAF Henlow | |
|     Brize Talkdown/Tower | 123.725 |     Para drop zone | 130.525 |
|     Ground | 121.725 | RAF Honington | |
|     Zone | 119.000 |     Approach | 123.300 |
| RAF Chivenor | |     Tower | 122.100 |
|     Air/Ground | 130.200 | RAF Kinloss | |
| RAF Church Fenton | |     Approach | 119.350 |
|     Approach (MATZ) | 126.500 |     Radar | 123.300 |
|     Talkdown | 123.300 |     Tower | 122.100 |
|     Tower/Ground | 122.100 | | |
| RAF Colerne | | | |
|     Approach/Tower | 122.100 | | |
| RAF Coltishall | | | |

# UK and Irish Airports

| Airport | Mhz AM | Airport | MHz AM |
|---|---|---|---|
| **RAF Lakenheath** | | **RAF Northolt** | |
| MATZ | 128.900 | Approach | 126.450 |
| Radar | 123.300 | ATIS | 125.125 |
| Tower | 122.100 | Departure | 120.325 |
| **RAF Leconfield** | | Queen's Flight Ops (D) | 132.650 |
| Leconfield Rescue | 123.050 | Radar (Director) | 130.350 |
| **RAF Leeming** | | Radar | 124.975 |
| Approach | 123.300 | Talkdown | 125.875 |
| Approach/Director | 127.750 | Tower | 120.675 |
| Tower | 120.500 | **RAF Odiham** | |
| Tower | 122.100 | Approach | 125.250 |
| **RAF Leuchars** | | Helicopter Ops | 119.900 |
| Approach (LARS and MATZ) | 126.500 | Talkdown | 123.300 |
| Tower/Ground | 122.100 | Tower/Odiham Information | 122.100 |
| Tower/Radar | 123.300 | **RAF Shawbury** | |
| **RAF Linton-On-Ouse** | | Approach (LARS and MATZ) | 120.775 |
| Director/Radar and Departures | 129.150 | Talkdown | 123.300 |
| Radar | 123.300 | Tower | 122.100 |
| Tower/Ground | 122.100 | **RAF Spadeadam** | |
| **RAF Lossiemouth** | | SRE | 122.100 |
| Approach (LARS/MATZ) | 119.350 | **RAF St Athan** | |
| Director | 123.300 | Approach | 125.850 |
| Tower | 118.900 | Cardiff Information | 119.475 |
| Tower | 122.100 | Talkdown | 123.300 |
| **RAF Lyneham** | | Tower | 122.100 |
| Approach/Radar (Director) | 118.425 | **RAF St Mawgan** | |
| Ground | 129.475 | Approach (LARS and MATZ) | 126.500 |
| Radar (Zone) | 123.400 | Approach | 125.550 |
| Talkdown | 123.300 | Approach/Tower | 122.100 |
| Tower | 119.225 | Radar | 123.300 |
| Tower/Ground | 122.100 | Tower | 123.400 |
| **RAF Marham** | | **RAF Ternhill** | |
| Approach | 124.150 | Approach | 122.100 |
| Radar | 123.300 | **RAF Topcliffe** | |
| Tower | 122.100 | Approach/Tower | 122.100 |
| **RAF Mildenhall** | | Director | 125.000 |
| 100th Refuelling Wing | 118.000 | Talkdown | 123.300 |
| 100th Refuelling Wing | 119.000 | **RAF Valley** | |
| 100th Refuelling Wing | 133.000 | Director/Talkdown | 123.300 |
| Air to air tanker flights | 121.125 | Radar (LARS and MATZ) | 134.350 |
| Tanker flights Air/Air (discreet) | 134.475 | Tower/Ground | 122.100 |
| Tower | 122.550 | **RAF Waddington** | |
| **RAF Mona** | | Director | 123.300 |
| Air/Ground (weekends only) | 122.000 | Radar (LARS and MATZ) | 127.350 |
| Radar | 134.350 | Zone | 125.350 |
| **RAF Newton** | | **RAF West Drayton** | |
| Tower | 119.125 | Air Traffic Control | 118.375 |
| Tower | 122.100 | London Military Radar | 135.150 |
| | | London Military Radar | 135.275 |

# UK and Irish Airports

| Airport | Mhz AM | Airport | MHz AM |
|---|---|---|---|
| RAF Wittering | | Scatsa Aerodrome | |
|   Radar | 123.300 |   Approach/Tower | 123.600 |
|   Radar | 130.200 |   Radar | 122.400 |
|   Tower | 118.150 | Scilly Isles (St. Marys) | |
| RAF Woodvale | |   Approach/Tower | 123.150 |
|   Approach | 121.000 | Scotland | |
|   Tower | 119.750 |   Bonzai Sqn Air-Air | 122.675 |
| RAF Wyton | |   Air Mountain Rescue | 123.100 |
|   Approach | 134.050 | Scottish Air Traffic Control Centre, Prestwick | |
|   Tower | 122.100 |   Scottish ACC (Entire Route) | 133.675 |
| Rathkenny | |   Scottish ACC (Information) | 119.875 |
|   Air/Ground (Rathkenny Radio) | 123.600 |   Scottish ACC (Information) | 127.275 |
| Redhill Aerodrome | |   Scottish Air Traffic Control | 134.850 |
|   Ground (Airshows Only) | 121.925 |   Scottish Air Traffic Control | 135.675 |
|   Tower/AFIS | 120.275 |   Scottish Control (0700-2145) | 124.825 |
| Retford | |   Scottish Control (2145-0700) | 126.300 |
|   Air/Ground | 130.475 |   Scottish Control (Information) | 126.250 |
| RNAS Culdrose | |   Scottish Control (Stornoway) | 131.300 |
|   Approach/Radar | 134.050 |   Scottish Control (TMA) | 128.500 |
|   Tower | 122.100 |   Scottish Control TMA | 123.375 |
|   Tower/Talkdown | 123.300 |   Scottish Control UIR | 135.850 |
| RNAS Merryfield | |   Scottish Control | 123.775 |
|   Tower | 122.100 |   Scottish Control | 124.050 |
| RNAS Predannack | |   Scottish Control | 124.500 |
|   Culdrose Approach | 134.050 |   Scottish Control | 125.675 |
|   Tower | 122.100 |   Scottish Control | 126.850 |
| RNAS Yeovilton | |   Scottish Control | 129.225 |
|   Approach/Radar | 127.350 |   Scottish Control | 132.725 |
|   Director/Talkdown | 123.300 |   Scottish Control | 134.775 |
|   Display director | 132.900 |   Scottish Information | 133.200 |
|   Tower | 122.100 |   Scottish Military | 134.300 |
| Rochester Aerodrome | |   Scottish Military | 134.475 |
|   AFIS | 122.250 |   Scottish VOLMET | 125.725 |
| Ronaldsway, Isle of Man | |   Shanwick Oceanic (Clearances) | 135.525 |
|   Approach/Radar | 120.850 | Seething Aerodrome | |
|   Island Aviation | 130.625 |   Air/Ground | 122.600 |
|   Radar | 118.200 | Shannon Airport | |
|   Radar | 125.300 |   ACC | 127.500 |
|   Tower | 118.900 |   ACC | 135.600 |
| Rufforth, York | |   Approach | 120.200 |
|   Air/Ground | 129.975 |   Approach | 121.400 |
| Salisbury Plain (Army) | |   ATIS | 130.950 |
|   Ops | 122.750 |   Ground | 121.800 |
| Sandown, Isle of Wight | |   N Altantic Track Broadcasts | 133.800 |
|   Air/Ground | 123.500 |   Shanwick Oceanic ACC | 127.650 |
| Sandtoft Aerodrome | |   Shanwick Oceanic ACC | 135.525 |
|   Tower | 130.425 |   Tower | 118.700 |
| Scarborough | | | |
|   Air/Ground Glider Ops | 130.125 | | |

# UK and Irish Airports

| Airport | Mhz AM | Airport | MHz AM |
|---|---|---|---|
| Shannon | | Southend Airport | |
|    ACC | 134.275 |    Approach/Radar | 128.950 |
|    Aerofolt Ops | 131.625 |    Approach/Tower | 127.725 |
|    Clearance Delivery | 121.700 |    ATIS | 121.800 |
|    Servisair | 131.450 |    British Air Ferries Ops | 130.625 |
|    Shannon Control ACC (Cork sector) | |    British World Ops | 130.025 |
| 131.150 | |    Express Flight | 129.700 |
|    Shannon Control ACC | 132.150 |    Heavilift Ops | 122.050 |
|    Shannon Control Southern Sector | 135.225 |    Radar | 125.050 |
|    Shannon Control | 124.700 | Spalding (Crowland) | |
|    Shanwick Oceanic ACC (Shanwick Radio) | |    Tower | 130.100 |
| 127.900 | |    Tower (Gliders) | 130.400 |
|    Shanwick Oceanic ACC | 123.950 | Spanish Point, Eire | |
| Sheffield City | |    Air/Ground | 123.300 |
|    AFIS | 128.525 | St Angelo | |
|    Tower/Approach | 128.525 |    Tower | 123.200 |
| Sherburn-in-Elmet Aerodrome | | St Kilda | |
|    Tower | 122.600 |    Tower | 128.100 |
| Shetlands | | Stansted | |
|    East Shetland Information | 119.000 |    Air Foyle | 131.775 |
|    Radar | 134.150 |    Air UK Leisure Ops | 130.600 |
|    Viking Approach | 129.950 |    Approach/Radar | 120.625 |
| Shipdam | |    Ground | 121.725 |
|    Air/Ground and AFIS | 119.550 |    Radar | 126.950 |
| Shobdon Aerodrome | |    Servisair Ops | 129.750 |
|    Air/Ground | 123.500 |    Tower | 123.800 |
| Shoreham Aerodrome | |    Tower | 125.550 |
|    Approach/Tower | 123.150 |    Universal Air Handling | 130.575 |
|    ATIS | 132.400 | Stapleford | |
|    Tower (when directed) | 125.400 |    Aeromega Ops. (Helicopter ops) | 122.050 |
| Silverstone | |    Air/Ground | 122.800 |
|    Air/Ground | 121.075 |    Stapleford Ops | 130.620 |
|    Tower | 122.700 | Stevenage Aerodrome | |
| Skegness Aerodrome | |    British Aerospace | 123.050 |
|    Tower | 130.450 | Stornoway Airport | |
| Skye | |    Approach/Tower and AFIS | 123.500 |
|    Tower | 130.650 | Strathallan Aerodrome | |
| Sleap Aerodrome | |    Air/Ground | 129.900 |
|    Air/Ground | 122.450 | Strubby Aerodrome | |
| Sligo | |    Air/Ground gliders | 130.100 |
|    Tower/AFIS | 122.100 | Strubby Heliport | |
| Solent | |    Air/Ground | 122.375 |
|    Initial Contact Frequency | 120.255 | Stubton Park | |
| Southampton Airport | |    Air/Ground | 119.425 |
|    Approach (as directed)/Radar | 128.850 | Sturgate Aerodrome | |
|    Approach Solent | 120.225 |    Air/Ground | 130.300 |
|    Ops | 130.650 | | |
|    Radar | 128.250 | | |
|    Tower | 118.200 | | |

# UK and Irish Airports

| Airport | Mhz AM | Airport | MHz AM |
|---|---|---|---|
| Sumburgh Airport | | Warton (BAe) | |
|    Tower | 118.250 |    Radar | 124.450 |
|    Approach/Radar | 123.150 |    Ops | 127.975 |
|    ATIS | 125.850 |    Radar | 129.725 |
|    Helicopter Information | 129.950 |    Tower | 130.800 |
|    Radar (Offshore Advisory) | 131.300 | Waterford | |
| Sumburgh | |    Tower and AFIS | 129.850 |
|    Radar | 130.050 | Wattisham (Army Airfield) | |
| Swansea Airport | |    Approach | 123.300 |
|    ATC Glider Training | 129.975 |    Approach | 125.800 |
|    Air/Ground | 119.700 |    Tower | 122.100 |
|    Air Sea Rescue | 132.650 | Wellesbourne Mountford | |
| Swanton Morley Aerodrome | |    Air/Ground | 124.025 |
|    Air/Ground | 123.500 | Welshpool | |
| Swindon (Draycott) | |    Air/Ground | 123.250 |
|    Air/Ground | 129.825 | West Drayton | |
| Tatenhill Aerodrome | |    London Control (Bristol) | 132.800 |
|    Air/Ground | 124.075 |    London Control (Cardiff) | 135.250 |
| Teesside Airport | |    London Control (Cardiff) | 135.325 |
|    Approach/Radar | 118.850 |    London Control (Hurn) | 134.450 |
|    Tower | 119.800 |    London Control (Standby) | 136.600 |
|    Air Cam | 122.350 |    London Control ACC | 118.825 |
|    Radar | 128.850 |    London Control ACC | 120.525 |
|    Teesside Information | 121.825 |    London Control FIR Information | 124.600 |
| Thirsk (Sutton Bank) | |    London Control Inbound | 120.175 |
|    Air/Ground gliders | 130.400 |    London Control Inbound | 126.300 |
| Thruxton Aerodrome | |    London Control Inbound | 126.875 |
|    Air/Ground | 130.450 |    London Control Information | 124.750 |
| Tibenham | |    London Control Information | 125.475 |
|    Air/Ground | 129.970 |    London Control Irish Sea | 134.425 |
|    Air/Ground (Gliders) | 130.100 |    London Control North East UIR | 131.050 |
| Tiree | |    London Control North Sea | 128.125 |
|    AFIS | 122.700 |    London Control North Sea | 133.525 |
| Tresco | |    London Control North Sea | 134.250 |
|    Civil Heliport | 130.250 |    London Control Radar Departure | 125.800 |
| Trim, Eire | |    London Control SIDs | 120.475 |
|    Air/Ground | 123.300 |    London Control SW Approach | 132.600 |
| Truro Aerodrome | |    London Control TMA | 121.325 |
|    Air/Ground | 129.800 |    London Control TMA | 130.925 |
| Turweston Aerodrome | |    London Control Upper East | 127.425 |
|    Air/Ground | 122.175 |    London Control Upper West | 134.750 |
| Unst (Saxa Vord) | |    London Control | 118.475 |
|    Ops | 123.450 |    London Control | 119.775 |
|    Air/Ground | 130.350 |    London Control | 120.025 |
| Walton Wood | |    London Control | 121.225 |
|    Air/Ground | 123.625 |    London Control | 121.275 |
| | |    London Control | 124.275 |
| | |    London Control | 126.075 |
| | |    London Control | 127.100 |
| | |    London Control | 127.700 |

# UK and Irish Airports

| Airport | Mhz AM | Airport | MHz AM |
|---|---|---|---|
| West Drayton (cont.) | | Weston on the Green | |
| London Control | 127.875 | Weston Radio | 133.650 |
| London Control | 128.425 | Weston-super-Mare | |
| London Control | 129.075 | Tower | 122.500 |
| London Control | 129.100 | Whitchurch (Tilstock) | |
| London Control | 129.200 | Air/Ground | 122.075 |
| London Control | 129.375 | White Waltham Aerodrome | |
| London Control | 129.425 | Air/Ground | 122.600 |
| London Control | 129.600 | Wick | |
| London Control | 131.125 | Air/Ground | 119.700 |
| London Control | 132.450 | Fuellers (FarNor) | 130.375 |
| London Control | 132.950 | Wickenby Aerodrome | |
| London Control | 133.175 | Air/Ground | 122.450 |
| London Control | 133.450 | Wigtown | |
| London Control | 133.600 | Tower | 123.050 |
| London Control | 133.700 | Woodford | |
| London Control | 134.125 | Approach | 130.750 |
| London Control | 134.900 | Approach/Tower | 126.925 |
| London Control | 135.050 | BAe Ops | 130.025 |
| London Control | 135.425 | Tower | 130.050 |
| London Military Brize Radar | 133.900 | Wroughton | |
| London Military Northwest | 127.450 | Approach | 118.425 |
| London Military Radar | 128.700 | PFA Arrivals | 132.900 |
| London Military Radar | 133.300 | PFA Circuit | 129.225 |
| London Military | 128.250 | PFA Delivery | 121.850 |
| London VOLMET (Main) | 135.375 | PFA Ground | 121.925 |
| London VOLMET (South) | 128.600 | Tower | 130.700 |
| Oceanic Clearance (E of 30_W) | 127.650 | Tower | 133.650 |
| Oceanic Track Broadcasts | 133.800 | Wycombe Air Park (Booker) | |
| West Freugh (MoD) | | Ground | 121.775 |
| Approach | 130.050 | Tower/AFIS | 126.550 |
| Radar | 130.725 | Yeovil (Westland) | |
| Tower | 122.550 | Tower and Air/Ground (Judwin) | 125.400 |
| West Midlands | | Approach/Radar (Judwin) | 130.800 |
| Air Ambulance | 127.900 | Yeovil | |
| Weston (Dublin), Eire | | Westland Helicopter Tests | 118.000 |
| Air/Ground | 122.400 | Radar (LAKS) | 127.350 |

# Part 3

# European Frequencies

# European VHF/UHF Frequencies

The following European frequencies have been included because many of these stations can be heard from many parts of the UK and Ireland. The list will also be useful to our growing number of European readers and travellers.

## Austria

| Base | Mobile | Mode | Location | User and Notes |
|------|--------|------|----------|----------------|
| 171.4000 | 166.8000 | NFM | | Police & Gendarmerie Ch 1 |
| 171.4250 | 166.8250 | NFM | | Police & Gendarmerie Ch 2 |
| 171.4500 | 166.8500 | NFM | | Police & Gendarmerie Ch 3 |
| 171.4750 | 166.8750 | NFM | | Police & Gendarmerie Ch 4 |
| 171.5000 | 166.9000 | NFM | | Police & Gendarmerie Ch 5 |
| 171.5250 | 166.9250 | NFM | | Police & Gendarmerie Ch 6 |
| 171.5500 | 166.9500 | NFM | | Police & Gendarmerie Ch 7 |
| 171.5750 | 166.9750 | NFM | | Police & Gendarmerie Ch 8 |
| 171.6000 | 167.0000 | NFM | | Police & Gendarmerie Ch 9 |
| 171.6250 | 167.0250 | NFM | | Police & Gendarmerie Ch 10 |
| 171.6500 | 167.0500 | NFM | | Police & Gendarmerie Ch 11 |
| 171.6750 | 167.0750 | NFM | | Police & Gendarmerie Ch 12 |
| 171.7000 | 167.1000 | NFM | | Police & Gendarmerie Ch 13 |
| 171.7250 | 167.1250 | NFM | | Police & Gendarmerie Ch 14 |
| 171.7500 | 167.1500 | NFM | | Police & Gendarmerie Ch 15 |
| 171.7750 | 167.1750 | NFM | | Police & Gendarmerie Ch 16 |
| 171.8000 | 167.2000 | NFM | | Police & Gendarmerie Ch 17 |
| 171.8250 | 167.2250 | NFM | | Police & Gendarmerie Ch 18 |
| 171.8500 | 167.2500 | NFM | | Police & Gendarmerie Ch 19 |
| 171.8750 | 167.2750 | NFM | | Police & Gendarmerie Ch 20 |
| 171.9000 | 167.3000 | NFM | | Police & Gendarmerie Ch 21 |
| 171.9250 | 167.3250 | NFM | | Police & Gendarmerie Ch 22 |
| 171.9500 | 167.3500 | NFM | | Police & Gendarmerie Ch 23 |
| 171.9750 | 167.3750 | NFM | | Police & Gendarmerie Ch 24 |
| 172.0000 | 167.4000 | NFM | | Police & Gendarmerie Ch 25 |
| 172.0250 | 167.4250 | NFM | | Police & Gendarmerie Ch 26 |
| 172.0500 | 167.4500 | NFM | | Police & Gendarmerie Ch 27 |
| 172.0750 | 167.4750 | NFM | | Police & Gendarmerie Ch 28 |
| 172.1000 | 167.5000 | NFM | | Police & Gendarmerie Ch 29 |
| 172.1250 | 167.5250 | NFM | | Police & Gendarmerie Ch 30 |
| 172.1500 | 167.5500 | NFM | | Police & Gendarmerie Ch 31 |
| 172.1750 | 167.5750 | NFM | | Police & Gendarmerie Ch 32 |
| 172.2000 | 167.6000 | NFM | | Police & Gendarmerie Ch 33 |
| 172.2250 | 167.6250 | NFM | | Police & Gendarmerie Ch 34 |
| 172.2500 | 167.6500 | NFM | | Police & Gendarmerie Ch 35 |
| 172.2750 | 167.6750 | NFM | | Police & Gendarmerie Ch 36 |
| 172.3000 | 167.7000 | NFM | | Police & Gendarmerie Ch 37 |
| 172.3250 | 167.7250 | NFM | | Police & Gendarmerie Ch 38 |
| 172.3500 | 167.7500 | NFM | | Police & Gendarmerie Ch 39 |
| 172.3750 | 167.7750 | NFM | | Police & Gendarmerie Ch 40 |
| 172.4000 | 167.8000 | NFM | | Customs Ch 41 |
| 172.4250 | 167.8250 | NFM | | Customs Ch 42 |
| 172.4500 | 167.8500 | NFM | | Customs Ch 43 |
| 172.4750 | 167.8750 | NFM | | Customs Ch 44 |
| 172.5000 | 167.9000 | NFM | | Customs Ch 45 |
| 172.5250 | 167.9250 | NFM | | Customs Ch 46 |

| Base | Mobile | Mode | Location | User and Notes |
|------|--------|------|----------|----------------|
| 172.5500 | 167.9500 | NFM | | Customs Ch 47 |
| 172.5750 | 167.9750 | NFM | | Customs Ch 48 |
| 172.6000 | 168.0000 | NFM | | Fire Brigade Ch 49 |
| 172.6250 | 168.0250 | NFM | | Fire Brigade Ch 50 |
| 172.6500 | 168.0500 | NFM | | Fire Brigade Ch 51 |
| 172.6750 | 168.0750 | NFM | | Fire Brigade Ch 52 |
| 172.7000 | 168.1000 | NFM | | Fire Brigade Ch 53 |
| 172.7250 | 168.1250 | NFM | | Fire Brigade Ch 54 |
| 172.7500 | 168.1500 | NFM | | Fire Brigade Ch 55 |
| 172.7750 | 168.1750 | NFM | | Fire Brigade Ch 56 |
| 172.8000 | 168.2000 | NFM | | Fire Brigade Ch 57 |
| 172.8250 | 168.2250 | NFM | | Fire Brigade Ch 58 |
| 172.8500 | 168.2500 | NFM | | Fire Brigade Ch 59 |
| 172.8750 | 168.2750 | NFM | | Fire Brigade Ch 60 |
| 172.9000 | 168.3000 | NFM | | Fire Brigade Ch 61 |
| 172.9250 | 168.3250 | NFM | | Fire Brigade Ch 62 |
| 172.9500 | 168.2500 | NFM | | Fire Brigade Ch 63 |
| 172.9750 | 168.3750 | NFM | | Fire Brigade Ch 64 |
| 173.0000 | 168.4000 | NFM | | Fire Brigade Ch 65 |
| 173.0250 | 168.4250 | NFM | | Fire Brigade Ch 66 |
| 173.0500 | 168.4500 | NFM | | Road and Motorway maintenance Ch 67 |
| 173.0750 | 168.4750 | NFM | | Road and Motorway maintenance Ch 68 |
| 173.1000 | 168.5000 | NFM | | Road and Motorway maintenance Ch 69 |
| 173.1250 | 168.5250 | NFM | | Road and Motorway maintenance Ch 70 |
| 173.1500 | 168.5500 | NFM | | Road and Motorway maintenance Ch 71 |
| 173.1750 | 168.5750 | NFM | | User unknown Ch 72 |
| 173.2000 | 168.6000 | NFM | | User unknown Ch 73 |
| 173.2250 | 168.6250 | NFM | | Red Cross (Ambulance Service) Ch 74 |
| 173.2500 | 168.6500 | NFM | | User unknown Ch 75 |
| 173.2750 | 168.6750 | NFM | | User unknown Ch 76 |
| 173.3000 | 168.7000 | NFM | | User unknown Ch 77 |
| 173.3250 | 168.7250 | NFM | | Red Cross (Ambulance Service) Ch 78 |
| 173.3500 | 168.7500 | NFM | | Red Cross (Ambulance Service) Ch 79 |
| 173.3750 | 168.7750 | NFM | | Red Cross (Ambulance Service) Ch 80 |
| 173.4000 | 168.8000 | NFM | | Red Cross (Ambulance Service) Ch 81 |
| 173.4250 | 168.8250 | NFM | | Red Cross (Ambulance Service) Ch 82 |
| 173.4500 | 168.8500 | NFM | | Red Cross (Ambulance Service) Ch 83 |
| 173.4750 | 168.8750 | NFM | | Red Cross (Ambulance Service) Ch 84 |
| 173.5000 | 168.9000 | NFM | | Red Cross (Ambulance Service) Ch 85 |
| 173.5250 | 168.9250 | NFM | | User unknown Ch 86 |
| 173.5500 | 168.9500 | NFM | | User unknown Ch 87 |
| 173.5750 | 168.9750 | NFM | | User unknown Ch 88 |
| 173.6000 | 169.0000 | NFM | | User unknown Ch 89 |
| 173.6250 | 169.0250 | NFM | | User unknown Ch 90 |
| 173.6500 | 169.0500 | NFM | | User unknown Ch 91 |
| 173.6750 | 169.0750 | NFM | | User unknown Ch 92 |
| 173.7000 | 169.1000 | NFM | | User unknown Ch 93 |
| 173.7250 | 169.1250 | NFM | | User unknown Ch 94 |
| 173.7500 | 169.1500 | NFM | | User unknown Ch 95 |
| 173.7750 | 169.1750 | NFM | | User unknown Ch 96 |
| 173.8000 | 169.2000 | NFM | | User unknown Ch 97 |
| 173.8250 | 169.2250 | NFM | | Red Cross Ch 98 |
| 173.8500 | 169.2500 | NFM | | User unknown Ch 99 |

## Belgium

| Base | Mode | Location | User and Notes |
| --- | --- | --- | --- |
| 118.050 | AM | Brussels National | Ground |
| 118.250 | AM | Brussels National | Approach |
| 118.600 | AM | Brussels National | Tower |
| 118.700 | AM | Ostend Airport | Tower |
| 120.100 | AM | Brussels National | Approach/Radar |
| 120.600 | AM | Ostend Airport | Approach |
| 120.775 | AM | Brussels National | Tower |
| 121.875 | AM | Brussels National | Ground |
| 121.900 | AM | Ostend Airport | Ground |
| 121.950 | AM | Brussels National | Clearance Delivery |
| 122.500 | AM | Brussels National | Approach |
| 125.000 | AM | Brussels | Brussels Control South |
| 125.000 | AM | Brussels Airport | ACC |
| 126.750 | AM | Brussels Airport | ACC |
| 125.775 | AM | Brussels | Brussels Control West Low |
| 126.525 | AM | Brussels | Brussels Control South |
| 126.900 | AM | Brussels | Brussels FIS |
| 126.900 | AM | Brussels Airport | ACC |
| 126.975 | AM | Brussels | Brussels Control North Low |
| 127.225 | AM | Brussels | Brussels Control West High |
| 127.575 | AM | Brussels National | Final |
| 128.200 | AM | Brussels | Brussels Control East Low |
| 128.450 | AM | Brussels | Brussels Control East High |
| 128.200 | AM | Brussels Airport | ACC |
| 128.450 | AM | Brussels Airport | ACC |
| 128.800 | AM | Brussels | Brussels Control North Low |
| 128.800 | AM | Brussels Airport | ACC |
| 129.575 | AM | Brussels | Brussels Control East Low |
| 129.650 | AM | Brussels | Brussels Control East High |
| 129.650 | AM | Brussels Airport | ACC |
| 129.725 | AM | Brussels National | Final |
| 130.550 | AM | Brussels | Abelag Ops. |
| 131.100 | AM | Brussels | Brussels Control West Low |
| 131.450 | AM | Brussels | Speedbird Ops. |
| 131.475 | AM | Brussels | Servisair |
| 131.600 | AM | Brussels Airport | TWA Ops. |
| 132.200 | AM | Brussels | Maastricht Control West High |
| 132.475 | AM | Brussels | Maastricht Control West High |
| 132.750 | AM | Brussels National | ATIS |
| 165.810 | NFM | Belgium | Fire & Ambulance |
| 165.830 | NFM | Belgium | Fire & Ambulance |
| 165.850 | NFM | Belgium | Fire & Ambulance |
| 165.870 | NFM | Belgium | Fire & Ambulance |
| 165.890 | NFM | Belgium | Fire & Ambulance |
| 165.910 | NFM | Belgium | Fire & Ambulance |
| 165.930 | NFM | Belgium | Fire & Ambulance |
| 165.950 | NFM | Belgium | Fire & Ambulance |
| 165.970 | NFM | Belgium | Fire & Ambulance |
| 165.990 | NFM | Belgium | Fire & Ambulance |
| 166.010 | NFM | Belgium | Fire & Ambulance |
| 166.030 | NFM | Belgium | Fire & Ambulance |
| 166.050 | NFM | Belgium | Fire & Ambulance |
| 166.070 | NFM | Belgium | Fire & Ambulance |
| 166.090 | NFM | Belgium | Fire & Ambulance |
| 166.110 | NFM | Belgium | Fire & Ambulance |

| Base | Mobile | Mode | Location | User and Notes |
|------|--------|------|----------|----------------|
| 166.1300 | 166.1300 | NFM | Belgium | Fire & Ambulance |
| 166.1500 | 166.1500 | NFM | Belgium | Fire & Ambulance |
| 166.1700 | 166.1700 | NFM | Belgium | Fire & Ambulance |
| 166.1900 | 166.1900 | NFM | Belgium | Fire & Ambulance |
| 166.2100 | 166.2100 | NFM | Belgium | Fire & Ambulance |
| 166.2300 | 166.2300 | NFM | Belgium | Fire & Ambulance |
| 166.2700 | 166.2700 | NFM | Belgium | Fire & Ambulance |
| 166.2900 | 166.2900 | NFM | Belgium | Fire & Ambulance |
| 166.3100 | 166.3100 | NFM | Belgium | Fire & Ambulance |
| 166.3300 | 166.3300 | NFM | Belgium | Fire & Ambulance |
| 166.3500 | 166.3500 | NFM | Belgium | Fire & Ambulance |
| 166.3700 | 166.3700 | NFM | Belgium | Disaster Channel 1 |
| 166.3900 | 166.3900 | NFM | Belgium | Fire & Ambulance |
| 166.4100 | 166.4100 | NFM | Belgium | Fire & Ambulance |
| 166.4300 | 166.4300 | NFM | Belgium | Fire & Ambulance |
| 166.4400 | 166.4400 | NFM | Belgium | Disaster Channel 2 |
| 166.4500 | 166.4500 | NFM | Belgium | Fire & Ambulance |
| 166.4700 | 166.4700 | NFM | Belgium | Fire & Ambulance |
| 166.4900 | 166.4900 | NFM | Belgium | Fire & Ambulance |
| 166.5100 | 166.5100 | NFM | Belgium | Fire & Ambulance |
| 166.5300 | 166.5300 | NFM | Belgium | Fire & Ambulance |
| 166.5500 | 166.5500 | NFM | Belgium | Fire & Ambulance |
| 166.5700 | 166.5700 | NFM | Belgium | Fire & Ambulance |
| 166.5900 | 166.5900 | NFM | Belgium | Fire & Ambulance |
| 166.6100 | 166.6100 | NFM | Belgium | Fire & Ambulance |
| 166.6300 | 166.6300 | NFM | Belgium | Fire & Ambulance |
| 166.6500 | 166.6500 | NFM | Belgium | Fire & Ambulance |
| 166.6700 | 166.6700 | NFM | Belgium | Fire & Ambulance |
| 166.6900 | 166.6900 | NFM | Belgium | Fire & Ambulance |
| 166.7100 | 166.7100 | NFM | Belgium | Fire & Ambulance |
| 166.7300 | 166.7300 | NFM | Belgium | Fire & Ambulance |
| 166.7500 | 166.7500 | NFM | Belgium | Fire & Ambulance |
| 166.7700 | 166.7700 | NFM | Belgium | Fire & Ambulance |
| 166.7900 | 166.7900 | NFM | Belgium | Fire & Ambulance |
| 166.8100 | 166.8100 | NFM | Belgium | Fire & Ambulance |
| 166.8300 | 166.8300 | NFM | Belgium | Fire & Ambulance |
| 166.8500 | 166.8500 | NFM | Belgium | Fire & Ambulance |
| 166.8700 | 166.8700 | NFM | Belgium | Disaster Protection |
| 166.9100 | 166.9100 | NFM | Belgium | Disaster Protection |
| 166.9300 | 166.9300 | NFM | Belgium | Disaster Protection |
| 166.9500 | 166.9500 | NFM | Belgium | Disaster Protection |
| 167.0125 | 167.0125 | NFM | Belgium | Disaster Protection |
| 167.0375 | 167.0375 | NFM | Belgium | Disaster Protection |
| 167.0500 | 167.0500 | NFM | Belgium | Disaster Protection |
| 167.0700 | 167.0700 | NFM | Belgium | Disaster Protection |
| 167.0900 | 167.0900 | NFM | Belgium | Disaster Protection |
| 167.1100 | 167.1100 | NFM | Belgium | Ambulance - Hospital |
| 168.5500 | 168.5500 | NFM | Belgium | Gendarmerie Ch 1 |
| 168.5700 | 168.5700 | NFM | Belgium | Gendarmerie Ch 3 |
| 168.5900 | 168.5900 | NFM | Belgium | Gendarmerie Ch 5 |
| 168.6100 | 168.6100 | NFM | Belgium | Gendarmerie Ch 7 |
| 168.6300 | 168.6300 | NFM | Belgium | Gendarmerie Ch 9 |
| 168.6500 | 168.6500 | NFM | Belgium | Gendarmerie Ch 11 |
| 168.6700 | 168.6700 | NFM | Belgium | Gendarmerie Ch 13 |
| 168.6900 | 168.6900 | NFM | Belgium | Gendarmerie Ch 15 |
| 168.7100 | 168.7100 | NFM | Belgium | Gendarmerie Ch 17 |

| Base | Mobile | Mode | Location | User and Notes |
|------|--------|------|----------|----------------|
| 168.7300 | 168.7300 | NFM | Belgium | Gendarmerie Ch 19 |
| 168.7700 | 168.7700 | NFM | Belgium | Gendarmerie Ch 23 |
| 168.7900 | 168.7900 | NFM | Belgium | Gendarmerie Ch 25 |
| 168.8100 | 168.8100 | NFM | Belgium | Gendarmerie Ch 27 |
| 168.8300 | 168.8300 | NFM | Belgium | Gendarmerie Ch 29 |
| 168.8400 | 168.8400 | NFM | Belgium | Gendarmerie Ch 30 |
| 168.8600 | 168.8600 | NFM | Belgium | Gendarmerie Ch 32 |
| 168.8800 | 168.8800 | NFM | Belgium | Gendarmerie Ch 34 |
| 168.9200 | 168.9200 | NFM | Belgium | Gendarmerie Ch 38 |
| 168.9400 | 168.9400 | NFM | Belgium | Gendarmerie Ch 40 |
| 168.9600 | 168.9600 | NFM | Belgium | Gendarmerie Ch 42 |
| 168.9800 | 168.9800 | NFM | Belgium | Gendarmerie Ch 44 |
| 169.0200 | 169.0200 | NFM | Belgium | Gendarmerie Ch 48 |
| 169.0400 | 169.0400 | NFM | Belgium | Gendarmerie Ch 50 |
| 169.0600 | 169.0600 | NFM | Belgium | Gendarmerie Ch 52 |
| 169.0800 | 169.0800 | NFM | Belgium | Gendarmerie Ch 54 |
| 169.1200 | 169.1200 | NFM | Belgium | Gendarmerie Ch 58 |
| 169.1400 | 169.1400 | NFM | Belgium | Gendarmerie Ch 60 |
| 169.1800 | 169.1800 | NFM | Belgium | Gendarmerie Ch 64 |
| 169.2200 | 169.2200 | NFM | Belgium | Gendarmerie Ch 68 |
| 169.2400 | 169.2400 | NFM | Belgium | Gendarmerie Ch 70 |
| 169.2600 | 169.2600 | NFM | Belgium | Gendarmerie Ch 72 |
| 169.2800 | 169.2800 | NFM | Belgium | Gendarmerie Ch 74 |
| 169.3200 | 169.3200 | NFM | Belgium | Gendarmerie Ch 78 |
| 169.3400 | 169.3400 | NFM | Belgium | Gendarmerie Ch 80 |
| 169.3600 | 169.3600 | NFM | Belgium | Gendarmerie Ch 82 |
| 169.3800 | 169.3800 | NFM | Belgium | Gendarmerie Ch 84 |
| 169.4000 | 169.4000 | NFM | Belgium | Gendarmerie Ch 86 |
| 169.4200 | 169.4200 | NFM | Belgium | Gendarmerie Ch 88 |
| 169.4400 | 169.4400 | NFM | Belgium | Gendarmerie Ch 90 |
| 169.4600 | 169.4600 | NFM | Belgium | Gendarmerie Ch 92 |
| 169.4800 | 169.4800 | NFM | Belgium | Gendarmerie Ch 94 |
| 169.5200 | 169.5200 | NFM | Belgium | Gendarmerie Ch 98 |
| 169.5400 | 169.5400 | NFM | Belgium | Gendarmerie Ch 100 |
| 169.5600 | 169.5600 | NFM | Belgium | Gendarmerie Ch 102 |
| 169.5800 | 169.5800 | NFM | Belgium | Gendarmerie Ch 104 |
| 169.6200 | 169.6200 | NFM | Belgium | Gendarmerie Ch 108 |
| 169.6400 | 169.6400 | NFM | Belgium | Gendarmerie Ch 110 |
| 169.6600 | 169.6600 | NFM | Belgium | Gendarmerie Ch 112 |
| 169.6800 | 169.6800 | NFM | Belgium | Gendarmerie Ch 114 |
| 169.7200 | 169.7200 | NFM | Belgium | Gendarmerie Ch 118 |
| 169.7400 | 169.7400 | NFM | Belgium | Gendarmerie Ch 120 |
| 169.7600 | 169.7600 | NFM | Belgium | Gendarmerie Ch 122 |
| 169.7800 | 169.7800 | NFM | Belgium | Gendarmerie Ch 124 |
| 169.8200 | 169.8200 | NFM | Belgium | Gendarmerie Ch 128 |
| 169.8400 | 169.8400 | NFM | Belgium | Gendarmerie Ch 130 |
| 169.8600 | 169.8600 | NFM | Belgium | Gendarmerie Ch 132 |
| 169.8800 | 169.8800 | NFM | Belgium | Gendarmerie Ch 134 |
| 169.9000 | 169.9000 | NFM | Belgium | Gendarmerie Ch 136 |
| 169.9200 | 169.9200 | NFM | Belgium | Gendarmerie Ch 138 |
| 169.9400 | 169.9400 | NFM | Belgium | Gendarmerie Ch 140 |
| 169.9600 | 169.9600 | NFM | Belgium | Gendarmerie Ch 142 |
| 169.9800 | 169.9800 | NFM | Belgium | Gendarmerie Ch 144 |
| 170.0000 | 170.0000 | NFM | Belgium | Gendarmerie Ch 146 |
| 170.0200 | 170.0200 | NFM | Belgium | Gendarmerie Ch 148 |
| 170.0400 | 170.0400 | NFM | Belgium | Gendarmerie Ch 150 |

| Base | Mobile | Mode | Location | User and Notes |
|------|--------|------|----------|----------------|
| 170.0600 | 170.0600 | NFM | Belgium | Gendarmerie Ch 152 |
| 170.0800 | 170.0800 | NFM | Belgium | Gendarmerie Ch 154 |
| 170.1000 | 170.1000 | NFM | Belgium | Gendarmerie Ch 156 |
| 170.1200 | 170.1200 | NFM | Belgium | Gendarmerie Ch 158 |
| 170.1400 | 170.1400 | NFM | Belgium | Gendarmerie Ch 160 |
| 170.1600 | 170.1600 | NFM | Belgium | Gendarmerie Ch 162 |

## Czech Republic

| Base | Mobile | Mode | Location | User and Notes |
|------|--------|------|----------|----------------|
| 66.2000 | | WFM | Brno | Cesko Rozhlas [LBS] |
| 66.3200 | | WFM | Ostrava | Cesko Rozhlas [LBS] |
| 66.4400 | | WFM | Hradec Kralove | Cesko Rozhlas [LBS] |
| 66.8300 | | WFM | Praha | Cesko Rozhlas [LBS] |
| 67.1000 | | WFM | Jesenik | Cesko Rozhlas [LBS] |
| 67.3400 | | WFM | Pizen | Cesko Rozhlas [LBS] |
| 67.6100 | | WFM | Ceske Budejovice | Cesko Rozhlas [LBS] |
| 67.8800 | | WFM | Ostrava | Cesko Rozhlas [LBS] |
| 68.0000 | | WFM | Hradec Kralove | Cesko Rozhlas [LBS] |
| 68.6600 | | WFM | Jesenik | Cesko Rozhlas [LBS] |
| 69.0800 | | WFM | Ostrava | Cesko Rozhlas [LBS] |
| 69.2500 | | WFM | Usti nad Labem | Cesko Rozhlas [LBS] |
| 69.5600 | | WFM | Pizen | Cesko Rozhlas [LBS] |
| 69.9800 | | WFM | Liberec | Cesko Rozhlas [LBS] |
| 70.0700 | | WFM | Ceske Budejovice | Cesko Rozhlas [LBS] |
| 70.1600 | | WFM | Jesenik | Cesko Rozhlas [LBS] |
| 70.3400 | | WFM | Pizen | Cesko Rozhlas [LBS] |
| 70.5800 | | WFM | Usti nad Labem | Cesko Rozhlas [LBS] |
| 71.1800 | | WFM | Liberec | Cesko Rozhlas [LBS] |
| 71.6300 | | WFM | Ceske Budejovice | Cesko Rozhlas [LBS] |
| 71.8700 | | WFM | Brno | Cesko Rozhlas [LBS] |
| 72.2000 | | WFM | Usti nad Labem | Cesko Rozhlas [LBS] |
| 72.7400 | | WFM | Liberec | Cesko Rozhlas [LBS] |

## Denmark

| Base | Mobile | Mode | Location | User and Notes |
|------|--------|------|----------|----------------|
| 84.0000 | 85.0000 | NFM | | Police |
| 118.100 | | AM | Copenhagen Kastrup | Tower |
| 118.450 | | AM | Copenhagen Kastrup | Approach |
| 118575 | | AM | Copenhagen Kastrup | Tower |
| 119.350 | | AM | Copenhagen Kastrup | Tower |
| 119.550 | | AM | Copenhagen | ATC |
| 119.800 | | AM | Copenhagen Kastrup | Approach |
| 119.900 | | AM | Copenhagen Kastrup | Tower |
| 120.250 | | AM | Copenhagen Kastrup | Departure |
| 121.600 | | AM | Copenhagen Kastrup | Ground |
| 121.725 | | AM | Copenhagen Kastrup | Ground |
| 121.900 | | AM | Copenhagen Kastrup | Ground |
| 122.750 | | AM | Copenhagen Kastrup | ATIS Arrivals Information |
| 122.850 | | AM | Copenhagen Kastrup | ATIS Departure Information |
| 123.725 | | AM | Copenhagen | ATC |
| 124.000 | | AM | Copenhagen | Copenhagen FIS |
| 124.550 | | AM | Copenhagen | ATC |
| 124.975 | | AM | Copenhagen Kastrup | Departure |
| 126.050 | | AM | Copenhagen | ATC |

## Denmark (cont)

| Base | Mobile | Mode | Location | User and Notes |
|------|--------|------|----------|----------------|
| 127.075 | | AM | Copenhagen | Copenhagen FIS |
| 127.325 | | AM | Copenhagen | Copenhagen FIS |
| 128.150 | | AM | Copenhagen | ATC |
| 128.750 | | AM | Copenhagen | ATC |
| 129.475 | | AM | Copenhagen | Copenhagen FIS |
| 129.800 | | AM | Copenhagen | Air to Air |
| 133.150 | | AM | Copenhagen | ATC |
| 134.675 | | AM | Copenhagen | ATC |

## Finland

| Base | Mobile | Mode | Location | User and Notes |
|------|--------|------|----------|----------------|
| 118.125 | | AM | Helsinki Vantaa | Clearance Delivery |
| 118.600 | | AM | Helsinki Vantaa | Tower/Approach |
| 119.100 | | AM | Helsinki Vantaa | Approach/Radar |
| 119.700 | | AM | Helsinki Vantaa | Approach/Tower |
| 119.900 | | AM | Helsinki Vantaa | Arrivals |
| 121.300 | | AM | Tampere | Tampere Control |
| 121.800 | | AM | Helsinki Vantaa | Ground |
| 125.400 | | AM | Tampere | Tampere Control |
| 127.100 | | AM | Tampere | Tampere Control |
| 127.500 | | AM | Tampere | Tampere Control |
| 129.850 | | AM | Helsinki Vantaa | Radar |
| 132.325 | | AM | Tampere | Tampere Control |
| 132.675 | | AM | Tampere | Tampere Control |
| 135.075 | | AM | Helsinki Vantaa | ATIS |
| 164.1000 | 170.1700 | NFM | | City Police |

## France

| Base | Mobile | Mode | Location | User and Notes |
|------|--------|------|----------|----------------|
| 35.8250 | | NFM | | PMR [LBS] |
| 87.3875 | 87.3875 | AM | | Nuclear Alert Channel |
| 88.3000 | | WFM | Normandy | Melody FM |
| 89.2000 | | WFM | Cherbourg | Culture |
| 89.4000 | | WFM | Brest | Musique |
| 89.9000 | | WFM | Renns | Musique |
| 90.9000 | | WFM | Normandy | CFM |
| 91.4000 | | WFM | Cherbourg | Culture |
| 91.6000 | | WFM | Brest | Musique |
| 92.1000 | | WFM | Renns | Musique |
| 93.000 | | WFM | Brittany | Bretagne Ouest |
| 93.1000 | | WFM | Normandy | Fun Radio |
| 93.4000 | | WFM | Normandy | Radio Manche |
| 93.5000 | | WFM | Rennes | Inter |
| 93.8000 | | WFM | | Inter |
| 94.1000 | | WFM | Cherbourg | Inter |
| 94.2000 | | WFM | Brittany | Culture |
| 94.4000 | | WFM | | Inter |
| 94.5000 | | WFM | Normandy | Fun Radio |
| 94.6000 | | WFM | Brittany | Fun Radio |
| 95.1000 | | WFM | | Cherie FM |
| 95.4000 | | WFM | Brittany | Inter |
| 95.5000 | | WFM | Brest | Inter |

| Base | Mobile | Mode | Location | User and Notes |
|---|---|---|---|---|
| 95.6000 | | WFM | Caen | Musique |
| 95.9000 | | WFM | | Musique |
| 96.2000 | | WFM | | Radio Cote d' Armor |
| 96.3000 | | WFM | Normandy | Inter |
| 96.4000 | | WFM | Normandy | Nostalgie |
| 96.6000 | | WFM | | Radio France Mayenne |
| 97.5000 | | WFM | Normandy | Radio France Nornandie-Caen |
| 97.9000 | | WFM | Normandy | Melody FM North |
| 98.5000 | | WFM | Brittany | Musique |
| 98.9000 | | WFM | Brittany | Musique |
| 98.9000 | | WFM | Normandy | CFM |
| 99.0000 | | WFM | Brest | Musique |
| 99.1000 | | WFM | | Radio Boule |
| 99.3000 | | WFM | Normandy | NRJ |
| 99.4000 | | WFM | France | RFM |
| 99.5000 | | WFM | Renns | Musique |
| 100.100 | | WFM | Normandy | Radio France Normandie-Rouen |
| 100.400 | | WFM | Normandy | Radio France, Cherbourg |
| 100.700 | | WFM | Normandy | Radio France, Cherbourg |
| 101.100 | | WFM | Normandy | NRJ |
| 102.400 | | WFM | Normandy | Musique |
| 102.600 | | WFM | Caen | Radio France Normandie-Caen |
| 103.100 | | WFM | Renns | Armorique |
| 104.000 | | WFM | Normandy | RFM |
| 104.300 | | WFM | | RTL |
| 104.800 | | WFM | | Europe 1 |
| 105.100 | | WFM | | NRJ |
| 105.200 | | WFM | | Nostalgie |
| 105.500 | | WFM | Normandy | France Info |
| 105.600 | | WFM | Normandy | France Info |
| 106.100 | | WFM | Normandy | RTL2 |
| 106.200 | | WFM | Normandy | RTL2 |
| 106.700 | | WFM | | Europe 1 |
| 118.100 | | AM | Calais Airport | Tower |
| 118.100 | | AM | Charles de Gauulle | Ground |
| 118.150 | | AM | Charles de Gauulle | Radar |
| 118.225 | | AM | Paris | Paris Control - high |
| 118.300 | | AM | Deauville Airport | Tower |
| 118.300 | | AM | Le Touquet Airport | Tower |
| 118.350 | | AM | Brest | ACC |
| 118.700 | | AM | Paris Orly | Tower |
| 118.725 | | AM | Paris | Paris Control - all levels |
| 118.875 | | AM | Paris Orly | Approach/Radar |
| 119.000 | | AM | Dieppe | AFIS |
| 119.250 | | AM | Charles de Gauulle | Tower |
| 119.300 | | AM | Toussus Airport | Tower |
| 119.400 | | AM | St. Brieuc Airport | Tower |
| 119.700 | | AM | Dinard, | Radar |
| 119.700 | | AM | Toussus Airport | Approach |
| 119.900 | | AM | Beauvais Airport | Approach |
| 120.150 | | AM | Dinard Airport | Approach |
| 120.250 | | AM | Dinard Airport | Tower |
| 120.350 | | AM | Deauville Airport | Approach |
| 120.500 | | AM | Paris Orly | Ground/Tower |
| 120.650 | | AM | Charles de Gauulle | Tower |
| 120.500 | | AM | Renns Airport | Tower |

## France (cont.)

| Base | Mobile | Mode | Location | User and Notes |
|------|--------|------|----------|----------------|
| 120.750 | | AM | Toussus Airport | Approach |
| 120.900 | | AM | Charles de Gauulle | Tower |
| 120.950 | | AM | Paris | Paris Control - all levels |
| 121.050 | | AM | Paris Orly | Ground |
| 121.150 | | AM | Bordeaux Airport | Approach |
| 121.150 | | AM | Charles de Gauulle | Approach |
| 121.400 | | AM | Beauvais Airport | Tower |
| 121.600 | | AM | Charles de Gauulle | Ground |
| 121.700 | | AM | Paris Orly | Ground |
| 121.725 | | AM | Charles de Gauulle | Ground |
| 121.800 | | AM | Charles de Gauulle | Ground |
| 121.975 | | AM | Charles de Gauulle | Ground |
| 122.575 | | AM | Paris | Paris Control - low |
| 122.750 | | AM | Le Bourget | Universal Ops |
| 122.800 | | AM | Brest | VFR Control |
| 123.600 | | AM | Charles de Gauulle | Ground |
| 123.875 | | AM | Paris Orly | Approach/Radar |
| 124.000 | | AM | Paris | Paris Control - all levels |
| 124.050 | | AM | Paris | ACC/UACC |
| 124.350 | | AM | Charles de Gauulle | Approach |
| 124.450 | | AM | Paris Orly | Approach/Radar |
| 124.625 | | AM | Paris | Paris Control - low |
| 124.800 | | AM | Renns Airport | Approach |
| 124.850 | | AM | Paris | Paris Control - all levels |
| 125.075 | | AM | Paris | Paris Control - all levels |
| 125.150 | | AM | Paris | VOLMET |
| 125.300 | | AM | Le Touquet | Approach |
| 125.325 | | AM | Charles de Gauulle | Tower |
| 125.450 | | AM | Paris | Paris Control - lowl |
| 125.500 | | AM | Brest | Control |
| 125.550 | | AM | Brest | IFR Control |
| 125.700 | | AM | Paris | FIS - Northl |
| 125.825 | | AM | Charles de Gauulle | Approach |
| 126.000 | | AM | Paris | VOLMET |
| 126.100 | | AM | Paris | FIS - South |
| 126.175 | | AM | Charles de Gauulle | ATIS (French) |
| 126.400 | | AM | Bordeaux | VOLMET |
| 126.425 | | AM | Charles de Gauulle | Radar |
| 126.500 | | AM | Paris Orly | ATIS |
| 126.575 | | AM | Charles de Gauulle | Approach |
| 126.650 | | AM | Charles de Gauulle | Departure |
| 127.125 | | AM | Charles de Gauulle | ATIS (English) |
| 127.300 | | AM | Cherbourg Airport | Tower/Approach |
| 127.300 | | AM | Paris | Paris Control - all levels |
| 127.750 | | AM | Paris Orly | Departure |
| 127.850 | | AM | Reims Airport | ACC/UACC |
| 128.100 | | AM | Paris | Paris Control - all levels |
| 128.275 | | AM | Paris | Paris Control - all levels |
| 128.375 | | AM | Paris Orly | Approach/Radar |
| 128.875 | | AM | Paris | Paris Control - low |
| 129.000 | | AM | Brest Airport | ACC/UACC |
| 129.000 | | AM | Paris | UIR Control |
| 129.150 | | AM | Paris | Paris Control - low |
| 129.350 | | AM | Paris | ACC/UACC |

## France (cont.)

| Base | Mobile | Mode | Location | User and Notes |
| --- | --- | --- | --- | --- |
| 129.500 | | AM | Brest Airport | UACC |
| 129.625 | | AM | Paris | FIS - West |
| 129.850 | | AM | Charles de Gaulle | Air France Ops. |
| 130.225 | | AM | Paris | Paris Control - high |
| 130.325 | | AM | Paris | Leadair Ops. |
| 130.450 | | AM | Paris | EuroAir Ops. |
| 131.250 | | AM | Paris | Paris Control - high |
| 131.175 | | AM | Brest Airport | UACC |
| 131.250 | | AM | Paris Airport | ACC/UACC |
| 131.350 | | AM | Paris Orly | ATIS |
| 131.550 | | AM | Dinard, | Aurigny Air Service |
| 131.600 | | AM | Charles de Gaulle | TWA Ops. |
| 131.775 | | AM | Charles de Gaulle | British Airways |
| 132.000 | | AM | Paris | ACC/UACC |
| 132.050 | | AM | Brest Airport | UACC |
| 132.100 | | AM | Paris | Paris Control - all levels |
| 132.125 | | AM | Brest Airport | UACC |
| 132.375 | | AM | Paris | Paris Control - high |
| 132.500 | | AM | Reims Airport | ACC/UACC |
| 132.625 | | AM | Reims Airport | ACC/UACC |
| 132.675 | | AM | Paris | Paris Control - high |
| 132.825 | | AM | Paris Airport | ACC/UACC |
| 133.000 | | AM | Brest | ACC/UACC |
| 133.375 | | AM | Charles de Gauulle | Approach |
| 133.475 | | AM | Brest | UACC |
| 133.500 | | AM | Paris | ACC/UACC |
| 133.575 | | AM | Reims | Control |
| 133.825 | | AM | Reims Airport | ACC/UACC |
| 133.925 | | AM | Paris | ACC/UACC |
| 134.200 | | AM | Brest Airport | ACC |
| 134.400 | | AM | Reims Airport | ACC/UACC |
| 134.825 | | AM | Brest Airport | UACC |
| 134.875 | | AM | Brest Airport | UACC |
| 135.000 | | AM | Paris Orly | Tower |
| 135.300 | | AM | Paris | Paris Control - all levels |
| 135.500 | | AM | Reims Airport | ACC/UACC |
| 136.275 | | AM | Charles de Gauulle | Radar |
| 135.650 | | AM | Brest Airport | UACC |
| 135.800 | | AM | Paris | ACC/UACC |
| 135.900 | | AM | Paris | ACC/UACC |
| 136.07 | | AM | Paris | Paris Control - all levels |
| 136.375 | | AM | Paris | Paris Control - high |
| 145.3250 | 144.7250 | NFM | Caen, Normandy | Amateur Repeater (F5ZBF) |
| 145.3500 | 144.7500 | NFM | Various | Amateur Repeater R9b |
| 145.3750 | 144.7750 | NFM | Tours | Amateur Repeater (FZ0THF) |
| 145.4000 | 145.8000 | NFM | Clermont-Ferrand | Amateur Repeater (FZ8THF) |
| 145.4250 | 144.8250 | NFM | Various | Amateur Repeater R12b |
| 145.6125 | 145.0125 | NFM | Evreux | Amateur Repeater (F5ZBL) |
| 146.6250 | 145.0250 | NFM | Quimper | Amateur Repeater (FZ3VHD) |
| 145.6375 | 145.0375 | NFM | Chateauroux | Amateur Repeater (F5ZDE) |
| 145.6625 | 145.0625 | NFM | Vernon | Amateur Repeater (F5ZCR) |
| 145.6750 | 145.0750 | NFM | Rennes | Amateur Repeater (F1ZBF) |
| 145.7750 | 145.1750 | NFM | Les Herbiers | Amateur Repeater (FZ3VHB) |
| 165.2000 | 168.4000 | NFM | | DGT |

| Base | Mobile | Mode | Location | User and Notes |
|------|--------|------|----------|----------------|

## France (cont.)

| | | | | |
|------|--------|------|----------|----------------|
| 166.2000 | 168.3000 | NFM | | TEC |
| 173.0000 | 173.5000 | NFM | | TEC Alphakage |
| 182.5000 | | WFM | | French TV Channel 5 sound |
| 190.5000 | | WFM | | French TV Channel 6 sound |
| 198.5000 | | WFM | | French TV Channel 7 sound |
| 206.5000 | | WFM | | French TV Channel 8 sound |

# Germany

| | | | | |
|------|--------|------|----------|----------------|
| 38.4600 | 34.3600 | NFM | | Emergency Channel Ch 801 |
| 38.4800 | 34.3800 | NFM | | Emergency Channel Ch 802 |
| 38.5000 | 34.4000 | NFM | | Emergency Channel Ch 803 |
| 38.5200 | 34.4200 | NFM | | Emergency Channel Ch 804 |
| 38.5400 | 34.4400 | NFM | | Emergency Channel Ch 805 |
| 38.5600 | 34.4600 | NFM | | Emergency Channel Ch 806 |
| 38.5800 | 34.4800 | NFM | | Emergency Channel Ch 807 |
| 38.6000 | 34.5000 | NFM | | Emergency Channel Ch 808 |
| 38.6200 | 34.5200 | NFM | | Emergency Channel Ch 809 |
| 38.6400 | 34.5400 | NFM | | Emergency Channel Ch 810 |
| 38.6600 | 34.5600 | NFM | | Emergency Channel Ch 811 |
| 38.6800 | 34.5800 | NFM | | Emergency Channel Ch 812 |
| 38.7000 | 34.6000 | NFM | | Emergency Channel Ch 813 |
| 38.7200 | 34.6200 | NFM | | Emergency Channel Ch 814 |
| 38.7400 | 34.6400 | NFM | | Emergency Channel Ch 815 |
| 38.7600 | 34.6600 | NFM | | Emergency Channel Ch 816 |
| 38.7800 | 34.6800 | NFM | | Emergency Channel Ch 817 |
| 38.8000 | 34.7000 | NFM | | Emergency Channel Ch 818 |
| 38.8200 | 34.7200 | NFM | | Emergency Channel Ch 819 |
| 38.8400 | 34.7400 | NFM | | Emergency Channel Ch 820 |
| 38.8600 | 34.7600 | NFM | | Emergency Channel Ch 821 |
| 38.8800 | 34.7800 | NFM | | Emergency Channel Ch 822 |
| 38.9000 | 34.8000 | NFM | | Emergency Channel Ch 823 |
| 38.9200 | 34.8200 | NFM | | Emergency Channel Ch 824 |
| 38.9400 | 34.8400 | NFM | | Emergency Channel Ch 825 |
| 38.9600 | 34.8600 | NFM | | Emergency Channel Ch 826 |
| 38.9800 | 34.8800 | NFM | | Emergency Channel Ch 827 |
| 39.0000 | 34.9000 | NFM | | Emergency Channel Ch 828 |
| 39.0200 | 34.9200 | NFM | | Emergency Channel Ch 829 |
| 39.0400 | 34.9400 | NFM | | Emergency Channel Ch 830 |
| 39.0600 | 34.9600 | NFM | | Emergency Channel Ch 831 |
| 39.0800 | 34.9800 | NFM | | Emergency Channel Ch 832 |
| 39.1000 | 35.0000 | NFM | | Emergency Channel Ch 833 |
| 39.1200 | 35.0200 | NFM | | Emergency Channel Ch 834 |
| 39.1400 | 35.0400 | NFM | | Emergency Channel Ch 835 |
| 39.1600 | 35.0600 | NFM | | Emergency Channel Ch 836 |
| 39.1800 | 35.0800 | NFM | | Emergency Channel Ch 837 |
| 39.2000 | 35.1000 | NFM | | Emergency Channel Ch 838 |
| 39.2200 | 35.1200 | NFM | | Emergency Channel Ch 839 |
| 39.2400 | 35.1400 | NFM | | Emergency Channel Ch 840 |
| 39.2600 | 35.1600 | NFM | | Emergency Channel Ch 841 |
| 39.2800 | 35.1800 | NFM | | Emergency Channel Ch 842 |
| 39.3000 | 35.2000 | NFM | | Emergency Channel Ch 843 |

| Base | Mobile | Mode | Location | User and Notes |
|---|---|---|---|---|
| 39.3200 | 35.2200 | NFM | | Emergency Channel Ch 844 |
| 39.3400 | 35.2400 | NFM | | Emergency Channel Ch 845 |
| 39.3600 | 35.2600 | NFM | | Emergency Channel Ch 846 |
| 39.3800 | 35.2800 | NFM | | Emergency Channel Ch 847 |
| 39.4000 | 35.3000 | NFM | | Emergency Channel Ch 848 |
| 39.4200 | 35.3200 | NFM | | Emergency Channel Ch 849 |
| 39.4400 | 35.3400 | NFM | | Emergency Channel Ch 850 |
| 39.4600 | 35.3600 | NFM | | Emergency Channel Ch 851 |
| 39.4800 | 35.3800 | NFM | | Emergency Channel Ch 852 |
| 39.5000 | 35.4000 | NFM | | Emergency Channel Ch 853 |
| 39.5200 | 35.4200 | NFM | | Emergency Channel Ch 854 |
| 39.5400 | 35.4400 | NFM | | Emergency Channel Ch 855 |
| 39.5600 | 35.4600 | NFM | | Emergency Channel Ch 856 |
| 39.5800 | 35.4800 | NFM | | Emergency Channel Ch 857 |
| 39.6000 | 35.5000 | NFM | | Emergency Channel Ch 858 |
| 39.6200 | 35.5200 | NFM | | Emergency Channel Ch 859 |
| 39.6400 | 35.5400 | NFM | | Emergency Channel Ch 860 |
| 39.6600 | 35.5600 | NFM | | Emergency Channel Ch 861 |
| 39.6800 | 35.5800 | NFM | | Emergency Channel Ch 862 |
| 39.7000 | 35.6000 | NFM | | Emergency Channel Ch 863 |
| 39.7200 | 35.6200 | NFM | | Emergency Channel Ch 864 |
| 39.7400 | 35.6400 | NFM | | Emergency Channel Ch 865 |
| 39.7600 | 35.6600 | NFM | | Emergency Channel Ch 866 |
| 39.7800 | 35.6800 | NFM | | Emergency Channel Ch 867 |
| 39.8000 | 35.7000 | NFM | | Emergency Channel Ch 868 |
| 39.8200 | 35.7200 | NFM | | Emergency Channel Ch 869 |
| 39.8400 | 35.7400 | NFM | | Emergency Channel Ch 870 |
| 39.8600 | 35.7600 | NFM | | Emergency Channel Ch 871 |
| 39.8800 | 35.7800 | NFM | | Emergency Channel Ch 872 |
| 39.9000 | 35.8000 | NFM | | Emergency Channel Ch 873 |
| 84.0150 | 74.2150 | NFM | | Emergency Channel Ch 347 |
| 84.0350 | 74.2350 | NFM | | Emergency Channel Ch 348 |
| 84.0550 | 74.2550 | NFM | | Emergency Channel Ch 349 |
| 84.0750 | 74.2750 | NFM | | Emergency Channel Ch 350 |
| 84.0950 | 74.2950 | NFM | | Emergency Channel Ch 351 |
| 84.1150 | 74.3150 | NFM | | Emergency Channel Ch 352 |
| 84.1350 | 74.3350 | NFM | | Emergency Channel Ch 353 |
| 84.1550 | 74.3550 | NFM | | Emergency Channel Ch 354 |
| 84.1750 | 74.3750 | NFM | | Emergency Channel Ch 355 |
| 84.1950 | 74.3950 | NFM | | Emergency Channel Ch 356 |
| 84.2150 | 74.4150 | NFM | | Emergency Channel Ch 357 |
| 84.2350 | 74.4350 | NFM | | Emergency Channel Ch 358 |
| 84.2550 | 74.4550 | NFM | | Emergency Channel Ch 359 |
| 84.2750 | 74.4750 | NFM | | Emergency Channel Ch 360 |
| 84.2950 | 74.4950 | NFM | | Emergency Channel Ch 361 |
| 84.3150 | 74.5150 | NFM | | Emergency Channel Ch 362 |
| 84.3350 | 74.5350 | NFM | | Emergency Channel Ch 363 |
| 84.3550 | 74.5550 | NFM | | Emergency Channel Ch 364 |
| 84.3750 | 74.5750 | NFM | | Emergency Channel Ch 365 |
| 84.3950 | 74.5950 | NFM | | Emergency Channel Ch 366 |
| 84.4150 | 74.6150 | NFM | | Emergency Channel Ch 367 |
| 84.4350 | 74.6350 | NFM | | Emergency Channel Ch 368 |
| 84.4550 | 74.6550 | NFM | | Emergency Channel Ch 369 |
| 84.4750 | 74.6750 | NFM | | Emergency Channel Ch 370 |
| 84.4950 | 74.6950 | NFM | | Emergency Channel Ch 371 |
| 84.5150 | 74.7150 | NFM | | Emergency Channel Ch 372 |

| Base | Mobile | Mode | Location | User and Notes |
|------|--------|------|----------|----------------|

**Germany** (cont.)

| Base | Mobile | Mode | Location | User and Notes |
|------|--------|------|----------|----------------|
| 84.5350 | 74.7350 | NFM | | Emergency Channel Ch 373 |
| 84.5550 | 74.7550 | NFM | | Emergency Channel Ch 374 |
| 84.5750 | 74.7750 | NFM | | Emergency Channel Ch 375 |
| 84.5950 | 74.7950 | NFM | | Emergency Channel Ch 376 |
| 84.6150 | 74.8150 | NFM | | Emergency Channel Ch 377 |
| 84.6350 | 74.8350 | NFM | | Emergency Channel Ch 378 |
| 84.6550 | 74.8550 | NFM | | Emergency Channel Ch 379 |
| 84.6750 | 74.8750 | NFM | | Emergency Channel Ch 380 |
| 84.6950 | 74.8950 | NFM | | Emergency Channel Ch 381 |
| 84.7150 | 74.9150 | NFM | | Emergency Channel Ch 382 |
| 84.7350 | 74.9350 | NFM | | Emergency Channel Ch 383 |
| 84.7550 | 74.9550 | NFM | | Emergency Channel Ch 384 |
| 84.7750 | 74.9750 | NFM | | Emergency Channel Ch 385 |
| 84.7950 | 74.9950 | NFM | | Emergency Channel Ch 386 |
| 84.8150 | 75.0150 | NFM | | Emergency Channel Ch 387 |
| 84.8350 | 75.0350 | NFM | | Emergency Channel Ch 388 |
| 84.8550 | 75.0550 | NFM | | Emergency Channel Ch 389 |
| 84.8550 | | NFM | | Emergency Channel Ch 390 |
| 84.8950 | 75.0950 | NFM | | Emergency Channel Ch 391 |
| 84.9150 | 75.1150 | NFM | | Emergency Channel Ch 392 |
| 84.9350 | 75.1350 | NFM | | Emergency Channel Ch 393 |
| 84.9550 | 75.1550 | NFM | | Emergency Channel Ch 394 |
| 84.9550 | | NFM | | Emergency Channel Ch 395 |
| 84.9950 | 75.1950 | NFM | | Emergency Channel Ch 396 |
| 85.0150 | 75.2150 | NFM | | Emergency Channel Ch 397 |
| 85.0350 | 75.2350 | NFM | | Emergency Channel Ch 398 |
| 85.0550 | 75.2550 | NFM | | Emergency Channel Ch 399 |
| 85.0750 | 75.2750 | NFM | | Emergency Channel Ch 400 |
| 85.0950 | 75.2950 | NFM | | Emergency Channel Ch 401 |
| 85.1150 | 75.3150 | NFM | | Emergency Channel Ch 402 |
| 85.1350 | 75.3350 | NFM | | Emergency Channel Ch 403 |
| 85.1550 | 75.3550 | NFM | | Emergency Channel Ch 404 |
| 85.1750 | 75.3750 | NFM | | Emergency Channel Ch 405 |
| 85.1950 | 75.3950 | NFM | | Emergency Channel Ch 406 |
| 85.2150 | 75.4150 | NFM | | Emergency Channel Ch 407 |
| 85.2350 | 75.4350 | NFM | | Emergency Channel Ch 408 |
| 85.2550 | 75.4550 | NFM | | Emergency Channel Ch 409 |
| 85.2750 | 75.4750 | NFM | | Emergency Channel Ch 410 |
| 85.2950 | 75.4950 | NFM | | Emergency Channel Ch 411 |
| 85.3150 | 75.5150 | NFM | | Emergency Channel Ch 412 |
| 85.3350 | 75.5350 | NFM | | Emergency Channel Ch 413 |
| 85.3550 | 75.5550 | NFM | | Emergency Channel Ch 414 |
| 85.3750 | 75.5750 | NFM | | Emergency Channel Ch 415 |
| 85.3950 | 75.5950 | NFM | | Emergency Channel Ch 416 |
| 85.4150 | 75.6150 | NFM | | Emergency Channel Ch 417 |
| 85.4350 | 75.6350 | NFM | | Emergency Channel Ch 418 |
| 85.4550 | 75.6550 | NFM | | Emergency Channel Ch 419 |
| 85.4950 | 75.6950 | NFM | | Emergency Channel Ch 421 |
| 85.5150 | 75.7150 | NFM | | Emergency Channel Ch 422 |
| 85.5350 | 75.7350 | NFM | | Emergency Channel Ch 423 |
| 85.5550 | 75.7550 | NFM | | Emergency Channel Ch 424 |
| 85.5750 | 75.7750 | NFM | | Emergency Channel Ch 425 |
| 85.6150 | 75.8150 | NFM | | Emergency Channel Ch 427 |
| 85.6350 | 75.8350 | NFM | | Emergency Channel Ch 428 |

## Germany (cont.)

| Base | Mobile | Mode | Location | User and Notes |
|------|--------|------|----------|----------------|
| 86.0750 | 76.2750 | NFM | | Emergency Channel Ch 450 |
| 86.0950 | 76.2950 | NFM | | Emergency Channel Ch 451 |
| 86.1150 | 76.3150 | NFM | | Emergency Channel Ch 452 |
| 86.1350 | 76.3350 | NFM | | Emergency Channel Ch 453 |
| 86.1550 | 76.3550 | NFM | | Emergency Channel Ch 454 |
| 86.1750 | 76.3750 | NFM | | Emergency Channel Ch 455 |
| 86.1950 | 76.3950 | NFM | | Emergency Channel Ch 456 |
| 86.2150 | 76.4150 | NFM | | Emergency Channel Ch 457 |
| 86.2350 | 76.4350 | NFM | | Emergency Channel Ch 458 |
| 86.2550 | 76.4550 | NFM | | Emergency Channel Ch 459 |
| 86.2750 | 76.4750 | NFM | | Emergency Channel Ch 460 |
| 86.2950 | 76.4950 | NFM | | Emergency Channel Ch 461 |
| 86.3150 | 76.5150 | NFM | | Emergency Channel Ch 462 |
| 86.3150 | 76.5150 | NFM | | Emergency Channel Ch 462 |
| 86.3350 | 76.5350 | NFM | | Emergency Channel Ch 463 |
| 86.3350 | 76.5350 | NFM | | Emergency Channel Ch 463 |
| 86.3550 | 76.5550 | NFM | | Emergency Channel Ch 464 |
| 86.3750 | 76.5750 | NFM | | Emergency Channel Ch 465 |
| 86.3950 | 76.5950 | NFM | | Emergency Channel Ch 466 |
| 86.4150 | 76.6150 | NFM | | Emergency Channel Ch 467 |
| 86.4350 | 76.6350 | NFM | | Emergency Channel Ch 468 |
| 86.4550 | 76.6550 | NFM | | Emergency Channel Ch 469 |
| 86.4750 | 76.6750 | NFM | | Emergency Channel Ch 470 |
| 86.4950 | 76.6950 | NFM | | Emergency Channel Ch 471 |
| 86.5150 | 76.7150 | NFM | | Emergency Channel Ch 472 |
| 86.5350 | 76.7350 | NFM | | Emergency Channel Ch 473 |
| 86.5550 | 76.7550 | NFM | | Emergency Channel Ch 474 |
| 86.5750 | 76.7750 | NFM | | Emergency Channel Ch 475 |
| 86.5950 | 76.7950 | NFM | | Emergency Channel Ch 476 |
| 86.6150 | 76.8150 | NFM | | Emergency Channel Ch 477 |
| 86.6350 | 76.8350 | NFM | | Emergency Channel Ch 478 |
| 86.6550 | 76.8550 | NFM | | Emergency Channel Ch 479 |
| 86.6750 | 76.8750 | NFM | | Emergency Channel Ch 480 |
| 86.6950 | 76.8950 | NFM | | Emergency Channel Ch 481 |
| 86.7150 | 76.9150 | NFM | | Emergency Channel Ch 482 |
| 86.7350 | 76.9350 | NFM | | Emergency Channel Ch 483 |
| 86.7550 | 76.9550 | NFM | | Emergency Channel Ch 484 |
| 86.7750 | 76.9750 | NFM | | Emergency Channel Ch 485 |
| 86.7950 | 76.9950 | NFM | | Emergency Channel Ch 486 |
| 86.8150 | 77.0150 | NFM | | Emergency Channel Ch 487 |
| 86.8350 | 77.0350 | NFM | | Emergency Channel Ch 488 |
| 86.8550 | 77.0550 | NFM | | Emergency Channel Ch 489 |
| 86.8750 | 77.0750 | NFM | | Emergency Channel Ch 490 |
| 86.8950 | 77.0950 | NFM | | Emergency Channel Ch 491 |
| 86.9150 | 77.1150 | NFM | | Emergency Channel Ch 492 |
| 86.9350 | 77.1350 | NFM | | Emergency Channel Ch 493 |
| 86.9550 | 77.1550 | NFM | | Emergency Channel Ch 494 |
| 86.9750 | 77.1750 | NFM | | Emergency Channel Ch 495 |
| 86.9950 | 77.1950 | NFM | | Emergency Channel Ch 496 |
| 87.0150 | 77.2150 | NFM | | Emergency Channel Ch 497 |
| 87.0350 | 77.2350 | NFM | | Emergency Channel Ch 498 |
| 87.0550 | 77.2550 | NFM | | Emergency Channel Ch 499 |
| 87.0750 | 77.2750 | NFM | | Emergency Channel Ch 500 |
| 87.0950 | 77.2950 | NFM | | Emergency Channel Ch 501 |

| Base | Mobile | Mode | Location | User and Notes |
|------|--------|------|----------|----------------|
| **Germany** (cont.) | | | | |
| 87.1150 | 77.3150 | NFM | | Emergency Channel Ch 502 |
| 87.1350 | 77.3350 | NFM | | Emergency Channel Ch 503 |
| 87.1550 | 77.3550 | NFM | | Emergency Channel Ch 504 |
| 87.1750 | 77.3750 | NFM | | Emergency Channel Ch 505 |
| 87.1950 | 77.3950 | NFM | | Emergency Channel Ch 506 |
| 87.2150 | 77.4150 | NFM | | Emergency Channel Ch 507 |
| 87.2350 | 77.4350 | NFM | | Emergency Channel Ch 508 |
| 87.2550 | 77.4550 | NFM | | Emergency Channel Ch 509 |
| 118.025 | | AM | Frankfurt Main | ATIS |
| 118.500 | | AM | Frankfurt Main | Approach |
| 119.075 | | AM | Frankfurt | ATC |
| 119.900 | | AM | Frankfurt Main | Tower |
| 120.150 | | AM | Frankfurt Main | Departures |
| 120.425 | | AM | Frankfurt Main | Departures |
| 120.450 | | AM | Frankfurt | ATC |
| 120.575 | | AM | Frankfurt | ATC |
| 120.800 | | AM | Frankfurt Main | Approach/Radar |
| 121.700 | | AM | Frankfurt Main | Ramp/Apron |
| 121.800 | | AM | Frankfurt Main | Ground |
| 121.850 | | AM | Frankfurt Main | Ramp/Apron |
| 121.900 | | AM | Frankfurt Main | Ground |
| 121.950 | | AM | Frankfurt Main | Ramp/Apron |
| 123.325 | | AM | Frankfurt | FIS |
| 123.525 | | AM | Frankfurt | ATC |
| 124.200 | | AM | Frankfurt Main | Approach |
| 124.025 | | AM | Frankfurt | ATC |
| 124.375 | | AM | Frankfurt | ATC |
| 124.425 | | AM | Frankfurt | ATC |
| 124.475 | | AM | Frankfurt | ATC |
| 124.725 | | AM | Frankfurt | ATC |
| 124.850 | | AM | Frankfurt Main | Tower |
| 124.900 | | AM | Frankfurt | ATC |
| 125.200 | | AM | Frankfurt | ATC |
| 125.400 | | AM | Frankfurt | ATC |
| 125.600 | | AM | Frankfurt | ATC |
| 127.050 | | AM | Frankfurt | ATC |
| 127.125 | | AM | Frankfurt | ATC |
| 127.500 | | AM | Frankfurt | ATC |
| 127.725 | | AM | Frankfurt | ATC |
| 127.925 | | AM | Frankfurt | ATC |
| 129.675 | | AM | Frankfurt | ATC |
| 130.975 | | AM | Frankfurt | ATC |
| 131.300 | | AM | Frankfurt | ATC |
| 131.7500 | 131.7500 | AM | Frankfurt Main | Lufthansa Ops. |
| 135.725 | | AM | Frankfurt | ATC |
| 169.8100 | 165.2100 | NFM | | Emergency Services Ch 101 |
| 169.8300 | 165.2300 | NFM | | Emergency Services Ch 102 |
| 169.8500 | 165.2500 | NFM | | Emergency Services Ch 103 |
| 169.8700 | 165.2700 | NFM | | Emergency Services Ch 104 |
| 169.8900 | 165.2900 | NFM | | Emergency Services Ch 105 |
| 169.9100 | 165.3100 | NFM | | Emergency Services Ch 106 |
| 169.9300 | 165.3300 | NFM | | Emergency Services Ch 107 |
| 169.9500 | 165.3500 | NFM | | Emergency Services Ch 108 |
| 169.9700 | 165.3700 | NFM | | Emergency Services Ch 109 |

## Germany (cont.)

| Base | Mobile | Mode | Location | User and Notes |
|---------|----------|------|----------|-------------------------|
| 169.9900 | 165.3900 | NFM | | Emergency Services Ch 110 |
| 170.0100 | 165.4100 | NFM | | Emergency Services Ch 111 |
| 170.0300 | 165.4300 | NFM | | Emergency Services Ch 112 |
| 170.0500 | 165.4500 | NFM | | Emergency Services Ch 113 |
| 170.0700 | 165.4700 | NFM | | Emergency Services Ch 114 |
| 170.0900 | 165.4900 | NFM | | Emergency Services Ch 115 |
| 170.1100 | 165.5100 | NFM | | Emergency Services Ch 116 |
| 170.1300 | 165.5300 | NFM | | Emergency Services Ch 117 |
| 170.1500 | 165.5500 | NFM | | Emergency Services Ch 118 |
| 170.1700 | 165.5700 | NFM | | Emergency Services Ch 119 |
| 170.1900 | 165.5900 | NFM | | Emergency Services Ch 120 |
| 170.2100 | 165.6100 | NFM | | Emergency Services Ch 121 |
| 170.2300 | 165.6300 | NFM | | Emergency Services Ch 122 |
| 170.2500 | 165.6500 | NFM | | Emergency Services Ch 123 |
| 170.2700 | 165.6700 | NFM | | Emergency Services Ch 124 |
| 170.2900 | 165.6900 | NFM | | Emergency Services Ch 125 |
| 172.1400 | 167.5400 | NFM | | Emergency Services Ch 200 |
| 172.1600 | 167.5600 | NFM | | Emergency Services Ch 201 |
| 172.1800 | 167.5800 | NFM | | Emergency Services Ch 202 |
| 172.2000 | 167.6000 | NFM | | Emergency Services Ch 203 |
| 172.2200 | 167.6200 | NFM | | Emergency Services Ch 204 |
| 172.2400 | 167.6400 | NFM | | Emergency Services Ch 205 |
| 172.2600 | 167.6600 | NFM | | Emergency Services Ch 206 |
| 172.2800 | 167.6800 | NFM | | Emergency Services Ch 207 |
| 172.3000 | 167.7000 | NFM | | Emergency Services Ch 208 |
| 172.3200 | 167.7200 | NFM | | Emergency Services Ch 209 |
| 172.3400 | 167.7400 | NFM | | Emergency Services Ch 210 |
| 172.3600 | 167.7600 | NFM | | Emergency Services Ch 211 |
| 172.3800 | 167.7800 | NFM | | Emergency Services Ch 212 |
| 172.4000 | 167.8000 | NFM | | Emergency Services Ch 213 |
| 172.4200 | 167.8200 | NFM | | Emergency Services Ch 214 |
| 172.4400 | 167.8400 | NFM | | Emergency Services Ch 215 |
| 172.4600 | 167.8600 | NFM | | Emergency Services Ch 216 |
| 172.4800 | 167.8800 | NFM | | Emergency Services Ch 217 |
| 172.5000 | 167.9000 | NFM | | Emergency Services Ch 218 |
| 172.5200 | 167.9200 | NFM | | Emergency Services Ch 219 |
| 172.5400 | 167.9400 | NFM | | Emergency Services Ch 220 |
| 172.5600 | 167.9600 | NFM | | Emergency Services Ch 221 |
| 172.5800 | 167.9800 | NFM | | Emergency Services Ch 222 |
| 172.6000 | 168.0000 | NFM | | Emergency Services Ch 223 |
| 172.6200 | 168.0200 | NFM | | Emergency Services Ch 224 |
| 172.6400 | 168.0400 | NFM | | Emergency Services Ch 225 |
| 172.6600 | 168.0600 | NFM | | Emergency Services Ch 226 |
| 172.6800 | 168.0800 | NFM | | Emergency Services Ch 227 |
| 172.7000 | 168.1000 | NFM | | Emergency Services Ch 228 |
| 172.7200 | 168.1200 | NFM | | Emergency Services Ch 229 |
| 172.7400 | 168.1400 | NFM | | Emergency Services Ch 230 |
| 172.7600 | 168.1600 | NFM | | Emergency Services Ch 231 |
| 172.7800 | 168.1800 | NFM | | Emergency Services Ch 232 |
| 172.8000 | 168.2000 | NFM | | Emergency Services Ch 233 |
| 172.8200 | 168.2200 | NFM | | Emergency Services Ch 234 |
| 172.8400 | 168.2400 | NFM | | Emergency Services Ch 235 |
| 172.8600 | 168.2600 | NFM | | Emergency Services Ch 236 |
| 172.8800 | 168.2800 | NFM | | Emergency Services Ch 237 |

## Germany (cont.)

| Base | Mobile | Mode | User and Notes |
| --- | --- | --- | --- |
| 172.9000 | 168.3000 | NFM | Emergency Services Ch 238 |
| 172.9200 | 168.3200 | NFM | Emergency Services Ch 239 |
| 172.9400 | 168.3400 | NFM | Emergency Services Ch 240 |
| 172.9600 | 168.3600 | NFM | Emergency Services Ch 241 |
| 172.9800 | 168.3800 | NFM | Emergency Services Ch 242 |
| 173.0000 | 168.4000 | NFM | Emergency Services Ch 243 |
| 173.0200 | 168.4200 | NFM | Emergency Services Ch 244 |
| 173.0400 | 168.4400 | NFM | Emergency Services Ch 245 |
| 173.0600 | 168.4600 | NFM | Emergency Services Ch 246 |
| 173.0800 | 168.4800 | NFM | Emergency Services Ch 247 |
| 173.1000 | 168.5000 | NFM | Emergency Services Ch 248 |
| 173.1200 | 168.5200 | NFM | Emergency Services Ch 249 |
| 173.1400 | 168.5400 | NFM | Emergency Services Ch 250 |
| 173.1600 | 168.5600 | NFM | Emergency Services Ch 251 |
| 173.1800 | 168.5800 | NFM | Emergency Services Ch 252 |
| 173.2000 | 168.6000 | NFM | Emergency Services Ch 253 |
| 173.2200 | 168.6200 | NFM | Emergency Services Ch 254 |
| 173.2400 | 168.6400 | NFM | Emergency Services Ch 255 |
| 173.2600 | 168.6600 | NFM | Emergency Services Ch 256 |
| 173.2800 | 168.6800 | NFM | Emergency Services Ch 257 |
| 173.3000 | 168.7000 | NFM | Emergency Services Ch 258 |
| 173.3200 | 168.7200 | NFM | Emergency Services Ch 259 |
| 173.3400 | 168.7400 | NFM | Emergency Services Ch 260 |
| 173.3600 | 168.7600 | NFM | Emergency Services Ch 261 |
| 173.3800 | 168.7800 | NFM | Emergency Services Ch 262 |
| 173.4000 | 168.8000 | NFM | Emergency Services Ch 263 |
| 173.4200 | 168.8200 | NFM | Emergency Services Ch 264 |
| 173.4400 | 168.8400 | NFM | Emergency Services Ch 265 |
| 173.4600 | 168.8600 | NFM | Emergency Services Ch 266 |
| 173.4800 | 168.8800 | NFM | Emergency Services Ch 267 |
| 173.5000 | 168.9000 | NFM | Emergency Services Ch 268 |
| 173.5200 | 168.9200 | NFM | Emergency Services Ch 269 |
| 173.5400 | 168.9400 | NFM | Emergency Services Ch 270 |
| 173.5600 | 168.9600 | NFM | Emergency Services Ch 271 |
| 173.5800 | 168.9800 | NFM | Emergency Services Ch 272 |
| 173.6000 | 169.0000 | NFM | Emergency Services Ch 273 |
| 173.6200 | 169.0200 | NFM | Emergency Services Ch 274 |
| 173.6400 | 169.0400 | NFM | Emergency Services Ch 275 |
| 173.6600 | 169.0600 | NFM | Emergency Services Ch 276 |
| 173.6800 | 169.0800 | NFM | Emergency Services Ch 277 |
| 173.7000 | 169.1000 | NFM | Emergency Services Ch 278 |
| 173.7200 | 169.1200 | NFM | Emergency Services Ch 279 |
| 173.7400 | 169.1400 | NFM | Emergency Services Ch 280 |
| 173.7600 | 169.1600 | NFM | Emergency Services Ch 281 |
| 173.7800 | 169.1800 | NFM | Emergency Services Ch 282 |
| 173.8000 | 169.2000 | NFM | Emergency Services Ch 283 |
| 173.8200 | 169.2200 | NFM | Emergency Services Ch 284 |
| 173.8400 | 169.2400 | NFM | Emergency Services Ch 285 |
| 173.8600 | 169.2600 | NFM | Emergency Services Ch 286 |
| 173.8800 | 169.2800 | NFM | Emergency Services Ch 287 |
| 173.9000 | 169.3000 | NFM | Emergency Services Ch 288 |
| 173.9200 | 169.3200 | NFM | Emergency Services Ch 289 |
| 173.9400 | 169.3400 | NFM | Emergency Services Ch 290 |
| 173.9600 | 169.3600 | NFM | Emergency Services Ch 291 |
| 173.9800 | 169.3800 | NFM | Emergency Services Ch 292 |

# Hungary

| Base | Mobile | Mode | Location | User and Notes |
|------|--------|------|----------|----------------|
| 66.0200 | | WFM | Miskolc | Magyar Radio [LBS] |
| 66.1400 | | WFM | Kemadi | Magyar Radio [LBS] |
| 66.2900 | | WFM | Szentes | Magyar Radio [LBS] |
| 66.6200 | | WFM | Budapest | Magyar Radio [LBS] |
| 66.8000 | | WFM | Miskolc | Magyar Radio [LBS] |
| 66.9200 | | WFM | Kemadi | Magyar Radio [LBS] |
| 67.0400 | | WFM | Gyor | Magyar Radio [LBS] |
| 67.1900 | | WFM | Pecs | Magyar Radio [LBS] |
| 67.4000 | | WFM | Budapest | Magyar Radio [LBS] |
| 67.8500 | | WFM | Szentes | Magyar Radio [LBS] |
| 67.9700 | | WFM | Pecs | Magyar Radio [LBS] |
| 68.2500 | | WFM | Kemadi | Magyar Radio [LBS] |
| 68.3600 | | WFM | Nagykanizsa | Magyar Radio [LBS] |
| 68.4800 | | WFM | Miskolc | Magyar Radio [LBS] |
| 69.3800 | | WFM | Budapest | Magyar Radio [LBS] |
| 69.9800 | | WFM | Nagykanizsa | Magyar Radio [LBS] |
| 70.1000 | | WFM | Kekes | Magyar Radio [LBS] |
| 70.4000 | | WFM | Sopron | Magyar Radio [LBS] |
| 70.4300 | | WFM | Tokaj | Magyar Radio [LBS] |
| 70.6400 | | WFM | Kabhegy | Magyar Radio [LBS] |
| 71.0300 | | WFM | Nagykanizsa | Magyar Radio [LBS] |
| 71.2100 | | WFM | Kekes | Magyar Radio [LBS] |
| 71.3300 | | WFM | Tokaj | Magyar Radio [LBS] |
| 71.4200 | | WFM | Kabhegy | Magyar Radio [LBS] |
| 71.8100 | | WFM | Pecs | Magyar Radio [LBS] |
| 71.8600 | | WFM | Sopron | Magyar Radio [LBS] |
| 72.0800 | | WFM | Sopron | Magyar Radio [LBS] |
| 72.1100 | | WFM | Tokaj | Magyar Radio [LBS] |
| 72.7700 | | WFM | Kekes | Magyar Radio [LBS] |
| 72.9800 | | WFM | Kabhegy | Magyar Radio [LBS] |

# Iceland

| Base | Mobile | Mode | Location | User and Notes |
|------|--------|------|----------|----------------|
| 118.000 | | AM | Reykjavik Airport | Tower |
| 119.000 | | AM | Reykjavik Airport | Approach |
| 119.700 | | AM | Reykjavik | ATC |
| 121.700 | | AM | Reykjavik Airport | Ground |
| 123.700 | | AM | Reykjavik | ATC |
| 123.900 | | AM | Reykjavik | ATC |
| 125.700 | | AM | Reykjavik | ATC |
| 126.550 | | AM | Reykjavik | Iceland Radio |
| 127.850 | | AM | Reykjavik | Iceland Radio |
| 128.100 | | AM | Reykjavik Airport | ATIS |
| 132.200 | | AM | Reykjavik | ATC |
| 123.300 | | AM | Reykjavik | ATC |

## Netherlands

| Base | Mobile | Mode | Location | User and Notes |
|------|--------|------|----------|----------------|
| 86.0750 | 77.6750 | NFM | | Police Ch 804 |
| 86.0875 | 77.6875 | NFM | | Police Ch 805 |
| 86.1000 | 77.7000 | NFM | | Police Ch 806 |
| 86.1125 | 77.7125 | NFM | | Police Ch 807 |
| 86.1250 | 77.7250 | NFM | | Police Ch 808 |
| 86.1375 | 77.7375 | NFM | | Police Ch 809 |
| 86.1500 | 77.7500 | NFM | | Police Ch 810 |
| 86.1625 | 77.7625 | NFM | | Police Ch 811 |
| 86.1750 | 77.7750 | NFM | | Police Ch 812 |
| 86.1875 | 77.7875 | NFM | | Police Ch 813 |
| 86.2000 | 77.8000 | NFM | | Police Ch 814 |
| 86.2125 | 77.8125 | NFM | | Police Ch 815 |
| 86.2250 | 77.8250 | NFM | | Police Ch 816 |
| 86.2375 | 77.8375 | NFM | | Police Ch 817 |
| 86.2500 | 77.8500 | NFM | | Police Ch 818 |
| 86.2625 | 77.8625 | NFM | | Police Ch 819 |
| 86.2750 | 77.8750 | NFM | | Police Ch 820 |
| 86.2875 | 77.8875 | NFM | | Police Ch 821 |
| 86.3000 | 77.9000 | NFM | | Police Ch 822 |
| 86.3000 | 77.9000 | NFM | | Police Ch 822 |
| 86.3125 | 77.9125 | NFM | | Police Ch 823 |
| 86.3125 | 77.9125 | NFM | | Police Ch 823 |
| 86.3250 | 77.9250 | NFM | | Police Ch 824 |
| 86.3250 | 77.9250 | NFM | | Police Ch 824 |
| 86.3375 | 77.9375 | NFM | | Police Ch 825 |
| 86.3375 | 77.9375 | NFM | | Police Ch 825 |
| 86.3500 | 77.9500 | NFM | | Police Ch 826 |
| 86.3625 | 77.9625 | NFM | | Police Ch 827 |
| 86.3750 | 77.9750 | NFM | | Police Ch 828 |
| 86.3875 | 77.9875 | NFM | | Police Ch 829 |
| 86.4000 | 78.0000 | NFM | | Police Ch 830 |
| 86.4250 | 78.0250 | NFM | | Police Ch 832 |
| 86.4375 | 78.0375 | NFM | | Police Ch 833 |
| 86.4500 | 78.0500 | NFM | | Police Ch 834 |
| 86.4625 | 78.0625 | NFM | | Police Ch 835 |
| 86.4750 | 78.0750 | NFM | | Police Ch 836 |
| 86.5000 | 78.1000 | NFM | | Police Ch 838 |
| 86.5125 | 78.1125 | NFM | | Police Ch 839 |
| 86.5250 | 78.1250 | NFM | | Police Ch 840 |
| 86.5375 | 78.1375 | NFM | | Police Ch 841 |
| 86.5500 | 78.1500 | NFM | | Police Ch 842 |
| 86.5625 | 78.1625 | NFM | | Police Ch 843 |
| 86.5750 | 78.1750 | NFM | | Police Ch 844 |
| 86.5875 | 78.1875 | NFM | | Police Ch 845 |
| 86.6000 | 78.2000 | NFM | | Police Ch 846 |
| 86.6125 | 78.2125 | NFM | | Police Ch 847 |
| 86.6250 | 78.2250 | NFM | | Police Ch 848 |
| 86.6375 | 78.2375 | NFM | | Police Ch 849 |
| 86.6500 | 78.2500 | NFM | | Police Ch 850 |
| 86.6625 | 78.2625 | NFM | | Police Ch 851 |
| 86.6750 | 78.2750 | NFM | | Police Ch 852 |
| 86.6875 | 78.2875 | NFM | | Police Ch 853 |
| 86.7000 | 78.3000 | NFM | | Police Ch 854 |
| 86.7125 | 78.3125 | NFM | | Police Ch 855 |

| Base | Mobile | Mode | Location | User and Notes |
|------|--------|------|----------|----------------|
| 86.7250 | 78.3250 | NFM | | Police Ch 856 |
| 86.7375 | 78.3375 | NFM | | Police Ch 857 |
| 86.7500 | 78.3500 | NFM | | Police Ch 858 |
| 86.7625 | 78.3625 | NFM | | Police Ch 859 |
| 86.7750 | 78.3750 | NFM | | Police Ch 860 |
| 86.7875 | 78.3875 | NFM | | Police Ch 861 |
| 86.8000 | 78.4000 | NFM | | Police Ch 862 |
| 86.8125 | 78.4125 | NFM | | Police Ch 863 |
| 86.8250 | 78.4250 | NFM | | Police Ch 864 |
| 86.8375 | 78.4375 | NFM | | Police Ch 865 |
| 86.8500 | 78.4500 | NFM | | Police Ch 866 |
| 86.8625 | 78.4625 | NFM | | Police Ch 867 |
| 86.8750 | 78.4750 | NFM | | Police Ch 868 |
| 86.8875 | 78.4875 | NFM | | Police Ch 869 |
| 86.9000 | 78.5000 | NFM | | Police Ch 870 |
| 86.9125 | 78.5125 | NFM | | Police Ch 871 |
| 86.9250 | 78.5250 | NFM | | Police Ch 872 |
| 86.9375 | 78.5375 | NFM | | Police Ch 873 |
| 86.9500 | 78.5500 | NFM | | Police Ch 874 |
| 86.9625 | 78.5625 | NFM | | Police Ch 875 |
| 86,9750 | | NFM | | Water Companies |
| 86.9750 | 78.5750 | NFM | | Police Ch 876 |
| 86.9875 | 78.5875 | NFM | | Police Ch 877 |
| 87.0000 | 78.6000 | NFM | | Police Ch 878 |
| 87.0125 | 78.6125 | NFM | | Police Ch 879 |
| 87.0250 | 78.6250 | NFM | | Police Ch 880 |
| 87.0375 | 78.6375 | NFM | | Police Ch 881 |
| 87.0500 | 78.6500 | NFM | | Police Ch 882 |
| 87.0625 | 78.6625 | NFM | | Police Ch 883 |
| 87.0750 | 78.6750 | NFM | | Police Ch 884 |
| 87.0875 | 78.6875 | NFM | | Police Ch 885 |
| 87.1000 | 78.7000 | NFM | | Police Ch 886 |
| 95.2000 | | WFM | Amsterdam | Radio Noord Holland |
| 103.000 | | WFM | Amsterdam | Radio 10 Gold |
| 118.075 | | AM | Amsterdam Schipol | Approach |
| 118.100 | | AM | Amsterdam Schipol | Tower |
| 118.275 | | AM | Amsterdam Schipol | Tower |
| 118.400 | | AM | Amsterdam Schipol | Arrivals |
| 118.800 | | AM | Amsterdam Schipol | Radar |
| 119.050 | | AM | Amsterdam Schipol | Approach |
| 119.175 | | AM | Amsterdam | FIS Low |
| 119.225 | | AM | Amsterdam Schipol | Tower |
| 120.550 | | AM | Amsterdam Schipol | Radar |
| 120.825 | | AM | Amsterdam | Dutch Military High |
| 121.200 | | AM | Amsterdam Schipol | Approach |
| 121.700 | | AM | Amsterdam Schipol | Ground |
| 121.975 | | AM | Amsterdam Schipol | Clearance Delivery |
| 122.200 | | AM | Amsterdam Schipol | ATIS Departure Information |
| 123.700 | | AM | Amsterdam | Centre High |
| 123.850 | | AM | Amsterdam | Centre High |
| 124.300 | | AM | Amsterdam | Centre High |
| 124.300 | | AM | Amsterdam Schipol | ACC |
| 124.775 | | AM | Amsterdam Schipol | Tower |
| 124.875 | | AM | Amsterdam Schipol | ACC |
| 124.875 | | AM | Amsterdam | Centre High |
| 125.750 | | AM | Amsterdam Schipol | ACC |

## Netherlands (cont.)

| Base | Mobile | Mode | Location | User and Notes |
|------|--------|------|----------|----------------|
| 125.750 | | AM | Amsterdam | Centre High |
| 127.625 | | AM | Maastricht | Eurocontrol |
| 126.675 | | AM | Amsterdam Schipol | Approach |
| 128.350 | | AM | Amsterdam | Dutch Military Low |
| 129.300 | | AM | Amsterdam Schipol | ACC |
| 129.300 | | AM | Amsterdam | Centre High |
| 130.950 | | AM | Amsterdam Schipol | Radar |
| 131.150 | | AM | Amsterdam Schipol | Arrivals |
| 131.425 | | AM | Amsterdam | KLM Computer Ops. |
| 131.450 | | AM | Amsterdam | Phillips Ops. |
| 131.450 | | AM | Amsterdam | Martinair Ops. |
| 131.550 | | AM | Amsterdam Schipol | Ground Control |
| 131.600 | | AM | Amsterdam Schipol | TWA Ops. |
| 131.650 | | AM | Amsterdam Schipol | KLM Ops. |
| 131.800 | | AM | Amsterdam Schipol | Ogden Aviation Ops. |
| 131.825 | | AM | Amsterdam Schipol | KLM Maintance |
| 131.850 | | AM | Amsterdam Schipol | Singapore Airlines Ops. |
| 132.200 | | AM | Maastricht | UAC |
| 132.350 | | AM | Amsterdam | Dutch Mititary Primary |
| 132.525 | | AM | Amsterdam | Dutch Military Low |
| 132.850 | | AM | Maastricht | UAC |
| 132.975 | | AM | Amsterdam Schipol | ATIS Arrival Information |
| 133.100 | | AM | Amsterdam Schipol | ACC |
| 133.100 | | AM | Amsterdam | FIS Low |
| 133.250 | | AM | Maastricht | UAC |
| 133.350 | | AM | Maastricht | UAC |
| 133.850 | | AM | Maastricht | UAC |
| 133.950 | | AM | Maastricht | UAC |
| 134.375 | | AM | Maastricht | UAC |
| 135.150 | | AM | Maastricht | UAC |
| 135.450 | | AM | Maastricht | UAC |
| 135.975 | | AM | Maastricht | UACC |
| 145.0875 | 149.4875 | NFM | Reusel | Customs |
| 145.7000 | 145.1000 | NFM | Eindhoven | Amateur Repeater PI3EHV |
| 146.0500 | 146.0500 | NFM | | Disaster Ch 23 |
| 146.0700 | 146.0700 | NFM | | Disaster Ch 24 |
| 146.0900 | 146.0900 | NFM | | Disaster Ch 25 |
| 146.1100 | 146.1100 | NFM | | Disaster Ch 26 |
| 146.1300 | 146.1300 | NFM | | Disaster Ch 27 |
| 146.1500 | 146.1500 | NFM | | Disaster Ch 28 |
| 146.1700 | 146.1700 | NFM | | Disaster Ch 29 |
| 146.1900 | 146.1900 | NFM | | Disaster Ch 30 |
| 146.1900 | 146.1900 | NFM | | Trauma Teams Ch 71 |
| 146.2300 | 146.2300 | NFM | | Disaster Ch 31 |
| 146.2700 | 146.2700 | NFM | | Disaster Ch 33 |
| 146.2900 | 146.2900 | NFM | | Disaster Ch 34 |
| 146.3100 | 146.3100 | NFM | | Trauma Teams Ch 72 |
| 146.3700 | 146.3700 | NFM | | Disaster Ch 36 |
| 146.3900 | 146.3900 | NFM | | Disaster Ch 37 |
| 146.4300 | 146.4300 | NFM | | Disaster Ch 38 |
| 146.4500 | 146.4500 | NFM | | Trauma Teams Ch 73 |
| 146.4700 | 146.4700 | NFM | | Trauma Teams Ch 74 |
| 146.4900 | 146.4900 | NFM | | Disaster Ch 39 |
| 146.5100 | 146.5100 | NFM | | Disaster Ch 40 |

## Netherlands (cont.)

| Base | Mobile | Mode | Location | User and Notes |
|---|---|---|---|---|
| 146.5300 | 146.5300 | NFM | | Disaster Ch 41 |
| 146.5500 | 146.5500 | NFM | | Disaster Ch 42 |
| 146.5700 | 146.5700 | NFM | | Trauma Teams Ch 75 |
| 146.6100 | 146.6100 | NFM | | Disaster Ch 43 |
| 146.6300 | 146.6300 | NFM | | Disaster Ch 44 |
| 146.6500 | 146.6500 | NFM | | Disaster Ch 45 |
| 146.6700 | 146.6700 | NFM | | Disaster Ch 46 |
| 146.6900 | 146.6900 | NFM | | Disaster Ch 47 |
| 146.7100 | 146.7100 | NFM | | Disaster Ch 48 |
| 146.7300 | 146.7300 | NFM | | Disaster Ch 49 |
| 146.7500 | 146.7500 | NFM | | Disaster Ch 50 |
| 146.7700 | 146.7700 | NFM | | Disaster Ch 51 |
| 146.7900 | 146.7900 | NFM | | Disaster Ch 52 |
| 146.8300 | 146.8300 | NFM | | Disaster Ch 53 |
| 146.8500 | 146.8500 | NFM | | Disaster Ch 54 |
| 146.8700 | 146.8700 | NFM | | Disaster Ch 55 |
| 146.9300 | 146.9300 | NFM | | Disaster Ch 56 |
| 146.9500 | 146.9500 | NFM | | Disaster Ch 57 |
| 147.0500 | 147.0500 | NFM | | Disaster Ch 58 |
| 147.0700 | 147.0700 | NFM | | Disaster Ch 59 |
| 147.0900 | 147.0900 | NFM | | Disaster Ch 60 |
| 147.1700 | 147.1700 | NFM | | Disaster Ch 61 |
| 147.1900 | 147.1900 | NFM | | Disaster Ch 32 |
| 150.5125 | 150.5125 | NFM | Eindhoven | Fire Brigade DAF Trucks |
| 151.7125 | 151.7125 | NFM | | Disaster Ch 62 |
| 151.7375 | 151.7375 | NFM | | Disaster Ch 63 |
| 151.7625 | 151.7625 | NFM | | Disaster Ch 64 |
| 151.7875 | 151.7875 | NFM | | Disaster Ch 65 |
| 151.8375 | 151.8375 | NFM | | Disaster Ch 66 |
| 151.8875 | 151.8875 | NFM | | Disaster Ch 67 |
| 151.9625 | 151.9625 | NFM | | Disaster Ch 68 |
| 151.9875 | 151.9875 | NFM | | Disaster Ch 69 |
| 152.3625 | 152.3625 | NFM | Eindhoven | Animal Ambulance |
| 152.7625 | 152.7625 | NFM | Eindhoven | Fire Brigade DAF Trucks |
| 153.7875 | 153.7875 | NFM | | Fire Brigades Ch 01 |
| 153.8375 | 153.8375 | NFM | | Fire Brigades Ch 02 |
| 153.9375 | 153.9375 | NFM | | Fire Brigades Ch 03 |
| 154.0125 | 154.0125 | NFM | | Fire Brigade Ch 04 |
| 154.2375 | 154.2375 | NFM | | Police Ch 161 |
| 154.2625 | 154.2625 | NFM | | Police Ch 162 |
| 154.2875 | 154.2875 | NFM | | Police Ch 163 |
| 154.3625 | 154.3625 | NFM | | Police Ch 164 |
| 154.3875 | 154.3875 | NFM | | Police Ch 165 |
| 154.4125 | 154.4125 | NFM | | Police Ch 166 |
| 154.4875 | 154.4875 | NFM | | Police Ch 167 |
| 154.6625 | 154.6625 | NFM | | Police Ch 168 |
| 154.8375 | 154.8375 | NFM | | Police Ch 169 |
| 154.8875 | 150.2875 | NFM | Eindhoven | Electricity and Gas Ch 6 |
| 164.1700 | 164.1700 | NFM | Eindhoven | Fire Brigade Philips |
| 164.7500 | 160.2500 | NFM | | Fire Pagers Ch F1 |
| 164.7700 | 164.7700 | NFM | | Fire Pagers Ch F2 |
| 166.6700 | 166.6700 | NFM | Eindhoven | Railway Police Ch 3 |
| 166.8500 | 166.8500 | NFM | Eindhoven | Railway shunters |
| 167.1300 | 167.1300 | NFM | Eindhoven | Railway shunters |

## Netherlands (cont.)

| Base | Mobile | Mode | Location | User and Notes |
|------|--------|------|----------|----------------|
| 167.1700 | 167.1700 | NFM | Eindhoven | Railway Travel Service |
| 167.5500 | 167.5500 | NFM | | Ambulance Service Ch 06 |
| 167.5700 | 167.5700 | NFM | | Ambulance Service Ch 08 |
| 167.5900 | 167.5900 | NFM | | Ambulance Service Ch 09 |
| 167.6100 | 167.6100 | NFM | | Ambulance Service Ch 05 |
| 167.6300 | 167.6300 | NFM | | Ambulance Service Ch 02 |
| 167.6500 | 167.6500 | NFM | | Ambulance Service Ch 01 |
| 167.6700 | 167.6700 | NFM | | Ambulance Service Ch 07 |
| 167.6900 | 167.6900 | NFM | | Ambulance Service Ch 03 |
| 167.7100 | 167.7100 | NFM | | Ambulance Service Ch 04 |
| 167.7300 | 167.7300 | NFM | | Ambulance Service Ch 12 |
| 167.7500 | 167.7500 | NFM | | Fire Brigades Ch 11 |
| 167.7700 | 167.7700 | NFM | | Fire Brigades Ch 13 |
| 167.7900 | 167.7900 | NFM | | Fire Brigades Ch 12 |
| 167.8100 | 167.8100 | NFM | | Fire Brigades Ch 14 |
| 167.8300 | 167.8300 | NFM | | Fire Brigades Ch 16 |
| 167.8500 | 167.8500 | NFM | | Ambulance Service Ch 10 |
| 167.8700 | 167.8700 | NFM | | Fire Brigades Ch 15 |
| 167.8900 | 167.8900 | NFM | | Ambulance Service Ch 13 |
| 167.9100 | 167.9100 | NFM | | Ambulance Service Ch 11 |
| 167.9100 | 167.9100 | NFM | Eindhoven | Ambulance Ch 11 |
| 167.9300 | 167.9300 | NFM | | Fire Brigades Ch 03 |
| 167.9500 | 167.9500 | NFM | | Fire Brigades Ch 04 |
| 167.9700 | 167.9700 | NFM | | Fire Brigades Ch 01 |
| 167.9700 | 167.9700 | NFM | Eindhoven | Fire Brigade Ch 1 |
| 167.9900 | 167.9900 | NFM | | Fire Brigades Ch 07 |
| 168.0100 | 168.0100 | NFM | | Fire Brigades Ch 09 |
| 168.0300 | 168.0300 | NFM | | Fire Brigades Ch 05 |
| 168.0500 | 168.0500 | NFM | | Fire Brigades Ch 06 |
| 168.0700 | 168.0700 | NFM | | Fire Brigades Ch 02 |
| 168.0900 | 168.0900 | NFM | | Fire Brigades Ch 08 |
| 168.0900 | 168.0900 | NFM | Eindhoven | Fire Brigade Ch 8 |
| 168.5900 | 168.5900 | NFM | Airports | Fire Brigades Ch 17 |
| 170.3500 | 170.3500 | NFM | Eindhoven | Fire Brigade Philips |
| 171.0900 | 166.4900 | NFM | Eindhoven | Railway shunters Ch 3 |
| 171.2100 | 166.6100 | NFM | Eindhoven | Railway shunters Ch 9 |
| 171.4500 | 171.4500 | NFM | Eindhoven | Railway information |
| 171.7100 | 171.7100 | NFM | | Police Ch 100 |
| 172.3300 | 172.3300 | NFM | | Police Ch 101 |
| 172.3500 | 172.3500 | NFM | | Police Ch 102 |
| 172.3700 | 172.3700 | NFM | | Police Ch 103 |
| 172.3900 | 172.3900 | NFM | | Police Ch 104 |
| 172.3900 | | NFM | | Riot Police |
| 172.4100 | 172.4100 | NFM | | Police Ch 105 |
| 172.4300 | 172.4300 | NFM | | Police Ch 106 |
| 172.4700 | 172.4700 | NFM | | Police Ch 107 |
| 172.4900 | 172.4900 | NFM | | Police Ch 108 |
| 172.5100 | 172.5100 | NFM | | Police Ch 109 |
| 426.5500 | 416.5500 | NFM | Eindhoven | Buses, Hermes |
| 426.6250 | 426.6250 | NFM | Eindhoven | Buses, Hermes |
| 430.1000 | 431.7000 | NFM | Eindhoven | Amateur Repeater PI2EHV |
| 460.1000 | 158.1000 | NFM | Eindhoven | Railways Ch 37 |
| 467.6000 | 457.6000 | NFM | Eindhoven | Railways Ch 17 |
| 467.6750 | 457.6750 | NFM | Eindhoven | Railways Ch 20 |
| 467.7000 | 457.7000 | NFM | Best | Railways Ch 21 |

## Netherlands (cont.)

| Base | Mobile | Mode | Location | User and Notes |
| --- | --- | --- | --- | --- |
| 467.7500 | 457.7500 | NFM | Eindhoven | Railways Ch 23 |
| 467.8250 | 457.8250 | NFM | Eindhoven | Railways Ch 26 |
| 468.0000 | 458.0000 | NFM | Eindhoven | Railways Ch 33 |
| 468.0750 | 458.0750 | NFM | Eindhoven | Railways Ch 36 |
| 469.6700 | 459.6700 | NFM | Veldhoven | Wegenwacht (AA) |

## Norway

| Base | Mobile | Mode | Location | User and Notes |
| --- | --- | --- | --- | --- |
| 88.7000 | | WFM | Oslo | P1 |
| 93.5000 | | WFM | Oslo | P3 |
| 100.000 | | WFM | Oslo | P2 |
| 103.900 | | WFM | Oslo | P4 |
| 118.300 | | AM | Oslo Gardermoen | Tower |
| 118.825 | | AM | Oslo | Oslo Control North |
| 118.875 | | AM | Oslo | Oslo Control |
| 120.100 | | AM | Oslo Gardermoen | Approach/Radar |
| 120.375 | | AM | Oslo | Oslo Control West |
| 120.725 | | AM | Oslo | Oslo Control |
| 120.650 | | AM | Stavanger Airport | Radar |
| 121.600 | | AM | Oslo Gardermoen | Clearance Delivery |
| 121.675 | | AM | Oslo Gardermoen | Ground |
| 121.725 | | AM | Oslo Gardermoen | Ground |
| 121.925 | | AM | Oslo Gardermoen | Ground |
| 123.325 | | AM | Oslo Gardermoen | Tower |
| 124.700 | | AM | Stavanger Airport | Radar |
| 124.775 | | AM | Oslo | Oslo Control |
| 125.050 | | AM | Oslo | Oslo Control East |
| 126.125 | | AM | Oslo Gardermoen | ATIS Arrivals Information |
| 127.150 | | AM | Oslo Gardermoen | ATIS Departure Information |
| 127.250 | | AM | Oslo | Oslo Control |
| 128.875 | | AM | Oslo Gardermoen | Tower |
| 131.350 | | AM | Oslo Gardermoen | Oslo Director |
| 131.975 | | AM | Oslo Gardermoen | Ramp Deicing |
| 134.050 | | AM | Oslo | Oslo Military |
| 134.175 | | AM | Oslo Gardermoen | Handling |
| 134.350 | | AM | Oslo | Oslo Control South |
| 167.000 | 168.000 | NFM | | Mobile Phones |
| 172.125 | 172.275 | NFM | | Fire Service Ch 2 |

## Poland

| Base | Mode | Location | User and Notes |
| --- | --- | --- | --- |
| 66.4700 | WFM | Siedice | Polskie Radio I Telewizja [LBS] |
| 66.5600 | WFM | Poznan | Polskie Radio I Telewizja [LBS] |
| 66.6800 | WFM | Zamosc | Polskie Radio I Telewizja [LBS] |
| 66.9500 | WFM | Koszalin | Polskie Radio I Telewizja [LBS] |
| 67.2500 | WFM | Olsztyn | Polskie Radio I Telewizja [LBS] |
| 67.4000 | WFM | Poznan | Polskie Radio I Telewizja [LBS] |
| 67.4600 | WFM | Luban | Polskie Radio I Telewizja [LBS] |
| 67.6100 | WFM | Zamosc | Polskie Radio I Telewizja [LBS] |
| 67.6400 | WFM | Klodzko | Polskie Radio I Telewizja [LBS] |
| 67.9400 | WFM | Warszawa | Polskie Radio I Telewizja [LBS] |
| 68.0300 | WFM | Siedice | Polskie Radio I Telewizja [LBS] |
| 68.2400 | WFM | Luban | Polskie Radio I Telewizja [LBS] |
| 68.5100 | WFM | Kudowa | Polskie Radio I Telewizja [LBS] |
| 68.7800 | WFM | Jelenia Góra | Polskie Radio I Telewizja [LBS] |
| 69.3800 | WFM | Zamosc | Polskie Radio I Telewizja [LBS] |
| 69.5600 | WFM | Luban | Polskie Radio I Telewizja [LBS] |
| 69.5600 | WFM | Olsztyn | Polskie Radio I Telewizja [LBS] |
| 69.7400 | WFM | Klodzko | Polskie Radio I Telewizja [LBS] |
| 70.2200 | WFM | Siedice | Polskie Radio I Telewizja [LBS] |
| 70.7900 | WFM | Olsztyn | Polskie Radio I Telewizja [LBS] |
| 71.1200 | WFM | Suwalki | Polskie Radio I Telewizja [LBS] |
| 71.7200 | WFM | Jelenia Góra | Polskie Radio I Telewizja [LBS] |
| 71.7200 | WFM | Zielona Góra | Polskie Radio I Telewizja [LBS] |
| 71.8100 | WFM | Lublin | Polskie Radio I Telewizja [LBS] |
| 71.8400 | WFM | Bydgoszcz | Polskie Radio I Telewizja [LBS] |
| 72.0200 | WFM | Bialystok | Polskie Radio I Telewizja [LBS] |
| 72.0200 | WFM | Pila | Polskie Radio I Telewizja [LBS] |
| 72.4400 | WFM | Klodzko | Polskie Radio I Telewizja [LBS] |
| 72.5900 | WFM | Lublin | Polskie Radio I Telewizja [LBS] |
| 72.6200 | WFM | Bydgoszcz | Polskie Radio I Telewizja [LBS] |
| 72.6800 | WFM | Suwalki | Polskie Radio I Telewizja [LBS] |
| 72.8000 | WFM | Bialystok | Polskie Radio I Telewizja [LBS] |
| 72.8000 | WFM | Pila | Polskie Radio I Telewizja [LBS] |

## Romania

| Base | Mode | Location | User and Notes |
| --- | --- | --- | --- |
| 65.9600 | WFM | Gheorgheni | Radioteleviziunea Romana [LBS] |
| 65.9600 | WFM | Zalau | Radioteleviziunea Romana [LBS] |
| 66.1700 | WFM | P. Neant | Radioteleviziunea Romana [LBS] |
| 66.3600 | WFM | Birlad | Radioteleviziunea Romana [LBS] |
| 66.4400 | WFM | Sibiu | Radioteleviziunea Romana [LBS] |
| 66.5600 | WFM | Baia Marea | Radioteleviziunea Romana [LBS] |
| 66.7600 | WFM | Cluj | Radioteleviziunea Romana [LBS] |
| 67.0100 | WFM | Bacau | Radioteleviziunea Romana [LBS] |
| 67.2500 | WFM | Vilcea | Radioteleviziunea Romana [LBS] |
| 67.3400 | WFM | Varatec | Radioteleviziunea Romana [LBS] |
| 67.6700 | WFM | Zalau | Radioteleviziunea Romana [LBS] |
| 67.7900 | WFM | Constanta | Radioteleviziunea Romana [LBS] |
| 67.8800 | WFM | Focsania | Radioteleviziunea Romana [LBS] |
| 68.1200 | WFM | Baia Mare | Radioteleviziunea Romana [LBS] |
| 68.2500 | WFM | Bucuresti | Radioteleviziunea Romana [LBS] |
| 68.3600 | WFM | Cluj | Radioteleviziunea Romana [LBS] |
| 68.5200 | WFM | Resita | Radioteleviziunea Romana [LBS] |
| 68.8700 | WFM | Bacau | Radioteleviziunea Romana [LBS] |

| Base | Mobile | Mode | Location | User and Notes |
|------|--------|------|----------|----------------|
| 68.8700 | | WFM | Comanesti | Radioteleviziunea Romana [LBS] |
| 69.1100 | | WFM | Varatec | Radioteleviziunea Romana [LBS] |
| 69.6500 | | WFM | Timisoara, | Radioteleviziunea Romana [LBS] |
| 69.6800 | | WFM | T. Severin | Radioteleviziunea Romana [LBS] |
| 69.7400 | | WFM | Bistrita | Radioteleviziunea Romana [LBS] |
| 69.9200 | | WFM | Iasi | Radioteleviziunea Romana [LBS] |
| 70.0100 | | WFM | Constanta | Radioteleviziunea Romana [LBS] |
| 70.2200 | | WFM | Focsania | Radioteleviziunea Romana [LBS] |
| 70.4000 | | WFM | Bucuresti | Radioteleviziunea Romana [LBS] |
| 70.6100 | | WFM | Suceava | Radioteleviziunea Romana [LBS] |
| 70.6400 | | WFM | Deva | Radioteleviziunea Romana [LBS] |
| 70.7900 | | WFM | Arad | Radioteleviziunea Romana [LBS] |
| 71.0000 | | WFM | Oradea | Radioteleviziunea Romana [LBS] |
| 71.0600 | | WFM | P. Neant | Radioteleviziunea Romana [LBS] |
| 71.0600 | | WFM | Petrosani | Radioteleviziunea Romana [LBS] |
| 71.7200 | | WFM | Timisoara, | Radioteleviziunea Romana [LBS] |
| 71.8400 | | WFM | Iasi | Radioteleviziunea Romana [LBS] |
| 71.9600 | | WFM | Topolog | Radioteleviziunea Romana [LBS] |
| 72.2000 | | WFM | Cimpulung | Radioteleviziunea Romana [LBS] |
| 72.2000 | | WFM | Deva | Radioteleviziunea Romana [LBS] |
| 72.3200 | | WFM | Birlad | Radioteleviziunea Romana [LBS] |
| 72.3600 | | WFM | Resita | Radioteleviziunea Romana [LBS] |
| 72.4400 | | WFM | Bistrita | Radioteleviziunea Romana [LBS] |
| 72.5600 | | WFM | Arad | Radioteleviziunea Romana [LBS] |
| 72.6800 | | WFM | Vilcea | Radioteleviziunea Romana [LBS] |
| 72.7100 | | WFM | T. Severin | Radioteleviziunea Romana [LBS] |
| 72.8000 | | WFM | Petrosani | Radioteleviziunea Romana [LBS] |
| 72.9200 | | WFM | Ploesti | Radioteleviziunea Romana [LBS] |
| 72.9800 | | WFM | Bihor | Radioteleviziunea Romana [LBS] |
| 72.9800 | | WFM | Suceava | Radioteleviziunea Romana [LBS] |

## Slovakia

| Base | Mobile | Mode | Location | User and Notes |
|------|--------|------|----------|----------------|
| 66.3800 | | WFM | Kosice | Slovensky Rozhlas [LBS] |
| 67.2800 | | WFM | Poprad | Slovensky Rozhlas [LBS] |
| 67.6700 | | WFM | Bratislava, | Slovensky Rozhlas [LBS] |
| 67.9400 | | WFM | Kosice | Slovensky Rozhlas [LBS] |
| 68.0600 | | WFM | Poprad | Slovensky Rozhlas [LBS] |
| 68.8400 | | WFM | Bratislava | Slovensky Rozhlas [LBS] |
| 68.8700 | | WFM | Kosice | Slovensky Rozhlas [LBS] |
| 69.5000 | | WFM | Zilina | Slovensky Rozhlas [LBS] |
| 69.6800 | | WFM | Banska Bystrica | Slovensky Rozhlas [LBS] |
| 70.8200 | | WFM | Zilina | Slovensky Rozhlas [LBS] |
| 70.9400 | | WFM | Banska Bystrica | Slovensky Rozhlas [LBS] |
| 71.1200 | | WFM | Bratislava | Slovensky Rozhlas [LBS] |
| 71.6000 | | WFM | Zilina | Slovensky Rozhlas [LBS] |
| 72.0200 | | WFM | Namestovo | Slovensky Rozhlas [LBS] |
| 72.5000 | | WFM | Banska Bystrica | Slovensky Rozhlas [LBS] |

# Sweden

| Base | Mobile | Mode | Location | User and Notes |
|------|--------|------|----------|----------------|
| 79.0000 | 80.0000 | NFM | | Scandanavian Police |
| 89.600 | | WFM | Stockholm | Stockholm International P6 |
| 92.400 | | WFM | Stockholm | Sveriges Radio P1 |
| 96.200 | | WFM | Stockholm | Sveriges Radio P2 |
| 99.300 | | WFM | Stockholm | Sveriges Radio P3 |
| 100.800 | | WFM | Stockholm | Golden Hits |
| 101.900 | | WFM | Stockholm | Radio Rix |
| 103.300 | | WFM | Stockholm | Sveriges Radio P4 |
| 104.300 | | WFM | Stockholm | Megapol |
| 105.100 | | WFM | Stockholm | Energy |
| 105.500 | | WFM | Stockholm | Bandit 105.5 |
| 105.900 | | WFM | Stockholm | Radio City |
| 107.500 | | WFM | Stockholm | Classic FM |
| 118.200 | | AM | Stockholm | Stockholm Control |
| 118.400 | | AM | Stockholm | Stockholm Control |
| 118.500 | | AM | Stockholm Arlanda | Tower |
| 119.000 | | AM | Stockholm Arlanda | ATIS Arrival |
| 119.400 | | AM | Stockholm Arlanda | Approach |
| 120.150 | | AM | Stockholm | Stockholm Control |
| 120.500 | | AM | Stockholm Arlanda | Approach/Tower |
| 121.625 | | AM | Stockholm Arlanda | ATIS Departure |
| 121.700 | | AM | Stockholm Arlanda | Ground North |
| 121.950 | | AM | Stockholm Arlanda | Tpwer/Ground South |
| 123.100 | | AM | Stockholm Arlanda | Tower |
| 123.300 | | AM | Stockholm Arlanda | Approach/Tower |
| 123.750 | | AM | Stockholm | Stockholm Control |
| 124.100 | | AM | Stockholm | Stockholm Control |
| 125.125 | | AM | Stockholm Arlanda | Tower |
| 126.650 | | AM | Stockholm | Stockholm Control |
| 131.125 | | AM | Stockholm | Stockholm Control |
| 133.450 | | AM | Stockholm | Stockholm Control |
| 133.700 | | AM | Stockholm | Stockholm Control |
| 134.450 | | AM | Stockholm Arlanda | Clearance Delivery |
| 167.000 | 163.000 | NFM | | Gothenburcreft |

# Turkey

| Base | Mobile | Mode | Location | User and Notes |
|------|--------|------|----------|----------------|
| 118.100 | | AM | Ankara Esenboga | Tower |
| 119.100 | | AM | Ankara Esenbiga | Approach/Radar |
| 119.600 | | AM | Ankara Esenboga | Approach/Radar |
| 121.900 | | AM | Ankara Esenboga | Ground |
| 122.100 | | AM | Ankara Esenboga | Approach/Radar |
| 123.600 | | AM | Ankara Esenboga | ATIS |
| 127.300 | | AM | Ankara | Ankara Control East |
| 128.100 | | AM | Ankara | Ankara Control East |
| 128.750 | | AM | Ankara | Ankara Control South |
| 128.800 | | AM | Ankara | Ankara Control West |
| 129.300 | | AM | Ankara | Ankara Control East |
| 129.450 | | AM | Ankara | Ankara Control East |
| 131.050 | | AM | Ankara | Ankara Control South |
| 132.900 | | AM | Ankara | Ankara Control Southeast |
| 133.550 | | AM | Ankara | Ankara Control West |
| 135.300 | | AM | Ankara | Ankara Control East Merzifon |

# Part 4

# Scanning Log

---

# Scanning Log

| Date | Base | Mobile | Mode | Location | User |
|------|------|--------|------|----------|------|
|      |      |        |      |          |      |
|      |      |        |      |          |      |
|      |      |        |      |          |      |
|      |      |        |      |          |      |
|      |      |        |      |          |      |
|      |      |        |      |          |      |
|      |      |        |      |          |      |
|      |      |        |      |          |      |
|      |      |        |      |          |      |
|      |      |        |      |          |      |
|      |      |        |      |          |      |
|      |      |        |      |          |      |
|      |      |        |      |          |      |
|      |      |        |      |          |      |
|      |      |        |      |          |      |
|      |      |        |      |          |      |
|      |      |        |      |          |      |
|      |      |        |      |          |      |
|      |      |        |      |          |      |
|      |      |        |      |          |      |
|      |      |        |      |          |      |
|      |      |        |      |          |      |
|      |      |        |      |          |      |
|      |      |        |      |          |      |
|      |      |        |      |          |      |
|      |      |        |      |          |      |

# Scanning Log

| Date | Base | Mobile | Mode | Location | User |
|------|------|--------|------|----------|------|
|      |      |        |      |          |      |
|      |      |        |      |          |      |
|      |      |        |      |          |      |
|      |      |        |      |          |      |
|      |      |        |      |          |      |
|      |      |        |      |          |      |
|      |      |        |      |          |      |
|      |      |        |      |          |      |
|      |      |        |      |          |      |
|      |      |        |      |          |      |
|      |      |        |      |          |      |
|      |      |        |      |          |      |
|      |      |        |      |          |      |
|      |      |        |      |          |      |
|      |      |        |      |          |      |
|      |      |        |      |          |      |
|      |      |        |      |          |      |
|      |      |        |      |          |      |
|      |      |        |      |          |      |
|      |      |        |      |          |      |
|      |      |        |      |          |      |
|      |      |        |      |          |      |
|      |      |        |      |          |      |
|      |      |        |      |          |      |
|      |      |        |      |          |      |
|      |      |        |      |          |      |

# Scanning Log

| Date | Base | Mobile | Mode | Location | User |
|------|------|--------|------|----------|------|
|  |  |  |  |  |  |
|  |  |  |  |  |  |
|  |  |  |  |  |  |
|  |  |  |  |  |  |
|  |  |  |  |  |  |
|  |  |  |  |  |  |
|  |  |  |  |  |  |
|  |  |  |  |  |  |
|  |  |  |  |  |  |
|  |  |  |  |  |  |
|  |  |  |  |  |  |
|  |  |  |  |  |  |
|  |  |  |  |  |  |
|  |  |  |  |  |  |
|  |  |  |  |  |  |
|  |  |  |  |  |  |
|  |  |  |  |  |  |
|  |  |  |  |  |  |
|  |  |  |  |  |  |
|  |  |  |  |  |  |
|  |  |  |  |  |  |
|  |  |  |  |  |  |
|  |  |  |  |  |  |
|  |  |  |  |  |  |
|  |  |  |  |  |  |

# Scanning Log

| Date | Base | Mobile | Mode | Location | User |
|------|------|--------|------|----------|------|
|      |      |        |      |          |      |
|      |      |        |      |          |      |
|      |      |        |      |          |      |
|      |      |        |      |          |      |
|      |      |        |      |          |      |
|      |      |        |      |          |      |
|      |      |        |      |          |      |
|      |      |        |      |          |      |
|      |      |        |      |          |      |
|      |      |        |      |          |      |
|      |      |        |      |          |      |
|      |      |        |      |          |      |
|      |      |        |      |          |      |
|      |      |        |      |          |      |
|      |      |        |      |          |      |
|      |      |        |      |          |      |
|      |      |        |      |          |      |
|      |      |        |      |          |      |
|      |      |        |      |          |      |
|      |      |        |      |          |      |
|      |      |        |      |          |      |
|      |      |        |      |          |      |
|      |      |        |      |          |      |
|      |      |        |      |          |      |
|      |      |        |      |          |      |

# FREE Books for You!

These new guides list by county the radio frequencies used by the police in Britain, and now include the other emergency services. There are hundreds of frequencies, many have never been published before. The country is covered in four comprehensive parts: London, Southern England, Northern England, and Scotland and Wales.

All you have to do to receive your free copy is to send us 25 or more VI IΓ/UI IΓ frequencies and their users from your area. The frequencies must not be listed in any edition of *The UK Scanning Directory*, and must include location and user. Taxis, parcel couriers, telephones and other undefined users are not acceptable. It's that simple!

To get your free book set out your list under these headings:

Base     Mobile
<u>Freq.</u>     <u>Freq.</u>     <u>Mode</u>     <u>Location</u>     <u>User & Notes</u>

*Good luck!*

---

**Important:**
To qualify for your copy of the *UK Police Radio Guide,* please send the appropriate voucher which is on the last page, for the one you would like along with your frequency list. Please do not send photocopies of the voucher as only the original will be accepted.

### THESE PUBLICATIONS ARE NOT FOR SALE

# North Atlantic
# Flight Communications

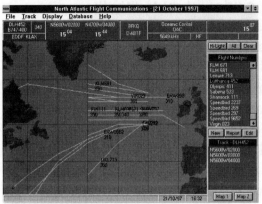

*New!*
*2nd Edition*

**Greatly Improved Free Software**
**Displays 160 Simultaneous Flights**
**Stores 500 Flights Daily**
**Automatically Displays Flight Plan**
**Routes**

This new 2nd edition has not only been completely revised and updated but the software now covers so many features it will like being one of the air traffic controllers at Shanwick! Enter the flight details you hear on your receiver and watch in real time as the programme plots the flight's progress across the North Atlantic on high-resolution charts, which now cover a much wider area. From the position reports you receive over the air the flight path can be updated at each waypoint, and now the software displays these waypoints as well as the airports. The new Flight Management System gives the active Latitude and Longitude, headings, altitude, true air speed, ground speed, Mach Number, tail and head winds, fuel consumption and forward estimates of flights in real time! In addition tracks, which are colour coded, display the flight number, altitude, heading and ground speed. The new searchable database of all flights entered is updated daily and also stores flights and weather details.

The accompanying large book (171 pages A4) clearly explains all the procedures from filing the flight plan right through to landing at the destination and describes the radio communications system in depth.  Over 1,900 flight routings are listed, 730 plus airports, waypoints, VORs and NDBs and all the relevant frequencies.  Comprehensive list of geographical waypoints and ICAO codes are also included. New chapters include ACARS, navigation and aviation weather. Software on three 3.5" disks requires IBM/PC running Windows 95 with minimum 8MB RAM.

*See demo at our web site www.interproducts.ukf.net*
**Price: £16.50 + £1.75 UK post. Postage for Europe add £2.75 or £6 airmail to other destinations.**

"Through it's first rate presentation and accompanying software, simplicity of operation and detailed chapters, *North Atlantic Flight Communications* will encourage a large number of aviation enthusiasts to listen to flights over the North Atlantic"
*MegaHertz* magazine, France

## INTERPRODUCTS
8 Abbot Street, Perth. PH2 0EB, Scotland
Tel. : 01738-441199  Fax: 01738-626953
e-mail: interproducts@ukf.net
www.interproducts.ukf.net

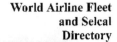

# Scanner Busters 2

by D. C. Poole

*Overcome New Technology and listen into what you want to hear*

*Covers the Latest Encryption Systems, PMR, New Digital Telephones, Pagers and the Emergency Services*

### How to Tune into More Frequencies and beat new Technology

The Police continue to scramble more of their frequencies, trunked radio systems are making it harder to eavesdrop on conversations, and there are more and more strange noises heard on the bands. To overcome this new technology *Scanner Busters 2* guides you through the maze, showing you how to deal with these systems, and to tune into the things you really want to hear. The book has clearly explains in simple terms the workings of PMR, new digital telephone systems, spread spectrum, new pager systems, frequency hopping, encryption systems such as MASC used by the Police and the latest communication methods of the emergency services. *Scanner Busters 2* will be of great help to both new scanner owners and veterans.

**Price:  £6.00 Special Offer £5 incl.  UK postage. Overseas post add  £1.25 for Europe (airmail) and sea mail worldwide, airmail outside Europe add £2.**

## Shortwave Eavesdropper CD-ROM

A huge step forward in the accessibility of shortwave utility information has been made with the *Shortwave Eavesdropper* CD-ROM.  It gives instant access to well over 32,000 frequencies, over 42,000 call signs both ITU and military tactical, country by country information containing QSL addresses, schedules, examples of traffic, and maps.

That is not all!  The DX Edge shows you in real time where to monitor throughout the day, there are extensive help menus, tutorials and a very large list of aircraft and ARQ SELCAL codes. There are even audio samples of data modes and number stations. *Shortwave Eavesdropper* runs on an IBM PC or compatible computer with CD-ROM drive, at least 4MB of RAM running Microsoft Windows 3.0 or higher and sound board which is optional.

**Price:  £16.50 Special Offer £12.00 including UK postage and airmail worldwide.**

## INTERPRODUCTS

8 Abbot Street, Perth. PH2 0EB, Scotland
Tel. : 01738-441199  Fax: 01738-626953
e-mail: interproducts@ukf.net
www.interproducts.ukf.net

# Scanning the Maritime Bands
## by FF O'Brian

*2nd Edition*

It is so easy to pick up maritime radio communications on your scanner because transmissions are in the clear and there are so many ships. *Scanning the Maritime Bands* gives you the Channel Number for each port, harbour and coast radio station in the UK, Ireland, Western Europe and right up to Iceland. All you have to do is to key into your scanner the corresponding frequency from the foldout maritime frequency list. When travelling at home or abroad, take along your scanner to hear ports controlling ships and ferries, weather and navigation broadcasts, the supplies and spare parts required, problems they are having with the crew and lots more. From weekend pleasure craft to super tankers all are fitted with VHF radios. By monitoring Channel 16 you can learn when disaster strikes, and then switch to the appropriate channels to hear the whole of the search and rescue operation (156 pages A5).

**Price: £9.75 + £1 UK postage. Overseas post add £2 for Europe (airmail) and sea mail worldwide, airmail outside Europe add £3.**

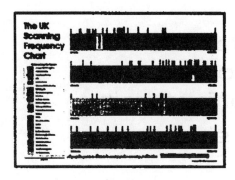

## UK Scanning Frequency Chart

Stunning full colour A3 wall chart covering 25 MHz to 1.8 GHz showing in graphic details all major users of the VHF/UHF spectrum. It will show you quickly

where to scan to pick up your favourite transmissions.

### *Only £3 including UK postage!*

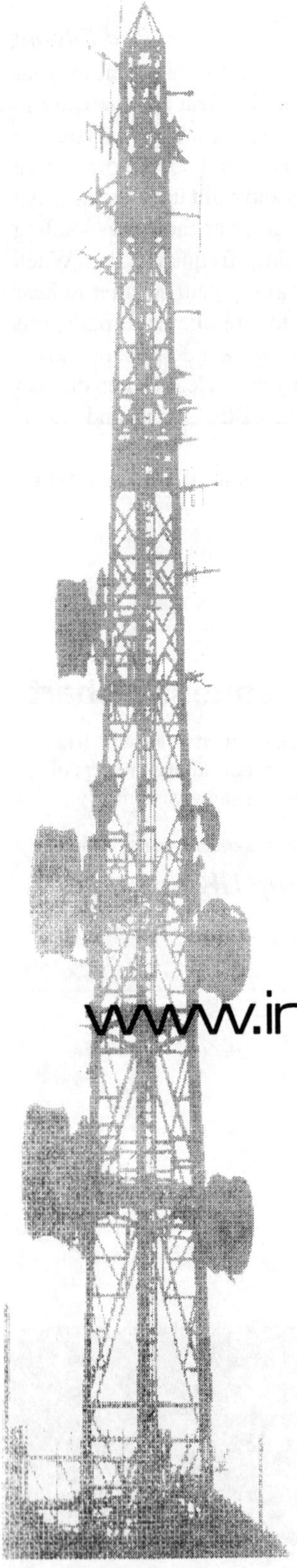

# ORDER FORM

To: **Interproducts**
    **8 Abbot Street**
    **Perth,**
    **PH2 0EB,**
    **Scotland.**

**Tel.: 01738-441199**
**Fax: 01738-626953**
International: +44-1738-441199
              +44-1738-626953
email: interproducts@ukf.net

Name:

Address:

e-mail:

Date...........................................

| Qty | Items | Each £ | Postage £ | Total £ |
|-----|-------|--------|-----------|---------|
|     |       |        |           |         |
|     |       |        |           |         |
|     |       |        |           |         |
|     |       |        |           |         |
|     |       |        |           |         |
|     |       |        |           |         |

UKSD7            **Total £**

I am enclosing a cheque/postal orders/draft for £.........................

Please charge to my credit card

| | | | | | | | | | | | | | | | |
|-|-|-|-|-|-|-|-|-|-|-|-|-|-|-|-|

**MasterCard**

**VISA**

Expiry date.......................     Signature.........................................

Books normally available from stock.
For better service fax or email your order.
UK credit card orders under £10 have a services charge of 75p.
Please allow 2 weeks for delivery of orders.
If you wish to be informed of Special Offers and new Products please give us
your e-maill address.
www.interproducts.ukf.net

# ORDER FORM

**To: Interproducts**
**8 Abbot Street**
**Perth,**
**PH2 0EB,**
**Scotland.**

**Tel.: 01738-441199**
**Fax: 01738-626953**
International: +44-1738-441199
          +44-1738-626953
email:  interproducts@ukf.net

| Name: |
|---|
| Address: |
|  |
|  |
|  |
| e-mail: |

Date...........................................

| Qty | Items | Each £ | Postage £ | Total £ |
|---|---|---|---|---|
|  |  |  |  |  |
|  |  |  |  |  |
|  |  |  |  |  |
|  |  |  |  |  |
|  |  |  |  |  |
|  |  |  |  |  |

UKSD7                                          **Total £** |      |

I am enclosing a cheque/postal orders/draft for £.........................

Please charge to my credit card

| | | | | | | | | | | | | | | | | |
|---|---|---|---|---|---|---|---|---|---|---|---|---|---|---|---|---|

Expiry date.......................     Signature..........................................

Books normally available from stock.
For better service fax or email your order.
UK credit card orders under £10 have a services charge of 75p.
Please allow 2 weeks for delivery of orders.
If you wish to be informed of Special Offers and new Products please give us
your e-maill address.
www.interproducts.ukf.net